To Randy

Alice Birnbach

NEXT YEAR,
GOD WILLING

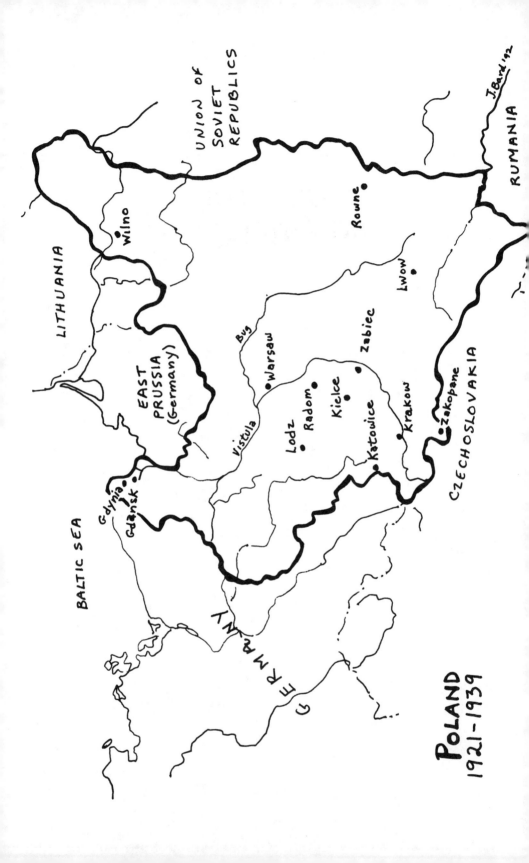

POLAND
1921-1939

NEXT YEAR, GOD WILLING

by
ALICE BIRNHAK

with

Patricia Defer Bonadonna

SHENGOLD PUBLISHERS, INC.
New York

Dedication

To the memory of my perished family, and to my son Adam, his wife, Carol, and my grandson, Andrew, so they will keep the memories.

Acknowledgments

To my cousin, Janush Peltz, who let me use the material from his memoirs and from the letters that he got from Poland in the thirties from his mother and brother.

To Pat Bonadonna, for her friendship and devotion.

To my son Adam, his wife, Carol, for being my severe and constructive critics.

To the faculty of New Utrecht High School; Mr. Citron, Mr. Iacono, and Mr. Waine for their technical advice and coming to our aid whenever there were problems with the computer.

To Ronald Kronheim, who encouraged me to start the project.

To First Lieutenant of the American Army, Jack O. Birnhak, for Zeireis' statement.

ISBN 0-88400-174-1
Library of Congress Catalog Card Number: 94-065517
© 1994 by Alice Birnhak

Published by Shengold Publishers, Inc.
18 West 45th Street
New York, NY 10036

Printed in the United States of America

CHAPTER 1
Prologue

The Pleszowskis settled in Poland in the early fourteenth century. They adopted their Polish name only after centuries had passed and they had grown wealthy and prosperous. Since the 12th century, Poland had provided a haven for persecuted Jews from western Europe. They were welcomed and they spurred commerce and industry.

The Pleszowskis served kings and princes and had been granted privileges unknown to the general Jewish population. They were one of the few Jewish families in Poland that could own land. They spoke Polish at home and, except for their religion, they could not be told apart from the Polish landed gentry. Nevertheless, they were aware of the deep-seated anti-Semitism of their country. Many Jews served as middlemen between the nobility and the peasants, and the exploited peasants blamed the Jews for their misery. Anti-Semitism was also fueled by a powerful clergy. At the end of the eighteenth century, Poland stopped existing as an independent state. Poland was partitioned between Russia, Austria and Prussia. The Pleszowskis lived in the Russian part. Still, the Jews in that part of Poland suffered less persecution than those in Russia proper.

Janush Pleszowski was born in the mid-1800's. He traded in land and, by the time he was twenty-five, he had amassed a fortune. Janush married Leah Slecka, the daughter of a rich merchant from Warsaw. They had three children, Adam, Ida and Regina. Regina, the youngest, was the favorite. She was the only one of the three who loved the land and horticulture. It was obvious to her parents that she would always want to live in the country. The other children complained of being bored and dreamt of living in the city.

When Regina was twelve her father acquired Zabiec, an estate of 20,000 acres located on the river Vistula. At that time, the Vistula was the dividing line between Russian and Austrian Poland, or Galicia. Zabiec was located on the Russian side. A bridge over the river led to the

1

little town of Szczucin. The nearest town on the Russian side was Pacanow. The frontier between Russia and Austria was open and the local people could cross both ways with practically no formalities.

Janush intended Zabiec as an eventual dowry for Regina, but the family resided on a vast country estate, Pierscien, near the city of Radom. Their house was large and comfortable, with many servants and every possible convenience. Janush was an outdoorsman and a gentleman farmer. His children attended school in Radom, where Regina took a special interest in agriculture.

One summer day, a young man in a shiny new carriage appeared in Pierscien. He had come to deliver the carriage to the family from his father's blacksmith's shop. Regina, who was seventeen, was the first to greet him. He looked different from the rest of the boys who came to court her and her sister Ida. His Polish was good, and there was no trace of the ghetto in him. Tall and masculine, with a charming smile, he was the handsomest man Regina had ever met. They talked for a while and then the entire family came out on the porch. Ida was already engaged, but it was obvious that she was taken with the young blacksmith. However, everyone saw that he liked Regina, who decided ; right then and there, that he was the man for her. When she told her father, he was shocked. "He's a nice boy," he said, "but he's only a blacksmith's apprentice."

Janush sent spies to town to find out about the young man and his family. The Warmans were simple people. The father was a blacksmith. They had four children, three girls and Mark. Mark had been a problem, he was thrown out of Yeshiva, joined the circus as a strong man, sung with a cantor in a synagogue and now was learning a trade in his father's shop.

Regina told her father that she would never be interested in another man and would be an old maid unless she married Mark.

Mark was invited to Pierscien. He entertained the whole family by singing and telling funny stories. He had a powerful tenor and knew many operatic arias. Even Janush was charmed by him, and Ida was jealous.

Mark and Regina married in 1898. As was customary in those times, women did not own property. Zabiec, the estate that was Regina's dowry, was put in Mark's name. Their first child, Paula, was born in 1899 and Guta, the second, just a year later. They all lived in Pierscien for a time. When Paula was six and Guta five the Warmans left Pierscien and settled in Zabiec.

Mark's older sister, Yentl, moved with them. She was thirty years old and considered a spinster without any prospects. Regina welcomed her and Yentl became the chief housekeeper, while Regina assumed the responsibility of managing the estate. Mark did not know much about agriculture and was not eager to learn.

The two little girls were their parents' joy. Paula was a beautiful child with black hair and deep green eyes. Guta was blond and shy, always living in her sister's shadow.

The girls were raised in the manner of aristocratic young ladies. They had a French governess and, by the time they were eight years old, they spoke French fluently. They also knew Russian. Their favorite novel was *War and Peace* by Tolstoy. They attended school in the city only part-time. Most of the year they studied at home with a governess. Paula loved to ride, and by the time she was twelve she was an accomplished horsewoman.

Zabiec was surrounded by other large estates that belonged to the Polish nobility. They were all hostile to the Warman family. They considered a Jewish landowner a trespasser and thought that owning and cultivating land were the exclusive privileges of the Poles.

In the early 1900's, a flour and saw mill was built in Zabiec. Adding industry to the property protected the estate from land reforms instituted by the Russian government. Mark took a great interest in running the mill, and Regina was in charge of everything else. She was lucky to have able help. She had realized, early in her marriage, that she couldn't rely very much on her husband. She was also aware of his weakness for good-looking women.

It was winter 1914. Paula was fifteen years old and her sister was fourteen. It was terribly cold that January and both Regina and Guta came down with a bad case of flu. A carriage was dispatched to Szczucin to fetch Dr. Markowski, who always looked after the Warman family. In the meantime, Paula and Aunt Yentl cared for the sick women. When it was Yentl's turn, Paula decided to get some fresh air. She got on her horse and galloped toward the bridge. She rode across the frozen fields, and when she reached the bridge, she turned and saw Zabiec's carriage going toward the estate. She caught up with it as it stopped in front of the porch. To her surprise, instead of old Dr. Markowski, there was a young man inside. Paula had been told many times that when she rode with her hair inside her cap, she looked like a boy. Now, with a young man in the carriage, she did not want to look like a boy. As she dismounted she shook her head and a black braid escaped from under her hat. The young man, who had begun to descend from the carriage, stopped in his tracks and stared at the boy who had miraculously changed into a beautiful girl.

He was tall and blond; she thought he was probably in his mid-twenties.

"You're not Dr. Markowski," she said.

"I am Dr. Moses Peltz," he replied, "Dr. Markowski isn't feeling well; I'm his assistant."

"Welcome to Zabiec," she said.

She looked directly into his face with her sparkling green eyes. Though she was only fifteen, she was aware of the impression she made on people, especially men.

"For a moment I thought you were a boy," he said. "Now I can see that you're the most beautiful girl in the world."

"Take it easy," she laughed. "That's only your first impression. Wait till you know me better."

"I'll try. My friends call me Monek," he said. From that day on he visited Zabiec under one pretense or another.

Monek had many patients in the village, and both Paula and Guta accompanied him on his rounds. The two girls realized that he was a devoted and talented physician. Paula dreamt about being a doctor herself. She had a way with sick people and they loved and trusted her.

Mark and Regina were happy with the way things were going between Monek and Paula. "He's eleven years older than she," Mark said to

Regina, "but she'll have a solid marriage with him and, as a doctor, he'll always be able to provide for her."

The outbreak of war in 1914 interrupted the courtship. Doctor Peltz was inducted into the Austrian army and became the chief surgeon of a hospital train on the eastern front.

Russian and Austrian soldiers faced each other across the Vistula. Zabiec became a battleground. In 1914 and 1915 it kept changing hands between the Russians and Austrians. The Warmans fled to Pierscien to avoid the Russian army, who respected neither people nor their property. There were frequent cases of rape and other violence. From Zabiec the Russian soldiers stole pictures and whatever else they could lay their hands on. They also took the horses and dismantled the mill.

Eventually the Austrians attacked and captured the entire region. They stayed in Zabiec until the end of the war. They reorganized the estate for the intensive production of food. The mill was rebuilt and the farm buildings modernized.

When the situation stabilized, the Warmans came home. Zabiec was now an important center for the Austrian army. There were many officers in the area, and frequent dances, balls and picnics. Paula and Guta had a wonderful time. Doctor Peltz was in the front lines of the now distant Russian front and leaves were rare.

Among the Austrian officers stationed in Zabiec was Lieutenant Eric Von Neugarten. He was in his early twenties and fell madly in love with Paula. He was a Roman Catholic from a good Austrian family. Tall, good-looking, an excellent dancer, a good horseman and a gentleman with a great sense of humor, he was fun to be with. Paula was swept off her feet. Eric presented himself before Mark and formally asked for Paula's hand in marriage. He declared that, if necessary, he was prepared to convert to Judaism.

Mark tried to explain to Eric how impractical the whole idea was. The differences in social standing and religion would wreck such a marriage. Eric's parents were equally shocked; they threatened to disinherit him. How could a proper Austrian boy marry a Polish girl who was also Jewish? This was a thing they could not tolerate.

Eric took a leave. He went to Vienna to impress on his parents that his whole life's happiness depended on marrying Paula. He wrote her love letters, which Mark managed to intercept at the post office and destroy. Paula waited in vain to hear from Eric. She cried every night, thinking that he had forgotten her.

Mark decided to contact Dr. Peltz. He traveled east and managed the almost impossible task of reaching a field hospital right behind the front lines. There he found Dr. Peltz. At first Mark barely recognized the man who had once courted his daughter. Monek Peltz had lost a lot of weight. His eyes were sunken and his face was haggard. "We work very hard here; sometimes it's not very pleasant," he said.

Monek's superior officer told Mark that the surgeons worked almost twenty-four hours a day. They had very little time to sleep or eat and sometimes didn't change their clothes for weeks. Doctor Peltz, he added, was a very conscientious and skilled surgeon.

Mark told Monek about the situation with Paula and Eric and Monek managed to get a leave of absence. When they arrived in Zabiec, he fell asleep in the bathtub, Mark carried him to bed, where he slept all night and the entire next day. It took him a few days to recover from his exhaustion. Once he felt better, he picked up his black bag and went with Paula and Guta to visit the sick in the village. Often he took long walks just with Paula.

Paula could not help comparing her two suitors. Monek was serious and dedicated to his work, while Eric had a happy-go-lucky attitude toward life, his main activities being dancing, riding horses and generally having a good time. Eric was not around and, not knowing about his letters, Paula made up her mind.

To her surprise, Eric returned to Zabiec. He was exuberant, having managed to persuade his parents to accept Paula as their future daughter-in-law. But he was too late. Paula had already said yes to Monek.

Still, Paula was not happy. It seemed to her that this was the end of her beautiful, carefree youth and that she had given up her prince charming for the serious business of marriage to Monek.

Guta guessed her sister's doubts. "You can't have both a solid marriage and a romantic love affair with another man," she said.

"Why not?" Paula said. "How about Father? We all know about his liaisons."

"Men can do it, not us," Guta said.

"I don't see why," Paula answered.

Monek took Paula to see his parents. They lived in a little Galician shtetl. His father was a barber who also pulled teeth and applied vacuum cups and leeches, which supposedly drew out fever and bad blood. Everybody in the town was proud of Monek; he was a real doctor.

Monek warned Paula about his mother. "She doesn't approve of you," he said. "She had arranged for me to meet a girl from Lwow. She told me that the girl would be obedient, keep a kosher house, go to Mikvah and bring up children properly."

"That certainly isn't me," Paula laughed.

"My mother heard that you ride a horse like a Cossak and dance with goys on Friday and Saturday nights."

"What did you answer?" Paula asked.

"I said to her that I don't mind you riding horses but I assured her that you will only dance with me."

Paula became sad. No dancing all night long with dashing young men, she thought.

Paula and Monek got married in October 1916. Paula accompanied her husband to the front and served as his nurse and assistant.

Guta felt lost without her sister. The two girls had never been separated before. Guta was different from Paula, who was always willing to take a chance and court danger. Guta was full of fears and superstitions; she washed her hands often, was afraid of germs and made sure no one used her towels. She got upset when a black cat crossed her path, expected the worst on Friday the 13th and believed in dreams. Most of the time, however, she was a rational young woman. When she and her sister started dating, the boys Guta brought home invariably fell in love with Paula.

During the war years Zabiec was financially successful. The Austrians paid well for flour, dairy products and vegetables. Mark and Regina decided to send Guta to Vienna to attend a fancy prep school for well-born girls. They realized how lonely she was without her sister.

Guta enjoyed her year in Vienna. When she returned in the spring of 1917, she found that her grandfather Janush had died. He had already been ill at Paula's wedding but he hadn't wanted to worry the family. Early that spring he died peacefully in his sleep.

Paula came to Zabiec that summer. She was heartbroken about her grandfather's death. She was in the last two months of her pregnancy, and her son was born in August. He was named after his late great grandfather. Janush was abbreviated to Jas. Paula and the baby stayed in Zabiec for six months. Then she rejoined her husband.

To baby Jas, Zabiec was home. There were plenty of people to take care of him. He had a nanny and Aunt Yentl, Guta and grandparents. They all adored him.

Old Janush had tried to straighten out his affairs before his death. He knew that none of his children would be able to manage his land holdings. Ida lived in Kielce, Adam had bought a furniture store in Krakow and Regina had enough on her hands running Zabiec. Janush had not trusted Mark and he regretted having allowed Regina to marry him. He intended to sell everything and divide the money among his children. But death came too soon. Bitter quarrels about the inheritance ensued among his three children. As a result, Regina became estranged from her sister Ida, and her relations with Adam were poor at best. Pierscien was sold and the widow Pleszowski moved to Zabiec to live with Regina and Mark. She became very religious after her husband's death.

The end of the Great War and the treaty of Versailles brought a new order in Europe. Poland, which had been partitioned for over a century, gained its independence. The three parts were reunited to form one republic. Marshal Pilsudski became the head of state. He had been a warrior against czarist Russia, and had spent many years in various prisons, including in Siberia. During the war, he formed a fighting force named the Legions that fought for Polish independence. When the Polish republic was reborn, Pilsudski's Legions became the regular army. But unlike in western Europe, the year 1918 was not the end of the war for Poland. There were protracted campaigns over frontiers that involved Poland, the Soviet Union, the Ukraine and Lithuania. In 1920 the Soviets approached Warsaw and were repelled by Poland in a battle subsequently called "the Miracle on the River Vistula." This victory turned the tide of war in favor of Poland. Pilsudski claimed that he had saved Europe from the Bolshevik hordes. Finally, in 1921, Poland and the Soviet Union signed a treaty establishing the Polish eastern frontier. Poland also gained access, through a narrow corridor, to the Baltic sea, and the city of Gdansk became a free city under the jurisdiction of the League of Nations. By 1921 Pilsudski had resigned his position and withdrawn to his country house. Perhaps he wanted to give democracy a chance.

In 1920, Paula was pregnant with her second child. Again she stayed with her parents in Zabiec. Her husband was now serving in the Polish army as a surgeon.

Dr. Peltz had met another officer and doctor with a background similar to his. In appearance, Dr. Eisig Strum was the opposite of Dr. Peltz. He was not tall, had dark eyes and hair and a wry sense of humor. He was very impressed with Monek's commanding personality. Eisig came from a small Galician shtetl. His family was poor and strictly orthodox. Until he was twelve he received only a religious education. At home he spoke Yiddish, and in school he read Hebrew. His father had been ambitious for his eldest son. He had hired a tutor and, within one year, the boy spoke and wrote both Polish and German. He was admitted to a Polish gymnasium and from there went to medical school in Vienna. His family tried to help him financially, but there wasn't much money to go around. Eisig often went hungry. When he met Monek he was twenty-nine, and already a specialist in dermatology and venereal diseases. He planned to establish his own practice after the war.

Both doctors were scheduled for leave at the same time. Monek had often spoken about his wife and her family. "Why don't you come with me and meet my wife's younger sister?"

"I really should go see my own family," Eisig answered.

"Do something for yourself for a change," Monek said. "I think you'd like my sister-in-law."

Eisig allowed himself to be persuaded.

They traveled by rail to Szczucin. When the doctors were picked up at the station by the estate's deluxe coach, Eisig wondered if Monek's family were millionaires.

It was May and the lilacs in Zabiec were in full bloom. Eisig had never imagined being invited to such a place in his wildest dreams. The host and hostess were elegant and warm. The house was spacious and beautifully furnished. There were servants all around.

When Eisig saw Guta, he couldn't take his eyes off her. She was tall, slim and blond, with a light, translucent complexion. There seemed to be something ephemeral, almost unreal, about her. If she had wings, he thought, she would be an angel. It paid to have worked so hard to become a doctor just to have looked at her. He did not dare hope that she would condescend to consider him as a suitor. After dinner, the gentlemen retired to the smoking room. Mark asked the young doctor about his plans. Eisig told him that he was saving money in order to start up a private practice.

Mark winked. "I noticed that you like my daughter, and I think she was impressed by you. If things go well between you two, you won't have to worry about money for your office."

Eisig was stunned—a beautiful girl, rich and cultured parents and a dowry for him.

During Eisig and Guta's courtship, they talked about Vienna. His memories were different from hers. He remembered studying long hours, memorizing the names of every little bone and ligament in the body. During his vacation he had worked as an orderly in a hospital, emptying bedpans and mopping floors.

To Guta, Vienna meant Strauss waltzes, operas, the theater and elegant balls. She told Eisig a story about going with her class to see "Aida"; it was a great event because Caruso was singing Radames; "Everyone was applauding," Guta said, "but I told the headmistress that my father sang better than Caruso. Everyone thought I was joking."

Eisig realized that they came from different worlds. But he was in love and he wasn't going to worry about it. Guta told him something else: "If my father has promised you a dowry, don't believe him. He lost a great deal of money when the Polish marc was devalued. Whatever he has left he needs for himself. Believe me, he never has enough."

Eisig did not want to believe her. After all, he had seen the luxurious estate. He thought that Guta was trying to find out whether he wanted to marry her for her money or for love.

In October 1920, Paula gave birth to her second son, Jerry. Both doctors were discharged from active duty. They remained in the reserves for an indefinite period. Guta and Eisig got married in May 1921 at Zabiec. It was a great event; an orchestra played and hundreds of people from the neighboring towns and villages ate, drank and sang.

Eisig's family wasn't there. They claimed it was too far for them to travel, but Eisig knew better. They just would not be comfortable in Zabiec. They weren't used to that kind of life. Eisig did not approve of the extravagance but had agreed to a big wedding to please his bride.

Both doctors and their families settled in the city of Kielce. A girl was born to Eisig and Guta in June 1922, and they named her Alicia. Dr. Peltz gave up the scalpel to specialize in internal medicine and pediatrics He still had nightmares about ghastly injuries and amputations. He had had enough of surgery.

CHAPTER 2

Alicia looked at herself in a large mirror. She jumped up and down and sang, "My mommy says that next month I'll be four." She admired her blond curls and the blue ribbon in her hair. The ribbon was tied in a fancy bow. On her father's desk there was just such a photograph of Guta with Alicia sitting on her back, her arms around her mother's neck and wearing the same blue ribbon.

The child was playing in the drawing room, with its oriental rug, mirrors and crystal chandelier. This was where Guta entertained and held her card parties.

It was early afternoon in May 1926, and the sun was pouring through the window. Its rays reflected off the golden curtains and the little girl watched streams of light playing on the specks of dust.

The door to the balcony was open. It was Tuesday, market day in the square, which had lately been called "Freedom Place" in memory of Poland's independence from Russia.

Not seeing her mother, the child ventured out onto the balcony. She knew it was a "no no" to go there alone, but it was so much fun to watch the peasants displaying their wares: colorful paper flowers, real flowers colored violet, yellow and red, fruits and vegetables, and a variety of everyday clothes. On the sidewalk bearded Jews in their traditional garb were walking along gesticulating and talking in Yiddish.

Guta entered the room. She looked around for her daughter, "Alicia, where are you?" she said.

The little girl was so absorbed with the sights that she didn't hear her mother.

Guta saw Alicia out on the balcony. She pulled her back into the room. "How many times must I tell you not to go out there alone? You're always jumping and climbing and mommy is afraid that one day you might fall onto the street." She called Kasia the servant girl: "Kasia, please don't

12

leave the door to the balcony open. That child behaves like a boy. She tries to imitate her wild cousin Jas."

At the mention of her cousin Alicia started to clap her hands, "Mommy, can I go upstairs to play?"

"Upstairs" in the Strum household meant the Peltzes'. They lived on the second floor of a two-story building, which in Kielce was as high as they came. A back yard divided the one-story apartment house that faced Freedom Place from the two-story one that fronted Hipoteczna Street. On the first floor of the house lived another physician, Dr. Levin, with his wife and daughter Greta.

Kasia offered to take Alicia.

"I have to check with Aunt Paula first," Guta said.

"Mucia, Mucia!" Alicia exclaimed.

This was the nickname she had given her aunt. In her mind it meant another mommy, one different from her own but loved just as much. Though she knew that Paula was Jas and Jerry's real mother, Paula was nobody's Mucia but Alicia's. Even at her age, the little girl was aware of Paula's beauty, wit and talent. Who else could make pigs, horses, dogs and cats from leftover bread? Or play a tune on a comb?

Alicia and Kasia followed Guta to the kitchen. Guta opened a little window overlooking the back yard. She called, "Paula, Paula!"

On the other side of the yard Mrs. Kubicka, the Peltzes' maid, opened her window and yelled back, "I'll call the Mrs."

Paula came to the window.

"Can Alicia go over and play for a while? She's very restless."

"Of course she can."

Guta turned from her window and admonished the child, "Hold on to Kasia when you go and don't run up the stairs. Be careful."

They left. Guta watched with her heart in her mouth. Alicia was running ahead, paying no attention to Kasia.

Alicia arrived at the Peltzes' door and rang the bell. Kasia was short of breath trying to keep up.

Kubicka opened the door and the little girl flew into the boys' room. It was a large room and the furnishings were quite Spartan: two wooden beds on opposite walls, one for Jas and one for Jerry. A wardrobe stood against Jerry's headboard, a folded ping pong table was leaning against the wall and a desk stood near the window. The wooden floor was highly polished; no wonder Guta was afraid her child would slip and hurt herself.

When Alicia entered the room, Jerry was sitting on the floor playing with model cars. He was six years old, quiet, a beautiful child who resembled his mother. He had just finished kindergarten and next fall was scheduled to go into the first grade. Alicia didn't pay any attention to him. She ran to the window sill, where she found the jar of marinated cherries. It was her uncle's hobby to make preserves from the fruits and vegetables that were sent to them from Zabiec.

Alicia loved the cherries. Jerry was not very interested in food. Kasia stood helpless. "You will spoil your appetite and your mother will blame me," she said. "I've got to go. Behave yourself."

Then Jas came in. He was nine, very tall for his age, blond and blue-eyed, with a big nose like his father's. He was holding a stick in his hand. He went over to Jerry and yelled, "I am Pilsudski and you are the Senate. Get out of here, I'm taking over!" He waved the stick.

Jerry looked up at him with his large green eyes. "I was elected by the people," he said. "You can't just dissolve me with your stick."

"Of course I can," Jas said. "I am Pilsudski and you can kiss my ass. Now get out!"

Alicia kept eating cherries. Paula entered the room. Alicia stopped eating and ran to her Mucia. "Why?" she asked.

"Why what?"

"Why did Pilsudski tell them to kiss his ass?"

Paula laughed and picked up her niece. "Jas must have told you that. You shouldn't repeat everything Jas says. He is a naughty boy, but you are a gorgeous little girl. I wish I had a little girl like you, instead of these two cowboys."

Uncle Monek walked into the room. He was tall and completely bald. He never seemed to smile or joke. Alicia was afraid of him. He was the doctor who examined her whenever she was sick. She dreaded those visits and would always put a blanket over her head and shiver. "Why can't my daddy examine me?" she would ask her mother. "He's a doctor too." Guta tried to explain that different doctors had different specialties.

Alicia cuddled closer to her aunt, burying her head in Paula's bosom.

Uncle Monek was holding a newspaper in his hand. "So it's finally happened," he said to Paula. "That was quite a coup d'état Pilsudski and his Legionnaires staged in Warsaw. I'm glad it happened. There was too much chaos. Poland needs a strong chief like Pilsudski. There will be more stability. Besides, he stands for religious tolerance. No more economic boycott of the Jews." He looked critically at Jas. "Shouldn't you be doing your homework?" he asked.

Kubicka's entrance saved Jas. "You have a patient waiting, Dr. Peltz."

When he left there was a sigh of relief in the room. Paula put Alicia down. "You're getting big and heavy," she said. "You must weigh almost 20 kilograms."

Alicia was pulling at her aunt's skirt. "Mucia," she asked, "what is a boycott?"

Paula shook her head in wonder and said to Jas, "Our little girl loves to pick up strange and complicated words. Jas, why don't you explain to Alicia what boycott means."

Jas was only too happy to oblige. It made him feel important. "My father and yours," he explained, "are boycotted by other doctors. They won't refer patients to them."

"Why?" Alicia asked.

"Because they, along with Dr. Perlstein, opened a clinic that treats poor people for very little money. The other doctors are afraid that the clinic will take away their business."

"Perlstein is a traitor," Paula said. "He joined the others recently, and Dr. Levin, our neighbor and close friend, isn't talking to us. When he sees us on the street, he ignores us."

"He, and his retard of a daughter Greta," Jas said.

"You shouldn't talk that way about unfortunate children," Paula admonished him.

Alicia tried to pronounce Perlstein. She missed him because whenever he came for dinner he brought her toys. Lately he hadn't been coming.

"But," Paula said to her son, "that's not the boycott I wanted you to tell her about. I was thinking about Endeks and the way they tell people not to patronize Jewish stores or do business with the Jews. We're hoping that from now on things will get better and there will be no more quotas for Jews in the universities.

Jerry raised his eyes from his cars and asked his mother, "What does Endek stand for?"

Paula was surprised. She thought that her younger son was so busy playing that he wasn't paying attention to the conversation. "That is an intelligent question," she said. "Endek is an abbreviation for National Democratic Party."

Alicia tried hard to say "abbreviation."

"She's just a little monkey. She has to repeat everything," Jas said.

"Don't taunt our little girl," Paula said.

"Don't taunt our little girl," Alicia echoed. She stuck her tongue out at Jas.

"I'll cut it off."

"And I'll cut off your nose."

Now Paula and Jerry were laughing. Jas was self-conscious about his big Jewish nose. "That little Alicia," Paula said, "can stand up for herself. She doesn't need anyone to protect her."

Guta came to pick up her daughter. "You have such a bright, wonderful child," Paula told her sister. "Enjoy her and don't worry so much."

"That's easy for you to say; you have boys. Anyway, I have to take Alicia home for her afternoon snack."

"Mommy," Jas asked, "can I go to eat at Aunt Guta's?"

Jerry said seriously, "Jas will do anything to get away from his homework."

"Well," Paula said, "your father is busy with a patient, so there's no harm if you go, but come back soon."

"Can I go too?" Jerry asked.

"Of course," Guta answered, "but Jas, please don't run down the stairs or slide on the banisters because Alicia will follow." Guta was surprised to see Jas holding Alicia's hand as they walked slowly down the stairs. They crossed the back yard without jumping or running. "Jas," Guta said, "thank you for setting such a good example for your brother and cousin." The snack that Guta had prepared was more like a meal, with rolls, bread and butter, and all kinds of cold meats, chocolate pudding and an assortment of fruits.

Eisig came in. He was wearing his white coat. Alicia ran to her father.

"Don't touch your daddy, he just finished with a patient and there are a lot of germs on him," Guta exclaimed.

Eisig just shrugged his shoulders. "I changed my coat and washed my hands. I have a few minutes before my next patient."

Alicia wanted her father's attention. She pulled at his coat and asked, "Daddy, what is a coup d'état?"

"That child, I think I'll start teaching her French," Guta said.

Eisig thought for a moment and said, "We call it a 'coup d'état' when one group of hooligans takes power from another group."

Guta was not happy with her husband's answer. "How can you talk that way about Pilsudski? He is a great national hero; he fought for Polish independence. He was sent to Siberia and was imprisoned by the Germans. If it weren't for him and his Legions, there would be no Poland the way it is now."

"So who needs independent Poland?" Eisig answered. "I felt safer in Galicia under old Franz Joseph." Then he added, "I heard there was fighting on the streets of Warsaw and 600 people died."

"Monek thinks that things will be better in the future because Endeks will be out of power," Guta said.

Alicia was still pulling her father's coat. "Daddy, why don't Endeks like Jews?"

Eisig and Guta looked at each other in amazement. From a child who was three weeks short of being four years old, it was quite a question.

Jas butted in. "I don't worry about Endeks. The kids in my class wouldn't dare say anything against Jews when I'm around. They know I would beat them up." Jas was attending a fancy prep school where very few Jews were accepted.

Eisig said, "Did you do your homework? Never mind beating up Endek kids. We Jews have to excel in other ways."

Alicia wanted her father's attention exclusively. "Why?," she asked.

Eisig had forgotten the original question. His mind had drifted to other matters.

Jerry got into the conversation. "Because Endeks are stupid and jealous."

Now Eisig remembered. Talking more to himself than to his little girl, he said, "Endeks call the Jews 'Godless Bolsheviks' who want to abolish private property. At the same time they maintain that Jews control all commerce and industry and are filthy rich. They say that Jews don't want to be integrated into Polish society because they have their own language, religion and customs. But those who try hard to assimilate and even convert to Christianity are not accepted either."

Now Jas interrupted. "My friends say that the Jews didn't believe that Christ was the son of God, so they crucified him and now they need the blood of a Christian child for Passover Matzoh."

Guta was getting upset over the direction in which the conversation was going. "Jas, those kids aren't your friends; you shouldn't listen to them. Did they ever tell you that Jesus was a Jew and that without Judaism there wouldn't be Christianity? She said to Eisig, "Let's stop analyzing Polish anti-Semitism. You should eat something while you're waiting for your patient. Jerry," she said, "you are smart enough to know that a boy your age has to eat to grow properly. You have been sitting over your plate and daydreaming. Alicia, sit at the table, finish your meal and stop annoying your father."

Eisig was still absorbed in his thoughts. "We shouldn't complain," he said, "the zloty is quite stable. We can buy food, not like in Germany, where it takes 100,000 marks to get a loaf of bread."

"Eisig," Guta said, "we already had our financial crisis when the Polish mark collapsed and my parents lost a fortune."

"Who would know better than I? That was your father's excuse for not giving you a dowry."

The three children and their mothers spent summers and spring holidays in Zabiec with their grandparents. The two doctors remained in the city and visited occasionally.

Guta, Paula and the children traveled to Zabiec by bus. The trip was fun. Jas always sat near the driver, trying to learn how to drive. The bus stopped in small, mostly Jewish, towns along the way. Chmielnik, Busko spa, Busko town, Stopnica and finally Pacanow. Bearded men would come over to the bus extolling, in sing-song using broken Polish mixed with Yiddish, the wonderful bargains they had to offer.

Pacanow was a typical Jewish shtetl in what had been Russian Poland. It was without electricity, sanitation or running water. Women carried water from a distant well. A putrid smell came from the outdoor latrines. The townspeople lived in crude wooden houses or thatched peasant huts. The only brick structure was the synagogue. The wooden Yeshiva was attached to it, along with a shack for the slaughter of poultry under kosher law.

When Guta, Paula and the children arrived at the bus station in Pacanow a coach with four horses was waiting for them. The children jumped and ran. They knew the names of the horses, two chestnuts and two whites. They were greeted by Kazimierz, chief stableboy of the estate. He was the oldest son of Stefka, the maid. She had several other children and no one, including Stefka, knew who their father was. They all lived in the servants' quarters.

On special occasions, such as picking up the "girls" and their children, Kazimierz donned his official coachman's uniform and cap and took the best carriage and horses.

"We're going to Zabiec!" The children were jumping for joy.

Jas sat near Kazimierz, trying to take the reins. They rode on dirt roads and peasant boys gaped at them. Some were Jas's playmates and he waved at them. They passed the mill, barns and stables, cowsheds and other farm buildings. Then they passed an iron gate.

The path to the house was lined with acacia trees. The sweet smell of their white flowers was the first thing that hit them. The coach stopped in front of the white stone house. Grandfather Mark was sitting on the porch, looking big and strong. As usual, he was eating. Grandmother Regina ran out of the house at the sound of the horses' hoofs. So did Aunt Yentl. The dogs jumped on the children, barking happily. There was much kissing and hugging. It felt like home, even more than Kielce.

The children loved being in Zabiec. During the summer meals were served outside on a big table under a linden tree. Alicia and Jerry had all the freedom they needed to play outdoors. There was a lawn and a lane of chestnut trees leading to an orchard. On the other side there were two ponds where they could watch ducks and geese swimming. The ponds were abundant with frogs; thus the name Zabiec (*zaba* is frog in Polish). The path between them led to a lane of elm trees, whose branches were cut on top to form a canopy so thick that the sun's rays could not penetrate. The orchards were full of apple, pear and plum trees. For the summer, Mark leased the orchard to a family who harvested the fruit and sold it at market. As a part of their agreement, a certain portion of the yield had to go to the estate. The children were allowed to climb the trees and eat whatever they picked. There were frequent rumors of rabid dogs running loose in the area. They felt safe sitting high up in the branches.

A fence surrounded the orchard. Beyond it were the servants' quarters, forbidden territory for the children. Jas disobeyed and would visit the help. He told Alicia and Jerry how crowded and squalid their quarters were, dirty and damp even in the summer.

A wooden house was attached to the main residence. It was occupied by Regina's mother, widow Pleszowska. The children called her "Grand Baba." Jas, being the eldest, knew her better than the others. To them, she was a very old lady who always carried her prayer book. She had a special kitchen and her food was prepared separately. The main kitchen was not kosher enough for her.

In the summer of 1927, the children did not see Grand Baba for a couple of weeks. Jas told them she was sick. Alicia had never been inside the wooden house. She was curious and finally sneaked in and crouched in the corridor. The maid left the bedroom with the door slightly open. Alicia crawled inside the room and hid behind a dresser.

Aunt Yentl was sitting by the bed, putting cold compresses on Grand Baba's forehead. Alicia was used to seeing her great grandmother with black hair. She didn't know Grand Baba was wearing a wig. Now her hair was white and thin and her face was pale. She was breathing with difficulty, as if there was something in her chest that she was attempting to get out. Baba was making wheezing noises. Maybe she was trying to talk.

Aunt Yentl tried to prop her up with more pillows. "Try to spit it out," she kept repeating.

She spoke Yiddish, but Alicia could understand her gestures. She was aware of the penetrating smell in the room. She was nauseated and sneaked out unseen.

The fresh air felt good. Through the slats in the henhouse she watched the rooster in his fancy plumage as hens cackled around him. Birds were singing high in the birch trees.

Jas appeared from behind the trees. "Where have you been? Your mother has been looking for you."

"I saw Grand Baba," the child whispered.

Jas was surprised. "You mean you were in her room? If I tell your mother she will make you wash your hands for two hours."

"Why?"

"Because, stupid, Grand Baba has pneumonia and there are plenty of germs in the room. After a while he added, "Grand Baba is very sick. I think she will die soon."

Alicia forgot about the germs. One word stuck in her mind: "die." "Will I wheeze like Grand Baba before I die?" she asked.

Jas was kind for a change. "She's sixty-five; you have sixty years before you have to worry."

Alicia stared at him blankly.

Jas waved his hand. "You don't even know what sixty is."

"I do, too; my daddy will teach me numbers."

They ran back to the main house. The grown-ups were nowhere to be seen. Even grandfather was not in his usual seat on the porch. Jas picked up his bike. He rode it through the acacia lane toward the gate, then turned around and started riding fast. As he gained speed he stood with one leg on the crossbar and the other extended in the air, while his arms were spread like an eagle. He coasted that way for several hundred meters.

Alicia and Jerry jumped, cheered and applauded. Paula came out on the porch. "Stop making all that noise. We're all concerned about Grand Baba. Your father," she said to Jas and Jerry, "is coming tomorrow to see her."

Jas got off his bike. He didn't look very happy. "Why can't Dr. Markowski come?"

He's certainly not looking forward to seeing his father, Paula thought. He's being spoiled rotten here by his grandparents and Aunt Yentl, while his father tries to be a strict disciplinarian; and I'm caught in the middle. "Don't you think," she said to Jas, "that your father knows more than Dr. Markowski?"

Dr. Peltz arrived. He only stayed for two days. Everybody, including the children, was subdued and quiet. He prescribed some medication for Grand Baba. Jas took his bike and got it from the pharmacy in Szczucin.

"He is a wonderful kid," Paula told Guta. "Sometimes he's wild, but you can count on him when you need him. He's only ten and I don't worry about sending him on his bike to Szczucin."

Grand Baba died a few days after Dr. Peltz left. She was buried in a Jewish cemetery in Pacanow. Alicia and Jerry were judged to be too small to attend the funeral, but Jas went. Afterwards Regina, Yentl, Paula and Guta cried for days and days.

One day that week, the children were playing in front of the house. Stefka was sitting on the stairs to the porch, watching the children. A few horse carriages pulled up in front of the house. The children watched as people arrived. Some men wore yarmulkas, kaftans and other orthodox paraphernalia; others were dressed in regular dark suits. The women wore black dresses and carried packages.

"The grown-ups are sitting shiva," Jerry explained.

Alicia asked, "Why?"

"So you should ask," Jas said.

"What's in the packages?"

"Mostly food and don't ask me why. They think that our grandmother and mothers are too busy wailing and screaming to prepare meals."

"But Aunt Yentl sees to it that we eat." After a while Alicia said, "My mommy told me that Grand Baba will go straight to heaven because she prayed and fasted."

"You'll go to hell because you don't pray and fast," Jas said.

Alicia was about to cry. If her mother were there she would complain that Jas had said she would go to hell. She turned around and said to Jas, "You'll get there first because you're older and you are a bad boy. Besides, my mommy told me that children don't have to fast on Yom Kippur."

"Your mommy doesn't fast on Yom Kippur either," Jas said.

"Oh, yes she does. She doesn't eat until dinner."

Dinner was served early in the afternoon.

"But my daddy eats breakfast," she said.

Jas looked at her with a mischievous smile, "Well, then we will all meet in hell."

"What's in hell?"

Jas startled Alicia by making a sudden scaring noise. "There are big fires that burn you continuously and it hurts like hell," he told her.

Jerry, the wise old man at seven interrupted, "In hell, it hurts like hell. Don't worry, Alicia, my father told me that there is no such place as hell. Let's play. I will be Skrzetuski* and you will be Cossack Chmielnicki* and we'll have a life and death duel."

"And I will be Count Poniatowski,*" Jas said, "and beat you both." Then he changed his mind. "I am Lindbergh." He spread his arms and pretended to fly. "Now I'm landing in Paris," he swooped and crouched.

Alicia heard the name Lindbergh mentioned quite often in the past few months. "Can Lindbergh fly to heaven?" she asked.

"Yes. He'll say hello to God but I think he'd rather be in Paris. I would too," Jas answered.

"Why?"

"All there is up there," Jerry said, "is the moon, planets, the sun and the stars."

Alicia wanted to ask where was God but she was afraid they would laugh. Instead she said, "My mommy told me that she will teach me French and then she will take me to Paris."

Paula came onto the porch wearing her riding habit. "I need a distraction," she told Stefka. "I can't take the crying and mourning any longer. Jas, find Kazimierz, he must be in the stables. Tell him to saddle up my chestnut and bring her here."

Jas was only too happy to run to the stables.

"Mommy, can I get a ride with you?" Jerry asked.

"Me, too," Alicia said.

"One at a time, please."

Jas appeared on Paula's horse. Kazimierz was walking helplessly

---

* Characters from "Fire and Sword," a historical novel by Henryk Sienkiewicz.

beside. Jas dismounted in front of his mother. Kazimierz helped Paula up, then picked up Jerry and sat him in the saddle with his mother.

Paula rode slowly down the acacia lane, to the gate and back. Now it was Alicia's turn. The routine was repeated.

Paula went for a ride alone. Once she was outside the gate and had passed the farm buildings, she took her usual route to the Vistula bridge. It felt so good to be on a horse, to breathe fresh air, to see the river and the fields where wheat and rye had grown high. It was good to be alive. Enough of mourning; the old lady was beyond suffering.

The children had another encounter with death that summer. A puppy from their favorite dog's litter died. They were grief-stricken and decided to hold a formal ceremony and funeral. Jas knew the procedure, as he had been present at the funeral and burial of Grand Baba.

A shoebox served as a coffin. Alicia and Jerry acted as pallbearers. They marched solemnly across the lawn, Jas in front with an old scarf around his shoulders. He said it was his prayer shawl. They chose a spot under an anthill. Jas told the other two that they were no longer pallbearers; now they were gravediggers. He handed them two shovels.

As they dug, Alicia noticed ants crawling all about. They put the box with the puppy, whom they named Blossom, in the hole. Jas sprinkled some dirt on top of it and said a Hebrew prayer that his grandfather had taught him.

"Won't the ants eat through the box and then eat Blossom?" Alicia asked.

"That's the way it is," Jerry said. "My father told me that ants help the body decompose and the minerals will return to the earth to feed the flowers, grass and trees."

"Will Grand Baba's body also decompose?" Alicia pronounced the word with difficulty.

"No," Jas said, "she was buried with her prayer book and her prayers will scare the bugs away."

Alicia looked at Jerry for help.

"He is just kidding you," Jerry said.

"How will she go to heaven? How will she get out of her coffin?"

"Her body will not go to heaven, her soul will."

"Does everybody have a soul?"

"All people do," Jerry answered.

"Did Blossom have a soul? She was so tiny when she died, her soul should go to heaven."

"I don't know if animals have souls." Jerry was irritated by now. "How should I know?"

They covered the hole in the ground and went back to play.

When August came death, sickness and mourning were far from everybody's mind. It was harvest time and, as the Bible said, "it was time to pluck up what had been planted." Everyone had to help. Regina was in charge of the operation. Since Mark was not very interested in the workings of the estate, she relied mostly on Michal. Michal was officially a gardener, but he was Regina's right hand in practically everything. During harvest time, he managed the labor force. Besides the peasants, who lived permanently in the estate's servants' quarters, many outsiders were temporarily employed.

Aunt Yentl was the queen of the kitchen. She was in charge of the servants, who cooked huge kettles of stew for people returning from the fields.

Mark's interest in the estate was limited to the mill, where, with his great bulk and amazing strength, he heaved large sacks of grain. If any of his customers or mill hands gave him trouble, he would pick them up by the collar and throw them out. His victims would be out of their wits. His strength was known far and wide and was the subject of many tales. Nobody in his presence would dare to make an anti-Semitic remark. Mark could be both charming and persuasive, especially toward the people he owed money. His daughters wondered at how men who were boiling with anger when they came to see their father left smiling and joking after only a brief conversation with him. Apparently, they had forgotten what they came for.

Harvest time did not interest Mark. The busy season at the mill began in September. But Jas was in his element in the fields. He was far from Kielce, far from school and, most of all, far from his father. The farmhands were his friends; they called him Master Jas. He knew everyone by their first name: Wojtek, Staszek, Franek, Wladek. Although he was the beloved and pampered grandson of Zabiec's owner, he played with the peasant boys, many of whom were rumored to be the illegitimate offspring of his prodigious grandfather. During harvest time Jas got up at dawn and followed the workers.

Guta, Paula and the two younger children would ride to the fields later. The crops consisted mainly of wheat and rye. Oats were grown for the horses and grass for hay. The estate owned two horse drawn harvesting machines. But the machines could not do enough; most of the work was done manually, using scythes. Jas usually managed to drive the harvester despite the protests of the man in charge, who complained that Squire Warman or Michal would give him hell.

When Paula saw Jas in the driver's seat, she laughed. "Can you imagine," she said to Guta, "if his father saw him? He'd probably tell him to study Latin instead."

Alicia and Jerry watched the row of peasants mowing with the scythes, and the women following them tieing the crops into sheaves.

"Why are they cutting it?" Alicia asked. "It looked so nice before."

Guta patted the child's hair. "Don't worry, it will grow back." She tried to explain the process, from harvest to bread and rolls. "In the fall, the fields will be plowed and the grains sowed, and next August, God willing, when the wheat and rye are high, we'll have harvest again."

In the afternoon, they rode back on top of the sheaves to the barns where the crops were stored for threshing. It was a wondrous ride. Alicia and Jerry laughed and rolled between the sheaves and watched the fields where the grass was piled high to dry for hay.

The harvest was over in late August. Paula and the boys had to leave for Kielce. Jas was proud that he had been admitted to the first year of gymnasium in September. He was enrolled in a Polish public school which had a quota for Jewish students. Jerry had been promoted to second grade in the same school that Jas had attended. But Jerry at seven could read like a twelve-year-old. He loved adventure stories and read them without help. Alicia had turned five in June.

"Shouldn't you be sending Alicia to kindergarten?" Paula asked her sister. "You're always complaining that she has no girls to play with."

"She's too young to be exposed to all the germs, measles, chicken pox, mumps and God knows what else," Guta answered.

"The sooner a child gets over these diseases, the better," Paula said.

"They don't learn much in kindergarten," Guta insisted. "Eisig and I can teach her more at home."

"That child of yours will never have a learning problem, but she could benefit in other ways from going to school. Don't ever complain that your daughter is a tomboy."

"Well," Guta said, "Monek is in Kielce and Eisig is not at home, so I decided to stay in Zabiec for at least one more month."

The children came in and overheard the end of the conversation. "Why isn't my daddy at home?" Alicia asked.

"He's in Vienna," her mother answered. "He has to take some more courses."

Jas interrupted. He was eager to show off. "Your daddy is learning Roentgenology. Can you pronounce it?"

Before the little girl had a chance to answer, he said, "Roentgen invented rays that can photograph inside you and see all the dirt."

"I don't have any dirt," the girl protested. After a while, she asked, "Can he see my soul?"

Guta shrugged her shoulders helplessly. "Where does she get these ideas?"

Paula said to Jas, "Shame on you, Alicia is the only girl we have in our family. You should be nice to her."

"It wasn't me who told her about souls, it was Jerry."

Jerry didn't defend himself. Paula was worried about him. She felt that even little Alicia was more of a fighter than he was. "I'm sure," she said, "Jerry wasn't trying to scare Alicia. Then she said to the girl, "Your daddy will use Roentgen rays for sick people to find out what makes them ill. You are too small to worry about this. Nobody knows where souls are or where they go after people die. The best thing is not to think about it."

Jas had something to add. "I thought that Dr. Perlstein was an expert in Roentgenology, so why does Uncle Eisig have to study in Vienna?"

"Perlstein is a con artist," Guta said. "He took one miserable course at the University of Wilno. He introduced himself to your father under false pretenses."

All of a sudden Alicia interrupted. "Like 'Motke Ganef,' the thief."
Everyone burst out laughing.

"She didn't get it from me," Jas said. "That's what Uncle Eisig calls
Grandfather Mark."

Guta's thoughts reverted to her husband. She was afraid that Eisig
relied too much on his brother-in-law's judgment.

Doctor Peltz was a man whose ideas were far ahead of his contemporaries. He believed that doctors should be socially conscious and
contribute time and skills to those who could not afford private care.

In 1925, Dr. Peltz and Dr. Strum opened a medical center where poor
people could be treated for reduced fees. They invited other doctors to
join them, but the majority of physicians not only boycotted the center,
but didn't refer private patients to Dr. Peltz and Dr. Strum. The two of
them started an X-ray clinic and diagnostic center and brought in Dr.
Perlstein from Lublin as an expert in the field, but it soon became obvious
that he knew little.

The two doctors were innovators, resented by the establishment. Dr.
Peltz suffered from diabetes and persuaded Eisig to experiment with
varied amounts of insulin, with himself as the guinea pig. Neither Paula
nor Guta knew anything about it. One day Dr. Peltz went into a coma.
Paula was in a panic; she called on Eisig, who gave her husband an
injection that saved his life. She never forgave Eisig for experimenting
without her knowledge.

Dr. Peltz started his own laboratory, where he conducted urine
analysis and blood sugar determinations. He imported equipment from
Warsaw that was unknown in Kielce: incubators, a centrifuge and a
sterilizer.

Eisig also used techniques that were then unknown to other doctors in
Kielce. For infected boils and other skin inflammations, he injected his
patients with sterile milk, on the principle that a foreign protein would
stimulate the patient's natural immune system. He was quite successful.
After a few days the infection was gone.

Eisig saved many people from surgery. He believed that a knife should
be used only if everything else failed. In the summer of 1927 he was in
Vienna learning how to use x-ray therapy for skin conditions.

Paula seemed to read her sister's thoughts: "I know that Monek seems like a stiff Prussian officer, but, believe me, there is warmth and compassion in him."

The summer was over. Paula and the boys left Zabiec. The blossoms of the linden tree were gone and the leaves started turning different shades of yellow and red. The days were getting shorter and, though the weather was still balmy, crisp autumn breezes could be felt in the mornings and evenings.

The orchard man folded his tent, gathered the fruits, packed up his possessions and left Zabiec. The fields were bare and the cowherds roasted potatoes on an open fire.

Sometimes Guta took Alicia to visit the cowherds to taste the potatoes. They were often burned to the crisp, but the flavor was unmatched by anything cooked indoors. For a while, Alicia enjoyed being the only grandchild, Jas was usually the favorite.

With Jas and Jerry gone, it was Alicia's turn to be spoiled and pampered. Her grandfather, who did not pay much attention to her in the summer, now enjoyed playing cards with the little girl.

Regina, as usual, was preoccupied with getting things done. The crops had to be threshed, grain had to be brought to the mill, hay and oats had to be stored in the barns for winter, horses had to be tended and sent to the Vistula to be washed. Regina had to make all the important decisions: what crops would be rotated, which fields had to be plowed, and what sowed and where.

Produce was gathered in the gardens and most of it packed for export, first to the railroad station in Szczucin and then to the larger city of Tarnow. Some of it was stored in the wagons and eventually sent on the long trip to Kielce to Paula and Guta.

A huge barrel buried in the garden contained slabs of ice insulated with straw. The ice had been taken from the Vistula the winter before and was expected to last an entire year until the river froze again. The ice was used to pack the produce.

Some days Guta rose at dawn to oversee the milking so that Regina could sleep a little longer. Alicia liked to join her mother in the cowsheds.

They watched the women sitting on stools milk the cows. The buckets were poured into large cans, most of which were loaded onto wagons and covered with ice to be exported. The estate produced its own cream, butter and sour milk.

Later during the day Alicia watched the threshing machines at work and the horses being led to troughs for drinking.

Stefka, who was taking care of the child, often approached the mill to wave hello to her new sweetheart. The little girl just stood there fascinated by the sacks of grain sliding down an unloading ramp.

Usually only Jas was allowed inside the mill because, with all the machines and workers, it was judged unsafe for little children. But now Mark, without asking Guta, was only too happy to let Alicia in. She watched the workers and listened to their talk. She quickly picked up their peasant slang and curses. At times Mark had to yell at them for their language in front of her.

When Guta heard Alicia talking and swearing in coarse language, she was horrified. "Oh God," she would say to Regina. "Paula was right. I should have sent her to kindergarten."

"When Jas talks that way," Alicia whined, "everybody loves it. Why can't I?"

"You're a girl," her mother answered. "I hope you'll grow up to be a lady."

Something else happened that convinced Guta that she should take Alicia back to Kielce. One morning Regina had a neck and back pain. She had had a pinched nerve in her neck for a few years and often had to wear a neck brace and sometimes a corset. Guta went to her parents' bedroom with some aspirins and Alicia followed. On the nightstand stood a picture of Jas. He must have been five or six when it was taken: a little blond urchin, stark naked, sitting on a studio swan with his genital area covered by a towel.

Alicia pointed her finger at the photograph. "The swan is naked; why is Jas's penis covered?"

Mark laughed, but Regina and Guta were shocked. "I told you," Guta said to her mother, "it's time to take Alicia home."

Guta and Alicia took the usual route, the carriage to Pacanow and the bus to Kielce. The trip was not much fun for Alicia without her Mucia and her cousins.

Eisig was home from Vienna, Kasia, the maid, was back and there was always "upstairs."

But "upstairs" was not much fun this fall. Jerry had a new friend, a boy named Tadek. They played ping-pong and afterwards they did their homework together. When Alicia asked to play ping-pong she was told by the boys that she was too small and, besides, she was a girl.

Once Paula walked in on this conversation. "I'm a girl," she said, "and I'm much bigger than you. I can probably play ping-pong better than you 'men.' Give me the racket and I'll show you."

Then she turned to Alicia and said, "Get another racket." Alicia could barely reach the table but she managed to hit the ball back to her Mucia. From then on the boys occasionally played ping-pong with her. Most of the time, though, the little girl had no one to play with.

CHAPTER 3

One morning in December 1927, Alicia woke up in her room in Kielce and found what looked like a new toy near her bed. It consisted of rows of beads strung on wires; each row was a different color and all of them were attached to two wooden boards. She burst into her parents' room.

Eisig and Guta were still in bed. "I told you to knock first," Guta said. She saw the board in Alicia's hand and said, "St. Nicholas has brought you a new toy."

"Why do you feed that nonsense to the child?" Eisig asked Guta. "I bought it for you," he said to Alicia. "It's called an abacus and it's how the Chinese learn their numbers."

Alicia could not get St. Nicholas out of her mind. "Does St. Nicholas bring gifts to Jewish children?" she asked.

"St. Nicholas is a Christian saint, but he loves all of the children," Guta answered.

Alicia looked at her father. She knew how to please him. "Eh," she said, "it's only make believe. I know my daddy bought it for me and he's going to teach me numbers."

The following week she was busy playing with the beads. Soon she was able to add and subtract.

"She'll be very good with numbers, unlike you," Eisig said to Guta.

Once, when Alicia was playing with her abacus, she told her parents, "Jas said that I don't know what sixty is." She arranged six tens, one underneath the other. "That's what sixty is," she said proudly.

Eisig said, "Tell Jas that you know more than him."

Guta didn't like his suggestion. "You're asking for trouble. If Alicia taunts him, they will fight worse than ever." Then she said, "My family is known for their ability with languages." She decided to teach her daughter French.

Eisig was jealous: "I should be teaching her German."

32

Guta did not like the idea. "French is more important for a girl," she added. "I could also teach her Russian so she could read *War and Peace* in the original."

There was no mention of religion in Alicia's education. Eisig remembered his rigorous training in Heder, which he now considered a waste. He thought of himself as a man of science. From Guta, Alicia got a sense of an omnipotent God watching over them all, though she still remembered Jerry's telling her that there were only a moon, planets and stars in the sky.

It was a cold winter. The apartment was heated by coal. Every morning the maid started the fire in tall, white-tiled stoves with doors in front. The rooms on Freedom Place were large, with high ceilings, and hard to heat. Alicia and her mother often huddled by the stoves to keep warm.

Alicia's nose was always stuffed; she breathed through her mouth and snored at night.

"It's a good thing we didn't send her to kindergarten," Guta told Eisig. "Breathing through her mouth makes her susceptible to infection. Monek says that she'll eventually have to have her tonsils and adenoids removed."

"Never mind that," Eisig answered. "It's not her throat, it's her nose. She probably has polyps."

Monek has a friend in Krakow who's an eminent ear, nose and throat specialist."

"We'll decide what to do this summer," Eisig concluded.

One afternoon, the Peltzes had a party. Everybody who was anybody in the Jewish society of Kielce was there: lawyers, engineers, business people and doctors who had given up on the boycott.

The children played in Jas and Jerry's room. There were three of them: Jerry, Alicia and a redheaded boy named Rick, the son of one of the guests. Their game consisted of climbing on top of the wardrobe and jumping off, one at a time.

Paula didn't mind this game because Dr. Levin lived on the floor underneath. "Maybe the ceiling will fall on his head, that lousy boycotter."

Alicia jumped down first. Jerry waited until she picked herself up; then he jumped. But Rick did not wait long enough; he landed with all his weight on Jerry's leg. Jerry screamed. Alicia yanked Rick off Jerry's leg and hit him. The noise brought the others. The first thing Dr. Peltz did was cut open his son's sock, cut the laces of the shoes and pull them off and carry Jerry to bed.

It proved to be a compound fracture. A cast was not enough; the boy had to stay in traction. He would have to miss at least two months of school.

Alicia spent a lot of time with her cousin, who was usually reading books. Once the little girl tried to make out a title. The first three letters were easy: D, O, N.

"That's 'Don,'" Jerry said. "You won't be able to figure out the other word because it's Spanish, 'Quixote.'" Then he told her about the knights errant and Sancho Panza, the steed Rocinante and how Don Quixote attacked windmills because he thought they were wicked giants. And how he imagined that a simple peasant girl was the great lady Dulcinea.

When Paula walked in, Alicia ran to her and said, "Jerry can read a big book, but I can speak and sing French."

Jerry protested from bed, "Oh, no more singing. I heard enough."

Paula said to Jerry, "When you enter the gymnasium, your father will insist that you take German. In the meantime I should teach you French."

"I'm not interested," Jerry answered. "I want to learn Spanish so I can read *Don Quixote* in the original."

Paula was flabbergasted. "Nobody in Poland studies Spanish. Look at French literature: *The Three Musketeers, The Count of Monte Cristo* or *The Hunchback of Notre Dame.*

"But I want to read *Don Quixote*," Jerry insisted.

"I don't think I can get a Spanish reader and a Spanish/Polish dictionary," Paula said. After two months, Jerry was ready for school again.

That winter Guta would take Alicia for walks in Kielce's park. The trees were bare and covered with snow. By January the pond was solidly frozen and served as a skating rink.

"I want to skate," Alicia told her mother.

"Next year, God willing, St. Nicholas will bring you skates."

Uncle Monek stressed physical conditioning for children before anyone else did. His pet idea was that from the earliest age, children should be hardened by not being overdressed in cold weather. As with everything else, he was quite strict in enforcing the rules. Jas and Jerry wore short pants and socks. Alicia, wanting to be like her cousins, refused to wear heavy woolen stockings. She ran around with bare legs in the coldest weather.

"You see," Guta told her daughter, "the girls at the skating rink are wearing tights and short skirts, and nobody is bare-legged."

Kasia helped Alicia build a snowman in the yard. Jerry had not completely recovered and Alicia missed her playmate.

The cold Polish winter gave way to warmer weather, but spring was slow in coming. The snow that had been on the streets for weeks started melting, leaving slush underfoot.

The Passover holiday that year came at the end of March. This meant a trip to Zabiec for at least two weeks. The weather was still damp, chilly and windy. But Zabiec was always Zabiec and some mornings you could smell spring in the air.

Some days the three children wandered around the strawberry patch through the birch tree lane and over a ditch to the wired fence that separated the estate from public grounds. They could see the narrow siding of railroad tracks equipped for small trains. People from this side of Vistula took the connecting line to Szczucin, where they could take regular trains to Tarnow and other towns in old Galicia and, finally, to Krakow.

"Soon I'll be taking a big train to Krakow, where a doctor will unstuff my nose," Alicia bragged to her cousins.

"He'll cut it off," Jas declared.

"You don't know everything." As Guta had predicted, Alicia continued, "My daddy said that I know more than you. I can read and count better."

This time Jas laughed. The claim was too preposterous to be taken seriously.

The important events during their spring vacation were two Seders, especially the first, as Jerry and Alicia were judged too small to stay up late on two successive nights. Many people were invited; there were relatives the children never saw during the year. The long table, covered with a white lace tablecloth, looked imposing, with glowing crystal goblets, silver flatware and festive dishes used only for Passover. Mark conducted the services in Hebrew and sang in his great voice. Servants stood underneath the windows just to listen to him, even though they didn't understand a word.

Alicia and Jerry knew the story of Passover from their mothers. To them it was simple: Moses and the Jews were good, Egyptians were bad. They made the Jews work many hours under the broiling sun to build pyramids. God was on the side of the Jews. That is why He sent ten plagues on Egypt and parted the Red Sea for Moses, while the Egyptians drowned.

Everybody had a *Hagadah* in front of him, with Polish translation on one side and Hebrew on the other.

The children enjoyed every step—reading, drinking and singing—though they knew that their goblets contained colored soda water instead of wine. The food was delicious, with all the traditional dishes—gefulte fish, chicken soup with matzo meal kneidls, and so on.

When it came time to ask the Four Questions, Jas walked confidently to his grandfather.

Jerry and Alicia could read in their *Hagadahs*, "The youngest child present asks the Four Questions." Alicia pushed herself up from her chair and ran to her grandfather. "I am the youngest," she said.

Everyone burst out laughing. Paula laughed the most. "That girl has spunk," she said to Guta.

Mark took Alicia on his knee. "You're a girl," he said, "and Jas is the only one who knows a little Hebrew."

"Well, why did you teach Jas and not me?"

Regina was appalled at her nerve. "That child has too much chutzpah," she told her daughters.

Mark was more diplomatic. "I'll teach you and Jerry next year."

Paula laughed again and said to Guta in a low voice, so her mother wouldn't hear, "Another one of his promises. I wonder what other promises he'll make today and how he'll manage to break them all."

"You're unfair to father."

"How many times has he sworn on your health, on the childrens' health and even on his own health that, next year after harvest, you will get your dowry? You've been married almost seven years and you haven't received one cent. At least I got a set of furniture for Monek's study and a grand piano for me."

Now Paula picked Alicia up and said, "My little suffragette."

"What's that?" Alicia asked.

Paula put a finger on the child's lips. "I'll explain later. Now let's listen to Jas."

Jas donned a yarmulke on his head and proudly asked in Hebrew, "Why is this night different from all other nights?"

Afterwards, the children watched their grandfather break a matzoh and wrap it in a cloth napkin. They knew the custom. The matzoh was hidden somewhere and, after the meal, the children were free to look for it. Whoever found it would bargain with Mark for a gift. When the time came, the three of them went crazy running around, looking under chairs and crawling between people's legs. Finally Jas found it on a window sill behind a curtain. He brought the matzoh to his grandfather and the bargaining began. When it was over, Jas had been promised a new bicycle.

Paula and Guta shook their heads. "I told you," Paula said, "another promise." They knew that, as usual, he was short of money. It was doubtful that he could spring for a new bicycle.

Jerry and Alicia forgot their disappointment when the singing began anew. Mark led and everyone else was the chorus. They kept repeating a line in Hebrew: "Ahad Eloheinu shebashamaim u baerez" (One is eternal who is above heaven and earth). Alicia and Jerry enjoyed repeating the words as long as they knew what they meant. "Why are there such funny letters on the other side?" Alicia wanted to know.

"That is the Hebrew alphabet," Guta explained.

By the time the dinner and services were over, Alicia and Jerry were exhausted, but Jas and his grandfather were still going strong.

After two weeks of vacation it was time to leave. "We don't have to go back. I don't have school," Alicia said to her mother.

Guta agreed that it would be nice to see spring in Zabiec, with the lilacs in bloom. "But your daddy is home," she said, "and you'll be lonely in Zabiec without Jerry. Spring will come to Kielce."

When they got home, Alicia ran to her father. "Daddy, teach me Hebrew. Next year I'll ask the Four Questions."

Eisig shrugged his shoulders. "I don't think that a girl is allowed to do that." He didn't like Alicia's idea. His early experiences had turned him off anything that remotely referred to religion.

June arrived, with another trip to Zabiec. It was strawberry season. The children watched the rows of women crouching and picking berries. Sometimes, Alicia and Jerry helped. The berries were packed in wooden boxes and shipped to neighboring towns. Regina realized a nice profit from the sales. The children's favorite dish was strawberries and fresh cream.

June was also a month of birthdays. Alicia turned six, Paula twenty-nine, and Guta twenty-eight. Guta knew that she could no longer postpone her daughter's entry into school. Alicia's breathing problems had to be attended to this summer.

Toward the end of June, Guta came down with a bad case of migraine headaches. Mark was supposedly on business in Warsaw, looking for grain merchants. He had told the women that he could get better prices in a big city. However, Paula doubted his motives. "I won't tell mother," she said to Guta, "but I think he is going to sell the crops before they are harvested for a fraction of what they are worth. He probably needs money right now for his escapades."

Guta could not imagine her father being so devious.

They received a letter from Dr. Peltz. He had arranged an appointment for Alicia to see his friend, an ear, nose and throat specialist. Paula offered to go. She was looking forward to seeing her cousins and browsing in her uncle's furniture store, and would perhaps look at the latest fashions.

"You are going to meet your family in Krakow," Paula told Alicia. Mr. Adam Pleszowski is grandmother's brother, so he is my and your mother's uncle. His son Wladek, who is a lawyer, is our cousin.

On the morning of July 4th Paula, Alicia, Guta, Jas and Jerry were driven to Szczucin by the estate's deluxe carriage. The road to Szczucin ran in the opposite direction to the road to Pacanow. Though Szczucin and Pacanow were the same size, they seemed like two different countries and cultures. Szczucin was clean, had sidewalks, sanitation and electricity. It had a doctor, a dentist, a lawyer, a pharmacy, a notary public and a few nice stores. Pacanow, in contrast, looked like a medieval hovel. The difference reflected the chasm between the pre-war living standards of the occupying powers, Russia and Austria. Now both towns were in the independent Republic of Poland.

When they arrived in Szczucin, they went to the ice cream parlor first. Guta was nervous. She kept kissing her daughter and telling her to mind Mucia.

From the ice cream parlor they went to the railroad station. There was much hugging and kissing. Paula and Alicia boarded the train. They kept waving as it pulled away.

There weren't too many people on the train. Paula and Alicia had a compartment all to themselves. Alicia was excited. As they traveled across the flat Polish countryside, she watched the green meadows and grazing cattle.

In Krakow, Wladek was at the station to meet them. He was a medium sized young man with broad shoulders. When he saw Paula, his eyes beamed with pleasure and admiration. They hugged and kissed. She was a head taller than he, as with most men, her husband being the exception.

"Oh, Polusha," Wladek said, "you become more beautiful every year. Your gorgeous green eyes will never stop fascinating me."

"Are you sure," Paula asked, "I'm not related to you on my father's side? You sound just like him."

"How's that old reprobate?" Wladek asked.

"He's gallivanting someplace in Warsaw, nobody knows with whom, while my mother is working hard to keep the estate going."

"So what else is new?"

Alicia watched and listened. Wladek finally noticed her.

"So this is Alicia. What a beautiful child." He picked her up and kissed her. "Is she as gentle and sweet as her mother?"

Paula laughed. "That's also an old story," she said. "Guta is gentle and sweet, while Paula is a devil."

"You sure are. I'll always remember you as a wild horsewoman with a fiery temper." He put the little girl down.

Paula pointed to Alicia. "She's more like me than like her mother. You should have heard her giving her grandfather an argument during the Seder. Guta tries to tame her, but I don't think she'll succeed."

"Ah, those great Seders in Zabiec. I must get myself invited again," he said. "Does that old scoundrel still have his beautiful voice?"

"Better than ever."

"That man missed his vocation. He could have been a great cantor or an opera star, and what an actor he would be!"

"Could have. Would have. Those things would require persistence and commitment. It's easier for him to live off his wife's inheritance than to work."

"Polusha, you are really hard on the man."

"Somebody has to be. My mother is bewitched by him and blind to his faults. Guta is too naive and gentle. And to Jas, his grandfather is the best. He worships him. I wish he looked up to his father instead."

Wladek helped them with their luggage. As they waited for a taxi to take them to the hotel, he said, "After you check in and refresh yourself, I'd like to invite you both to dinner."

He looked at Alicia and said, "I gave up hoping that your Mucia would fall madly in love with me and leave her husband. I've gotten engaged to a bright, pretty girl who's a second-year law student. I want you both to meet her."

"Oh, how wonderful," Paula said. "I can't wait to meet her and to congratulate you both."

Alicia was jumping and hopping in front of them. "Tomorrow a doctor will unstuff my nose," she sang.

Wladek was amused. "She doesn't seem worried at all."

Paula laughed. "The only doctor that she is afraid of is Monek. This child doesn't seem to have any fears and she drives poor Guta crazy."

"Guta," Wladek was now laughing, "tying knots on her towels to make sure that nobody else uses them and gives her germs."

A taxi pulled up. Paula and Alicia checked into the hotel, and after a couple of hours they met Wladek and his girlfriend in the lobby. She was an attractive girl with brown hair and eyes.

"This is Eda Weinberg," Wladek said, "and this is Paula Warman." Then, correcting himself, "No, Paula Peltz."

"So you are Paula," Eda said. "I've heard so much about you. Now I can see what Wladek means when he says you're the most beautiful girl in the family. I've resigned myself to the fact that no other woman will ever equal you and he'll have a crush on you for the rest of his life."

"I'm sure you're exaggerating," Paula said. "We're only cousins."

Alicia did not like to be ignored. "Like me and Jerry," she piped in.

Eda looked at her. "So this is cousin Guta's little girl. I love your hair," she said to the child.

"I see Wladek has filled you in about our family," Paula said.

Wladek got into the conversation. "I told you something interesting about Paula," he said to Eda.

"If you want Paula to know, tell her yourself!" Eda said.

Paula laughed. "I think I know the secret. I've heard it from other people."

"I guess I'm not the only one to wonder," Wladek said, "why you married that humorless, stiff, pompous Austrian Lieutenant-Doctor?"

"Maybe I wanted someone completely different from my father. What good does his charm do my mother?"

"But did you have to go to the other extreme, Polusha?" Wladek asked.

"Monek is a reliable, hard-working person. He takes his profession and responsibilities seriously, he is dedicated to medicine and he loves me."

"Bravo," Eda said. "Now that you've heard it yourself, you'll have to settle on me. Let's go eat."

Alicia was not used to eating in a restaurant. She enjoyed having waiters treat her like a grown-up and, as always, she watched Mucia make little animals from the dough she removed from inside the rolls. While they were waiting for the main course the conversation turned serious.

"Did you hear," Wladek asked the women, "about that crazy maniac running around Germany, blaming the Jews for Germany's losing the war? He has a bunch of goons who beat people up and loot Jewish stores."

"Who is he?" Paula asked.

"His name is Hitler, and nobody takes him seriously. While he was in a Bavarian jail he wrote a book, *Mein Kampf*, full of fantastic and ridiculous ideas, hate and stupidity. He looks a bit like Charlie Chaplin, a clown with a silly mustache."

Eda smiled at the mention of Charlie Chaplin. "We saw 'City Lights' last night," she told Paula. "Chaplin is funny, and sometimes pathetic, but he also seems to me to be very human and full of compassion." She turned to Wladek and asked, "How can you compare this gifted human being to a vicious maniac?"

"I am only talking about physical appearance," Wladek said defensively. "Sometimes I worry whether Hitler will turn out to be dangerous."

"Does he have many followers in Germany?" Paula asked.

"Not many," Wladek answered. "The economic situation in Germany has improved a lot in the last few years. People are generally prosperous and happy. A rabble-rouser and hate-monger like him has no chance."

"Last year I visited my girlfriend in Berlin," Eda said. "It was my impression that the Jews there are more assimilated than Polish Jews. They were brought up on German literature and music and fought in the war. To them we are inferior 'Ost Jude' (Eastern Jews)."

Wladek shrugged his shoulders. "To hell with them, I feel Polish. After all, how many men can claim that they ran away from home at fourteen to fight for Polish independence?"

"I bet you lied about your age!" Eda laughed.

After dinner Paula excused herself and explained that they had to go home early, Alicia needed rest. "You must have a good sleep tonight," she told her niece. "Tomorrow morning we go to see the doctor." Wladek offered to walk them to their hotel.

Alicia asked, "Will we go sightseeing while we're in Krakow?"

"I hope so, but first let's see what the doctor says," Paula said.

The next day, Paula took Alicia to the doctor. The diagnosis of polyps was confirmed. Surgery was performed the same day in the office; it was quick and almost painless. The doctor recommended lots of fluids and ice cream. He also advised Paula to keep Alicia quiet for a few days, as sudden jumps could open up the stitches.

"Can I go out tomorrow?" Alicia asked.

"If you feel all right you may, but don't run and jump," the doctor told her.

"I promise, I promise. I'll pretend I'm an old lady, like my Mucia."

"Thank you," Paula said.

The doctor laughed. He was not a young man, but he was aware of Paula's extraordinary beauty and charm. "Children," he said. "Anybody older than twenty is considered old."

Alicia had to spend the rest of the day in her hotel room. Wladek came over and brought her a container of ice cream.

"Go out," he told Paula. "I'll babysit."

"I'm six years old," Alicia declared. "I'm a big girl and I don't need a babysitter."

"Sorry," Wladek answered, "I'll just keep you company."

"I'm going to look for a shop that might have something for Alicia to read. She's already finished the book she brought with her."

"Get a Spanish dictionary for Jerry," Alicia reminded her aunt.

Paula laughed. "I have such precocious children on my hands. Jerry, at eight, wants to read *Don Quixote* in the original." She could find her way around Krakow quite well. She remembered a store that carried children's books and toys. As she entered, the first thing she noticed was a doll that came with different outfits and a makeup kit. Alicia would not appreciate a doll, Paula thought. Maybe I should buy it anyway and see what she says. Guta worries, but I don't. I remember being mostly interested in horses, but it didn't keep me from growing up as a woman. She thought back to all the men who had been in love with her and how she had first met Monek. She had been only fifteen at the time. He was a mature man of twenty-six already a doctor and surgeon. Later, he told her that when he saw her dismounting her horse that winter day, he knew that he could never think about another woman. And Eric; she wondered where he was now, whether he'd married and what her life would had been like with him, what kind of children she would have. Paula smiled to herself; I still like to flirt

with men, no wonder Monek is jealous. If I gave Wladek the slightest
encouragement he would leave Eda and she knows it, too. I won't get
this doll for Alicia, she decided. She chose some cowboys-and-Indians
books and a few puzzles. These should keep her busy, she decided. When
she got back to her room, Eda was there too. The three of them played
gin rummy.

"How nice of you to spend the afternoon with Alicia," she said to Eda.

"I just wanted to see how she was doing. I'd love to meet her mother
someday," Eda said.

"Oh, definitely," Paula said. "In the winter we usually come to Krakow
to shop for clothes and furniture."

"Mucia, Mucia," Alicia interrupted, "Wladek said that tomorrow he'll
show me the city."

"Do you remember your promise? No running or jumping."

As usual, Eda was encouraging. "I'm sure a big girl like Alicia will
follow the doctor's instructions."

"Now that everything is settled," Wladek said, "how about browsing
around in our furniture showroom tomorrow morning? Afterwards we'll
have something to eat and I'll show Alicia the city."

"I hope we won't be keeping you from something important," Paula
said.

"Don't worry. It's the middle of the summer; we were planning on
going to see my mother and sister in the mountains but I prefer spending
the time with you."

The showroom occupied an entire block of a busy street. When Paula
and Alicia arrived, Wladek and Eda were waiting for them. Adam
Pleszowski, Wladek's father, came in to say hello. He was a tall man
with a goatee. When Paula looked at him she thought she was seeing her
late grandfather Janush. Memories of her magic childhood in Pierscien
flooded her mind.

"It's uncanny how much you resemble your late father."

He smiled and said, "Well I guess there is a family resemblance." He
asked about Regina's health. Then he expressed regret that he could not
attend his mother's funeral the past summer. "The entire family was

abroad. We didn't learn of her death until we returned that August. Did my other sister, the venerable Ida Rodbard, come to the funeral?"

"She did," Paula answered. "Just her, no family. She attended the service and the burial, didn't say hello to anyone and left. I understand she stayed overnight in a hotel in Szczucin."

"My, my," he said, "I would think that the death of a mother would bring two sisters together. I hear that the Rodbards are doing all right buying apartment houses in Kielce."

Then he apologized for not inviting them to dinner at his house but, as they already knew, his wife and daughter were away in the mountains.

A customer walked in. It was difficult not to notice her; she was tall, slim, elegant and dressed in the latest fashion.

She looks like a movie star, Paula thought.

The lady approached them. Alicia was wandering around the store. Paula noticed that the woman was not young anymore, but she was certainly well preserved.

She said hello and Adam introduced her to Paula: "This is Mrs. Dankowa. She and her husband are dear friends and preferred customers." Then, pointing to Paula, "This is my niece, Paula Warman. I think you know the Warmans; Paula is Mark and Regina's daughter."

Dankowa, Paula thought; where have I heard that name?

"Oh yes," the woman said to Paula. "A few years ago, my husband and I stayed in the same hotel in Krynica as your parents. We became quite friendly."

She stayed in the same hotel as my parents, Paula thought. Then it came to her. She was my father's mistress for a long time; it was one of his more serious affairs. Now she has the nerve to stand here and tell me she was a friend of both my parents. Paula felt like spitting in the woman's face. Mrs. Dankowa extended her hand. Paula looked at Adam and Wladek, evidently they were not aware of the connection. She didn't want to make a scene. She stared at the woman's extended hand and said as coldly as she could, "Adam forgot to tell you that I've been married for quite a few years and I have two big boys. My name is Mrs. Peltz."

Adam was confused, the conversation was not going well. "Oh yes," he said, "Paula is married to a prominent physician in Kielce."

Paula finally shook the woman's hand, but her eyes were still hostile.

"I don't want to bother you," Mrs. Dankowa said to Adam, "you're busy with your company. The salesclerk will show me around. If I need you I'll call you."

In the meantime, Alicia noticed an upright piano that looked like the one in the Peltz's apartment. She ran back to Paula and pulled at her skirt.

"You're not supposed to run," Paula said wearily.

"Oh, I forgot. I'm sorry, but I saw your piano over there."

"It just looks like mine. Grandfather Mark bought mine here.

Then Paula told Wladek, "That piano and the furniture for Monek's study are the only things we ever got from my father. Guta just got his promises."

Wladek laughed. "Should I tell her?" he asked his father.

Adam shrugged his shoulders.

"I hate to disappoint you," Wladek said, "but it's really a gift from me."

Paula looked at him skeptically.

"You see, we never collected from Mark. My father was ready to sue him, but I convinced him to consider it a gift from our family to you."

Paula was embarrassed. It was one thing when she berated her father, but she didn't like to hear it from someone else. She felt she was out of control, first meeting Dankowa and now this. "That son of a bitch," she said. Then, pointing at Alicia, "I shouldn't talk like this in front of the child."

"Why are you calling grandfather a son of a bitch? My daddy calls him 'Motke Ganef'." Whenever she said this, the grown-ups laughed.

Paula grew more and more irritated. "It's not funny, Alicia."

Noticing her annoyance, Wladek said, "I'm sorry I told you." He added, "You shouldn't worry about Jas looking up to his grandfather. When we were growing up, he was also my hero." Then he tried to describe Mark to Eda. "He's a huge man, well over six feet tall, and he weighs about 250 pounds, all muscle. As I remember, he could bend steel with his powerful hands, lift a grown man above his head and toss him up like a puppet. He was always full of fun and sang with a fantastic tenor voice. And he was never boring, like my father." He poked Adam lovingly in the ribs.

Paula was not impressed by the description of her father. "Your 'boring' father is building a great fortune, while mine is in the process of squandering one."

"Polusha, you can't blame the man for land reform. Many great Polish magnates were ruined overnight."

"Zabiec is getting smaller and smaller. He put his inheritance money in the bank in order to have easy access to it for his adventures. Your father bought his furniture store and the Rodbards bought apartment houses; they didn't lose anything during the devaluation of the Polish mark. Our fortune in cash was lost overnight."

"Come on, Paula. How could your father foresee what was going to happen to the money? My family was just lucky."

"I'm talking about the way he lives. I'm sure he has a mistress in Krakow, another one in Warsaw and one in Zabiec, right under my mother's nose."

"Like a sailor," Wladek laughed. "A girl in every port."

Eda put her arm around Wladek. "So that's the man who was your childhood hero. I hope you're not planning to take after him."

Now it was Paula's turn. "Don't worry, the Pleszowski men are good providers, steady, reliable husbands and affectionate fathers."

"Thank you, Polusha. I hope we're not too boring. I'm hungry, let's go eat."

History had always been Wladek's hobby; now he enjoyed explaining things to the child: "Krakow was once the capital of Poland the Polish kings ruled from that castle. For many centuries Poland was united with Lithuania, together they stretched from the Baltic to the Black Sea. They were one of the most powerful countries in Europe."

After lunch, the four of them went to see the ancient Polish castle Wawel. It stands high on a hill overlooking the river.

"It's the same Vistula as in Zabiec," Paula explained to Alicia, "but here it is narrower and brisker because it is close to its source."

There was a strange rapport between Paula and Eda. Though they'd only met two days before, Paula felt she'd found a kindred soul, as if Eda were an old friend. She wanted to talk to another woman. Guta was too involved with her own problems; Paula needed an outsider. "Wladek thinks that I'm fixated on my father and Zabiec. But what bothers me is my mother and sister. Mother never says anything detrimental about Father. She wouldn't let us criticize him. If she knows about his philandering and infidelities, she doesn't show it, but I'm sure she suffers deeply and it affects her physical well-being. The only person she might discuss her feelings with is Aunt Yentl."

"Who is she?" Eda asked.

"She's not a Pleszowska. She's my father's sister, but she is totally devoted to my mother and doesn't like her brother."

Eda's interest was mounting. "Women in our society are such helpless creatures; what about your sister?"

"Lately my father has been endorsing bad checks by falsifying his younger son-in-law's signature. He's a bit afraid of my husband."

"Oh my God," Eda said, "that's a criminal offense; he could go to jail for it."

"Eisig usually covers the check, but then he vents his anger on Guta."

Eda started to laugh: "No wonder he calls his father-in-law 'Motke Ganef'."

"That's another story," Paula said. "We shouldn't laugh at Alicia when she repeats her father's choice expression. She should be taught to respect her grandfather. We all tend to talk too much in front of her."

"She's a smart girl; she would find out anyway."

They were looking for a coffeehouse where they could get ice cream for Alicia. As they walked they came upon an old wall with a broken gate.

Alicia looked inside. "What's in there?" she asked Wladek.

"Behind this wall was a ghetto," Wladek answered.

"What's that?"

"In the middle ages, Jews were only allowed to live in a certain part of the city, and couldn't go outside without special permission. This section of the city is named Kazimierz, in memory of King Kazimierz The Great, who in the middle ages invited Jews to Poland."

Eda laughed. "Now many Poles would like to disinvite us. They think that if the Jews left, their woes would be over."

Alicia peeked inside at the narrow, winding streets. She noticed men in caftans and fur hats and boys with sidelocks hanging from underneath their yarmulkes. It was a warm July day.

"They're still there," she said.

"They want to be there, but those who want to leave may do so. They can become doctors, like your father, lawyers, like me and businessman, like my father," Wladek told her.

Then he said to the women, "I think the time will come when most Jews will lose their Jewish identity. They'll be Poles, Germans. French, Italians and so on. Occasionally they might observe traditional holidays."

As usual, Eda did not agree. "I read about that infamous Dreyfus affair in the most liberal and enlightened country of Europe. I think that others will never let us forget where we came from. Sometimes I'm inclined to join a Zionist movement."

"Come on Eda, that's a pipe-dream. I was born in Poland, educated here and I fought for my country, so why should I leave?"

"It's a dream all right," Eda answered, "to take people from the shtetls—people who have never smelled a flower—and transform them into farmers and pioneers. They are turning the desert back into a land of milk and honey, the way it was 2000 years ago."

Paula wondered how Eda and Wladek would get along in the future. Eda always contradicted him.

Wladek said, "That's what I get for falling in love with an independent, strong-minded woman. I should find me a 'three K' girl."

"What's three K?" Paula asked.

"Oh, you don't know?" Wladek chuckled. "That's "Kinder, Kuche and Kirche—children, kitchen and church."

"Oh, how typical of the Germans," Eda laughed. "Not to mention bed."

"For that," Wladek said, "a gentleman has a mistress. He does it occasionally with his wife, just enough to make her pregnant."

Eda nudged Wladek playfully. "I wouldn't stand for it," she said. "I'd throw the bum out."

Wladek pulled her to him and kissed her.

Alicia looked at them and squinted. "They're kissing now, but when they get married they'll argue," she declared.

Eda was surprised. She said to Paula, "That's a funny statement from a little girl." Then she said to Alicia, "Your mommy and daddy must have kissed after they were married. How else would they have had you?"

Paula pulled Eda aside. "That is still forbidden territory," she whispered.

"But Paula, Alicia is a bright six-year-old who grew up on a farm. She must have some idea of how babies are made."

"She's not my daughter, she's Guta's. As far as I know she doesn't connect the birth of a baby with anything that happens between a man and a woman. She believes that when people get married God gives them children."

Eda shook her head. "You mean, a Jewish child believes in immaculate conception?"

Paula laughed. "In his professional life, Eisig sees so many men who could spread venereal diseases to women that he would like to protect his daughter from the knowledge of sex as long as possible."

"That's strange logic. From the way Alicia reacted when Wladek and I were kissing, she can't see much affection between her parents."

"Well," Paula said, "I'm sure that Eisig loves Guta, but he was a poor, struggling doctor when he married her and he expected some help from his father-in-law to establish his practice. All he got from that direction was trouble. The stress doesn't help my sister; she gets bad migraine headaches and suffers from severe menstrual cramps. I know Eisig wants a boy, but I doubt that Guta, in her present condition, could carry a baby to term. She's already had a couple of miscarriages."

All of a sudden Eda started to laugh.

Paula was shocked; there she was, spilling her guts to her, and she thought it was funny.

"I'm sorry," Eda said. "I wasn't laughing at your family's problems. I just remembered something. My father still feels guilty because he made my mother pregnant with me twenty-five years ago, causing her much discomfort and pain."

Paula flopped on a bench and said, "Let's sit. I'm ashamed of only talking about myself. I don't know anything about you."

"But I love to hear about Wladek's family. As he aptly pointed out, his immediate family is boring, just like mine. My father is a lawyer; my mother used to be a schoolteacher, but she has a heart condition and has to take it easy. I'm an only daughter and my father always encouraged me to use my mind. I was never expected to be a 'three K' girl. I got my Matura and now I'm going to the university and following in my father's footsteps. Your gang is fascinating; I would love to meet all of you. You'll hate me if I tell you that I'm especially looking forward to meeting your father."

"I'm sure you will be charmed, like all other women, so be forewarned."

Wladek said, "You two women just keep on gabbing." He was happy that his favorite cousin and fiancée got along so well.

They walked together to the hotel. When they parted Paula agreed to come to Eda's parents' house that evening for supper.

When Paula and Alicia entered their hotel room, there was a bouquet of red roses on the bureau. "Roses are my favorite flowers, they are so beautiful," Paula exclaimed. "I wonder who sent them." She found a card: "To a beautiful lady with ebony hair and to a little girl with golden curls, for the privilege of watching you both." It was signed, "An anonymous admirer." Paula read the card out loud. She was used to this kind of adoration from strange men.

"See, sometimes it's fun being a girl. Now, we've got to wash up and rest, then dress for dinner."

Alicia lay down on the bed. She was asleep in a moment. Paula opened the child's suitcase and found a pink organdy dress with ruffles. She decided Alicia would wear it that evening.

Paula was ready to lie down herself, but there was a knock at the door. A bellboy brought her a letter. "It was just delivered," he said.

Paula gave him a tip and took the letter. To her surprise it was from Mrs. Dankowa. How did she find out where I'm staying? That woman has some nerve to write to me. Paula was tempted to tear it up and throw it in the garbage, but curiosity overcame her. She opened it and read:

I saw the hate and contempt in your eyes and I don't blame you, but I would like you to know my side of the story. Once I was deeply in love with your father. I don't have to describe to you the impression that man makes—dashing, handsome, suave. I could not resist his advances.

I have a good and secure marriage and, believe it or not, until I met your father I was never unfaithful to my husband. But I was ready to leave him if your father would leave your mother. I settled for a clandestine affair just to be with my lover; you probably know that it lasted a few years. Like all cheating husbands, he told me bad things about his wife. I believed him, though deep inside I had my doubts.

One summer before the war, I stayed with my husband in a hotel in Krynica; to my embarrassment, both Mark and Regina were staying in the same hotel. I found your mother a lovely and intelligent woman and we became friends during that summer. At the end of our stay she told me that she knew about my affair with her husband. She felt sorry for me.

I also felt sorry for her. At least I could break the relationship; she was stuck for life. I could not in good conscience keep my affair with your father going anymore. I simply would not have been able to live with myself.

I still love both of your parents very much and I hope that you and your sister will not hold a grudge against me. I'm sorry that I caused your mother so much pain. She really deserves better.

With love and respect,

Helena Dankowa

Paula felt like tearing the letter into tiny pieces, but instead she threw it into her bag. I'll show it to Guta, she thought.

Alicia was now half awake. Paula handed her the dress.

"Do I have to put it on?" Alicia complained.

"Sometimes a girl has to dress up. You can't pretend to be a wild cowboy all the time."

"But it itches." Alicia wished she were wearing her everyday clothes and climbing trees in Zabiec with Jerry. She was even getting tired of all the ice cream she was eating. In Zabiec, the strawberries were gone, but

July was the season for raspberries and red currants. The bushes were in the back of the vegetable garden, her grandmother's pride and joy. Grudgingly she slipped into the dress.

Paula put on a flowered dress that emphasized the sparkle in her eyes. She placed a red rose in her hair. She took Alicia by the hand and twirled her around the room. Alicia no longer minded the organdy dress.

Paula jingled her bracelet. "I feel like Carmen," she said.

"Who's Carmen?"

"Oh, a gypsy woman."

Alicia remembered gypsies coming to Zabiec. The women were usually dirty, told fortunes and stole from people. Her Mucia did not look or act anything like them. Something else occurred to her. "When grandfather sings 'Toreador' Jerry told me it's from the opera 'Carmen.' Carmen was a gypsy."

Paula stopped her dance. "It's just like Jerry to know the names of all the operas. We both miss Jerry."

Paula's good mood didn't last long. When they were walking to Eda's parents' apartment, her thoughts returned to the letter. Alicia noticed that her aunt was not her usual self. "Mucia," she asked, "did I do anything wrong? I put on the dress."

"Oh, no," Paula hugged her niece, "it has nothing to do with you."

"I know," Alicia said. "It's because of grandfather."

Paula laughed, "I should be used to his tricks by now, shouldn't I?"

The supper was uneventful. As usual, the men admired Paula, but she was tired, and couldn't wait to go back to her hotel.

The next morning they were ready to leave. Wladek and Eda met them at the station. Paula was wearing a white summer dress with a sailor collar, red tie and a red belt that emphasized her slim waist. She wore a white cloche hat and white shoes.

"Isn't my cousin beautiful?" Wladek asked Eda.

"For once, I have to agree with you," she answered. She herself was wearing a smart pink linen suit.

"You don't look so bad yourself." Wladek looked at her appreciatively.

"Well, thank you for noticing me," she answered.

"I'm in the company of the three most beautiful ladies in Poland,"
Wladek said.

"He sounds just like my father," Paula laughed.

Paula and Alicia boarded the train. Once they were settled in their
compartment, they decided to go to the dining car for something to eat.
As usual, men were looking at Paula.

"Are they all in love with you?" Alicia asked.

"Love is a big word. These are just innocent flirtations and maybe a
way to start an interesting conversation."

They went back to their compartment. The train stopped at Tarnow,
the biggest city on the way to Szczucin. Alicia looked out the window
and saw boys in uniform selling newspapers, cigarettes and candy.
Suddenly she started to jump with excitement. "Mucia, Mucia!" she
exclaimed.

"I told you not to jump."

"Look who's there!" the child insisted.

Who could it be? Paula wondered. She looked out the window and
saw a large man shaking hands with the conductor and a blond boy with
a shiny new bike. No doubt about it, it was Jas and Mark. Jas had gotten
a new bike.

"Jas, Jas!" Paula shouted.

The conductor was pointing to the bike and the train, trying to explain
something. He spread his hands helplessly. Mark was gesticulating and
patting the man on the back. Inside the train, Alicia read the sign, "No
bikes allowed." Paula was still waving and yelling. Mark and Jas noticed
her as the conductor announced, "All aboard." Mark, Jas and the bike
got on the train and joined them. Some people were annoyed by the
commotion, but Mark smiled and talked his way past them. All four of
them found themselves in a large compartment, while Jas moved Paula
and Alicia's luggage.

Paula wondered if Mark had bought new tickets for them and if he had
paid the difference. She hugged her father and son. Mark picked her up
and twirled her in the air. He was just as she had known him as a girl: the
smartest, funniest and strongest man, a man who could charm a stone.
He had gotten the family out of trouble during the war when Zabiec was

changing hands from the Austrians to the Russians. She forgot his extramarital affairs, his spending habits and forgeries. Maybe it's not all his fault, she thought. Mother is probably not interested in sex anymore and a man like this. . . . Her thoughts trailed off.

When they settled down Paula noticed that Jas was rubbing his eye. "I think I have something inside," he said. The children trusted Paula. She skillfully removed splinters from fingers, examined their throats and, when she put iodine on their scrapes and scratches it did not sting them as much as when others did.

Now Paula made Jas tilt his head back, and removed a speck of dust with the corner of a handkerchief. "Now close your eye," she instructed, "and let the tears wash it out."

"It's fine now," Jas said, blinking.

Alicia pulled at her aunt's dress: "I think I have a splinter in my finger."

"She's just jealous of the attention I'm getting. She doesn't have a splinter," Jas interrupted.

Paula gave her niece the benefit of the doubt and looked at her finger. "Jas is right," she said. "No splinter."

Then the bantering between the children started.

"I see they didn't cut off your nose," the boy said.

"I see yours got longer," Alicia answered.

"We should be pulling out soon," Paula said.

Jas looked at the clock across the platform. "Can you tell time, Alicia?"

Alicia knew quite well how to tell time, but she could not make out the numbers on the distant dial. She was squinting and trying hard.

"You are either stupid or blind like a hen," Jas told her.

So he noticed it too, Paula thought. She said to her father in a low voice, "It looks like this little girl will have to wear glasses. This won't make Guta very happy, with all the dreams and plans she has for her daughter. She pointed to the two children, "They are always fighting; maybe there's some strange attraction between them." She quoted: "Cousinage dangereux voisinage."

Krakow and the train rides had been exciting for Alicia, but it was good to be back in Zabiec, play-acting with Jerry, watching Jas's crazy bike stunts and eating raspberries and currants from the bushes. To her, the sounds and smells of Zabiec were unique. At night, before she fell asleep, she listened to croaking frogs, neighing horses and barking dogs. She would awake to the sounds of a crowing rooster and chirping birds. The linden tree was in bloom now and its sweet scent permeated the house.

On hot days Guta, Paula and the children liked to bathe in the Vistula. The sandy beach on the river bank was only a few kilometers from the estate. Kazimierz would harness the horses to the everyday buggy and they would ride to the shore. They had to stop in front of a tall, massive dike that had been built after the war by the Polish government to protect the fields from flooding. The dike built during the Russian occupation had disintegrated and eroded into the river.

The family crossed the dike on foot and went to the beach. For some strange reason none of them could swim. It was odd that Paula, who was a great equestrian and had even contemplated learning to ski, could not swim. Jas, who was well-coordinated, never expressed an interest in water sports.

One day they were sitting in knee-deep water, splashing each other. Jas and Jerry ventured a little farther, until the water reached their waists. Alicia tried to follow them. Guta became hysterical. "Come back, come back!" she called. "There are bad currents in the river and deep holes on the bottom."

That was all Jas had to hear. "Go back to your mother, Alicia," he teased.

Some boys were bathing on the other side of the river. They picked up Jas's taunt and repeated, "Alicia, go back to your mother." Both banks of the Vistula reverberated with "Alicia, go back to your mother." By now the little girl was in tears.

That afternoon, she "ran away." She settled high in a willow tree whose branches extended over a ditch next to a fence. From there, she watched the small train puffing as it passed. Jerry was the only one who knew about the hiding place.

Paula comforted her sister. "When it's time to eat, Jerry will bring her back." She was right, as usual.

A few days later, Zabiec had a visitor. It was Mark's niece, the daughter of his youngest sister, who lived in Lublin. She was twelve years old and, to Alicia, she seemed very mature. The girls became friends. On the clear August evenings, they walked together, trying to count the stars. Frania told her cousin that she knew how to swim; she had learned how at summer camp the year before. Alicia was impressed.

One hot day, Alicia decided to persuade Frania to go with her to the river. She knew she would never get permission from her mother to go bathing without her, but if Jerry went with them, her absence would not be noticed. The grown-ups would assume that the children were off playing somewhere in the bushes.

Jerry looked for an excuse not to go. "It's too far," he said, "and we can't take the buggy."

"We can walk," Alicia declared. She sneaked on her bathing suit underneath her dress.

When they got to the river, Frania went right in, showing off her breaststroke. Alicia followed her in. The floor of the river was sandy, with few pebbles. The sand felt good underneath her feet and the cool water was pure delight after the long walk in the hot summer sun.

Jerry stood on the bank, throwing pebbles and watching the ripples in the water. Alicia wished she could throw the way he did, but, as she was told, a girl could never do it quite the same as a boy. Right now she was more interested in watching Frania; she had never seen anyone actually swim before. She admired Frania's well-coordinated arm and leg movements. She turned around and waved to Jerry.

"Come on," she called. "Frania will teach us how to swim." While Jerry was making up his mind, Alicia tried to walk a little farther out, closer to Frania. Then a strange thing happened; she couldn't walk either forward or backward. She was stuck; the only way her body could move was down. The more she tried to step up, the more she went down.

"Come on," Frania called, "it's not deep where I am. The water only reaches my waist." Then Frania noticed there was something wrong. "Flap your arms," she yelled, "and try to get your legs up."

Alicia tried hard to imitate Frania's swimming stroke, but to no avail. Frania did not realize the seriousness of the situation. A strong undercurrent prevented her from going to her little cousin. Alicia was sinking fast.

In her mind she saw her mother's face and heard her saying, "How many times have I told you not to go to the Vistula without me? You didn't ask permission." A thought flashed through her mind: What would my mother say if I drowned? The treacherous holes that Guta had warned her about were now a reality. Down, down she sank into the sticky, wet sand, which was already up to her neck.

Then she saw Jerry. He was standing in shallow water with a young peasant cowhand next to him. He was holding a long stick. Jerry extended the stick toward Alicia; it just about reached her. "Hold on with all your might and don't let go," he yelled.

The boys pulled hard. It was not easy but Alicia was finally able to step out of the quicksand. She was covered with mud.

Frania came to the shore and kissed Jerry, who turned red. "You knew exactly what to do," she told him. "I didn't and I'm much older than you."

"I read someplace," he said, "that this is the thing to do when someone falls off a boat." Then he added, "My father knows what to do in an emergency." Alicia was quite shaken, but she remembered how quickly her uncle had reacted when Jerry broke his leg.

Jerry shook the boy's hand. "Thank you, it was lucky that I found you and that you had a stick." The boy was eager to get back to his cows. "You must think," Jerry said, "that we have nothing else to do but get ourselves into trouble."

As Alicia washed the mud off, she worried about how she was going to explain her absence and her wet bathing suit to her mother. Frania calmed her by saying that by the time they got home, they would be dry and they would manage to put away their suits before anyone noticed.

Alicia still anticipated trouble. "When I run away this time, I won't come back to eat. Jerry, you'd better bring me my meal." Jerry nodded.

When they got home, no one asked them where they had been. The grown-ups seemed distracted and preoccupied. Alicia almost felt neglected. Even Aunt Yentl didn't try to offer them food.

"Something must have happened," Jerry concluded. "Maybe Jas

knows." But Jas was not around that morning; he was away washing horses with some stable boys.

"It's a good thing he didn't see us. He definitely would have told on us," Alicia said to Jerry.

"He would not," Jerry answered indignantly. "He would just tease you."

They were right; something disturbing had happened in their absence. Paula and Guta had heard Yentl screaming in the bedroom. They were curious. When Yentl heard them coming, she opened the door and said, "Come in girls, you'd better hear this."

They entered. Mark was there; he tried to leave. Yentl had blocked the door and he was reluctant to use force. She screamed in Yiddish to make sure that the servants or children passing under the open window could not understand.

"Do you know what he did?" she screamed. "You probably wondered where he got the money for his fancy trip."

"Don't listen to that frustrated spinster," Mark said. "She has nothing else to do but start trouble."

"Where did you take the money from, Father?" Paula asked.

"I'll tell you where," Yentl shouted. "Michal mentioned it; he assumed that we knew. Zagroba inherited money from America and decided to pay the debt he owed to the estate. And this," she pointed at Mark, "good for nothing grabbed the money, didn't tell anyone and took off to see his whores."

She came very close to her brother and yelled straight into his face, "The barn's roof is leaking, we could use another thresher and we need a couple of pairs of work horses, the grinding stones of the mill should be replaced, we need more farm equipment and nothing has been modernized since the Austrians paid for it during the war. There are many other things that could make Regina's life easier. We need a foreman so Michal can concentrate on the gardens. The stove is falling apart and so is some of the furniture. And he goes," she almost poked her finger in his eye, "and spends it all, and then he makes a big deal out of buying a new bike for Jas. If anyone needs a vacation, it's

Regina. She should go to a spa in Busko, drink mineral water and take
mud and sulfur baths for her arthritis."

Why should such a beautiful summer, with the interlude in Krakow,
have to end like this? Paula wondered. I was almost reconciled to my
father's way of life, and had started loving him again. Now this had to
happen. Am I as naive as my mother, Mrs. Dankowa and Guta? Is Yentl
the only one who can stand up to him?

CHAPTER 4

At that time in Poland, school consisted of four years of elementary school and eight years of gymnasium, followed by rigorous examinations and then the certificate called Matura.

In Kielce there were two public gymnasiums for boys and one for girls. They were supported by the central government. Under the law of the new Republic, all citizens were eligible for public education. In practice it didn't work that way. Though one-third of the population of Kielce was Jewish, Jewish children in the public schools comprised 1% of the student body. They were mainly children of doctors, lawyers, engineers and rich businessmen. It was a matter of prestige to those people to send their children to Polish schools; perhaps it was a way of asserting their rights. The majority of Jewish children went to private schools.

Mrs. Zima's school for Jewish girls ranged from kindergarten through elementary school and then gymnasium. It was accredited by the central government and its Matura was supposed to be accepted by all Polish universities. There were some classes in the religion and history of the Jews, but the main emphasis was on a traditional European education.

Mrs. Zima was the owner and headmistress. She was a tall, distinguished-looking graying lady, with a Ph.D. in philosophy and education. She tried to be more Polish than the Poles and her goal was to make the girls entrusted to her good citizens, rejoicing in the independence of their country after years of partition. For many of her students, Polish was the second language; at home they mostly spoke Yiddish. Mrs. Zima put a great emphasis on fluency in the main language of the country.

The school was only one block away from Freedom Place, which was why Guta sent Alicia there. Alicia took an admittance test. "She reads like a seventh grader," Mrs. Zima told Guta, "but she is only six and we cannot send her to seventh grade."

61

Alicia was placed in the second grade. The girls in her class were at least one year older than she was, and had two years of school behind them. They were more advanced socially and had already learned arts and crafts and some knitting and sewing in kindergarten.

Alicia disliked these classes. In the six years of her life, she had never played with girls. Every afternoon, when she came home, she complained to her mother, "Why can't I go to the same school that Jerry goes to?" She had no problems with academic subjects, but for a while it was hard for her to make friends with girls.

She enjoyed the gym classes. The exercise room was well-equipped because of generous donations from a rich Jewish manufacturer whose daughter had graduated from Mrs. Zima's.

The second graders had gym together with the first-graders. Alicia found a kindred spirit in a little first-grader, a dark girl with smiling black eyes. She was Alicia's age and physically well-coordinated. Her father, Mr. Rapaport, was their gym teacher. He was a tall, handsome man who was always laughing and kidding.

Mr. Rapaport adored his daughter. Occasionally he served as a drama coach, staging plays with the first- and second-graders, and Basia was always his star.

Basia told Alicia that, last summer, when her family was at the lake, her father had taught her how to swim. Alicia was impressed. "Now you have to teach me," she told her friend. The memory of sinking in the quicksand was still in her mind.

Slowly Alicia made other friends. Leah was a skinny, quiet girl with a sallow complexion, light brown hair and green eyes that seemed bigger than her whole face. Leah was very smart; she could read and count well above her grade level. Then there was Hania, another bright girl, who came from a Hassidic family and would only eat strictly kosher food. Sabina was prim and self-conscious about her kinky hair, which was pulled tight in braids. She tried to keep up with the other three; she studied hard but could never quite make it. She was very jealous. Alicia's other friend was Fryma, who didn't care much about her grades but was a lot of fun. The girls helped Alicia with her sewing and drawing, and she started to like school.

Leah lived in the suburbs of Kielce. Her father was a mining engineer who was working on a mountain, Kadzielnia. He was in charge of a crew that was dynamiting limestone. It was a long walk from the city to Kadzielnia. First there was the path along the park, then a road where trees were rare, and finally a bare limestone mountain.

One spring afternoon Alicia and Jas took a walk to Kadzielnia. Julek, Leah's brother, was Jas's classmate in the second level at the Polish gymnasium, Zeromski.

As usual, Guta warned her daughter, "Don't talk to strangers; if anyone offers you candy don't accept it; be careful when you cross the streets; hold onto Jas."

As they were walking, Jas said to his cousin, "You can't keep up with me; your legs are too short."

"So when you walk, I'll run" she answered.

It was late May and the two were already dreaming about the summer vacation and Zabiec. Jas was somewhat worried about being promoted. If a student failed two subjects, he had to repeat the whole year. Jas knew his father would not look kindly on it if that happened to him. Julek will help me in math; he's very good in it, he thought. He's going to be an engineer like his father.

It was a beautiful, warm spring day with a clear sky. Suddenly, dark clouds rolled in, followed by a heavy downpour, thunder and lightning. Alicia was overwhelmed by the beauty of the sky and the violence of the storm. It didn't even occur to her to be afraid. "Let's stand under a tree so we won't get wet," she said.

"Don't!" Jas screamed. "That's where the lightning strikes first."

Alicia was amazed to see fear and terror in his eyes. She never imagined that Jas could be afraid of anything or anybody.

He pointed to a ditch alongside the road. "We're going to lie down flat," he told her.

Alicia followed his instructions. When she tried to look up to see the lightning flash through the sky, he pushed her head down. She had never known him to be so cautious—the same Jas that performed crazy stunts on his bike and rode a horse like a maniac.

The summer storm passed as quickly as it had come. The two children were soaked, but the sun was strong, and by the time they arrived at their destination they were almost dry.

In the house Mr. and Mrs. Bloom greeted them. She was a dark, handsome woman, who treated them to home-baked cookies and milk and talked about her "Litvak" origins. She had been born near Wilno. She told them, "I always thought of it as a Lithuanian city, but now it's Polish."

In the next room Julek tried to help Jas with his math homework. Mrs. Bloom was telling the girls how smart her son was. "He's a real genius," she declared. Mr. Bloom, a pleasant man, patted Leah's head and said, "Both of my children are smart."

After milk and cookies the four children decided to climb the mountain. It wasn't easy; there wasn't anything to hold on to. The mountain was bare.

The boys managed to get to the top first. "You'll never get this high," they teased the girls.

But I'm not afraid of a storm, Alicia was tempted to say, but she decided against it. She didn't want to embarrass him in front of his friend. The girls climbed to the top laboriously.

Leah told Alicia that her brother was going to go to the summer camp for boys. "He's a good swimmer," she said. "When I go to visit him, he promised to teach me."

"I wish I could go with you, so he could teach me, too," Alicia said.

At the end of June, Guta, Paula and the children took their usual trip to Zabiec. Everything seemed the same. Alicia, who was seven, and Jerry, who was nine, still loved to enact scenes from "By Fire and Sword," made up their own adventure stories, pretended to engage in duels and talked non-stop to each other. Jas got a new dog, a black Doberman with long legs, and they ran around the estate together.

That summer, Regina was subdued and depressed. She could no longer overlook or pretend to be blind to Mark's transgressions. He confessed and swore as usual on his children's and grandchildren's health that the next time he got some money back, he would give it to his wife right away to do with as she saw fit. After thirty years of marriage she didn't believe him anymore; she had neither the strength nor the will to do anything about it. He was the owner of Zabiec.

Then a bombshell fell: The new populist government in Poland was planning to encourage the growth of small- and medium-sized farms by breaking up the large estates of the nobility, who for many centuries had controlled most of the land. A moratorium was declared on all outstanding debts. For Mark and Regina, the hope of getting their money back were practically lost forever. Zabiec was heavily mortgaged.

For the next few years, the same scenario was repeated every fall. In October a big candle was lit in the mortgage house in Kielce; as long as the flame lasted, the owners had a chance to pay the interest due. Once the flame went out, the estate would go to the highest bidder. Mark would come to Kielce to try to scramble enough money to pay his debts. Usually he managed to do it, promising his sons-in-law and friends that he would pay them back after the crops were sold. Year after year he would arrive at the mortgage house out of breath, and pay the money at the last moment, with the candle almost melted and the flame already flickering.

Something else happened that was especially hard on the children. One day early in August, Uncle Monek came to visit. They were all used to his serious and unsmiling face, but now he looked gloomier than ever.

Jas was never happy to see his father. This time he was afraid that he was going to be taken back to Kielce. He knew his father intended to hire a tutor for the last month of the summer vacation to prepare Jas for the next school year.

Paula went to her husband and kissed him. Most of the time she could dispel his dark moods. What could be wrong? she wondered. The children are all here and everyone is in good health.

He came to the point right away, without trying to soften the impact of the news. "Julek Bloom is dead," he said.

"Julek Bloom is dead?" It rang through Alicia's mind. How is it possible? She had seen him and Jas on top of the mountain, waving to Leah and her; how could he be dead? As lifeless as Blossom? If he could be dead, so could any of us.

Uncle Monek told the story: Julek was considered to be one of the best swimmers in the summer camp where he was spending his vacation. One afternoon, when the campers were supposed to be resting, he and a friend sneaked a canoe out and paddled it on the lake. The boys were fooling around and pushing each other and the canoe overturned. Julek's friend was not a swimmer; Julek managed to push him into shallow water, but he got entangled in the weeds and drowned.

Julek was twelve years old, a nice, bright boy full of promise. "What a tragedy!" Paula said.

"Why didn't the other boy hand him a stick?" Alicia asked. Nobody but Jerry knew what she was talking about.

That fall it wasn't much fun to visit Leah. Her mother was dressed all in black. She talked continually about Julek—how good-looking and brilliant he was, what a good son. Mr. Bloom had gone all gray in the last few weeks and looked like an old man. He looked at his wife and said to the girls, "Maybe talking will help her get over her grief." He had tears in his eyes. He said to his wife, "You're not the only one. I lost a son and Leah lost her brother, but we have to go on. I have you and Leah to support, just as you have me and your daughter to take care of. All that wailing and crying will not bring Julek back."

Mrs. Bloom continued her lamentations. She looked at Leah and waved her hand in despair, as if she wanted to say, If God had to take one of my children, why did it have to be my boy?

"Girls," Mr. Bloom said, "go out, climb the mountain, run, play and laugh. There is no use staying in this house."

It was the fall of 1929 and the end of a decade. It had seemed that, in the Twenties, things would be getting better and better. People believed in progress and thought that technology would cure all human ills in time. The war to end all wars had already been fought. Prosperity was spreading from America to Europe and the rest of the world. The stock market kept going up. It was the age of the flapper, short skirts and bobbed hair, prohibition, gangsters, and the Prince of Wales and his sweethearts.

After their victory over the Bolsheviks in 1920, Poland felt secure in her borders. She had access to the Baltic Sea through her Corridor, the port of Gdynia was built to make her independent from the free city of Gdansk; the coal mines in Silezia were operating at capacity; the agrarian policy was paying off, and the country was proceeding on its way to reconstruction after the long nightmare of occupation, partition and war.

In October 1929 the stock market on Wall Street crashed. This was followed by the Great Depression, which precipitated an economic crisis all over the world. Poland, which depended chiefly on its agriculture, was weathering the crisis. Its currency remained stable. It was a different story in neighboring Germany, which depended heavily on American investments. Banks failed, people lost their life savings, factories shut down, unemployment rose to astronomic proportions, and there was misery, hunger and rage in the land.

Hitler, considered a gruesome joke and a crazy megalomaniac in the twenties, was no longer funny. He promised people jobs and food, and vowed to make Germany the most powerful country in the world. He made Germans believe that they were members of a superior race destined to enslave and rule the world. He also gave the average citizen someone to blame for all his defeats and humiliations. It was the Jews who had caused all their troubles. They had made Germany lose the war and had brought all their economic woes upon them. Hitler rose to power on the hopelessness, distress and misery of his people to become the greatest mass murderer in the sad history of murderous tyrants.

In December, Alicia said to her mother, "You promised that, God willing, St. Nicholas would bring me skates when I was seven."

As usual, Guta had reservations. "You're not careful enough," she said.

"Basia is getting skates; her father said that he would teach us both," Alicia whined.

Guta spoke to Mr. Rapaport, and then to Eisig. He complained about the expense; money was getting tighter.

"Rapaport is only a teacher," Guta said. "Doctors are still better off."

Eisig took his daughter to be fitted for shoes and skates. Alicia's feet were unusually big for a girl her age, she wished they were small like Basia's.

"Did you have skates when you were a boy?" she asked her father.

"I was happy when I had a piece of bread to eat," he answered.

After a month of lessons with Mr. Rapaport, both girls were pretty confident on the ice.

One Sunday morning in January, Alicia went with her skates to Basia's. Basia was an only child, like Alicia. Mrs. Rapaport was a small woman with a pretty face, but she dragged one of her legs. Alicia had heard her mother's friends gossiping and wondering why a tall, strong man like Mr. Rapaport had married a frail, slightly crippled woman.

Though Alicia was only seven, she noticed the unusually warm relationship between the three Rapaports. Father and daughter were concerned about the mother; you could almost touch the love between them. They lived modestly; their apartment was much smaller then the ones Alicia was used to.

That morning Mr. Rapaport was busy. "You girls," he said, "can manage without me. I might join you later."

The park was only a few blocks away. This morning, the skating rink was full of children of all ages, the girls in short skirts, fancy tights and gaudy sweaters and the boys in more conservative clothes. For a while Alicia and Basia were so busy skating that they didn't realize they were the only two Jewish children in the rink. Slowly they became aware of the dirty looks they were getting. Alicia didn't understand why. They behaved, they didn't bother anyone; but Basia had an inkling of what was going on.

"Maybe we should get out of here," she told Alicia.

"Why?" Alicia said, "I'm enjoying myself."

A girl much bigger than Basia and even bigger than Alicia bumped hard into Basia, who had to grab Alicia's arm not to lose her balance. The two of them almost fell to the ice. The girl didn't excuse herself; she was ready to move on. Alicia stretched her leg across the girl's path, who tripped and fell.

"I'm sorry, I hope you're not hurt," Alicia said.

The girl looked at her and mumbled, "You Jews always push yourselves where you're not wanted."

A group of children now surrounded the three girls. Someone gave the one sitting on the ice a hand and helped her pick herself up. She brushed herself off and patted her back. Evidently she was not hurt. Basia and Alicia felt surrounded. They were getting menacing looks. Basia was scared and cuddled up to Alicia. Alicia put her arm around her. They won't beat us up, she thought. They might chase us out of here. Then she heard a familiar voice: "What's going on here?" To her relief, it was Jas.

"Nothing much," someone answered. The circle opened and they all resumed skating. Now Alicia and Basia felt safe.

Jas was a very good skater. At twelve he looked at least fifteen, and the biggest compliment the Polish children could pay him was that he didn't look or act like a Jew.

The girls in the rink flirted with him, including the one who had tried to cause trouble for Basia and Alicia. Though he ignored his little cousin and her friend, the others somehow knew they were related and nobody bothered them anymore.

Later on Mr. Rapaport picked up the two girls. When they were walking home he noticed that they were not as lively as usual. "What happened?" he asked. "Did you have any problems?"

Alicia answered, "We're just tired." She and Basia somehow felt humiliated by the incident. Alicia had heard about anti-Semitism, but she had never really been exposed to it herself. In Zabiec she considered Michal, Stefka and Kazimierz not only friends, but people who took care of the family and the estate. Now, at the skating rink, she had seen a hate and resentment in that girl's eyes that she was not prepared for.

Jerry was sick again that winter. There was an enlarged gland at the side of his mouth, which later proved to be full of tuberculi bacilli. He had a low-grade fever and had to stay in bed. It took him only a week to finish all the fourth-grade textbooks, and he knew more than enough to be promoted to the first level at the gymnasium. Then he read mostly adventure stories and historical novels.

There were two more Jewish boys in his class of forty, both of them competitive, outstanding students. They were resented by their classmates.

Jerry was not competitive. He didn't have to exert any effort at school. He let others copy from him and everyone liked him. He could play the piano quite well, but he preferred to listen to records of great arias.

When Jerry was sick, Alicia spent many afternoons with him. Sometimes Tadek came over, and when Jerry didn't feel up to it, she played ping-pong with his friend.

At home, Eisig was worried. "If Jerry has T.B.," he told Guta, "Alicia shouldn't be spending that much time with him." Then, as always, he blamed his wife's family: "If your sister weren't so busy trying to seduce all the men around, she'd put her foot down and see to it that Jerry ate properly. He fills up with sweets, he doesn't get enough vitamins and minerals or other essential nutrients; no wonder he's always sick."

Guta defended her sister. "Jerry is a problem eater and there is nothing that Paula can do about it; we're lucky with Alicia."

Eisig placed great importance on proper nutrition for children. Alicia always ate fruit and vegetables. She had to have two oranges a day, though they were imported from California and very expensive. When Jerry broke his leg and Jas broke an arm at the skating rink, Eisig told Guta that they didn't have enough calcium in their diet. He also blamed his brother-in-law. "Monek," he said, "should know better; diabetes runs in his family and he has it himself. He should keep sweets away from his children. He's too lenient with Jerry and too strict with Jas. It seems to me that Jas is failing in his subjects just to spite his father. He's a smart boy and he could do well in school."

Lately Jas had spent a lot of time in the apartment on Freedom Place. His relationship with his father was stormy. After every Parent–Teacher Conference or report card, there was a the great crisis in the Peltz household.

Alicia enjoyed having Jas stay with them. She loved to play with Jerry and fight with Jas.

One day in May, Alicia, Fryma and Leah were walking along Chestnut Lane in the park. They met Guta and Paula, who were taking a shortcut through the park on the way to their usual window shopping on Railroad Street, the main street of Kielce, which had lately been renamed Sienkiewicz Street.

Guta looked at the girls critically. Later she said to Paula, "Their accent is terrible. It sounds more Yiddish than Polish. That is typical of Mrs.

Zima's girls. I'll have to look for a different school for Alicia; she'll never get to the university with that kind of speech."

"She's only in third grade, you have time to worry," Paula said.

"You shouldn't be giving me advice," Guta answered. "Both your boys are in state schools. Besides, the tuition at Mrs. Zima's is too high for Eisig. Because he's a doctor they expect him to contribute more than his share."

For the 1930/31 school year, Guta found Alicia a small, private school for Polish girls from wealthy families. There were a few Jewish girls scattered throughout the classes, and the tuition proved to be no higher than at Mrs. Zima's.

In the summer of 1930 it rained heavily throughout the month of July. The Vistula in Zabiec rose to a dangerous level; it was pounding at the dike and threatening the fields. The Warman's house was situated high in the valley, but as a precaution, Paula, Guta and the children moved to Pacanow. There they stayed with a strictly orthodox family. One evening they went to a wedding and Alicia wondered why the men and women were not allowed to touch. When they danced, they held hands through a handkerchief.

"Those are real Jews," Alicia told her mother the next day.

"What do you mean real, we're Jews, too," Guta answered.

Paula was laughing. "She's right. We're not very real at being Jewish."

"Jas," Alicia said, "doesn't like 'real' Jews. He always makes fun of the boys from the Jewish gymnasium in Kielce. He prefers to play with goys."

Guta waved her hand. "She must have gotten that word from Mrs. Zima's girls. By the way, where is Jas?"

Paula would not let her sister see how worried she was. "I'm not like you, a hen sitting on eggs. Jas is a big boy; he can manage. I don't blame him for not wanting to stay with women and children."

Jerry told Alicia that Jas was helping the men reinforce the dike. They were trying to plug the holes that were developing as the river got higher and more violent.

Alicia was getting excited. "Let's go join Jas," she said.

Guta was horrified. "She's ready to jump head first whenever there's an opportunity."

"Don't worry," Paula said to her sister. "She won't go without Jerry."

"Why couldn't that girl of mine be more like Jerry?" Guta sighed.

Later in the afternoon, Jas and Michal came to the family's quarters. Jas was pale. He was wearing oversize peasant clothes and carried his own, completely soaked garments in a bag. Now even Paula got panicky.

"What happened?" she asked.

Jas shrugged his shoulders. "Nothing much," he said.

"Nothing much!" Michal repeated. "Your son almost floated down the river all the way to the Baltic."

"Michal saved my life," Jas said flatly.

"We were standing on the dike," Michal said. "We were watching the river. A big wave swept over right where Jas stood; it made a hole in the dike and picked up Jas."

Paula was shivering, but Jas was laughing. "Michal picked me up by the collar and pulled me out," he said. "Another second would have been bye, bye Jas."

Alicia couldn't control herself; she ran to Jas and kissed him. "Hey, stop it," he said.

"I know how it felt," she said. Me, buried in a bottomless river, Jas floating to the Baltic, and Julek tangled in weeds. The fear of water and drowning was becoming an obsession.

In September Alicia began fourth grade in her new school. She was still a year younger than the other girls, but she was big for her age and ready to socialize. The class was small, with only fifteen girls, and Alicia was the only Jew. At first she was not even aware of that fact. She noticed that the girls whispered to each other and pointed their fingers at her. Nobody wanted to sit with her, and when they marched in pairs to gym she found herself alone in the back.

One day during recess, the girls were playing "Ring Around the Rosy." Alicia tried to enter the circle, but the girls wouldn't break the chain to let her in. She stood and watched them.

Students in Polish schools carried their pencils and pens in oblong wooden boxes. Alicia picked up her box and started hitting the girls on top of their heads. The box was solid wood and heavy; every time it landed on a head, it made a hollow sound. The girls were crying. The noise brought the teacher and she confiscated the box.

The next day the parents were called to see the principal. Guta knew the story from her daughter. It was a private school and Eisig paid full tuition. There were some rich Jewish girls in the upper classes and it was important for the administration to keep them in the school. Alicia was not punished at all.

The priest, who was also a religious instructor, lectured the girls on religious tolerance. From then on Alicia's classmates talked and played with her. Even the leader of the gang tried to be friendly.

Alicia still was not very happy at this school. When the class had religious instruction she wandered the hall, occasionally meeting other Jewish girls. In the mornings, when they recited prayers to the Virgin Mary and crossed themselves, she stood there feeling isolated and different from everyone else. There were no morning prayers at Mrs. Zima's. At the end of the year, the school lost its accreditation and Alicia landed back at Mrs. Zima's. That whole year she hadn't made one friend in her class.

Guta became pregnant. Alicia heard her father saying, "Now we'll have a boy." Alicia had been told by Guta that Eisig had wanted his firstborn to be a boy. As the story went, not only was Alicia a girl but she was very small at birth. Eisig had been disappointed, but later had learned to love her and was now spoiling her rotten.

Alicia looked at her mother's stomach. Guta had told her that a baby was growing inside her, but she had never explained how it got into her.

Alicia discussed the matter with Jerry. She maintained that parents "did it" on their wedding night and that God gave them children. But Jerry said she was wrong. "They have to do it separately for every child." Alicia didn't believe him. "They only did it once," she insisted. It was hard for her to imagine her parents "doing it" at all. Jerry would take two stuffed animals and show her how it was done.

"My parents only did it once," she repeated.

Jas said, "If adolescents don't have sex, their hormones will drive them crazy."

Sometimes, when Alicia came from school, there were patients sitting in separate rooms of the apartment. Why aren't they in the waiting room, she wondered? The maid told her that they didn't want to see each other

"Why not?" Alicia asked.

"Because they have diseases that they are ashamed of," Kasia answered.

Alicia looked at her father's shingle on the front door: "Dermatology and Venereal Diseases." Once, when the maid was emptying the buckets in Eisig's office, Alicia heard Guda tell her to be careful and wear rubber gloves.

"I'm only going to get it," Kasia said, "if someone sticks it in me."

It took Alicia another year to figure that out, along with what "Venereal Diseases" meant.

Alicia didn't think much more about her mother's pregnancy. She was busy in school, going to movies with Basia and talking endlessly with Jerry.

At night, before falling asleep, she watched the shadows on the walls. She was not afraid of the dark. She listened to the neighing horses from the cabs parked across the square and she would fall asleep thinking of Zabiec.

That spring Eisig went to Vienna again to take additional courses. Guta went into labor two months prematurely. She was well attended by her gynecologist, Dr. Levin; Dr. Peltz; and a midwife, Mrs. Friedman; and of course by her sister Paula. Only poor women gave birth in hospitals.

After school, Alicia went "upstairs," where she, Jas and Jerry were fed by Mrs. Kubicka. "Your mother must be screaming something terrible," Jas said. "It hurts awfully to have a baby."

"Be quiet," Mrs. Kubicka said. "Don't scare the children. As soon as the baby is born, the woman forgets all the pain. It's a wonderful feeling to have a tiny infant in your arms. She's ready for another one."

"I was never a tiny infant," Jas declared.

The next day Alicia went home and looked at the baby girl in the cradle. She was all swaddled and very red.

Guta was crying. Eisig had been notified and arrived the next day. The baby was premature and very underweight. One of her legs was too short. She died four days later.

Guta blamed the doctors. "They didn't make any effort to save her," she told Alicia. "She could have lived a long, happy life the way she was."

That June, Alicia took a trip with her mother to Krynica, a resort and spa in the Karpathian Mountains whose waters were supposed to be good for female problems. It was hoped that a stay in the spa would help Guta carry a baby full term.

It was the same wondrous train ride that she had taken two summers ago with Paula. From Krakow, a little mountain train brought them to Krynica. They stayed in a fancy hotel; the guest next door was a famous opera singer. Guta was thrilled when he knocked at their door and asked if she could lend him a needle and thread. He even commented on Alicia's blond curls.

They took long walks on the winding path of the park mountain. Alicia would run, jump and skip ahead, and Guta would admonish her to stay close and not talk to strangers.

Still, it was nice to go back to Zabiec.

Late in 1931, Guta was pregnant again. She spent long hours in bed to prevent an onset of bleeding, which, in the past, had caused her miscarriages.

When the school year was over, Paula took Jerry and Alicia to Zabiec; then she went back to Kielce to stay with her sister. Jas, at his father's insistence, stayed in Kielce, where he was supposed to study with a tutor.

Late one afternoon, Jerry and Alicia were in their room washing up for supper. Since there was no running water in the house, Stefka brought a pitcher of fresh water from the well. Their room, like all the other rooms in the house was on the ground floor and the windows faced west. The sun was just setting, and the big red orb forecast a clear day. Suddenly Jerry pointed his finger at the window. "Look" he exclaimed.

Alicia stared. She saw a tall figure casting a long shadow. She was scared. Her grandparents were in the next room, so she knocked at their door and called her grandfather. Mark came in, Alicia turned around and they saw Jas standing in the middle of the room. "I came on my bike," he said. "I couldn't stay home anymore."

Mark didn't have a chance to answer. The door swung open and Dr. Peltz, all red in the face, burst into the room. "I figured this was where you went," he screamed. He went straight for Jas. He's going to hit him hard, Alicia thought. Jas ran to the window, his father almost upon him.

To the astonishment of the children, Grandfather grabbed Dr. Peltz by the collar, lifted him in the air and held him there. That gave Jas a chance to jump out the window, get on his bike and disappear.

Mark put his son in law down.

"Wow," Jerry said.

Dr. Peltz was angry. He never liked Mark. "How dare you?" he said. "Jas is my son."

"He's also my grandson," Mark replied.

They would have come to blows if Regina hadn't have entered. Doctor Peltz controlled his temper. He hadn't seen his mother-in-law for a year. Now he was struck by her appearance. She was wearing a neck brace and looked worn and tired to the point of exhaustion.

"Mother," he said, "you haven't been taking good care of yourself."

"I have that rash that bothers me," she said. "Doctor Markowski said that it must be sensitivity to weeds."

"Why didn't you write to us about it?" Dr. Peltz asked. "Eisig should come and look at it."

"It's going away already," she said. "I didn't want to bother you with my problems. Its important that Eisig and you stay in Kielce and see Guta through her last two months of pregnancy."

"Guta is fine. I'm worried about you," he said.

"Why are you here?" she asked.

"It's between me and Jas," he answered. His anger was returning. He waved his hand at Mark: "He had to interfere."

"Monek," Regina said, "quiet down, have something to eat. Then get a good night's sleep and go home in the morning. You're one of the best doctors in Poland, and I'd feel better knowing you were available to Guta."

Doctor Peltz found it impossible to be angry at Regina. "You probably know where Jas is," he said.

"I have an inkling," Regina said. "It's summer. He'll do much better next year if you let him enjoy it."

"He shouldn't get away with defying me."

"I'll make him promise," Regina answered, "that he'll work hard in school."

The next morning Dr. Peltz left. He intended to write a letter to Dr. Markowski to ask his opinion about his mother-in-law's health, but when he returned to Kielce, he found himself very busy. Besides carrying on his practice he was serving as a councilman, the only Jew in Kielce in that position. He was also an organizer and director of the Jewish Orphanage and Home for the Aged. He kept postponing writing the letter and decided to wait till the fall to discipline Jas.

Back in Zabiec, Regina told the children to get Jas and tell him that it was safe to come home. They guessed that he was at Michal's house in the village, not too far from the estate. Michal was a widower whose spinster daughter took care of him. Paula and Guta had always suspected that he was secretly in love with Regina.

Jerry and Alicia were playing in the trees. They were on a safari in Africa with Alicia's unborn brother, who had been kidnapped by the natives, and they were trying to recapture him.

Grandmother Regina called: "Children, come fast!" As they emerged from the bushes they saw the old, bearded peddler Zajoc, who circulated between the villages from Szczucin to Pacanow. He wore his usual attire: a long kaftan and beaver hat. He was waving a piece of paper and yelling, "Mazel Tov, Mazel Tov, it's a boy!"

Regina grabbed the telegram and they all formed a circle—she, Jas, Jerry, Alicia, Zajac, Stefka, Aunt Yentl and a few servants. They danced and jumped. Regina sang, "We have a son, we have a son!" In pure joy, they went around and around, up and up, celebrating the arrival of new life. "He weighs three-and-a-half kilograms," Regina shouted. "Guta

finally did it after ten years of trying." Aunt Yentl tried to tell her to take
it easy. "You haven't been well" she kept saying. "I feel wonderful,"
Regina said. "Guta has had a healthy baby."

Alicia couldn't wait to go home to see her new brother. The whole
household routine had been adjusted to his needs. Guta had engaged
Rosie, Kazimierz's half-sister, as a nanny.

Alicia was disappointed by the baby. "He's so tiny," she said to her
mother. "And all he does is sleep and suck at your breast."

"He's big for a newborn baby," Guta answered, "and he's beautiful.
Some babies have no hair at all, he has black hair and eyes like his father."
Than she promised her daughter, "You'll see, when he's three months
old he'll smile and try to sit up, he'll be a real *mentsch.*"

Many of Guta's friends had been pregnant at the same time that she
was, and there was a crop of Jewish babies born in Kielce that summer.

Guta tried to postpone the ceremony of circumcision; she kissed her
baby and moaned, "it will hurt him."

Rosie came home almost every day with stories about how people had
stopped her on the sidewalk and asked, "When will the boy have the
Bris?"

Eisig suggested that Monek should do it; after all, he had been a
surgeon. But Guta didn't want to tempt God. It was supposed to be a
religious ritual, performed by a *Mohel* especially trained for these occasions.

They found the best and most expensive one in Kielce, who circum-
cised the babies of the most important people.

On the scheduled day, the three doctors, the baby's father, uncle and
Doctor Levin watched the *Mohel* and made sure that all of his equipment
was sterile. The man was nervous; his hands shook; but everything went
smoothly. The baby got a Jewish name, Chaim Jeremiah. In Polish this
was Henryk Jeremi. At home he would be called Henius.

In October 1932, news came from Zabiec that Regina was sick. It was
Yentl who wrote, not Mark. "So typical; he doesn't even care," Paula
raged. "He's too busy with his latest love affair." Paula left for Zabiec.
Guta was breast-feeding the baby and couldn't go.

One afternoon Alicia came home from school and found her mother sobbing and tearing her hair. "She was only fifty-two," she kept repeating. "Why did she have to die so young? If I had been there maybe it wouldn't have happened."

Alicia guessed that her grandmother was dead. Just two months ago she had seen her jumping, dancing and full of joy. Dead? Did that mean that when they went to Zabiec, Grandma would not be there? This was not like when her Grand Baba died; she had been only a shadowy figure in Alicia's life. And she had only met Julek a few times. But since Alicia could remember, Regina and Zabiec went together.

Eisig came into the room.

"Daddy," Alicia asked, "where is Grandmother?"

Guta was still sobbing. "She's in heaven," she said.

"If she's in heaven, why are you wailing? She certainly didn't have it so good with your father." Then he said to his daughter, "We'll never see her again."

"She died from aggravation, overwork and a broken heart," Guta said through her tears.

Eisig grew irritated. "She died simply because her heart was too weak to pump blood through her body and nobody, no doctor could do anything about it."

Guta was crying, "With all the doctors in this family, only one inferior, inefficient guy from Szczucin attended her. They treated her for arthritis and it was a heart condition that killed her."

"Daddy," Alicia asked, "will your heart and Mommy's heart stop pumping blood; will mine?" One of Alicia's friend's mother had died of cancer.

Eisig patted his daughter on her head. "Eventually we will all die, but we have many years of life ahead of us, and all you have to worry about is doing well in school." He left the room.

Guta looked at Alicia through her tears. "Until now," she said, "when things were bad between me and your father, I could always pack up, take my children and go to Zabiec. With my mother gone I have no home anymore. Fathers don't make homes."

When Alicia went "upstairs," to her surprise Jas was crying. She had never imagined him doing that. Even when he broke his arm skating, he had just clenched his teeth without uttering a peep. "I only made her angry once," he kept saying.

Everybody was blaming himself for something, Alicia thought; her mother for not being there with Grandmother, and now Jas. She tried to remember the incident Jas was talking about. Regina had sent him to Szczucin with four chickens to have them slaughtered the kosher way. Jas had tied them in the basket in back of his bike and started pedaling toward Szczucin. On his way he met Kazimierz. The two boys decided that Kazimierz could do the job; it would be a waste to give the money to the "Shohet." Kazimierz cut the birds' throats and they hung the basket high in a tree on the side of the road. They split the Shohet's fees and made off to Szczucin. Jas got ice cream, and Kazimierz cigarettes. When they returned, the basket was gone. The boys went back to Zabiec and tried to catch another four chickens.

Regina caught them in the act. She put two and two together and was very disappointed and unhappy with her favorite grandson.

Was that why Jas was crying now? Alicia remembered her father's reaction when he heard the story; "What can you expect from the grandson of Motke Ganef?"

"They wouldn't let me go to Pacanow for the funeral," Jas cried. "I'm fifteen, but my father announced that funerals are not for children. He was afraid I'd miss some precious school. I wanted to see her before they put her in some cold grave. I loved her and I wanted to pay her my last respects."

"But you went to Grand Baba's funeral when you were only ten," Alicia said.

"Father was not in Zabiec at the time and I just went."

Paula came back from Zabiec furious at Mark. "He neglected her," she kept saying. "He didn't call a doctor on time. He was cavorting with his *shikse* while mother was on her deathbed."

CHAPTER 5

Guta's milk went sour from grief and little Henius cried all the time. Back in Zabiec, Stefka had had another baby, and Guta imported her as a wet nurse. Now Stefka and Rosie managed the household.

Guta slowly recovered. Henius made up for the baby she had lost the year before, and taking care of him restored her peace of mind. She sent Stefka back to Zabiec: "You must take care of your own baby and help Aunt Yentle run the house."

Alicia waited patiently for Henius to become a *mentsch*. Sure enough, by November he was turning around, smiling, kicking and following people with his eyes. In school Alicia kept talking to her girlfriends about her brother, and the girls wanted to come and look at him.

Guta voiced her objections: "Babies are very vulnerable to infections."

"Mommy," Alicia said, "Daddy told me that infants are born with natural immunity."

One day Alicia brought Leah, Hania and Fryma home. They circled the crib, asking, "May we hold him?"

Guta and Rosie watched. Guta shivered and prayed to God that none of the girls would drop the baby. When they put him back in his crib, she sighed with relief.

"I'll probably have nine babies, like my mother," Hania said. "They've already chosen a husband for me." There was sadness in her voice.

Hania is so smart, Alicia thought, but she'll never go to a university. "I might not even have a child, but I'll be a great writer or scientist," she said.

A letter arrived from Yentl in Zabiec; it was written in Yiddish and the sisters tried to decipher it. Guta knew the Hebrew alphabet better than Paula.

"What does she write?" Paula asked, as Guta laboriously plodded through.

"Yentl wants to leave Zabiec to go live with her sister in Lublin." She began to translate: "Regina needed me and I loved the children, but now they are big. Henius will have to grow up without me. I'm just too disgusted with my brother and I cannot stand by while he carries on with his peasant girlfriend Jozka. I don't want to witness the complete deterioration of Zabiec after Regina worked so terribly hard to keep it together."

"My God," Paula exclaimed, "she was with us for thirty years, and now what? No one to take care of the estate and no one to care of the house. What will happen to Zabiec with Mother and Yentl gone?"

Paula went to her bedroom and found an old pocketbook. She fished out a letter. It was the one she had gotten four years ago from Helena Dankowa. Paula had seen Eda and Wladek at Regina's funeral, and Eda had mentioned that Mr. Dankow had recently died, leaving gorgeous Helena a very rich and grieving widow. This news and the letter gave Paula an idea. "I'm going to write to the woman," she told her sister.

Guta said, "How can you contemplate such a thing? Mother has only been dead a month."

"Dankowa still loves Father. Maybe she'll take him to Krakow and let him spend her money instead of what's left of Mother's." Then she added, "Between the two of us, maybe we can save Zabiec from complete ruin."

Guta was well aware of how bad things were in Zabiec. Before the moratorium there had still been some money coming in from the peasants; now it was mainly the income from Regina's vegetable garden that kept the place going. The machinery in the mill had broken down and the mill closed. In order to meet his mortgage payment every fall, Mark often sold or leased more acreage or sold the crops before they were harvested. Guta knew more than Paula about farming. She had often supervised milking and the production of butter, cheese and yogurt, and she loved to work in the garden with her mother. She had sat in on Regina's discussions with Michal and had helped decide what to plant, what fertilizer to use and how to improve certain strains of vegetables by crossing them with other varieties.

"But I have Henius. How do you expect me to run Zabiec?" she asked.

"Rosie is good with the baby," Paula answered. "Starting this spring, one of us will take care of Zabiec, while the other one will stay in Kielce and be responsible for the children. We'll alternate between spring and fall. In the summer, we'll both be in Zabiec, and we'll close the house for the winter." Then she added, "The first thing we have to do is try to get Father out of Zabiec.

She sat down to write the letter:

> Dear Mrs. Dankowa,
>
> You have probably heard from the Pleszowskis in Krakow that our mother passed away. My sister and I learned from the same source about the death of your husband. It is very painful for me to write to you, but we all have to worry about the living. Father is very depressed, dejected and moody. He mopes around the house and looks at old pictures. You wouldn't recognize him these days; he's lost his usual zest for living. You must be lonely too. From that memorable letter of four years ago I learned that you still love my father. I know it is presumptuous for me to suggest that you and he meet again, but if you would consider it, please let me know.
>
> P.S. Father has no idea I'm writing to you. He's still in deep mourning, but life must go on. He's a relatively young man, and mourning and depression can't last forever.

Paula read the letter to her sister.

Guta shook her head: "How can you write such a letter? Does that poor woman have any idea how many affairs he's had since their's ended?"

"What's the matter with you?" Paula answered. "How can you feel sorry for her? She and Father deserve each other."

A few days later, Paula came downstairs waving a letter triumphantly. "It didn't take the lady a long time; she's eager and willing."

Later that month, Paula took another trip to Zabiec. Though, in the last months of her life, Regina had tried to finish the chores connected with the farm, there were still plenty of odds and ends to be attended to. Yentl was ready to leave. She had packed away all of Regina's clothes, giving a lot away to the servants, saved the good ones for Guta and Paula. She hardly took anything for herself, claiming that nothing fitted her. "It is so sad and hard to realize that Regina is gone forever," she cried.

One night Paula and Yentl went to Mark's room and found him in bed. They were suspicious, and Yentl quickly ran over and pulled off his quilt. Sure enough, there was Jozka. The girl, scared out of her wits, ran away half naked.

Mark's face was red as he screamed, "How dare you! I'm an adult, this is my home; I'll throw you both out!"

"Father," Paula said slowly, "you have to behave yourself. Dankowa wants to see you; she's a very rich widow and she still loves you."

Mark was amazed. "Dankowa? How did you manage that?" After a while: "She must be an old woman by now."

"Not as young as Jozka, but still very attractive, elegant and rich. You can't stay in Zabiec alone. Even your torrid romance with Jozka won't help you through the miserable fall and winter."

The climate in Zabiec was good for the soil, but the dampness from the river was bad for human bones, and lately there had been leaks in the roof of the stone house. Mark suffered from rheumatism and often had to use a cane.

"It would be a blessing if you could marry Dankowa and move to Krakow," Paula said. "So stop fooling around with Jozka."

By early December, things had settled down. Yentl went to Lublin and Mark moved to Krakow, to the dry and beautifully furnished apartment of Helena Dankowa. They planned to marry in the spring.

Kielce is situated in the Swietokrzyski Mountains. It is geologically an old range; its peaks flattened by billions of years of erosion are more like gently sloping hills. The mountains are covered with thick pine woods.

In the early Thirties the city started to clear a place in the woods, not far from the center of town, in order to build an entertainment and sports complex with tennis courts, a swimming pool and a restaurant. Farther in the forest were ski trails and a ski jump. The complex was named Stadion. Jas got his skis when he was fourteen years old and, by the time he was fifteen, was already an expert skier.

Paula decided that, after everything that had happened last fall, she needed a vacation. "During the school break," she told Guta, "I'll take the three children to Zakopane."

In Polish Zakopane means "buried in." The resort is deep inside the Tatra mountain range, where the peaks are steep and challenging.

"We'll get skis for everyone, and as soon as we arrive there, we're going to sign up for lessons and get as good as Jas," Paula said.

Eisig protested: "It seems like yesterday that I spent money on skates."

"It was three years ago," Alicia whined. As usual, her father gave in and Alicia got an outfit and a pair of skis. Since Henius was born, she had felt less pressure from her mother. It was easier for Guta to let her daughter go.

On the day of departure they were all in a good mood. School was out for two weeks and they would be with Paula. For Jas, that meant freedom from his father; and for Alicia, being away from her mother.

The train was packed with teenagers holding their skis and in a holiday mood. Jas met many of his school friends. As the train started to move the crowd began to sing Christmas carols. Paula and the children sang with everyone else. There was joy and happiness in the air.

It was beautiful in Zakopane. They spent many hours on the slopes with their instructor and, at the end of a week, Paula, Alicia and Jerry were climbing and sliding down beginners' slopes, while Jas went for the most advanced slopes. Even Paula was anxious when she saw Jas jump.

At the end of the first week, Alicia spoiled the fun by coming down with a sore throat and fever.

A doctor paid them a visit. Alicia had to stay in bed, drink a lot of fluids and take aspirin to bring down the fever.

"One of us will have to stay with her during the day," Paula sighed.

Jerry was eager to do it. He had had enough of the strenuous activities and was looking forward to sitting quietly and reading.

Paula didn't like the suggestion. "You're too susceptible; it will have to be Jas and me."

At first, Jas protested, but he was engrossed at the time in reading *Sherlock Holmes* and was looking forward to finding out what happened.

Lately, Paula and the children had been taking English lessons. Jas was also learning Hebrew. There was no chance for a Jewish boy to get into a Polish university. Jas would have to go to America or Palestine. Paula was learning English, which was becoming fashionable, almost to the point of replacing French. Now, in the hotel in Zakopane, Jas had two editions of *Sherlock Holmes*, one in English and one in Polish, and he tried to read them both.

At home, when Alicia was sick, she got one hundred percent service. Since Guta did not let her get out of bed to go to the bathroom, someone in the little girl's "entourage" would give her a bedpan. In the hotel the bathroom was down the hall, so Alicia asked Jas for a bedpan.

"What?" he yelled. "You can move your ass and go!"

"But my Mommy said that when I have fever I should stay in bed."

"Your mommy is not here." He threw her a heavy robe. "If you don't want to pee in bed, go!" From then on he called Alicia "Miss Bedpan." If she asked him for a glass of water, he yelled, "Miss Bedpan wants water; elementary Dr. Watson, here's your water."

"I am Miss Bedpan, not Dr. Watson," Alicia objected.

The second week of their vacation was coming to an end and it was time for them to go home, but Alicia was not yet ready to travel. Paula decided that they would stay a few more days.

Jas was very happy. "Hurray!" he exclaimed. "Miss Bedpan did something good."

"I'm Dr. Watson, not Miss Bedpan," Alicia said.

"Your father won't like it," Paula said to Jas, "but I've decided that we'll all go home together. I'm not going to send you boys back alone."

After the school holidays, most of the people left. The hotel and the slopes were empty and Paula and the children got a lot of attention. Paula, as usual, had an admirer following her. She confided in Alicia, "Don't say anything to the boys; they might tell their father." She promised

Alicia that when she turned fourteen, she would be told the story of her Mucia's greatest love.

Finally it was time to leave Zakopane. This time they traveled first class. "Alicia still needs a lot of rest," Paula told them.

They had a large compartment all to themselves. Two well-dressed gentlemen knocked on the door, asking permission to join them. Paula agreed with a smile. The men came in and made themselves comfortable. One of them commented, "This first-class travel is expensive, but at least we don't have to sit with all those dirty Jews who crowd every compartment on this train."

It didn't take Paula long to answer: "You came to the wrong place. I am Jewish and so are these children. If you don't like it, you can get out of here, and I suggest that you do so."

The man was speechless for a moment. Then he stood up. He was standing near Paula and breathing hard. "You get out of here, you shameless Jewish whore!"

Alicia and Jerry were afraid. Jas was about to jump up, but he didn't have to. Paula didn't get up; she just raised her arm and slapped the man hard in the face.

The man moaned, grabbed his face with his hands and started to choke. Jas laughed, "That was quite a slap," he said.

The conductor came in and tried to find out what had happened. The men didn't have a chance against a beautiful woman with three children, especially when she told the conductor that they had tried to attack her physically.

Afterwards Alicia asked Paula, "What are we, Jews or Poles?"

"We're both, stupid," Jas said.

Jerry had the last word: "Most of the time we consider ourselves Polish, but often we are rudely reminded that we are also Jewish."

"Elementary, Dr. Watson," Alicia said.

When Alicia returned to Kielce she tried to persuade Mr. Rapaport to get a pair of skis for Basia. It was an expensive proposition for a teacher, but for his daughter he scrambled enough money together.

Saturdays and Sundays, the girls were pulled to Stadion by a horse sled. Paula and Jerry sometimes accompanied them. Jerry was very shy around girls other than Alicia. He barely talked to Basia. Paula joked that she would give Basia five zlotys if she succeeded in making Jerry kiss her.

Even in winter there was construction going on around the future swimming pool. Rumor had it that it would open sometime in the coming summer.

"You teach me how to swim," Alicia told her friend, "and I'll show you everything the skiing instructor taught me in Zakopane."

In school Alicia sat in the first row, but she still could not read from the blackboard. She was taken to an eye doctor, who told Guta that her daughter was near-sighted and needed glasses.

Guta wasn't happy about it. Alicia had been named after her late grandmother, whose Jewish name was Alta; but she also shared the name with a popular actress. Guta had dreamt that her daughter would grow up to be a beautiful actress, dancer or musician. Alicia had a deaf ear for music, did not like to dress up and was not interested in her mother's make-up or clothes. Now glasses, Guta thought. She's going to be a scholar.

Alicia herself felt awkward. She was taller than most of the girls in her class, she had big feet and now she wore glasses.

Her classmates were older than she was, and slowly, one after the other, they were getting their periods. They formed a club for those who had it; every week another one joined.

Alicia didn't quite understand what it was all about. She knew that her mother was sometimes very sick with it. "When will I get my period," she kept asking.

"God willing, in a year or two," Guta answered.

Alicia was told that Mucia had gotten it when she was nine years old, but Mucia did everything early. She had Jas when she was only seventeen. Guta, on the other hand, was late. She didn't start to menstruate until she was seventeen. I wouldn't care, Alicia thought, if I didn't get it at all. She gave up the idea of ever being as popular with men as Paula or as attractive as her mother. Lately, in her science class, they had talked about Marie Curie. I'll be like her, she decided.

The big attraction in Zabiec that summer was the baby. Alicia and Jerry watched him crawl on the blanket. He tried to stand, up holding onto Rosie, and started to talk. Jerry and Alicia chased butterflies. When they caught a big, colorful Monarch they brought it to Henius and he screamed with delight. In the evenings he didn't want to go to sleep. He cried for Jerry and Alicia to play with him. Jas had to come to his room and tell him to shut up; somehow he listened to him.

Mark and his new wife came for a visit. It was hard for his daughters to see Mrs. Dankowa sleep in their mother's bed. She realized this, and she and Mark didn't stay long.

Alicia received a letter from Basia. She was excited by the opening of the swimming pool in Stadion. "As soon as you come back, I'll teach you how to swim," she wrote.

Alicia didn't know if she should be happy or scared. She still had bad dreams about falling in a hole and not being able to get out.

No one cared that Hitler was now the Chancellor of Germany—not that summer, anyhow.

In 1933, there was a change in the Polish school system. Elementary school would consist of six grades. Four years of gymnasium followed, then two years of lyceum. The last two years were designed only for those who intended to attend universities. After the gymnasium the students who wanted to attend lyceum had to pass an exam. Alicia was eleven when she entered the first level in the new system of gymnasium at Mrs. Zima's. According to the regulations, students in this grade had to be twelve years old, but an exception was made for Alicia.

That fall it was Guta's turn to stay in Zabiec. Rosie and Henius stayed in Kielce, as the autumn months could be cold and rainy in Zabiec. Usually on Saturdays and Sundays, Paula, Alicia, Rosie and Henius took a bus to the Stadion. Paula had a game of gin rummy going, and tables and chairs were placed for that purpose on the patio of the Stadion's restaurant.

In the early Thirties, the Peltzes and Strums resumed their social contact with other doctors' families. The only exception was Dr. Perlstein and his new wife. His betrayal during the boycott had hurt too much.

One of Paula's partners in the game was Mrs. Katz, the wife of a gynecologist. She and her husband had two sons, Pawel, aged 9, and Stas, one year older than Henius. That September was an unusually warm month and the swimming pool stayed open.

One day Alicia was sitting on the bench at the pool watching the swimmers. Basia had recently learned to dive. Although she didn't dare try the highest board, she was slowly working her way up. Pawel, a skinny kid with an upturned nose, was jumping cannonball style, holding his nose and landing with a great splash. He was having a lot of fun.

Alicia felt warm and wished she had the nerve to go in, but she was embarrassed to tell Basia that she was afraid of sinking into a hole in the bottom of the pool. She stood up to stretch. Pawel ran past, splashed some water and playfully pushed her in. Alicia could have stood up, but she panicked. She remembered Frania saying, "Flap your arms and lift your legs." Basia was nearby. "Come on," she yelled, "you're not far from the side of the pool; you can stretch your arms and hold onto the edge." Alicia desperately grabbed the edge.

Mr. Wisniecki, the man in charge of the area, was passing by. He saw the girls and said to Alicia, "if you can't swim you shouldn't be so far out. You can barely stand where you are, so please walk to the shallow end."

Alicia was still terrified. "What if there's a hole in the bottom and I fall in?"

He was intrigued. "What do you mean, a hole? This isn't a lake or a river. The floor of the pool is solid concrete."

"It's all right," Basia said, "I'm watching her." She stood up, the water was up to her neck, and she jumped up and down. "You see, there's no hole. You can stand up."

Alicia continued to hold on for dear life. Mr. Wisniecki asked, "Do you know Archimedes' principle?"

Alicia tried to remember her science lessons. "It's something that makes you weigh less in the water than in the air," she answered.

"Yes, and you are buoyant in the water."

Alicia slowly lowered her legs and touched bottom. She made sure there wasn't any hole there. She felt like pushing herself up and getting out of the pool, but she decided to stick it out. Pawel and a group of kids were watching. Alicia let go of the edge and took a step toward the shallow end.

That's all Basia and Pawel needed. Basia dunked Alicia's head into the water. "Blow," she yelled, "I'm holding you."

Pawel picked Alicia up by the legs and pushed her. She was now floating, but she was still afraid to stand. Mr. Wisniecki jumped into the pool. "It's all right." He caught her by her hands. "You're in shallow water now. Stand up!"

Alicia shook the water out of her eyes and ears and looked around at the others. "That's all? It's much easier than skiing; push me back," she said to Basia. As long as there was someone to catch her and she didn't have to stand up by herself, she wasn't afraid. Everyone laughed and applauded.

"Now go to the edge and practice leg movements for the breast stroke," Basia told her. Alicia was still very scared but did as she was told.

"That girl will make a very good swimmer," Mr. Wisniecki stated, "even with her fear of the hole in the bottom."

Within a week Alicia was swimming. The following week she was jumping into the pool like Pawel. She knew the water was deep enough and she would never touch bottom. She now had confidence in Archimedes' principle and her own buoyance.

In early October, while Guta was still away, Eisig's father came to Kielce. Alicia had never heard of him; she knew only one set of grandparents. Sometimes she wondered why Jas and Jerry occasionally visited their paternal grandparents. She asked Paula. Paula tried to explain.

"I know," Alicia said. "It's because mommy didn't get a dowry from Grandpa Mark."

"It is more complicated than that," Paula answered. "Your father's parents expected him to help them financially after he became a doctor, but because of the boycott and heavy investments in Roentgen equipment, your father was always short of money. Your mother isn't to blame; anyway, she finally got her dowry."

Paula was referring to the fact that recently Guta had had a sizable piece of meadowland placed in her name. Now that Mark was married to Mrs. Dankowa, he could afford to be generous. "I'm glad your mother now has something of her own."

"Why," Alicia asked, "does he come to Kielce when my mother is away? I'm sure she would welcome him."

"His coming to Kielce has nothing to do with your mother, Paula answered. "He's a sick man and he came to his son for help. It's good for you to meet your paternal grandfather."

One morning Alicia, Rosie, the baby and the grandfather went to the park. The old man was very weak and Alicia had to support him. They sat on a bench overlooking the pond and watched the rowboats and canoes. It was a beautiful autumn day, still warm, with a gentle breeze. The leaves were turning gold and red. Henius got out of his carriage and tried to walk, holding onto Rosie's hand. Alicia called to the baby encouraging him to take a few steps toward her without holding on. He toddled to her and she picked him up, hugging and kissing him.

Her grandfather was smoking and coughing. Alicia gave the baby back to Rosie and sat down near him.

"You know," he said, "you have cousins in America."

"Cousins in America?" Jas and Jerry were cousins, and she had cousins in Lublin. But America? She was always interested in faraway countries.

"Both your father's brothers are in America. They have children your age, and your father's sister lives in Katowice with her husband and three children."

Alicia knew the map of Poland quite well. Katowice was a Polish city in Silezia. "How come, they never visit us in Kielce? Katowice is not very far."

My other daughter, your Aunt Bertha, married a "no-goodnik." During the war he left her with two small boys and escaped to Switzerland to avoid the draft.

"Anyhow," he said, "in the early Twenties, Bertha, with the two boys, smuggled herself from Poland to Germany, trying to join her husband. He really didn't want to leave Switzerland—he probably had another woman there—but finally he went to Berlin. He was never any good for Bertha and the boys. The only positive thing that came out of Bertha's marriage to Max is that he has a brother Louis in New York, a decent guy and a prominent lawyer. When Hitler came to power last January, Louis managed to get his brother and his family to America."

Grandfather had a heavy spell of coughing. With an effort, he added, "Things in Germany are no good for Jews."

"My father says," Alicia said, "that Hitler just talks big, but he won't last long."

"Your father is very optimistic. Things in America are not good either. They're having a depression; people can't get jobs." His eyes lighted up. "Bertha's younger son, Jack, has a good job already; he's a movie technician in New York, He's doing quite well, even though he's only been in America a few months."

Alicia was still watching the children in the park.

The old man kept talking: "The older boy, Kurt, was very good in school, but now he feels lucky if he can get work as a laborer in New York. Jack's good-looking and smart." Then he said with a twinkle in his eye, "I hope you'll meet him sometime in the future."

Grandfather fished out a photograph of a boy and girl on bicycles from his wallet. "Those are your cousins in Toronto, Canada," he said. "You should write to them." He took out a pen and scribbled the Toronto address on the back of the photo.

Alicia put the picture in her pocket. "I'll glue it into my album," she said.

The old man was still smoking and coughing. Later Alicia found out that he had throat cancer and had come to his son for x-ray therapy. He stayed for a week, went for treatment each day and then left. He didn't live long after that visit. As promised, Alicia put the picture of her American cousins into her album.

That month, Jas took his bike and disappeared. Paula assumed that he had gone to Zabiec and stayed with Guta, but when Kazimierz came to

Kielce with a wagon of vegetables and fruits, she learned that Jas wasn't there.

"If he was staying with Michal or somebody else around, I would know," Kazimierz said, adding sadly, "Since Mrs. Regina died and Squire Warman left, the place isn't the same."

Guta returned to Kielce and there was still no sign of Jas. He came back as suddenly as he had disappeared. Instead of going home, he stayed "downstairs." His father had given up on him, everyone else waited to hear his story. Then, after missing ten days of school, an amazing thing happened. Jas settled down and, studied hard, at the end of the fall term, he passed everything, with very good marks in Latin, Polish and history. "Maybe he should always stay with us," Guta said to Paula.

The spring term began and Jas moved back home. He and his father managed to ignore each other. Paula tried to navigate between the two of them. "I think," she told her sister, "that the peace in my home is only temporary. Monek and Jas are always on the brink of war." She was right. With Jas around, you couldn't expect peace for long.

It happened at the beginning of the spring term, during a geography lesson in the sixth level of gymnasium in Zeromski. The boys had a new teacher, a tall, skinny man whom no one liked. A map of Asia hung on the wall. The teacher pointed to a narrow strip of land on the Mediterranean coast of the westernmost part of Asia Minor. "This is Palestine," he said. "We hope that all the Jews will go there. We don't need those filthy parasites here."

Jas looked at him. He hadn't expected anything like that from a teacher. He remembered the train from Zakopane and stood up: "I'm a Jew, but I'm also a Pole. My father served in the Polish army during the Bolshevik wars. He's a highly decorated officer, a distinguished physician, a city councilman, and director of an orphanage and home for the aged. He's certainly not a parasite, and we are not filthy."

The class was completely silent. The boys had all known Jas since elementary school, and they were sure he wouldn't let anyone step on him.

The teacher was caught off guard. He was used to Jews who would take insult and abuse without daring to answer, and he himself was usually applauded for his anti-Semitic remarks. Now he was eager to save face with the class. "If your father is not a dirty parasite," he said, "he's an exception for the Jewish race. I still think that if you're Jewish, your family should go to Palestine," he said.

"We'll go to Palestine when we want to; you aren't going to tell us what to do."

The class was breathlessly sitting at the edge of their seats, waiting to see what would happen.

Jas picked up an open ink container on his desk and threw it at the teacher. Ink splashed all over his suit. Everybody laughed; only Jas would dare throw an ink bottle at a teacher.

The incident ended in the principal's office. Jas was threatened with expulsion, which would mean that he wouldn't be admitted to any other gymnasium.

His classmates circulated a petition. They described the provocation, and, to Jas's surprise, his father also took his side. As a result, Jas was asked to leave the school voluntarily, with a clear record. The geography teacher was reprimanded and asked to refrain from anti-Semitic remarks.

Paula suggested that Jas go to Krakow to live with his grandfather and his new wife and attend the last two years of gymnasium there. His father was reluctant, but finally admitted that it would be better for everyone.

In May Alicia was scheduled to take an entrance exam to the Polish public gymnasium named "Blessed Kinga." She didn't like the idea; she still remembered her experience at the other Polish school. Guta explained that money was getting tight and they couldn't afford the tuition at Mrs. Zima's. There was another stipulation. Since Alicia was now too young for the second level of gymnasium, she would have to repeat the first level if admitted to Kinga.

She cried and protested, "I'm doing so well, my marks are all excellent; I even got a "sufficient" in sewing. In French all the girls are still trying to conjugate 'être and avoir,' while I read novels and magazines."

Alicia as a student of "Mosaic Faith" as it was called, had to test very high and have well connected parents to be admitted to the public gymnasium. When the notification came that she had been accepted she had been not very happy about it.

By June Alicia wasn't thinking about the new school. The pool in Stadion had opened again, and both Alicia and Basia signed up for swimming classes with Mr. Wisniecki. Basia was in an advanced class, while Alicia was put into the intermediate one. "At least," she laughed, "I'm not with the beginners, even if I'm still afraid of holes in the bottom."

Mr. Wisniecki asked Mr. Rapaport to help with the lessons. "Maybe if you got involved, your presence would bring more Jewish kids to the pool."

Mr. Rapaport was surprised.

"I hope that swimming together would promote better understanding between the young people of our city," Mr. Wisniecki said.

"You don't often hear anything like that in Poland," Mr. Rapaport answered.

It was the first summer in Alicia's life that she was not enthusiastic about leaving Kielce and going to Zabiec. It meant saying goodbye for two months to her swimming lessons, Basia and the crowd around the pool.

"Pawelek has a crush on you," Basia said to Alicia, "He's always following you."

"You're crazy. He's ten years old, hardly older than Henius."

"How about Bolek? He's probably thirteen and he's really cute," Basia said to Alicia.

"I think he likes you," Alicia answered.

Alicia heard her parents talking about Bolek's father, Dr. Brazen. On market days his relatives positioned themselves at the entrances to the city and told the farmers about the magical healer, Dr. Brazen. Another group of relatives would sit in the waiting room, talking about the miraculous cures that the doctor performed. Mrs. Brazen, unlike other doctors' wives, had a profession of her own; she was a medical technician. Bolek was tall and handsome and girls were generally crazy about him.

Once in Zabiec Alicia forgot about the Stadion. Henius, at almost two, was running around and coming out with new words every day. He was being spoiled by everyone. And there were visitors, grandfather Mark with his wife and some cousins from Lublin.

The Warmans, unlike the Pleszowskis, were poor people and two of Mark's sisters had married poor men. Frania and Hela were the daughters of Luba Warman Brody; Beryl was the only son of Sura Warman Czarny. The three of them stayed in Zabiec for a few weeks. Guta and Paula were annoyed at Yentl staying away. "I want her to see Henius," Guta complained.

Beryl was two years older than Jas. He was an honor student and had gotten his Matura that year. He wanted to be a doctor, but, as a Jewish boy, the only place he could go to medical school was Italy. His parents could not afford to send him abroad. Paula persuaded her husband to give the Czarnys the job of managing the home for the aged in Kielce. This, plus some help from the family, made it possible for Beryl to make his dream a reality.

Occasionally Alicia and Jerry had political discussions with the Lublin cousins. Beryl and Frania were telling them about the wonders of communism.

"When the revolution comes," Beryl said, "I won't have to go to fascist Italy to study medicine. I'll go to Warsaw or Krakow. It won't matter that my parents are poor; education will be free and nobody will ask me if I'm a Jew. Then he quoted, "Religion is the opium of the people."

Alicia knew about communism only vaguely. Jerry knew more. "I don't like communism in Russia," he said. "Stalin is a ruthless dictator, just like Hitler and Mussolini."

Beryl and Frania tried to explain to them that Stalin's dictatorship was just a stepping stone toward a workers' paradise. But Alicia believed Jerry.

Jas was studying English and Hebrew during their vacation. "I'm going to try to go to Palestine and study at the University of Haifa," he told Alicia.

Jas in Palestine? He always considered himself a Pole; all his friends were gentiles; socially he had no contact with the boys from the Jewish gymnasium. He practically never dated Jewish girls. Now he wanted to go to Palestine?

"There's no room for me in Poland," Jas declared. "I would like to meet Jews who are farmers and fighters."

Alicia was reminded of a conversation of long ago. "That's what cousin Eda once said."

Jas looked at her blankly. "Oh," he said, "is she a Zionist?"

"I think so," Alicia answered.

Alicia turned twelve that summer, and she got her period. She thought how nice it would be to discuss her experience with her friends. She would belong to the club now. But then she remembered that, the next school year, she would not be seeing these girls very often. They would no longer be in the same school.

CHAPTER 6

In the fall of 1934, Jas entered the seventh level of gymnasium in Krakow. Jerry began the fifth level at Zeromski and Alicia entered the first level of the new system at Kinga.

Alicia was used to small classes of fifteen or twenty girls, but at the public gymnasium everything was big—big building, unfriendly atmosphere and fifty girls in her class. Alicia had to walk the entire length of Sienkiewicz Street to get to her new school. The teachers no longer called her by her first name; everything was strange and formal.

To her surprise, Sabina was in the same class; she and Alicia were the only Jewish girls. Of her old group at Mrs. Zima's, Alicia liked Sabina the least. She had never invited her home. The previous year Sabina had been considered boy crazy. Now her braids were pulled tighter than ever, her skirts were drabber than everyone else's, and she was a real drudge, only interested in books and grades.

Even though Alicia and Sabina did not look alike and sat at opposite ends of the classroom, teachers often mistook them for each other. They called Sabina by Alicia's name and vice versa. Polish girls' surnames usually ended with "ski" or "icz," but the Jewish girls' names derived from German or Hebrew. It was Alicia Strum and Sabina Levy. "I wish," Alicia told her mother, "we'd kept the name Pleszowski."

Since both girls were mostly shunned by other students, of necessity they became friendly. Alicia was aware of Sabina's jealousy of the ease with which she got her good grades.

Alicia had very little social life that year. She lost touch with her old crowd. They were now in the second level at Mrs. Zima's and most of the girls had started dating. To the boys at the Jewish gymnasium, Alicia appeared to be too tall and too athletic. She didn't speak Yiddish and she was too remote to be approached. Polish boys did not ask Jewish girls for dates.

Sabina resented Basia; she wanted Alicia for herself. She lived with her mother and brother in a small apartment on Sienkiewicz Street. Her father was long dead. Her brother Carl was twenty years older than her; he was the bread-winner in the family and owned the only radio store in Kielce. Not many people had radios. Alicia occasionally met Basia. They went to the movies together, and in the winter, skating and skiing. Alicia visited Sabina to do homework and to listen to far off stations on her brother's radio. They dreamt about leaving dreary Poland and going to warmer and friendlier countries.

One morning in May 1935, Alicia was walking to school. The kids from Jewish schools and Polish schools rarely mixed. They walked on opposite sides of the street. Alicia sometimes joked that, since she was a Jewish girl in a Polish school, she should walk in the middle. Sometimes a Jew in the company of a gentile friend walked on the Polish side, but a Pole crossed to the Jewish side only if he had to go to a store. There were many nice stores on both sides of the street, some of them belonging to Jews. This day, Alicia walked on the Polish side, which seemed to her wider, brighter and cleaner. She passed by a fancy café where Jews were not welcome. People were drinking coffee, eating pastries and reading their papers. She noticed that many were crying. She stopped a passerby.

"What has happened?"

"Don't you know?" he answered. "Grandad is dead."

For a minute Alicia didn't know who he meant, but there was only one man in Poland whom everybody called "Grandad." Death and Pilsudski did not go together; he had performed deeds and was involved in situations that no ordinary human could survive. She had lived in Pilsudski's Poland all her life and could not imagine the country without him.

The man continued, "Independent and united Poland is practically his creation. I wonder if there's anybody who can step into his shoes."

In school that day there was very little regular instruction. The teachers spoke about Pilsudski. Some were ex-Legionnaires and cried openly.

When Alicia came home from school, she saw fear in her parents' eyes. Guta was wondering, "Will Poland survive without Pilsudski, sandwiched between Communist Russia and Nazi Germany? Russia never accepted our Eastern frontiers and Germany would like to occupy our Corridor to the Baltic."

Eisig said, "Who cares about the Polish Corridor, Vilna and Bielorussia. What I'm worried about is that without Pilsudski, the Endeks will run wild again. At least the old man was fair to the Jews."

"But," Guta answered, "we must be concerned about the situation. If there's a war, you'll have to put on your uniform and report to duty."

"Eh," Eisig said, "there won't be a war. We have treaties with Germany and Russia, and Polish frontiers are also guaranteed by France. So I think we are safe."

"You should still try," Guta suggested, "to write to your brother in America. Maybe as a physician you have a chance to immigrate with your family. There's no future for our children here."

Guta knew very well that if Eisig ever seriously considered the matter, she could not leave her sister, her nephews, even her father, not to mention whatever remained of Zabiec and her life in Kielce. She didn't have to worry.

"You're talking crazy," Eisig answered. "There's a depression in America. What would I do there? I don't know the language; I'd probably have to start over as an intern."

Marshall Pilsudski was succeeded by another Legionnaire, General Smigly Rydz, who became Marshall and Chief of State.

In the fall of 1935, Alicia entered the second level at Kinga. Jas returned from Krakow for his last year of gymnasium. He was studying for two Maturas, the standard one at Zeromski and a Hebrew one at the Jewish gymnasium. Doctor Peltz was on the board of directors of the Jewish gymnasium. Though it was against his principles, he intended to give his son a push.

"He'll do anything to get rid of him," Paula joked. But she had tears in her eyes. "It will be very hard for me to let him go, especially to Palestine, with the Arabs and riots. I wish we could find something safer and closer for him."

There were clouds gathering over Mark's marriage. The new Mrs. Warman had a young, pretty maid. She was quite sure that both Jas and his grandfather had slept with her.

The fall as usual was Guta's turn in Zabiec. Alicia missed her mother, she was thirteen and developing fast. It was hard for her father to accept that his little girl was maturing into a woman.

Mr. Rapaport was staging a school play; Leah was his assistant and Basia his star. The two were always busy and Alicia barely saw them. She was sick and tired of Sabina, who wouldn't even go to the movies. Alicia sometimes wound up going alone and she hated it.

There was a new girl in class, a repeater for the second time, two years older than most of the other girls. She was pretty and Alicia thought she looked sophisticated and mature. She wore makeup and high heels. Her name was Olga Czeladin; she was an Ukrainian.

Though Ukrainians were reputed to be the greatest anti-Semites in the world, known for many pogroms, in the context of "Blessed Kinga" the three girls, two Jewish and one Ukrainian, were non-Catholics and therefore members of minorities.

During religious instruction they sat outside the room, waiting for the period to end. Olga was very friendly.

Alicia had met Mrs. Czeladin, who was desperate about her daughter. "If she isn't promoted this time," she told Alicia, "she'll have to leave school."

Alicia never asked where Olga's father was. She tried to tutor her friend, but Olga's mind was someplace else, mostly on a new boy in the eighth level of Zeromski. She saw him often with Jas. "All the girls here are crazy about him. You must convince your cousin to introduce me," she said.

Now I know, Alicia thought, why she's so friendly to me. It was still considered a grown-up thing to arrange a date for Olga with Jas's friend Jurek.

The four of them, Jas, Jurek, Olga and Alicia, met in front of a movie theater. After introductions they went inside. They sat in the balcony, which was dark and almost empty. Olga made sure she had Jurek exclusively on her side, while Alicia sat between the two boys. The film took place in the African desert. Cary Grant was wearing a large helmet and was in the Foreign Legion.

They didn't pay much attention to the movie. The boys told funny stories about their physics and chemistry teacher. Alicia thought that whatever Cary Grant was doing was not as dramatic as throwing a piece of sodium metal into a beaker of water and watching it explode up to the ceiling. Olga found the conversation boring.

Later on she told Alicia, "I've never met a boy like Jurek; we sat in a dark balcony for two hours and he never made a move. He didn't even touch me."

"I thought they were funny," Alicia said.

"Who cares about a stupid teacher," Olga answered. "I bet if I sat next to your cousin, he'd try something."

Alicia was sure of it.

As for Jurek, he told Jas that he wouldn't ask Olga for another date; she was not very interesting to him. He preferred more intellectual girls, but Alicia was a little too young.

Grandfather Mark came to Kielce for a few days to pay the interest on Zabiec's mortgage. This year, with his wife's money, he was not as strapped as before; still, he was forced to sell more acreage and Zabiec was shrinking.

Mark flirted with Olga. To Alicia he was an old man, but fifteen-year-old Olga thought that he was very attractive.

"Your grandfather likes pretty young girls," Rosie noted.

One day, Alicia met Basia. "Hello stranger," she said.

"Why don't you come tomorrow after school to our auditorium," Basia suggested, "and watch the dress rehearsal of the play?"

To Alicia, this was something to look forward to. The next morning, before she left for school, she told her father that she would be late for dinner and she explained why. Dinner was served at 2 P.M. Alicia had no idea how long the rehearsal would take.

Alicia watched the play, fascinated. It was "Blue Bird," by Metternich. She admired the costumes, the little dancing girls and, most of all Basia, who looked like a real actress.

When it was finished, everyone was excited and very hungry. Mr. Rapaport took Basia, Alicia and Leah to a coffee shop for sweet rolls and hot chocolate. "This will hold you until you eat your regular meal," he said.

By the time Alicia came home, it was 5 o'clock. Her father was fuming and screaming, "You're getting to be a tramp like Olga. Your Aunt is supposed to keep an eye on you, but she's not home, probably running around who knows where and with whom. You're growing up like your grandfather."

He was ready to hit her, chasing her around the table. Alicia ran to her room, slammed the door and locked herself in. Where is my mother? I told him this morning where I was going to be. Even if he forgot, he could at least listen to me now. She was getting really angry: I'll run away from home; if Jas can do it, I can too. But where? To Zabiec, to my mother? It didn't seem very romantic.

She remembered when running away meant hiding on a branch of a weeping willow tree in Zabiec, but now things were more complicated.

The next day in school she discussed the matter with Olga. "My mother," Olga said, "wouldn't mind if I ran away and never came back."

"Where could we go?" Alicia wondered.

"I would like to say hello to someone in Gdynia," Olga answered.

"That's very far from Kielce," Alicia said.

Now Olga was talking: "The ship, Stefan Batory, is anchored at Gdynia. It will sail to America in a few days, I just got a letter from a very good friend of mine." She winked at Alicia, "He's an officer on Batory, he writes that he is in love with me, maybe he will take us to America."

Alicia was getting enthusiastic, "I never saw a sea, first we will see the Baltic and then we will go to America." She reminded herself of the photograph of her cousins from Toronto with the address of her uncle written on the back. Canada and the United States - at that point it seemed the same. Once in America, she'll find them.

"Maybe Leszek will marry me and take me with him as his wife," Olga said.

"I'll smuggle myself through as a cabin boy."

"But you are not a boy."

For Alicia it started to sound like one of the make believe plays that she used to make up with Jerry, the stories of girls disguised as boys always appealed to her. It was supposed to be only a temporary disguise, a prince charming would discover that the boy was actually a beautiful girl.

Olga woke her up from her dream, "Where would we take the money?" she asked.

Alicia knew that there was some money put in her name in the postal saving account, she noticed that the saving book was hidden in the credenza in the dinning room. "I'll take care of it," she said.

"We have to hurry, because I don't know how long Batory will stay in port," Olga said.

The wheels of the plan started rolling. They would run off to sea from Gdynia. Eisig learned of Alicia's whereabouts from Mr. Rapaport on the afternoon of his outburst. He bought a large box of chocolates for his daughter as a gesture of reconciliation.

Alicia was not very impressed. "If he gave me money to buy myself material for a dress or a pretty blouse, I'd appreciate it more," she told Rosie. Her father never enjoyed seeing her dressed nicely and looking pretty. She had heard him saying to her mother, "All it will do is get Alicia into trouble."

She said to Rosie, "My father can be so good, but at other times, when I deserve it the least, he is, . . ." Alicia tried to find a word to describe him; "a dictator, a tyrant."

Now Eisig tried to be very nice. Alicia loved to play with Henius and home wasn't such a bad place. She wished she hadn't made plans to escape, but she couldn't back out and lose Olga's friendship. She was going through all the steps, found her savings book, withdrew the money and had her hair cut very short to look like a boy. She was so absorbed with the details of organizing the adventure, that she didn't think how preposterous the whole plan was.

When she went "upstairs" nobody was home; Jerry was at Tadek's, Jas someplace with his friends and Paula was either playing cards or busy with her committee of charitable organizations. Alicia certainly could not talk to Uncle Monek. Where is my mother? She sighed again, wishing Guta was here to stop her.

Alicia went to Jas's and Jerry's room, noticing Jerry's pants on the bed. If I'm going to pretend to be a boy, I have to sneak those pants. Jerry will never miss them.

She picked up the pants and looked at herself in the mirror, she was developing a big bust and had to wear a bra. It was another thing that made her feel self-conscious, both her mother and aunt had small shapely, conical breasts. How am I going to hide these? she wondered. Olga got herself a fresh permanent for my money, she looks now even prettier than before, while I look like a jerk.

The afternoon before the scheduled getaway, Eisig, as usual, was busy with his patients. Alicia locked herself in her room and told Rosie not to disturb her because she had a lot of studying to do. She packed. She put Jerry's pants into her suitcase, having decided to leave the house in a skirt so as not to arouse suspicion. Deep inside she still hoped that someone would stop her.

The next morning, when Alicia got up at her usual time, Eisig was still asleep. His first patient was not scheduled until 10 o'clock. Alicia was served breakfast by Kasia. It tasted so good. If my mother were here, she thought, I would tell her everything and tomorrow I could have the same breakfast at home.

Rosie and Kasia were in the kitchen, Henius was jumping in his crib. Alicia went to her room and brought the suitcase. She kissed her little brother. He pointed to her suitcase, "Why are you taking it Ala?" She felt like dropping it and taking her school bag instead, but she kissed Henius and said, "I'll tell you later."

She went through Eisig's office unseen by Rosie and Kasia and left through the front door. It was the usual walk on Sienkiewicz Street, but this time she wasn't going to school. She kept walking until she reached the railroad station. There she met Olga. They bought their tickets and boarded the train. They were traveling third class. The train was full of peasants and small children, it was noisy and smelly. Alicia looked around and wished it were years ago, when she'd traveled with Mucia, Jas and Jerry to Zakopane or with her mother to Krynica. Where was she going now?

It was still unbelievable to her that she'd managed to carry out her plan without anyone discovering anything strange. She tried to give herself and her companion courage. "We are independent," she kept saying.

The train stopped at Radom. They had to wait until the next morning for their connection to Gdynia, so they got a small room in a cheap hotel. "We're on our own," Alicia said. But somehow it did not sound as hopeful as intended.

That night she had a dream about sinking into a hole and not being able to get out. She tried to convince herself that she knew how to swim now.

In the morning she put on Jerry's pants, they were too loose in the waist and Alicia was afraid that she would lose them. Olga found a safety pin for her to use. "What a silly looking boy I am," Alicia said.

It was a long and not pleasant ride to Gdynia. Nobody paid much attention to the two girls or wondered if Alicia was a boy or girl. Even Olga could not find anybody to flirt with.

The whole thing turned into a tremendous fiasco. Batory left for America the day before their arrival in Gdynia. The weather was terrible; it was drizzling and windy, and the sea looked angry, with billowing waves and white, frothing whitecaps. Even the seagulls seemed sad and mournful. This was not the blue sea and clear sky of Alicia's dreams. All the romance had gone out of the adventure and the reality of her boundless stupidity hit her.

They stayed in a hostel waiting for what? They didn't know; maybe for another ship to take them to America. Their money was getting short.

"My mother's in Zabiec, and I'm afraid to contact my father," Alicia told Olga. She thought about her mother, and how worried she had been when she read about Lindbergh's baby's kidnapping. She may think that's what happened to me. How could I do such a thing? There's only one person who can help me, she decided. She sent a telegram to Aunt Paula: "Come, but please don't tell Daddy." It only took two days and then Paula was there, Alicia's one and only beautiful Mucia.

Alicia ran to her, crying. "You didn't tell my father?"

"Of course I told your father."

Alicia's face dropped, she was scared and disappointed with her Mucia. "He must be very angry with me," she said.

"Don't worry," Paula said, "he was worried sick about you. He'll be so happy when he finds out you're all right, he won't mind the rotten thing you did."

"I spent so much money and I missed school." Alicia was filled with remorse now.

"It's not the money or school." Paula said, "it's all the worry that you caused us. Henius misses you more than he misses his mother; he kept on repeating, "Where is Ala, my Ala?"

At the mention of her mother and Henius, Alicia began to cry.

"It's a good thing your mother's in Zabiec. She's due back in four days; we'll be in Kielce by then."

"I'll bet nobody worried about me," Olga said.

"When I got the telegram from Alicia, I notified your mother," Paula said coldly. "I arrived in the nick of time. The man in the hostel started to suspect that you were runaways and he was ready to notify the police."

They checked into a decent hotel. Paula brought good weather with her; the sun was shining again and the sea looked calm, so who cared if Batory left without them. Alicia still felt bad about her short hair, which she thought emphasized her big glasses, four eyes, blind hen, Jas would have said. They made a little vacation out of the misadventure, going to Sopot, a resort on the sea. They walked on the beach, watched the sailboats and the diving seagulls and met some vacationing friends from Kielce. Paula, as usual, had an admirer who showed them around. After a week of near-starvation, food tasted delicious. They went to the movies and saw a lavish American musical with Ginger Rodgers and Joan Blondel. After Sopot they visited Hel peninsula, a little sliver of land jotting into the sea. There was water all around it. The most fascinating thing was the lighthouse; they climbed it and watched ships entering the ports of Gdansk and Gdynia.

After two days they took the train back to Kielce, traveling first class. They stopped in Warsaw for a few hours. It was the largest city Alicia had ever seen, much larger than Krakow. It was the same Vistula, only much wider, meandering north to its mouth in the Baltic. The bridge between Warsaw proper and its suburb Prague was so much more imposing than the little bridge over the Vistula in Zabiec. They walked the wide boulevards and admired the store windows.

Guta came back to Kielce at almost the same time as Alicia. She looked at her daughter's hair and noticed the suitcase in the middle of the living room. "What happened?" she asked. "I had disturbing dreams; I knew something bad was happening." When she was told, she lamented, "My place is here with my children; this Zabiec arrangement is not working."

Alicia went back to school. Olga dropped out and Alicia didn't hear from her again. She considered her Gdynia adventure a bout of temporary insanity, and she wished her parents thought about it the same way. Guta never spoke about it, but whenever Eisig was angry at his daughter, he would tell her to go to "Gdynia."

One day in the spring of 1936, a lot of baking was going on in Guta's kitchen in preparation for her card party. Both Kasia and Rosie were busy breaking eggs, sifting flour, cracking nuts, washing raisins and measuring sugar. Alicia and Henius enjoyed licking the leftover batter from the mixing bowls.

Eisig was critical of all the activity. "I hope," he said, "your guests don't eat everything." Once he caught one of Guta's friends sitting on the lap of a married man in a room by themselves. To her delight, Alicia overheard him yelling at Guta, "Your guests are making a whorehouse out of our home."

The day of the party, Alicia listened for a while to the conversation of the adults. The main subject was the romance of the new King of England with Mrs. Simpson. Alicia had to go to her room and do the math homework she'd neglected for a couple of weeks. On the last quiz she'd gotten an "unsatisfactory."

My friend Sabina, she thought, was still at the door yesterday when she informed my father about my bad grade. Tonight I know he'll inspect my homework. I really like Trig; it's just that I had more interesting things to do.

Eisig was especially keen on math and Latin. Alicia had to be at least two chapters ahead of her class. When he lost his temper he would throw a book at her, but most of the time both father and daughter enjoyed working together on math problems and Latin translations. It was just like his teaching her to read years ago.

When Alicia went to her room, Henius and Stas, Pawel's younger brother, were sitting on the floor, playing with blocks. Henius tried hard to imitate his older friend. Alicia didn't quite approve. "If Stas climbed on the roof and jumped down, Henius would do the same," she had once told her mother.

The boys kept asking her questions. "Go someplace else," she said. "I have to concentrate." Where is Rosie? she wondered.

The boys left. Alicia decided to go tell Rosie to watch the children.

Rosie was busy serving the women. Alicia went to the kitchen to get a glass of water. The boys were chasing each other. They approached the stove, Stas first, Henius following. With his elbow, Stas knocked down a kettle of boiling water, which fell on Henius. Alicia screamed, Eisig ran from his office and the ladies burst into the kitchen.

Henius suffered third degree burns over most of his body. Alicia didn't know who to feel sorrier for, her mother or her brother. Eisig, of course, blamed Guta for the terrible mishap. "Instead of watching the children, you play cards," he repeated over and over.

"If anybody is to blame, it's me," Alicia said. "I told them to get out of my room."

Eisig put the little boy into a gypsum cast to give the skin a chance to heal. Alicia and Jerry spent many afternoons playing with him. The child didn't feel any pain, and he enjoyed the attention he was getting.

One afternoon Alicia looked at the headline in the newspaper: "Hitler defies Versailles Treaty, German troops march into demilitarized Rhineland, France and England issue a formal protest." "Why didn't the French troops chase them out of there?" Alicia asked Jerry.

"The French are too busy making love and eating frogs' legs," he answered.

That was one subject that Alicia and Jerry always disagreed on, She loved the French language and everything French, while Jerry considered France a nation of playboys. "I read that France has the largest and the best equipped army in the world." she said.

"Yes," Jerry answered, "but the French can't form a stable government and nobody knows who is in charge."

Alicia tried to defend her favorite country. "Don't forget, the French fought for Liberté Fraternité and Egalité, and Napoleon was the greatest military leader in history."

"That was a long time ago," Jerry shrugged.

The Rhineland was far away, but something very bad had happened quite near.

"Do you remember Yona Fisher?" Jerry asked Alicia a few days later.

Alicia had met Yona "upstairs" a couple of times. He was a sturdy, muscular boy, very smart in school and occasionally was Jas's skiing partner. Yona was two years ahead of Jas at Zeromski. After he'd gotten his Matura, he was the only Jewish boy in Kielce who had managed to get into medical school in Warsaw. There was already a "bench ghetto" in Warsaw University; the Jews had to sit separately from the Christian students.

Jerry told Alicia that Yona had been attacked by an Endek assault squad on the steps leading to the medical school. He had tried to fight, but he was overwhelmed and severely beaten with heavy sticks.

"Oh, my God," Alicia said. "How is he now?"

"Not so good," Jerry answered. "Luckily he was picked up by a Christian student, a Kielce boy who brought him to Kielce's hospital. My father just saw him. He told me that Yona is in a coma and that he suffered severe damage to his liver and kidneys."

"Did they ever catch the people who did it?" Alicia asked.

"I doubt if the Warsaw police ever made a real effort," Jerry answered.

A few days later, Yona died. "He barely recovered consciousness enough to say goodbye to his parents," Jerry told Alicia.

Even little Henius noticed how upset his sister and cousin were. When Guta walked in, Alicia asked her to finish the story she had been reading to the little boy. "I want to talk to Jerry. I don't want Henius to see me crying."

"Everybody is shocked," Jerry told Alicia. "Nothing else is being discussed in school. I took notes of what Professor Graza said."

"Is he that science teacher that Jas and his friend Jurek always joke about?"

"Yes," Jerry answered. "We call him 'Mongol' because of his slanting eyes. He likes doing crazy and spectacular experiments, but today I found out that he's a fine Pole with a lot of civil courage." Then he read the notes to Alicia: "That is what happens when hooligans get into universities. With their insane mentality they invent all kinds of racial nonsense and then they use clubs, cudgels and brass knuckles to profane the solid and holy science. The tragic thing is that a good, decent fellow with great potential is dead."

Eisig removed the cast from the little boy. Henius's skin looked new, pink and healthy. He was now even more precious to his family than before.

It was June again, the good month. To Alicia it meant birthdays and the end of the school year. Alicia and Basia got tennis rackets; now they had another attraction besides swimming. Alicia managed to persuade Jerry to play with them. He was still extremely shy around Basia.

"He's such a beautiful boy," Basia told Alicia.

Alicia was used to Jerry. She wasn't aware of his striking appearance, his huge, deep green eyes and long eyelashes, dark hair and engaging smile. He probably was not aware of it himself. "Yes," she told Basia, "I should have those eyes, instead of my small eyes with no lashes. Henius has big eyes and long lashes, too. I'm the only girl in our family, and I have to wear glasses. I also have big feet," she added, "and I like math. My mother thinks that all those things are not too good for a girl."

Basia laughed. "I wish I were tall and blond and as smart as you. I guess, when I grow up I'll find a good-looking, rich husband, while you'll be a famous scientist."

Alicia picked up her balls and racket. "Let's play," she said.

People around the tennis court looked at them. The girls were a striking pair in their short, white tennis outfits—one tall, with long slim legs; the other smaller and darker, a bundle of energy with strong, shapely legs. It seemed as if all the parts of Basia's body worked in unison.

Alicia noticed Mr. Wisniecki cheering them on. She waved to him. The tennis court was in the middle of pine woods. The birds were chirping and a gentle breeze swayed the trees.

Alicia looked at the hills of the Swietokrzyski range. This winter Yona would not be sliding the slopes and Jas would be far away. In such a magnificent world, with swimming pools and tennis courts, why couldn't everybody be like Mr. Wisniecki?

Jas passed both Maturas. He and his father were almost on speaking terms. When his mother complained about him leaving for Palestine, he would say, "Look what happened to Yona in Poland; in Palestine I'll have a gun to defend myself with."

That summer was his last in Zabiec. He tried to absorb all its beauty and keep it inside.

To Alicia, Zabiec was a paradise, but that summer she found out that most of the peasants' children were growing up illiterate. There was no school in Zabiec, and only the few prosperous farmers could send their children to distant towns.

Jas, Alicia and Jerry ran a little school in the barn.

"No wonder," Jerry said, "they listen blindly to whatever the priest tells them. They can't read for themselves. It's a good thing the priest in Zabiec is a decent guy."

"I know," Alicia said. "He used to play chess with our grandfather on the porch."

"They discussed Talmud," Jerry said.

"What's that?" Alicia asked.

"You are very ignorant," Jerry replied.

Beryl arrived in August. He had done well the past year in medical school in Italy, but he had a strange idea now. "I'm going to Spain to enlist in the Republican Army to fight the Fascists."

Paula and Guta were shocked. "You'll break your mother's heart. You're an only son; do you realize what a sacrifice it was for your parents to send you to Italy?"

"Yeah," Beryl said. "All the plans and dreams that my mother has for me; but I have to do what I think is right."

Somehow they managed to persuade him to go back to the university in Bologna.

"I'll see how things are going next year," he said.

CHAPTER 7

Summer gave way to fall, and the school year of 1936–37 began for Alicia and Jerry. Jas was now in Palestine, attending the Technion in Haifa. Jerry was a year away from his Matura. The quotas for Jewish students at Polish universities were getting smaller; the Endeks claimed there were already too many Jewish professionals in Poland. The memory of what had happened to Yona Fisher kept many boys from even applying.

Doctor Peltz had cousins in the United States who were well established and quite wealthy. They promised to get Jerry a student visa when the time came.

"As I understand," Paula said one day, "it isn't easy to get a visa for a Jewish boy from Poland. The Americans think that European Jews are communists, working for the Soviet Union."

Alicia laughed. "I can just imagine Jerry starting a revolution."

"I can do it single-handed," Jerry declared.

"Anyhow," Paula said, "because of Hitler, German Jews have priority."

All of a sudden Alicia said: "I would like to go to Spain with Beryl to fight the Fascists."

Paula was amused, Guta was worried.

"I brought you back from Gdynia; don't expect me to come to Spain," Paula said.

"Oh! Mucia, you would love Spain," Alicia threw her arms around Paula and kissed her. "Can you imagine a torrid romance with a dashing Toreador? I did not forget you dancing like Carmen."

"She gets these ideas from you," Guta said to her sister. "From you and Jas, and now Beryl."

"Don't worry," Paula said. "Beryl is going back to Italy to finish medical school. I'm sure that once he is a physician and starts making

115

money, he'll forget about the 'exploited proletariat.' In the meantime, he should keep his mouth shut, they send communists to jail in Poland and Italy."

"In Russia they're murdered or sent to Siberia," Jerry said, "by the arch communist himself, Joseph Stalin."

"We can't worry about the whole world," Paula said.

That year, the students in Alicia's class were allowed to take an additional foreign language besides their compulsory French or German. The language being offered was English. Both Alicia and Sabina enrolled in the new course.

Alicia also prevailed on her parents to get her a private tutor to teach her Hebrew. She wasn't even familiar with the Hebrew alphabet.

Eisig and Guta wondered why their daughter felt Jewish all of a sudden. For centuries the Hebrew language had only been used for prayer and studying Torah. But for Alicia it was the language of a new country and a new kind of a Jew, who, like Jas, would stand up and fight for his rights.

Her tutor was a young woman, Miss Lina, who had spent a few years on a kibbutz in Eretz Israel. She had returned to Poland to be with her aging parents and planned to go back as soon as possible.

"When I first came to Eretz Israel in 1928," she told Alicia, "there was no limit on Jewish immigration and the Arabs were quite happy to sell the land to Jewish settlers. But only the idealists came. It's a shame that more people didn't take advantage of the situation. I can't blame them; they felt safe in Europe and Palestine is a hard country. Now it's a different story; many people are anxious to leave Europe, but the British are restricting immigration."

"It's a good thing Jas got in when he did. It would be harder now," Alicia said.

"Maybe. You should join a Zionist youth organization, like Hashomer Hapoel. You might be able to get into Palestine through them."

Alicia wasn't sure about Palestine. She had never given up her dream of going to Paris or going with Jerry to the United States.

A new directive came from the Central Board of Education: All children who had not received religious instruction in their schools had to take private lessons in their own religion and bring back a grade.

Alicia had never had any religious instruction. She had taken two years of Jewish history at Mrs. Zima's, but she had never really paid much attention. She did not enjoy the class. The Jews had been slaves in Egypt and in Babylon, and they were always being persecuted and victimized. She preferred learning about Polish heros. Lately she'd been reading novels about David slaying Goliath, the Maccabees and Masada, and she was changing her mind about the history of the Jews. Now she needed a grade in religion.

Guta solved the problem by going to a local rabbi and donating money to the synagogue. In exchange, she got a signed note from the rabbi himself, stating that Alicia had passed a course in Mosaic religious studies with a grade of Excellent.

For money I can even be a good Jew, Alicia thought. She firmly believed that her parents could solve all her problems; if they weren't available there was always Mucia.

That fall Mark and his new wife came to Kielce. They stayed in a hotel, Dankowa did not want to impose on Guta and Paula. As usual, Mark waited till the last minute of the last day to rescue Zabiec from its creditors. But there was unexpected treachery from within his own family. Eisig accidentally discovered that Dr. Peltz, with some wealthy friends, was planning to buy Zabiec at auction just before the candle went out. It ended with a race along Sienkiewicz Street, with Eisig and Mark on one side and Peltz and his friends on the other. Eisig and Mark got to the mortgage house first, where Mark, with Dankowa's money, redeemed Zabiec. Dankowa was appalled. "It's like Chicago and the warring gangsters."

This wasn't the first time Eisig had felt bitter towards his brother-in-law. They had had a parting of the ways when they owned a Roentgen clinic together. This incident was the last straw. From then on Eisig had a new name for his brother-in-law: "Mojsie Kak (Mojsie Crap). He's like a circus horse who performs all those intricate tricks. People think he's a great wonder, but just as the horse at the end, he stands in the middle of the stage and, all his grand schemes turn to crap."

An odd situation developed between the two families. Eisig did not talk to the Peltzes and vice versa. Guta did not talk to Monek. The two sisters no longer visited each other at home, but they continued to call each other through the back yard, and they went out shopping and to the social club together. The Peltzes ignored Mark and his wife. To Alicia it did not make much difference; she'd never seen much of her Uncle Monek anyhow; Aunt Paula was still her "Mucia" and Jerry remained her best friend.

Occasionally, Alicia came down with a fever and sore throat, but it was not Uncle Monek who came to examine her now. Their new family doctor was Dr. Breitman, a pleasant young man who often referred patients to Eisig.

"I like him better than Uncle Monek," Alicia told her mother. "He tells jokes and makes me feel comfortable."

"Uncle Monek is probably a better doctor, but with his personality he should have remained a surgeon," Guta laughed.

"Will Daddy ever make up with him?"

"Oh, who knows; it will take time."

Later that fall a letter arrived for Guta from Dankowa. She had decided to divorce Mark. "I still love him," she wrote, "but I don't want to end up like your mother, without a penny of my own and dying prematurely."

Guta showed the letter to her sister, "What is father going to do alone in Krakow?" she wondered.

"It serves him right." Paula answered. "Dankowa is a good woman, but she is smart and knows how to protect herself and her money." Then she confided, "I have enough to worry about without thinking about him. There are riots in Palestine and next year Jerry might go to the United States. I know I shouldn't be concerned about Jas; he knows how to manage. But Jerry's a different story. Jas used to say that he and Alicia knew only what they read in books."

Guta said, "But Jerry will be safe in the United States."

This didn't seem to comfort Paula. "Alicia is a plugger, but Jerry only needs his books and records to be happy. I hope he'll find a girl in the United States who will take care of him and give him a little push."

"Most likely," Guta smiled, "a girl will find him; all of Alicia's friends are crazy about him." She was thinking how lonely her sister would be, when both of her boys were gone. She hoped that by the time Alicia got her Matura, things would be better in Poland and her daughter would be able to stay home. "God willing," she said to Paula, "in a year or two Hitler will be gone and we'll be able to breathe easier."

A couple afternoons a week Paula and Guta played Gin Rummy in their social club. Usually Paula won, while Guta lost.

Alicia often lent her mother the contents of her piggybank. Guta was afraid to tell her husband that she lost her household allowance playing cards.

One afternoon, Eisig and his daughter were reading Cicero. Eisig picked up Alicia's piggybank and shook it: "It's almost empty, your mother robbed you again."

Alicia was angry at him, "When mother sells her meadowland, she'll be independent from you, she'll have money of her own."

"No she won't," Eisig answered, "she'll lose it to her sister in a card game."

"Come on Daddy, the women are playing for small stakes." Alicia vowed to herself, that she would have her own profession before she gets married.

Haifa, May 1937
From Jas to Jerry,

Dear Jerry,

I would like you to be the first to hear about my decision. I realize that Father and Mother will learn about it eventually and won't accept it gracefully.

I simply couldn't concentrate on studying (I've always had that problem) with everything that's going on. I'm joining the Jewish Auxiliary Police. They're attached to the British police charged with squelching Arab riots. I'm not going to be a student anymore and completely dependent on father.

The lousy Arabs are attacking peaceful agricultural settlements and murdering people. They are a bunch of ruthless terrorists. They plant bombs on school buses. The bastards have forgotten that they sold the land to the Jews for exorbitant prices. They want it back now that the Kibbutzniks, through backbreaking work and sacrifice, have transformed the desert into flourishing farms. The British are not our friends either; they think they can bring law and order to the country by limiting Jewish immigration. They're issuing one "White Paper" after another, with more and more restrictions, just when European Jews desperately need a place to go.

I've met many new German arrivals. They are a stuck up bunch, but they are bringing culture to the country. There are many highly talented people among them—scientists, doctors, artists and musicians. I even met an opera singer. He sang for us but, you know me, I think nobody can measure up to our grandfather.

Hitler's loss is our gain. These people will be contributing and enriching the future Jewish state, instead of Germany and the rest of lousy Europe.

Now back to my decision. I figure, who but a strong, healthy guy should try to protect the Jewish settlements? At least, if I get myself killed, I'll take a few Arabs with me. I'm the kind of Jew Palestine needs.

Maybe you should break the news of my not being at the university to Mother. It's up to her to talk to the "Pater familiae."

I miss you all: Mother, you, Alicia and little Henius. I hope he doesn't play near the kitchen stove anymore. Poor kid, he never knew Grandmother Regina, or saw Zabiec in its glory. How is the old place doing? Is it true that Dankowa is divorcing Grandfather? I still dream about Zabiec the way it was years ago—all the horses, dogs, the great harvests, the mill all lighted up, the orchards, flowers, strawberries and raspberries and the great seders.

Henius will never sit at a seder table in Zabiec and listen to Grandfather conducting services, but maybe when he's our age there will be a better world, without Hitler, Stalin, Mussolini, the Endeks or murderous Arabs.

I hope, God willing, as Aunt Guta would say, that next year
you'll be able to go to America.
> Love to everybody,
> Jas

Jerry showed Alicia the letter. After she had finished reading it, he
said, "Jas forgot about the other bad ones, Franco and the Grand Mufti
of Jerusalem. We Jews must be good people because all the tyrants of
this world hate us. Jas writes about the Arabs wanting the land they sold
back. I read someplace that Dutch settlers in America bought Manhattan
island from the Indians for some trinkets and beads. Can you imagine the
Indians trying to get Manhattan back?"

Alicia laughed. She always appreciated the way Jerry put ideas
together. He was her encyclopedia. When she needed information for her
compositions, she didn't bother to look it up, she just asked Jerry. Who
else would know about Manhattan island?

She noticed that Jerry was a little worried. "I don't know if I should
show the letter to my mother; she cannot sleep at night thinking about
Jas."

Alicia was surprised. "But she's always laughing and joking."

"That's my mother," he answered. "Only Baldie and I know how upset
she gets when she reads about Palestine in the papers. Now Jas is not
only there, he's actually fighting the Arabs."

Alicia tried to figure out who "Baldie" was, then she realized that it
was an endearing name, that Jerry gave his father. To my father he is
"Mojsie Kak," to Jas he is a father to run away from, but Jerry lovingly
calls him "Baldie."

"My parents will find out soon. They send money and packages
through friends who have relatives in Palestine. One of them is going to
tell them that Jas is no longer a student at the University of Haifa."

"Jas will always find adventure," Alicia stated.

As predicted, the Peltzes soon found out about Jas. At her social club
Paula appeared to be as vibrant, witty and flirtatious as ever, but her
family knew how worried she was. She confided in her sister that
Monek's diabetes was almost out of control. "We are trying to persuade

Jas to come back to Poland. He always got along here, and after Jerry gets his Matura, maybe the two of them will go to the United States."

In June, Alicia and Basia befriended a girl at the pool. Lisa was a physician's daughter. Her father was a decorated ex-Legionnaire, now in the active reserve with a rank of colonel. Lisa's parents would not dream of sending their daughter to a Jewish school; her marks were not high enough for Kinga, so she attended a small, private Polish school. She was on the plump side, but for a girl of fifteen she was immaculately groomed, with manicured nails and hair done in a beauty parlor. She was a good swimmer, but she rarely went in the water for fear of ruining her hairdo. Mostly she sunned herself at the pool and flirted with boys. She had a crush on Bolek, but everybody knew that Bolek liked Basia.

Jerry never came to the pool. Lisa had only seen him once at Alicia's house, and wanted to meet him badly.

One day Basia said to Alicia, "Lisa is a stupid creep. I may never talk to her again."

"What happened? Did she try to steal Bolek from you?"

"It has nothing to do with Bolek," Basia answered. "Do you remember, a couple of days ago I lent her my history notes? Yesterday I went to her house to get them back; she didn't ask me in, but told me to wait in the hall. I couldn't figure out why she was acting that way. I did her a favor and she treats me like a poor relation."

"I think I know the reason," Alicia said. "I bet Lisa had a gentile classmate in the living room and didn't want her to find out she had a Jewish friend from Mrs. Zima's."

"How do you know?" Basia asked.

"I know her type," Alicia said. "Her cousin Janka Buchhalter is the same way."

"I know Dr. Buchhalter, he is our dentist," Basia said. "He's a nice guy."

"Janka is one grade higher than me in Kinga. You can always see her walking on the Polish side of Sienkiewicz Street with her gentile classmate Wanda. The Buchhalters feed, dress and entertain Wanda. They're buying her friendship for their daughter."

Basia laughed. "I guess that's what a Jew has to do if he wants the honor of having a gentile friend."

Alicia reminded herself of something funny. "Jas's friend, Lolek Golebiewski, is a devout Catholic. He tried to convince Jas to convert to Christianity. He worried about Jas's immortal soul. Jas told him, that it must be boring in heaven and that he will meet more interesting people in hell. Lolek yelled at him for being blasphemous." Then she added, "My mother is always serious; she told me that Jews stress behavior right here on earth and don't worry about the hereafter. We just assume that good people will go to heaven. My Mucia is seldom serious. She said that since we're condemned to hell, we might as well enjoy ourselves here and forget about after."

One afternoon at the Stadion Guta and Alicia were sitting on a bench watching Henius chasing pigeons. They were joined by Mrs. Koslow, a dentist's wife, with her two daughters Lucia and Rita. Mrs. Koslow was a heavy set lady dressed in old fashioned and ill fitting clothes. The women gossiped that her husband, a good looking man, had many extra marital affairs. Mrs. Koslow's younger daughter Rita was Henius' age and they both became busy playing.

Lucia was ten years old, she was a skinny kid with thin arms and legs. To Alicia she looked like a sick child.

Mrs. Koslow carried a big ball, she handed it to Alicia. "Try to play with Lucia," she said.

Alicia threw the ball straight at Lucia, the little girl tried hard to catch it, but she had problems. I hope, Alicia thought, that she is not backward like Greta. Greta, Dr. Levin's daughter, at twenty-two was not able to cross the street by herself.

"Make sure," Mrs. Koslow told Alicia, "that Lucia does not try to run, she's not supposed to get herself overtired."

She's ten years old, Alicia thought, and she is not supposed to run. All the jumping, that Basia and I did at that age, even now we, never stop. Alicia vaguely knew Lucia's story, she had a strep throat, which led to rheumatic fever and according to Doctor Peltz the child suffered permanent heart damage.

After catching the ball a few times Lucia was out of breath. Both girls sat on a bench opposite their mothers. "Your uncle, Doctor Peltz," Lucia said, "said that maybe next year I will be able to go to school, I will have to be careful, another throat infection might affect and damage my heart valves even more."

Alicia was surprised, I thought she was backward, but at ten her vocabulary is better than Lisa's at fifteen.

"Next year I might go to Kuszewska."

Kuszewska was the Polish private school that Lisa attended.

"I have a tutor and I read well above grade level."

I bet, Alicia thought, she said: "Do you like my uncle as your doctor?"

"He's supposed to be the best doctor in town, but my parents think that at the beginning of my sickness I was misdiagnosed by him and that aggravated my condition."

Alicia was more and more surprised, "Where did you learn to talk that way?" she asked.

"I've been around doctors so much that I talk like them, when I grow up I will be a doctor."

"You certainly will," Alicia answered. Poor kid, she thought, she is sick so much, she doesn't have much of a childhood. It's a lousy way to start life with permanent heart damage at ten.

Mrs. Katz with Stas came over, now Stas, Henius and Rita were running around together. Stas as usual was the leader. It was Rosie's day off. "Watch them," Guta begged Alicia.

"Oh mother," Alicia answered, "there's no kettle of boiling water here."

That summer in Zabiec, Alicia and Jerry felt an emptiness. No Grandmother or Aunt Yentl, no Grandfather. They even missed Mrs. Dankowa. It still seemed unbelievable that Jas was not there.

The mill had closed permanently and everything else was deteriorating. They still remembered when there were twenty-eight pairs of work horses in the stable. Now the number had dwindled to two pairs. With so much land sold and leased, no more were needed. The harvest, which used to be a big event, didn't amount to much anymore. Most of the servants had been discharged, though Stefka, Kazimierz and Rosie were still in Zabiec.

Henius was approaching his fifth birthday. He once asked Paula, "Will Jas come and visit us this summer?"

Paula wanted to cry. "Maybe next summer," she said.

In the meantime Kazimierz stood in for Jas. He carried Henius on his shoulders, and sometimes when Guta was not around, he put him on a horse and held him there, to the boy's delight.

Rosie would get excited. "Miss Guta will kill me if she finds out that I let you do this." Rosie loved Henius, and the boy was very attached to his nanny.

"When are we going to see Father?" Guta wondered one day.

"Don't tell me you miss him," Paula said.

"I wish we could get together just to listen to him sing; maybe it would dispel the gloom and bring back the old days."

"They're gone; without Mother there's no hope for Zabiec."

The day after that conversation took place, a letter came from Mark. It was addressed to both of his daughters.

"I don't want to see it," Paula said. "I don't give a damn what he's doing."

"I think," Guta said cautiously, "that last fall he was right, and you and Monek were wrong."

"It would be better for everyone concerned," Paula said, "if we had gotten Zabiec away from him."

Guta opened the letter and began reading. "Oh my God!" she said.

Paula could not contain her curiosity. "What's so interesting?"

"He has a woman he intends to marry; he wants to bring her to Zabiec this month to meet everybody."

"I assure you," Paula said, "that I won't be included in 'everybody.' I'm going to Busko; I need sulpha baths for my rheumatism anyhow."

"Aren't you interested at all?" Guta asked.

"I still remember when he slept with Jozka while mother was dying. You forget too easily. Now you can have the honor of playing the hostess to his new flame. I hope she's not as smart as Dankowa and has enough money to support him in the style that our mother accustomed him to.

Then she added, "Be sure to write to me at Busko and describe her to me."

Guta could not keep from laughing.

Mark's new wife didn't make a very good impression on Guta. Later she wrote to Paula, "She is short, fat and doesn't know how to dress. Her name is Tina and the only tiny thing about her is her brain. What a difference from Dankowa! I wish father had stayed married to her; she was elegant and intelligent. What a letdown this hapless creature is after his two previous wives. She's not interested in anybody or anything but Father; she even ignores Henius. I think that she must be quite stupid; why else would she do everything to antagonize the family? Remember how Dankowa respected our feelings about sleeping in our mother's bed? Tina doesn't care; she's ready to make love right on the front porch. I get the impression that no one ever made love to her, or even kissed her before. Now she's overwhelmed by Father's attention and charm.

I asked Father how old she was, but he was ashamed to tell me. I asked her myself, and she told me, without batting an eye, that she was thirty-five. That means she's younger than me. To me she is a piece of mindless flab, but I think that Father enjoys all her attention, as naive and stupid as she is. She must have money; why else would he bother with her? They're leaving for Krakow by the end of the month. If you are interested in meeting her, come back earlier. You must be back here in August to help me with the harvest, such as it is."

For Jerry 1937–38 was the last year at the gymnasium. The news from the American Peltzes was not encouraging. They doubted that Jerry could immigrate to the United States the following summer or even in the fall.

"Jerry's name," they wrote, "is on the list and his number will eventually come up, but with quotas getting tighter, it might take a long time."

Polish anti-Semitism was on the rise. The Jews were being blamed for the deteriorating economic situation. On Sienkiewicz Street, young men were distributing leaflets saying, "Don't Patronize Jewish Stores, Support Your Own." There were pickets in front of the Jewish shops.

Once Alicia came across a group of elementary school children escorted by their teacher. The children were singing:

> A Pole looks for a job in vain
> While a Jew spends money in a cabaret,
> The Germans are expelling Jews, so should we,
> There will be more work for our people.

The teacher smiled approvingly at his charges. Later on, Alicia said to Jerry, "This is the country that Cousin Wladek and Lisa's father fought so hard for. I don't understand your mother; she's still trying to convince Jas to come back."

"Well," Jerry said, "if Jas had stayed at the university, my parents would feel differently." He smiled. "Parents are not very logical people. When Jas was home, Baldie couldn't find anything good about him. Now he misses him and wants him back in Kielce. He's trying to find a pilots' school for Jas in Poland."

"Yes, I remember. Lindbergh was always Jas's hero."

That fall Guta managed to sell her meadowland in Zabiec. She felt good about it. As usual, the two sisters went to Krakow to shop for clothes. Guta could now afford a dress for the New Year's Eve ball. The ball in the Jewish social club was a big event every year. People drank, danced and gossiped, and no one worried about politics. "Things had hit bottom," someone concluded. "From now on it can only get better. Poland is still not Germany."

Then it was 1938. In March Germany annexed Austria. They began to stir trouble in Czechoslovakia.

"Hitler wouldn't dare move against the Czechs," Eisig told Guta and Alicia. "They have a treaty with Russia and France."

"Just a few years ago Britain and France guaranteed Austria's independence," Guta said.

Eisig had an explanation for that, too: "That's different; after all, the Austrians are Germans."

"There are many Germans living in Czechoslovakia," Alicia observed.

Kielce, June 1938
From Jerry to Jas

Dear Jas,

I hope my letter reaches you, since you don't have a permanent
address. I'm glad that my exams are behind me, especially the
orals. They were a drag. You can congratulate me; my Matura
certificate was mailed to me and I even got honors. All my
transcripts have been sent to the United States. It might take
another year for me to get a visa.

I took the admissions test for medical school in Krakow.
Would you believe that during testing, students were distributing
anti-Jewish leaflets to the professors and the candidates? The
"Bench Ghetto" in all of Poland's universities is being enforced.
Sometimes I think that the majority of Polish people are not so
bad, but now the Endeks are in control.

Smigly Rydz is not Pilsudski. I have no idea how he feels about
religious tolerance and equality of opportunity, but he's in no
position to enforce anything. Maybe he was a hero as a Legionnaire, but that doesn't make him a good head of state.

Coming back to good Poles. There were riots at the University
of Wilno. The Jewish students refused to sit on "Ghetto
Benches." The dean announced that all the Jews had to sit on
their designated side, but that non-Jews might also sit there. Lo
and behold, the majority of students joined the Jews and the
Endeks were in the minority. When one of the students was asked
by a reporter why he identified with the Jews, he answered, "If
Jesus were now attending a Polish university he would have to
sit on a 'Ghetto Bench.' "

Unfortunately, very few professors have the courage to appeal
to the students' better instincts. I'm rambling on. "Baldie"
suggested that, next year, while I'm waiting for American
papers, I should learn a practical trade. He got me a job for next
fall in a garage. I'll try to be an auto mechanic for a while. My
physics might come in handy.

None of the Jewish kids that graduated with me have any
prospects. The ones that can work in their fathers' businesses are
lucky. With the economic boycott against the Jews, there is not

much future in that either. It seems that we are not needed anywhere. I don't have to tell you that the only way to get to Palestine is illegally, and even our good and wealthy relatives can't get me to America. It took centuries for Jewish youths to get out of ghettos and be able to get a modern education. Now the clock is turning back.

Alicia has finished the gymnasium. Now she has to go to lyceum for two years, then the Matura. There are entrance exams to lyceum, but both Alicia and her friend Sabina were exempted because of their high marks. Alicia is very proud of herself, and we hope that maybe in two years, when she's finished, things will be better.

Beryl came home from Italy for vacation. Since Mussolini became Hitler's pal, things there have changed for the Jews. Beryl loves the Italian people—he says they're warm, friendly and not warlike at all—but their fascist government stinks and he hopes that he'll be allowed to finish medical school next year. Then his troubles will only have begun: He'll have to find an internship in Poland.

Mother will probably get a visa to visit you in Palestine. If she tries to convince you to come back to Poland, don't listen to her. Last year we all had to attend army exercises, and unless I get to America, I might be drafted. We all miss you very much. Please stay away from Arab bullets.

Love, Jerry

At the end of June it was Zabiec again. One day in July, Guta, Paula and the children went to Pacanow to visit the cemetery. It was a beautiful park with big trees and green grass, so different from the town in which it was located. When they entered, bearded men were asking for alms and offering to say prayers for the dead. It was peaceful and quiet. Pacanow seemed to be nicer for the dead than for the living.

They came to the Pleszowski plot and stopped in front of two monuments: Laja Slecka Pleszowski, Wife, Mother, Grandmother, Greatgrandmother, Born 1860, Died 1927, and Regina Warman Pleszowski, Wife, Mother, Grandmother, Born 1880, Died 1932.

"Grandmother," Paula said, "helped Grandfather amass a great fortune, while our mother, in spite of all her efforts, couldn't prevent its decline."

Alicia looked around. "How come no one brings any flowers?"

"We just put pebbles on top of monuments, so a passerby will know that these dead are not forgotten," Guta said. "Next year, if we want to visit these graves, we'll have to stay in a hotel."

Alicia and Jerry did not grasp the meaning of what she was saying. "The roof isn't leaking that bad," Jerry said.

"You don't get it," Guta said. "It looks as if, next fall, your grandfather is not going to redeem Zabiec."

Alicia and Jerry still did not understand. "What's going to happen to Zabiec?" Alicia asked.

"Unless someone buys it at auction, the banks are going to repossess it. The redemption rate this fall will be so high that it would probably be cheaper to buy a whole estate at auction. Whoever buys it will have it debt-free."

"So why don't we?" Jerry asked.

"It's not so easy," Paula said. "The former owners and their heirs are barred from the auction. Even if we could get someone to buy it for us, it wouldn't be any good. There's no one to manage Zabiec."

"But you two have been doing it for a few years," Alicia said, pointing to her mother and aunt. "Why can't we try to keep the place?"

Guta said, "We have our homes in Kielce with our husbands and children, and Grandfather is in Krakow. The only person who could make this estate function again is Jas, but he won't come back to Poland."

That afternoon Alicia and Jerry watched the ducks and geese on the ponds. They looked at the weeping willow trees and the birch trees, they walked the elm and chestnut lanes and they stood on the hill where they had buried Blossom. They could not believe that this would all belong to someone else.

Paula watched them moping around. "I don't think," she told Guta, "that I'm going to write to Jas about Zabiec. He would take it even harder than the other two. Kielce was never as much of a home for him as Zabiec was. Whenever he was in trouble in school or with his father, he came here."

"How about us?" Guta said. "This place has been in our family for almost half a century. We lived through the Great War here. Even after I got married, Zabiec was always home number one to me." Guta was ready to cry: "How about Michal, Stefka and Kazimierz, where will they go? They have been with us since I can remember. At least Rosie has a home with us in Kielce."

Now Paula was also close to tears. "Let's not get sentimental," she said. "We did everything we could to save the place. Anyhow, next week I'm going to Busko when Father comes. You'll discuss the details with him. Since Mother's death, I've stopped caring."

"Whom do you have in Busko?" Guta asked suspiciously.

"I'll take Alicia, she'll keep an eye on me," Paula said.

"It's her last summer in Zabiec." Guta didn't want to hurt her sister's feelings, but she said it anyhow: "Sometimes I don't like the influence you have on my daughter."

Paula flashed her green eyes at her sister. "You mean that you're afraid she won't grow up to be a prude like you."

Guta said, "I'm just trying to impress on her that a girl can't be too careful." She was upset. She threw her arms around Paula: "Since mother died, you're the only person I can rely on. Now everything is falling apart."

"Don't worry so much," Paula said. "Things will work themselves out. I won't take Alicia to Busko. I'll come back as soon as Father leaves.

Paula left for Busko.

Alicia and Jerry were busy teaching reading. Rosie and Henius were among their students. The school consisted of nine youngsters and Rosie. "We should have more adults," Jerry said. "Most of the peasants around Zabiec are illiterate."

"Henius is the youngest," Alicia said, "but he's picking up the fastest. He can't even go to school next year; a child has to be seven years old to be admitted to the first grade." Then she remembered, "I was six when I entered second grade, and then I lost a year when I went to Kinga."

"Look at me and Jas," Jerry said, "parents put all the pressure on their first born, like "Baldie" with Jas, with the second they take it easier."

"What should they pressure you for?" Than she laughed, "If some superior force would average you and Jas, than we would have two normal persons."

"You don't mean normal, you mean ordinary and who wants to be ordinary?"

In September 1938 Jerry started working in a garage. Alicia entered the first class at the lyceum. The students had a choice of two different curriculums, humanities or sciences. Alicia loved literature, languages and history, but lately the sciences, especially the physical sciences, appealed to her. She found logic and order in chemistry and physics.

"I've had enough of Latin translation and memorizing dates; I'm taking sciences," she told Sabina.

Sabina had always preferred the humanities. "I bet your mother won't be happy about it."

"You're right," Alicia said. My mother thinks that science is not a feminine pursuit. She's worried that I'll have problems finding a husband. My father will probably approve, even though he enjoys reading Latin with me."

Sabina still did not give up, "How will you manage in the labs? You know, you are not handy."

"You will help me," Alicia said.

"But I'm not going to be in your classes."

"Oh yes, I forgot," Alicia said, "good luck."

Sabina, as Alicia expected, changed her mind and settled on the sciences. They were both learning how to light Bunsen burners. "Jerry and I," Alicia joked, "work everything out in our minds. I wonder what kind of auto mechanic he'll make."

That afternoon she told Jerry about her experiences in lab.

"Did you ever hear about the 'Gedanken' experiment?" Jerry asked.

Alicia gave him a blank look.

"Einstein developed his Theory of Relativity without ever going to the laboratory."

"I assure you, I'm no Einstein," Alicia laughed. "I might try for Madame Curie. On the other hand, I'd like to write fiction."

That September, Hitler claimed that all he wanted was to "liberate" poor, persecuted Germans in Czechoslovakia. Eisig still maintained that Hitler would not dare make a military move against the Czechs. Hitler didn't have to dare. Neville Chamberlain achieved "peace in our time" by conceding a section of Czechoslovakia to Germany. Poland and Hungary took advantage of the situation and also grabbed a piece.

"Poor Czechoslovakia," Jerry said to Alicia. "Smigly Rydz hasn't learned much from history. He forgot how, at the end of the eighteenth century, the Big Three partitioned Poland."

"Maybe he remembers more recent lessons," Alicia said. "In 1920 Pilsudski took Wilno from Lithuania and tried to incorporate much of the Ukraine into Poland."

"Where did you learn such history? They don't teach you these things in Polish schools." Then he said, "Pilsudski, crazy as he was, was shrewd and knew what he was doing, unlike our idiot Smigly. Anyhow, Poland, with her history of martyrdom, shouldn't participate in the gang rape of Czechoslovakia. One day it will come back to haunt us."

Alicia said, "You'll be in America by then. You're criticizing Poland, how about England? Chamberlain gave the Sudetenland away like it was his."

Early in October Paula received a visitor's visa to Palestine.

Tel Aviv, October 1938
From Jas to Jerry

Dear Jerry,

Mother is here with me. I've got two weeks' furlough to spend with her. She looks young and beautiful; my friends think that she's my girlfriend.

We sit at night on her hotel porch, look at the Mediterranean and talk. You know what a storyteller she is. I'll never be tired of hearing about her and Aunt Guta's life in Pierscien and Zabiec. This is the first time she's told me about the great love of her life. Alicia knows this story, but I doubt if you do.

It happened during the war. Mother met him again a few years
ago in Karlsbad. He's married and has a family. Would you
believe that he was willing to leave his wife and children if
Mother agreed to divorce Father? She told me how she met our
father. I still don't understand what made her marry him. I realize
that we two wouldn't be here if she hadn't.

I'm trying to persuade Mother to stay in Palestine. She only
has a visitor's visa, but many people stay here illegally, and the
British can't do much about it. I know people in the right places,
and after you go to America, I could bring Father here also. You
know how I feel about him, but for her I would do anything.

She might have considered it until she heard the news on the
radio about an Arab ambush of a bus. Those things happen here
almost every day. Do you know what she said? I quote: "This is
a wild country, like cowboys and Indians. Nobody shoots at me
on the streets of Kielce. I have a husband there, Jerry is still
home, my sister, Alicia, Henius and many friends. I've lived in
Poland all my life and in Kielce for almost twenty years. I know
everybody and everybody knows me. Why should I stay in this
crazy place?"

I tried to tell her that now, with half of Czechoslovakia gone,
Poland is in a vulnerable position. She said that I was talking
nonsense, that Hitler had already gotten what he wanted and has
no reason to move against Poland.

I personally think that Hitler will not stop with the Sudetenland. It's the nature of the beast to keep wanting more and more.
Don't forget that Germany always resented the Polish Corridor
to the Baltic and the free city of Gdansk.

The Arabs are not as dangerous as the Germans. We Jews here
are a closed community and we are prepared to fight. I feel that
European Jews are trapped.

I know that all my arguments are in vain. Not only doesn't she
want to stay here, but she tries to lure me back to Kielce. She
says she worries constantly about my fighting Arabs.

I hope your American papers come through soon, before
you're drafted into the Polish army.

                              Love,
                              Jas

Paula left Palestine in early November. After a journey by ship on the Mediterranean and a long train trip through central Europe, she arrived in Krakow on the morning of November 10th. She felt rested after having spent the night before in a first class sleeping compartment. Wladek and Eda met her at the station.

"Like old times," Paula said.

By now, both Eda and Wladek were successful lawyers. Eda was stylishly dressed and looked very attractive. Paula looked at her slim waist. "Nothing cooking yet," she said. "You've been married almost ten years."

"It's not a good world to bring up children in," Wladek said.

Paula noticed that Wladek was not his usual self; he was not joking or kidding with her. "Hey cousin, what's going on?"

"Did you see the newspapers this morning?" Wladek asked.

"Hell no," Paula said. "I've been in Palestine for the last three weeks and I read and heard enough about Arabs planting bombs, shooting people and attacking settlements. Jas is in the line of fire. I don't want to hear any more about Palestine or Czechoslovakia. I want to go home to Kielce. I wish Jas would come too."

Eda shook her head. "It's better to be in the line of fire in Palestine than to be a sitting duck in Europe."

Wladek laughed. "My wife is an ardent Zionist. I'm still trying to be a Polish patriot."

Paula now looked at the paper. "Let me see what got you so upset."

It was a Jewish paper published in Polish: "Hitler Avenges* Killing of German Diplomat by Jewish Boy in Paris. SS Organizes 'Spontaneous' Demonstrations Throughout Germany. Many Jews are Robbed, Beaten, Arrested and Sent to Concentration Camps, Jewish Homes, Synagogues Set on Fire, Store Windows Broken, Store Owners Murdered. Streets Covered with Glass."

Paula could not believe her eyes. "It's a Jewish newspaper; they must be exaggerating."

"Uh, uh," Eda said. "I don't think they know the half of it."

---

* Refers to "Crystal night."

"This is something new," Wladek said. "The atrocities were organized by the government and performed by Hitler's elite guards. Even in czarist Russia the pogroms were carried out by fringe groups such as Cossaks. The government didn't do much to prevent them, but they weren't the instigators."

"Monek always thought that Germans were the most civilized people in Europe," Paula said. "It's barbarism to punish a whole group of people for the crazy act of one individual, not even committed in Germany. Can the world just stand by?"

Wladek grinned. "I would expect a question like that from Guta; you were never naive. The world stood by when Mussolini invaded Abyssinia, when Franco destroyed a legitimate government in Spain, and Hitler was even rewarded for repeatedly breaking the Versailles Treaty. Do you expect the world to do anything for the Jews?"

Paula was not convinced. "In Poland," she said, "the Jews have full citizenship rights." Essentially she was an optimist. As a child of privilege, she had an inbred feeling of security; she could never imagine that events in Germany could affect her life. She worried about Jas being in a foreign country and away from the safety of home.

Eda didn't share her feelings. "Lately our rights haven't been actively upheld and I'm afraid it will get worse."

Wladek started feeling sorry for his cousin. "Leave Polusha alone, she's had a long trip. Let her rest up at home and enjoy herself."

Paula went back to Kielce. The atmosphere there was depressing. Young Jewish graduates were walking back and forth on Sienkiewicz Street with nothing to do.

In Germany, the racial laws had now been fully implemented. A person was considered a Jew if one of his grandparents was Jewish. The Jews were barred from civil service jobs, forced to sell their businesses and houses at bargain prices to the Aryans, and were made to move to special sections of the cities. The Jewish children could not attend school. That was the law of the country. Besides that, there were outbreaks of violence and hooliganism.

When Alicia visited Sabina, she met her uncle, Mr. Hochberg, Kielce's resident pessimist. He was a bitter fifty year old man who had never married. Sabina's mother was completely different, a woman with a sunny disposition who loved to eat. It was hard to believe that Mr. Hochberg and Mrs. Levy were brother and sister.

"It won't end with robbing and beating Jews," he told the girls. "They're going to kill all of us."

"Don't listen to him," Sabina told Alicia.

"First in Germany," he said, "they're going to line up the Jews on the streets and drive tanks over them. The same thing will happen in Czechoslovakia, Austria and eventually Poland."

This all seemed so exaggerated.

"The scary thing," he went on, "is that the German medical profession is endorsing Hitler's racial theories."

The girls stopped paying attention to him. "Leave us alone," Sabina said. "We have studying to do."

In March, 1939, Germany occupied all of Czechoslovakia. The Munich agreements and Hitler's promises were now a joke. Poland was next on his list. There were German riots in the free city of Gdansk, and Hitler announced his intention to build a highway through the Polish Corridor connecting Germany proper with east Prussia.

On March 31st, England and France vowed to protect Poland against Nazi aggression. This time, even Eisig had doubts. Marshall Smigly Rydz, comparing Poland to a coat, declared that the Polish people would not concede even one small button.

It was June 1939 and the end of a another school year. It was the first summer without Zabiec. Jerry was working in a garage and Alicia was promoted to the second and last class of lyceum. Her old classmates from Mrs. Zima's already had their Maturas and Alicia was envious. She ran into Leah on Sienkiewicz Street. Leah was no longer the pale, skinny kid of old. She had filled out and her large green eyes illuminated her face, which was set off by wavy brown hair. At eighteen, she was a beautiful girl.

"It's a shame," Alicia said, "that we drifted so much apart. You used to be my closest girlfriend."

"Why don't you come to Kadzielnia, like in the old days? We'll climb the mountain, talk and reminisce."

It was early in the afternoon. "I'm ready," Alicia said. "If you have the time, let's go."

Leah had the time. From the top of the mountain they could see the hills of the Swietokrzyski range on one side and the city on the other.

"Everybody's talking about politics and the threat of war," Alicia said. "Why don't we talk about something else? Now that you have your Matura, what are your plans?"

"It looks like I'll be working as my father's secretary," Leah answered.

"Are you applying to any universities abroad?"

"My mother wouldn't even consider it; my father would let me try, but he doesn't want to upset my mother."

"It's still possible for a Jewish kid to get into a university. Jerry will probably get his American papers this fall, Jas went to the University of Haifa and my other cousin Beryl finished medical school in Italy.

Leah just shrugged her shoulders, "You know my mother," she said.

Alicia said, "My mother will give me a million warnings, but I know she realizes that unless things in Poland change drastically, she'll have to let me go." She smiled now. "I might have a bigger problem with my father; he doesn't believe that young women are safe alone."

But enough about me. Tell me, how are your parents?" Alicia knew that Mrs. Bloom wore black clothes and a black veil over her face.

"My father is working hard and my mother is still mourning. She constantly talks about Julek and the accident."

"But it's been almost ten years."

"Tell that to my mother!"

"I don't know much about religion, but I'm pretty sure that most of them teach you to bury the dead and proceed with your own life."

"Maybe for Christians it's easier," Leah said. " They believe in an afterlife. Julek saved another person's life before he drowned; he should have gone straight to heaven."

Alicia said, "The other boy wasn't Jewish."

"What difference does it make?"

Alicia was ashamed. "I just wonder if he's picketing Jewish stores now. Did he ever contact your family?"

"He came to my father's office, but my father didn't invite him home;

he was afraid it would upset my mother. I feel sorry for my father. Since Julek's death he hasn't had much of a life. He's only forty-five years old. If Julek were alive," she said dreamily, "he would probably have gone to Palestine like Jas, or to England, where we have relatives. But me, forget it. I'll either have to run away from home or get married to the first guy who proposes to me."

Despite their resolve, the conversation drifted to the political situation.

"What a stupid statement Smigly Rydz made comparing the country to a coat and the Corridor to a button," Alicia said. "Pilsudski would say, 'Go to hell.' He'd order a general mobilization to show Hitler that we were ready for him."

"I think," Leah said, "that Poland has been advised by her allies not to provoke Hitler."

"I'm sure that Pilsudski would not have listened to Chamberlain. I hope that Britain and France mean business, and that Hitler won't risk going to war with them."

It was getting late and Alicia said goodbye. "Don't settle on being a secretary, and make sure you hold on until you find the right guy."

July was hot that year. Alicia spent most of her time at the pool. Basia was now going steady with Bolek. Alicia became closer to Lisa. Lisa's mother spoke to Guta about a cousin of hers who belonged to a Zionist organization and was running a summer camp for young adults in the Karpathian Mountains.

Guta was surprised that Zilbergs' cousin was a Zionist; the family tried to be 100% Polish. I guess when things are rough, we find out who we really are, she thought.

"The girls are a little tired of the Stadion. They would enjoy a camp for a change," Mrs. Zilberg told Guta. "I was there last May, and they have very good accommodations. The campers live in two-room cabanas. There's a lake with a dock and boats on the premises, and the countryside is very picturesque."

When Guta heard the words "lake" and "boats," she jumped. "They are very well supervised," Mrs. Zilberg assured her.

Later, Guta discussed the idea with her sister. "Maybe Jerry could join the girls. The poor kid works so hard in the garage, he needs a vacation," Paula said.

Guta felt a little better: Jerry would watch the girls.

"We got an encouraging letter from America," Paula told her sister. "Our relatives hope that they'll have a visa for Jerry this October. It's about time. It's been a year and a half since he got his Matura."

"I forgot to tell you, I also have good news," Guta said. "Henius has been accepted to the prep school that Jas and Jerry went to. Next year, God willing, he'll start first grade."

"Maybe soon there'll be no quotas at the universities," Paula said.

Mrs. Katz heard about the camp and asked if Pawel could join them. She suggested that Pawel share a room with Jerry.

Paula and Guta knew that the Katzes had tickets for themselves and their children to go to the World's Fair in New York in August.

"We decided to return the tickets," Mrs. Katz told them. "The political situation is so uncertain, we don't want to leave our property unattended."

When Guta told Eisig what had happened,he shrugged his shoulders. "Property, apartment houses, all the physicians in Kielce are rich, except for me."

"You're a better doctor than most of them," Guta said.

Alicia was not too happy about Pawel joining them. "I get enough of his silly antics at the pool," she said to Lisa.

"He's in love with you," Lisa joked.

"That's all I need, Pawel dragging himself after me."

"He's quite mature for his age, but most of all he's very funny," Jerry said.

Lisa was excited about Jerry going with them and Paula hoped that maybe she'd succeed in getting Jerry interested in girls. "She's quite a number," she told Guta.

To allay her sister's fears, Paula took the trip with the four of them. She promised to look the place over and see that they got good accommodations. She left for Kielce after two days.

The four kids got a little house to themselves, with two adjacent rooms. Lisa had been to camp before, but it was a new experience for Alicia and Jerry. "I guess," Alicia said to Jerry, "we might as well learn how to make our beds in the morning and how to straighten out our rooms."

They were always busy. They played volleyball and tennis, went swimming and boating, took long hikes in the mountains, and at night went dancing in the main hall. Most of the other campers were university students in their twenties.

Late one evening, Alicia and Lisa didn't feel like walking to the latrine. Their room was on the ground floor. They opened their window wide; Lisa stuck her bare behind and watered the grass underneath. Alicia stood guard. They could not stop laughing. Suddenly they heard someone whistling. "I told you not to laugh so loud," Lisa whispered.

"Oh God, I hope it's not one of the counselors," Alicia said. She thought about Rick, her usual dancing partner. "Who is it?" she yelled.

"Shut up!" Lisa implored.

"Hello girls," a voice said, "just wanted to join in the laughter."

"Breathe with relief, it's only Pawel. You're a pest," Alicia told him.

They laughed again. For a minute the girls got serious, "You know," Alicia said to Lisa, "My mother told me that since my grandmother's death, she hasn't been able to laugh as freely as before. There is always sadness in the back of her mind. But I have young parents and a very young brother, so I'll be able to laugh without restraint for a very long time."

Lisa said, "My mother wrote that my father had to report to the army for maneuvers."

"Don't worry," Alicia told her. "There won't be a war." Soon they found something new to laugh about.

The four of them often went to the lake. Alicia and Pawel did most of the swimming. Lisa and Jerry would sit on the pier. Lisa was trying to encourage Jerry to neck.

There was a large, flat marker planted firmly in the bottom of the lake, not too far from the shore. They were not supposed to swim beyond the marker. Rick was the lifeguard. "Make sure this kid," he said to Alicia, pointing to Pawel, "doesn't swim any farther."

Once, when Alicia and Pawel were sitting on the marker, they noticed that Jerry was actually touching Lisa.

"Oh, oh," Pawel said. "There's progress in that department. May I touch you?"

"Wait until you're a little older," Alicia said.

"All right, I'll wait two years until I'm seventeen like you."

"That's a good age," Alicia said, "but don't forget, by then I'll be nineteen."

"So I'll wait until I'm nineteen, and don't tell me that you'll be twenty-one then."

"Pawel, by the time you'll be nineteen, you'll fall in love many more times."

"I like older girls; smart ones not brainless creatures like Lisa."

"Lisa is far from brainless," Alicia said. "She's just interested in boys to the exclusion of everything else."

"Do you like Rick?" Pawel asked.

"None of your business. He's more my age than you."

"Your age? He's at least four years older than you are."

"That's the way it's supposed to be. My father is eleven years older than my mother."

"Is that good?" Pawel asked.

"Maybe that's too much of a difference," she agreed. She was pensive for awhile, then she started laughing again. "Let's swim back, and save Jerry from Lisa's advances."

Once, all the campers took a mountain trail to get to a neighboring town. The leader had announced that whoever arrived first would get free ice cream.

The four of them were ahead of everyone else. Alicia noticed that Lisa kept pulling at her side. "What is the matter?" she asked.

"My girdle is pinching," Lisa answered.

"You're wearing a girdle on a hike!"

For a while Lisa managed to keep the pace, but the girdle was really bothering her. They hid behind a bush and Alicia tried to help her pull it off. They were laughing loudly when Alicia noticed Pawel watching them from behind another bush.

"Must you peek?" she yelled. She took the girdle and hit Pawel over the head with it. Now all three of them laughed. They hid the girdle in

Jerry's knapsack. In spite of the delay, they were the first to reach town and were awarded the ice cream.

On one of their hikes, they came to the Czech–Polish border. It was a beautiful, warm summer day. The sky was clear and the air was easy to breathe. It was the kind of a day that made everyone feel good to be alive. But something ominous and threatening lurked across the border. They looked at the German soldiers and shivered. They no longer felt like laughing. Their mood changed.

Every day the group got together for the noon meal. August 21st seemed like every other day in camp. Alicia sat near Rick, Lisa was practically on Jerry's lap and Pawel wasn't very happy about the situation.

The camp director walked in waving a newspaper.

"Use it for toilet paper," somebody yelled. "We're enjoying ourselves. We don't want to hear about Hitler, Mussolini, Chamberlain or Smigly Rydz."

"How about Stalin?" the director asked.

"What about him? Did he force more people to confess?"

The director showed them the headline: "Germany and the Soviet Union Concluded a Non-Aggression Treaty. The Formal Signing by Joseph Stalin and Joachim von Ribbentrop will take Place in Moscow in Two Days."

There was silence in the room. It seemed unbelievable. The Nazis hated communists almost as much as they hated the Jews; they often equated them with each other. After a while everyone started talking at the same time.

"Maybe now that Germany has a treaty with Russia," Lisa said, "they'll leave Poland alone."

"It takes a brilliant mind like yours," Pawel said, "to come to a conclusion like that."

Alicia kicked him. "Shut up, her father's already on active duty."

The camp director began to speak. "We've decided not to wait until the end of the month to close the camp. Tomorrow everyone will pack up and go home."

The train was full of frightened people. Everyone was in a hurry to get home to safety. Jerry and Lisa found a corner to themselves. They were necking and were oblivious to the general atmosphere.

Alicia nudged Pawel: "Finally Jerry's hormones are acting up."

"How old is Jerry?" Pawel asked.

"Nineteen."

"I'm only fifteen," Pawel said, "and mine are acting up already. I have a crush on an older woman of seventeen."

"Oh shut up, Pawel." Alicia decided to say something light to alleviate the tension. "You rotten kid, I'll never forget your pushing me into the pool."

"You should be thankful. If I hadn't done it, you'd still be afraid of the hole in the bottom."

They laughed, but the joy was missing. There was a nagging uncertainty in the back of their minds.

They arrived in Kielce on August 24th.

"Now that Hitler has a treaty with Russia," Eisig said, "he doesn't have to attack Poland."

Is my father as naive as Lisa? thought Alicia.

"The government must know something," Eisig continued. "There's no mobilization order."

On August 30th, the Polish government issued orders for a general mobilization. Both Dr. Strum and Dr. Peltz had to report to their units on September 5th. By September 1st, bombs were falling on Kielce.

CHAPTER 8

Although no bomb hit the house on 2 Hipoteczna Street directly, the reverberations from a nearby strike dislodged the roof. Pieces of the ceiling fell on Dr. Peltz and injured his collarbone. He was in acute pain. In desperation, Paula called Eisig. There was a war on. Past disagreements and resentments no longer seemed important.

After that initial attack, it was quiet for a while. Eisig managed to take x-rays and get a surgeon to set Monek's collarbone.

During the following two days there were sporadic bombings in the city. People were afraid to leave their houses. No one knew how many buildings had been destroyed or how many people had been killed.

On September 3rd the news was broadcasted that Britain and France had declared war on Germany. People sighed with relief. Everyone thought in terms of the last war and expected that the Polish army would retreat for a while, then dig in. There would be a front. The Allies would attack from the west and the war couldn't last very long. In the meantime the people in Kielce tried to flee east, away from the bombs and the Germans.

Eisig and Monek, as officers of the reserve, had orders to report to their units by the fifth. Guta, Paula and the children tried to get out as soon as possible. The trains were taken by the army, and it was very difficult to find means of transportation.

Sabina's brother Carl owned a van that he used for business. He didn't want to drive anyone but his mother and sister. Sabina insisted that he take Alicia and her family, and threatened not to go with him otherwise.

"In spite of her jealousy, she's a real friend," Alicia told her mother.

Guta took the money from the meadowland sale and Paula took money and jewelry. Then the two sisters, Jerry, Alicia, Henius and the three Levys packed into the van and started east. The roads were filled with panic-stricken people. Many of them were on foot and were carrying heavy backpacks; some were in horse-drawn carriages. There were few private cars.

The van couldn't quite escape the German bombs. Often everyone had to get out and lie flat in the fields. The German planes flew low, diving still lower to shoot at the civilians.

The farther east they traveled, the quieter and less crowded it became. Finally they were as far east in Poland as possible, in the little Bielorussian town of Rowne. In czarist Russia, Rowne had been situated in the Jewish Pale*, it was still predominantly Jewish.

This was Paula and Guta's first experience of being refugees. During the last war, when the Russian army was stationed in Zabiec, the family had fled to Pierscien. It was like going from one home to another. When, a few years ago, they had to stay in Pacanow because of a flood, they were still Warmans, rich landowners from Zabiec. Now they were just refugees.

They rented two rooms in a large two-family house. Their landlords were a middle-aged couple with three teenage sons. The men wore yarmulkes and the woman wore a traditional wig. The first thing Mrs. Kaner told Paula and Guta was that she didn't allow strangers to touch anything in her kitchen. "Everything is strictly kosher and I don't trust anyone." They were allowed to use a hot plate in their room.

Generally the Kaners were suspicious and unfriendly. They kept on admonishing their tenants to turn off the lights, not to use too much hot water and not to keep the hot plate on for too long. Mrs. Kaner complained that Henius was making too much noise.

The Kaner boys ignored Alicia and Jerry. Their lives centered on the synagogue and the Yeshiva; their main language was Yiddish. To them, Alicia and Jerry were strange creatures—they looked and spoke like goys, but they were supposed to be Jews.

"We're not accepted by the Poles because we're Jews," Alicia said to Jerry, "but real Jews consider us goys."

"I'm not interested in being accepted by Polish anti-Semites or by

---

* A part of a country reserved for one ethnic group, which is not allowed to live anywhere else.

people like the Kaners. I have plenty of Polish and Jewish friends who are simply decent human beings."

"So do I," Alicia echoed, but still she thought, it would be nice to know where you belonged.

There were many refugees from western Poland in Rowne. Paula and Guta found Beryl, who had recently gotten married, and his wife, and two young men, Mietek and Szlomek, who were distant cousins on Eisig's side.

People looked in the newspapers for news of France and England attacking Germany. Everyone was excited when there was a brief mention of French patrols penetrating 15 kilometers into Germany, but that was all. There was no mention of it the following day.

There was plenty of bad news: Warsaw was under siege. The Polish government had first moved east to Lublin, but as the German army advanced, Lublin was not safe enough. The government, army brass and some lucky soldiers escaped to Romania. People still hoped that a defense line would be established on the River Bug.

Paula and Guta were worried about their husbands; Kielce and Krakow were occupied by the Germans. Warsaw was still resisting, as were isolated Polish units. Then the Germans mysteriously stopped in the middle of Poland.

Carl had a proposition. "While there's still time, we'll drive south, cross to Romania, Bulgaria and Greece, and from there the Jewish underground will get us to Palestine. With money and jewelry we can do it." He looked at Paula and Guta.

"Lets go!" Alicia yelled, "we'll join Jas in Palestine."

"How can you suggest such a thing? You are just thinking about yourself!" Guta was screaming now, "Your father and uncle are someplace in Poland and you just want to run."

Carl tried to calm her down. "Women and children can remain, but young people should get out as soon as possible."

Alicia was enthusiastic: "Carl, Sabina, Jerry and I will go to Palestine." She looked at Beryl and his wife. "I guess you would prefer to go to Russia."

Guta quieted down a little. "A family should stick together during a war. Maybe the Germans aren't advancing because they had to pull their army over to the western front. The war will end soon. We'll find daddy and go home, and life will resume, God willing."

Carl had given up on Guta, but he knew that Paula could finance such a trip. "How about it, Mrs. Peltz?"

Paula spread her hands. "I can't do it," she said. "My husband is in Poland."

"But Mucia," Alicia said, "during the last war you were ready to leave your parents and elope with Eric."

"I was seventeen then, and I had no responsibilities."

Mrs. Levy piped in. "What kind of son are you?" she said to Carl. "How can you even think of leaving me here alone?"

"You don't have a husband someplace in Poland; you can come with us!"

"I'm too old for a trip like that."

Carl was losing his patience. Alicia remembered Paula joking that it took both Carl and Sabina to lace their mother's corset. Mrs. Levy liked to have her children with her.

Alicia still wouldn't give up. "Jerry, say something," she yelled. "This is our chance to get out of here, the Germans may take us for forced labor or even send us to concentration camps."

But Carl was resigned. "I can't leave my mother in a strange city," he said.

On September 17th the mystery of why the Germans had stopped their offensive was solved. The reason they hadn't occupied eastern Poland was not because of the western front, as people had hoped. There was no western front; the French were sitting on the Maginot Line and waiting. It was not the Germans who had occupied eastern Poland; it was the Russians.

The refugees in Rowne felt both relief and horror. This was a disaster for Poland. History was repeating itself and Poland was once again disappearing from the map of Europe. The Poles fought valiantly, but the Polish cavalry was no match for German tanks. The Germans took more than half a million prisoners, and the Russians took several hundred thousand.

Amazingly, Warsaw, which by the end of September had been almost completely destroyed, its population decimated and starving, was not giving up. Neither was a garrison at the naval base of Hel Peninsula, but by the end of September, even they were forced to surrender.

Paula and Guta were mainly concerned about the situation in Kielce and their husbands. The border between the Russian and German Polands was on the River Bug, and it was not very well guarded in September. People were moving back and forth easily. Some young men from Kielce arrived in Rowne. They brought the news that Doctor Peltz and Doctor Strum never had a chance to report to their units. The events were moving too fast. The Germans arrived in Kielce and took some prominent citizens, both Polish and Jewish, hostage. The two doctors were in the group. Money was collected and paid and the hostages were released. A Jewish Council was formed to administer the affairs of the Jewish community; Dr. Peltz was made president because of his stature and fluency in German. Reportedly, the situation had stabilized.

Alicia asked about the schools and libraries. She was told that everything was closed and there was a curfew at 8 o'clock in the evening.

On the Russian side of Poland things were relatively normal. The children went to school and the one and only movie theater in Rowne stayed open. But food was getting scarce, and by the end of September there were long lines to the bakery and for potatoes; meat was practically impossible to get.

A young, unattached man from Kielce hung around Paula and Guta. "I wonder who he's in love with, me or you?" Guta joked. "Maybe it's Alicia," Paula said.

Weinstock was very useful. He had a talent for getting food without standing in long lines. He managed to bring bread and butter and sometimes a delicacy from a Jewish restaurant called "ciulent" (stuffed derma with kasha).

The Jews in Rowne felt superior to their unlucky brethren from German-occupied Poland. Like the Kaners, they did not accept them with open arms or generosity.

The Jewish New Year arrived, and then Yom Kippur. On Yom Kippur good Jews spend the whole day in the synagogue, praying and fasting. The Kaners left the house early in the morning.

"Do you see what I see?" Paula asked her sister. "An empty house, a kitchen and plenty of dishes."

"You couldn't!" Guta exclaimed. "It's Yom Kippur, a Day of Judgment!"

"Lately our God has not been too good to his chosen people. I trust he won't judge us too harshly for making a hot meal for our children."

Guta and Paula were like magnets for the Kielce colony. Now Weinstock arrived first. He was carrying something under his coat. Looking apprehensive and hesitant, he said, "You know a Jew is not supposed to carry packages on Yom Kippur."

"What makes you think you have to apologize to me," Paula said. She couldn't keep from laughing. "Let's see what goodies you have under that coat."

He was hesitant, but he finally produced two chickens and a slab of beef. "I got it from a peasant this morning; I saw your landlord entering the synagogue. I hope you'll have a chance to cook it."

"You hoped right," Paula said.

Other people came in. Beryl brought some good Russian vodka. "I don't feel guilty eating on Yom Kippur," he announced.

Guta got upset. "Communist, atheist, I don't care what you believe now, but I bet you had to fast in your mother's house, and you must have some reservations today."

"Well, what my mother doesn't know won't hurt her. Anyhow, with the Russians here, the synagogues and churches will soon be closed. It's lucky that the Kaners have a synagogue to go to today." Then he winked at Guta. "What about you?" he said. "I assume you're going to cook these chickens today."

"It's an emergency situation," Guta answered. "There's a war on and Henius is losing weight, but I wish I didn't have to cook on Yom Kippur."

"Oh, come on," Paula said, "you never fasted at home."

"I did before I got married, but then Eisig insisted I eat."

"Okay, blame Eisig, but now we have to go to the kitchen and start working. We don't have very much time."

Everyone who came brought something.

It felt good to cook in a regular kitchen and prepare a meal for the children and their friends. Paula and Guta forgot about their husbands and Guta lost her scruples.

The meal itself was a lot of fun. Everyone laughed and joked; even the always serious Sabina joined in. They felt like children getting away with mischief.

"I'll bet," Paula said, "the Kaners are filthy rich. He is a successful grain merchant. They're stingy from habit and meanness. We're using their kitchen for a good purpose, to feed a hungry bunch of people."

They were all young and full of hope, and felt that their situation was temporary. At the end of the meal Mrs. Levy spoiled the fun. "I can't take it anymore," she said. "I want to go home. Doctor Peltz is running the community and things are quiet."

"The Germans are there," Carl said.

"Take me and Sabina home," his mother said. "You can come back."

"I can go to school here," Sabina protested.

"When the war ends you'll go to school in Kielce. All the reports about the Germans killing and robbing Jews are exaggerated in the Jewish papers."

"Maybe you should listen to your brother," Carl said, "and his opinion of what the Germans will do to the Jews."

"I don't pay any attention to that crazy bachelor uncle of yours." Then she sighed. "What a family. I'm a widow, my brother is a bachelor, at seventeen my daughter dresses and behaves like an old maid, and my son, instead of settling down and getting married, has a different woman every night."

Being a refugee along with the Levys is quite an experience, Alicia thought. I'm finding out all kinds of things about them. "Mr. Hochberg predicted that the Germans would come to Poland," she said, "and the Nuremberg laws are a fact."

"Those are laws for Germany, not for Poland," Mrs. Levy answered.

"My sister and I will wait for instructions from our husbands; maybe they'll try to join us here," Paula said.

"They should." Carl said. "I'll have to take my mother and sister back
to Kielce, but I doubt that I'll stay there."

Everyone became serious for a while. The joking and bantering were
over. The kitchen and the dishes had to be thoroughly cleaned to erase
the traces of the feast.

When the Kaners came back that evening, they looked tired and pale.
Then—a miracle!—they invited their tenants for sponge cake and tea.
"We have to eat something light to break the fast; the stomach has to get
used to food," Mrs. Kaner said. It was beyond her comprehension that
there were Jews who didn't fast on Yom Kippur.

"We'll be with you in a few minutes." Once in their room Paula said
to Guta, "Maybe all that praying made them more human. The rabbi must
have told them to be kind to refugees."

"How can we sit at their table and drink tea after what we did to their
kitchen?" Guta wondered. "The food we cooked wasn't even kosher."

"As Beryl said, what they don't know won't hurt them. Just make sure
Henius doesn't give us away," Paula said. "We didn't have any dessert;
let's go and have it now. But I'll bet the sponge cake is lousy."

In October the Levys went back to Kielce. The rest of the people from
Kielce decided to leave Rowne and go to Lwow. Lwow was a metropolis
in southeast Poland with large Ukrainian and Jewish minorities. Now the
city was the center of Russian-occupied Poland. People were still crossing the border back and forth, and it was easier to get news from Kielce
in Lwow than in Rowne.

Guta, Alicia and Henius rented a room with a middle-class Jewish
family. Paula and Jerry found their own accommodations not too far
away.

Life in the city was proceeding as usual. The university was open, as
were the schools, libraries, museums and other cultural establishments.
Alicia began the second class of lyceum and Henius entered the first
grade of elementary school. The lights were turned on in the evening;
Russia was not at war and the war in Poland was over.

Basia and her parents were in Lwow. They were staying in a different
part of town, and Basia and Alicia attended different schools. In Alicia's

class there was a group of girls from Warsaw, Krakow, and other Polish cities under German occupation. The refugees kept together and were mostly ignored by the indigenous group.

The people of Lwow didn't like the mob that had invaded their city, and the Lwow Jews were afraid that the influx of so many Jews would give rise to anti-Semitism.

Alicia liked belonging to the group of refugees. After school, they would walk in the street and in the parks and do the things that girls their age did. They talked and laughed and looked in store windows, which still had nice displays.

Dana, one of the girls from Warsaw, told Alicia about the trips abroad that she had taken with her parents. Every year they went someplace else: the Norwegian fjords, Paris, London and Rome. Alicia felt like a provincial hick; she'd never left Poland. Dana didn't have Zabiec, Alicia thought, but then Zabiec was no more. After the war I'll go to Paris, she mused.

There were school dances, but none of the Lwow boys would ask a refugee girl to dance. Alicia and Dana danced with each other. "I'm having a good time," Alicia said, "and I don't give a damn if those prigs are trying to make us feel inferior."

Dana invited Alicia to meet her parents. They occupied a spacious suite in a first-class hotel. To Alicia they appeared to be a very distinguished couple. The mother was dressed in the latest fashion and the father smoked expensive cigars. No wonder, she thought, they took all those trips. They must be very rich. They were much older than her parents, especially older than Guta. Dana was an only child and Alicia concluded that she was even more spoiled than she. Dana's mother reminded Alicia more of Mrs. Dankowa than of Guta and Paula, but she had always considered her mother and aunt to be young and beautiful, and no one else's mother could compare to them.

The doctors sent instructions to their wives; Doctor Peltz wanted Paula to come home, but Jerry, he wrote, should stay in Lwow. It was no good for a young Jewish male to be in German-occupied Poland. Eisig wanted everyone back. Henius was small and Alicia was a girl; they'd be safe.

"Did the schools open?" Alicia asked the messenger.

"You must be kidding," he said. "There are no schools for Poles; you can't expect schools for the Jews."

Alicia did not want to go home. She enjoyed her life in Lwow. "Daddy should join us here," she told Guta. "I don't want to go to Germany."

"We're not going to Germany," Guta said, "we're going home to Kielce."

"There are Germans in Kielce," said Alicia.

"Our family survived the Great War together; we'll manage now," answered Guta.

"There was no Hitler during the Great War."

"But there were Russian soldiers rampaging and raping women," replies Guta. She reflected at the memories. "Zabiec changed hands between the Russian and Austrian armies. One time, the Austrians accused grandfather of being a Russian spy. But you know grandfather; he duped them and we escaped to Pierscien in the nick of time."

Alicia had heard the story many times. "What an adventure you had," she said. "We could have had more exciting adventures if we went along with Carl's plan and take that bus trip south. It's too late for that now, but at least Daddy should join us here," she repeated.

Guta was annoyed. "It's easy for someone your age to say that. Your father has an established practice in Kielce. That's our home. He's not a young man. He would have to start all over in a strange city." Young people are so inconsiderate, she thought.

"If Uncle Monek joined Mucia and Jerry here, I'm sure Father would follow. It would be nice for Jerry to have his parents with him."

"You're dreaming again," her mother answered. "Your uncle has an important job in Kielce and the whole community depends on him. He feels responsible for softening the impact of the occupation on the Jews in Kielce."

"What if the war lasts a long time, like the Great War? Are Henius and I supposed to lose all that time in school? If you must join Father, go, but Henius and I should stay here."

Guta was tired and could not decide. She kept repeating again that a family should stick together during the war. As planned, Paula left and Jerry remained. At night Alicia listened to Russian soldiers marching beneath her window and singing their haunting ballads evoking distant steppes. She thought of her mother's and aunt's favorite book, *War and Peace*. She was disappointed in her Mucia. She had set a bad example by going back; Jerry probably needed her more than Uncle Monek.

Then something happened that changed life in Lwow. Overnight the Russian ruble became the official currency; the zloty was not worth much any more. Guta had most of her money in zlotys, but luckily she also had some jewelry. Lwow began to look like Rowne and Russia. There were long lines for food; the displays in store windows disappeared. The Russian army sequestered most of the available food and goods for themselves. People hoarded whatever they could. The lucky ones, who had money and space, put sacks of potatoes, jars of lard and preserves in their cellars. For a while, Weinstock helped Guta get food. Then he left for Kielce.

One day Henius returned from school with a high fever and a rash. Guta became panicky. "I'm used to having all those doctors available at home; here we're alone and helpless," she said to Alicia. She found a doctor in the neighborhood who diagnosed the illness as scarlet fever. Luckily, it was a mild case. After two weeks the fever and rash were gone and Henius was happily jumping on his bed.

"We're going home," Guta declared. "If we wait much longer I won't have the money to pay a guide to take us to the border. At home, everybody knows me as a doctor's wife; if I don't have cash, I can always get credit."

Alicia was desperate. "I'm not going," she said.

"I can't force you," her mother said, "but I'm taking Henius with me. What would you do if he got sick again?"

"I want to stay with Ala," the boy said.

"You are too small; you need mommy and daddy"

"He also needs school and books to read."

"He can't eat books."

"We'll manage," Alicia said. "We'd probably move in with Jerry. The Rapaports will help us, and maybe Dana's parents will adopt us."

"That's wishful thinking," Guta said.

She and Henius left for the border.

Alicia was now alone. The rent for the room was paid for for the month of November and her mother had left her some money. The freedom felt good for a while. She never thought about what she would do when her money ran out and she would have to pay rent again. On the first afternoon of her independence, she visited Basia.

"My classmate's brother," Basia told her, "asked me about you."

"I can't imagine who he could be. I don't know any boys in Lwow."

"Yes, you do," Basia laughed. "As soon as he found out that I was from Kielce, he asked me if I knew a cute blond girl who wore glasses."

Alicia still didn't know who it was. Then she remembered that Rick, from summer camp, was a student at Lwow's university. Last summer seemed like a lifetime away. It was unbelievable that so many things could change between August and October.

It was Rick. Basia told Alicia that he would be at a dance in her school the following week and would like to meet Alicia there.

"I never thought he'd remember me," Alicia said.

"You seem surprised," Basia said.

Alicia said, "I guess I'm used to seeing boys following you around and Lisa running after boys, but I always felt like a spectator." Alicia looked at Basia closely. She was a pretty girl all right, but there was something else. Mr. Rapaport treated his daughter as if she were the most beautiful girl in the world, while my father, Alicia thought, considers being a girl a curse. All he ever cared about was whether I got good marks in school and ate well.

"I know a lot of boys back in Kielce who would like to date you," Basia told her.

"Don't tell me about that little pest Pawel." Then Alicia added, "I know I could never be as attractive as my aunt or my mother, so I've given up trying."

"Oh, cut it out. Are you coming to the dance?" Basia asked.

"Yeah," Alicia said, "it will be something to look forward to."

"It's a week from today," Basia told her.

On her third afternoon alone, Alicia was invited to Dana's for afternoon tea. I wish I had nicer clothes, she thought. Maybe, as Mucia once said, it's not so bad to be a girl. Why did she have to go back?

There was a knock at the door. Maybe it's Jerry, Alicia thought. She opened the door and found Guta and Henius standing there. Alicia almost felt guilty that, during the last two days, she hadn't thought much about her mother and brother. Now she picked up the heavy suitcase Guta was lugging and patted Henius on the head. "What happened?" she asked. "I thought by now you'd be in Kielce."

"We were turned back by a Russian border patrol," Guta told her. "Its 'beshert' that next time you should come with us."

"What's 'beshert'?"

"It's the will of God," Guta said.

"Since when is a Russian Bolshevik patrol the will of God?"

"Your father insisted in his last communication that you come home. Uncle Monek can send Jerry money, but I've spent practically everything I got from Zabiec. We can't support you here."

My mother finally got her dowry and now it's all gone, Alicia thought.

For the next few days Guta was busy making arrangements with a guide. Toward the end of 1939, taking people across the border was a lucrative business for some young enterprising men.

Alicia was preoccupied with the next week's dance and meeting Rick again. One afternoon, when she returned from school, she found her mother packing. "The guide just notified me that we're going tomorrow," Guta said.

"I've been invited to a dance tomorrow."

She looked for her silk stockings, which she'd rinsed and hung in the bathroom that morning. She had planned to wear them for the dance. They weren't there.

"Where are my stockings?" she asked.

"I sold them," Guta said. "We're trying to take as little luggage as possible. We need money, so I sold everything we didn't need."

"My stockings?" Alicia started to cry. For her, these stockings were a symbol of the life a seventeen-year-old should have: school, dances, flirtations, friendship, laughter. "You sold my silk stockings!" she wailed. "And now I'll be living in darkness, where there is no normal life."

Jerry came over and Alicia threw her arms around him. "Take care of yourself. Try to eat solid food if you can find any and forget about the sweets."

"Don't cry," Jerry said. "You're going home, while I have to stay here."

"I wish I were a boy," Alicia sighed.

The next day Guta, Alicia and Henius were taken by a guide to the border. Again they were stopped by a Russian patrol. In fluent Russian, Guta convinced the captain that they were lost and had come from the German side. He let them cross.

They were walking to the nearest railroad station through a bleak Polish village on the western bank of the river Bug when they came eye to eye with a German patrol. "Just walk and pretend that you belong here," Guta said to Alicia and Henius.

It was the first time Henius had seen German soldiers. He could not resist turning around. They called them.

I wish they'd send us to the Russian side, Alicia prayed silently. Then maybe my mother would say it's "beshert" for us to stay in Lwow.

The Germans were polite. "Are not the ladies from the other side?" the officer asked as he pointed east.

This time Guta pretended that she didn't understand a word they were saying. Only Jews spoke German; plain Poles did not. She smiled innocently at them and pointed west. The German gave up and waved them on.

It was a cold and drizzly November afternoon when they arrived at the station. In the train, it seemed to Alicia that everyone was looking at them suspiciously, trying to figure out if they were Jews. They arrived in Kielce in the afternoon, and managed to get a horse cab home just before the curfew. Henius ran to Rosie before he even noticed his father. Guta, crying, hugged and kissed her husband. It was the first time in her life that Alicia had seen her parents kissing. She waited her turn and then hugged her father. Then something on the table caught her eye. It was a black arm band with a yellow Star of David and the word "Jude" printed in the middle. "What is that?" she asked her father.

"All Jews over six years old have to wear them," Eisig told her.

This was unbelievable. "You mean Henius will have to wear one?"

The band was very ugly. The bright yellow star, particularly, invoked certain images: a Jew with a bent back, a coward, a shylock, a dirty, despised pariah. "I'm not wearing it. Jas would never put it on."

Guta was scared. "You'll have to do it for the time being."

"I know, next year, God Willing." If Yehovah won't help us, maybe Zeus will."

"It's not funny, Alicia," Guta said, disturbed by her daughter's irreverence.

Henius was busy running around the house. As long as he had his mother, father, sister and nanny he didn't care about the ugly arm band. At seven he still considered his parents infallible.

"Tomorrow all of you will have to go to the offices of the Jewish Council to register and get your ration cards and arm bands," Eisig said.

The next morning, when Alicia woke up, she thought she was still in Lwow. I have to get ready for school, she thought. She smiled to herself. In the afternoon I'll meet Basia and we'll go to the dance. Then she realized that she was in Kielce. It felt good to be in her own bed, but then she remembered the curfew and the arm band. She didn't feel like getting up. Rosie brought her breakfast. Guta tried in vain to convince her daughter to get out of bed. Henius came in with a book and asked her to read it with him, but she didn't even feel like doing that. "I have nothing to get up for," she said.

Early that afternoon Rosie came into her room. "You have a visitor."

Alicia had heard Guta talking with someone in the living room.

"Who is it?"

"Your dream boy, Bolek," Rosie answered.

"Bolek?" She got up hastily, dressed, and even combed her hair.

Bolek looked well and happy. He was wearing the band on his left sleeve.

"Must you wear it in the house?" Alicia asked.

"We have to get used to it," he answered. He wanted to know about Basia.

"She's fine. She's going to school. We should be there."

"Did you hear the tragic news?" he asked her.

More tragic news? Alicia wondered.

"Lisa's father is dead. Doctor Zilberg was in the Polish army in the east and he was killed by the Russians. Some soldiers from his command came to Kielce and notified the family."

"Oh, my God, poor Lisa. Already last summer she was worried about her father."

Bolek told her about his life in Kielce. He and a few other boys and girls met in each other's houses to play cards and chess and listen to records. "There are many new interesting people in Kielce, mainly from Lodz. They're afraid there will be a ghetto in Lodz and Kielce seems to be the best place for Jews in Poland. Your uncle is a very good administrator; even the Germans respect him."

Alicia was reminded of the old ghetto in Krakow. That was a part of history; now a ghetto was becoming a reality.

Bolek also told her that German and Austrian Jews were being transported to Poland. Many found themselves in Kielce. "We don't have much contact with them. They don't speak Polish and they keep to themselves."

Slowly Alicia became part of a group of young, privileged Jewish youth. Her circle included Lisa, Bolek, Pawel and a few other boys and girls from Lodz. Alicia was the niece of the president of the Jewish Council and the council was the main source for jobs for the Jews. Thus, Alicia had status. Sometimes she felt like the princess of the Jewish community. She had many friends and enjoyed it for a while.

The poor and orphans had priority in getting jobs in the offices of the council. Lisa got a job as a clerk. Doctor Peltz didn't want to play favorites, so it took a long time for Alicia to get a job. She had to begin at the bottom, filing papers.

The most eligible bachelors in Kielce were young doctors, mainly from Lodz. They had gone to Polish medical schools in the early Thirties, before the wave of discrimination.

Working in the office Alicia met the majority of people, the poor and hungry who lived on rations that could only keep them near starvation level. People with money could still buy food from the Poles. The offices of the council were always busy; every Jew had to have special identity papers, a ration card and an arm band; the refugees depended on the council to find living quarters for them.

It was the responsibility of the council to form work battalions at the request of the Germans. The councilmen and the clerks had special privileges, bigger rations and exemptions from labor gangs.

Guta kept asking Eisig to try to get a seat on the council. "If you ask Monek, I'm sure he would arrange it for you."

"I don't want it," he said. "I don't want to have anything to do with a council that takes orders from the Germans."

The council was instructed to organize a Jewish police. Many young men volunteered; this could mean survival for their whole family. The majority of them were refugees from Lodz or Germany and Austria. The policemen were issued uniforms and carried clubs; otherwise they were unarmed.

Eisig again disapproved: "No decent young Jewish boy would volunteer for a job like that. Let the Germans enforce their laws themselves; the Jews shouldn't help them."

One day a tall, handsome man came to the office. He was wearing his shiny new police uniform and swinging his club. Alicia knew him and his wife as the prosperous owners of a dry goods store. The store had belonged to the family for generations; now it was closed. Mr. Goldberg was always friendly and polite. Why does he need a club? Alicia wondered. She couldn't imagine him hitting people. He told her how proud he was to serve the council headed by Dr. Peltz. My father, Alicia thought, doesn't think that it's an honor to be a Jewish policeman.

When she left the office, another policeman was standing in the door. He was screaming at people in German and threatening them with his club. He even hit a woman. Alicia looked him straight in the eye and said in Polish, "Who do you think you are, a Jewish Gestapo?" She guessed he was a German Jew and hoped he didn't understand her. He looked at her menacingly, getting ready to hit her. Another policeman nudged him and whispered in his ear. The bully smiled at her and, in very polite German, asked her to pass. "I want everyone to get home before curfew," he said. Alicia wondered what he would have done if she weren't the president's niece.

She seldom spoke to her uncle. But she said to Paula, "Some of those Jewish policemen, especially Germans, try to behave like real Aryan Germans."

Paula just smiled. "It can't be helped, it's human nature; even a little power corrupts."

Almost every week there was a new regulation limiting Jewish mobility and freedom. Sienkiewicz Street reverted back to its original name, Railroad Street. Sienkiewicz was a writer identified with Polish nationalism. Railroad Street was now off limits to Jews. Signs saying "Juden Verboten" (Forbidden to Jews) were posted at the entrances. Shortly after, the same signs appeared in Kielce's park, thoroughfares and other important areas.

Sabina lived on Railroad Street. If Alicia wanted to visit her she had to use the back streets and back entrance. Carl had disappeared and Uncle Hochberg was predicting doom. Mrs. Levy was more cheerful in Kielce than she had been in Rowne. Carl had left Sabina a radio, which was buried in the linen closet behind many pillows and comforters. Mrs. Levy didn't know about it. Sometimes the girls took it out and managed to get France or England. They kept the volume very low and practically sat on the receiver. They learned that Europe was going through what was called a "phoney war"; it wasn't phony for them.

Eisig received an official letter denying him permission to treat Aryans. Most of his patients were gentiles. "How will I make a living? It was hard before, but now it's going to be almost impossible," he complained.

The next regulation hit even harder. Jews could not employ gentiles. Rosie had to be discharged. She had come from Zabiec to Kielce when she was seventeen, and she felt like a member of the family. She had brought up Henius and the boy loved her. "Where will I go?" she lamented. Her mother had remarried and moved away and Kazimierz had a girlfriend.

"I'll write you a good recommendation," Guta offered.

"Polish people don't like to employ girls who worked for Jews."

Rosie went back to Zabiec.

Alicia wondered who was running Zabiec now. Thanks to Jerry and herself, Rosie could now read and write. She wrote a letter to Alicia, saying that there were rumors that the man who lived in the big house had bought Zabiec at auction with Warman's money.

Alicia showed the letter to her mother. "Are you in touch with Grandfather?" she asked.

"Not at all," Guta said. "You know how I feel about his new wife. If the rumor is true, then Zabiec was bought with her money. Probably, after a reasonable time, it will revert back to Grandfather."

"Maybe we'll get it back eventually. Wouldn't that be wonderful!"

Guta was not thinking of Zabiec. It was very hard for her to manage the household without Rosie. The apartment consisted of seven large rooms with high ceilings, which made it hard to heat. It was an art to start a fire in the tile stoves, you had to build layers, first of paper, then wood, then coal. Coal was getting harder to get.

One of the rooms was assigned by the council to a middle-aged Viennese couple. Frau Hilda told Guta that she belonged to a family that had lived in Vienna for generations. They were barely aware of the fact that they were Jews. Her husband was a veteran of the Great War. Now they were forced to sell their house for next to nothing, leave their country and become refugees in Poland, without knowing a word of Polish. "I love Vienna," she kept repeating, "and I dream of going back."

Guta told her that both she and Eisig had studied in Vienna. The women cried. Guta's memories brought her back to her childhood and youth in Zabiec and Pierscien. Alicia is right, she thought, Henius has no childhood. When she looked at Frau Hilda she realized that she and her family were still much better off than the poor refugees. "Next year, God willing, you will go to Vienna and I'll visit you."

Alicia could not communicate in German, but she liked Frau Hilda, who despite of all her hardships seemed cheerful. She liked to prepare pretty hors d'oeuvres for Alicia's card parties. Frau Hilda tried to help Guta out, but she was not young anymore. Eventually the council found an apartment for her and her husband, and a refugee woman from Lodz came to help Guta.

A ghetto in Lodz was now a certainty. A wall was being built in Warsaw, which was a sure sign of a ghetto. Many more people arrived in Kielce, but travel was dangerous, as Jews were not allowed to use public transportation. People took their chances. They knew that, once locked behind walls, they would not get out.

Cold weather was settling in. "Can I have skates?" Henius asked.

"How am I going to explain to a seven-year-old," Alicia wailed, "that because he's a Jew he's not allowed in the park or even to walk on Railroad Street? Rosie used to build a snowman in the yard for him, but she had to leave."

Alicia had tears in her eyes; she considered Rosie her friend. Rosie had a peasant's earthiness and a rough sense of humor. Every December she decorated a little Christmas tree for herself. Alicia and Henius enjoyed buying gifts for her: scarves, gloves and chocolates. They left the gifts under the tree on Christmas Eve.

"Last year," Alicia told her mother, "we took a horse-drawn sleigh to Stadion. There were Pawel, Stas, Henius, Bolek, Basia and myself. We had our small sleds with us. All of us slid down the hills and then we had a snowball fight. It was a lot of fun, especially for the little ones. This year we would have taken them skiing."

She sat down with her head in her arms. "When I was Henius' age," she said, "I had school, the library, the city with its streets and parks, Stadion and Zabiec. This winter, Henius will be stuck in the house. When he goes to visit Stas, he'll have to use the back streets and wear that hateful arm band. Maybe in Lwow he could have had a childhood."

"Don't complain so much," her mother said. "Henius has both his parents, his sister and a home. That is more than many other kids have these days. Look at all those poor refugees from Austria, Germany, Lodz and Warsaw."

Alicia spent a lot of time with Paula. Books were forbidden, and they were very expensive on the black market. Somehow Paula managed to get the American best seller *Gone With The Wind* in Polish translation. They both read the book. Paula identified with Scarlet and Tara was Zabiec.

"We should try to read it in English," Alicia suggested.

Paula tried to persuade her husband to tell Jerry to come home. Doctor Peltz insisted that Jerry stay where he was. Paula assumed that he knew more than other people, being in contact with the German authorities.

Luckily, the winter was not too severe, but Kielce was overcrowded and many people were cold, homeless and hungry. Some people from Kielce took advantage of the situation, buying clothes, linens and heirlooms from refugees at rock bottom prices. The most notorious was Mrs. Perlstein. She expected these things to be worth a lot of money after the war. As during any war, there was hoarding, especially of potatoes, which were very important.

It was a bright day in February 1940. The temperature was well above freezing for the first time in months. Everything was melting and the sun was shining. Alicia felt like going someplace. She decided to take a long walk to Kadzielnia without her arm band. Her mother would assume that she was either with Mucia, Lisa or Sabina. She didn't bother to take her identification papers either. I'll just imagine, she thought, that it's the old days. But when she approached the familiar path, she realized she'd been dreaming. The large sign, "Juden Verboten," could not be missed. She kept on walking. It was a country road. There was plenty of snow on the sides, but the air felt so much better than in the city. There were very few people around. Two boys were playing in a ditch on the side of the road, the same ditch in which, many years ago, Jas and she had hidden from a storm. The boys looked at her. One of them squinted and smiled maliciously. "Jew," he yelled, "where is your arm band?"

That little bastard, Alicia thought, he can smell a Jew. A German would ask for papers. She knew that she had to react quickly. "Do I look like a Jew, you moron?" she yelled. "I'll complain to my German friend Hauptman Schreiber, and he'll beat you up." The kids ran away. Alicia sighed with relief. She thanked God that she had some of Grandfather Mark's genes.

When she finally arrived at Leah's house, everything seemed unchanged. Her father had kept his job and he had a pass to the city, but Leah did not. She was not allowed to walk on the long road that Alicia had just taken. The peasants brought them food. Leah and her mother were isolated in the little house. When she saw Alicia she was very happy, but also worried about her friend taking a chance by coming to her house.

Alicia said, "I was here last July. Our biggest problem then was that we couldn't go to the universities in Poland. Now we can't even walk on most of the streets." She laughed. "I'll use my imaginary German friend from now on."

Leah showed her a letter she'd received from the Russian side. It was a love letter. The boy was not doing well. He was cold, hungry and sick, he wrote that the only thing that kept him going was thinking of Leah.

"Do you love him?" Alicia asked.

"Oh no," Leah answered. "He probably doesn't love me either; he's just lonely."

They talked, laughed and cried, hoping that "soon" the "world" would be a world again.

Alicia walked back to the city. This time, no one bothered her.

Passover was in the second part of March. The holiday brought back many happy memories for Paula, Guta and Alicia. They remembered the seders in Zabiec. Now Zabiec was gone and they were not allowed to travel anyway. Guta tried to make a festive supper. Alicia suggested that they invite Lisa. "I'm sure," she said to her mother, "that Mrs. Zilberg won't prepare anything. This is her first holiday without her husband and, according to Lisa, she's depressed."

The seder was not a real seder in the Strum household. Eisig absolutely refused to conduct services and tell the ancient story of the escape from slavery.

"It would be so relevant this year," Alicia said.

"This summer, when Hitler is defeated, I promise I'll return to religion," her father answered.

Their dinner was a little better than usual, Guta managed a roast and the traditional symbolic dishes—bitter herbs, lamb shank and hardboiled eggs. Paula and Monek didn't come; Paula could not face a seder without her sons.

Lisa kept crying, "I miss my father most during the holidays. My mother is so distant; she doesn't seem to care about anything."

"Do you remember how much we laughed last summer?" Alicia asked, trying to distract her.

"Last summer my father was alive and Jerry was here."

"We don't need these bitter herbs," Eisig said. "It's bitter enough." He said to Guta, "We planned to put away the money you got from Zabiec for the children's education. But you spent all of it on your escapade east."

He blames her again, Alicia thought, just like a husband.

Guta didn't feel very well, but when she looked at Lisa and thought about Mrs. Zilberg, she realized again how lucky they were.

War, overcrowding and hunger bring epidemics. "Fleck typhus" and war go together. The disease is spread by the bite of a body louse and is characterized by very high fever and a rash. It is known to affect the brain, usually temporarily but sometimes permanently. Once someone has had it, he develops an immunity to it. Both Dr. Peltz and Dr. Strum went through it during the last war. There was a vaccine available in 1940, but it was impossible for Jews to get it.

Alicia and Lisa worked in the office giving out ration cards and forever stamping the word "Jude" on them. They were in contact with many people. In the beginning of April both girls came down with typhus.

Lisa had a mild case and recovered in three weeks, but Alicia almost died. For weeks she was in a fog. She heard her mother crying and blaming herself: "I should have left her in Lwow like she wanted. She wouldn't have contracted typhus there."

Alicia heard her father talking to God. He was asking Him for permission to trade places with Alicia. "I've already lived most of my life; she is only seventeen and has her whole life ahead of her."

In her delirium, Alicia wondered that her father, who always claimed to be an unbeliever, was now appealing to God.

It was her uncle, Dr. Peltz, who saved her life. When her temperature remained at 104° for four days in a row, he wrapped her in ice cold sheets. The other attending physician, Dr. Levin, protested that she would get pneumonia.

"Pneumonia is better than brain damage and death," Dr. Peltz answered.

One night Alicia felt she had actually crossed over. She was in heaven and she saw all kinds of people there. She spoke to Plato and Madame

Curie. Then she felt a cold rag hitting her in the face and heard voices saying, "Come back, come back." They were her father's and uncle's voices. She improved, the cold sheets brought down her temperature and the worst crisis was over.

Convalescence began. Eisig walked miles to a village to get a chicken for a soup. The fog was gone and she was aware of things around her. Eisig showed her some cans of coffee and canned food and told her that they had received a Red Cross package from the United States from Bertha Knopf. Alicia remembered her dead grandfather and the day in the park when he told her about Bertha and her sons, who lived in Brooklyn.

Maybe by the time I'm well, she dreamt, I'll be able to go to the park again. Spring will be in full bloom. Then there's the summer. I'll walk in the pine woods in Stadion. The swimming pool will open. We'll get Zabiec back. Jerry will come from Russia and we'll go visit Jas.

Bits of conversation drifted over from the adjoining room. Alicia heard her father talking. Regulations or not, Polish patients still came to see him and they brought newspapers. The only papers available were the German ones. Eisig read between the lines. Now he was telling Guta, "The Germans have been badly beaten in Norway. Their Navy has been destroyed by the British."

Alicia hoped that her father was right for a change.

Guta told her that she had found a real bargain. It was a piano. "After the war, God willing," she said, "Henius will take piano lessons."

"Where is the piano?" she asked her mother.

"We stored it," Guta told her, "with Mr. X."

"Who is Mr. X?"

"I guess you should know where we're going to put some of our things. Now the Germans can come to any Jewish apartment and confiscate whatever they feel like."

Guta told her the story of Mr. X. For many years Eisig had treated a Polish gentleman for syphilis. For all practical purposes, the man was cured. But nobody could be absolutely sure the disease would not flare up again. One day Mr. X brought a young woman with some skin eruptions. He was frightened. Eisig assured his patient that it was only a skin irritation. Mr. X was relieved and asked the doctor if it was all right for him to marry the woman. Eisig realized that his patient had never told his fiancée about his syphilis. He assured him that, being a doctor, he was bound by his oath of confidentiality. Mr. X got married and Eisig never found out if he had divulged his secret to his wife. Periodically they both came to Eisig for tests to see if they were all right. There was a rapport between doctor and patient. When Eisig spoke about him, he always referred to him as Mr. X, though Guta knew his real name. Now the piano was stored in the man's basement.

Aunt Paula told Alicia about the opening of a new Jewish hospital on Warsaw Street. It was badly needed because of the epidemic. Warsaw Street was the main thoroughfare in the Jewish section of the town. Doctor Peltz was the organizer and president of the hospital and Dr. Levin was vice-president. It was a big building with many modern facilities, financed by money still available in the Jewish community. Once a week a Polish surgeon came to perform operations. There was no shortage of doctors, but there were not enough nurses. Anne was the only one who had been certified before the war; she served in the capacity of head nurse and was training other girls. Alicia didn't know her, now she listened: According to Paula, Anne and Doctor Sepple, a young, handsome physician from Lodz, were involved in some sort of scandal. She was fired but he was not.

Slowly Alicia recovered. By May she was ready to see her friends. Lisa was now completely well and Leah managed to get a pass to come to the city. Sabina was a frequent visitor. Many girls from her years at Mrs. Zima's whom she hadn't seen for years came to see her.

She was glad to see Fryma. Fryma's father, a merchant, had made a lot of money at the beginning of the war. Fryma had three sisters. The two older ones got married during the war. Fryma had a steady boyfriend and her younger sister, at fourteen, was going steady. To them the war was just a nuisance. Bolek brought over a few boys from Lodz and Warsaw. It was great to feel her health coming back. Her hair was falling out, but that was considered normal after typhus. She didn't worry about it, since she had naturally thick hair.

The war news was bad. Eisig was still reading between the lines.

"They're beaten in Norway and France," he kept saying. By the beginning of June it was getting hard, even for Eisig, to have illusions about an Allied victory. Norway, Denmark and Belgium had gone the way of Czechoslovakia and Poland. When he read about the evacuation at Dunkirk, he said, "Now the whole German army is going to be trapped."

"Where," Alicia asked, "in the Channel?" Then she added, "Maybe God will part it for the British and French and drown the Germans."

The realization of a complete French defeat was sinking in. Sabina and Alicia often discussed the situation. Sabina whispered, "The Germans will never invade England."

Alicia looked at her, surprised. "What makes you so sure?" Only the Channel stands between occupied France and Britain."

"The British navy is in the Channel," Sabina said.

"But the British navy was supposed to prevent the invasion of Norway."

Now Sabina got really close to Alicia, and her whisper became almost inaudible. "I managed to hear the speech by the new English Prime Minister, Mr. Churchill, on our radio."

Alicia was excited. "What did he say? What did he say?"

"He said," Sabina quoted, " 'Though large tracts of Europe and many old and famous states have fallen or may fall into the grip of the Gestapo and all the odious apparatus of Nazi rule, we shall not flag or fail.' " She could not remember the rest, but she quoted, out of context, "We shall never surrender."

"Those are inspiring words. I hope that it's more than words."

Sabina continued, "I also learned that the evacuation at Dunkirk was a great success. The whole British army was rescued and brought safely to Britain."

"God," Alicia said, "be careful with that radio. You and your mother could be shot for listening."

Sabina laughed. "My mother still doesn't know that I have it."

"Where is Carl?" Alicia inquired.

"Before he left, he told us that he'd find us after the war. It's best that we don't know where he is."

June 15, 1940 was Alicia's eighteenth birthday. Hitler was marching to the Arch of Triumph and the flag covered with the swastika was hoisted to the top of the Eiffel Tower. Paris, the city of Alicia's dreams, was now in the hands of the Nazis.

The people of Kielce watched and listened as German soldiers marched and sang their triumphant songs of conquest. "Germany, Germany above all!" They ruled Europe. For Guta, "Soon, God willing," became "Sometime, God willing." "We have to survive day by day," became her philosophy. "We're in this situation together with many other people; we'll do whatever they do."

Summer is always easier on the poor than winter. But the epidemic still raged, the hospital was full and beds had to be put in the halls. Alicia and Lisa resumed their jobs in the council. They were now both immune to typhus. Lisa forgot about Jerry and let Bolek console her.

Mucia was always cheerful and smiling. Occasionally she had attacks of rheumatism and her back and neck hurt. Twice a week a masseuse came "upstairs." Mrs. Friedman was also Kielce's best known midwife. She was Dr. Levin's assistant and had helped deliver Jerry, Alicia and Henius. She was a large woman with powerful arms and hands. Mrs. Friedman was always talking about her son Benjamin. According to her, he was brilliant. She was sure that he would be a doctor. Alicia knew Benjamin slightly; he'd gotten his Matura in the Jewish gymnasium in 1939.

One day Alicia found her aunt crying. Things must be really bad, she thought; her Mucia hadn't even cried when Grandmother Regina died. Then she just cursed Grandfather.

"There's bad news from the Russian side," Paula told her. "Somebody arrived from Lwow yesterday. It's not that easy to cross the border any more; the security is much tighter and the man is very happy he made it."

Alicia couldn't believe her ears. "Is he a Jew?"

"Of course," Paula answered. "We are not in touch with Poles."

"It seems so preposterous for a Jew to be happy to be in the German part of Poland."

Paula stopped crying. "The Russians are deporting refugees east, nobody knows how far. Maybe all the way to Siberia."

Siberia, Alicia reflected. She associated Siberia with Polish heroes
who were sent there by the czarist regime to prison camps. After the
revolution Stalin had kept the camps occupied. "Why the refugees?" she
asked.

"It's a ploy. The Russian authorities announced that people who
wanted to go back to the German side of Poland could register and were
then free to leave. Many homesick and lonely boys registered. I suspect
that Jerry did too."

Alicia still didn't understand. "So they registered," she said. "So
what?"

"It's the devious Russian mind. They figured that people who wanted
to go back to Germany were security risks for them." Paula started crying
again. "I'm trying to convince your uncle to send somebody to Lwow to
bring Jerry home before it's too late."

Doctor Peltz walked in on the conversation. "We don't know if they'll
deport Jerry or, if they do, how far east he'll be sent. Take my word for
it, wherever he goes, even Siberia, he'll be better off than here."

Alicia was shivering. Uncle Monek sounded like Mr. Hochberg, but
Mr. Hochberg had only been guessing.

In October Guta learned from her sister that all furs were being
confiscated. Sometimes the council had advance knowledge of these
kinds of "actions." Guta had a beautiful black Persian lamb coat. It was
time to store not only her fur, but all things of value with Mr. X. Whatever
the Jews owned was in jeopardy.

The apartment began to look empty. The best furniture had been
hidden. Alicia missed the Persian rugs, the chandeliers and the curio
cabinet with crystals. Guta had bought these things at Pleszowskis in
Krakow. At the time, Eisig had complained about the amount of money
she was spending. He never admitted how much he liked his apartment
and the way Guta had furnished it.

"It's a good thing," Guta said, "that these confiscations are done
through the Jewish Council and the police; it would be terrible having
the Germans coming into Jewish homes."

Eisig just shrugged his shoulders. "The Germans are making the Jews
do the job on their own people. It frees them to fight the war."

Guta didn't pay attention to his words. "God willing, after the war, we'll get our things back."

The battle for Britain raged throughout that fall. People had once believed in the might of France; now England was the last bastion of democracy in Europe. Alicia and Sabina tried to find solace in broadcasts from beleaguered London.

One day Alicia was sitting with Pawel in her room. The room was still full of books. "You'd better pack them up and bury them somewhere; they can get you into trouble," Pawel said.

"Books, too," she said. "Look at our apartment; everything that made it look like home is hidden now."

"Sometimes I feel lousy, too. If my father hadn't canceled our tickets to the World's Fair, we'd be stuck in the United States. I'll bet my parents would have been upset if they hadn't been able to come back home last fall. Stas and I would be driving them crazy running around the fair." Then Pawel became pensive. "On the other hand, I would have missed that summer in the mountains and wouldn't be talking to you now."

Alicia almost cried.

"Do you still think that I'm a pest?"

"Yes," she said, "but a lovable one." She kissed him lightly on the cheek.

At the beginning of November Doctor Peltz resigned from his post as President of the council. "I cannot in good conscience keep the job," he told his wife. "The Germans are using the council to rob and persecute the Jews, and who knows what else. They call me "Stolze Jude" (a proud Jew), but if I keep my position I will lose my pride and self-respect. I'm a doctor and it's enough for me to be a director of a hospital and to be in charge of a Jewish orphanage and house for the aged."

Doctor Peltz's successor was Herman Levy. The first thing he did was to put his entire family on the council's payroll. His son, Lenny, who had once been a clerk with Alicia, was now in charge of all the offices.

Mr. Levy was tough on his own people and very compliant and humble toward the German authorities. Alicia lost her job in order to make room for one of Mr. Levy's relatives. Lisa, being an orphan, now worked in the hospital's pharmacy.

At the beginning of December Eisig received a letter from the two cousins Guta had met the past year in Rowne. They were somewhere in Russia; the return address was only a post office number. They wrote that they envied Eisig's father. Evidently their letters were being censored, and this was their way of saying that they would rather be dead than be in Russia. Guta did not mention the letter to her sister.

The young Lublin cousins were also in Russia: Frania, her sister Hela, and Beryl and his wife. Eda was in the Russian part of Poland. Wladek, who had been in the Polish army in 1939, also found himself in Russia, Eda occasionally heard from him. Mark and Tina were in Krakow. In December 1940, Jerry was deported to Russia. Mr. Rapaport worked as a teacher in Lwow and remained there with his family.

Despite their wishful thinking, the Jews of Kielce were not spared a ghetto. Theirs came later than those in Lodz, Warsaw and Krakow; in March 1941, all Jews had to move to a small section of the old part of town. The original population there was mostly orthodox Jewish. Before the war, Guta had gone there to hunt for bargains in the crowded little stores. To Alicia it was strange territory.

It was the job of the council and the police to see that people moved in an orderly manner. The council assigned apartments. Fences were built around the ghetto and the Jewish police patrolled them.

Both Alicia and Henius had been born in the apartment on Freedom Place and had lived there all their lives. It was in the center of the city, close to the park, and they had shared their back yard with the Peltzes. When Henius asked why they were moving, no one could think of a rational answer.

Alicia gave most of her books away to the gentile neighbors and took a few of her favorites to the new apartment, even though Guta complained that it was dangerous for Jews to own forbidden books.

Although Dr. Peltz was no longer Council President, he continued to command great respect from the community. The new president made a special effort to assign him and Paula one of the nicest apartments available. It was on Okrzejowa Street. Sabina and her mother also moved to that street. The advantage of living in that part of the ghetto was that there were many small gardens in back of the houses.

The Strum family got an apartment in a relatively new apartment house on Warsaw Street. The street itself was forbidden to Jews, and the front gate of the house was nailed shut. The tenants had to use the back entrance.

The Koslows were the Strums's next-door neighbors. Alicia hadn't seen Lucia since the day she'd played ball with her five years ago. Now she almost didn't recognize her. She was a well-developed fifteen-year-old, the picture of health. It would be hard to guess that she had once been a very sick child. The Koslows' nephew from Warsaw, Franek, was staying with them.

The young people still met in each other's apartments. Boys and girls paired off, Bolek and Lisa, Alicia and Franek. Guta once asked her daughter why she never invited Sabina over with the others. Alicia sometimes wondered about it herself. She knew that Sabina loved her, she did not want to go to Rowne without her. But Sabina was once jealous of Basia and now she resented Lisa. Besides that she did not fit in with the group.

It was getting hard for Alicia to treat Pawel as just an obnoxious kid. "I'd thought things were looking up. You even kissed me. Now Franek's moved in," he complained one day.

"Why don't you try getting friendly with Lucia?" Alicia suggested. "She's more your age."

"That shrewd little bitch. When she wants to be, she's the sweetest, most innocent wide-eyed thing, but I can see right through her."

Alicia laughed. At sixteen, Pawel was remarkably perceptive. "She can turn her amiability on and of; she'd be a great actress."

"I understand Lucia had a sore throat recently," Pawel said with his impish grin.

Doctor Steiner was an ear, nose and throat specialist, and he was considered the biggest catch in Kielce. He was well bred, suave and cultured, unlike the boorish Dr. Sepple. Many girls were developing upper respiratory problems.

"You, being the hospital director's niece, would have a good chance with him. Your mother could say, 'My husband the doctor and my son-in-law the doctor.' "

"If my uncle were still the President of the Council, all the doctors would be fighting over me," Alicia joked. Then she became serious: "I'm not really impressed by them. Someday I'll be a doctor myself."

Alicia told Pawel that Dr. Steiner had managed to bring his mother and sister to Kielce from Lwow. "His sister is cute and all the nurses are trying to make friends with her. Steiner figures that, as a doctor, he can always make a living here, and the ghetto is better than Siberia."

"What wonderful choices we have," Pawel said.

Chapter 9

It was early in May, 1941. Henius and Stas were playing in the back yard. Alicia sat on the trunk of an old tree, reading "Ashes" a romantic novel by Stefan Zeromski. Her mind was far from the dirt and garbage that surrounded her, lost in the vast expanses of Polish estates, ponds, trees, orchards and fox hunts.

A voice brought her back to reality. "If a German sees you reading a book, you'll be in serious trouble. You could be shot."

Alicia looked up. It was a policeman, a refugee from Lodz. At least he was speaking Polish. Though he was not a German Jew, he was still a stranger. These policemen were tougher on people than those born and bred in Kielce. She said, "What would a German be doing in one of our back yards? They're afraid of filth and infectious diseases; besides, they have you. There's no need to come here themselves."

"I'm only doing my job," he answered. "You're just as stubborn as your uncle. No wonder he couldn't last as President of the Council."

"Who the hell are you to talk about my uncle? You came here from Lodz and are getting rich on other people's misery."

He was getting angry. "You're not wearing your arm band; someone else would beat you up for that."

Alicia said, "You mean one of those German-speaking bastards who think they're special Jews."

Suddenly Henius and Stas started yelling at her. "You 'farfluchte Jude'—damn, stinking rotten Jew, why aren't you wearing the band with the yellow star? You should be kicked and shot."

Alicia was stunned. The kids are victims more than anyone else, she thought.

The boys acted as if it were a big joke.

"It's not funny," Alicia told them. "We're all human beings, loved by our families, and we're not damn and stinking."

177

"But we are Jude," Stas insisted.

"Of course you are," Alicia answered, "and you should be proud of your heritage." She told them about the Maccabees, about David killing Goliath with a sling, and about zealots in Masada. "The Jews have made great contributions in medicine, science, philosophy and literature," she added.

"But now we are 'farfluchte Jude,' " Henius repeated.

"You are who you believe you are."

"Then, why aren't the Jews fighting now?"

"Sometimes the odds are overwhelming," Alicia answered. "All we can do is wait and try to make it day by day. There were ghettos in the middle ages; the Jews were separated from the general population just like now. They survived pogroms and got out of the ghettos."

The policeman listened for a while. Then he waved his hand and said, "Make sure you obey the rules. If you want to get out of the ghetto, don't talk about the Maccabees."

The next day Alicia and Sabina were lying on the grass behind Sabina's house. It was a bright spring afternoon, and the flowers were in bloom. It had been an oversight on the part of the Germans to leave these gardens in the ghetto. The Jews were actually allowed to enjoy the flowers, and the Germans could not take the beautiful spring day away from them.

Alicia told Sabina about the discussion she had had with the boys the day before.

"Since when," Sabina asked, "do you know so much about Jewish history? You were never an eager student of the subject."

"Oh, I read a lot of novels based on the Bible. I'm sorry for the children to be growing up in the ghetto."

"How about feeling sorry for us?" Sabina said. "We only needed one more year to get our Maturas. By now we would have been at a university. How will we ever make up those lost years?"

Alicia said, "Basia is a student at Lwow's university. She got her Matura last year." Then she remembered something. "We tried to go to school in Kielce last fall."

It had happened in the fall of 1940. Doctor Peltz was still the president of the council and people hoped that there would be no ghetto in Kielce. Sabina told Alicia that she had learned through the grapevine that some teachers from Kinga were running gymnasium and lyceum in the basement of a house. "They even have a couple of microscopes and a few chemicals to demonstrate simple reactions."

The girls decided to find the secret school. The house was located on a small side street that was not yet forbidden to the Jews. They still did not wear their arm bands. Sabina had brown, kinky hair with a reddish tint, it was considered to be Jewish hair. It was tightly braided, but it still didn't look straight. They found a path leading to the back of the house, climbed down a narrow staircase and knocked on a door. "Come in," they heard a voice. Their eyes slowly adjusted to the dark. A woman was sitting at a table. She raised her head, and there was surprise in her eyes. She evidently expected someone else. Then surprise gave way to apprehension. "What do you want?" she asked. The girls sighed with relief; it was Mrs. Kubelska, the principal of Kinga, who had also been their biology teacher.

Alicia came right to the point. "Mrs. Kubelska," she said, "we would like to attend your school."

For a moment there was recognition in the woman's eyes, acknowledgment of their old teacher–student relationship, but then her eyes turned stone cold. "I don't know what school you're talking about. I've never seen you before."

"But Mrs. Kubelska, Sabina and I went to Kinga for five years. I loved your biology class. You called me by my first name. I was the first in the class to learn how to focus a microscope; you made me draw my diagrams over and over again." Alicia was talking very fast.

"Please leave," the woman said. There was something definite and final in her voice.

The girls were shaken, but there was nothing to do but leave. Sabina said, "She looked through us as if we didn't exist. The whole world seems to be doing that. We're poison to the Poles. I hope the Polish partisans accepted Carl."

Alicia concluded that Sabina knew more than she let on.

Now, a few month later, Alicia said, "There was fear behind those stone eyes of Mrs. Kubelska, I almost felt sorry for her. I'll bet they moved the school to another house after our visit; it's dangerous enough to teach, but to be associated with Jews makes it doubly so." Then she added, "The war won't last forever. We'll be students again. In the meantime we should teach the kids history. They should know about the French Revolution, the American Declaration of Independence and Bill of Rights and about the Poles fighting against czarist tyranny."

"It might be dangerous to teach them about revolutions and uprisings while we're in the ghetto," Sabina said.

"Who would tell the Germans?" Alicia asked.

"I'm sure they have informers, including Jewish policemen."

"Speaking of the devil, there's one coming," Alicia said.

He was a young, handsome man who had recently married one of their schoolmates from Mrs. Zima's. He was a native of Kielce, usually friendly and cheerful, but this afternoon he looked grim.

"Having a bad day, Aron?" Alicia asked. "Tell us something good. It would be nice to hear that there were fewer typhus admissions in the hospital, there was more food available, you guys no longer hit people and the political situation has changed for the better."

There was no trace of a smile on Aron's face.

Alicia sensed that something very close to her was wrong.

"What's happened?"

"They arrested Dr. Peltz, Dr. Koslow and Dr. Harkavi."

"When, why?" she screamed.

"About an hour ago. I decided that you should know."

"Thank you, Aron. Do you know why?"

"That's a silly question."

My uncle, my neighbor and my parents' friend, she thought. "Where are they now?"

"In Gestapo headquarters," Aron answered.

"I've got to see my aunt. They've arrested her husband and she doesn't know where her sons are."

"Don't assume the worst," Sabina consoled her. "Maybe they took the doctors for interrogation and will let them go afterwards." Sabina and Alicia left to see Paula.

Paula was sitting in the garden, looking at the flowers. Alicia wondered if the flowers reminded her of the past and of Zabiec. How much could anyone take before breaking down? She tried to tell her aunt that the doctors would be released, and wished she could believe it.

Paula didn't believe it either. "He was too prominent, too unyielding and commanded too much respect in the community. They couldn't possibly let him be," she said.

"Why Koslow and Harkavi?" Alicia asked.

"I have a theory," Paula answered. "On the Russian side, they deport the refugees to Siberia, and on the German side, they are arresting people of Russian origin. Koslow originally came from Bielorussia."

"And Harkavi?" Alicia asked.

"He is a young man and was an officer in the Polish army."

Alicia remembered that her father was also an officer in the reserves.

Paula seemed to guess her niece's fears. "Your father never took part in anything but his medical practice. They'll leave a quiet man like him alone. Go see how your parents are taking it and how the Koslows are doing. I'll be all right." She asked Sabina about her mother's health and if they had heard anything from Carl. "Wherever he is, he's better off than here."

Alicia quickly jumped in: "Like Jas and Jerry."

"That's what your uncle always said," Paula answered.

When Alicia arrived home, Guta was crying. "Monek, Monek, my poor sister is all alone now."

"You're carrying on more than Mucia," Alicia said.

"Paula keeps everything inside and that's no good either."

Alicia kissed her mother. Then, looking at her father, she saw fear in his eyes. "I can understand why they arrested Monek," he said, "but the other two? Who knows who will be next."

"Let's not assume the worst. They might be released," Alicia repeated. "I'm going to see the Koslows."

Little Rita opened the door; Mrs. Koslow was washing the dishes. When she looked up, to Alicia's surprise, she did not seem upset. She said, "You're wondering about Herman. There must be some misunderstanding about his practice (Dr. Koslow was known to have German patients). I expect him back this evening or tomorrow for lunch."

Alicia noticed that Lucia, unlike her mother, was close to tears. "Tell me what happened." she asked.

Lucia said, "There was a knock at the door. I opened it and there was a Gestapo man. I was scared, but my father assumed that he was a patient. He told my father to finish what he was doing and come with him. We realized that he wasn't a patient. My mother started packing sandwiches for my father in case he didn't get back for supper. I looked out the window and there was another Gestapo man standing with Dr. Peltz. It was the first time I ever saw Dr. Peltz with his head down. My mother gave my father the sandwiches and they left. I decided to follow them. When we crossed the ghetto gates, I dropped my arm band. They went down Railroad Street in the direction of Gestapo headquarters." Lucia was crying. "I was scared; I was outside the ghetto and without my arm band. I ran back home."

Mrs. Koslow ignored her daughter. Her mind was on the sandwiches. "I hope I gave him enough to eat."

Rita was crying. "When will daddy be back?"

"Maybe tonight," her mother assured her.

It wasn't that night, or the next. They were in the city jail for three weeks.

At night Alicia and Guta heard Mrs. Koslow crying.

Alicia wondered if the prisoners had been interrogated, beaten or tortured. It was known that they were being held together with a group of Polish political prisoners.

"Why don't you cry?" Alicia asked her aunt.

"He's strong, he can take it and so can I."

But after three weeks Alicia was not so sure. The council was notified that the entire group from the city jail, including the Jewish doctors, would be deported to Auschwitz.

Auschwitz, a concentration camp built in a sleepy Polish village, Oswiecim, was already notorious in 1941. On the day of deportation the women were allowed to go to the railroad station to see their husbands off. Mrs. Koslow, Lucia, Mrs. Harkavi, Paula and Alicia were escorted by two Jewish policemen. Guta stayed home with Henius and Rita. The Jewish women walked down Railroad Street, joined the crowd of Polish women and children, passed the café, the movie theater and the school of Blessed Kinga. Maybe this is just a terrible nightmare, Alicia thought. I'll wake up any moment and be walking on old Sienkiewicz Street. She looked at the two Jewish policemen, Aron and Goldberg, and at all the crying women around her. She wasn't dreaming.

It seemed that all the women of Kielce were at the station that day. Goldberg explained the situation: "This is a large transport, mainly of Polish intelligentsia, judges, lawyers, doctors, teachers and a few Jewish physicians."

"They're trying to get rid of all our prospective leaders," someone whispered.

The train stood empty, waiting. Slowly the buses from the jail began to arrive. The prisoners jumped out in pairs, handcuffed to each other. The women frantically yelled and waved their hands. The Polish police kept them behind a line. Paula and Alicia were much taller than most of the women at the station; they could see above the crowd. As more buses arrived, there was still no sign of the doctors. Paula pinched Alicia. "Maybe they're not sending them to Auschwitz."

Alicia began to jump and wave.

"I don't see your uncle. Who are you waving to?" Paula asked.

Alicia had tears in her eyes. "It's Mr. Wisniecki." That kind man who had taught her how to swim, who had applauded her when she played tennis, was now handcuffed and kneeling in front of the train.

"Why is he there?"

"He's a decent goy, Aron whispered. "That's enough of a reason."

The last bus arrived and the Jews got off. Doctor Peltz was handcuffed to Doctor Koslow. Paula waved and waved. Monek knelt in front of the train like everyone else. His head was bent and he would not look up. At the last minute he raised his eyes and saw her. He put his free hand to his mouth and blew her a kiss. Then he was gone, together with the others. The train had swallowed them all. Paula stood there transfixed. This was the man with whom she had spent twenty-five years. They had had many triumphs together; they had had their defeats; but he had always been proud and kept his head high. It seemed to her that no one could ever humiliate him.

How would he manage? Would they give him insulin? Lately he had been getting it through a Polish physician friend; a Jewish policeman was helping smuggle it into the ghetto, for a fee of course. She closed her eyes and saw a scene from many years ago, when she had been a sixteen-year-old girl and he, a physician and highly decorated Austrian officer. He was courting her in Zabiec. They decided to go horseback riding. The stable boy mistakenly saddled a wild stallion that hadn't been broken. Paula instructed the boy to change the horse for Dr. Peltz, but Monek insisted that, as an officer, he could ride any horse. The horse threw him onto a dirt road. There he stood in his dress uniform, all splashed with mud, while Paula, sitting tall on her horse, could barely keep from laughing. Monek was angry and humiliated; it was almost the only time in their lives together that she had realized how vulnerable he could be.

Paula awoke from her reverie. What a silly thing to think about at a time like this. She had always prided herself on being down to earth. The train left slowly. The women and children filed in a sorrowful march back to their homes, some sniffling, some weeping openly. They wondered what was going to happen to their husbands. They themselves faced an uncertain future without their men. The Jewish women, escorted by their policemen, went back to the ghetto.

"After the war," Paula kept saying, "I'll find Jas and Jerry."

In June 1941, Germany launched an attack on Russia. The infantry and mobilized units kept on going day and night east and east.

The Jews living in houses along Warsaw Street were not allowed to look out their front windows. Eisig and Alicia peeked through the slats in the blinds. They watched the marching soldiers, trucks and tanks. The soldiers were singing.

"Soon they will sing no more," Eisig said. "They're going to get stuck in Russia, just like Napoleon and his army. They'll freeze to death."

It didn't seem that way in the summer of 1941. In July the Germans occupied all of Poland and were on Russian soil. They expected to wind up their campaign, take Moscow and annihilate the Red Army. Millions and millions of Russians were taken prisoner and millions lost their lives. The Germans were winning on the northern, central, and southern fronts. They stretched from Leningrad to the Black Sea. It was the "blitzkrieg" all over again. Now it became obvious that the people deported to Siberia were the lucky ones; maybe they were far enough from the Germans.

Life in the ghetto kept going. There were many beggars on the streets, people were coming down with typhus, and there was the continuous fear of nightly knocks at the door. But the president of the council, Mr. Levy, was getting richer and richer and so were some of the policemen who controlled the trade at the fences. To add to the overcrowding, more people were drifting into Kielce.

Stories circulated about murderous battalions that followed the German army in the east, rounding up and killing Jews, but most ghetto dwellers refused to believe them. Natives of Kielce who had been on the Russian side of Poland and had managed not to be deported to the depths of Russia now tried desperately to return to to Kielce. The Rapaports were among them. They were arrested en route and sent to Auschwitz. The news traveled to the Kielce ghetto.

In the first week of September, the Jewish council received a telegram from Auschwitz. It was a notification that Dr. Peltz was dead. According to the telegram, he had hung himself. A councilman told Alicia that such telegrams were sent automatically, even if the prisoner was alive. It did not make much difference either way, as the estimated life span of a concentration camp inmate was short. But a miracle could happen and, if Dr. Peltz was alive, there was a glimmer of hope.

The following week identical telegrams came about Drs. Koslow and Harkavi. It was becoming routine; people just shrugged their shoulders. The average ghetto dweller reasoned that he had already suffered enough, even for the Germans, and only the prominent and well educated would be arrested and sent to concentration camps.

Paula presented a smiling face to the world. She often invited people to her apartment, but she cried at night.

The situation was bleak everywhere. The only bright spot was that Germany did not win the Battle of Britain. In December, the Germans were 25 miles from Moscow. The Red Army seemed nonexistent. But, as Eisig had forecast, the Russian winter stopped the Germans. In December 1941, the temperature dropped to 40 degrees below zero and the German drive collapsed. A fresh Russian army from Asian Russia now fought, not for communism but for their country. On December 6th they opened a counteroffensive, and the following day the Japanese bombed Pearl Harbor. Now the United States was at war. The Germans were stopped in North Africa, and Egypt and Palestine were safe.

There was a little more hope in the ghetto, but nothing had really changed. Lucia, as an orphan, got a job in the hospital's laboratory. After Dr. Peltz's arrest, Dr. Levin became the director of the hospital. Anne got her job back as chief nurse and Lisa worked in the hospital pharmacy.

Alicia had lost her status as the niece of the most powerful leader in the Jewish community. Now she was just Alicia and Dr. Peltz was dead. She felt that many people who had tried to ingratiate themselves with her in the past had stopped. Doctor Steiner, once very attentive, ignored her in his own polite way.

The council got bigger as the ghetto became more crowded. Mr. Levy had absolute power over its complicated bureaucracy. The typhus epidemic never subsided, and in early 1942 the hospital staff decided to give a six-week emergency nursing course. It was hoped that it would produce more nurses and give the girls who already worked in the hospital some background.

Alicia registered for the course. She began in February, along with Lisa and Lucia.

Lisa had enrolled at the insistence of her mother. By now she was Bolek's girlfriend and that was the only thing on her mind. Lucia was bored by the work in the laboratory. She would go to the wards to watch the nurses and follow the doctors. Anne considered her a nuisance. Lucia pushed herself into the retinue of the visiting surgeon, Dr. Kalish. She was pretty and engaging, and he allowed her to watch him in the operating room. In spite of her scanty education, she did well in the theoretical part of the nursing course. Laura, an attractive, statuesque redhead, was another good student. In practice she was already a nurse, and it was a not-too-well-kept secret that she was trying to land a doctor for a husband. The urbane Dr. Steiner was first on her list. Her younger sister Rebecca also worked as a nurse. Alicia had heard Dr. Peltz say that she was able and devoted to her job. Both sisters had pleasant personalities and the patients liked them.

The doctors lectured on their specialties. All the girls laughed when Eisig told them that every man had gonorrhea at least once in his life, but would always deny it.

Doctor Brazen, Bolek's father, lectured on internal medicine and Dr. Katz, Pawel's and Stas's father, on gynecology. The venerable director of the hospital, Dr. Levin, often came to listen. At any moment, Alicia expected to feel the formidable presence of her uncle. The man who had organized the entire operation was now forgotten. At times it was hard for her to remember that he was dead. Still, the hospital felt like home, safe and sane. All the doctors were her parents' friends. Sick people were treated and recovered. The old, too ill to be helped, died from natural causes. Alicia almost forgot about the world that had gone mad.

For the practical part of the course, Alicia was assigned to Anne. Anne was a thin, small, wiry girl always on the move. Alicia only knew her slightly, as Anne was a few years older and she and Alicia were from different worlds. Alicia was curious about Anne. She thought, that's the girl that my uncle fired. Alicia felt that Anne did not like her: To her I'm a spoiled brat who has never worked, while she's been on her own for years. On top of that, I'm Dr. Peltz's niece.

Anne did not mince words and she could be quite unpleasant. On their first day together, Anne instructed Alicia to straighten out the supply closet. Alicia had just come from an interesting lecture on acute appendicitis. Now she was faced with a mundane task.

"I hoped I was going to learn something," she said.

Anne shrugged her shoulders. "Like what?"

Alicia felt intimidated, but she decided to tell her anyway. "I would like to be shown how to administer injections."

"Not so fast, my dear. The first job of a student nurse is to keep a ward in order. You must also follow the instructions of the nurse in charge. If you don't comply, I won't sign any papers saying you've completed a practical in nursing."

A man stumbled into the room. He was legless, and rolled on two stumps.

"Do you need help?" he asked Alicia. He was a fixture in the hospital; after the amputation, he had had no place to go.

Anne looked down at him and said, "You can help her with the lowest shelf; I have to go to the ward."

Alicia knew about Pete from her aunt. He had frozen his legs in the winter of 1941 while crossing the border from Russian to German Poland. When he came to Kielce, gangrene set in in both his legs. Doctor Peltz admitted him to the hospital and Dr. Kalish operated.

"Don't be afraid of nurse Anne," Pete told Alicia. "I like her the best. She's the only one who says what she means. Your uncle was the same way. The rest of them. . . ," he waved his hand.

Alicia was glad Pete had spoken. To her Anne was an independent woman who had studied nursing at a time when most girls with Maturas studied languages and literature. She figured that Dr. Sepple had been at least as guilty as Anne, but it was the woman who'd gotten fired.

Anne came back in the room and looked into a neat closet. "Well, you're not as big a pain in the ass as the other 'princess,' your friend Lucia."

Alicia almost burst out laughing. "Shame on you, Anne, Lucia is an orphan."

"I'm sorry about that."

In March they took their final exams. Four of them received A's: Alicia, Lucia, Laura and Rachel. Unlike Anne, Rachel was once Doctor Peltz's favorite. He was impressed by the way she was taking care of her father when he treated him for typhus in 1940. At that time the hospital was being organized and he advised Rachel to apply for a nursing job. Her way with sick people reminded him of Paula during the last war.

The girls gave a party for the lecturing doctors and staff. Everyone needed a party; it evoked memories of happier times. Anne didn't attend. According to Laura, she felt that someone had to stay in the wards to take care of the patients.

Dr. Sepple was dancing cheek-to-cheek with Irene, a tall, beautiful girl with green eyes who worked as a nurse. She was from a little town near Kielce. Her parents were poor and Irene only had an elementary school education. She didn't pass the final nursing exam, but she was a hard worker and kept her job.

Alicia thought, Irene is younger and prettier than Anne, so what if she isn't well educated.

Laura was dancing with Dr. Steiner, and was in seventh heaven. Lucia flirted with another young doctor.

Alicia danced with her father; she was thrilled that he'd come. Eisig was not a party-goer. She looked at Lucia. How fast time flies, she thought; it's almost a year since the telegrams about her father and my uncle arrived. Is Lucia envious because I'm dancing with my father? Seeing Lisa, she couldn't chase away a horrible thought: Who is going to be the next orphan?

Since last spring, many more people had been arrested and deported to concentration camps. Alicia studied her father. He seemed to be happy and proud of her this afternoon. She suspected that, deep down inside, he was afraid. Guta had told her that he had bad dreams at night.

It was time for Alicia to present a short play that she'd written. Lucia, Laura and Rebecca helped her. She played the main character, a hypochondriac nurse. Everyone applauded, laughed and enjoyed himself. The stage and the play reminded her of Basia. Was she still alive in Auschwitz? What about her parents, especially her mother who is crippled?

Afterwards, when refreshments were served, Dr. Levin proposed a toast: "To next year, hopefully we'll all be out of the ghetto and free."

Anne appeared. She picked up a glass of wine: "Next year in Jerusalem."

Next year, God willing, my mother would say, Alicia thought.

It was March 1942. On the eastern front, the Germans and Russians were stuck in the mud, waiting for drier weather so they could begin killing each other. In the west, German U-boats ruled the Atlantic.

Guta and the children looked out their back windows. Everyone knew that the only time the Gestapo trudged through the back yards of the ghetto was when they came to arrest someone. The routine was always the same: Two Gestapo men were accompanied by two Jewish policemen, who served as their guides.

Even if we saw them approaching, what could my father do? Alicia wondered. There was no place to go or hide. Eisig's ex-patients were storing his possessions, but they would never risk their lives hiding a Jew. She still considered her father's fears exaggerated. Why would they come for him?

They came at night. Aron was one of the Jewish policemen. They banged on the door and Guta opened it. Henius awoke and ran to his sister, who took him in her arms. One of the Gestapo men cracked his whip and yelled to Alicia and Henius to go to the other room. Henius clung to his sister. Through the open door Alicia looked at her mother. Guta's pale green eyes were fixed on Aron, pleading for an explanation; Aron stood there helplessly and spread his hands.

It dawned on Alicia that this was real, not like her mother's stories of the last war, when the temporary setbacks would pass and they would all return to Zabiec in one piece. Even if Grandfather Mark were here tonight, he could not talk himself out of this situation.

The Gestapo men ordered Eisig to get dressed and come with them. Eisig asked for permission to go to the bathroom.

Alicia was shivering. She tried to divert Henius's attention away from the room where the Gestapo was. He was staring at the Germans and she was afraid that he would provoke them. Terror overcame her. The Germans could do anything they wanted and nothing and nobody in the whole world could prevent it. It seemed to her that her father had been in the bathroom for a long time. Why was he procrastinating? She wanted him to leave and take the Gestapo with him so she, her mother and brother would be safe. A sense of order was returning to her. They will question him, and as soon as they find out they made a mistake, he'll be home.

Eisig emerged from the bathroom and slowly dressed. The Gestapo, policemen and Eisig left.

Alicia went to her mother. "Don't worry, it's just a misunderstanding."

Guta's eyes were enormous. "You sound like Mrs. Koslow last year."

"Doctor Koslow was born in Russia and had German patients," Alicia said. Despite overwhelming evidence, the fact that the Germans did not need an explanation for an arrest or execution had still not penetrated her consciousness. After all, even with Polish anti-Semitism, they had lived in safety, protected by the law, for the twenty years of her life.

"I hope you're right," Guta said.

Alicia kissed her mother. She was ashamed of herself for having wanted her father to leave. She had always loved her mother and brother more than him. "Let's go to sleep now; there's nothing we can do. Tomorrow we'll find out where Daddy is."

The next morning, Guta and Alicia got up early. Henius was fast asleep. "I'm going to the council as soon as the offices open," Alicia said.

She made breakfast. Then she woke Henius up and gave him his food. He didn't seem to remember last night. Guta was staring at the wall.

"Don't worry, mom, I'll be back soon." She ran out of the apartment. It was only morning, but the beggars and cripples were out in force, with outstretched hands. Nobody cares about my father, she thought. Everything is normal; the policemen are strutting in their uniforms, waving their sticks, and the narrow streets are as filthy as ever.

Alicia knew practically everyone at the council's main office. When the clerks and secretaries saw her, they suddenly got busy. No one looked up to acknowledge her presence. They act as if I had leprosy, she thought. To her relief, she spotted Bolek and Pawel; however, when she looked at their faces she knew right away that something was wrong. Pawel, the mischievous kid with smiling eyes and a charming smile, looked old and gray, his eyes dull and lackluster. "Alicia," he yelled.

She noticed that he was crying. "What's happened to my father?" She was panic-stricken.

"My father and yours were shot right beneath our windows."

"They came for my father, too." Bolek was almost apologetic. "He's in prison."

Pawel looked at Alicia and said through his tears, "They can't take our fathers to prison anymore, or torture them or send them to concentration camps."

Aron came over. He was crying, "I was once your father's patient. I was only seventeen and I came down with gonorrhea. My parents didn't know; I was desperate. Your father was kind and understanding and he charged me very little. Gestapo Chief Herr Thomas wasn't satisfied with simply killing the man; he had to deprive his body of its dignity. He kicked it and gloated over it and said, 'You were a doctor.' He was proud of his great achievement."

"Why?" Alicia asked.

Aron had slowly regained his composure. "It was an 'action' on reserve officers."

Alicia stood there as the awareness of what she was hearing slowly penetrated her consciousness. My father is dead; he was a physician, he was my father, he was my mother's husband, he will never be again.

"Where is his body?"

Aron said quickly, "We're ordered to dispose of corpses right away. We had to wake Jankiel, the grave digger, in the middle of the night."

Pawel looked at Aron with hatred and contempt. "It was just one of those routine 'actions,' " he said. "All in a day's work for Aron and his pals. The Gestapo simply comes to the council, asks for the list of the day and requests Jewish police to guide them. Last night it was the list of reserve officers."

Aron was already feeling bad; now he was devastated. "What could I do?"

Pawel continued mercilessly. "Just doing your job, Aron? Enjoying it, eh? Making it easy for the Germans? They don't have to look for the addresses in the dark. Last night you brought murderers to the houses of innocent people." He smiled maliciously. "In the future they'll give you guns and you'll become the executioners of your fellow Jews."

Alicia considered Aron a basically decent fellow who now found himself in a role he hadn't bargained for. She had known Pawel since he was nine years old, and this was the first time she'd seen this bitter, angry side of him. It almost frightened her to see him this way.

Bolek joined the conversation. "Come on, Pawel, Aron could never shoot a fellow Jew."

"I don't know about that," Pawel said. "But if you had a gun, Aron, would you shoot a German?"

Aron now protested. "You're a crazy, foolish kid. If a Jew ever did that, the Germans would level the ghetto to the ground."

Alicia thought about Mr. Hochberg; his predictions were coming true. "Aron," she said, "the Germans might kill us all anyway." She had had enough of the conversation. She was thinking of her mother and of how she was going to break the tragic news to her. "I have to go home; you do the same," she said to Pawel, and she left the council.

The day was clear and beautiful. It was close to the Passover holidays. Alicia looked up at the sky and almost said out loud, You once sent plagues on the Pharaoh, You parted the Red Sea for Moses; where are You now?

Henius was outside in the yard, playing with Stas. Guta waited inside for her daughter. She was dry-eyed and composed, and there was hope in her eyes. Alicia didn't know what to say. Aunt Sura knocked at the door. For a moment, Alicia was relieved. But then Aunt Sura ran to Guta, crying and hugging her. "Thank God, Beryl and Zlata are in Russia, far from the Germans."

Alicia was bitter; it was just like Aunt Sura to think about her son and daughter-in-law when her niece's husband had been murdered.

Guta grew pale. Alicia was afraid that her mother would faint. "Where is Eisig?" Guta asked.

"You mean she doesn't know?" Sura said to Alicia.

"When you stop worrying about Beryl, you'll tell her." Then she repeated what Pawel had said. "They won't be sending Daddy to a concentration camp now. They shot him. They shot Dr. Katz, too, and Dr. Brazen is in jail. It was an 'action' on the reserve officers."

Guta did not understand what her daughter was saying. She looked at her aunt, who was nodding her head. Then the realization came and she began to wail. "If only I hadn't opened the door so quickly, maybe Eisig could have escaped."

She always blames herself, Alicia thought. She said. "If you hadn't opened the door they would have broken it and probably shot all of us." Her mother's favorite expression came to mind: "Next year, God willing." Where was her God now and where would He be next year? He must be in some distant galaxy, light years away from his chosen people.

Henius walked in. He was hungry. Guta wiped her eyes and turned her face away. The boy wasn't paying any attention to his mother. Alicia wondered if he was pretending or if he really didn't remember last night. He had not asked once about his father. It was just as well; she wasn't ready to answer his questions.

She gave Henius his lunch. He couldn't wait to start playing again. She recalled her favorite English poem:

> From too much love of living
> From hope and fear set free
> We thank with brief thanksgiving
> Whatever gods may be
> That no life lives forever
> That dead men rise up never
> That even the weariest river
> Winds somewhere safe to sea

My father and my uncle have already wound up "safe to sea."

My father was the lucky one; he died quickly. A dead man is beyond caring where he is buried.

Paula came in and hugged and kissed her sister and niece. Obviously she knew what had happened.

Guta had stopped crying. She asked Paula, "Can we claim the body and arrange for a funeral?"

"We're not allowed to do that," Paula said. "You and I are not supposed to mourn. We have to act as if our husbands never lived."

Alicia said, "Aron told me that Father and Dr. Katz were buried last night. That's how the Gestapo wanted it."

Her mother was crying again. "Your father was not observant, but I know he would want a Jewish funeral, with his son saying Kaddish. From the dawn of civilization the human race has paid respect to the dead. Now we're forbidden to do even that. Your father worked his way through medical school, he became an outstanding physician, he was a good husband and father. He didn't deserve this kind of end."

"No man deserves this kind of end," Alicia said.

Many of the gardens on Okrzejowa Street belonged to the council.

Their produce was collected and sold to the general population, with the proceeds going to the council. Since that April night Alicia had the privileges of an orphan. She got a job as a cashier in the store where the produce was sold. To her pleased surprise, the salesgirl was Leah. Leah was unusual because she had both parents. The Blooms had moved to the ghetto like all the other Jews, but Mr. Bloom had a daily pass to go to Kadzielnia and was still in charge of the quarry. His job was deemed essential by the Germans.

Should I be envious? Alicia wondered. She thought about herself and all the other orphans. Sabina's father had died a long time before the war, and now she did not know the whereabouts of her brother; then there were Lisa, Lucia and Rita, Pawel and Stas, Henius and herself and probably Bolek. Doctor Brazen, after a week in jail, had been sent to Auschwitz; people waited for a telegram.

The man in charge of the store was a ruddy councilman, Mr. Rodbard. The name was vaguely familiar to Alicia. When the man looked at her, he shook his head in wonderment. "You must be Guta Warman's daughter; you look exactly the way she looked at your age. The only difference is that you're wearing glasses."

Alicia was puzzled.

He smiled, "I'm your mother's first cousin, Stefan Rodbard."

"Oh yes, I know," she finally said. "Your mother and my grandmother were sisters." The irony of the situation struck her. "Isn't it funny that our families lived nearby in Kielce for years and there was never any contact between them?"

"I don't remember how the feud started," he said.

"I think it was because of Zabiec."

"Even before, there were bitter arguments in Pierscien," he said. "Both my parents are dead and now, looking back, the whole thing seems ridiculous. Pierscien is gone and, I understand, so is Zabiec."

Later, Alicia told the story to Leah. "I think it's more important to have friends than relatives."

"It's nice to have both," Leah answered. "I wish my mother was all right and I still had my brother."

Alicia's thoughts reverted back to that rainy afternoon in August, eight years ago, when Uncle Monek brought the news of Julek's drowning. It was such a tragedy then. Incredible as it now seemed, there had been disasters in peoples' lives even before the war.

Customers were coming and both girls were glad to stop their fruitless speculation.

The great advantage of the job was that Alicia could bring home fruits and vegetables. After Eisig's death, her family's financial situation had not been very good. Guta, Alicia and Henius lived mainly on potatoes.

Guta was reluctant to ask Mr. X to raise money for her by selling some of their possessions. She said to Alicia, "After the war, without your father to support us, we'll need money. You and Henius still have to be educated." She added nostalgically, "Zabiec is gone."

"If what Rosie wrote me is true, Zabiec will become Grandfather's again," Alicia said.

"Then Tina will get it," Guta answered.

Alicia laughed. "If I know Grandfather, he'll get rid of her. He'll find himself a younger, more attractive version. He's going to be like King David, sleeping with a young girl in the last years of his life."

"Where do you get these ideas?" Guta asked.

"I can dream, can't I? Anyway, we won't need Zabiec; we'll go with Mucia to Erez Israel."

Some of the money Alicia got from sales in the store went into her pocket. Why should the policemen and councilmen get everything? I'll take some and leave less for them to steal. After all, I am "Motke Ganef's" granddaughter. My father was scrupulously honest, and a lot of good it did him. Now I'm the main provider and I don't care how I do it.

Leah suspected that Alicia was taking produce home, but she would never believe that her friend was actually stealing money.

At home, Henius was becoming wild and hard to handle. Alicia tried to explain the meaning of death to him, but he wasn't interested. He just wanted to play. "I was his age when Grandmother died," she told her mother. "I think I already understood the finality of it. I remember the unveiling in the cemetery in Pacanow and the frequent visits we made later on. We left pebbles on the stone as a remembrance."

Guta had tears in her eyes. "Do you remember the final visit we made to the cemetery the summer before we lost Zabiec?"

Alicia followed her own train of thoughts. She said, "I was only five when Jerry and I staged a funeral for our little dog while Jas played rabbi. It's more than we were able to do for Father. At that time I thought that only the old and sick died. We were young and healthy. I felt that you and Daddy would live forever. No wonder Henius can't face what's happening."

In May Paula sublet a room to her old friend Weinstock. He was as enterprising as ever; the fence around the ghetto did not stop him from making money. He bought food from gentiles and sold it to the Jews. He gave Paula and Guta bread and potatoes in exchange for the room.

Weinstock had a girlfriend. She had left her family in a small town in order to be with him. They planned on getting married.

Paula encouraged them. The wedding took place in her apartment, with a reception afterwards. Everyone tried to act happy, but it was really a sad affair. Too many people had been murdered, arrested and sent to concentration camps in the last year. The bride was crying because her family was far away.

"It's important to show the children that life must go on no matter what," Paula said.

Guta thought about her wedding in Zabiec twenty-two years ago. Alicia remembered Jas's Bar Mitzvah, when she was eight and Jerry was ten. Both of them ran and played, paying little attention to the religious ceremony. Are those times gone forever?

She went to the garden to see what Henius and Stas were doing. Stas was holding a stick to Henius's head and yelling, "This is an 'action'; all children under ten will be shot. You're a child; soon you'll be a rotten cadaver."

Alicia screamed, "Stop that!" She took the stick away from Stas. "This madness will not last forever; we have to survive as human beings."

"What will be the next 'action?' " Henius asked.

"Let's hope that the Germans have run out of 'actions' for the year," she answered. She hugged her brother.

When Alicia went inside, Weinstock and his bride were kissing.

Happier thoughts came to her mind. Weinstock will manage to get himself and his wife through the war and then they'll have a proper wedding.

They all drank a toast to better times.

One day early in June, Paula told her niece that she was going to a fortune teller. Alicia was surprised. "It's something my mother would do."

"At times like this, we all become superstitious. Come with me," her aunt said.

They visited a woman in a dark room in a basement. She was of an indeterminate age and was dressed in a sheer, bejeweled gown. She sat at a table. There was a ring on every finger and they could hear her bracelets clicking as she signaled them to come in. The woman was a Viennese Jew. Alicia wondered if she had been a fortune teller before being deported from her native city.

The woman examined Alicia's palm. She told her that there was an ocean voyage in her future, and that she would find a man who loved her very much. She said almost the same thing to Paula, but in different words.

Alicia had to admit that it felt good hearing words of hope in that dark, mysterious room.

As they, left Paula said to Alicia, "Maybe June will turn things around. Tadek visited me the other day."

"Tadek? How did he get here?"

"He took a chance coming to the ghetto. He was anxious to know if I'd heard from Jerry. Somehow he knew about your uncle, your father, Dr. Katz and Dr. Brazen."

Old images flooded Alicia's mind: Jas and Jerry's room "upstairs," the long ping pong table, she, Tadek and Jerry alternating hitting the ball back and forth.

"Tadek brought lard, potatoes and some canned food," Paula said. "We'll invite our friends and have a party.

"I can contribute some vegetables from the shop," Alicia said.

On June 15th, Alicia turned twenty. The family gathered in the garden in back of Paula's apartment. The day was warm and clear, and the flowers were in bloom. For a while they forgot about the misery around them. The men of the family were dead or gone, but they assumed that women and children could present no danger to the Nazis.

As usual, Paula talked about joining Jas in Palestine after the war. In the meantime, she was contemplating getting Aryan papers for herself, her sister, Alicia and Henius, so they could live outside the ghetto.

Alicia felt that her world was still there.

Besides the ever-present new cases of typhus, there was an epidemic of dysentery in the ghetto. First Paula had it, then Guta. Alicia took care of both of them. In spite of Anne's reservations, I would make a good nurse, she thought.

One day Guta fainted in the bathroom. Alicia picked her up from the floor. Her mother's face was drained of color. Alicia remembered a very sick woman in the hospital ward who had died soon after being admitted. Guta had the same look of being ready to give up. As Alicia led her mother back to bed, Guta's color returned. She smiled at her daughter and assured her that she was all right. After a couple of weeks she felt better.

With Eisig gone, they rented out a room. A young Jewish policeman, about to get married, took it. The couple spent their wedding night in that room.

Where would I want to spend the first night with my husband? Alicia wondered. In a fancy hotel in the mountains or at a seaside resort? Krynica, Zakopane, Sopot—will I ever see those places again?

The rented room was adjacent to what used to be Guta and Eisig's bedroom. Now Guta slept there alone.

The morning after the wedding night, Guta was pensive during breakfast. "I heard them; it is a wonder the bed didn't collapse." Alicia was surprised to hear it from her mother; she considered her prudish. It sounded more like something Paula would say. Does my mother think about her wedding night? she wondered. Does she miss my father that way? Does a forty-two-year old woman still need it? Alicia thought about Franek, next door, who had tried to convince her to have sex with him. At this point in her life she was not interested.

By the beginning of August there were vague rumors circulating in the ghetto. There was talk about resettlement to work camps in the east. Guta got her information from her tenant. He told her that people had already been deported from other ghettos. Those who remained had received postcards from them stating that they were doing fine. To Alicia, this seemed logical. First German and Austrian Jews were sent to Poland; now everyone would go farther east. But where? Why? For how long?

"Who will stay in Kielce?" Alicia asked the policeman.

The assumption was that they would be people with skills useful to the German war effort: workers in two important factories, Henrykow and Ludwikow, the policemen, councilmen, doctors, nurses and hospital staff.

Nobody knew anything for certain. Alicia had an identification card that stated that she was a clerk in the council. Guta also wanted her to get a certificate stating that she was a nurse.

"I'm not a nurse," Alicia protested. "I've never worked as one. I just took a brief course."

Guta was not deterred. She went to the hospital to see Dr. Levin. The place was a madhouse. The doctor was too busy to talk to her. She insisted on seeing his assistant, Dr. Breitman; she knew that he had respected Eisig very much. But he had his hands full that day. Besides the new admissions, it was the day Dr. Kalish performed operations. Dr. Breitman told Guta that he had only a few minutes to spare and asked her to his office.

"How come Alicia has no proof that she completed the nursing course?" Guta asked.

"None of the girls have received their certificates yet. We simply did not have time to get to it. It might take a few more weeks."

Guta, however, was persistent. "I'm not leaving your office until I get a certificate for my daughter."

In order to get rid of her, he took a piece of official hospital stationery and began to write.

"Make sure," Guta said, "you mention that Alicia completed the course with an 'A.' "

He complied. It won't matter what I write, he thought. As a result,

Alicia was the only person out of about fifty girls who was a nurse on paper.

On August 19th, everyone was ordered to pack. Guta, looking at their meager possessions, tried to decide what to take and what to leave behind. She thought about Zabiec, the affluence of her childhood and her twenty-one years of marriage. It had taken hard work to make a home for a husband and children. Now she, Alicia and Henius had to leave everything behind. They had very little money and their only security was a large diamond engagement ring that Eisig had given Guta. They had no contact with Paula because Okrzejowa Street was on the other side of the ghetto.

Alicia cried. It was the first time since her father's death that she had allowed herself that luxury. Usually, she was too busy making a living and keeping her chin up. Now she cried for her father, dead at fifty-three, never to see his children grown to full maturity or to have grandchildren. She cried for her mother and aunt, widows in their forties, and for her brother, for not having had a childhood and for believing himself to be a "damn stinking Jew." She cried for Jerry, somewhere alone in Russia, and for herself and the end of her dreams. She actually had to steal not to see her family hungry. Guta consoled her daughter. "You'll make it," she said. "You have your whole life ahead of you. Remember what the fortune teller told you."

It had seemed traumatic in 1941 when they had had to leave their apartment on Freedom Square and move to the ghetto. Her father and uncle had been alive then. In retrospect, it had been no more of a problem than moving from one apartment to another. They were still in Kielce. Now they were just two women and a child. The future was unknown.

On August 20th, policemen came to their home. "Everybody, leave and report to the marketplace. Schnell, schnell, hurry up. We have many more places to go." Some tried to be polite, but most were harried and overwhelmed by their task. Others were drunk with power; over and over, they said, "Whoever is not out of this apartment on time will be shot by the Germans."

Guta, Alicia and Henius left and followed the crowds going towards the marketplace. Children were crying, women were pushing infants in carriages, old people were dragging along and those on crutches tried to keep the pace. No Germans were in sight. There were Jewish policemen all over controlling the crowds. Though it was early morning, it was already hot. People were carrying as much of their belongings as they could. They wore layers of clothes, figuring that what was on their backs could not be taken from them. Valuables were sewn into their garments, precious things that had taken them a lifetime to gather, and maybe the lifetimes of their ancestors.

The three of them walked as if they were in a dream. Guta held Henius' hand tightly, while Alicia tried to carry most of the bundles.

The August sun beat mercilessly. Everyone knew there would be a selection that would decide who stayed and who would be sent away.

When they arrived at the marketplace, they saw many German soldiers assisting the Gestapo. The Jewish policemen directed people to a selection committee composed of Germans.

Alicia trusted her mother, she remembered how she had behaved when they had crossed the border in 1939. Guta was Mark's daughter and had had similar experiences in the last war.

They came before a soldier. He was polite and sympathetic. When Guta told him that she was the wife of a physician, he pointed her and Henius to the "good" side. Alicia showed him the two pieces of paper that she had, one saying that she was a clerk and the other that she was a nurse. He glanced quickly at the papers and said, "From now on, tell everybody that you're a nurse; forget the other job." Despite her limited understanding of German, she got the message.

Alicia joined her mother and brother. She kept saying to herself that she was a nurse.

She was relieved to see most of her friends from Kielce—Mrs. Katz, Pawel and Stas, Lisa and her mother, Mrs. Koslow, Lucia and Rita, Mrs. Brazen and Bolek. As families of doctors, they were allowed to stay. The Germans did not ask if the physicians themselves were present. Mucia will have no problem during the selection on Okrzejowa Street; neither will the Blooms, Alicia thought. She didn't know about Sabina and wondered about Weinstock and his new bride; knowing him, he would escape the transport. Fryma, her sisters, parents and boyfriends, with all their money, will probably arrange something. She realized that the elderly, the weak and small children had the least chance of remaining. She watched all the people who had not made the selection move slowly towards Railroad Street.

The day before, work battalions had built tents under the supervision of the council and the police for the people who remained in Kielce.

It was already afternoon when Guta, Alicia and Henius entered their assigned tent. Rumors were circulating about what and who was left in the apartments. Gruesome stories were told by the boys returning from cleaning details. The Germans were making a sweep through ghetto apartments, shooting those who did not get out and throwing their bodies on the streets for the boys to pick up and bury. The people in the tent felt grateful that they had gotten out in time, that they were alive and had not been sent away.

It was hot and sweaty. Some people peeled off their clothing and placed them on top of their bundles. The council's kitchen helpers brought kettles of soup to the tents. Bread was distributed. Alicia forced herself to get in line, telling Guta and Henius to sit and wait for her. The people on line were patient; some even joked and laughed.

"That's us Jews," a man told Alicia. "We're used to this; joking helps us survive." Alicia didn't want to be Jewish that way; Maccabees and Zabotinsky were Jews also, she thought.

When she brought back the soup, Henius asked, "Where are we going after this?"

"Probably back to our apartment," she answered. She tried to sound matter-of-fact.

As the afternoon progressed, people became confident that things would assume a sort of normalcy. After all, the Jewish council and Jewish police were still in charge, and they were still in Kielce. Some felt that the expendable Jews had boarded the trains, and the rest would be left alone.

Doctor Sepple walked into the tent, Alicia barely recognized him. It was hard to believe that this was the same man she knew—tall, blond, debonair, joking and slapping the nurses' behinds. Now his face was ashen. He was crying and shaking. It was embarrassing to see a man in his position behave that way.

People surrounded him and asked, "What's happened? What's happened?" He kept saying, "This is the end. We are all doomed."

Alicia noticed Rachel, who was clinging to her sister Stella and crying. Alicia approached her. "What happened in the hospital?"

"Leave her alone," Stella yelled. "She's very upset and she hasn't even told me why."

Rachel wiped her tears. Looking at Alicia, she said, "I might as well tell you. Then maybe you and the others won't have any more illusions about our future."

Alicia sensed that Rachel had a terrible story to tell.

"Thomas came to the hospital," Rachel said.

Thomas, Thomas, went through Alicia's mind. He's the one who murdered my father.

Rachel continued: "He called a meeting of the staff and told us to open the hospital gates and let the patients who could walk leave and join the people in the tents. The others were to be liquidated within two hours. If we didn't comply, he told us, we'd all be dead by this afternoon. He didn't care how we did it as long as no bedridden person was left alive."

By now, a crowd had gathered around the girls. "Haven't you heard enough?" Stella screamed.

Rachel was determined to continue. "We administered lethal injections. Some people didn't respond fast enough." She was sobbing now. "We had to strangle them."

Alicia was sinking into the quicksand, only this time there was no Jerry to pull her out. She thought about the day in the hospital when she had straightened out the supply closet with Pete. "What happened to Pete?" she asked.

"Pete," Rachel said. "His upper body and hands were very strong, so he was able to strangle people easily. As usual, he was helpful."

"Is he alive?" Alicia asked.

Stella was becoming hysterical. "Stop asking her questions," she yelled.

Rachel ignored her. "Pete had to be eliminated too. He didn't want an injection. He fought. It took several people to strangle him."

"Who finally did?" Alicia asked.

"If you must know, it was Steiner."

Alicia closed her eyes. She could imagine Steiner strangling Pete. Who had held him down? Rachel, the most compassionate nurse? Anne? Anybody but Anne. What would my father and uncle have done had they been alive?

From then on the mood in the tent was grim. Nobody felt like laughing and joking any more. A woman moaned in the corner. Someone said that it was Genia Borman, an electrician's wife who was having labor pains. What a time for a baby to come into this world!

On August 21st, the policemen brought news of a selection on Okrzejowa street. People learned that many of their friends and relatives had been sent away to the unknown. Paula remained and so did the Weinstocks.

Alicia saw Mr. Bloom. What was he doing here, she wondered. She knew he didn't belong in this tent. And where were Mrs. Bloom and Leah? She tried to push her way through the crowd to talk to him. Her glasses fell and she had to crawl between peoples' legs to find them. When she finally did, one lens was cracked. It is better than nothing, she thought.

Mr. Bloom looked dejected and forlorn.

"Where is Leah?" Alicia asked.

"I lost them in the crowd," he told her. "My wife was confused and Leah wouldn't leave her. They went with many others to the trains."

This was too much. Alicia was very angry. "You have an important job," she screamed. "You certainly could have prevented their deportation."

He looked at her in desolation.

Alicia felt guilty for blaming him. Her attention was drawn to something else. Doctor Levin and Mrs. Friedman were standing around Genia, who was screaming in agony. Mrs. Friedman yelled, "Push, push," and suddenly they all heard the lusty cry of a newborn baby.

"Mazel Tov!" someone exclaimed.

The crying stopped abruptly. Genia was sobbing; her husband was speaking to her softly.

Mrs. Friedman turned around, holding a little bundle wrapped in a blanket and trying to make her way through the throng of people. Alicia blocked her way. There was unbelievable pain in the woman's eyes. She said, "I've been delivering babies for twenty-five years, all kinds of babies, boys and girls. Most of them normal and healthy. Some had defects. But I never had to do anything like this."

Alicia made a move to unfold the blanket to look at the infant.

"Don't," Mrs. Friedman told her. "I strangled him with his own umbilical cord. There's going to be another selection tomorrow. Genia, as the wife of an electrician, has a good chance of remaining, but not if she has an infant at her breast. Let me go," she told the people around her. "I'll give the bundle to my son Benjamin; he is working on a detail burying corpses, and he is very busy."

A woman with an infant has no chance, Alicia thought. Then she remembered something she had heard: Children were being sent away and mothers with children were being sent away. Alicia decided to learn more about the situation. She was surprised at her own reaction to the tragedy she had just witnessed. I'm getting numb and indifferent to human suffering. I kept going after my father's murder, so why should the death of a newborn baby make any difference? What sane Jewish woman living in Poland in 1942 would carry her pregnancy to term? I have to worry about my mother, brother and myself.

The "first family" of the ghetto, the Levys, stayed in a corner of the tent behind a curtain separating them from the rest. Lenny Levy, the power behind the throne, stood before the curtain, surrounded by people. He and Alicia had once worked together in the council and had been friendly, especially when her uncle was the president and his father a councilman. Now she managed to get close to him.

He saw her. "What happened to your glasses? Come in," he said, opening the curtain slightly.

She realized that he was using her as an excuse to get away from the others. She walked in. The little space was filled with suitcases, boxes and cartons. The "first lady" was standing in the middle, a dowdy, gray, middle-aged woman. No wonder, Alicia thought, there were so many rumors about Papa Levy's extramarital affairs.

Mrs. Levy was wringing her hands. She addressed Alicia: "How am

I going to transport all of these things to our new quarters?" She lamented, "My daughter-in-law, Rega, has disappeared someplace. I could use her help. At least she could wrap the silver so it won't tarnish."

Alicia was taken aback. "Nouveau riches" of the ghetto! For a moment she thought of her friend Fryma and her family and all their wealth. Did they remain?

Lenny was embarrassed. He tried to turn the whole scene into a joke. "She has more stuff now than she did before the war."

Alicia didn't find this funny. "I heard there will be another selection tomorrow."

"I'm tired of answering questions," Lenny said. After a while he looked Alicia straight in the eyes: "It doesn't look good."

Alicia stood there hoping he would tell her more.

He could not decide how much to confide in her. He was tired of avoiding the truth and deceiving himself and others. "Thomas told my father that he's not happy with the way things are going. There are still too many people left in Kielce, and the trains are leaving half-empty."

Thomas again. "Do you know where the trains are going?" she asked.

"I have my suspicions."

Alicia did not want to hear any more.

"If I were you, Alicia, I wouldn't wear broken glasses in front of Thomas. I wouldn't wear glasses at all."

"I've got to go to my mother," Alicia said. She made her way to their corner of the tent. Henius, uncharacteristically, was clinging to Guta. They were sitting in a part of the tent that was exclusively occupied by women and children. Mrs. Katz, Pawel and Stas, Mrs. Kozlow, Lucia and Rita were there. Sitting nearby with her little daughter Betty was Mrs. Spitz, an extremely attractive woman. Alicia had heard of her vaguely, she was an opera singer who had performed in the European capitals. In the ghetto, she had entertained patients in the hospital. There was no hospital anymore, and no patients.

Betty looked about five or six years old. She had long, blond curls and was dressed almost as beautifully as her mother. Alicia felt like hugging and kissing her.

Where was Mr. Spitz? Alicia thought. Had he already been sent to a concentration camp? Or had he left his wife and child to join a group of able-bodied men? All the children born in the Thirties, once loved and cherished, a claim to immortality, were now shunned and avoided. People were staying away. Even Mrs. Brazen and Bolek and Mrs. Zilberg and Lisa were nowhere near that corner.

The policemen and doctors were the only ones who were promised by President Levy, who got it from the mouth of Thomas himself, that they would be allowed to remain in Kielce with their wives and children.

Henius was whining, "Where is Aunt Paula?"

"She's in a different tent with the Weinstocks," Alicia improvised. They'll take good care of her." Then Henius said something that made Alicia jump. "I wish Daddy was here." It was the first time he had mentioned his father since that awful April night. Should I tell him that, after what happened in the hospital, his daddy is better off "winding safe to sea"? But she said, "I wish he were here too, but we'll manage."

"I have to go to pee," Stas said to Henius. "Do you want to come with me? Pawel will take us."

Guta was reluctant to let Henius go.

"Mother," Alicia said, "Pawel can take care of them." She was glad to see that Pawel had his smiling eyes and impish grin back. Or was it just for his mother's and brother's sake?

Once they were gone, Guta stopped pretending that everything was all right. "They're sending away all the old people, the handicapped and children."

Alicia tried to act irritated. "Ma, we've already passed the selection. Please take it easy." She hoped her mother did not detect the doubt in her voice.

"If they take Henius away from me," Guta said, "I won't go on living."

To distract her mother from her thoughts, Alicia pointed to the other side of the tent, where the relief station was located. "Look at the way those kids are running and laughing. Then she said to Mrs. Katz, "I'm glad Pawel is back to his usual self. Ever since that horrible April night I've been worried about him."

"He'll never be back to his usual self. Neither will you, Alicia," Mrs. Katz said.

Alicia had tears in her eyes. I love that obnoxious, crazy kid, she thought. She closed her eyes and saw little Pawel jumping into the pool cannonball style, splashing and making everyone laugh. Their mothers were sitting in the Stadion's restaurant, playing cards on the patio. How did all those intelligent, happy people get from the Stadion to this miserable tent? How did we lose control of our lives so completely?

The boys came back, giggling. They crouched around the women. "Cover me," Pawel said to Stas and Henius. Then, to the women, he said, "I've got something here that's worth money, people are so desperate." He produced working papers with the council's stamp. "You've got to sign your name and a photograph would help."

A sense of reality was returning to Alicia. "We are here as physicians' families. Do you think these phony documents will fool the Germans?"

"Don't forget," Pawel answered, "that our fathers are dead. Phony or not, these papers might help."

"How did you get them?" Alicia asked.

Henius and Stas giggled again. "Pawel told us to bump really hard into the guy who was selling them. The man dropped the papers and Pawel picked them up. We all ran."

After Pawel gave the papers to his mother and Guta, he distributed the extras to the other women. They were all grateful; everyone was grabbing at straws.

Mrs. Spitz hugged little Betty. "I think I'm safe as a hospital worker," she said.

To everyone's surprise, Pawel had a couple of decks of cards. "Let's play Gin Rummy before we go to sleep," he suggested. Alicia knew how much her mother loved the game, but Guta wasn't interested in cards this evening. Alicia started playing with the boys, but she couldn't concentrate. They were homeless and destitute, at the mercy of whom? Thomas? She looked at Pawel and thought again about the night when their fathers were murdered.

Her mother used to say, "We're in this with a lot of other people; we'll do what everyone else does." But this evening Guta was silent. Since her husband's death she no longer believed that following others was the thing to do. "Let's go to sleep," Alicia suggested. "We need our wits for tomorrow."

They spread some of their clothes on the floor. It was still hot and humid and they heard people talking, crying and moaning. Could tomorrow be better?

After the night came the morning. The sun rose early. Its red disk foreshadowed another hot day. Mornings come after nights for eons of time from the beginning of earth's history. Why should it be different on that August 23rd in 1942? Some natural disaster? Earthquakes were unrecorded in Kielce history but there must be some faults under the Swietokrzyski mountains. Or maybe a dust storm could block the sun and turn the morning back into the night.

It was the day of the final selection in Kielce. Once again, people gathered in the marketplace. Alicia and Pawel suspected something that they did not admit even to themselves: The families of the murdered doctors were expendable; It had been an oversight to let them remain during the previous selection.

Mrs. Zilberg and Lisa approached Thomas first. They told him that they were the family of a physician. When he learned that the man of the family was gone, he waved his hand and sent them to the side of deportation. The same thing happened to Mrs. Brazen and Bolek, Mrs. Katz, Pawel and Stas, Mrs. Kozlow, Lucia and Rita, Guta, Alicia and Henius.

Pawel's fake papers did not help. This time the jobs in the council did not matter at all. All the councilmen and clerks and their families were directed to the transport side. As expected, the Levys, the policemen and the surviving doctors were allowed to remain in Kielce with their wives and children. Most of the other men eligible to stay had to remain alone. Thomas told them that, if they wished, they could join their families for transport. Some couples stood together, but at the last moment many men changed their minds and crossed to the "good" side, leaving their wives and children.

Thomas asked the hospital staff to come forward. Nurses, orderlies, clerks, pharmacists, aides and volunteers like Mrs. Spitz stepped out. Some of them had children with them.

Suddenly, Alicia felt someone pulling her arm. It was Lucia. "Let's go, let's go!" she kept on repeating.

"Go where?" Alicia asked.

"Let's stand with the nurses."

I'm not a nurse, Alicia almost said. Then she remembered the certificate, and the voice of the German soldier came to her: "Tell everyone you're a nurse." She looked at her mother and brother, at Lucia's mother and little sister, and at all the women, children and older people. For a moment she stood there, frozen, then in a split second she realized that unless she joined the young working people, it would be an end to all her dreams—no Paris, no Sorbonne, no Palestine or America, no love. She turned to her mother. "Ma, should I go?" She saw how pale her mother's face was. She had looked that way last month when she'd fainted in the bathroom. She had never completely recovered from dysentery. Alicia heard Guta's voice. "It's your decision." Alicia had always wanted to leave home, but like this?

Henius held tight to Guta's hand. He was not afraid. He believed, like Alicia at his age, that he would always be safe in this world with his mother.

"Ma, what should I do?" Alicia repeated. But she already knew what she was going to do.

Alicia and Lucia joined the nurses, Anne, Laura and her sister Rebecca, Rachel, Irene and many other girls Alicia did not know. They looked at Alicia and Lucia as if to ask why they were there.

"Let's go back to our mothers," Lucia cried, pulling at Alicia's arm again. With all her shrewdness, she was only fifteen.

A feeling of inertia overcame Alicia. The decision to leave her mother and brother had cost her too much. She could not undo it now. "Do what you want," she told Lucia, "I'm staying." She looked at Lisa on the other side, standing with her mother. Why isn't she joining us? She worked in the hospital pharmacy. A new thought flashed through her mind. Lisa, unlike me, is staying with her mother. She was almost ready to go back and take Lucia with her. Then her eyes caught Pawel's eyes. He waved to her, gesturing to stay where she was. It was too late anyhow; Thomas was standing in front of the group.

First he called out women who had children and sent them to the transport side. Mrs. Spitz and little Betty were between them. Next he sent all the people over forty, then those between thirty and forty, and then between twenty-five and thirty. He was left with a group of boys and girls aged seventeen to twenty-five. They were all young, nice-looking and in good physical shape. Alicia became aware of her broken glasses. At this point she didn't care anymore. She no longer knew which side was good. Maybe I should be on the transport side; he might shoot all the young people.

Thomas inspected the group. There were twenty-five girls and fifteen boys. He still had more people than he needed. He directed all the girls to one side and all the boys to the other. Then he took a stick and started tapping some of the girls on the shoulder. Anne was tapped, then Laura, but not her sister Rebecca, who stood right by her side. Alicia, Lucia, Rachel and a few others, ten altogether, were tapped. The rest were sent away.

Mr. Levy was pushing Tekla to the "good side." She was a big, strong girl who had taken care of him when he had typhus. But Herr Thomas just waved his stick and said, "Raus."

Laura tried to interfere for her sister, but to no avail. It seemed to Alicia that both Mr. Levy and Laura were telling Thomas that she was not really a nurse and had no business standing there, and that Tekla and Rebecca should remain instead. Those girls had worked hard in the hospital, had cared for typhus victims, made beds, changed bedpans, taken temperatures and performed innumerable chores. They had earned the privilege of remaining in Kielce.

Herr Thomas would not be bothered. He chose ten boys the same way.

All of a sudden a woman ran up to him. It was Mrs. Spitz, and little Betty was tagging along. Mrs. Spitz spoke quickly in fluent German, desperately trying to explain something. Maybe, Alicia thought, she imagines herself on a stage, like Tosca begging for her life.

Mrs. Spitz was blond, handsome and had blue eyes. She looked positively Aryan. Thomas ogled her with amusement and appreciation.

Then he looked at the child hugging her mother's skirt. He pointed his index finger at Betty and then at the transport side. Mrs. Spitz tried to push the little girl away. "I want to stay with you, Mommy!" the child cried. "Go with the other children," the mother yelled. "I'll be with you later." She pushed her daughter hard and ran to the Kielce side.

The boys and girls chosen by Thomas were now surrounded by the Jewish police. The great majority of the Jews of Kielce began the torturous walk towards the railroad.

Alicia saw her mother in the distance. She was holding Henius by the hand and following the crowd. Alicia tried to cry, but the tears would not come. My mother must be exhausted, she thought, frightened and thirsty. Maybe Henius is beginning to see that everything may not turn out all right. Alicia did not know what was in store for the people who remained, but there was a feeling that it did not matter, that nothing mattered anymore. There was a nagging thought in the back of her mind, Is my mother angry at me?

Thomas reviewed the scene, those who were leaving and those who were staying. He swirled his cane and it seemed to Alicia that he was gloating over his great achievement, like Napoleon at Austerlitz after a triumph over a great Austrian army. Only this was a victory over thousands and thousands of helpless people.

Thomas left with his entourage and a policeman whispered that he was going to another selection on Okrzejowa Street.

After an hour, Alicia noticed Aron walking, downcast and exhausted. She ran to him. "Aron," she said, "what happened on Okrzejowa Street?" She hoped against hope that Paula remained. Paula looked at least as good as Mrs. Spitz, and she didn't have a child with her. Her Mucia was the most beautiful, most intelligent and wittiest person she knew; she could talk or flirt her way out of any predicament.

Aron looked as bad as he had the morning after Eisig's murder. "It was worse than here," he said. "Thomas was tired and irritated; he sent almost everyone away."

"My Aunt Paula?"

Aron pointed to Railroad Street.

"Weinstocks?" Alicia asked.

"Yes. Together with my parents, two sisters and three brothers," he answered. "I'm going to resign. I don't want to be a policeman any more. At least I saved my wife," he added after a while.

Alicia thought of all her other friends. Leah had been sent away yesterday. She asked Aron about Sabina, Fryma and other girls from her old class at Mrs. Zima's. He told her that they had all been deported with their families.

Aron called Alicia to the side and handed her a sealed envelope. "Hide it," he told her. "I don't know what's in it, your Aunt Paula gave it to me."

"Did you see my mother and brother?"

"I saw them," he said. "Your mother and brother met with your aunt at the station". Aron didn't feel like saying any more.

Alicia kept talking. "They must have been thirsty and heat-prostrated. My mother didn't feel well today."

"Like everyone else," Aron answered. "Some people were trading jewelry for a glass of water."

"Did you give my mother and Henius water?"

"I tried my best."

Did my mother trade her diamond ring for a glass of water for Henius? Alicia wondered. Did a Pole or a Jewish policeman take the diamond and then not give them the water? They boarded those horrible trains while I, Alicia, an ungainly klutz, as Jas used to call me, who sometimes walks in a dream, remained.

Jankiel, a shoemaker by trade who now worked as a grave digger, passed by. He looked at Alicia standing there dejected, with broken glasses on her nose. He was talking to Aron in Yiddish. He pointed to Alicia. "Look whom Thomas smelled out. What a nose! He sent away so many beautiful, able people, but he tapped her on the shoulder."

Aron hoped that Alicia didn't understand.

A mean smirk curled Jankiel's lips. He switched to Polish to speak to her. "Hey, princess," he said, "I buried your father a few months ago. His eyes were bulging and his pants were full of shit."

Aron began to scream, "You brutish, vile man. Haven't we all suffered enough? Go away or I'll beat you up."

"Thank you, Aron," Alicia said. "Now go to your wife."

Policemen were lugging suitcases, picking up what was left behind by people who could not carry all their possessions. Alicia was flabbergasted to see two of them fight over a piece of expensive luggage. Her lethargy gave way to disgust. How can they think about suitcases after what happened? Then she wondered what Pawel would say. Pawel had become a man lately, more than that heartthrob Bolek was. Liza could have Bolek. She felt almost a physical stab of pain in her chest, realizing that all her friends were gone and that she'd never told Pawel that she loved him.

She had only what was on her back. Guta had their suitcase. I should be with her, helping to carry all the bundles, she thought. Guta had the cash and the diamond. My mother didn't expect me to leave her. She has Henius to think of. She wondered what was in the envelope Aron had given her, and she placed it inside her brassiere. It's from my Aunt Paula, I'll keep it until the day I die or until I meet my Mucia again.

Alicia looked at the other girls. Even at that horrible time there was comradeship between Anne, Laura and Irene, as well as the few remaining nurses' aides. They were taking care of each other. She felt like an unwelcome outsider, resented because she had taken the place of a legitimate nurse.

Lucia was talking to a policeman. She seemed overwrought. Rachel hugged her sister, who had remained as the wife of a policeman. Both girls were crying. They were a rare exception, their tears were tears of joy. The girls' parents were there with them. It seemed like a miracle that an entire family had somehow managed to remain.

Laura was speaking to Dr. Steiner. Alicia closed her eyes. He strangled Pete, she thought. She approached them. "Did your mother and sister remain?" she asked the doctor. She knew how much effort it had taken to get them to Kielce, the best ghetto in Poland.

Laura's expression said, "butt out."

Alicia regretted having asked the question.

The doctor answered, "I didn't think fast enough. I should have claimed my sister as my wife. I could at least have saved her." After a while he added, "I don't know if Debbie would have wanted to leave her mother."

Leave her mother, leave her mother, buzzed through Alicia's mind. Save Debbie. He just assumed that those sent away had no chance.

Benjamin Friedman was speaking to Anne. He was stocky and well-built, and, like most Jewish boys, shorter than Alicia. He probably doesn't like me, she thought. I was never friendly with boys from the Jewish gymnasium. To him I'm a deposed princess who doesn't even speak Yiddish. She approached him anyhow. "What happened to your mother?"

To her surprise he was friendly. "My mother went with the transport. She was too old to remain as a hospital worker."

Alicia could not erase the image of Mrs. Friedman running through the tent with a dead infant. "And Genia?" she asked Anne.

Anne was annoyed with Alicia, but she was too tired to be nasty. "You probably know that Genia was running a high fever during the selection, but Thomas mistook her redness for a sign of health. He let her stay in Kielce with her husband. It's ironic that Mrs. Friedman was sent away while Genia, her patient, with a postpartum infection, remained."

It's a good thing, Alicia thought, that he didn't have an X-ray of Lucia's heart. She noticed Mrs. Spitz. The glow and smile were gone. Instead, there was a vacant and empty expression.

Slowly, the extent of the devastation was sinking in. Everyone she had ever loved or respected was dead, resettled east or far away. She was left with people like Anne, who thought she shouldn't be there. Jankiel was crude enough to express it in words, but most people probably felt that way. Maybe those policemen are grabbing suitcases because they have wives and children to think about. I have nothing and nobody. The only connections to her past were doctors and their families, especially the two older ones, Levin and Perlstein, and the two dentists, Buchhalter and Grauer, and their grown children.

It was late in the afternoon when all the policemen finally returned from the railroad station. It was time to take the eight hundred remaining people to their quarters. Few streets in the corner of the old ghetto were assigned to them. From then on this part of the town would be called

"Jewish Quarters." Lenny came over to the group of young hospital workers. He told them that they would live in a house that would serve as a hospital for factory workers.

Anne laughed. "Do you need twenty people, Lenny?"

"I wouldn't be asking questions if I were you," he answered.

Then Alicia yelled, "Do you know where the trains are going?"

Lenny pointed his finger heavenwards and left.

As they started walking Alicia noticed Greta crying and shaking, barely able to move. "Where are your parents?" she asked.

"I remained with my father but I don't know where he is now. My mother got lost in the crowd."

Poor Mrs. Levin, just like Mrs. Bloom. They both could have stayed with their husbands, Alicia thought. She remembered how she used to help Greta step off the curb to cross the street. "Hold onto me" she now said, "we'll go together to our new quarters and we'll find your father." Greta leaned heavily on Alicia.

On August 23rd, 1942 the Germans attacked Stalingrad and the Americans won their first land battle against Japan. The Germans needed 300,000 men to attack Stalingrad, and had to use many trains for transportation.

Somehow they managed to find enough resources for the liquidation of the Kielce ghetto. In three days the Gestapo had achieved victory: The patients in the Jewish hospital were killed by their own doctors; over 29,000 men, women and children, some in their prime, some elderly and infants, were put in sealed box cars in 95 degree heat without water, food or the most rudimentary sanitary conditions. Herr Thomas thanked the president of the Jewish Council, Mr. Levy, the chief of Jewish police, Mr. Spiegel and the director of the hospital, Dr. Levin, for helping organize the great operation. As a reward, Mr. Levy, all the policemen and the doctors remained in Kielce with their wives and children.

CHAPTER 10

Doctor Levin awaited his staff in front of the house that was to become the hospital in the new Jewish Quarters. He was getting on in years after practicing medicine for almost half a century. He had always envied his neighbor, Dr. Peltz, for his reputation and the respect he commanded in the profession. He had envied the Strums their tall, blond, bright daughter who, unlike his poor Greta, could ski, skate, swim and play tennis. Once he had led the ill-conceived boycott of the two doctors. Now, the whole thing seemed insignificant. He almost wished that, like Peltz and Strum, he weren't here any more. It was ironic that only after Peltz's death had he become the director of the hospital. Once it had employed 200 people; now he was waiting for 20 and he didn't know why he needed so many for the remaining population. Where was Greta? She was with him during the selection, but then he had lost her in the crowd. And his wife? She was old before her time, but he still loved her. There had been other women, his patients, nurses, he also had a long standing affair with his co-worker, the mid wife Mrs. Friedman. They were gone now. His wife could have avoided deportation, like all the other living doctors' wives. Poor old woman. In all the confusion, she didn't know what was going on. He was getting frantic about Greta; she was all he had left. Then he saw the hospital workers walking towards him and there she was, holding onto Alicia. He ran to them. Thanking Alicia profusely, he hugged his daughter.

"Mommy, mommy," Greta cried.

Doctor Levin tried to comfort her. "She is in another camp," he told her. "We'll find her after the war."

Alicia watched them. Did he really believe what he said? She couldn't stop thinking of Lenny pointing heavenwards when asked where the trains were going. An empty feeling in the pit of her stomach prevented further speculation. She realized how hungry she was.

218

Benjamin Friedman approached her and gave her a piece of bread and butter. "My mother liked you very much," he said.

Someone was looking at her. It was Anne. Oh my God, she thought, now Anne will have one more reason to hate me. I bet Benjamin is her boyfriend.

Doctor Levin took charge. "We have to organize," he said wearily. "Anne, how many nurses do we have?"

Anne answered, "There are four of us: me, Laura, Irene and Rachel. Rachel isn't here, she's with her parents. Ruth and Fanny served as aides. The rest," she glanced at Lucia and Alicia and waved her hand.

Doctor Levin said to Anne, "Let's go inside and look the place over." He turned to Alicia. "Take care of Greta for me for a few more minutes."

The group waited. Then the doctor and his chief nurse came out and described the situation. "Tomorrow," Anne said, "the boys, along with some policemen, will bring beds, blankets and other things from the abandoned apartments. There is one big room downstairs which we will convert into a hospital ward. We have a sizable kitchen and a few smaller rooms that the aides will use. The room upstairs will be used by the nurses."

Alicia wondered where Anne was going to put her.

They spent the first night in the room downstairs, lying on old blankets. Some cried, others whined; a few sang old Yiddish songs.

After two days, Anne assigned Alicia and Lucia to a small place in the attic with a narrow bunk bed beneath a small, dusty window. At least it was cooler there than in the other rooms.

The boys moved out and got jobs either in the Quarters or in one of the two factories.

Food was available for money. The policemen had passes to the old ghetto and even to the city proper, and that meant that their families would be well fed. The next most privileged class was the ex-policemen, some of whom, like Aron, had resigned as a matter of conscience, the others of necessity—far fewer were needed now than in the original ghetto. Gentiles would come to the fences, selling things discreetly.

Alicia had no money and she was hungry. She had found out what was in the envelope that Aron had handed to her. It was a beautiful diamond necklace. She hoped she wouldn't have to trade it for a bowl of soup or a few potatoes.

She was often sent, in a work detail, outside the Quarters to office buildings in the city. The Jewish policemen were in charge. One day, gentile boys were working in the building. Sonia, a well-developed teenager, and Alicia were assigned to wash windows. Sonia disappeared. Alicia went to look for her and found her fooling around with the boys in the attic. The policemen followed Alicia and the gossip started.

When they went home, they told their wives that Alicia slept with all the "goys." They didn't mention Sonia, who was notoriously promiscuous. Alicia was at a point where she didn't care. It's not enough that I have nothing to eat and only one dress to wear; now I'm also considered a whore, she thought.

One afternoon after work, Alicia and Lucia sat on a stone in back of an abandoned house. Once the yard had served as a vegetable garden; now it was overgrown with weeds. Lucia, though younger than Alicia, was managing somewhat better. But that afternoon, neither of them felt like doing anything. Lucia complained of the pain in her heart.

What a choice Thomas made, Alicia thought; Lucia, with a history of rheumatic heart disease, and me with my broken glasses. She put her head down in her arms and brooded: If only the earth were flat, I would walk to the edge and jump into the void; if the force of gravity didn't pull me to the center, I'd just float away—from Poland, the Germans, the Jewish Quarters, the Jewish police and the Council. Damn, Issac Newton. Then she realized that the war would end eventually, she wanted to be here to witness it, not floating around someplace. Though, deep inside, she doubted that she would ever see her mother, Mucia and her brother again, there was still some hope left.

She said, "Lucia, let's try to think logically. We can't survive without help. The Jewish policemen and their families are not our friends and neither are the nurses. Our only hope is the doctors. They were our fathers' colleagues. Doctor Levin was very grateful when I helped Greta after the deportation. Doctor Perlstein was once my father's and uncle's friend and partner. I'm sure they still eat regular meals. We could suggest that they ask us to dinner."

The girls got themselves invited to the Grauers. Papa Grauer was a dentist. When the Germans specified "doctors," they didn't bother to find out who was in the hospital that fatal afternoon in August. They didn't differentiate between medical doctors and dentists. The Grauers were an intact family, with a mother, a father, a son, Abe, and a daughter, Lina. Abe was in his late twenties; he was a dentist like his father, pleasant and uncomplicated. Lina was a couple of years younger, a dark, heavy-set girl who, after getting her Matura at Mrs. Zima's, just floundered around without much to do. Alicia liked both of them.

"Why don't you go to the Perlsteins?" Lina suggested to Alicia. "Mrs. Perlstein has a lot of clothes and I'm sure she could spare some."

Abe joked, "Mrs. Perlstein probably managed to get all her rags out of the ghetto."

The next day, Alicia visited the Perlsteins. Swallowing her pride, she asked Mrs. Perlstein point blank if she could spare any dresses.

"Yes, I have some that will fit you. I can sell them to you at a reasonable price."

Her husband had a hard time persuading her to just give the clothes to Alicia.

During the following week Alicia had more opportunities to get clothes. She and Lucia, along with other women, went to a storeroom outside the Quarters to sort clothes left over after the deportation. The room was supervised by a German, Herr Wirtz. While the girls worked, they discreetly stuffed whatever they could into their underwear.

Mr. Wirtz liked women and, like most Germans, was intrigued by blond, blue-eyed Jewesses. Gretchen suited his taste perfectly, especially since she was a German Jew.

The other women watched the two of them talking, laughing and joking. He seemed to be falling for her.

One day Gretchen found a beautiful dress. She put it on and modeled it for Wirtz. At first, he seemed amused. But suddenly he grew red in the face and started screaming, "You damned Jew! How dare you take a dress without my permission?" He pulled out a gun and shot Gretchen on the spot. Her guts spilled all over the floor, Wirtz ordered some girls to clean up the mess.

Alicia put her hand over Lucia's eyes and said, "Don't look. Let's try to get out of here alive." They were panic-stricken. When they got back to the Quarters, they sighed with relief because they had not been searched. Looking for rags had lost its allure.

That afternoon Alicia found Fanny, an industrious girl, who served as an aide in the big hospital of the ghetto. Now she was tearing a dress, kissing it and sobbing. Alicia noticed that it was blood-stained. "It was my mother's," Fanny said.

Alicia closed her eyes. God, she thought, if only I could close my mind to reality, the way Henius did after they murdered our father, maybe I would be able to go on. Henius, Henius; where is he?

Fanny looked at Alicia through her tears. "I see you got a few decent dresses," she said. "Some need fixing; I could do it for you."

Alicia knew that Fanny was handy with a needle. She sewed for Mrs. Levy and Mrs. Spiegel and other policemen's wives. How can she think about helping me after finding her mother's dress? Alicia put her arms around Fanny and kissed her.

Doctor Levin used his influence to get Alicia a job in the kitchen, where women cooked large kettles of thin soup for the returning factory workers. In the morning they peeled potatoes. Most of them were experts, able to peel only the skin, leaving the entire vegetable underneath. Alicia had never peeled a potato in her life. "Why bother?" she would say. "We should just scrub them well; most of the vitamins are right under the skin." She remembered the fall in Zabiec when she, Jas and Jerry had watched the peasant boys roast potatoes in an open fire. They ate them, skins and all.

The little hospital was slowly filling up with sick and injured factory workers. They suffered from broken bones, infected boils, wounds and fevers. There were plenty of doctors available to serve the population of the Jewish Quarters. Anne, Laura and Irene worked as nurses; Ruth was the housekeeper for the Levys; Fanny was the resident seamstress; Lucia worked in the office and Alicia in the kitchen.

At night, Alicia and Lucia tried to sleep on the narrow bunk in the attic. They listened to the sound of distant trains. Whom are those trains transporting, and for what reason? They didn't dare to voice their thoughts: Did our people reach their destination alive or did they die of heat and dehydration? Or were they shot by guards? Did Henius and Rita stay with their mothers or were they separated? Many nights the girls cried themselves to sleep.

As time went on they realized that, though their whole world was gone, they could not simply get off. The earth kept rotating, and spinning, the sun rose and set, day followed night, fall followed summer, and when winter came, if they were still alive, they would need food and clothes. My mother got me a nurse's certificate, Alicia thought, and my aunt sent me the necklace from the station. The least I can do is put up a fight.

By the middle of September, Alicia felt better. The girls in the hospital had begun to accept her. All of them were in the same boat. What mattered most to Alicia was that Anne did not resent her as much as before. Anne had assumed the role of mother to the girls living in the hospital and, though Laura was her favorite, Alicia was a member of her brood. Alicia felt that she and Anne would eventually become friends.

On some evenings the girls had visitors, Abe and Lina Grauer, Janka Buchhalter with her boyfriend, Dr. Sepple and Dr. Steiner, Benjamin and his friend Ira and Lucia's boyfriend Joseph.

Everyone brought something to eat. Alicia and Laura would laugh at how men, before the war, had brought flowers and chocolate to girls; now it was black bread and potatoes. It was a luxury when they had kielbasa and sardines.

It was becoming more and more obvious that Dr. Sepple and Irene were in love. It was taken for granted that Dr. Steiner was interested in Laura, though no one could be sure about Steiner. Then it was Anne and Benjamin and Abe and Alicia.

Alicia put her cracked glasses away. She didn't need them in the small room. Abe complimented her on how much better she looked than she had right after the deportation. They danced to old records, talked and laughed.

Sometimes, when the men left, Anne and Alicia talked late into the night. Anne would say, "We're on a sinking ship, but we're young, so let's try to have fun."

Alicia told Anne all about herself. She even showed her the necklace and confided about Mr. X. Anne was closed-mouthed about her own life. Alicia noticed that there was still a lot of hostility between Anne and Dr. Sepple. She wanted to know the details of what had happened in 1940. Anne didn't have much luck with men, Alicia thought. Benjamin had roving eyes, especially for beautiful Laura, who was only interested in her doctor.

Anne seemed satisfied. "We'll always remember this as a carefree time. Our families are gone and all we have to worry about is each other."

The original group of girls became smaller. First Lucia moved out and joined Joseph. He was twenty years her senior, a nice, gentle man who had owned a small factory before the war. Now he was managing it for the Germans. He had a pass to the city and therefore access to food. Lucia was well taken care of.

Irene and Dr. Sepple decided to get married. It was impossible to legalize a union. All the rabbis and justices of the peace had been deported. But the group in the hospital had an excuse for a party. Benjamin assumed the role of rabbi. They broke a glass, stepped on it and yelled "Mazel Tov!" Irene had a bouquet of flowers and threw it into the air. Laura caught it. Everyone laughed and kidded Steiner, who seemed embarrassed.

Alicia moved to the big room. There were two beds; one was occupied by Anne and Laura and Alicia shared the other one with Ruth. Ruth was a big, buxom, friendly girl. "She looks like 'Mother Earth' " Alicia said to Anne.

Anne laughed. "She certainly is generous like Mother Earth. I wonder who she's sleeping with, Papa Levy or the son. Alicia didn't want to speculate. She liked Ruth.

In the evenings Alicia helped Anne distribute the evening snacks and medication in the ward. Many boys needed sleeping pills, which were scarce, like everything else. Some of them had worked during the deportation, burying the bodies of people who had been shot because they hadn't left their apartments on time or were unable to make the trains. They didn't want to talk about it, but they couldn't stop the nightmares. During the waking hours, they reminisced about the past.

In the factories the Jews were in contact with Poles who listened to the BBC. The word was that the Germans were being stopped at Stalingrad. There was also good news about the African campaign.

Stalingrad is so far away, Alicia thought. How long will it take for the Germans to get out of Russia and Poland? Who cares about Africa? We'll all be dead before anything happens.

Alicia was especially friendly with two of the boys in the ward. One was Andrew, a short and skinny fellow, whose mother and younger brother were deported last August. He had uncles and aunts in the United States. He studied English before the war and expected to go to America after gymnasium. Now he had a bad case of bronchitis.

Alicia recited English and Polish poetry to him; she kept on repeating her favorite English poem about "Weariest river, that winds up safe to sea." Anne sometimes listened to their conversations. "How come you know English and Polish poetry by heart," she asked Alicia, "but you wouldn't learn to speak German?"

The "princess" doesn't want to speak Yiddish either," the boys kidded.

"I wouldn't want to live in a world where German is necessary. The Germans wouldn't let me live in it anyway," Alicia answered.

"But right now," Anne said, "it would be so much easier for you if you could communicate with the people in charge."

Alicia ignored her remark. "I don't speak Yiddish, because I never liked the language. My parents and grandparents spoke it if they didn't want us children to understand what was going on. I know the Hebrew alphabet and I can speak a little Hebrew."

"So the princess admits that she is Jewish," the boys kidded her.

Saul was another patient Alicia had befriended. He had a multiple fracture of one leg and was lying in traction. He was working in Henrykow when he had an accident. The man on duty in the emergency room was the medic, Rutkowsky. He set Saul's leg improperly.

Anne screamed at Saul, "From all the doctors, you had to have that idiot set your leg."

Saul was an idealist, a utopian socialist, his dream was to go to Eretz Israel and live on a kibbutz.

Alicia didn't feel alone anymore; she had friends.

The cold weather was setting in fast. Alicia didn't have a warm coat, boots, or a sweater.

Ruth, through her job, knew what was going on in the ruling circles. She told Alicia to go to the storeroom and look for winter clothes that fit her.

Anne said, "The Germans couldn't move everything that was left in the old ghetto, so they very generously gave some stuff to the Jewish workers. Now our policemen are in charge of the storeroom."

"You might get something," Ruth told Alicia, "after the policemen's wives take their pick."

The man in charge of the storeroom was policeman Rudek, a dark, stocky man in his early thirties. Since his wife was President Levy's cousin, he had a lot of influence in the Quarters. Alicia didn't like or trust him. She stated her business right away.

He tried to make conversation. "You look a lot like my wife—tall, blond. Even with glasses you are quite attractive."

She didn't pay any attention to him. She stared at the piles and piles of clothes and household goods and thought about the people who had once worn these coats and dresses, used the pots and pans and slept on the sheets.

"What will I get from you for letting you look for things you need?" Rudek asked.

She came out of her reverie. "I was under the impression," she said, "that everything in this storeroom is supposed to be distributed free to the people in the Quarters."

"But," he said, "the way I heard you've been behaving, we could do it right here between the sheets."

She was still too amazed to respond. Then it dawned on her that he expected to fornicate with her for a coat.

"Unless," he said, "the rumors about you are not true, and you are a virgin. I would not want to be first." He thought he was being fair and decent.

Alicia almost burst out with laughter. "It's none of your damn business," she said, "if I am a virgin or not. Even if I would like to sleep around, you would be the last person on earth I would sleep with. I wouldn't let you touch me."

Rudek tried to come closer. Alicia moved behind a carton and he realized that she wouldn't hesitate to throw it at him. He decided to turn the whole thing into a joke. Alicia found a winter coat and, without even a "thank you," left the storeroom.

When Alicia returned, she told the story to Anne. Anne said, "Well, at least you got a warm coat and it doesn't need a lot of fixing. But how long can you walk around with a cracked lens? A piece of glass could get in your eye and you'd be in serious trouble."

"What do you expect me to do? Even if we had an optician in the Quarters, I have no money to get a new lens."

"Ask a policeman to get them fixed in the city," Anne answered. "Don't worry about money; we'll all contribute."

Alicia was surprised. Maybe, she thought, Anne likes me after all. I'm not sorry I showed her the necklace and told her about Mr. X.

Anne seemed to guess her thoughts. She said, "You'd better get hold of some money. Either sell the necklace or get in touch with your father's ex-patient."

She's right, Alicia thought; I can't subsist on soup and potatoes or depend forever on dinners at the doctors'. She said, "Mr. X lives on the other side of the city; nobody gets a pass to go that far. I have no way of getting in touch with him and I'd rather keep my aunt's necklace." She thought for a moment and then said, "Maybe nothing matters anymore."

Anne was getting angry now. "Look," she said, "I didn't ask you to leave your mother and brother and stand with us. I didn't ask Thomas to tap you; I had better candidates for him. But since all that happened, I feel responsible for you and you'd better shape up."

"Don't you have any feelings? " Alicia asked.

All of a sudden, Anne started sobbing. "I couldn't get my sister and her two babies out of my mind all day."

The next day, Alicia approached Goldberg. She asked him if he would go to an optician in the city to have her lens replaced. He took her glasses and returned them the following day. Alicia asked him how much it had cost.

"Forget it," he said. "I'm glad I could be of help. I knew your parents well. I knew your uncle and aunt and the whole family, and it's the least I can do for you."

Somebody remembers where I come from, she thought. Once I was known as the daughter of a prominent family, not as a destitute orphan. There will always be a piece of home in Kielce.

Alicia had clothes and her glasses were fixed. My mother would be proud of how well I manage, she thought. Paula and Guta often talked about how well they had managed during the Great War. Where were they managing now? She thought about Rowne and Lwow, and wondered again why they hadn't gone to Russia or any other place outside German occupied Europe.

Anne was right; she needed money. She remembered Tadek Wronski visiting Aunt Paula in the big ghetto and she knew his address in the city. If I could only get in touch with him, she thought, I'm sure he could find Mr. X and tell him to sell a few things to get me cash.

Tadek did not live very far from the Jewish Quarters. Alicia was ready to sneak out without a pass, without the band, and go to see him. There was a death penalty for leaving the Quarters without proper authorization.

One day, while she was still weighing her decision, she met Mr. Bloom. He looked at her with tears in his eyes. Alicia started to cry herself. Mr. Bloom said, "Leah was just following her mother."

"I left my mother and brother." She was overcome by grief.

Mr. Bloom still went to work every morning to Kadzielnia. "Can I do anything for you, Alicia?" he asked. "May I help?"

"Can you deliver a message for me? It's not far from here, on Wesola Street. It has to be delivered directly to Tadek Wronski; if he's not there you have to try another day."

"I'll try," he said, "but don't write anything down. Whatever your message is, I'll memorize it."

Alicia gave Mr. Bloom the addresses of both Tadek and Mr. X. She explained her plan of getting money with Tadek's help.

A couple of weeks after the conversation, Mr. Bloom told Alicia that Tadek had visited him in Kadzielnia and was holding money for her in his house. Mr. Bloom was reluctant to carry the money himself, he could be searched. Tadek was afraid to come to the fence of the Quarters. Now it was up to Alicia to get her money. Tadek left a message with Mr. Bloom telling which morning he would wait for her in his apartment. She was instructed to knock three times, pause and knock four more times.

The next morning, Alicia told Anne and Benjamin of her plans. It would not be easy. In the morning, the people who worked outside the Quarters were counted at the gate by the policemen and escorted directly to their destination. When they came back, they were counted again.

"If they see you and let you out, they will figure that you are bringing something back," Benjamin said. "They will follow you and take it away. Since getting out without a pass is illegal in the first place, if you complained to Levy, he would side with the policemen."

"Not all of them would do that," Alicia said. "I think Goldberg is a decent man and Aron brought me the necklace from the station."

"Aron brought her necklace." Anne laughed. You're too naive for your own good, princess."

Why is she calling me princess again? Everytime I consider her my friend, she has to say something to remind me of the gulf between us; a working, life-experienced woman who's been around and a princess.

Benjamin was kinder. "Don't you see, you don't know what else your aunt gave Aron at the railroad station. It was still decent of him to have given you the necklace. He could have taken everything. By the way, have you seen Aron lately?"

"I know he resigned as a policeman," she said. "Now that I think about it, he hasn't been around."

Benjamin said, "He vanished into thin air; he and his wife are probably living someplace on Aryan papers. Do you know how much money it takes to purchase false documents and establish a residence outside the ghetto?"

"I don't believe Aron stole my aunt's jewelry." She didn't dare to hope that she would ever see her Mucia again and learn the answer. "Anyway, now I trust Mr. X, Tadek and, of course, Mr. Bloom."

Benjamin laughed. "What choice do you have? You even have to trust me, Ira and Anne."

They agreed on a plan. Benjamin knew about an unguarded hole in the fence. "Let's hope," he said, "that nobody notices you sneaking out. It shouldn't take you more than an hour back and forth from Wesola Street. Either Ira or I will wait for you and we'll walk home together."

Alicia asked, "Won't they miss me at work?"

"I'll tell them you're sick," Anne offered.

"Do you really think I have to be that careful with the policemen? We're all more or less in the same position."

Benjamin said, "They think they are less. Besides, most of them are the scum of the earth. There were never many Jewish criminals, but the Germans found them all. They shipped them to Kielce and made them policemen. No wonder, Chief Spiegel is called a Jewish Gestapo man. Even Levy is afraid of him.

Alicia's thoughts were on her escapade. "If I get my money, I'll have to hide it. I can't carry it on me when I go to work."

"Don't worry about it. Just get it first," Anne said.

"We'll put it with my gun," Benjamin said. "They'll have to deal with that before they get to your money."

Alicia was not surprised that Benjamin had a gun.

Anne said to Benjamin, "You talk too much."

Benjamin ignored her and kept talking to Alicia. "It's a good idea to go in the morning, when there are a lot of people on the street going to work. Blend in with the crowd, keep your chin up, walk fast but don't run."

"Don't dream," Anne said. "Just attend to your business and get back as soon as you can."

On the agreed-upon morning, Alicia sneaked out through a small opening in the fence. In a few minutes she was in the old Kielce, out of the Jewish Quarters and past the streets that encompassed the old ghetto. She was almost ready to go to the apartment on Freedom Place and there would be her father and mother and little Henius waiting, or she would visit Sabina on Sienkiewicz street.

Freedom Place was now "Goebbel's Platz." Her father had been murdered. Railroad Street, where she used to walk back and forth from school, was also the place where her people had walked last August to the trains. Then, in her mind, she heard Anne's voice: "Don't dream, just tend to your business."

No one paid attention to her. She did not see many Germans. She turned off the main street onto a narrow side street. What if someone recognized her? Finally, there it was: Wesola 68. Alicia walked in. It seemed as if she had to climb the winding staircase forever. She knocked on the door of the attic: One, two, three. One, two, three, four. The door opened and there stood Tadek, the same Tadek, his face covered with pimples. Alicia threw her arms around him and kissed him. "I mustn't cry," she said.

"Sit down." He offered her some food.

It was a tiny, dark room with a single bunk, very neat. Alicia wondered where Tadek's parents were and why he was living alone. What did he do for a living?

He told her immediately not to ask him too many questions.

Alicia was always ready to eat. They had bread and sardines. Tadek insisted that she take a few cans home with her.

"But you probably don't have enough for yourself," she said. "I'm eating like a pig."

"Don't worry," he said. "Let's hope that the next time we meet, it will be under better circumstances."

She said, "It would take a miracle for the war to end soon. It looks like a long haul. Did you take a day off from work on account of me?"

"I had to take a day off anyhow. I had some things to take care of."

I'd better not ask what "things," she thought.

Tadek had a sizable sum for her. He told her that Mr. X had followed her instructions, but he advised her to postpone selling the more valuable items. "Maybe he can strike a better deal later on. Right now, with all the things the Jews left behind, everything is cheap. That guy loved your father and he'll do anything for you."

Alicia said, "He shouldn't sell too much; some things should be left for after the war for my mother and brother." She said it to test his reaction. She knew that he was well informed. She noticed that he was surprised and pretended not to hear her. He knows, she thought, that there will not be an "after the war" for the people who were deported. First Lenny and now Tadek.

Tadek quickly said, "Jerry will make it in Russia and so will Jas in Palestine."

"Some of my Lublin cousins are also in Russia." She thought about Frania with her sister and brother and Beryl and his wife. She was almost sure that Frania and Beryl were members of the Communist Party; they should like it in Russia. What about those who remained in Lublin—Aunt Yentl, Aunt Luba and her husband? Aunt Sura had been deported from Kielce; she and her husband, together with the people from the Jewish home for the aged and the children from the orphanage. And in Krakow Grandfather Mark and his wife? Alicia knew that Wladek had served in the Polish army shortly before the outbreak of the war; was he alive now? And Eda? Did she escape the Germans by being deported by the Russians? Alicia asked Tadek if he knew what had happened to the Jews of Lublin and Krakow.

Tadek hesitated. Then he said, "As far as I know, all the ghettos are being liquidated."

Alicia was overwhelmed by that word. "What does liquidation mean; where are they putting all those people?"

"I wish I could tell you," he answered.

Alicia thought, he knows but he doesn't want to tell me and I won't press him. She kissed him again. "Goodbye, pal. Take care of yourself, get yourself a girlfriend and avoid trouble."

She stuffed the money into her brassiere and walked back to the Jewish Quarters. She found the hole in the fence. Ira was waiting for her.

"Mission accomplished," she said. She kissed Ira. I'm in a kissing mood, she thought. Ira was a nice-looking boy, but Alicia did not feel any special attraction to him. All she knew about him was that he was Benjamin's friend and that whatever Benjamin was into, he was in it also.

After she kissed him, Ira's face became all red. He told her that Benjamin had to go to the factory, but he had an inside job this week fixing Mr. Levy's apartment. He used his lunch break to meet Alicia. As they were walking, Birnbaum, a policeman and a refugee from Lodz, passed them and started to yell at them in Yiddish. Ira yelled back at him and told Alicia to go home; he would take care of Birnbaum.

She did. The money was safe. She had regained some of her faith in humanity, and she wasn't indigent anymore.

Alicia was still peeling potatoes and scrubbing pots and pans in the main kitchen. One afternoon she was returning from work to the hospital. She felt lucky because her pockets were filled with boiled potatoes and carrots. There was something else on Alicia's mind; the women in the kitchen were talking. They had heard from someone who had heard from someone else, that letters had been received from "our people," resettled east. They wrote that they were doing fine. Alicia wondered if she should believe those stories.

She was deep in thought when someone bumped into her and said her name. She raised her eyes and saw a ragged, unkempt young man. All the beggars have been deported, she thought. In our new quarters, only policemen and workers walk the streets.

"Alicia," he repeated.

Where have I heard that voice? She could not believe her eyes. "Pawel!" she shouted. She didn't know whether to laugh or cry with joy. For a second, she had an illusion: If he's here, everybody will be back—my mother, Mucia, Henius and on and on. . . . "Pawel, how come you are here and where have you come from?" Filthy as he was, she was ready to kiss him.

"I ran away from Treblinka," he said.

Somehow Alicia knew that kissing would not be appropriate. She had never heard of Treblinka. "What's there?" she asked.

"Gas chambers and crematoria," he answered.

She didn't grasp the meaning of this. "Gas chambers and crematoria?"

"They are for people, Alicia, to gas them and incinerate their bodies. No work camps in the east!"

Alicia was sinking into the quicksand, but to her surprise the earth remained firm under her feet. If I could only block out this nightmare and be back in the normal world.

"As soon as we got off the train," he told her, "they pulled out a group of tall, husky boys to work in the Special Squad."

"Our mothers? The children?"

"Don't ask me!" he screamed. "They're all gone. Do you want the details?"

"Did they suffer? Were they afraid?"

"They thought they were going for a shower. But instead of water, a poisonous gas came out of the faucet. I hope they died fast. Try not to think about it. They are all dead, they are not suffering anymore, they are ashes. It is final. You are alive."

In spite of her previous suspicions, this sounded unbelievable, insane. "Henius, Stas?" she asked.

"Get it into your head, everybody! Only the few men who tend to the gas chambers and crematoria are alive. They won't live very long. Special Squad members are changed periodically, and you can guess what happens to those discharged."

It seemed like the death of the entire world, and of all the assumptions that rational and sane people take for granted. If she were a little girl, she would ask, 'Why'?"

"Final," she repeated. It was almost a relief to know for sure. "Like our fathers, 'they wound up safe to sea.' "

"It's that poem of yours again." In the same breath he asked, "Do you have anything to eat?"

She said, "My Pawelek, you must be starved." She produced a boiled potato from her pocket. He grabbed it and devoured it.

"Take it easy," she said, "I have a few more. I know a place where we can sit and talk."

They went to the same patch, overgrown with weeds, where Alicia had sat with Lucia and felt like walking off the earth. Walking off the earth, sinking in the quicksand. . . . They sat on a stone and Alicia kept feeding Pawel potatoes. She said, "I have a job in the kitchen; that's how I get extra soup and potatoes."

He said, "The best jobs in the camps are in the kitchens, storerooms or Special Squads. They fed me well in Treblinka, but when I was making my way through the Polish countryside I almost starved. The peasants wouldn't give me anything to eat without money. If they'd known I was a wandering Jew, they would have killed me or called the partisans to do the job."

Alicia said, "We'll go to Dr. Levin; he was your father's friend and colleague. I got my job through him. I'm sure he'll help you get settled here."

He looked at her and his old grin was back. "I'm not going to stay here for more than a few weeks. When I'm ready, I'll leave and take you with me." He smiled at her and said, "I'm still hungry." For a change, Alicia gave him a carrot.

The early October dusk was descending fast. They munched on potatoes and carrots, the Pawel and Alicia of old. They forgot that they were marked for extermination. She was no longer aware of the age difference between them.

Then Pawel said, "The hope that you were alive and that I might find you made me keep my sanity and attempt an escape. Another day of 'work' and I would have become like an animal, trained to go through certain motions and ready to do anything for an extra plate of soup."

Alicia said, "Not you, Pawel."

"Oh yes, me. You don't know what it was like to see, day after day, those people herded from the trains, stripped naked and marching up the ramp. When the crematoria were filled, we threw the bodies into a mass grave. Sometimes we set fire to it."

So that's what the Special Squad is, she thought. She screamed, "Stop it! You managed to get out of there. How did you do it?"

"You wouldn't want to know."

"Try me."

Pawel said, "They had so many corpses that not only the crematoria, but also the pit inside the camp, was filled. We loaded a truck with the bodies to bury them outside the camp. I hid between the corpses. Luckily, my co-workers didn't miss me. When the truck left the camp's grounds I jumped out into a ditch on the side of the road. And here I am." He smiled at her again. "Give me another potato."

"What are your plans now?"

"You probably know," Pawel said, "that my parents owned a few apartment houses in Kielce. Before the deportation, my mother told me about cellars and attics where they hid money and jewelry. I'll try to sneak into at least one."

"Oh God, Pawel, be careful"

He laughed, "I got out of a death factory; I can certainly get into the cellar of an apartment house. Once I have money, decent clothes and I'm not starving anymore, I'll go to Warsaw. It's a big city and nobody knows me there."

Alicia said, "Every time you run out of money, you'll come back to Kielce and try another cellar or attic."

"No, no, I expect to be gainfully employed. I have a cousin in Warsaw. His mother isn't Jewish and he has Aryan papers. I'm sure he'll help me."

"I wouldn't count on it," Alicia said doubtfully.

"He's different than most of 'them.' "

"Them?" she asked.

"Half-Jews who deny their Jewish half." Then he said thoughtfully, "The Germans might let you be for a few months; they need Jewish labor in the two factories. But I'm sure they plan to kill all the Jews. I'll come for you long before that." He became very serious. "Will you come with me? Do you realize that I'm not a kid anymore and that I love you?"

Alicia was trying to absorb everything: gas chambers, crematoria, mass slaughter, Pawel's escape and love. "Pawel," she said, "I love you too." She kissed him. He was dirty and smelly, but it didn't bother her at all. Pawel pulled her close and they kissed long and passionately.

Alicia had been kissed by boys before, older than Pawel, but she never felt like this. Up to now, petting and kissing was more like physical exercise; everybody did it, so she did it, too. With Pawel it was a new, wonderful experience, a revelation. Alicia pulled away, shook her head and laughed. "Where did you learn to kiss like this?"

"I don't know, with you it comes naturally."

"Let's go see Dr. Levin before dark, before the policemen start chasing us. Despite herself, she could not leave things well enough alone and she asked, "Did you see 'ours' going up the ramp you told me about?"

There was pain in his eyes, "I waved to them. They stayed together, your mother, aunt, Henius, my mother and Stas." He felt like talking: "Sometimes I had to direct people to the gas chambers and reassure them that it was for disinfection. They were naked and bewildered, but it was comforting to them to see fellow Jews in a position of authority." Then he said something Alicia would never forget: "Believe me, death is not the worst thing that can happen to a person."

"For a while I was assisting a dentist."

"A dentist?" Alicia could not figure out what a dentist would be doing in the Special Squad.

"When bodies were thrown out of the gas chambers it was our job to remove gold fillings. Germans are too efficient to incinerate gold. Other men had to strip hair from the corpses. We smelled human fat melting, later to be used for soap."

Alicia was getting sick to her stomach. For some strange reason, she was back in the chemistry lab in her first class of Lyceum: they were treating beef fat with lye and came out with little cakes of soap. She could still remember the smell of hot lye. Pawel was talking about human fat. Her mother's? aunt's? Henius? Mrs. Katz? Stas?

"I am sorry," Pawel said, "I shouldn't be telling you these stories."

"It's all right. Talking about it will help."

"I guess I'll have to live with these images and smells for the rest of my life."

Alicia thought it was time to get out of the pit. She said, "If we survive, we'll try to replace the horrors with happy images."

"Like what?" he asked.

"Oh, children playing, lovers kissing, bright flowers and strawberries, sandy beaches, blue seas, waves, seagulls flying, mountain lakes, pristine ski trails."

"That's why I love you so much, for all those beautiful thoughts."

She kissed him. He grinned: "Wait till I clean up; we'll do some fancy kissing together.

The following week Pawel went to work in Henrykow. He moved in with Benjamin and Ira. Working outside the Quarters gave him the opportunity to sneak out to the city. There he found hidden money and jewelry.

One afternoon, he told Alicia that he was ready to leave. In the evening the two of them met in his room. Benjamin and Ira were at the hospital. Anne thought that Alicia was at the Perlsteins'.

Alicia couldn't stop crying.

"I'll come for you as soon as I can," he kept repeating.

They were kissing and touching each other. "You are so beautiful. I dreamt about your breasts," Pawel said.

Alicia laughed, "I was always self conscious about my big bust. My aunt, after giving birth twice and breast-feeding her children, still did not need a bra. I've needed one since I was twelve."

"Twelve," Pawel said, "I remember you at the pool when you were eleven, you already had quite a pair of tits."

"You mean at nine you ogled girls' tits as you call it."

"Not girls', yours."

"Sometimes you called me 'four eyes,' " she remembered.

"Yes, but I thought that all smart people wear glasses. I studied hard and read a lot, so you wouldn't think that I was stupid and ignorant."

She had to admit that for a boy, who finished only three classes of the new system gymnasium, he knew a lot. And what a man he was! She could feel his erection and was getting more and more excited. What the hell, she thought. In no time they were both naked, and found themselves on Pawel's bunk.

"Don't worry, I won't get you in trouble, my father told me how not to get a girl pregnant," he said. She remembered hearing gossip about Dr. Katz making a fortune by performing abortions. Poor man; he saw a lot of girls in trouble in his short lifetime.

She never touched a man's penis, she touched Pawel's, first timidly then stroked it. It was extended and hard. She was discovering a passionate side in herself, she did not know she possessed. When he caressed her breasts, she moaned with pleasure. She wanted him inside her. "Get in," she whispered hoarsely.

Pawel hesitated, he seemed confused. She sensed that it was the first time for him just like it was for her. She assumed her old role of an experienced mature woman. She took his hand and directed it between her legs. "Touch me inside," she whispered."

She remembered Franek once attempting to do it. The experience was disgusting. At the time Franek declared that she was not sexually awakened. She accepted it almost as a verdict. Maybe I will never be, she decided.

As Pawel's finger probed inside her, she was moist with desire and anticipation. When he finally entered her she felt a sharp pain at first and then it was pure delight. He withdrew early.

"Why?" she asked.

"You don't want my sperm inside you. Did I hurt you?"

"Hurt me some more, please! I am so glad you are my first!"

They made love a few more times and each successive time got better. "I am sure I didn't make you pregnant,' Pawel stated.

"Don't worry. If I die soon I will not have to go to heaven, I was already in paradise.

They both cried. She caressed him. "When did you get so tall, strong and handsome?" she said dreamily.

"You are probably thinking about my parents," Pawel smiled, "my father, plump with a paunch; my mother, round and a satisfied housewife; both of them content with their lives and indulging in their wealth, food and drink. I must be a throwback to some distant ancestor."

"You are wonderful and a great lover," Alicia said.

"In the last two hours," he said, "I didn't think about Treblinka and the corpses were far away like a horrible nightmare. I love you, I adore you, I will come for you as soon as I can."

"Must you go tomorrow? Stay a few more days," Alicia begged.

"If I stay another day, I may not leave at all. That wouldn't be good for either of us. We can't stay away from each other. I might get careless and get you pregnant. Most important, the Germans will not want to leave the witnesses to their crimes alive. I must get out and then come for you." He got very serious. "Promise me that if I don't make it, you won't give up."

"But you will make it, you must," Alicia said. She tried hard not to cry.

"I'll certainly try."

By November, the Jews who were left in Kielce had no illusion about the fate of the deported people. Pawel's story was confirmed by the Poles in the factories. A few more witnesses from Treblinka drifted into Kielce. The idea of gas chambers was now never very far from everyone's consciousness.

One day Anne suggested that Alicia try to get a job as a cook in the little hospital. "You'll be better off than in the main kitchen, and I need somebody for the job."

Alicia was stunned. "I never cooked a meal in my life."

"I know, my princess, but you'll learn."

Alicia had tears in her eyes."Don't call me princess anymore," she yelled. "I'll cook."

Anne said, "I know that in your previous life, you had more interesting things to do. Anyhow, we have to make it official. Go to Dr. Levin. He'll approve my recommendation and register you in the council as the official hospital cook. Just make sure he doesn't pull a 'Rudek' on you."

"Oh, Anne," Alicia said, "he's an old man. He delivered me, he was our neighbor and friend, and he owes me a debt for taking care of Greta after the deportation."

"He's also notorious, especially where young girls are concerned."

Alicia wondered. Anne and Levin? Anne and Sepple? Anne and Benjamin? Did she or did she not? With Benjamin, and if, when and where? If I could find the time and place with Pawel?

Alicia became the hospital cook. Ruth and Fanny were helpful, and she found it not very hard after all. Most of the time she had to prepare soup from whatever was available. She also made latkes (potato pancakes). She seemed to be forever peeling and grating potatoes. Occasionally there were eggs to add to the batter, and usually there was fat to fry the latkes in.

"Don't tell anybody about the fat," Anne once said.

"What kind is it?" Alicia asked

"Never mind," Anne answered.

It dawned on Alicia that it must be lard. "You mean," she said, "after all that has happened to us, there are people who still care about the Jewish dietary laws? It seems that God has given up on us."

"Some of the patients here come from Hassidic families, and tradition is all they have."

Anne and Alicia spent many evenings in the ward with the boys. Anne had a nice voice and she sang Polish and Yiddish songs. Benjamin and Ira were usually around. Someone managed to get a couple of decks of cards. Alicia organized a bridge game. It seemed like ages ago that Alicia, Lisa, Bolek and Pawel were the four for bridge in their apartment on Freedom Place. Now Lisa and Bolek had been murdered in Treblinka, and Pawel? Oh God, I hope I see him soon!

In the ward the four for bridge were Alicia, Andrew, Benjamin and Ira, and sometimes Abe. Saul, who was out of traction and on crutches, often kibitzed.

"I miss Pawel; I wonder where he is." Alicia once blurted out during a game.

Benjamin almost dropped his cards. "Alicia," he said, "when you miss someone, never ask where that person is and keep your observations to yourself."

Alicia realized that Benjamin knew what Pawel was doing. She had figured out a long time ago that Benjamin, Ira and maybe Anne were involved with some sort of Polish resistance. Benjamin had a gun and he always knew the war news.

She thought about Pawel and Tadek in his attic. She prayed, "If You are someplace, help these boys and bring Pawel back to me!"

Anne was worried that Saul and Andrew had stayed in the hospital as patients too long. "In case of any kind of 'action,' the sick will go first."

"Don't be a worrier," Alicia said. "Learn to have some fun."

Anne was not interested. "I always had to work hard," she said, "and I never had time to indulge in games."

The first snow came early this year. At dusk Ruth returned from her job. Even now she was full of life, laughter and hope. Ruth was one of eight children, the only one left alive. Maybe growing up with brothers and sisters had given her a cheerful personality.

Ruth told Alicia, "It's snowing. Let's go in the backyard and throw some snowballs."

"I don't have boots," Alicia answered, "and I don't want to ruin my only pair of shoes."

"Let's go barefoot. It's not very cold," Ruth suggested.

The two girls went to the yard, stamped in the snow and threw snowballs as they ran and laughed.

Alicia thought about the ski trails in the Swietokzyski mountains; the jumping board, who's using it now? The Germans? It is snowing for everybody, even for us.

They heard Anne's voice: "You're going to freeze your feet."

The magic was gone. The beautiful snow was turning into slush. Alicia dropped the snowball.

They went back inside. Anne handed them a towel. Laura was standing in front of a mirror. "This wet weather," she complained, "my pageboy won't stay put."

Always obliging, Fanny tried to fix Laura's hair into a roll. Everything was as usual.

The next day was a good one. Lucia brought a leg of lamb that Joseph had gotten in the city. They shared expenses; for a change, Alicia could pay for herself. They baked in the kitchen, they had a feast upstairs and there was food left over for the patients. They went to bed satiated and content. The lights were on and the girls talked and giggled, Ruth and Alicia in one bed and Laura and Anne in the other. They were twenty years old and everything else was forgotten.

Suddenly there was a knock at the door. Not banging but a dog was barking and they heard a voice in German, "Open up!"

Ruth squeezed Alicia's hand. Her nails dug into Alicia's palm. "That's it," she said. "It's our turn."

Alicia turned pale as the blood drained from her face. So soon, she thought. Why should it be any different for me? I only wish I had had more time with Pawel.

Laura put on her robe and opened the door. She was their representative, as she was fluent in German and spoke it without a Yiddish accent. A German soldier was standing there with a dog. He spoke to Laura, pointing to the windows.

Alicia was too frightened to hear what he said.

Laura went to the window and lowered the shade. The German raised his cap and left.

"We have to observe the blackout," Laura said. "The light was seeping out."

The girls burst out laughing and began to kiss each other.

"Not our turn yet," Alicia said.

PART II

This part of the book is dedicated to the brave women of Kielce.

These are the times that try men's souls.
Tyranny, like hell, is not easily conquered.

Thomas Paine

CHAPTER 11

1942–1943
Kielce Jewish Quarters

One morning in late November 1942, Irene appeared unexpectedly in the little hospital. Her eyes were sparkling and she looked excited and prettier than ever. No matter what, youth and love make people happy, Alicia thought, Irene and Sepple must be doing well together. Or maybe something important happened and the doctors learned of it. Was Hitler assassinated? Did someone in his entourage figure that he is leading his country to defeat?

"I came to say goodbye," Irene said. "All the Jewish Kielce doctors are going to work in hospitals inside Germany. They are allowed to take their immediate families and I might be able to serve as a nurse."

"Really?" Anne said. In that one word she conveyed doubt and disbelief.

Irene did not sense it, "I have to rush home to finish packing. Can you imagine they are actually giving us a bus so we can take all our luggage." She kissed everybody and whispered in Alicia's ear that she had a message from Abe. "You can join him and he will claim you as his wife. It's a great opportunity for you, Alicia."

Alicia smiled. My mother would be so happy, she told herself, to know that a young dentist, like Abe, practically proposed to me. How could she explain that she was waiting for Pawel, an eighteen-year-old nutty kid.

Irene left. Laura got out her suitcase and started packing. "I am going to join Herb Steiner," she told the others.

"He never asked you," Anne said.

"He'll be happy. He's very lonely and I will be of great help to him with my good German."

"I have two idiots on my hands," Anne said. "One thinks that her German will get her over being Jewish and the other speaks Polish, English, French and Latin but refuses to learn German."

Alicia watched Laura packing. It seemed logical that the doctors were not deported to Treblinka because they were needed, but then doubt entered her mind. The doctors knew too much. "How do they know where they are really going?" she asked.

"They don't," Anne answered. Suddenly she pushed Laura into a small room, where they kept the linen, locked the door and put the key in her pocket. Laura banged and yelled, "Let me out!"

Alicia stood there bewildered, "Anne, you have no right to make a decision like that for her! She's twenty years old, she has to make up her own mind."

Anne shouted, "I don't need you to tell me what to do!" She was getting excited. Benjamin walked in.

Anne sighed with relief. She needed somebody to take over. She threw the key at Benjamin. "You decide, I have to take the blame for everything!"

Benjamin put his arms around her and kissed her. That was the first time Alicia saw him express his feelings towards Anne. "Keep the door locked until the bus leaves," he said, "Jewish doctors are not going to work in German hospitals."

"What do you think will happen to them?" Alicia was now close to hysteria.

"If they are going to Germany, they are going to concentration camps" Benjamin answered. Then he began to yell through the door to Laura. "Don't you see it's a subterfuge? It's a lie like the resettlement east! It's just to get these people on the bus."

Benjamin opened the door and Laura came out crying. "They certainly could use doctors and nurses," he said to her. "Thousands, maybe millions are dying fighting around Stalingrad."

Alicia said, "My uncle ran a hospital train during the last war. My aunt was his nurse. Maybe there are those kinds of trains now."

Benjamin shrugged his shoulders, "That was the last war. In this war the Germans would rather let their wounded die than use Jewish doctors."

Anne was shivering. "I should have pushed Irene into that linen room, too."

"You didn't worry about me," Alicia said. "You heard what Irene told me."

"Yes, I did hear," Anne said. "But somehow I didn't worry about you. I knew you wouldn't go with Abe."

"I don't love Abe," Alicia stated flatly.

Laura was sobbing.

She's hurt that she did not hear from Steiner, Alicia thought, and aloud she said, "Steiner was probably smart enough to know that they were not going to be working in hospitals. Otherwise he would have asked you."

"You are so kind," Laura said, "not like her." She pointed at Anne.

Alicia got angry. "You have some nerve to criticize Anne. She might have saved your life."

"So for how long?" Laura answered. "Besides, who cares? Right now I don't give a damn!" Then, as if to fight her descending despair she added, "Benjamin doesn't know everything. Maybe they are going to work in hospitals." But the resolve to join Steiner was gone.

Ira came in. He worked that week for Levy and witnessed what happened in front of the council. Only one doctor and one medic remained in Kielce. Dr. Breitman was assigned to Ludwikow and medic Rutkowski to Henrykow. The rest of the doctors and dentists, with their families, boarded a bus. The exception was Janka Buchalter. She had a choice to remain with her boyfriend Meyer by claiming him as her husband or to go with her parents. Her father insisted that she come along. He even tried to persuade Levy to let Meyer join them. Levy advised against it. Did he know anything? So Janka remained with Meyer. Her father was very disappointed. The bus left with the doctors, a few Jewish policemen and SS men.

"Where did they go?" the girls asked.

Ira spread his hands and said, "Nobody knows, but there are some ugly rumors."

It took only two hours for the Jewish policemen to come back and then the people of the Quarters learned what had happened. The bus did not take the doctors to the trains for Germany, they went for a short

ride to a cemetery, which had been used for unclaimed bodies and in-
digents. The Gestapo employed a procedure learned from the SS death
squads in Russia and the Baltic states: The Jewish policemen and the
doctors were instructed to dig a deep pit, then the doctors and their
families had to take off their clothes, enter the pit, and lie down. The
policemen were afraid that they would be asked to join them, but apparently they had not yet played out their roles and would be needed
for future actions. The SS men sat down at the edge of the pit and
machine-gunned the people inside. When the shooting was over, the
policemen closed the pit. Hopefully everyone was dead, the ones only
wounded would be buried alive.

Alicia sat down and put her head in her hands, many images running through her mind: Dr. Levin watching Greta being killed, the girl
he had protected all her life. (Or did they shoot him first and then
Greta, who probably did not realize what was happening?) Dr.
Perlstein and his eight-year-old daughter. Did he beg them to kill him
but spare his little girl? Alicia knew that was what her father would
have done. Beautiful Irene, so full of hope just a few hours ago, is here
no more. Steiner had brought his mother and sister from Lwow so they
would not be deported to Siberia—they went to Treblinka instead, and
now it was his turn. Dr. Buchhalter was so sure that he was going to
work in a German hospital that he insisted his daughter come along
with the rest of the family. And the Grauer family. Abe had wanted to
give her a chance for a better life.

Alicia glanced at Laura, who was crying. Poor girl, this was the
end of her dreams; all the doctors are gone now. To Alicia it felt as if
the last link to the past was broken, her father's colleagues all but one
dead. Pawel, come for me soon!

She heard Anne's voice, "You two girls are sitting here like
statues. Laura, fix your hair, it's a mess. You have to come down with
me to help distribute food."

"I've got to go clean the kitchen," Alicia said.

Anne had planned something else for Alicia. "Never mind! I'll
take care of that. Do me a favor Alicia," she said. "Go down and play
bridge with the boys. Saul enjoys very much when you teach him the
game."

Alicia stared. Had Anne lost her mind?

Anne must have read her expression, she said, "We've got to pretend that everything is as usual. Those downstairs don't know anything yet."

"You can't keep it from them much longer. They have to be told."

"We'll give it to them slowly. Right now, all they have to know is that there is one doctor and one medic left and the rest went off to work in other hospitals.

Alicia went down and tried to play cards. Saul noticed that she was upset. He hobbled on his crutches and asked what happened. "We are not sure," Alicia told him. Then, to avoid more questions, she said, "I've got to get myself a drink of water." She went to the kitchen, Laura was drying the dishes, Benjamin and Anne were there too.

"They don't need ten nurses and ten medical assistants when they only have one doctor and one medic," Laura said "they will come for us next. They will probably decide that they don't need a hospital and they'll shoot all the patients."

"You might be right, Laura," Benjamin said, "but there is one thing in our favor."

"The way things are going, I wouldn't think so," Alicia said. "But tell me, what is it that works for us?"

"It's not 'what,' it's 'who.' Mr. Kramer, the civilian director of the two factories, is from an old German family and he is highly respected. He is not a member of the Nazi Party and, as far as I can figure out, he is not a Nazi sympathizer. His main purpose is to run the factories efficiently and he'll insist that there are some medical facilities for the Jewish slave workers. The proof of it is that one doctor and one medic (*felczer*) were left in Kielce. Those two factories are very important for the German war effort.

Laura was not buying it, "They still don't need twenty people to assist two doctors and take care of fifteen patients." She turned to Alicia; "You joined us once, now it is time to leave a sinking ship."

"Enough of this," Anne interrupted, "we are all in it together and we should help each other.

Maybe Anne finally has forgiven me for being alive, Alicia thought. I wonder about Laura.

Benjamin was, as usual, the voice of common sense. "Your only hope is that you are not important enough and that they will forget about you. Besides only three of you girls are working in the hospital, the rest of the ten have other jobs.

Still, Benjamin's theory of not being important enough was all very well, but Alicia thought about her father, a man who just minded his own business and was only interested in medicine. They came for him anyway.

Laura left the kitchen to distribute medication.

"We must consider other alternatives," Benjamin said. "Do you know what Pawel is doing?"

Oh, my God, I almost forgot about Pawel, Alicia thought. She was all ears.

"I might as well tell you, because we will probably all need him," Benjamin went on. "I wouldn't like Laura to hear this—she is too friendly with the administration. Pawel is in the business of getting Aryan papers for Jews in ghettos and labor camps."

Alicia did not know if she should be happy or anxious. It's just like him to go into business, she thought. Even that evening in the tent, before the final selection to Treblinka, he got hold of phony documents and distributed them to the women.

Benjamin turned to Alicia. "You're the only one in our group who could pass easily for a goy. I have a long nose, Anne is dark and has kinky hair, we all speak Polish with Yiddish inflection."

"How about Laura?" Alicia asked.

"She's a redhead," Benjamin said, "and there's something Jewish about her. Most Jews can communicate in German. The fact that you don't speak German would be to your advantage."

"I have curly hair," Alicia pointed out.

"Yes, but it's wavy and blond. Besides, once you are outside, Pawel intends to take care of you. Whatever happens to you two, if you can pass as Poles, you will not be transported to a cemetery or gas chambers."

"What will you do?" Alicia asked.

Ben looked around and whispered, "We'll get out also—Anne, myself, and Ira. They don't like to accept Jews, and Jewish women, forget it. But for us they will make an exception."

Who are "they? Polish partisans?" Alicia wondered. And how often and where does Benjamin see Pawel?

"What will Laura do?" Anne asked.

"She'll have to take her chances with the ruling classes. I'm sure they have some plans."

"But will they include her?"

"I can't worry about everybody!" Ben said sharply.

One evening, not long after the action on the doctors, Anne found Alicia sitting in the room alone with her eyes closed. "You are daydreaming again," she said.

Alicia opened her eyes and looked up at Anne. Anne acted differently lately. Her old belligerence was gone, she seemed subdued and tired. And pink circles around her eyes indicated that she had been crying. She sat down near Alicia. "Share some of your dreams," she said. "Right now I can use some."

"I just close my eyes," Alicia said, "and try to visualize the map of Europe. There are still a few places we could go.—Switzerland, Sweden, Spain, Portugal, Britain."

Anne shook her head. "Who needs Britain? I have enough of war. Spain reminds me of the Inquisition. How would we get there, anyhow?"

"Oh, that's simple. In my dream I see a big plane or a balloon, a dirigible filled with gas that's lighter than air."

"If we have it, why stick to Europe? Let's try the United States or Canada,"

"Australia or New Zealand."

"According to Benjamin, those two are not safe from Japanese invasion."

There was a moment of silence; then Alicia asked seriously, "Anne, do you really think Benjamin knows everything?"

"I don't, but you do." She was laughing now.

"Should we take Benjamin along?" Alicia asked.

"I wouldn't go without him. I hope, when the time comes, he'll do the same for me."

"Whom else shall we take?"

"Name your people first."

Alicia smiled, "Of course, first on my list would be Pawel, then maybe Lucia with her boyfriend and for sure Saul and Andrew. Let's hear your people."

"For a moment, I thought I would take Irene," Anne said. "And if she insisted, I would let Sepple join us. Then I reminded myself—"

"I would take Abe," Alicia broke in, "though Pawel might not like it."

Anne leaped up. "Stop it!" she snapped. "Your dream stinks!" Then as fast as she could, she started to enumerate people they would take: "Laura, Benjamin, Ira. How about Ruth and Fanny?"

Alicia spread her hands. "I don't know. I'll leave that decision to you."

Anne quieted down. "Let's go downstairs. I promised the boys I would sing to them."

The year 1942 was coming to a close, the worst of Alicia's life. Her whole world had disappeared and all the people in it. People she considered friends now had not been part of her life before. Pawel was the only exception. Pawel, she thought, in that most horrible year, he gave me the few happiest hours of my life: one afternoon filled with love and passion. Even if later she realized that the horrors were a reality, the memory of these few hours would make fighting for survival worthwhile.

Life settled into a routine. Saul and Andrew were finally discharged from the hospital. Saul was still limping and Andrew coughing. They both had jobs taking care of the streets in the Quarters. Ira and Benjamin were working in Henrykow. The factory workers were considered the proletariat of the Quarters.

Up to the last action, the girls in the hospital had felt secure in their jobs, because of the influence the doctors had with Levy.

One cold and nasty morning in January 1943, Ruth came running from the Levys' shaking and in tears. "They almost considered me a member of the family," she gasped incoherently. "I had to talk *Spiegel* into letting me go."

"Go from where and to where?" the girls asked

"They took Levy, his wife, two sons, and daughter-in-law in a bus. You know which bus. *Spiegel* is in charge now."

"*Levy?*" The girls were stunned. He had served the Germans faithfully. He would deliver to them anything and anybody they wanted. In fact, although Alicia's dream of a plane, blimp, or even magic carpet was only a dream, it was a concrete plan for Mr. Levy. He had bought himself a Gestapo man, who had a plane ready for him and his family to go to Switzerland. The plan backfired, someone squealed, and that was the end of the Levys.

That evening, Alicia was sitting alone in the kitchen. Slowly people drifted in: Anne, Benjamin, Ira, Saul, Andrew, and Laura. "What are you dreaming about now?" Anne asked Alicia.

"I wonder," Alicia answered, "if I should mourn the Levy family. He was a lecher and a crook, but his poor wife didn't know anything. She just enjoyed her good fortune. Lenny was his father's right hand, but Julian minded his own business.The rumor was that Julian's wife was pregnant, and if they could get to Switzerland, maybe the baby would have a chance. At least when they came for my uncle and my father, they only took them; now they're going for whole families. Still the Levys are last on the list of people I am crying for."

"I'm surprised at you, Alicia," Saul said. "It's irrelevant that they died, it's how they died that's important. If we are to survive the war, I'll be the first to bring charges in court against people like Levy."

"And I would love to be the prosecutor," Benjamin added grimly.

Anne laughed. "Let's hope that by that time you'll have a law degree."

Alicia looked at Benjamin. "When Benjamin, when? When will there be courts and trials and governments that uphold the law? When, if ever, we will be in control of our own lives, when can we come and go as we please? Will we ever live without the specter of gas chambers or nameless cemeteries?"

"You want a lot," Anne said. "I just want enough to eat for the near future." She added laughing, "Why do you ask Benjamin? Do you really think he knows more than you?"

Benjamin disregarded the remark. He was now lecturing on the world situation. "Too bad," he was saying, "that instead of opening a western front in France, the Allies went to North Africa. It looks as if the Germans will surrender in Stalingrad. Can you imagine German prisoners sent to Siberia?"

To Benjamin and Alicia, Anne said, "You two are in the clouds again. We have to be concerned about the new administration of the Quarters. Spiegel is not only chief of the Jewish police—now he's in charge of everything. Levy, whatever he was, was born in Kielce and he still was one of us. Spiegel, and his first lieutenant Glattstein, are two German pigs, and we don't know what to expect from them."

"You're exaggerating, Anne," Laura said. "They're not so bad."

"Oh, excuse me. I forgot that you're friendly with those ladies of leisure, Mrs. Spiegel and Mrs. Glattstein. Whatever you speak to them about in your perfect German, don't repeat what that other idiot said"—she pointed to Alicia—"that Ben knows everything." To Ben, she added, "You tell everybody else to keep their mouths shut. But you yourself repeat some rumors about Spiegel."

After the actions on the doctors and then on the Levys, everybody in the Quarters tried to get Aryan papers. Nobody could go as far as Levy did—actually to buy a German and a plane—but people with money paid Poles to hide them.

Benjamin suggested the same thing to the girls. "Pawel needs photographs. I am his representative for Kielce."

So Pawel is running a big enterprise! Alicia thought, Benjamin must be at least four years older than Pawel but he works for him. I am very proud of my Pawelek.

Andrew had a camera. (To have a camera was almost as dangerous as having a gun.) Benjamin got hold of some film. It was a dark gloomy day in February. There was a big lamp in the little hospital, which had once served as an additional light in the operating room of the original ghetto. Now it was used infrequently. Occasionally, Dr. Breitman needed it when he had to open a boil or when he was performing other minor procedures. That day in February, they used that lamp to take photographs. There were four girls: Anne, Alicia, Laura, and Lucia. Andrew took the pictures. They were all excited; it was quite a diversion for them. Laura kept on fixing her pageboy hairdo. It appeared that she had got over Steiner and was back to her usual self. The girls giggled and laughed; each one would pose and smile. When it was Alicia's turn, Andrew told her to take off her glasses. He took each one twice. Anne was the last. Just at the final click, there was banging at the door. Anne went to open it while Andrew hid the camera under the base of the lamp and turned off the light.

Birnbaum, the policeman Alicia had always disliked, walked in. "You had that big light on?" he said nastily. "I saw it through the crack in the door." He went for Andrew with his club, but Anne intervened.

"Leave him alone, you son of a bitch! He's a sick boy!"

"He's going to be a lot sicker after I get through with him, and if you don't shut up, I'll beat you too. I heard you were taking pictures for false identifications. Let me have the camera and film. This is a dangerous business—you can get us all into serious trouble."

Anne's reply was quick: "More serious troubles that what? If you're looking for something, find it."

Birnbaum released Andrew and tried to be reasonable. "You girls think you can get away with everything. Maybe with Levy you could, but Spiegel is different. You're jeopardizing the safety of the whole population of the Quarters by owning a camera and taking pictures. You know what kind of reprisals we would get if the Germans ever found out!"

"You have a lousy informer," Anne said, "because we don't have a camera. We just played around with the lamp."

"I'll talk to Spiegel," Birnbaum said.

When he left, the girls were a little panicky. Who had squealed?

The punishment came swiftly. It was decided that only one nurse was needed in the little hospital, and Laura got the job. Alicia thought it was unfair; it was Anne who was "the real nurse," who had trained everybody else, but the authorities disliked her and liked Laura. Ruth became the hospital's cook. Andrew, Anne, Lucia and Alicia lost their jobs inside the Quarters and had to go to Henrykow. Now, in the complete darkness of February mornings, they trudged to the gates, where everyone met and were counted by policemen and escorted to work. While she was marching to the factory, Alicia realized that there were holes in the soles of her shoes and that the coat she had managed to get last fall from the storeroom was not very warm. She could almost hear her mother, "Don't get your feet wet—it's the easiest way to catch cold, especially with your sensitive throat." Andrew kept on coughing; sometimes Alicia was afraid that he would spit out his lungs. Lucia complained about the pain in her heart and leaned heavily on Alicia. Anne was the only one who seemed to bear up well under the circumstances.

Alicia had another problem. As long as she was working in the small hospital, it had felt safe to keep Aunt Paula's necklace in an envelope inside her brassiere. Things were different now: The policemen at the gate were always ready to confiscate anything of value. She also did not trust some of her co-workers in the factory.

Luckily Henrykow was not far from the Quarters, and the factory was kept warm so that the cut wooden spokes could dry before they were used for wheels. The girls passed wooden boards from machine to machine. The machines were operated by the boys, the supervisors were Poles.

There was always heightened tension when the Gestapo agent, Herr Fuchs, a tall, skinny, menacing man, was on the premises. The boys assigned the girls to be on the lookout for him, and the news that he was approaching was a signal for everyone to start working feverishly. The factory was operating on a twenty-four-hour basis, and there were three shifts.

One day in the factory, Benjamin called Alicia aside. "Next week Pawel will be here; he will bring your papers and collect money from his customers. As I understand, he has other sources of money in Kielce. Both of you will leave for Warsaw and get lost in the crowd."

All that Alicia heard was that Pawel was going to be in Kielce next week and that she would finally see him.

They met in the factory, in a corner between stacks of spokes piled up high to dry. Andrew was standing guard. Pawel was dressed in coarse pants, heavy jacket, and a cap with a visor; he looked like a worker or peasant who had just come to town. But under the visor were the same mischievous smiling eyes that she loved so much. They kissed and then kissed more. It was hard to break apart. He rumpled her hair. "My golden princess, you are so beautiful, I missed you terribly."

Alicia had tears in her eyes. "I missed you too. Let's try to stay alive, maybe we will see the end of this nightmare."

"What a nice dress you have, and even the heavy stockings can't hide the shape of your legs," he said.

Stockings. She had "organized" them at Wirtz the same day that he shot Gretchen. The memory came back to her—Lucia standing panic-stricken that they might be shot next.

"Where did you get that dress?" Pawel asked.

Alicia smiled. "Oh, from Mrs. Perlstein."

"The yenta and rag lady that our mothers used to kid about?"

"Now she is buried in a nameless mass grave. I wonder if she took her rags to the cemetery."

Pawel said soberly, "At least she was spared the terrible train ride to Treblinka. Alicia, our fathers were murdered the same night, our mothers and our brothers died together. Now you and I have to try to survive."

"Will the memories always haunt us?"

"More or less, but as we make a life for ourselves, I hope it is going to be less. But right now we have very little time and plenty of things to talk about." He produced her papers. "How do you like your new name, Alicja Krystyna Buszewska?"

"Alicja is quite Polish, Alicia is more cosmopolitan. Krystyna is absolutely Christian. What is your name?"

He showed her his identification, Pawel Brzezinski. "There is no future in being Pawel Katz. Pawel—what a name to give a boy whose last name is Katz. But you know our parents—they wanted us to grow up as Poles."

Alicia had to laugh. "Alicia—my mother's dream of me becoming a famous ballerina or an actress. I certainly disappointed her."

"You did not disappoint me."

She looked at the picture on her new identification. "I don't like it too much."

Pawel kissed her again. "The original is better, but let's get down to business. I only need one day to get hold of some money. I'll meet you here the day after tomorrow, same time and place. Have your papers and no extra clothes. I will have tickets to Warsaw for us."

"What will we do in Warsaw?"

"I am going to have working papers for us. You are going to be a doctor's assistant and I a dental assistant. You must memorize certain names and addresses." He gave her the address of his cousin in Warsaw, the doctor, and the dentist.

She repeated the information a few times out loud. "I am good at it. I learned in school how to memorize things."

"After the war you'll go to school again—you'll be a great professor."

"You too, Pawel."

Pawel laughed. "Somebody has to make money for the family," he said.

"You'll be a great entrepreneur."

"In the meantime, as Poles, we will have more opportunities to do something. Even if they catch us and send us to a concentration camp, they don't gas Poles."

"Isn't it enough that you are selling Aryan papers?"

"We could join the partisans.," There was that old sparkle in his eyes. "We could try to sneak behind the front lines and find Polish units fighting alongside the Russians."

"Maybe we could just lie low and try to survive day by day." As she said that, she knew that Pawel could never do it and that she would not love him as much if he could.

He got serious. "Alicia," he said, "now that you have your papers, you must use them even if I don't make it."

"What are you saying?" Alicia gasped. "What good will my papers do me without you? What should I want to live for?"

"Listen to me: If one Jew survives, it will be a great victory. I surely hope it will be both of us. But in one day, a lot of things can happen, and I am in more danger than you."

"I can be shot tomorrow by Fuchs. Anything is possible."

"It is possible but unlikely. Just in case, please promise that you will go on."

"It works both ways—you have to try to live without me. By the way, keep this for me." Alicia handed him the envelope with the necklace. "It will be hard enough for me to worry about hiding my papers and the little money I have."

He took it reluctantly. "What if I don't make it?" he repeated.

"Oh, shut up, Pawel!"

They kissed. "I will see you the day after tomorrow," he said.

Andrew called to them, "You'd better break it up—the supervisors are on the floor." He motioned to Pawel. "Melt in with the workers and start stacking the spokes."

Alicia saw Pawel walking between Andrew and Benjamin. He put his hand to his mouth and sent her a kiss.

She was transfixed. She could see her Uncle Monek sending a kiss to Mucia at the station as he boarded a train to Auschwitz. My little Pawelek, now a grown and mature man, my lover. God, You took my mother and father, little Henius, my Mucia, and maybe Jas and Jerry— I don't know if they're alive or not. You took Leah, Sabina, and probably Basia. But please leave me Pawel.

But, of course, God had nothing to do with it—the Germans did it. God is light years away watching another galaxy.

She became disgusted with herself. Why am I getting all upset? Pawel will be here in two days.

The crucial day after tomorrow came. Anne was on the night shift that week, so Alicia kissed her in the morning. She had tears in her eyes. "Good-bye Anne, good luck. You and Ben will get out of here too. I'll see you when we're all free. Thank you, I would never had made it without you."

"Sure you would. You're stronger than you think." Anne, Benjamin, Ira, and Andrew were the only people who knew about Alicia and Pawel. Anne embraced Alicia and blinked back tears.

It was a bright March morning. The days were already longer, but it was still windy and cold, and Alicia's threadbare coat did not keep off March's winds. But she was hardly aware of discomfort. There could be a snow-storm this morning, and it would not bother her. She flew to the factory.

She waited in the same corner at the appointed time, but the hour was long gone, and there was no Pawel. She found Benjamin at his machine. When he looked at her, even in the gloom of the factory, she noticed how pale and upset he was. "I just learned about it. They've arrested him."

Him, who is *him*? She did not want to face the obvious. "Who do you think?" he answered.

Alicia had often wondered how people in the Quarters knew what was happening in the city. Benjamin probably had contact with a Polish co-worker, and he in turn probably knew somebody higher up. Maybe they were wrong? But when she looked at Benjamin's face, she realized that he was sure. "Pawel escaped from Treblinka. He can do it again."

Benjamin just shrugged. "From Gestapo headquarters?"

Alicia forced herself to keep calm and speak in a normal voice, so as not to attract too much attention in the factory. "You don't know Pawel like I know him."

"He will need a miracle to escape. It's possible that somebody inside here squealed," he whispered.

Alicia was sinking in the quicksand.

"You don't have to worry," he said. "You have your papers. But Pawel had photographs of his new customers and maybe a list of names. The Gestapo has a way of extracting information from their prisoners."

He means torture, Alicia thought. They're going to torture Pawel, mutilate his beautiful body. Maybe they're already doing it.

"Alicia, there's a panic in the Quarters. Don't forget, I'm his contact for Kielce. I don't know anything about what they're doing in Warsaw, who the forger is or where the documents are printed, but the Gestapo won't believe me. I should take my gun and just disappear, but I can't leave Anne behind. I had hoped to wait here until summer. I don't have Aryan papers yet—you do."

Alicia did not give a damn about her papers, about panic in the Quarters, about Benjamin, even about Anne. But Pawel? The idiot will not talk—what will they do to him? How much will it take to break him? She remembered what he had said, "Death is not the worst thing that can happen to a human being." Death?

The following day a few more people escaped from the Quarters, mostly ex-policemen with their wives. But then the panic was over. The Gestapo did not get any information from Pawel. He swallowed photographs and papers and then managed to hang himself in his cell.

Like Uncle Monek in Auschwitz, Alicia thought.

"You can now safely use your papers," Benjamin told her.

Safely, for what? It would be simpler just to drop dead. There is no mother or father to mourn over Pawel—I'm the only one. She remembered Pawel telling her, "Keep on plugging, Alicia."

Who the hell wants to live all alone?

> I am weary of days and hours
> Blown buds of barren flowers,
> Desires and dreams and powers
> And everything but sleep. (Swinburne)

Sleep forever, like Romeo and Juliet. It sounded peaceful. She had suffered enough in her twenty years and lost enough people to last a few lifetimes. Keep on plugging, try to survive and tell the story. Why me? Who cares about the story? If the world cared, these things would not be happening now.

The following week Alicia walked through the factory in a fog. She did not look anything like the girl who had met Pawel just a few days before. Her hair was uncombed, her dress was dirty, her shoes and stockings had holes, she had circles under her eyes. Andrew bumped into her. "Alicia, for crying out loud, look alive. If Fuchs sees you walking like a zombie, he might beat you up or shoot you."

She looked at Andrew with glazed eyes. "I wish he would. I don't have Pawel's courage to hang myself."

"Oh, drop it. Our turn will come soon enough. Why rush? I overheard what you promised Pawel. In his memory you must go on."

"I don't feel like going on." She quoted again from the same book of poems by Swinburne:

> And say at night "Would God the day were here,"
> And say at dawn "Would God the day were dead."

Andrew went into one of his coughing spells, but he managed to stammer, "You have more than I do. You're healthy—you have Gentile friends who'll give you money, and you have Aryan papers."

Alicia watched him coughing and spitting into a dirty handkerchief and felt compassion. "Andrew," she said, "warm weather will soon be here, and you'll feel better." Unbidden, a thought came to her: This underdeveloped sick kid is alive, while tall, strong, beautiful, Pawel, my lover, is dead.

Immediately, she was horrified at herself. I've become like the Germans—determining who should live and who should die. Tears filled her eyes.

"See—you can still cry," Andrew said. "You're not yet dead inside."

In the evenings Alicia sat on her bed, oblivious to everyone around her. She ate little, she did not change her clothes, and she did not wash.

"You are behaving like Mrs. Spitz," Anne told her.

Mrs. Spitz? The one who pushed her own daughter away so she herself could remain in Kielce "What about Mrs. Spitz?"

"She just sits and stares at the wall. The women of Ludwikow take care of her. They feed her and dress her. Don't expect me to do it for you. You can starve first and dissolve in your own filth."

"Why not? What's the point of surviving?"

"What's the point? If you survive, you'll have plenty of time to figure out what it's all about. Like I've told you before, if they want to kill you, don't make it easy for them—let them expend some energy."

"How much energy would it take to murder one little me?"

"There are still thousands of us left. If everyone gives up, they will not need gas chambers. The trouble is, since you started vegetating, Laura's been reminding herself of Steiner, and now I have two basket cases on my hands. Laura is our only nurse, and the patients need her to keep up their spirits." As an afterthought she asked, "What happened to your necklace?"

Oh, my God, Alicia thought. I forgot the necklace, the last momento from my Mucia. "I gave it to Pawel," she said tearfully. "I was afraid to lug it along."

Anne shrugged her shoulders. "Some German woman is lugging it now."

Laura walked into the room. She looked at Alicia and shook her head, "How could you be in love with that kid?"

Alicia got angry. "Kid? He was more of a man than your stuffy doctor! He hung himself so that he wouldn't betray anyone while under torture. Your doctor strangled his patients to save his own hide." Getting mad made her feel better.

Laura began to cry, "Most of the patients were injected and went fast. It was more merciful to die that way than to be shot by the Gestapo."

"Steiner was not the one to determine it," Alicia shouted at her. "Let the Germans do their own killings!"

Laura was still whimpering. "At the time, Herb still hoped that he could save his mother and sister and me."

Anne turned on them both. "Shut up you two. Isn't it enough that we are being murdered by the Germans? Do we have to be at each other's throats?" Then, more calmly, she said to Alicia, "Stop quoting poems about death to Andrew. If you want to be depressed and commit suicide, go ahead, but leave Andrew alone. He has enough problems without you adding your own."

"He likes to practice English," Alicia said feebly. She looked at Anne, and there was a new pain in her eyes. "Do you think what I think about his cough?" She suspected tuberculosis.

"Keep it to yourself," Anne said. Then, in another change of tone, she asked curiously, "Why did you memorize English poems about death?"

"I liked the way they were written—the words and the poetry. At the time, it wasn't death that interested me." She added dreamily, "Jerry and I used to memorize pages and pages of our favorite books. My mother had many books in French, Russian, and German. My aunt also bought books in English. My father and uncle read medical books in German. Do you remember Leon's bookstore on Sienkiewicz Street? You could order books in any foreign language, but they were quite expensive."

A memory from the past suddenly popped up in Alicia's mind. Her mother and aunt were sitting in the Paula's expensively furnished living room, having tea. Suddenly Eisig barged in, waving a bill from Leon's. Paula and Guta had not only been ordering literary masterpieces, but also modern French romances, and these were full of descriptions of explicit sex, quite risqué for the period. Since they were in French, the men and children of the house could not read them. "Look at these books listed on the bill," Eisig cried indignantly. "I've heard about these authors and their kind of writing. For the money the books cost, I could have had the best whore in Warsaw. Who needs their theories? Why not have the real thing? The books cost as much as a patient pays me for a treatment for syphilis. In fact, for that kind of money,"—he slapped the bill—"I can cure a person of clap and give him the next treatment gratis when he catches it again."

"Eisig!" Guta was scandalized, "How can you talk like this in front of the children?"

Eisig waved his hand. "Jas and Jerry are boys, and Alicia is too young to understand." Then he glanced at his wife and her sister. "You are both true Warman's daughters."

Guta was upset, but Paula simply laughed.

It was not until much later that Alicia realized how funny her father was. Later that afternoon, Jas got hold of one of the books. Alicia had always bragged to the boys that she understood French. "Translate it for us," Jas ordered.

She tried hard, but she was only eight, and the French words for unfaithful wives, adulterous husbands, and sexual gymnastics were unfamiliar to her. She was ready to cry. Jas snatched the book back, called her stupid, and said that he had an older girlfriend who took French in school.

The life that is no more, she thought. A bookstore where you could order mysterious books in different languages. Happy, smiling, beautiful faces of her mother and aunt. It was before Grandmother Regina's death and well before they lost Zabiec. My mother and the nursing certificate, Mucia and the necklace, Pawel and Aryan papers—they are all trying to tell me something.

Anne prodded her. "Wake up, Alicia. You're off in your own world again."

Alicia looked up at Anne and smiled. "I've got to go downstairs to the kitchen. Maybe Ruth has something there for me to eat. I'll try to rinse my clothes and wash up." She was talking fast, afraid that her resolve would fade away. "I've got to wear something different in the morning. Tomorrow is Tuesday, Tadek is usually home. I'll try to see him."

That week Anne and Alicia worked the same shift. "Cover for me in the morning," Alicia asked her. "If I find Tadek, I'll discuss my escape with him."

Anne was amazed at this sudden change in Alicia's mood. When Benjamin came later that evening, the girls told him of Alicia's plans.

There were only three of them in the room. "You might as well forget the addresses that Pawel gave you," Benjamin said to Alicia. "Somebody involved in the operation was arrested in Warsaw, and everyone else is scared stiff. They probably changed their addresses and maybe their names."

"Oh, God, I hope they didn't arrest Pawel's cousin."

"I don't think so, but I don't know for sure. These people used to help the ones who came to Warsaw with Aryan papers, but now it's all finished."

Alicia was losing her determination. I must do something, she thought, before I sink back into lethargy. "What do you suggest I do with these papers?" she asked Benjamin.

Benjamin started lecturing: "The best thing for you would be to work inside Germany. Nobody will recognize you there as a Jew. You won't have it easy—they're not exactly nice to Poles, either. After Jews and Gypsies, Slavs are next on their list of inferior races. But they won't murder you. Just make sure that you act dumb. Dumb Polak, you don't understand any other language except Polish. Even in your sleep make sure you don't quote your Polish, English, or Hebrew poetry. Never let them know that you have more than an elementary education."

Alicia laughed in spite of herself. She thought about the times in school when she listened to Polish girls praying to the Virgin Mary while she and Sabina felt like outcasts. "I know what I'll recite; Holy Mary of Czestochowa, Mother of God."

"And cross yourself as often as possible," Benjamin said.

"Before I become a 'dumb Polak,' I'd like to quote from Tuwim."

"Oh not again," Anne groaned.

"It's in Polish, you know."

> I pojdziemy znowu kazdy w swoja strone
> na wedrowki nasze dzikie i szalone
> Dokad nas zanioslo gdziesmy sie zgubili
> Swiatu ogromnemu obcy i niemili.

> Everybody will go his own way
> On crazy, mad escapades
> Wandering in an immense and strange world
> Always a despised alien.

"I know the poem," Benjamin said. "It's appropriate in our situation."

Alicia looked at Anne and Benjamin. They, Andrew, Saul, and the girls were her family now, the only family she had. Even Laura and Lucia were like sisters compared to strangers in Warsaw or—she shivered—in Germany. With Pawel, Alicia was ready to venture to the ends of the earth and would go along with his crazy schemes, but alone? Why do they expect me to do anything? Why can't I be like the majority, and wait for my turn or for a miracle? She thought about her mother: "We'll do what everybody else does." Then she and everybody else walked like sheep to the trains.

"You are in your dream world again," Anne said.

Alicia surprised herself by her own answer. "I ran away from home at thirteen looking for adventure. When I was in Rovno in 1939, I wanted to take a bus south with Carl and Sabina to cross many borders to get to Palestine. Later on, in Lwow, I was ready to remain alone rather than go back to German Poland."

The old doubt and despair clouded her eyes. "At that time the world did not seem to be such a horrible place and I did not perceive God as being light years away."

The following day Alicia sneaked out of the factory and went to see Tadek. Having Aryan papers in her pocket made her feel safer walking the streets of the city. Still in Kielce, there was always the danger of being recognized. It would be different in a big city like Warsaw where nobody knew her. By good luck, she found Tadek at home. When she saw him, she had to stop herself from crying. After Pawel's death, he was the only one alive who was a part of her previous life. He offered her bread and suggested that she take some with her.

"What's going on in the world?" Alicia wanted to know.

"I heard a broadcast from London from the Polish government in exile. They pledged that when they establish a government after the war, it will be a full-fledged democracy with rights guaranteed for all minorities."

Alicia almost laughed. "By then, they won't have to worry about a Jewish minority. There just won't be any. Do they know in London about gas chambers, *Einsatzcommando,* and other devices for murdering people?"

"They just talked in general about German atrocities. I don't understand why they don't give out details. Speaking of German devices, I heard about another one. They take people in buses, close all the windows, and let in poisonous gas."

"Your partisans are also killing Jews," Alicia reminded him. She had heard some painful stories.

Tadek spread his hands. "Some of them do," he admitted, "but some are trying to help. They're in constant danger themselves, and helping Jews would add to it. There are people of every nationality who just like to kill, and just now it's open season on Jews. If they hate Germans or Russians, they can't do much about it. Hating Jews takes away their guilt for getting property left behind by the Jews."

Somehow Alicia's thoughts drifted to "buses." "Do you remember the bus we used to take to Stadion when we were too lazy to walk, and the bus to Zabiec every June? All those little towns and shtetls must be all gone now."

"Poland will never be the same," Tadek said. "The Jews from the shtetls aren't there anymore—just gone forever."

"Well, I never did know much about that kind of life," Alicia admitted. "All I know I learned from reading Sholem Asch."

Then Tadek said idly, "Old Jerry invited me to Zabiec a few times, but I never managed to make it. Too bad it was sold. It would be nice for you, Jas, and Jerry to have a place to go back to after the war."

"You seem to be taking it for granted that we'll still be here after the war."

"You have Aryan papers. Hold on to them. Now, after Pawel's arrest and death, it is almost impossible to get papers."

So, Tadek knew about Pawel. Alicia felt her heart crushing her all over again. "I wonder who betrayed him, a Jew or a Pole?"

Tadek shrugged his shoulders. "Unfortunately there are too many of us who are willing to make it easy for the Germans."

"You know," Alicia said, "you're taking a terrible risk just allowing me in your apartment and talking with me? It's a death penalty for a Gentile who harbors a Jew."

"Do you know of the risk you are taking by talking to *me*?" Tadek answered. "You don't present any risk to me. How should I know that your papers are fake?"

"How do you think I should use them?"

"You are relatively safe working in the factory. The Russians are still far away. When they cross the old Polish borders, then you should get out. It will take a few more months."

"I wish I could be as sure as you that things will work out," she repeated.

"It will take time, Alicia, because the maniacs will never surrender until the Russians are in Berlin."

So they decided that Tadek would get some money for Alicia, leaving most of it for later. Alicia kissed Tadek good-bye. "You remind me of old times."

"I loved your aunt, Jerry's mother. What a lady she was," Tadek said.

At the mention of her Mucia, Alicia felt herself choke up. "It's hard for me to imagine her as a helpless victim. I remember coming back by train from Zakopane, she dislocated a man's jaw for insulting us and telling her that as Jews we had no right to travel first class. And my grandfather? He was such a powerful and cunning man. Did the Nazis get him also? The whole thing seems so improbable, I cannot get rid of a feeling that I will wake up any moment in old Kielce with all the problems that seemed so important at the time. How do you transport millions of innocent people to gas chambers and burn their bodies?"

"The Germans," Tadek said, "have an obsession to free Europe of all Jews. There is nothing spontaneous about their killings, they had devised a cast-iron system. But all that effort might make them lose the war sooner."

The chiming of a clock brought Alicia back to the reality of the moment. "I've got to run back to the factory before they miss me. I'll try to see you in a couple of weeks, and maybe you will have some money for me then."

"Be careful," he said. "Just try to blend in with the Polish workers."

One cold, wet morning in March, about a week after her visit with Tadek, Alicia was walking to the gate to join the groups on their way to the factories. It was bone-chilling weather, overcast and dark; sleet was falling, and there was ice underfoot.

Anne and Andrew were working the night shift that week; they were now sleeping. It was Tuesday, and Alicia had Aryan identification with her in case she decided to visit Tadek. But that morning it was too nasty to go anyplace. Nobody ever knew when the policemen would search people. It was too late to go back "home" to give her papers to Anne for hiding. On the way to the gate, she passed the abandoned shack behind which she once sat with Pawel when he first arrived at the Quarters. In the shack there was a loft full of straw. She placed her papers under the straw, noting the exact place, then proceeded to the gate.

It was the usual routine day of work at the factory. When she came back late that afternoon, it was still raining and dark. She went directly to the shack. It seemed even darker inside than outside, but she knew exactly the place where she had left her papers.

She could not find them. She went through the entire loft, throwing the straw all around, but they were nowhere. How could I let this happen? she thought in despair. Pawel died because of these papers. Did I want them stolen? Stolen, so that I don't have to do anything or go any place? She was crying inwardly. Pawel, I honestly tried, I was ready to take chances—I never suspected that somebody would steal them.

She tried to think logically. There was my photograph on the papers. Who could use papers with my photograph? Then she reminded herself of something Rudek had once said: "You look a lot like my wife—blond, light complexion, even with glasses. . ." Rudek and his wife Latka. Latka did not wear glasses. The photograph of Alicja Krystyna Buszewska was taken without glasses.

In her previous life, whenever Alicia had done something stupid, like almost drowning in the Vistula or running away to Gdynia, she would worry what her mother would say. Now she was afraid to face Anne. She imagined Anne disgusted with her: "You were in your dream world again. Wake up, Alicia—forget your poetry and start paying attention to what's going on around you!"

Alicia hated herself bitterly. What a schlemiel I am! No Pawel, no Aryan papers, no necklace.

To her surprise, when she confessed to Anne, the older woman was philosophical. "Maybe it's for the best," she said. "Who knows what would happen to you out there alone in a world full of enemies?"

"What will happen here?"

"Whatever is *beshaert*," Anne said.

My mother used that word, Alicia thought, when she was turned away from the border and came back to Lwow. "I think," she said to Anne, "it means 'preordained' like fate." Then she added, "Was it *beshaert* for our people to be gassed at Treblinka?"

The following morning, Andrew and Anne looked all over the loft, but, as Alicia suspected, they did not find the documents. A few days later Rudek and his wife disappeared from the Quarters.

Something strange was happening in the factory. One day in the middle of March, many policemen's wives, ex-policemen, and ex-policemen's wives reported to work. Until that day they had held jobs inside the Quarters, and now because there was not enough work for them in the factory, they hung around most of the time. Alicia had had very little contact with these people before. They were all well dressed and well fed, and she especially envied their boots. It rained a lot that March; the winter's snow had hardly melted yet, and she often got her feet wet. She knew if she got a fever and sore throat, Dr. Breitman would give her an admission slip to the hospital, but it was always dangerous to be sick.

That week Andrew was on the same shift as Alicia. He was still coughing, and it was a dry, rasping kind of cough that Alicia did not like. "Look at these women," he said to Alicia. "Some people just know how to take care of themselves under any circumstances."

"Oh, come on," Alicia said. "In this world there will always be haves and have-nots."

"This is not 'this' world. We're all doomed. The least we could do is be nice to each other and share our worldly goods. These might be the last few months of our lives." He pointed at Alicia's feet. "Look at your shoes. The soles are full of holes, and so are mine. We should both go to the storeroom and get shoes and socks."

"Rudek is gone," Alicia mused, adding, "probably with my papers. Our favorite creep, Birnbaum, is in charge."

"Yeah," Andrew said, "we don't stand a chance. The policemen's wives, as usual, have priority." Then he added, "There is a reason for all these people becoming factory workers so suddenly. Spiegel probably knows about some impending action. Factory workers have the best chance of remaining in Kielce."

Alicia had to laugh. "We were sent here for punishment."

The new bunch of women did not act as if they were awaiting doom. They talked about their husbands and children, chatter, chatter. Like my mother and Pawel's mother, Alicia thought, always bragging about their brood. It seemed to her that nothing had changed for these women. No wonder they look down on me. Then it occurred to her that these women were only in their twenties, and they had already lost their parents and maybe their sisters and brothers. Their husbands had bought life for them and their children by "devoted service." Alicia smiled to herself. Pawel would get a kick out of that—me calling whatever they did "devoted service."

The women thought that, as wives of policemen and mothers of their children, they were safe. Assigning them to the factory was just an extra precaution. Ex-policemen's wives did not feel quite so secure. The three German-Jewish women, Mrs. Spiegel, Mrs. Glattstein and Mrs. Breslau stayed inside the Quarters, babysitting for the forty children whose mothers went to work. Dora Oberman, the wife of the only Kielce born policeman in Spiegel's inner circle, worked in the factory in the privileged position of a secretary.

That evening, in the small hospital, they were discussing the situation. They had only four patients, so during the day, Laura helped the German ladies with the children while Ruth remained with the patients.

"Isn't it nice the way these three ladies are taking care of forty children?" Laura said. "The kids are very cute but still there's a lot of work taking care of them, and some are quite spoiled and obstreperous."

"I'm very much impressed," Benjamin said with heavy sarcasm.

Laura, as usual ignored Ben. "Mr. Spiegel told us that there might be a labor relocation. They need more workers in Pionki."

Pionki was a labor camp near Radom.

"You mean," Alicia said, "they don't have enough people in Radom to send there?"

"They sent too many to Treblinka," Ben said. "In case it's true that people are going to be sent to Pionki, I know for certain that it is not an extermination camp; it lacks the modern facilities for mass murder, which the German scientists and engineers so brilliantly devised."

"That's what Spiegel told us," Laura said, "Pionki is a labor camp just like Kielce." Then she became anxious. "I don't work in the factory—will I be deported?

"I wouldn't worry," Benjamin said. "Director Kramer will insist that there is at least one nurse left for his workers."

Anne turned to Laura and said, "Tell Dr. Breitman to discharge our four hospital patients as soon as possible."

Laura was troubled. "What are we going to do about Eddie?" Eddie, one of the patients. was running a high fever, and Dr. Breitman suspected spinal meningitis, so Eddie was kept in a separate room.

"We cannot discharge him. All we can do is hope," Anne said. "Thank God that Saul and Andrew are out."

Now Andrew looked worried. "What if, in the middle of the selection, I get one of my coughing attacks?"

"Don't Andrew, don't," Anne implored.

Laura promised to get some cough drops from Breitman or Rut-kowski.

"Now you," Anne said to Alicia, "this time try to take everything that you have with you, not like last time when you had no clothes and no money."

"Oh, God, Anne, by now I know how to take care of myself."

At the end of March 1943, the dreaded day of new selections came to the Jewish Quarters of Kielce. All eight hundred people gathered on the main street of the Quarters, and there was Mr. Thomas again. Eddie was taken out of the hospital, his fever so high that he was in a hallucinatory state. He did not know where he was. He never realized that a gun was pointing at him, and then he was dead.

The people working in the two factories, the Jewish policemen, their wives and children, one nurse, one doctor, and one medic went to the Kielce side. The others went to the transport side: Fanny, Ruth, Saul, Rachel, and many others that Alicia knew were between them. Then the last final act of the "labor relocation" was carried out. Children, all the children below the age of twelve, had to step out. Magnanimously, Thomas gave women a choice: They could stay with their husbands or go with their children. Out of twenty mothers, four joined the children.

There was one little girl, maybe eleven years of age, who stood inside her mother's many skirts, so that her feet could not be seen. She remained with the adult factory workers. They were escorted by the policemen to the new barracks attached to the factories. Thirty-nine children, four women, three Jewish policemen, with a few SS men, boarded a bus. Nobody had any illusion where they were going.

The majority of these children were below the age of five, after all, the policemen and their wives were young couples in their twenties. Though the children went through the selection before the deportation to Treblinka, they did not understand what was happening and they were never separated from their parents. The older ones sometimes asked about their grandparents, but their parents would only tell them that they had gone to another city. The three policemen chosen by

Spiegel to escort them had no children of their own. There was Glattstein, Viennese born and Spiegel's first lieutenant, Zubow, a big
husky refugee from Lodz, who did not have any family in Kielce, and
Stawski, a Kielce man who sent his wife and child to Treblinka and
remained with another woman in Kielce. They arrived at the cemetery
where the doctors with their families and the Levys had already been
taken care of. They descended from the bus, and the women and
children stood in a group watching the three policemen digging a pit.
The women told stories and sang to the kids. "Why can't we dig also?"
the children asked.

"We'll go to the sandbox tomorrow, where you can dig. There'll
be sandboxes and toys and love and laughter where we are going," the
mothers said.

Then the mothers were instructed to take off their clothes and to
take off their children's clothes and place them in a neat pile next to
the pit. It was still cold, and the children cried—they were freezing.
The mothers explained that it would be warm in the big sandbox. Then,
naked, they all entered the mass grave. The kids thought that the
machine gun pointing at them was a big toy gun. Then when the shooting started, and some actually saw their playmates dropping to the
ground, they started screaming. The surviving women tried to quiet
them down, and then it was all over. The policemen had the job of
closing the pit. Glattstein, from the corner of his eye, saw something
move under a bush. He glanced over at the Germans. They seemed not
to be paying attention. Smoking and laughing, they could relax, now
that the job was done. A limousine arrived and picked up most of the
Germans. The only ones left were the Polish bus driver and one SS
man, who were assigned to take the Jewish policemen back to the barracks. The SS man was tired; he climbed to the back of the bus with his
gun, sat down, and promptly fell asleep.

Glattstein told the bus driver that he had to take a piss. He went to
the bush where he had noticed the movement. There he found a little
boy, shaking, his eyes wide open with terror. Shlomo, nine years old,
sensed somehow that he was better off not following other children.

Glattstein had a wide jacket. He picked up the child and put him
under it. "Don't wiggle, don't say anything," he told him. They

boarded the bus. Glattstein put the jacket under the seat; he was worried that the child would die from fright. The SS man, with his big gun, was snoring in the back of the bus. Stawski and Zubow were also dozing off. The trip to the factory seemed to take forever. As Glattstein left the bus, with the kid under his jacket, the driver said, "Good luck, man."

Glattstein breathed deeply; he entered the relative safety of the barracks and let the little boy out. All he could hear was crying. The women were just lying on their bunks and wailing, some tearing their hair out. Then the little boy ran to his mother. "A miracle, a miracle," she cried. She grabbed him in her arms, hugged him, squeezed him almost to the point of hurting him.

The other women surrounded Glattstein. "Where are our children?" He spread his arms helplessly. "Could you not save our children? Why only Shlomo?" They were actually hitting and scratching him.

Glattstein was now crying himself. "I didn't do anything," he said. "It was all Shlomo's doing. He just didn't follow the others."

Alicia stood and watched. She had not expected that kind of humanity from Glattstein, a man who was always joking, pretending that he did not have a care in the world. Now she suspected that underneath that callous surface, he was compassionate and could suffer deeply. I should not be so prejudiced against German Jews, she thought. They are still Jews. She remembered Jerry quoting, from what book she did not know, "He who saves the life of one man saves the entire world."

She found something strange in herself. She really did not care about wailing women and their dead children. Thirty-eight children have just been murdered, and she did not feel a thing. But most important there was no rage left in her. At whom should she rage? At the insane system? Of course at the Germans. How about the Poles? And Jews themselves? At the Jewish God? At "whatever gods may be?" Even at her parents for staying in Poland? She simply stopped feeling anything.

For some strange reason she thought about Jerry again. She saw his tremendous, big deep green eyes, the eyes of a poet and dreamer. Jerry, please take care of yourself. It is better that you should cry for me, because I have no more tears left to cry for you.

CHAPTER 12

1943–44—Kielce, Barracks Labor Camp, Henrykow

It was arranged for the women who had lost their children not to report to work for three days. They used that time for a mass outpouring of grief. It seemed they competed, which one could cry the loudest. Most of them refused food. Laura walked between them trying to induce them to eat. Their husbands were dry-eyed and tried to hide their sorrow.

I never had the luxury of weeping like that, Alicia thought. I did not have even one day to mourn. Do these women feel guilty, that they did not go with their children for the final ride? I did not go with my mother, but I know that my mother would have gone with me. She remembered Guta wailing when her two-day-old daughter died. But the next year Guta had Henius. Will these women have another chance? If tiny Lala had lived and grown, in 1942 she would be eleven years old. She would be murdered like all other Jewish children. So it did not much matter that she died, nothing planned for and done in the 1930s really mattered. They were all doomed.

Whatever happens in human life, one has to get up and face the new day. The women went to work and started taking care of their husbands. That was supposedly the reason they remained.

In the barracks of Henrykow, there were two rows of double-decker bunks. Farther from the entrance was a partition, which separated the four "leading" couples from the rest of the population: the commandant Spiegel, with his pretty doll-like wife, who seemed to be completely dependent on him, Glattstein with his tall, dark handsome wife, a real Viennese belle; and Breslau with his wife. Breslau was the only one who was not a policeman. His job was to keep strict account of everybody. The fourth couple behind the partition were the Odermans; Kielce-born, their little boy was murdered.

The first three couples were German Jews; the Spiegels and Glattsteins were childless. The Breslaus' six-year-old son was hidden behind the partition. He was the third child of Henrykow. Everybody knew how eleven-year-old Bella and nine-year-old Shlomo were saved. How about Tommy Breslau? People whispered that Mrs. Breslau and her boy were not in the Quarters during the last action when thirty-eight children were murdered in the Kielce cemetery. They were already in Henrykow barracks. Who warned Breslau? A German? A Pole? The rumor was that it was a high-ranking member of the Gestapo. Whatever information Breslau had, and from whom, he kept to himself. Other parents did not suspect what was going to happen to their children.

Beyond the partition, there was a section occupied by the policemen, the medic, and ex-policemen. They had their wives or girlfriends with them. Then came the bunks of other couples like Lucia and Joseph. Next came the single girls: Laura the nurse, Alicia, Anne, and a few more. The workers lived in the longest section of the barracks; they had no status, no women, and were usually hungry and neglected. By the time the rations leaked to them, very little was left. Available girls would not bother with them. Andrew jokingly named this section "dungeons."

Attached to the factories were special workshops. In Henrykow there was a shoemaker and a tailor shop. The workers there were a little better off than the ones in the factory. Jankiel, Alicia's tormentor and a "jack of all trades," worked as the shoemaker. The ladies behind the partition employed the dungeon boys to clean and cook for them.

The barracks attached to the Ludwikow had similar arrangements. While Henrykow (Holzwerke) was based on work with wood, Ludwikow (Ludwigshutte) made iron products. Spiegel lived in Henrykow but was in charge of both factories. His lieutenant for Ludwikow was a Kielce-born policeman, Tarnow. Dr. Breitman was assigned to Ludwikow while medic Rutkowski and Laura to Henrykow. The entire group of people were in their early and mid-twenties; the few over thirty were the exception.

Alicia had a sore throat the first day they arrived at the barracks.

She asked Breslau to give her a separate bunk. "I don't want to give my germs to anyone," she said. There were not many single girls, and Alicia did not have to share a bunk with anybody. She slept on the lower level, on the upper level was Sonia, the same girl who once got her in trouble.

Kielce was rumored to be the best labor camp in Poland. Pionki, where so many Kielce people were transported, was supposed to be much harder. Alicia thought about Ruth, Fanny, and Rachel but especially about Saul; how was he managing with his bad limp? Kielce was Kielce, she still had access to Tadek and means to get money. Even some policemen like Goldberg were her friends. Goldberg and his wife Rhoda lost two small children in the last action.

Benjamin told Alicia not to sneak out of the factory anymore. "You don't have Aryan papers, and security is much tighter now. Occasionally, there are even Germans patrolling."

"I will soon need money," Alicia said.

Benjamin told her about a Polish worker who could get in touch with Tadek for her. "Maybe Tadek will meet you at a designated spot on the other side of the fence with some money."

And so it was arranged. One afternoon in May, Alicia and Tadek found themselves looking at each other across the fence. They had to attend to business fast before they were caught. They had no time to talk, yet still she noticed that he did not look well. He was pale and gaunt, and his skin seemed to hang loose on his bones.

Alicia got the money. The following week, she learned from Benjamin that Tadek had been admitted to a hospital with a case of typhus. "I thought that only Jews in the ghettos and work camps were getting typhus," she said. Some weeks later, Alicia was told that Tadek died. She felt like an old lady who reads obituary columns everyday to find out who from her circle of friends had died and wonders who will be next. Her enemies, doubt and depression, were descending on her. Why am I still here? "Keep on plugging, Alicia." You again, she said to the dead Pavel. She often talked to him.

Lucia became ill. She had strep throat and was running a fever. She lay on her bunk, worrying about her heart; Laura took as good care of her as she could. She told Alicia that it was hard to get an aspirin from Rutkowski. There were plenty of medical supplies in the infirmary, but he kept everything under lock and key and dispensed medication only to the "higher ups" like the Spiegels and the others behind the partition. Laura suspected that he planned to sell the rest and was disgusted.

One afternoon, Alicia was putting cold compresses on Lucia's head. Because of you, she thought, I am still alive. You're the one who pushed me to stand with the nurses. Then you wanted to go back to our mothers, but I made you stay. Maybe that's why I feel responsible for you.

It was even more dangerous to be bedridden in the barracks than it was in the Quarters. They were already hiding children, and any sudden inspection would reveal—well, she didn't want to think.

If Lucia and I had not left our mothers, Alicia thought, we would be beyond all suffering now—our ashes blown someplace in the wind and our bones ground up for fertilizer. Lucia would not have to sleep with a man she did not love or worry about her heart. I would not have to go through life alone and watch people I love being murdered or dying from sickness.

That afternoon, Lucia's fever broke. She smiled at Alicia and told her not to worry, that she would be all right.

Alicia suddenly felt ashamed of her gloomy thoughts. What right do I have to decide that Lucia would be better off dead than alive? She's only sixteen years old, and she will recover. Lucia is the type who usually gets what she wants. If there is ever again a "regular" world, there will certainly be a future for someone like her. Who knows? She might still become a doctor.

Suddenly Alicia decided that she was not yet ready to give up either. My father had a medical degree at my age, she thought. But I want to be a writer, and some writers produce their best work at middle age. I have plenty of time. I did not die from typhus, I was not sent to Treblinka or Pionki. . . . So maybe. Deep inside she could not imagine herself dead.

All these mood swings. At one moment she wished that she and Lucia had gone to Treblinka, and the next, she saw Lucia receiving the Nobel Prize for medicine and she getting one for literature. Just living in a regular world would be enough, she sighed. And with Pawel, it would have been heaven.

To Alicia's surprise, she had come to like most of the women. Genia was a tall pretty girl, always neat and well put together, cheerful and with a sense of humor. If Genia thought about her newborn baby, strangled during the selection to Treblinka, she did not show it. Alicia considered her a warm, lovely person.

Alicia often wondered what kind of a woman Mrs. Birnbaum was. Her husband was a vulgar man, full of filthy jokes, who seemed to know all of the most profane Yiddish expressions and who struck people left and right. But Lola, his wife, was a pleasant lady, well educated, intelligent, well read, polite, and friendly. Her two small children had been murdered. Sometimes when they were all together, she cried. However, most of the time she appeared cheerful.

Maybe I owe Birnbaum a debt, Alicia thought. If he had not reported us for posing for pictures, I would be in Pionki.

In the group of women, Zosia assumed the role of a leader. She was older than the rest, in her early thirties. Her husband was an ex-policeman, and they had lost two small children.

Marcia was the one who had saved her daughter by hiding her underneath her skirt. Her husband, a policeman, was one of the few that was liked by the dungeon boys.

Alicia was amazed at how well these women were able to leave their tragedies behind and resume their normal routine.

Normally, as people get older, they see their grandparents and their parents growing feebler and sicker and finally dying. And there are exceptions to the rule, as when young people die before their elders. Julek Blum died in a drowning accident, and his mother never recovered; she went to Treblinka in her black dress and veil. In 1943 Poland, many parents remained alive after the wholesale slaughter of their children. Did these women become numb after three days of crying, or did the fact that they shared the experience help them keep their sanity?

Alicia was only twenty when she lost her parents. In "normal" times she would probably have been on her own after she received her Matura. (Jas was only seventeen when he went to Palestine.) Alicia would have left home for a career, but home would still have been there for her to go back to. There would be a sense of permanency and continuity. She could have been alone but still never feel like a homeless waif.

She would close her eyes and see the things that should have been: food, apples, pears, and strawberries, walking in the mountains, looking at the river, smelling the flowers, playing with children, the ecstasy of intimacy with a man you love, but most of all being young and carefree, full of hope and not thinking about death anymore. "They destroyed my state of mind," she told Anne, "and I think forever."

"Don't give me that crap," Anne said crisply. "If you survive, you will still be young enough to build a new life for yourself. In the meantime, we have to pretend that we have a chance and do the best we can with each day. Once you tell yourself that you can't make it, then it's good-bye, Alicia. You should not feel sorry for the dead, as in your poem, they ended up 'safe to sea.' They won't be cold, hungry, or confused anymore."

Alicia was laughing now. "So you remember my poem, Anne."

As they were leaving the barracks to report for the afternoon roll call, they saw birds flying overhead. "What a magnificent creation of God a bird is," Alicia said, "a great engineering and artistic feat. Would you believe that the same God made Hitler? Maybe He should have stopped creating before He thought of man." Then Alicia thought for a while. "Of course, animals don't write poetry," she said. "Or explore the laws of the universe."

"Stop philosophizing," Anne told her. "We're late as it is."

But Alicia could not stop: "We live in an upside down world: Doctors, who are trained to save lives, have to kill their patients, and Jewish policemen deliver their own children for murder."

The first two weeks of June in 1943 found both Alicia and Andrew working the midnight shift at the factory. It was called a "dead" shift, because there was usually not much to do. They did not expect Fuchs to inspect the factory so late at night. Alicia and Andrew sometimes hid behind stacks of wood and talked. Andrew tried to get Alicia to memorize the names and addresses of his relatives in the United States. Just like Pawel, with his contacts in Warsaw, she thought.

"If you survive, let them know about me," Andrew told her.

Alicia tried to remember the names of her father's relatives in America. The name "Bertha Knopf" stuck in her mind; her father's sister who lived in Brooklyn. "Remember that name," she told Andrew.

"Don't be funny, Alicia, I will never make it. You just might. I am still coughing. Dr. Breitman says that I have a chronic bronchitis. It might soon affect my lungs and maybe my heart."

"What about my sore throats?" Alicia asked. "Any kind of breeze, and I get it."

"It never goes down into your bronchial tubes."

"The fact is," Alicia said, "that it doesn't follow any reason who will make it and who will not. Maybe it is fate or maybe none of us will survive. As Jankiel said, 'Thomas smelled me out.' Nobody cares about us. I expected that after Treblinka the earth would stop spinning on its axis, would stop rotating around the sun, fall out of its orbit and crash."

Andrew laughed. "Did you expect that 'whatever gods may be' would accomplish that? Maybe at least one of them is close enough to hear us. According to your theory, our one God is thousands of light years away."

"I know the story of Passover very well from the seders in Zabiec. The God I heard about then was very powerful and stood by his 'chosen' people. 'Let my people go,' He commanded the pharaoh."

"Therefore Hitler obeyed him," Andrew said. "Before the war, he was only too happy to let the Jews go. Poland was also. Nobody wanted to take us."

After a while they came back to the real world. "Now that Tadek is dead," Alicia said, "I've lost contact with Mr. X. Soon I will run out of money, and I'll be just as bad off as you and the boys in the dungeons."

"Don't expect these women, who you've been so friendly with lately, to help you. Do you think that because their children were murdered, somehow they've changed? They're just as greedy as ever, holding onto their possessions—they learned nothing from their experiences. Why else did they marry policemen or be policemen's girlfriends but for material advantages? The ladies behind the partition have butter, eggs, and fresh rolls every morning. I know it for a fact, because Mendel, my friend, sells it to them. He gets it from a Pole. In the afternoons, those ladies have high tea English-style, with tea and cake. They serve it on fancy dishes that the Spiegels inherited after the 'first family' Levy was taken to the cemetery."

Alicia burst out laughing.

"Did Dora Oderman ever invite you for tea?" Andrew asked. "She is a highfalutin secretary and acts like she is a great lady."

Alicia remembered when Dora and her husband brought their child to her father in the beginning of the war; the boy had a rash. Eisig treated him, but he looked suspiciously at the child's father; he did not like Jewish policemen. The baby was dead now, and according to Andrew, his parents did not learn anything. "Don't put these women down too much," she said, "Laura goes to the Ludwikow occasionally to assist Dr. Breitman in minor surgeries. She tells me that Mrs. Spitz is completely out of it by now, she does not report to roll calls or to work, and the women are taking care of her. Can you imagine that she was once an opera singer and spoke Italian, French, and German?"

"Madness does not discriminate," Andrew replied.

Alicia changed the topic. "What kind of surgery is Breitman performing?"

Andrew laughed. "Don't you know? It's mostly abortions. The policemen and their wives are busy."

It felt better to talk about sex than death and mental illness.

"Do you know about Stawski?" Andrew asked. "He is really getting rich. Do you know how?

Stawski was a powerfully built man, who sported a big mustache and looked like a Polish peasant. There was usually a group of young men surrounding him. Zubow, the coarse policeman originally from Lodz, was one of them. Stawski with his girlfriend had a bunk near the partition.

"So how is he getting rich?" Alicia asked. "And how come his bunk is so close to the partition?"

"Because," Andrew answered, "he gives kickbacks."

"Kickbacks from what?" Alicia wanted to ask, but she never had the chance. A Polish co-worker looked into their hiding place and told them that a supervisor was on the floor. "Get out, and at least pretend you're doing something."

"The Germans will not win the war if they're depending on our work," Alicia joked. The Pole joined in the laughter. Alicia never found out, that evening, how Stawski was getting rich.

One afternoon early in June, Alicia and Anne were returning from work. It was a warm, bright day, but not yet hot enough to make one uncomfortable—the kind of weather that one would want the whole year round. They had to cross the square that served for roll calls, which had a little grass plot. Alicia looked at the trees on the other side of the fence. Some lilacs and magnolias were blooming. She could almost smell the flowers. It was five o'clock in the afternoon, but the sun was still high on the horizon. There was at least two and a half hours left of sunlight. It would be so nice to be free on a day like this, but at that moment Alicia was thankful just to be still alive. Her diet consisted of thin soup, black bread, some extra potatoes that she could "organize"; most of the time she was hungry. This particular afternoon, a fellow worker gave her a couple of carrots. She shared them with Anne. Chewing slowly, Alicia savored each morsel as if she were trying to get all the sweetness and nutrients out of the humble vegetable.

"How can you enjoy a plain carrot so much?" Anne asked.

"Right now I would not exchange it for a piece of cake."

It was hard not to be hopeful on a day like that. The winter was far away, and they did not have to worry about keeping warm. The actions were forgotten. Until what? Nobody knew.

When Alicia and Anne walked into the barracks that afternoon, the first person they saw, standing by the bunk in the dungeons, was Saul. Alicia thought she was dreaming. She closed her eyes and then opened them again. Anne was kissing and hugging him. Alicia ran to them.

"Saul, how did you get here?" she said. "Did you grow wings and fly from Pionki?"

"I walked," he said.

Alicia looked down at his feet. He could barely stand on his bad leg.

"I was not limping as much when we started."

"But it is two hundred kilometers from Pionki!" Alicia exclaimed. "All mountains and forests."

"The boys wanted to leave me behind, but Chaim, the guy who organized the escape, would not hear of it. I didn't want to be a burden to the group, but he insisted that if I was left, he would stay with me. Nobody else knew the terrain as well as Chaim did, so they decided to drag me with them."

Alicia stared. "You mean you were with a whole group, free in the forests of Swietokrzyski Mountains, and you came to another labor camp?"

"It does sound crazy," Saul admitted, "but we could not make it in the forest. I was limping, and another fellow was running a fever. The Russians are still far away. I guess the others will try again in a few months." Saul looked around, and then he whispered, "Breslau told us not to talk about our experiences. He is going to try to incorporate us somehow into his registers."

"Dear old Breslau," Alicia said. "Paper work is so important to him. He still thinks that by complying strictly with the rules, we can make it."

Many more people drifted to the barracks of Henrykow that summer. There was a couple hiding in the forest for a while; the woman, though only in her twenties, was completely grey. As she told Alicia, they lived in constant terror, and her hair changed color in a few especially frightful nights. Two more couples came seemingly from nowhere, a man in his middle thirties with a big heavy woman, and another odd couple—a little girl who looked no older than fourteen, skinny with long pigtails and a stocky man, unkempt and dirty, drooling from the mouth, who appeared to be in his middle forties.

He could almost be her grandfather, Alicia thought. She felt sorry for little Hanka.

One day Alicia was talking to Lucia. "Why don't you try to meet Chaim?" Lucia said. "He is one of the very few men here who actually finished gymnasium."

"Oh, you mean the guy who led the boys from Pionki?"

"Yes."

Alicia was mildly interested. Finally here was somebody who did something. He did not just sit and wait, even if he came back to Kielce. But according to Saul, they could not do anything else. If it was Jas, she thought, he would rather die than stay in a labor camp. And if Pawel were alive, Alicja Krystyna Buszewska and Pawel Brzezinsky would probably join the partisans and blow up German supply trains going to the Eastern Front.

Lately Alicia was able to lump Pawel together with everybody else, the people whom she once loved who were now dead. She was twenty-one and alive and realized that she was practically the only girl in the barracks who did not have a steady boyfriend. Andrew and Saul were friends, and she could never consider them anything else. Lucia had Joseph, Anne had Benjamin. Laura had a serious admirer, Sid.

Sid was a gifted mechanic and electrician. He lived in the barracks but worked in the city directly for the Germans. He was tall and handsome, at a time when there were few tall Jewish men. Alicia remembered when he was trouble shooting for her father with X-ray machines. Sid had very little formal education, he was practically self-taught. Eisig called him the Jewish Edison. When they first moved to the barracks, Sid slept with Clara, another miracle girl, pulled out from those going to Treblinka because of her very blond hair and blue eyes. Sid got tired of Clara, left her bunk to sleep alone. He became the most eligible unattached man. He fell in love with Laura, the gorgeous redhead and gentle nurse. Laura, on the other hand, still had not given up her dream of marrying a doctor or at least a man with a higher degree. In the meantime, Majek Krakower, a short pudgy man, fell in love with the abandoned Clara. He was quite a bit older than she and not very attractive, and Clara still hoped that eventually Sid would come back to her. So the romance was one-sided.

As in *Midsummer Night's Dream*, Alicia thought, there's the same scenario in a slave labor camp as in an enchanted forest. Whenever young men and women are thrown together, these things happen; it doesn't matter if they are carefree frolicking fairies and elves, or a bunch of doomed Jews."

The women were always gossiping about who slept with whom and the latest hot item. A young pretty girl left the bunk she shared with her prewar husband, to sleep with her current lover. Genia sometimes kidded Alicia: "How about you, a healthy good looking girl?"

"You have enough people to gossip about," Alicia would answer. "Leave me alone."

Now Lucia said, "Chaim is not only educated, he's also handsome."

For a minute, Alicia did not know whom Lucia was talking about. Oh, yes, Saul's friend. Lucia wants to be my fairy godmother, she groaned inwardly. First it was her idea to stand with the nurses, now she's trying to find me a man.

And then, on midnight shift again, Alicia was bending over to tie her shoelaces when she heard Andrew's voice. "Alicia, meet Chaim, the guy who led the boys from Pionki."

Alicia looked up. He was tall and dark and had an aquiline nose. "I never met you before the war," she said.

"We moved in different circles," he said. "I was in the Jewish gymnasium while you were in Blessed Kinga. My father was a furrier, yours was a doctor."

His Polish had a Yiddish inflection, the same inflection that, so many years ago, made Guta take Alicia away from Mrs. Zima's.

"You seem to know a lot about me," Alicia said.

"Sure he knows, " Andrew put in. "Once he was your father's patient. Was it clap, Chaim?"

"That Andrew," Alicia said, "he can always make me laugh."

That week, on the midnight shift, Alicia and Chaim talked a lot. Andrew was sometimes there, but more often he was not. Alicia was impressed that that entire week Chaim did not make a pass at her. Lately, many boys who approached her wanted quick sex. Maybe, under the circumstances, it was understood. Chaim did not sound like a man who had obtained a Matura; he admitted that he had only had a few years of gymnasium. Chaim's main interest before the war was not school. He was satisfied just to pass from class to class with minimal effort. He had worked in his father's business cutting skins and making fur coats since he was twelve. Maybe that's what I need, Alicia thought, somebody with a tangible skill. Not like me and my other friends, full of hot air and no substance. Did Chaim have substance? He had lost his family to Treblinka, just like her. He was a policeman in the ghetto, but he resigned after the deportation, he could not stomach it any more. What weighed heavily on his conscience was that he did not save his fiancée, Racha. Alicia had known her slightly. Chaim said that he could not find Racha during the selections to claim her as his wife.

Chaim talked about Racha and Alicia about Pawel.

The second week, their relationship progressed from talking to necking. Alicia did not want to be pushed into an affair, but Chaim was insistent. "We're in the middle of the war, probably destined to be killed—why not go all the way and enjoy ourselves?" He often said that he loved her; Alicia did not quite believe him, but it felt good to hear it anyhow. She liked him, and there was definitely a physical attraction between them. She knew that Chaim was the best she could get in the barracks. She often felt alone. Anne, Benjamin, and Ira kept whispering to each other, and whenever she approached them, they would stop talking. My friends, she thought, I trust them but they do not trust me.

There was something that disturbed her about Chaim. She noticed that he hung out with "Stawski's boys." She instinctively disliked them. When she asked Chaim about his connection with them, he changed the subject.

Lately it was not Benjamin but Andrew who was her source of information. "Stawski and his gang," he told her, " have plans for leaving the barracks to live in the forest. They need Chaim as a guide."

The third week, Chaim was no longer working in the factory. He had gotten a job in the workshops attached to Ludwikow, where there was a furrier shop. They worked for the Germans stationed in Kielce. Chaim was redoing the furs grabbed from the Jews to fit German ladies.

"I thought," Alicia said, "that confiscated Jewish furs were for the soldiers on the Russian front?"

Andrew shrugged his shoulders. "Personally I don't mind if they freeze— hopefully to death." Then Andrew told Alicia that Chaim got the job through Stawski's influence.

She stared at him penetratingly. "You don't like Chaim," she remarked.

"I just don't trust him, and I don't think you should either."

Alicia wondered if Andrew was jealous. Did he resent her spending so much time with Chaim? If only I could combine Chaim and Andrew, she thought, then I could have a friend and a lover in one person. Her money was running out; summer and the warm weather would not last forever, and she dreaded the next winter.

Chaim had a good job, which meant more food, clothes, and generally better conditions. Sometimes he brought her potatoes and bread. She sensed that Chaim was not much different from other boys—he wanted sex. He just went about it slower and in a more sophisticated way.

Chaim had a suggestion: "I'll visit you at night in your bunk, and we will do it very quietly."

He wants to keep our relationship secret, Alicia thought. Especially if it develops into an affair. Why?

"If you and Stawski's gang escape into the mountains, would you take me along?" she asked.

"I don't think," he said, "that Stawski would even take Rywka with him and they've been living as husband and wife."

"You say that you love me. You should not leave me behind."

"If you sleep with me—maybe."

Alicia laughed.

The first week of July, Alicia was on the day shift. One afternoon, when she came back from work, she noticed Lucia standing by her bunk shaking and crying. Joseph was yelling at Stawski. "You almost gave her a heart attack."

"She's back isn't she? Safe and sound." Stawski growled.

"What is your friend Stawski up to?" Alicia asked Chaim.

"I think," he answered, "that Lucia is exaggerating and making too much out of what happened."

"You just came back from work—how would you know? And exaggerating what?"

"I know my man Stawski. I'm sure that he wouldn't abuse Lucia."

They heard Stawski telling Lucia, "Just keep your mouth shut, and we'll forget the whole incident."

No one would explain what had happened. Alicia was sure it wasn't sexual abuse; she didn't think Lucia would mind sex with a big virile guy like Stawski. Well, then what? Alicia was determined to find out. If Chaim is so devoted to his patron that he won't tell me, I'm never going to trust him. She was glad that after two weeks of night shift together, she had not slept with him.

Another strange thing happened. Alicia noticed that the big heavy woman, who had drifted in with her husband a few weeks ago, was not there anymore. The man had the bunk to himself. As usual, it was Andrew who explained the disappearance. "She was taken by the Gestapo." He pointed his hand toward the sky.

"Why?" Alicia asked.

"Pregnant," he replied curtly. "If a man wants to get rid of a woman, all he has to do is to tell Spiegel that she's pregnant. Then, it's up to him—either give her a pass to Dr. Breitman for an abortion or report her,"

No wonder, I'm afraid of sex, Alicia thought, appalled.

Then skinny little Hanka got pregnant. Laura went with her to Dr.Breitman. When they came back, Hanka was very pale and looked sick. Laura told Alicia that the pregnancy had progressed long past the first trimester. Breitman scolded her for waiting too long—the fetus was almost a baby. It was a boy, and his arms and legs were formed with all his fingers and toes.

"Did you hold it?" Alicia asked.

"I did, but I don't feel like talking about it."

Alicia thought with disgust of Hanka's dirty, drooling partner. "That contemptible pig of a man."

Late in August, Alicia was again working the midnight shift. The other women commiserated with her: "You get the midnight shift so often." But Alicia loved it. This time she was together with Lucia, who seemed to have recovered from her experience with Stawski. Alicia was still curious and asked her friend what had happened that day.

"I'll be glad to tell you," Lucia said, "because after the war I want you to write about it."

Lucia was the only one in the barracks who believed that there would be an "after the war." And she was the one with a bad heart. Amazing.

"But don't repeat this to anybody," she warned, "because Stawski is very powerful, and if I get pregnant, I might not get a pass to Breitman."

"So what happened?" Alicia prompted.

"During morning roll call, Stawski and Zubow approached me and told me not to go to the factory but to follow them. When I asked them where, Stawski said, 'Don't be scared—you'll soon see.' Zubow was laughing."

Alicia could well imagine the scene: Zubow, a coarse, vulgar, simple man. (What was he doing before the war? A prison guard? A grave digger? A butcher? Maybe a criminal?) Stawski was smoother and probably more evil. "So where did they take you?" she asked.

"We left the factory grounds, and there was a Gestapo man waiting for us. We started walking, the three men and I. For a while I was sure that we were heading for the cemetery. You can imagine how my heart was beating. Right there I thought I'd die of heart failure. Instead, we ended up in the backyard of our old ghetto apartment. Stawski asked me where my mother had buried her valuables. I told Stawski I didn't know, and the Gestapo man immediately pointed his gun at me. I wished I did know about some buried treasures—maybe it would save my life. Stawski told the Gestapo man not to shoot. Zubow got a shovel from someplace and started digging under the roots of an old tree, but found nothing. Then they took me to our pre ghetto apartment on Sienkiewicz Street. They didn't find anything there either. Some people saw us and were scared to death. Between my heart pounding and the Gestapo man with his gun, I was sure I'd never get through the afternoon alive. But a miracle happened, and somehow Stawski and Zubow brought me back to the barracks."

Now Alicia knew how Stawski was getting rich.

In September, Alicia was on the day shift. One day, just before the noon break, the people in the factory smelled smoke. The Polish supervisor told them not to worry; there had been a small fire in the workshops, but it was now under control.

When they returned to the barracks that afternoon, there was a lot of buzzing and whispering.

"They arrested your friend Jankiel," Andrew told Alicia. "The fire started in the shoemaker shop, and somebody has to be blamed."

The next morning at roll call, a group of boys, instead of going to their usual assignment, had to bring lumber from the factory to the front of the barracks. Alicia wondered what they were going to do with it.

That evening it rained. Whatever the boys had built during the day was covered by a rubber sheet. The next morning, everyone had to assemble in front of the barracks in orderly rows while Breslau took the roll call. Then the rubber sheet was removed, revealing a gallows. It was unusually cold for early fall. Alicia, in her thread-bare clothes, shivered more than the rest. Two Gestapo men brought Jankiel out. He still wore that arrogant smirk that Alicia remembered so well.

Now she wished he would taunt her some more. She wanted to run to him and tell him she was no longer angry: "I understand—it was your bitterness that made you so nasty. All the women in your life were murdered." But she could only watch.

They made Jankiel stand on the platform of the gallows. Then the Gestapo men summoned Goldberg and Birnbaum to carry out the hanging. They put the noose around Jankiel's neck and tightened it. Jankiel managed to yell out his last words, *"Haverim, Nkume Neme."* Alicia did not understand him. Later someone told her it meant, "Friends, avenge me."

They all stood there, in their orderly rows, and watched while Jankiel was hanged, and nobody could do anything at all. His body was left hanging there the whole day.

Alicia could not get the two policemen out of her mind. She did not know Birnbaum's background because he was from Lodz. He could even have been a hangman before the war, although she doubted it—Lola would never marry a hangman. But Goldberg, that nice, decent man, who once was proud to be a policeman because he could not only help his family but also ease things for other Kielce Jews. In the summer of 1942, he found that he had to help organize the deportation of thousands of people to gas chambers—his his wife and children were allowed to remain in Kielce. A few months later those children were murdered. Today he had hanged an innocent man, a fellow Jew. How did he feel about being a policeman now?

The false sense of security, which the group had had over the past few months, quickly evaporated. They were reminded once more of their position in the scheme of things. A sense of utter helplessness pervaded the barracks. Some people pinched themselves to make sure they were alive.

Winter weather was setting in once more. There were more and more holes in Alicia's shoes, and her clothes were getting shabbier. She did not have much money left and missed Tadek more than ever. She was still able to "organize" a little extra food, Sometimes, Chaim brought her bread and potatoes.

She remembered what Andrew had told her about Mendel selling eggs and butter to the ladies behind the partition. "Let's find out where he's hiding his basket of stuff," she suggested to Anne.

The two girls started sneaking behind Mendel's bunk when nobody was looking. They would pick up a few of the eggs, make little holes at the bottom, and suck out the contents, then put the eggs neatly back in the basket. They enjoyed listening to the "ladies" yelling at Mendel that some of the eggs he was selling them were empty shells.

Mendel was boiling mad. It did not take much detective work to find out who was behind the mischief. His first impulse was to beat up the two of them, but then he looked at the well-fed "ladies" and the two hungry girls, and he changed his mind. He made an agreement with them: If they would stop stealing, he would give them two eggs apiece every week. But he swore them to secrecy, afraid that other people would take advantage of him if they found out he was soft-hearted.

Alicia knew that there was a storeroom, someplace in the factory, where they had clothes for the workers. She decided to ask Oderman. He was a Kielce man who had known her parents, and now he was a bigshot. He would not pull a "Rudek" on me, she thought. Oderman was a tall, well-built man, who looked well fed and was well dressed. When Alicia approached him, he had just come in, and he wore a wool sweater underneath a fur-lined leather jacket, plus heavy pants and

long boots. Alicia told him what she wanted, and he looked down at
her and said, "Where's all the money you're getting from your Gentile
friends?" He grinned maliciously.

Alicia had never expected that kind of reaction. She said, "I
had money because of my father's hard and honest work. How
did you get that beautiful jacket and boots? I'll bet I know. After
taking people to the trains to Treblinka, you helped yourself to
their belongings. Now you're stealing clothes and food that
should go to the workers." She spat in front of him and went
back to her bunk. Some of the boys were listening, and they applauded.

The next day, Laura said to Alicia. "You shouldn't have spoken to
Oderman that way. I'll talk to Breslau," she offered. "He's a nice guy.
He'll find something for you."

Alicia went with her to Breslau. He was friendly and found her
some sort of boots, not too warm or too high but better than her old
shoes. She also got a few sweaters and some socks. Breslau, the
"Yekie" (a German Jew) and a stranger, was nicer than Oderman, the
Kielce man.

In October, Hanka needed another abortion. Laura went with her to
Dr. Breitman. When they came back, Hanka looked even sicker than
after her first abortion. She went straight to her bunk.

"Dr. Breitman thinks," Laura told Alicia, "that Hanka will not survive another pregnancy and certainly not another abortion. She always
waits too long. It was four months this time."

They noticed Moshe, Hanka's "husband," passing by.

Laura called him: "Moshe, Hanka is not feeling well. We hope she
won't get a bad infection."

The only adjective Alicia could apply to Moshe was "ugly." He
had small, squinting, watery eyes; his hair was greasy and dirty, and so
were his clothes.

He said, "Hanka is a woman."

"She's your wife," Laura said. "You should care about her."

"She's not my wife," he answered simply. "My wife and five
children were sent to Treblinka."

"So she's your girlfriend."

"She's my niece, my brother's daughter."

The girls were aghast. They sunk down on the bunk. "Whoever she is to you," Alicia said shrilly, "you should stop making her pregnant. Next time she'll die."

Moshe's stare seemed to undress her. "Would you like it if I made you pregnant instead?"

Alicia did not even find his statement insulting—it was too ridiculous. She started laughing. But then she reminded herself of poor Hanka, lying sick and exhausted on her bunk. Indignantly, Laura told Moshe that Hanka's insides were all mangled up by now.

Moshe spread his hands. "A man needs it. I have to have it."

"Maybe you should talk to the other men in the barracks," Laura suggested. "Most of them don't make their women pregnant."

Now Moshe was angry, "Nobody has to teach me how to do it," he said roughly. "I could show a few things to your boyfriend Sid." He turned and walked away, mumbling under his breath.

"You have influence with the administration," Alicia said to Laura. "Can't you ask Breslau to give her a separate bunk?"

"Both Breitman and I tried to persuade Hanka to sleep alone, but she wants to be with her Moshe."

"Did you ever think that she might be afraid of him?"

"I don't think so," Laura replied. "She just likes her life the way it is. I wouldn't be surprised that, as sick as she is, she will submit to him tonight. You heard him—he has to have it."

"They should be forced to separate," Alicia insisted. "In a normal world, this relationship would be against the law."

"It is not a 'normal' world," Laura reminded her wearily.

By January 1944 they knew that the Russians were approaching the old Polish borders. Alicia noticed that Chaim did not hang around with Stawski's gang as much as before. He now talked mostly with Ben, Ira, and Anne. Many people had "plans" of leaving the barracks; not only Stawski, but Oderman, if rumors were reliable, would lead a large group to freedom. Then there was Ben, Ira and Anne. With whom would Chaim go? And where would that leave her? Chaim still kept telling her that he loved her and that they would make their relationship permanent if they survived the war.

One day he said to her, "After the war, you probably won't want me—you'll consider me out of your class."

Alicia was surprised. Was he right? "Who do you think I am?" she asked. "A snob like Laura?" And she thought, So what if he's never read Tolstoy or Dostoevsky or Thomas Mann or Romain Rolland and doesn't know the difference between Chopin and Mozart? We could be happy together—if I could only trust him. Saul swears by him. Maybe I should stop listening to Andrew and drop my suspicions, especially since lately Chaim has been behaving like a gentleman.

In February, Alicia became ill. It started innocently when she developed a few boils on her legs. But by the end of the month, her legs were covered with festering sores. She looked at them and inwardly wept: My beautiful slim, strong legs! They served me so well once, for swimming, skiing, running, and climbing.

She went to the infirmary. Rutkowski was not pleasant or encouraging. Or much help. This damn quack, Alicia thought. Once there were my father, my uncle and Dr. Levin ready to take care of me. And now nobody but him. Rutkowski gave her a few red crystals of potash and told her to dissolve them in warm water and soak her legs. Laura managed to get hold of an ointment.

Alicia could not even wear stockings, for her legs were all bandaged. If there's an inspection, she thought, or if Fuchs just notices me, I might get shot. Sick women, pregnant women, and children—we're in the same category. She didn't mind her friends, like Andrew and Saul, to see her this way but she avoided Chaim. Somehow it embarrassed her that she looked "terrible." He respected her wishes and just said "hello" and "how are you?" Did he sense her feelings or had he already found a girlfriend in Ludwikow, who gave him more than she did? Most of the time she didn't care, but then there were times when she did. She was confused about her feelings toward him. She was confused about many things.

Lucia was bedridden with fever again. "Two chosen by Thomas," Jankiel would have said. Poor Jankiel, he has already wound "safe to sea." By the beginning of March, Alicia's legs were getting better, and Lucia was able to go back to work. Alicia had to agree with Rutkowski that soaking in warm water was beneficial; the few red crystals just made it look more important. My father, she reminded herself, always believed that you should get well by natural means.

She survived the winter. Will there be another winter? She would only be colder and hungrier, unless . . . Where were the Russians and what will the Germans do before they leave Poland?

One gloomy morning in the middle of March, Alicia stood during the morning roll call half asleep. She had a sore throat, and the pain had kept her awake most of the night. But even in her dulled state, she noticed that Breslau was unusually agitated. He kept walking back and forth along the rows of people, counting and checking his roster. He called three names over and over again.

Three boys were missing. Nobody knew when they had disappeared. Could it have been before the closing of the barrack doors for the night? Maybe in the morning when the doors opened?

That afternoon, when Alicia came back from work, she learned that two of the boys had been caught, one managed to escape.

"Maybe we should be thankful that one got away," Alicia said to Anne. "How come the other two were caught so soon?"

Anne was angry. "Breslau, that swine, wouldn't give the boys even one hour's head start. He notified the authorities immediately after roll call."

Alicia was tired of judging and hating people. She wished she could hate only the Germans. Breslau had always been nice to her.

Laura came over. She ventured only so far from the partition when she had to help a sick person.

"So Madam comes down to see us plain slobs," Anne said.

"Oh, stop it, Anne," Laura said. "What's happened to our friendship?"

"You tell me."

Laura ignored her and said to Alicia, "I have managed to get a couple of aspirins in case your throat bothers you again tonight."

Alicia did not have a chance to thank Laura, because Anne kept on talking: "So did you hear, Laura, that they caught the boys? Your friend Breslau, and Mrs. Oderman in the office, were very prompt in their duties."

Laura was close to tears. "Don't you realize that they had to do it. Can you imagine the reprisals? They would kill us all."

"And Breslau would be first," Anne said. "And that worried him most."

"I just thought about something," Alicia put in. "A lot of new people drifted into our barracks last summer and fall. Breslau did not seem to have any trouble incorporating them in his roster. I bet that if the Germans had not been notified about the three missing boys, they would never have known."

"But suppose the boys were caught anyway?" Laura said. "The Gestapo would soon find out where they came from."

"So our lives would be jeopardized, so what?" Anne commented.

Birnbaum passed by and told them to break it up: "Commandant Spiegel does not want people to congregate."

Alicia stuck out her tongue at Birnbaum as he was leaving. "You might have to perform another hanging," she yelled after him.

"You and Anne always have to make enemies," Laura commented.

The next morning the boys were building the gallows again. The following day all 150 people from the barracks were assembled to watch the second hanging of Henrykow. This time it was Oderman and Glattstein who had the honor of putting the noose around the necks of the two escapees. An overwhelming sense of doom descended on the men and women. They felt that there was no hope and that sooner or later it would be their turn.

Only two days after the hanging, Hanka had to go for an abortion again. This time she was in her fifth month. Laura was right. Moshe had gone to work on her right after the second abortion; she was probably still bleeding when they had sex. But three abortions in such a short span of time and so late in pregnancy proved too much for her frail body. This time, she died on the operating table.

Laura came back from Ludwikow crying. She told Alicia that Moshe wasn't even there, although Spiegel was willing to give him a pass.

"Where did they bury her?" Alicia asked.

"In the back of the factory near the garbage dump."

Now Alicia began to weep too. She thought about her father and the mass grave his body was thrown into.

Moshe approached them. He looked at the two girls sitting there crying. Then he said to Alicia, "Since Hanka is gone, you can share the bunk with me."

Alicia could not believe her ears. "You filthy pig and killer," she said. She spat in his face.

He wiped his face and said, "A man can try."

When he left, the two girls started laughing and for a time could not stop. But soon they were ready to cry again.

That night, it was hard for Alicia to erase from her mind the image of two limp bodies with broken necks swinging from the ropes, swaying in the wind, and Hanka dying on the operating table. Then, as always, she saw her father's corpse, the way Jankiel had described it, and her mother's pale face when she fainted in the bathroom during her bout with dysentery. Alicia always imagined that was how Guta's face had looked in the gas chamber.

To offset these images, she tried desperately to remember her parents when they were young: Eisig carrying his little girl on his shoulder while singing to her, Guta in a short dress with a low waistline, and a bobbed haircut, looking very pretty. Mucia telling her about her first love. She could almost hear Henius calling her, "*Ala, Ala, oj Aluniu.*" She longed to fall asleep and dream about them that way. Maybe I could accept these dreams as reality, she thought, and what's happening right now as just a nightmare.

Alicia knew only too well that it was not a nightmare but reality. In the upper bunk, Sonia was with her new boyfriend, making a lot of noise, moaning and groaning with delight. Alicia was used to it. She just had an abortion, she thought, and she's fooling around again. I hope she won't die like Hanka—no, not Sonia, she was a strong and healthy girl.

All of a sudden, she realized that somebody was sitting at the edge of her bunk. Her first reaction was that maybe it was Moshe, and instinctively she got hold of a wooden stick that she kept for defense.

Though the boys sometimes made crude jokes in Yiddish, that she pretended she did not understand, they really did not bother her. They knew that Benjamin and Ira were her friends, and everybody respected them. Chaim was still waiting for an invitation.

Somebody put a finger on her lips. "*Sha,*" he said, "I love you."

She knew then it was Chaim. He was now kissing her and stroking her hair. After the ghastly week, it felt very good to be kissed and to be told that she was loved. Somehow her suspicions disappeared; she just lay there, letting him kiss and caress her. For a while her old feeling of inertia overcame her, but then she started kissing him back. He was lying beside her now, on her bunk, lean and muscular. As he touched her, she felt beautiful and desirable. She was twenty-two years old, and under his hands she was coming alive. The stealth and filth of the barracks did not exist for her now. She wanted to get close to him, closer and closer almost into him, to bury herself and forget the last few years The tension and unhappiness soon evaporated. A stray thought entered her mind: I will close my eyes and imagine it is Pawel. But she was aroused and ready for Chaim.

"We will be very quiet," he whispered. "Nobody will know."

It was not even necessary to be quiet. Sonia and her partner were making so much noise that nobody could hear Alicia and Chaim.

"You don't have to worry," he told her. "I love you. I will be very careful. I will not get you into trouble."

He was fondling and kissing her breasts. He entered her, it only lasted for a short while. She almost didn't let him go; she wanted to keep him in her longer. But he kept his promise, he withdrew as soon as he felt his ejaculation coming. That's all? she thought. She wished it had lasted longer. It was still pleasant, but the ecstasy she once shared with Pawel was missing. He had a towel with him.

Alicia laughed to herself. He's an expert in the procedure, she thought. Now he is lying on his towel getting rid of his semen. Then her reasoning powers returned: He controlled himself this first time, but the next time he might not be able to, or I might not let him go. She was scared of her own body and deathly afraid of pregnancy. She hated the thought of abortion; too many children had already been killed. Maybe Moshe was not all that guilty. Maybe Hanka just didn't let him go, either. Hanka was a holder, she went for abortions late in her pregnancy because she wanted to keep her babies in her for as long ,as possible. It cost her her life.

As Alicia looked at Chaim, she realized something else. She really did not love him. They had very little in common. She was terribly lonely and unhappy that night, and she had needed somebody to make love to her. Chaim was kissing her again, and he sensed that her old tension and stiffness were back. Awareness of her surroundings returned—all the other couples making love or simply fucking in the same room.

Maybe if I survive, I will do it on green grass in the cool breeze or better at night under starry skies, or at least in a bedroom like the one I used to have with a canopy and clean sheets. It would be wonderful to have privacy and not to have that terrible fear of pregnancy. Would it be with Chaim? She did not know.

After a while, Chaim was ready to make love to her again. She buried her face in the torn, scanty pillow. She knew that if she let him kiss her, she might give in. Part of her wanted it very much. But her brain was functioning now. Besides her fear of pregnancy, she was wondering what Anne, Chaim, Ben, and Ira were whispering about and why Chaim didn't include her in whatever plans he was making.

"It is enough for the first time," she told him. "My throat is bothering me."

He respected her wishes, and he sneaked out. He still wanted her very much, but he was triumphant. Finally, he had got her. For him she was a great prize, not one of his "regular" women in Ludwikow. She almost didn't let him get out of her on time. But still he had doubts about doing it again. If he sneaked into her bunk every night from now on, people eventually would find out about them and talk. They would have to make it formal by sharing a bunk. He could not afford to feed Alicia regularly, as other men fed their women. But mainly, when the time came to go, it would be very hard to leave her behind. Maybe, in the "normal" world, we could have made a go of it, he thought. She could teach me her poetry in Polish, English, and French, and I would make a beautiful and passionate woman out of her. He had watched her that afternoon when she was sitting with Laura and crying. His heart went out to her; he really wanted to kiss and console her that night. He did not quite expect that she would submit so easily.

The next morning, before roll call, Alicia approached Breslau. She despised him, but he would not guess it from the way she acted toward him. She wanted to volunteer for the night shift. He was surprised, Alicia was not due for it for another two weeks. She explained to him that there wasn't as much dust at night in the factory to irritate her throat. He accepted her explanation. Alicia knew that she could now avoid facing her feelings for Chaim for at least one week of nights. There was another reason she asked for the night shift: That week she would be working with Anne.

CHAPTER 13

Henrykow 1944

It was a long time since Alicia had talked to Anne the way they used to when they lived together in the little hospital.

"How close are you with Chaim?" Anne asked. "By all means, let him bring you food, but I wouldn't trust him if I were you."

Alicia got angry. "You expect me to take your advice about Chaim, but you won't tell me what you have against him."

Anne said, "I'm sorry, but I can't."

"So don't tell me, and let me fall madly in love with him."

After a couple of nights of working together, Anne changed her mind. She said, "Promise you'll keep your mouth shut, and I'll tell you what I think you should know. When we discuss our plans with Chaim, he never mentions your name."

Alicia was not really surprised. She thought, Once he said that if I would sleep with him, it would make a difference. But I did, and nothing has changed.

"There's something else I'd like to tell you, but please don't let it build up your hopes. We are planning to drop Chaim. I'm trying to talk the boys into including you instead."

Alicia was taken aback. Anne said, "You know how the boys feel about taking girls into the forest. I keep telling them that you are strong, and the way you look and speak, you could be our contact to buy food from the Polish peasants. Benjamin is worried about your legs and throat. He also says that if you break your glasses, you'd be helpless."

"Those are his excuses. Men always think women are helpless," said Alicia. She thought about the summer of 1939 when she, Pawel, Jerry, and Lisa had been climbing in the Karpathian peaks. She had no infected boils on her legs then, and she wasn't half-starved. But still, she knew she could do just as well as the boys. "It can't be too long before the Russians come," she told Anne, and then she started laughing.

"What are you laughing about?"

"I just thought," Alicia answered. "What if everybody escaped, and I'm left alone in the barracks for the Germans to liquidate before they withdraw."

Now Anne was laughing too, but then she sobered. "Life in the forest is extremely difficult and dangerous, Alicia. Here, we have a place to sleep, rations—meager as they are—most people have ways to get extra food. Sometimes, for a couple of months at a time, we forget the situation we are all in. We have an illusion of stability. In the forest, you have to be on guard every moment, day and night. You don't know where the menace and danger are coming from, where you are going to sleep or when you are going to eat. You have no roof over your head and no place to cook a meal. The thin soup we get here is at least warm, and it would be a luxury there."

"There are no gas chambers in the forest," Alicia said.

"If the Poles point you out to the Germans, that's the end of you. And sometimes Polish partisans kill Jews."

"But there are no gas chambers, " Alicia insisted, "and my legs are getting better, and the warm weather is coming, and I know I could make it."

After a while Anne admitted the boys weren't too eager to take her either. She looked hard at Alicia. "I really care for you," she said suddenly. Alicia wanted to kiss her. It was a personal triumph that Anne, who had once disliked her so much, was now her best friend.

The next week, which was the last week in April, Alicia was working the day shift again. She wished she could be on the night shift forever. The weather was still changeable, and her throat felt scratchy. That dumb throat of mine, she thought. This day she had not managed to organize extra food, and she was hungry. Maybe Chaim will have some potatoes and bread for me. To hell with trust, I've got to eat. I'll accept food from anybody.

She wondered, can a person be two different people at the same time? The one I could almost love—warm, tender, and considerate, the man who swears that he loves me, who changed a miserable night into pleasure. According to Saul, he carried him on his back almost the entire trip through the Swietokrzyski Mountains. And then there is the other Chaim: two-faced liar, not to be trusted, pretending love just to get laid. He'll wait for the Russians, hiding in the forest, leaving me behind for the Germans.

At the end of her working day, Alicia was marching with her group back to the barracks. The weather had cleared and it was a beautiful spring afternoon. But springs brought actions. This spring, two boys were hanged. Last year, thirty-eight children were murdered. And the year before in April, they came for her father. And then, more pleasant memories of springs long gone flooded here mind: all the Passover holidays spent in Zabiec, the big seders; her grandfather conducting services, singing in his great voice; Jas asking, *"Ma ni shitanu halaila haze mikol halelot*—[Why is this night different from all other nights?]" As they entered the barracks, she realized that this day *was* different from other days. In front of the partition, Herr Spiegel was trying to beat Benjamin while people stood around, watching. Benjamin was skillfully dodging Spiegel's club and, at the same time, was cursing in Yiddish. *"Gey in dreyed*—[be buried], you are just a *farfluchte Jude.* When the time comes, you will go like everybody else."

Spiegel was yelling, "Give it to me. Surrender it before the Gestapo finds out!"

Alicia pushed herself through and stood right behind Anne. Ben looked at Anne and stretched out his hand. Alicia guessed that Anne was hiding Benjamin's gun. Oh God, she thought, Benjamin is going to shoot Spiegel. That will bring in the "real" Germans, and they will burn the barracks with all of us inside! And that will end our tiny glimmer of hope that, maybe by some miracle, the Russians will come before the Germans have a chance to finish us all.

Suddenly she felt something heavy drop into her pocket. Anne, was spreading out her hands, showing them to Benjamin: She didn't have the gun. The gun was in Alicia's pocket. Slowly Alicia backed up to her bunk and slipped the weapon underneath her blanket and sat down on it. In that moment, she spotted Chaim, looking at her from across the barracks. Hastily, she switched her attention to the commotion up front. Glattstein was trying to separate Spiegel from Benjamin. Benjamin was calling the policemen "scum of the earth" and Spiegel "the filthiest of them all."

Oderman was talking Polish in a loud voice so everyone could hear: "We remaining Jews should not waste our energy on fighting each other; we should help each other to survive."

The "ladies" Spiegel and Glattstein had taken Anne behind the partition, apparently to search her. Jewish Gestapo! Alicia thought savagely. From the corner of her eye, she saw Chaim approaching. An unpleasant thought crossed her mind: How did Spiegel learn about Benjamin's gun? Was it Chaim? Was he spying for Stawski? No, that was going too far with her suspicions. Chaim doesn't even know that Benjamin and Ira were not going to include him in their escape.

"I haven't seen you in a week," Chaim said. "You almost disappeared from my life."

"It is not my fault that they've sent me on the night shift," she lied.

He couldn't resist kissing her, even if everybody saw it. But she did not return his kiss.

Funny bitch, he thought. Just last week she couldn't get enough of it. Now she pretends that that night didn't happen. "What's going on up front?" he asked her.

Alicia took off her glasses, blinked her eyes, and said, "You know I don't understand Yiddish, and without glasses I don't see very well. I have no idea what the fracas is all about." Then she looked at him innocently and asked, "Do you have anything to eat that you can share with me?"

"As a matter of fact, I do," Chaim answered. He was mad at himself. Why should I give her food? he thought. She acts so high and mighty. "I want you badly," he whispered in her ear.

Chaim went to his bunk and soon came back. He actually had a ham sandwich with him, good Polish ham. Alicia opened her eyes wide. Nothing mattered now but that sandwich. She seized it and sank her teeth into the tender meat.

Chaim was trying to kiss her again. In spite of herself she liked his touch.

"Let's do it again," he told her.

"Right now we are making a spectacle of ourselves," Alicia said. "Thank you for the sandwich."

"I'm glad I was able to get it for you. I'll see you later. I must go."

Ira came over. Alicia slipped into her jacket and managed to sneak the gun into the pocket. She and Ira walked together along the barracks. They were talking, but somehow the gun passed unseen from Alicia to Ira. Alicia breathed with relief. "How about another girl for your expedition?" she asked him.

"We'll consider it," Ira said.

Alicia knew he was lying. She returned to her bunk and lay down exhausted. The tension of hiding the gun made her weak. Her throat felt worse. Her legs hadn't healed completely yet. I am still sure, that I could survive in the forest just as well as the boys. What if, by next winter, the winter of 1945, the Germans are still in Kielce? It did not seem likely, according to the latest news from the Polish co-workers. Next summer, next winter, and she remembered her mother saying; "Next year, God willing." Next year, Henius will be seven, and he will start school. Alicia will get her Matura. . . Jerry will go to America to study medicine. . . we will take a trip. Nothing like that happened, only war, occupation, ghetto, deportations, and death.

Now, in April 1944, what is in store for the rest of us? For me? Will I ever live to expect survival and a life in a "normal" world where parents see their children grow up, where people marry and have families, where you are allowed to get older, where the sick are taken care of instead of exterminated? Why try to get eggs from Mendel, a sandwich from Chaim, money from my Gentile friends, to keep clean and to keep my clothes in decent repair, soak my legs in the solution of potash? I'll just lie on this bunk, disintegrate, and die. I wish I could love and trust Chaim, but I can't even face him with what I know about him, because of my promise to Anne.

Laura passed by. She was as pretty as ever, with her long red hair falling to her shoulders. As a nurse, she had better rations, and besides,

Sid, her boyfriend, always managed to buy food. Laura had a bottle of aspirins with her.

"How did you get a whole bottle out of Rutkowski?" Alicia asked.

"He had a headache, and took out a bottle of aspirin and forgot to put it back. I just took it. I'm getting more and more disgusted with him." She made a face. "Now that the Russians are getting closer, he's worse than before. Maybe he's planning to sell medicines to the Russian army."

"What do you expect, just like all of the other people from the front of the barracks."

"Oh, stop it," Laura said. "They're managing the place very well. The conditions in our barracks are still the best in Poland. That's why so many people come to us from other places."

Alicia was too weak and her throat was too painful for her to argue. Laura touched Alicia's forehead and concluded that she was running a fever. She gave her two aspirins. Alicia's stomach didn't feel too good, either. She wished she had not eaten the ham sandwich. I'm not used to meat, she thought. She dozed off. In the back of her mind, she knew that the evening roll call would be soon.

A dream came. She was in Zabiec, and the weather, in the April of her dream, was much warmer and sunnier than in the April of 1944. It was after a rain, and she watched a rainbow from the window in her bedroom. The sun was setting, there were high cumulus clouds scattered over still blue skies. She actually smelled the white blossoms of the acacia trees. Or maybe it was not April but June, because the strawberries were ready to eat. She jumped out of her window and joined Jerry in the strawberry patches. They were both crouching, picking the berries, laughing and eating, when her mother called: "You'll spoil your appetite for supper." They ran to the front of the house, where the long table under the linden tree was set for the evening meal. All kinds of foods were there. Not a lousy ham sandwich, but a lot of fruits and vegetables and sliced meats. Henius—he looked about five years old—was running around the house, his long hair blowing in the breeze. His nanny, Rosie, tried to catch him, clapping her hands and laughing. Guta told Rosie to stop running and to get Henius to wash his hands and to make him sit at the table. Alicia and Jerry were eating.

Jerry kept the food in his mouth forever. He looked like he was dreaming. Paula yelled at him to swallow already. For dessert, each of them got a big piece of chocolate. Alicia and Jerry went to play some more before going to sleep. Jerry chided Alicia because, although her chocolate was long gone, he still had a big piece left. She tried to figure out how to swindle him out of his chocolate. Her father would say that it was the touch of larceny that she inherited from her grandfather. She was now half asleep and half awake, and she desperately wanted to stay in her dream. A blow across her legs woke her up completely.

She sat up, and there was Birnbaum. "You're late for roll call," he yelled at her.

I wish I had the gun now, Alicia thought. No wonder Andrew and Saul call him a "little gangster."

Chaim, Andrew, and Saul were passing by Alicia's bunk. "Leave her alone," Chaim said to Birnbaum. "She's not feeling well—she just overslept. She'll come with us. We're a little late too."

Birnbaum smiled wickedly. "Oh, she's your girlfriend, is she?" He proceeded to make several vulgar and obscene remarks in Yiddish about the two of them.

"You know, Birnbaum," Andrew said, "in the not so distant future, you are going to get what you deserve—not from the Germans but from us."

Birnbaum drew back his arm to hit Andrew when Alicia said, "You're very strong against me and Andrew, but stood like a dummy when they took your children away. You were more concerned about saving your suitcases than about saving your children." All the starch went out of him, and the arm holding the stick fell to his side. His chin tightened as if he were trying not to cry, and his eyes got very shiny. It took a minute for him to get himself under control.

Alicia was ashamed of herself. She knew only too well there was nothing that Birnbaum could have done to save his children. "Come on," he said thickly. "Let's report for the roll call."

Chaim took Alicia's arm and escorted her to the roll call. Alicia couldn't help but compare him to Andrew, who was thin and small yet had enough courage to stand up to Birnbaum and his stick. Chaim who had been insulted along with her, tried to trivialize the whole incident.

At evening roll call, there was unusual tension in the air. To add to their dread, Fuchs was there with a huge black dog. Ordinarily he did not bother to attend roll calls; why was he here now? In her mind, Alicia marshalled the roster of their secret sins: The children hiding in the barracks? Some pregnant woman did not get an abortion on time? Benjamin and the gun? The afternoon sun gave way to drizzle and rain, but it was not cold. And why was Anne wearing her heavy winter coat?

Everybody was accounted for. They sighed with relief when Fuchs with his dog went to the office. After a while he left the factory ground in his chauffeur-driven limousine, and the gates were closed. Fuchs's presence must have had nothing to do with the trouble that afternoon. The recent hanging had left people nervous. There was stepped-up security. The workers of the night shift were marched to the factory. The rest lined up in front of the outside latrines; it was their last chance before they had to go inside. Once the doors closed for the night, they would have no chance to relieve themselves.

As Alicia walked into the barracks, she felt somebody's hand on her shoulder.

"How do you feel?" Chaim asked her.

"Oh," she answered, "I might be running a fever, but I feel a little better."

"Birnbaum didn't really hurt you, did he? I thought that he was mostly making noises."

Alicia had to admit that she was not hurt. "He's a filthy bastard. You didn't even answer him—little Andrew had to put him in his place."

"You also put him in his place," Chaim told Alicia. "You've got to be careful. He might be dangerous."

"So one more policeman hates me," Alicia said. "First was mighty Oderman, because I practically accused him of being corrupt. Now you know why I am so afraid of getting pregnant. I would not get a pass to Breitman; they would report me to the Gestapo."

They got to Alicia's bunk and found a place behind it where they could talk. "I love you, Alicia. You know by now that I'll be careful."

He's not lying about that, she thought. He believes now that he loves me, but when he makes his plans for an escape, I won't exist for him.

He was stroking her hair. "You have such beautiful hair."

"It's dirty now."

"I'll try to get you some soap." He took off her glasses and started kissing her eyes.

A policeman was walking along the barracks. "Fifteen minutes to curfew," he announced.

"I didn't see Anne at her bunk," Alicia said to Chaim. "She's not working the night shift like Ben and Ira. The winter coat that Anne had been wearing at the roll call bothered her.

"She must be talking to Laura," Chaim said.

"I doubt it, because Sid dislikes Anne, and lately, Laura and Anne's relationship has cooled off."

"It's hard to like Anne."

"You either love her or hate her. I'm the one who loves her. Many people resent her, because she's so outspoken." Alicia was getting hoarse. "You'd better get away from me," she whispered, "or you'll get my germs."

"I hadn't seen you for a whole week," Chaim complained again.

"I'm sure you have ladies in Ludwikow that can satisfy you."

"You're right, but I wanted you."

Somebody was passing in front of the bunk, calling Chaim. They went to see who it was. It was Szmul, one of Stawski's gang. Chaim was annoyed. He knew that Alicia despised Stawski and his boys.

"Did you see Zubow?" Szmul asked. When Chaim gave him a blank stare, Szmul was disgusted. "You have your girlfriend on your brain. You don't know or see anything."

"You're right," Chaim answered. "I don't keep Zubow in my pocket. I don't care where he is."

"I think he's patrolling the fence," Szmul said. "After the last escape, Spiegel ordered the policemen to patrol."

The lights were off, and everybody was supposed to retire. Chaim and Alicia were kissing in the back of her bunk. Her brain was telling her one thing while her body was pulling her in another direction. She forgot about her sore throat and fever, and when he put his hand in her blouse and touched her breasts, she groaned with pleasure. She felt his erection, and she was getting more and more excited.

His hands were on her belly now and then between her thighs. They were ready to get undressed and get into the bunk when suddenly the lights went on. They jumped away from each other and straightened out their ruffled clothing. A man and a woman were yelling at each other. Anne and Zubow were in the middle of the barracks, exchanging insults. Alicia and Chaim went to see what was happening.

"Son of a bitch!" Anne was screaming. "He wouldn't let me go!" She drew a sobbing breath and resumed at a lower pitch: "They notified the Gestapo right away—now they're combing the countryside for the boys. Benjamin, my beloved, he and Ira could not help me over the stupid fence, so they just left me there for Zubow to catch."

"Break it up now," they heard from the other side of the partition. Lights went out. Alicia remained at Anne's bunk. She told Chaim that he'd better leave. Sex, at the moment, was the farthest thing from her mind.

Anne whispered the story: The three of them, Benjamin, Ira, and she, were running toward the fence. It was dusk, and since the day was cloudy and foggy, the visibility was poor. They chose a good evening.

"Who had the gun?" Alicia asked.

"I wish I'd had it," Anne answered. "Then, for sure, they wouldn't have left me behind. I kept it during the roll call in case Benjamin got himself into more trouble, but then I handed it back to him."

Anne resumed: They tried to climb over the fence, but the heel of her boot got stuck in one of the spaces between the wires. She couldn't free herself. The boys jumped over to the other side and kept running. Once or twice they yelled back at her to join them. By the time she freed her heel, Zubow was there.

"Oh, Anne! Why didn't you insist that I come along? My legs are practically healed, and even with a fever, I'm an expert at climbing and jumping fences. I would *never* have left you hanging there."

"*Sha*," Anne whispered. "Don't you get involved in my problem."

After a while, Alicia asked, "Tell me, did Chaim know you were going to try tonight?"

"He couldn't have known. It was a spur-of-the-moment decision. We originally planned the escape for three weeks from now, but things were getting too tense in the barracks. I don't know what to tell you. I trusted Benjamin, and look where it got me. Our beloved policemen are not finished with me yet. They'll probably report me to Fuchs."

As the girls quieted down, they heard talk from the bunks near the partition. They couldn't believe what the women there were saying.

"She had to do it.She had to jump the gun. Why couldn't she have waited until we were all ready? She had to risk our safety and relative comfort."

Anne had to hold Alicia back. She was ready to jump at these women's throats. "Wait for what and for whom? Who will be the Moses to lead the Exodus? The crook Stawski, Spiegel? The bureaucrat Breslau? Or the hypocrite Oderman?"

"Shut up, Alicia," Anne whispered, "you'd better go back to your own bunk. They shouldn't know that I've talked with you. Whatever they do to me, I don't need you as my companion."

Anne was right—they weren't finished with her. The next morning she was taken to the office by two policemen.

During roll call, Alicia just waved good-bye to Chaim as he was leaving for Ludwikow. She didn't feel like talking to him—she was too worried about Anne. She couldn't even look the women straight in the eye. She hated them all.

"Don't you see?" one of them tried to explain to her. "Zubow had to bring Anne back. The police are responsible for us. It's bad enough that they allowed the two boys to escape. Maybe Zubow, by catching Anne, saved our necks."

"Well, let us hope," Alicia answered savagely, "that the Germans find Ben and Ira, and then Zubow and Birnbaum can hang them and thereby save us all for the gas chambers."

Andrew, carrying some wooden planks, paused beside them. "Alicia," he said, "they need you by the machine." As they walked off together, he whispered, "Bad news. I just heard that there are two Gestapo men, Fuchs and another one, in the office with Anne."

Alicia started to tremble. Images of the recent hangings flashed before her eyes. Andrew added, "You'd better stop talking with the women. You won't help Anne, and they'll take you for interrogations next."

"Oh, you mean they just have Anne there for interrogation?

"Don't be naive."

When they came for my father, I also hoped that they were just taking him for interrogation, she thought. Then Andrew told her, "If I were you, I wouldn't trust Chaim too much either."

Alicia almost laughed. Andrew and Anne are both so worried about me that they begrudge me a little illusion of happiness. She handed the boards to the fellows at the machines without replying. Her throat felt dry again from the dust, and her head ached.

Time dragged, but at least the monotonous work distracted her a little. Like everything else, the day shift came to an end, and they were all marched to the kitchen to get their rations of soup and bread. It was getting colder, and it looked like rain again. Alicia was rigid with nerves. Where was Anne? They reached the barracks, and there she was. She was standing at her bunk , holding on to the post. Alicia ran up to her.

"What happened?" she demanded. "What did they do to you?"

Anne pulled her behind her bunk, raised her skirt, lowered her panties. Alicia stifled a gasp. Anne was black and blue from the middle of her back to her thighs. "Who did this?" Alicia cried in horror.

"Fuchs. And those two Jewish bastards, Zubow and Birnbaum, held me, while Fuchs was hitting. They wanted to know where Benjamin and Ira were going, and what kind of connection they had. I think I managed to convince them that I don't know, so maybe you're safe talking to me. On the other hand, they might figure that I would pass information on to you, and you might be easier to break. It's best that we are not seen together too much."

Laura arrived with a cold compress for Anne. She reported in a whisper, "Spiegel was told by Fuchs that the next time there's an escape, everybody in the barracks will be responsible."

"They'll hang us all," Alicia said. "I wonder who'll be the hangman then."

The curfew was announced: "Everybody back to their own bunks."

The day's events kept Alicia awake. Was the cold compress helping Anne? She hoped so. For some strange reason, she thought about Benjamin's mother and her plans for her studious son and the way she was saving money to send him to medical school. Medical school? Hopefully, he and Ira had reached the forest by now. They would be reasonably safe from the Germans there, but what about the Polish gangs roaming about after stray Jews? Maybe the gun would help the boys.

Sonia, in the upper bunk, was asleep, exhausted from her sexual activities. Other couples were making love, trying to extract some enjoyment from their existence. Life, such as we have here, has to go on, Alicia thought. She missed Chaim. As long as he doesn't make me pregnant, what harm will it do if I have a little pleasure before I die?

Did Chaim guess Alicia's thoughts? He was there, right near her in the bunk. He was kissing her. "I know," he whispered, "that you must feel terrible. I want to make you happy."

She put her arms around him and kissed him back. His hands were all over her. This time, the sex act itself was wonderful. Somehow, Chaim was able to prolong it long enough for Alicia to reach a climax. If she could die at that precise moment, she wouldn't have to come back to the reality of Anne with her black and blue back and the miserable barracks. She kissed him and tasted salt—her own tears. "Thank you," she whispered. "I was in heaven for a while and now our hell seems almost bearable."

He kissed her wet eyes. "I'd better leave," he said. "We might fall asleep in each other's arms and then be discovered in the morning.

Alicia was left alone, feeling fulfilled and content. Then she heard Anne's moaning, and her sanity returned. She felt guilty about not feeling guilty. She knew that she would do it again, no matter what.

The next morning was like any other morning. Last night seemed like a dream. Love or infatuation? I was crazy last night, she thought. I used to have so many outlets for my body; skiing and skating in winter, tennis and long walks to Kadzielnia in the spring, and swimming in the summer. Now, there is only sex. No wonder everybody is doing it.

Anne was too sore and in pain to go to work. She stayed in the barracks. Alicia hated leaving her.

"I have two children to play with," Anne told her. "And Laura will come from the infirmary to help me." Then she said something that scared Alicia: "The boys must be far away by now. If there's another hanging, I would rather sway in the wind alone."

"Stop it, Anne! You've already been punished. They don't have to hang you!"

"Are you trying to apply logic to what is going on?"

During the day, Alicia avoided Andrew as much as possible. She wasn't interested in his gossip, and she didn't want him to know the truth about her and Chaim. She was not ashamed of it, just of the timing—the night that Anne was in pain. How could she explain to her friend that Anne's very pain had made her need Chaim.

The women, as usual, were gossiping: who was sleeping with whom. . . who left her husband for a lover. . . was Sid making out with Laura? It kept their minds away from the prevailing anxiety: Will Ben and Ira be caught? Will there be another hanging? Will they leave Anne alone and let her heal her wounds?

Toward the end of the day, Alicia felt cramps. Her period was coming. Usually, it was a great nuisance to her, but this time she was relieved. She remembered that after the deportations to Treblinka, she stopped menstruating for a few months, but she had no reason to worry then. Her monthly periods were an additional hardship for her. She had to find something to stop the flow of blood. This afternoon she managed to get some rags from the laundry.

When she came back from work she went to Anne's bunk. They shared their thin soup and bread. Anne could almost sit down that day, but she still needed a pillow. Chaim came over. With the warm weather, he didn't have much work and not much extra food. He still managed to get some bread. Laura brought a whole bottle of milk, which Sid had gotten from the outside. They sat there, three girls and Chaim, and ate the black bread and drank the milk.

It had been so long since Alicia had had any milk. The last time was when she visited Tadek, sardine sandwiches and milk. Then, like everybody else, he had to go and die. Damn you, Tadek, why did you die? At least when I talked to you, I was not confused. Right and wrong were clearly separated from each other: Nazism was an absolute evil, Russian Communism was close behind. Anyone who cooperated with them was not only morally wrong, but stupid. The Poles who were helping the Germans with the extermination of the Jews were very bad. The Western Allies were good, the resistance was good, the Polish government-in-exile in London was good.

As they drank the milk, each of them was immersed in his own thoughts. Chaim, looking at Anne, wondered if she ever told Alicia that once he had been included in Benjamin and Ira's plans. He felt bitter because he had told them about all the secret places he knew in the Swietokrzyski Mountains, and then they dropped him. Laura was thinking about Sid and how deeply she should commit herself. And Anne, it was hard for her not to remember about all the times when Ben and Ira had been a part of their little group.

After they finished their meal, Alicia decided to go back to her bunk. "I feel like lying down," she said.

Chaim followed her. "What's the matter?"

"You should be happy. I got my period."

"Oh, shit, and I had big plans for tonight. Wasn't last night wonderful?"

Alicia had to admit that it was. She regretted now that she did not try to get out of the night shift for the following week. Her period usually lasted for only three days, and Anne, all of a sudden, was not so important to her anymore.

"Next week," she blurted out, "I am on the night shift. I purposely asked for it, so I could spend some time with Anne during the day."

"What am I supposed to do in the meantime?" Chaim wanted to know.

Alicia laughed. "You'll manage. Find somebody else in Ludwikow."

"I don't want anybody else. But now that I will not see you for an entire week, it will seem like years ago when I used to dream about you."

"You're giving me that bull again."

"I used to watch you and Basia at the Stadion. There were all those boys around you, laughing and joking, all sons of doctors. I thought I didn't have a chance."

"It was Basia who was the main attraction. She was so pretty and full of life," Alicia said.

"But I was attracted to you. Basia had black and straight hair. It was your blond, wavy hair that caught my eye."

"I am sure you watched Basia also." After a moment, she said, "I wonder if Basia and her parents are alive. It's been three years since they were sent to Auschwitz. Her father was strong and athletic, but her mother was a semi-invalid."

Chaim began to kiss Alicia and he said; "Nobody knows who will make it."

Chaim left and Alicia drifted off to sleep. She was home again, not in Zabiec but in Kielce in the apartment on Freedom Place. She was sitting in the living room with Leah, there was a big bowl of cherries right there on the table, and they were eating and laughing. Before long, all the cherries were gone. Guta walked in and said, "You mean you girls finished all the cherries? I hope you don't come down with diarrhea."

Then Alicia, Pawel, Lisa and Jerry were climbing mountains. They were laughing—oh, how they were laughing. Jerry told Alicia not to laugh like a madwoman. What was she laughing about? Was it because she ate a bowlful of cherries or because she was in the mountains, under blue skies, breathing the clean air? Then cramps and a full bladder woke her up. She had to wait for the morning before the doors were opened. Mercifully it came at last, and their daily routine started all over.

The following week Alicia worked the night shift. During the day, she spent her time with Anne. She would change Anne's compresses and tried to make her as comfortable as possible. Anne was the only person in the barracks who knew the whole truth about Alicia and Chaim.

"I hope you won't get hurt," Anne once said to Alicia, "but I'm not the one to advise you about Chaim. I don't have much luck with men. Chaim is still here, and he cares for you. Ben left me."

"He couldn't come back," Alicia pointed out. "Once over the fence, he *had* to run."

"Yes, but there was only Zubow pursuing me, and Ben had the gun. Sometimes I think that they used me as a decoy. While Zubow was busy with me, they were able to put some distance between themselves and the factory."

"How can you say that, Anne? They didn't know that your heel was stuck in the fence."

"But once it happened, they took advantage of it. They could have come back, pointed the gun at Zubow, and helped me over the fence."

"I wish that Benjamin had shot Zubow." Alicia said. "But I still think that they didn't know that Zubow was alone."

"If it was the other way around, I would have come back for Ben. Men don't understand love. Anyhow, there'll be no escapes now. The fences are being patrolled by Polish and Ukrainian guards. In spite of Zubow's 'heroism,' they don't trust Jewish policemen anymore."

Alicia was ashamed, but her first reaction to the news was, Chaim won't leave me now. She was disgusted with herself over how much she had become dependent on the relationship.

Then Anne said something that Alicia would always remember: "It's good to have friends and a lover, but you survived until now mainly by your own devices. I hope I can do for myself as well as you did."

"And you are going to be okay," Alicia exclaimed.

At work this night, things were even slower than usual. Alicia was hidden behind a pile of wood, trying to doze off. She hadn't gotten much sleep during the day. Besides Anne, she had what she called another job—teaching little Shlomo. He was ten, and like his whole generation of Jewish kids—if by a miracle they were alive at all—he had never gone to school.

Shlomo's parents had taught him how to read, write, and count. Once Alicia explained to him fractions and decimals, and after that he would follow her, asking her to teach him more. Alicia tried to include Bella, the other barracks child, in the lessons, but the little girl couldn't keep up with Shlomo, so she lost interest. After a short while Shlomo was ready for algebra and geometry. Now Alicia tried to figure out which Polish co-worker she could ask for some textbooks.

She felt somebody touching her shoulder and opened her eyes, half expecting Andrew to tell her she was needed. But to her surprise, it was Chaim. "What are you doing here?" she asked. "You're supposed to be asleep in the barracks."

"I managed to get a key to the office," he whispered. "We'll have some privacy there and almost a whole night together."

"But they'll miss me at work."

"I took care of that. I bribed the Polish supervisor."

"Bribed him with what?" Alicia knew that he had no money.

"Come on, I'll tell you everything later."

She followed him down the dark corridor. He opened the door and there was a regular office: a desk, a typewriter, and even a couch.

"Listen, if you got the key through Zubow or Stawski, I don't want any part of this."

"I swear, Stawski and his people had nothing to do with it."

He's swearing again, Alicia thought. Should I believe him?

"Do you want to see what I bribed the Polish supervisor with? He promised to forget that you are supposed to be working."

"I hope it's something to eat."

"Oh, Alicia, that's all you think about."

He handed her a package and she opened it. At first she was puzzled by the contents. Some sort of rubber balloons? Then she started laughing.

"Condoms are hard to get. I got them from a German whose wife's fur I altered."

"More and more you remind me of my grandfather, a womanizer with a touch of larceny."

Chaim did not answer. He was already busy unbuttoning her blouse.

"Don't tear my blouse. I am running out of clothes." She was in Chaim's arms now with her breasts bare.

"Alicia," he said, "if we survive, I'll get you many beautiful clothes. You won't have to worry about one miserable blouse. I'll make you a little boy like Shlomo."

"Just don't do it now," she replied.

He turned off the light. It was wonderful to have all that privacy. It was the first night that they made love more than once. Finally it was almost dawn and they had to part.

"At least I'll be able to return to the barracks and sleep," Alicia said, "but you have to go back to work."

She was almost happy; Benjamin and Ira hadn't gotten caught, Anne was healing, and the Russians were not far away. Finally, the office was put to a good use. She could imagine the expression on Dora Oderman's face if she knew about it.

When they were marching back to the barracks that morning, Alicia told Andrew that she had fallen asleep behind the wood pile. "I hope I wasn't missed."

The second week of May, Alicia was on the day shift. One day, when she came back from the factory, she looked about for Anne, but she was not at her bunk. Saul came over and put his arm around Alicia. She knew that something was wrong. "Where's Anne?" she demanded fiercely.

"Take it easy. Take it easy," he said. "Sit down."

Alicia did. There are no gallows in front of the barracks, so there isn't going to be a hanging, she thought.

"Anne has been arrested," Saul told her. "She's in Kielce prison."

Like my uncle, like Lucia's father, like Pawel. She was crying now. Then she stopped crying and started yelling: "I will scream and yell the whole night, so nobody in this barracks can sleep. Anne is worth it. If Anne dies, and we survive, I'll charge Zubow with murder, and you"—she pointed to the partition—"as accomplices."

Chaim got back from work, and went to Alicia.

"Leave me alone," she snarled at him. "You belong to Stawski's gang. You and Zubow are in it together. No wonder Benjamin and Ira dropped you."

"Stop it, Alicia," Saul said. "Chaim had nothing to do with it. You should know better. He was with you when Anne was caught."

"He was here, but his friend Zubow was patrolling around the fence." She yelled at Chaim, "You don't have to take me anywhere. You're a two-faced liar. I wouldn't go with you even if you swear that you have a safe place for me to hide."

"Shut up," Chaim said. "Nobody is going anyplace now."

Zosia came over. "Listen," she said to Alicia, "Zubow was charged that evening with patrolling the fence. It was his decision to bring Anne back. Nobody else was involved. He thought that he was protecting all of us. No matter what you think of Jewish policemen, we are all Jews."

"I still can yell and cry," Alicia said. "You did it after you gave up your children."

"I did not *give up* my children," Zosia said angrily. "They were taken away from me. You sometimes act as if you were the only one who's lost your family. For your information, before I 'gave up' my children, I lost my parents, my sister, my brother, my nephews and nieces. My husband resigned from the police after Treblinka, and I thank God that at least he didn't have to hang anybody. I also hope that if he were still a policeman and patrolling the fence that night, he would have let Anne go."

Zosia addressed Chaim now: "Please talk to her. We all like Alicia, and we don't want her to get into trouble. It won't help anybody for her to make a scene."

Alicia was sobbing. Are they beating Anne? she wondered in sick despair. Or have they gone on to shoot her? At least my father was shot right away.

One week later, news came to the office of the Henrykow that Anne was sent to Auschwitz.

Things changed between Alicia and Chaim after that evening. No more nights like that night in the office. Chaim still sneaked at night to her bunk, but their sex became quick and mechanical. He seldom brought food, he claimed he didn't have anything extra.

Alicia was now subsisting on very little. Her gums were bleeding, and her teeth were loose. She remembered newspaper pictures of famine victims from India during the 1930s. Will I ever look that way—protruding belly, breast hanging to the thighs? When she dreamed now, it was mostly about food, and it was not apples, cherries, and strawberries. It was a roll with a lot of butter and a glass of sweet, rich chocolate.

By the end of May, something happened that helped Alicia arrive at a decision regarding Chaim. Her periods were due at the end of each month, and she was regular. At the end of this May, it did not come. This was life-threatening. They hate me up front, she thought. I'll never get a pass to Dr. Breitman. Somehow I will have to get out of here and walk east until I'm behind the Russian lines. She didn't even think about telling Chaim.

By June 5, there was still no sign of her period. Then on the morning of June 6, she got terrible cramps. Her periods had never been so heavy or accompanied by so much pain. She could barely stop the flow of heavy clumps of blood. (Later on, she would suspect that it was not her period, but a miscarriage.) The women noticed how pale she was and how wracked with pain. "My period is very heavy this month," she told them.

They were very nice to her. They did her share of the work as she sat in the back, holding her stomach.

"Go to the infirmary," they told Alicia. "Laura will help you."

"I'll be all right."

After a couple of hours, she was. They all went outside for a lunch break and sat on a pile of wood. It was a bright, sunny June day. There were six women, most of whom Alicia liked, especially Genia and Zosia. Genia brought Alicia her soup and some extra boiled potatoes. Alicia felt better. Now, her resolution to drop Chaim was very firm in her mind. He's going to have to get his sex some place else.

Luzer, Zosia's husband, passed by and showed them a "V" sign."Have you heard?" he said, low. "There's an invasion going on now in Normandy. Finally there is a Western front."

The women got excited. "How do you know?"

"All the goyim know it already. The news came over the BBC."

Alicia threw her potato in the air, yelping with joy. In the last moment, she caught the potato. Eastern front, Western front, at this moment, the potato was still the most important thing in her life. Then realization overwhelmed her: Humanity's greatest nightmare would soon be over. *And I am still alive—I, Alicia Strum.*

Even if I don't make it and if they send us all to gas chambers before retreating, I will die knowing that this obscene system is about to meet its just fate. My father knew it, but it will come too late for him and millions and millions of others. My father lived through the fall of Poland, Norway, France, the Balkans, the bombardment of Pearl Harbor, and the invasion of Russia. He never lost his faith. At least I've lived long enough to see the turning of the tide.

That evening Alicia said to Chaim, "Our relationship has run its course. The war will not last much longer, and if we survive, we will want to be free. I'll probably look for Jas in Palestine or my relatives in the United States. I would want to go to school."

"What are you saying, Alicia? I admit that things between us are not good at the moment. We should tell Breslau that we want to share a bunk. Then we'll have more time at night together—maybe that would help."

Alicia looked at Chaim. *Now* he's asking me! she thought wearily. I probably would have said yes if he had asked me in the beginning, when the attraction was strong. Living formally with a man gives a woman status in the barracks. Everybody would know that there was a man who cared for me. But I don't need it anymore. It would only mean that I would wash his socks and shirts, provide him with convenient sex, and be his maid. And I would still have to live with this terrible fear of pregnancy. Even if our sex was as good as it was at the beginning, it's still not worth it. "It's too late in the game," she told Chaim. "Our mutual craziness for each other is gone. If we survive the war and decide to be together in the 'normal' world, we can start all over again. Now you don't have to feel guilty leaving me behind if you want to go hide in the woods. Though," she said with a smile, "I know that, given an opportunity, guilt will never stop you."

"Oh Alicia," Chaim said, "when I planned the escape with Benjamin and Ira, you and I were not lovers yet." But to his surprise, he felt relieved. Alicia and I would probably not be good for each other, he told himself. She has too many highfalutin ideas.

"We still can be friends," Alicia said.

But as June progressed, she discovered that she didn't miss Chaim at all; except for sex, they didn't have much in common. She could talk with Andrew or Saul for hours, but somehow with Chaim there was not much to talk about.

It was becoming harder and harder to organize food. She lost a few teeth. But then, by the end of June, a minor miracle happened. As she returned from the factory one day, she found Mr. Bloom waiting for her. He lived in Ludwikow, and as far as she knew, he still worked in Kadzielnia. To Alicia, he looked the same as he had years ago—stocky, dark, jovial, always joking. Leah was in Alicia's dreams like Sabina, Basia, Lisa, and finally Anne. But when she got close, she noticed that Mr. Bloom's eyes were glinting with tears.

He said, "They gave me a pass to get in touch with Sid for professional advice. It was an excuse to get to see you."

He whispered, "I have some money for you from Tadek. Before he was admitted to the hospital, he gave it to his friend, who came to Kadzielnia and gave it to me to pass to you."

Tadek, my good friend! she thought weakly. He's helping me from beyond his grave. My father's money, his patient Mr. X, my friend Tadek, Leah's father—what a chain of decent people, both dead and alive. Money means independence. I'll be able to buy extra food, either from Mendel or directly from the Poles. I will not have to schnorr (beg) from the women who work in the kitchen. I will certainly not have to sleep with a man just to eat, as so many other girls do. The money will last me a few months, and the image of myself as a famine victim will be removed farther away. Alicia put her arms around Mr. Bloom and kissed him.

"I know," he said, "that I am doing what would make Leah happy. I hope that she is watching us from someplace, and she is winking with approval."

"Leah and Tadek both," Alicia said. "Maybe they're on that distant galaxy, thousands of light years away, where God is. Who knows, He might be getting closer. Speed of light doesn't bother Him. He can cover any distance in one minute."

"Now, I can see," Mr. Bloom said, "why Leah loved you so much. You always philosophized together. I have to get back to Ludwikow before curfew. I hope the next time we see each other, it's going to be in a 'normal' world."

In June and July, Alicia spent most of her free time with Shlomo. Both of us, she thought, are here by some crazy quirk of fate. I left my mother and brother, and then Herr Thomas (as poor Jankiel so vividly expressed it) smelled me out. And Shlomo is alive against all odds.

She sometimes thought about her own childhood, how short and precious it had been and how a person goes through it only once. Shlomo was not able to go outside and he had no other children to play with. He had to pretend that he didn't exist. If Shlomo ever enters a "normal" world, will he be able to adjust? A big piece of the usual growing-up process will be missing. Will he ever fit with other children his own age? Or will he be an old man prematurely?

And what about me? Will I be able to form friendships again, after remembering what happened to the friends of my childhood and youth? Will I have my own children after witnessing the murders of all those Jewish children? To what God should I pray now—that Shlomo should survive and enter the normal life that would lead him to a university to be a physician, philosopher, mathematician, scientist, to be married and have a family, or just to live a life?

Sometimes Alicia talked to Shlomo about the solar system, the perfect harmony that the planets have with their moons and with each other, revolving each with its own speed proportional to its distance from the sun, in its individual orbit, so none of them collide.

Shlomo asked, "If 'Whoever' created the sun, planets, and moon did such a perfect job, why did He mess up like this by creating people?"

Alicia replied, "He did not mess up. He just gave people free will. *They* messed up." She talked to Shlomo about the miracle properties of water, which makes life on earth possible. "A lake in winter does not freeze through and through, so life can go on under the ice. There must be 'Something' in the universe that has respect for life, but it does not apply to Jews."

The studying of algebra and geometry was comforting to both of them. The abstract concepts removed them from their everyday reality. Somehow, they both realized that there was more to life than just surviving. Once Shlomo asked why mathematicians had never determined the exact value of pi. Alicia explained that it was close enough for ordinary purposes. I wish somebody could figure out as closely why people behave the way they do, she thought: Why Benjamin did not come back for Anne? Why I slept with Chaim? Why some policemen resigned after Treblinka while others remained in the Jewish police? Why all the senseless murders of innocent people?

She missed Anne. She thought: If I knew they have killed Anne the way they did my father, I would not have to worry about her suffering. By now she would have wound up "safe to sea."

But still in July and August of 1944, Alicia felt pretty good about herself; she was not hungry, she had decent clothes, her throat didn't bother her, the sores on her legs had healed completely and her gums had stopped bleeding, and she managed to keep clean and neat. Though Anne was gone, she had friends left; there was Saul and Andrew, Lucia, Genia, and Zosia. She knew that Mr. Bloom was in Ludwikow. Most of all, she was free of her obsession with Chaim.

There was a place in the factory where water dripped through the wooden slats in the ceiling, washing the stacks of spokes piled on the floor. Female and male workers alternated in using the place to wash themselves. One day Alicia heard a lot of noise coming from the place—the boys were laughing and splashing. Above the others, she heard Andrew's voice: "Hey fellows, stop it, enough is enough."

She could not resist peeking. Some boys had no shirts on, but none were naked. Andrew was dressed but covered with some kind of gunk, which reeked to high heaven. "You are full of shit!" the boys were yelling at him as they poured water from a bucket over his head.

Later on Alicia found out what had happened. Andrew was fished out by Glattstein from the sewer under the latrine. Unlike Zubow, Glattstein did not report the incident.

"Since the fences are patrolled, it's the only way to get out of here," Andrew explained later.

"But, where would you go all covered with feces?"

"I know a place in the city in the back of an abandoned building where I could hide till night. Then I would make my way into the mountains. You know our little dirty stream Silniczna? Up there, it's brisk and clean, and I could wash up."

"And then what?"

"I would find a cave and wait for the end of the war."

"What would you eat?"

"For crying out loud, Alicia, that's why most of us just sit and wait. We ask too many questions. Don't you realize that the Germans will kill us before they have to withdraw?"

She laughed. "Next time you go through the sewers, take me with you, and I'll be your cave woman."

"Now they will not only be watching the fences but also the latrines," he said gloomily.

August 1944 was a month of hope. The Russians had already taken Lublin, which was only eighty-five miles from Kielce. There was a Polish uprising in Warsaw; the home army, under the direction of the Polish government-in-exile in London, tried to liberate the city before the Russians got there. On the Western Front, the Allies were advancing toward Paris. Things were happening so fast that there was reason to hope that the Germans would not have time to murder the remaining Jews.

CHAPTER 14

1944—Auschwitz

By late August 1944, people in Kielce claimed that they could hear Russian artillery in the distance. The Jewish administration of Henrykow and Ludwikow was notified that the Jewish workers would be deported west. Oderman was told by a 'reliable source' that they would go to a "good labor camp." By 1944 people knew how to prepare for a deportation. They packed their possessions and put many layers of clothes on themselves. It was a warm August day but not as unbearably hot as that August day in 1942 during the deportation to Treblinka. But still people were hot and uncomfortable. They gathered in front of the barracks as they used to for roll call, but everything else was different. Men and women were separated. They were surrounded by German, Ukrainian, and Polish guards, and Jewish policemen were no longer in charge.

Alicia wondered about little Bella. Would the guards notice that there was a young girl among them, maybe too young for a labor camp? Marsha, Bella's mother, was pale and nervous, but it didn't look as though she was hiding anyone. Then Alicia noticed a bulge between Zosia and Genia, and she concluded that Bella was hiding behind their full skirts.

Shlomo was smaller than Bella, and although she could pass for an adult, he certainly could not. Alicia looked across at the men. She noticed Shlomo's father wearing a bulky coat. He was standing behind the two tallest men, Oderman and Glattstein; Shlomo must have been hiding inside that coat.

Somebody pulled Alicia's arm. It was Lucia. What can she want now? It is not like two years ago. We are not standing with our mothers, brother and sister; they became ashes a long time ago. This time there is no other side that we can go. No Thomas to tap our shoulders with his stick; "You will stay in Kielce and live." No selection to the left or right. The entire group has to go to the trains to be transported to a "'good labor camp." "Lucia," Alicia said, "there is nothing we can do now, except follow everybody else."

The orders were given, and they started marching toward the Railroad Street. Even leaving Henrykow was painful. As long as I live, Alicia thought, I will remember my friendship with Anne, Andrew, and Saul, teaching Shlomo, the good times with Chaim, and the kindness of Mr. Bloom.

As they moved along the street, they passed the old gymnasium of Kinga; how many times did I use this street to get to school in the old, happy times? I complained about the boredom of the daily routine of school and homework. Will I ever come back to Kielce? What for? There will be nobody to come back to. Unless Jerry returns to Poland or Beryl with his wife and other Lublin cousins, Wladek and Eda and relatives from Katowice? Hopefully, they may survive in Russia. We will meet here.

They were joined by Ludwikow group. Alicia spotted Mr. Bloom and Dr. Breitman; they were the oldest in the group, but being engineer and doctor, they had a good chance. Mrs. Spitz was walking with a blank empty stare, following the other women, unaware of where she was. Maybe she was better off than everyone else. Then there was a gray haired lady in the group, disheveled and looking worried. She lived in Ludwikow with her fifteen-year-old son Jeffie. Jeffie was very dependent on his mother. Now they were separated.

They arrived at the railroad station, and the trains were waiting. Neither the station nor the cars themselves were crowded. In 1944, unlike 1942, not many Jews were left in Poland to be transported. The Kielce group boarded with all their problems; the three children, an "old" lady, and a "crazy" woman. A group of girls from Radom was already on the train. The guards were Ukrainians, big blond fellows in uniforms armed with clubs and guns.

As the train started moving, they read the names of small Galician towns they were passing through. They were traveling southwest. Alicia, like everyone else, realized where they were going. The "good labor camp" would be Auschwitz.

The same place where, in 1941, her uncle and Lucia's father were sent. Where Basia and her parents were sent in 1941 and Anne only two months ago. The only two people from both factories who weren't on board these trains were Benjamin and Ira. What a dismal record for Kielce people!

In the men's car, the policemen threw things out of the windows while the guards were not looking. Valuables? Guns? Oderman and Stawski must have had some. What happened to the grandiose plans? Oderman was supposed to have led "everybody" to freedom.

Alicia's eyes wandered to the girls from Radom. They were a ragged group, sitting dejectedly on the floor of the car. Some had their heads in their arms, and they were crying.

As one girl picked up her head, her face seemed familiar to Alicia. No, it could not be her! She had been a roly-poly lively person, who had black hair and sparkling eyes, mischievous smile, dimples. There was no sparkle in this girl, who was sitting on the floor of the train. She was thin, her face looked tired, her eyes were dull, she had the expression of an old woman. There were even some gray strands in her black hair, though she was still a young girl. A lot of suffering was written on that face. Alicia edged over to the group. "Do I know you?" she asked the girl.

The girl raised her eyes, and a glimmer of recognition appeared on her face. She smiled, and there was that old spark in her eyes and on her face.

"You are Dana," Alicia said. "We went to school together for two months in 1939 when we were refugees in Lwow."

"And you're Alicia," the girl said. "What a place to meet—in a train to Auschwitz. Are you alone like me? Or is anybody from your family left?"

"I'm alone," Alicia said. "My family, together with most Kielce people, were murdered in Treblinka. And you? And what are you doing with the Radom group? As I remember, you are originally from Warsaw."

"Treblinka," Dana said. "My parents were 'taken care' there too." Then she came alive. "I was in the Warsaw ghetto uprising," she whispered. "I served as a messenger between the ghetto and the Polish resistance. They would tell me when and where they would deliver ammunition. We fought on the streets from bunkers and caves dug under houses. I myself threw fire bombs at German tanks.

We actually killed Germans—can you imagine Jews killing Germans?"

Then resignation came back. Her voice became dull and monotonous, the enthusiasm was all gone. "My boyfriend and love of my life was shot next to me and fell dead into my arms."

Alicia was crying now, thinking about Pawel. "Love of my life is dead also. He managed to escape from Treblinka, but later"—She spread her hands. As an afterthought she asked, "Are people still being murdered in Treblinka?"

"There's nothing in Treblinka anymore," Dana answered. "The *Sondercommandos* blew up the gas chambers, the crematoria, and the railroad station. Most of them were caught, but some escaped."

Alicia noticed that the guards were watching them. "We are talking too long," she said. "The guards are trying to listen. Ukrainians usually understand a little Polish. We'd better separate now."

Lucia was talking and flirting with one of the guards, a tall blond fellow, who was laughing and baring his crooked teeth. What is she up to? Alicia wondered. Lucia must have some purpose for flirting with him. Sometimes she is too smart for her own good. She again felt responsible for her friend. I've got to see that she doesn't outsmart herself.

She approached the guard and Lucia. She heard him talking in his broken Polish: "Such a pretty girl, a little Jewish girl. What a pity that they will gas and burn you at Auschwitz. When I open the door of the train to empty the bucket, I'll let you jump out, and you can go and hide."

Alicia looked at the bucket; it had been used for the women to relieve themselves.

The guard noticed her. "She's blond. I'll let you both out," he said to Lucia.

Alicia just stood there. That old feeling of inertia came back. I don't want to make a life-and-death decision for both of us again, she thought. But then she looked at the bucket. If I jump from this train, I won't have to piss in that foul-smelling thing. I could piss under a tree, like I used to in Zabiec. I have some money in my bra. Lucia must have some also. Maybe we could both pay a peasant to hide us for a few months. Or we could just try to walk east to meet the Russians.

Walk with Lucia? She would pull her heart condition on me and then I would have to carry her.

Alicia remembered stories circulated in the barracks about women in these trains being encouraged to jump out only to be shot in the back. Now, when Lucia asked her, "Should we go?" a suspicion entered Alicia's mind. Does she want me to jump out first to see what the guard will do?

The guard had broad, Slavic features with slanted Mongol eyes. He was a descendant of the Cossacks. Cossacks were famous for pogroms. There was a malicious grin on his face. He's bored, Alicia decided. He wants to have some fun seeing us tumble, run, and then fall dead. Not that it makes much difference, but why give him the satisfaction? She pulled Lucia away.

"Do you trust him?" the younger girl asked.

"Not particularly."

"Neither do I. What should I tell him?"

"Tell him that you want to stay with your friends."

They came to Auschwitz. As they left the train, they realized that they were in a different world, the unique, obscene nightmarish world. They were a group of young frightened women and guards were all over with sticks and guns, hitting and cursing. A thick smoke permeated the air, and there was a smell that they could not quite identify.

Somehow Alicia thought about Aunt Yentl in the kitchen of Zabiec, burning a piece of liver over an open flame. "Aunt Yentl, why are you burning the liver?"

"By getting the extra blood out, I am making it kosher," Aunt Yentl answered. "A good Jew is not supposed to eat blood."

Then Alicia realized that the smell of Auschwitz was the smell of burning flesh. How many human livers are burning now? Will my liver burn?

As they marched toward the smoke, they passed a group of female prisoners. The woman in charge was wearing a striped prisoner's uniform. She looked well fed and robust, but the girls in her group were painfully thin, almost shriveled, had sunken cheeks, and their ribs were sticking out from their chests. They were dressed in rags, and could barely move. Their leader was beating them and yelling: "Walk faster, you stinking *Muzulmans*.*" Her charges seemed to be oblivious to the surroundings and to the pain inflicted on them.

Next the Kielce women came upon a group of male prisoners working in a garden. It was filled with brilliant flowers; red, yellow and violet. How can these flowers grow with all this smoke? Alicia wondered. Maybe they want us to believe that we're in some benign place. But it was a malignant place, a mass murder place. A place where one could buy human ashes wholesale.

The men working in the garden were in better condition than the girls they had met. And then a miracle happened. The supervisor was a Kielce man. He had been deported to Auschwitz a long time ago for smuggling food in the ghetto in 1941. Now he looked like he was far from becoming a *Muzulman*. He wasn't hitting his men, and the entire group functioned well.

Zosia recognized him first. She called his name, and he was amazed to see Kielce women. "Do you know where we're going?" Zosia asked.

He pointed his finger toward the camp, then toward heaven and said, "Either, or." He looked them over. "You look well. You are young and strong, you have a chance."

Their mood lifted a little. Stan had been in Auschwitz for three years and not only had he survived, but he was working and seemed all right.

Alicia practically had to carry Lucia, and her feet were hurting.

"We should have jumped when we had the chance," Lucia kept repeating.

Alicia was tired. "I didn't stop you, I just advised you. Stop hanging on me now. You heard Stan. He said that we have a good chance. Just walk straight and pretend that you're strong and healthy." She thought: Should I feel lucky that old, sick people and children are not among us? "Strong and healthy," she repeated.

They entered the bathhouses, and went through a row of women

---

* *Muzulman—Camp jargon for an emaciated prisoner ready for the gas chmber.*

who were giving instructions on what to do. They had to strip completely and throw out all their personal possessions. They were deprived of reminders of who they were, whom they loved, and where they came from; not a tiny medallion, a ring, a snapshot or other momento from a loved one remained. They were nameless new inmates of Auschwitz. All they had now was each other.

Alicia had to get rid of her precious brassiere. If I still had Mucia's necklace, she thought, I would have to throw it out now anyway. So nothing really matters. Maybe Lucia was right, we should have jumped from the train.

Naked, they went through other inspections. Their hair was inspected for lice. Since none were found, they were not shaved. No Germans were around and no doctor; they hoped that it meant that there would be no selection. Still by the time they were all led to the showers, they were numb with panic. What will come out of the faucets?

It was not poisonous gas—it was real water. Water never seemed so beautiful, so miraculous, so refreshing. Like the stuff that Alicia used to tell Shlomo about, with the wondrous, extraordinary properties that made life on earth possible. It felt so good after the ghastly trip, the heat, and the sweat, it almost took the fright away. It seemed like ages since Alicia had taken a shower. She even had a bar of soap. Then they were led to a pile of clothes, where they grabbed whatever garments they could; some were able to pick up better clothes than others. Alicia got some shabby leftovers. Even Mrs. Spitz had better clothes than she did. Lucia did well. Alicia's feet were larger than average, and the shoes she got were tight. I look miserable and that, in Auschwitz, is probably dangerous, she thought.

While marching toward the camp, they met another column of women going toward the railroad station. Another miracle happened. Kielce women were among that transport. These were the girls who were deported to Pionki in 1943. They saw Rachel and her mother, Fanny and Ruth and—wonder of wonders—Anne was there too!

Alicia had to close her eyes and open them again to believe what she had seen. She wanted to run and scream and hug her friends, but guards were escorting them. Stella, Rachel's sister, who stayed in Ludwikow was now ecstatic at seeing her sister and her mother. Rachel gave a sign to Stella, pointing to the train. Pionki people had been deported to Auschwitz before the people from the Kielce factories. Now they were going to some place unknown. Anne found herself with them. Kielce people seemed to be everywhere and that fact was heartening to the forlorn group of women who had just arrived.

There was no more hierarchy among them; no more wives of policemen or ex-policemen or waifs, like Alicia—just a group of frightened, humiliated women, huddling together.

They came to block 3B. A coarse, rough woman stood in the entrance, yelling and hitting the newcomers: "I'm your block chief," she cried. "You must obey me. You've come to a Paradise. You should have been here when I came in 1942. I saw my parents, sister, with her husband and children, go straight to the gas chambers. I was beaten so badly that I wished I had gone with them. Our bunks were filthy, the soup was almost water. Now, you are getting potatoes in your soup. It is a luxury hotel compared to what it used to be."

She spoke in a mixture of broken Polish, Yiddish, and German. "You didn't have your heads shaved. When I came here, no inmate had hair in Auschwitz."

She picked the two biggest girls, one was Rywka, Stawski's girlfriend, the other Hela, an ex-policeman's wife. She said, "My name is Salka, and the two of you are going to be my *stubenalteste* [barrack elders]. You will scrub the floors and see to it that the bunks are neatly made. Right now you will help me assign everyone to a bunk."

The bunks were double-decked, and Alicia and Lucia shared one with a few other women. They received a bowl of thin soup, and still hungry, they fell asleep.

A shrill whistle awakened them; it seemed like the middle of the night: "Get up, make your bunks, soon you will have to report for roll call," Salka hollered. The wake-up call in Auschwitz was at 3 A.M.

They were handed a piece of black bread that tasted like sawdust. Then they went outside and just stood there, not knowing why. It was dark and cold. The sun would not rise yet for three more hours. Although it was only the end of August, it was freezing at three o'clock in the morning, Auschwitz not being too far from the mountains.

Salka counted them.

Alicia had practically no underwear. Lucia was hanging on her as usual. "Don't expect help from me," Alicia told her. "I am not making it either. I'm freezing to death, my bladder cannot stand it, and I am going to pee right now on the ground. Salka will notice it and beat me."

Salka hit the girls who didn't stand straight and who huddled together to stay warm. It seemed like they had to stand there forever. As the sun rose, it grew a little warmer. It was almost nine o'clock in the morning when the German *Aufseherin* (female warden) came to receive the report from Salka. The *Aufseherin* was accompanied by a woman in an inmate's striped suit. The suit was well-fitted, and she wore boots which were almost as good as the boots worn by the German woman. She carried a stick and tried to walk and look like the German. The two women, the Nazi and the Jew, talked and laughed and gave the impression of being friends.

Salka saluted them, gave the tally, and said; "*Jawohl, Frau Aufseherin, Jawohl, Frau Lageralteste* [camp elder]."

Alicia noticed the awe and respect that Salka had for those two. She would not be surprised that at any moment Salka and the other Jewish woman would raise their arms and salute the German with "Heil Hitler."

Mercifully, that roll call of the first morning came to an end. Everybody was still alive. They were now all walking toward the latrines. They could still see the smoke, but the stench was not as powerful, since the wind was blowing the other way.

And then they saw it, a usual sight in Auschwitz: A ragged girl was hanging on a fence. Somebody whispered that it was a way of committing suicide. The wires were electrified. Salka said contemptuously: "It is only a lousy *Muzulman.*" She grinned at Alicia and Lucia. "You'll be there soon."

Lucia was whimpering. Alicia said: "Don't look at the fence. And don't tell me again that we should have jumped."

By the end of the first week, things started getting better for the Kielce girls; Jobs were available and that always meant more food. Rywka and Hela, with their housekeeping job, at times, gave some bread to the others. Genia was in charge of the bread distribution. That meant more bread for the Kielce girls. Zosia was a *Schreiberin,* the block secretary. She knew how to type and her German was passable.

Some girls worked in the main kitchen. They had thicker soup and
more potatoes and occasionally shared their good fortune with others.

Zosia and Genia assumed the leadership. Zosia, with her usual efficiency, made a list of who should help whom. These two women
took care of and fed Mrs. Spitz, and they protected little Bella. Genia
persuaded Salka to leave the two alone.

Salka had a preference for Genia and chose her as confidant. She
told Genia her story, then Genia told it to the other girls: Salka's father
was a rabbi in Warsaw, very prominent in the Jewish community. It
was because of this that he and his entire family were deported to
Auschwitz as early as 1941. Salka was the only survivor of the family.
She worked herself up to become the block chief of Barrack 3B at
Birkenau, a "suburb" of Auschwitz.

To the Kielce girls, Zosia and Genia were the heroines of 3B. Because of them, and especially Genia's friendship with Salka, they were
not starving. There was a limited supply of bread for distribution.
When the Kielce girls got more the Radom girls got less. When they
complained to Salka, she would scream and beat them with her stick.

The inmates (*Häftlinge*) of Auschwitz proper were working
people: members of Special Squad, workers "processing" the new arrivals, sorters of clothes, office workers, and skilled laborers. On the
other hand Birkenau was a transition camp; people there either waited
for their turn in gas chambers, or for transports to other camps. They
only worked occasionally.

One day in September, the girls from block 3B went on a working
detail. It was senseless work of piling bricks one on top of the other.
The day was warm, but they couldn't get rid of the cold that seeped
through their bones during the morning roll call. Still moving and
working was better than just standing there freezing and watching
Salka beat girls who were near fainting.

When Alicia and Lucia came back to the barracks, they were exhausted and hungry. Zosia called them: "A man was looking for you
two. He is a Pole from Kielce, and he works as a plumber."

As Zosia was talking, a young man appeared. He was wearing
overalls and carrying a toolbox, and he held a package. He must have
been in his early twenties. He held himself straight, was tall, and didn't

look downbeaten. He was like a fresh breeze blowing through the bar-racks. Alicia didn't recognize him, but Lucia knew who he was. She became excited. "Mietek!" She was ready to hug him.

"You certainly grew up since I last saw you," he said.

Lucia turned to Alicia. "Don't you remember Mietek? He was in the same class with my brother and your cousin Jerry. His father was a superintendent of a building my family owned."

Mietek said to Lucia, "I was also a friend. Whenever I came over, your mother fed me. For some reason, she thought I didn't get enough to eat at home."

Lucia laughed. "I remember! My mother called you that nice *shaygets* [Gentile boy]. What are you doing in Auschwitz and how are your parents, brothers and sisters?"

"As far as I know, they are still in Kielce, and they are alive. I am a political prisoner. I heard from Tadek that you and Alicia did not go to Treblinka. Last week, when I learned about the Kielce transport, I decided to find out if you two girls were in it."

Mietek brought them black bread, boiled unpeeled potatoes, some raw carrots and turnips.

It was nice for the two girls to know that somebody would actually look for them in order to help.

The Kielce women came over, wanting to know if he had seen their husbands. Alicia noticed that Lucia wasn't interested in finding anything out about Joseph, the man she had lived with for more than a year.

When Mietek spoke to the women, he was evasive. He told them that he had seen their men, but now he didn't know where they were.

Once he was left alone with Alicia and Lucia, he told them what he knew: "The leader of the Kielce group, the German speaking guy, and another man were badly beaten."

"Was the German guy's name Spiegel?"

"I think that was his name," Mietek answered.

"Was the other man from Kielce?"

"He was Polish, but not from Kielce, maybe from Lodz."

"Probably it was Birnbaum," Alicia guessed. She wondered if it was other inmates that beat the two.

Then he told them something that was more important than what happened to Spiegel and Birnbaum: "You know your neighboring lager is a hospital lager; some Kielce Jewish doctors are working there."

The girls were stunned. "How is it possible? All the Kielce doctors were murdered."

"Well, not all of them. Two are just there across the fence, which is not electrified," he said.

"Who?"

"Brazen and Feinstein. You should try to see them. They could probably help you."

The two girls were getting more and more amazed. Brazen? Bolek's father. They came for him during that terrible action on the reserve officers. Alicia's and Pawel's fathers were murdered on the spot. But Dr. Brazen was sent to Auschwitz. At that time it seemed equivalent to death. Now they were learning that after more than two years in Auschwitz, he was working in a hospital and doing well. Other doctors sent there—Dr. Peltz, Dr. Koslow, Dr. Harkavi—lasted only a few months. So how come Brazen? What was he doing that the others didn't?

Alicia and Lucia managed to get to that fence the following day. They saw an orderly and asked for Dr. Brazen. He came right away. He didn't seem to have lost weight. To them he looked the same as when he lectured during the nursing course on internal medicine, two and a half years ago. He had a florid face, a little pot belly, and all his hair. His wife and son died in Treblinka. If he had not been sent to Auschwitz in April 1942, he would have been murdered in Kielce cemetery the following October. They were living in a crazy world.

From that day on, the two girls tried to see him as often as possible, and Dr. Brazen always had some food for them. The best was thick pea soup, which he handed them in small canteens through openings in the fence. To Alicia, who had been used to the best before the war, nothing ever tasted as good as that soup. She could actually find pieces of meat in it.

Dr. Brazen was usually accompanied by a young doctor from Katowice. He was handsome and very pleasant. He introduced himself as Dr. Kaplan and told the girls that he had once been married and had watched his wife go into the gas chambers. He took a fancy to Lucia, and she promptly fell head over heels in love with him. The doctors knew Margo the *Lageralteste* well, and through her, they could get jobs for the Kielce girls.

The other doctor from Kielce was Dr. Feinstein. He was in his early thirties. In 1939 he married Tania, Laura's girlfriend. At that time the Kielce girls were jealous of Tania for marrying a doctor. Then Dr. Feinstein was sent to Auschwitz and later Tania was murdered in Treblinka. Now Dr. Feinstein managed to persuade Margo to give Laura an assistant block chief's job in 5B. It was the next block to 3B.

Alicia wondered. Would Laura—mild and gentle Laura, a nurse who sometimes appeared as an angel of mercy—learn to beat the inmates the way the other block chiefs did?

The big filthy, smelly latrines were a meeting place for girls of different blocks. They tried to stay there as long as they could. Occasionally the block chiefs and Kapos came, hit them, and chased them.

Alicia met some French girls in the latrine. They told her that they were in the last transport from Paris. When their train started moving east on August 19, Paris was being liberated. General De Gaulle, with his Free French, were marching up the Champs Elysées.

"How did it feel to be leaving Paris, destination Auschwitz, at a time like that? Did anybody manage to jump off and escape?"

"We could not. We were guarded well. But it was good to know that there would be no more deportations."

"Are there any Jews left in free Paris?" Alicia asked.

"*Peut etre* [perhaps]," the girls answered.

It felt good to speak French.

Everybody who still was able to think straight knew that the Germans would have to surrender soon. Last August the Russians were near Warsaw. Were they there already? What about Kielce?

Occasionally Alicia visited Dana in block 5B. The block chief was Bronia, a girl from Lublin, and her assistant was Laura. Bronia complained that between her and Laura there was nobody to hit people.

Alicia worried about Dana. Dana had told her that if she got hungry enough, she might walk into the fence and electrocute herself.

Alicia was appalled. "Try to get a job. If you have some food, you will feel better."

Dana just shrugged her shoulders. "Do you think I would consider being a Kapo or a block chief after I threw fire bombs at German tanks?"

"But you have to eat."

"If you serve them, you become part of the system. You start behaving and thinking like them. I saw your friend Laura hitting a girl."

It was hard to believe it about Laura.

But to Alicia's surprise, one day the following week, she found Dana cheerful. She looked at Alicia, smiled, and there was that old dimple in her cheek.

"I have some bread for you," Alicia told her. "Dr. Brazen was quite good to me the last time I saw him."

"Thank you," Dana answered, "but I have something better." From underneath her blanket she took out a package and handed it to Alicia.

Alicia opened the package. She couldn't believe her eyes. It was warm underwear, a sweater, and a pair of shoes, the biggest women's size that could be found. These clothes could mean the difference between life and death, between surviving the roll calls and developing some fatal infection. "How did you get these?"

"Bronia told me that for a long time she was in the same block with a Kielce girl. Now that girl has a job in Canada.

Alicia gave Dana a blank stare. "Canada in Auschwitz?"

Dana laughed. "In Auschwitz it means a place where people sort clothes. The sorters find all kind of things sewn in clothes. The Jews from the Netherlands especially brought a lot of riches."

"Who is the Kielce girl working in Canada? she asked.

"Try and guess."

It could only be one person, Alicia thought. "Basia," she exclaimed. "Basia is alive! She is the only one who knows about my big feet." Both Basia and Anne, she thought. Maybe He *is* coming back from that distant galaxy.

Bronia approached them. She told them that she saw Basia in Auschwitz quite often. Basia found out about the Kielce transport and that Alicia was in it. She sent some clothes for Dana also; she remembered her from Lwow.

"How about her parents?" Alicia asked eagerly.

"Basia's mother did not last long at all in Auschwitz," Bronia told them. "Her father outlived his wife by a few months. He went together with my parents."

"He was such a strong and fit man," Alicia said. She closed her eyes. She remembered how very much Basia was attached to her parents, how protective she was of her mother and how she adored her father. "How is Basia doing now?"

"We both had some very tough times. But then she got a job in Canada, and I became a block chief."

"Can you eat a diamond or a piece of gold?"

Bronia was laughing: "You are very naive. Girls from Canada barter stuff with the kitchen girls. There is a definite rate of exchange, how many plates of soup for a karat."

There was a way of living and dying in Auschwitz, Alicia thought. She kissed the two girls, said hello to Laura, hid the package under her clothes, and went back to 3B.

Janka Buchhalter became a problem for the Kielce group. Alicia remembered her from before the war: an only child, spoiled rotten, fat, lazy, a bad student, living on cake and chocolate. She remained alive by refusing to get into the bus with her parents for that fatal ride that took all the remaining doctors and dentists to the cemetery. Now, she could barely make the roll call. She lay prostrate on the bunk, and unless someone like Zosia or Genia brought her food, she did not bother. Most of the time she kept her blanket over her head. She was almost as bad as Mrs. Spitz.

One morning, Alicia pulled the blanket off Janka. "Dr. Brazen wants to see you," she said. "You've got to come with me and Lucia. He knew your father well. If Brazen sees you, he'll find food for the three of us."

Janka didn't feel like moving. "Leave me alone. We're going to the gas chambers soon."

Alicia got mad. "Maybe so, but you are alive today so you have to eat." Then it came to her: That's all that mattered—today. No yesterday, no tomorrow. Got to eat and not to freeze at roll calls. No figuring where God is or why the earth did not fall out of its orbit and crash into the sun. If I survive, I will try to think about what happened and why and probably I will go crazy.

Mrs. Rothman and Shlomo's mother were crying and worrying

about their sons. "Jeffie was never without me," Mrs. Rothman was saying. "I always took care of him. How will he manage by himself?"

"Shlomo is only ten years old. What chance does he have?" the other woman wailed.

Alicia moved over to them. "Small or not small, I know Shlomo. If there's any way of getting out of here alive, he'll take it. He even got out of Kielce cemetery." To Mrs. Rothman, she added, "Kielce men will take care of Jeffie."

One afternoon Lucia and Alicia stayed in the latrine. Both girls were in a good mood. Lucia was in love. Alicia learned that Basia was alive; she wanted badly to see her. It was five years since they had said good-bye to each other in Lwow. It seemed like ages ago. The world had not collapsed on them yet, and they were young and full of hope.

Lucia managed to get paper and pen from Zosia and now, sitting in the latrine, tried to compose a love letter to Dr. Kaplan. She was only twelve when the war started; her education had stopped abruptly. She didn't know how to write very well. "Please, Alicia, write a letter for me."

Alicia laughed: "I'll be your Cyrano."

"Who is he?"

Alicia told her the story.

"Please be my Cyrano," Lucia said.

They had a lot of fun, and they wished they could stay in the latrine forever. When they came back to 3B, Salka was shouting that the girls were undisciplined, they came and went as they pleased, they didn't make their bunks straight and were late for roll calls; she threatened that she would complain to Margo, the *Lageralteste.*

Genia told everyone that Salka was really mad and she couldn't quiet her down. "Lucia and Alicia have to be especially careful. Salka thinks that they are too independent."

The next day, the roll call whistle blew at 3 A.M., as usual. It was colder that dawn than it should have been for the month of September. Alicia and Lucia huddled together, shivering. Their warm underwear was helping, but it wasn't enough. At this rate, Alicia thought, I doubt we'll get through the winter.

Then Margo appeared. The German supervisor was not with her. Margo was wearing boots and a fur-lined jacket. She looked warm and comfortable. Alicia wondered with whom Margo slept. Was it the German woman supervisor? According to the rumors, she was also a mistress of a German commandant of the entire camp. Was she doing both? Whichever was true, Margo had power over life and death and the distribution of jobs to the inmates. She looked down at the shivering, half-starved women.

She gave a speech: "Your block chief complained to me about your behavior." She pointed her thumb to the smoke of the crematoria. "Better people than you have gone there, and if you don't obey Salka, I will see to it personally that you are next."

Alicia felt like laughing. It struck her as ridiculous. One Jewish woman threatening a group of Jewish women with gas chambers and the crematoria. It was obscene.

Margo swung her whip, hit herself across her boots, and walked away nonchalantly. Her gait and demeanor would make people believe that she had been raised a proper member of the Nazi party.

Alicia looked up and saw the sun rising over Auschwitz. Half of the yellow disk was seen on the eastern horizon; the sky was red. It promised to be a clear, cool autumn day. The leaves in Kielce park would be starting to turn yellow, red, and brown. How could so much beauty coexist with Auschwitz? "Youth give me wings" (Mickiewicz). I'll fly back to Kielce. I can't do it now, but after my death, I will soar free; my flesh will be ashes, but my spirit will not feel hunger or cold.

Salka was talking to them. As usual, she sounded coarse and illiterate. If Salka had been born at another time, Alicia thought, she would be an ordinary Jewish woman. If she was married, she would be wearing a wig and once a month would go to Mikvah. Now Salka was devoted to Margo.

Salka was talking: "Do you remember what the *Lageralteste* said to you? Better people than you have gone to the gas chambers. Last year—" (Alicia half-expected her to say "in the good old days"—when Auschwitz was still Auschwitz, not a resort town) "there was a family transport from Holland. They lived in a model block and slept on real mattresses. Instead of blankets they had silk quilts. The men, women, and children were together. There were older people among them. Everyone was allowed to keep their possessions. The Orthodox men wore yarmulkas. One evening, Herr *Obersturmführer* came to visit. A representative of the Orthodox group asked him about the possibility of obtaining kosher food. The *Obersturmführer* promised that he would consider it. Then he gave chocolates and candy to the children and told the people that they would see for themselves what lies were told about the German camps. The next morning, while the orchestra was playing, the entire model block—children, grandparents and all—were marched to the gas chambers. They didn't believe even to the last moment, that they were going to their death."

Finally, the gruesome roll call was over.

The following day's roll call was uneventful. Salka handed her report to the German supervisor. It was nine o'clock in the morning, and the girls were waiting for a signal to go back to the barracks. The sun was already high in the sky; they tried to catch its warming rays.

Salka looked them over. "We are not going back to the barracks," she said. "I want you to march in orderly fashion, not like a rabble."

"Where are we going?" the girls asked.

Salka just stood there and grinned.

The women got hysterical and began to wail and cry. "Kielce girls," someone yelled, "let's say good-bye to each other." They started kissing.

Alicia's mind became a blank; she was detached from the entire scene. She felt like a spectator and couldn't care less what was going to happen to her. Mrs. Spitz looked more agitated than her. Mrs. Rothman was crying. "I hope my Jeffie will save himself. Somebody have pity on him."

Lucia held her hand over her heart and was very pale. She has even less living behind her than I have, Alicia thought.

Nobody noticed that Zosia was missing. She came out and eyed the scene. She waved bunch of papers in front of Salka's face and said: "You crazy sadist. Why didn't you tell the girls where we were going."

"Nobody asked me," Salka said.

"We are going to be tattooed," Zosia announced to the women.

Alicia took a deep breath. Was it relief? It would be nice to wind "safe to sea," or to be a free spirit floating someplace in the universe near God. Then she became aware that Lucia was having trouble breathing. Alicia put her arm around her. "Take it easy," she said. She tried to support her as they were marching. Lucia slowly recovered.

They came to a little house, which served as a place for tattooing prisoners. As they stood in line, waiting their turn, the girls were happy because it wasn't a line for the gas chambers.

"No, not yet," Janka said. "We will be marked and duly registered. When they send us to the gas chambers, they will know who they took care of and what series is next."

"Shut up, Janka," Alicia snapped. "Lucia is not feeling well. Haven't you heard of the expression, 'Where there's life, there's hope?' After all—you, like me and Lucia—come from a family of healers."

Genia came out of the shack and showed her arm. There was a small tattoo inside her left forearm: Letter A. and a number. "It's not a big deal.—L'Haim—to Life, we are alive one more day."

When the girls returned to 3B, Lucia was crying. She told Alicia that her heart was giving up. Alicia suggested that they should get to the doctors to see what could be done for her.

Lucia brightened up instantly. "I'll hand over the love letter that you wrote for me." She was so enthusiastic now that she forgot about her heart. They went to the fence and found Dr. Kaplan.

"I'm glad you came," he said to Lucia. "I have good news for you." He looked at her with a father's concern, yet he still thought of her as an attractive girl. Lucia handed him her love letter. "What is the good news?" she asked.

"I managed to get a job for you. Tomorrow morning, you are to report to a model block Eight B. You'll be in charge of bread distribution."

Model blocks in Auschwitz were used in case of an inspection by the Red Cross or some other international commission. The conditions there were immeasurably better than in the ordinary barracks, and the girls usually had a trade. Eight B was a block of seamstresses, who had arrived on a Hungarian transport. They slept on real mattresses and under silk quilts. Salka told the truth when she described the "luxurious" conditions of the model blocks. The girls didn't have to stand for long roll calls, they were counted and sent off to work. Lucia didn't have to go out at all. She had an "inside" job. Alicia would visit her and get extra bread.

One day in October, the smoke from the crematoria was very thick

and heavy, carried by the wind. "Don't you know why?" Genia said to
Alicia. "Today is the first day of Rosh Hashanah. It is an Auschwitz
tradition to gas and cremate three times as many people as usual on
this day." Auschwitz also has traditions, Alicia marveled. Obscene
traditions.

That afternoon, she visited Lucia. Most of the girls in the block
were back from their jobs. They were now lying under their silk quilts
and crying. They had come from traditional Jewish families, and the
memories of past holidays at home were in their minds. They were
young girls, and like Lucia and Alicia had lost their entire families.

Wailing, crying, the smoke, the stench—how did the "luxurious"
model block fit in? A ragged, stinking blanket would make more sense
then these silk quilts. But there was no sense to Auschwitz. It defied
rationality. Perfidy. Incongruent. How did the word "incongruent"
come to my mind? Alicia wondered. She remembered teaching
Shlomo about incongruent triangles. Why couldn't life be like
geometry? Pythagoras and Euclid had such beautiful, logical minds.
What kind of mind devised Auschwitz?

One day, three of the Kielce girls who worked in the kitchen
brought a keg of soup for the others in 3B. The soup was less watery
than usual. Most of the girls did not question the reason for sudden
abundance. Alicia noticed that Genia was not eating. Did she have so
much more bread than everyone else? "How come you are not eating?"
she asked.

Genia said, "Don't you know why we have so much extra today?
Some girls working in the kitchen are fasting."

Alicia still did not get it. "Not eating on purpose in Auschwitz?"

"Today is Yom Kippur," Genia said. Then she added, "I just don't
feel like eating myself."

Alicia had never fasted on Yom Kippur at home. But now it was
different, even different than when they were refugees in Rowno and
Yom Kippur was the only day that her family could use the kitchen.
She had no family now, maybe that's why it became important to
prove to herself that not only was she Jewish but that she was still
human, and there were things more important than food. She was ready
to return the soup to the keg.

Salka appeared. "You pigs. How dare you eat on Yom Kippur?" She hit the girls with her club.

Alicia said to Salka, "How come you are hitting people on Yom Kippur?"

Salka turned on her viciously, but Alicia ducked the blow.

Genia interfered. "We are Jewish girls, and it's Yom Kippur. Stop this nonsense."

Salka was confused. She was not used to anyone questioning her authority.

"I know you're a rabbi's daughter," Genia said to her. "But we didn't know what day it was, and we were hungry." Genia knew she was on dangerous ground, questioning Salka's judgment.

"You don't look like *Muzulmans* yet," Salka said. "On judgement day, you shouldn't be eating."

"But we have been judged already," Alicia said. "We must have been found guilty. The verdict is sealed. Why else are we in Birkenau?"

"You see," Salka said to Genia. "She has no respect for her block chief." Nobody felt like eating anymore.

Later Genia called Alicia. "You'd better watch out," she warned her. "I will not always be here to bail you out and save you from a real beating."

A few days later, the real beating came. Salka was looking for an excuse. She found that Alicia's bunk was not made smooth enough. After the roll call she got help from a Slovakian girl from a neighboring block. While the Slovakian girl held Alicia, Salka had a go at her. "This is the way we do things in Auschwitz," she yelled.

Genia was there once again. "Salka," she said, "if we survive the war, you will have to learn to do things differently."

Somehow, Salka was awed by Genia. She stood there with her whip hanging by her side. "I've been in Auschwitz so long."

"You will not be here much longer," Genia said. "Let Alicia go," she told the Slovakian girl. "Make your bunk right," she told Alicia.

That evening, Genia reported to the girls that later on Salka began to cry and talk about her parents. "I think deep down she knows the difference between right and wrong."

In the blocks of Birkenau, there were recurring cases of skin rash. Salka, who now watched Alicia carefully, noticed that she was scratching herself. Alicia was sent to an isolation block, called the *Kratze* (scratch) block. To her surprise Alicia found Dana among the inmates, and managed to share a bunk with her. Things in *Kratze* block were easier than in regular blocks; the roll calls came later and didn't last long. But they were isolated and had to depend only on their rations. Alicia was already taking for granted the extra food that she was getting either from Genia or her doctor friends. Now she was always hungry. After roll call they had nothing to do. The girls would either sit on their bunks or sleep.

"We'd better get out of here fast," Alicia said to Dana. "We will become *Muzulmans* soon, *Muzulmans* with skin rashes."

"At least we're not expending much energy; your arm is still black and blue from the beating you got from Salka. What's your hurry to go back there?"

"The longer we stay here, the closer we are to—"Alicia pointed upward with her thumb.

"You're talking as if you had a guarantee that in Three B you won't go up in the smoke."

"Even in a 'normal' world, there's no guarantee for anything. We just have to make informed choices."

Dana told Alicia that in the Warsaw ghetto, she had been taking Bible lessons. She remembered by heart from Ecclesiastes:

1. To everything there is a season, and a [proper] time for every purpose under the heaven.

2. A time to be born, and a time to die; a time to plant, and a time to pluck up that which hath been planted.

3. A time to kill, and a time to heal; a time to break down, and a time to build up.

4. A time to weep, and a time to laugh; a time to mourn, and a time to dance.

5. A time to love and a time to hate.

       .   .   .   .

"Why are you quoting that particular chapter?" Alicia asked.

"Don't you see," Dana said. "Even if we survive, we've lost our timing."

"Timing for what? Right now I would settle for not being hungry and not living under the shadow of you know what." She again pointed her finger upward.

"Timing is very important. You're twenty-three now. If things had gone as planned, you would have had five years in the university and would have been a doctor or some other professional. If you see the end of the war, you'll be a strange animal, an oddity; people will wonder how come you were not gassed together with millions of 'ordinary Jews.' "

"Are you trying to be funny, Dana? It's not funny." But Alicia started laughing.

"If it's not funny, why are you laughing?"

"I just remembered a story of long ago. I was ten at the time and Jas, my cousin, was fifteen. His father was angry with him because he had failed German. Jas came to stay at our house and he asked my parents why his mother had to marry his father. My father told Jas that if his mother had married somebody else, there would be no Jas. If she had a son, he would be a completely different person. Don't you see? We are all accidents. The whole thing is a random process."

"So what? Everybody knows that."

"But with us it's not only accidental that we're who we are. It is also miraculous that we are still alive at all. Who knows? A miracle might happen, and we will survive."

The block chief of *Kratze* came over to them. She was a nice-looking, pleasant woman; she wore a white coat and comfortable white shoes with laces. The girls assumed that she was a professional nurse. Alicia noticed that she spoke Polish to the girls from Poland; most of the block chiefs in Auschwitz only used German even if they were not fluent in it.

Her face seemed familiar, though Alicia could not quite remember where and if she had ever met her. It was hard to figure out how old she was, somewhere between thirty and forty. For an Auschwitz inmate it was old. But maybe as a nurse she had a longer life expectancy.

She looked the girls over. "The rash is practically gone," she said. "You'll be soon ready to return to your original blocks."

"You see, Alicia," Dana exclaimed, "we *are* going to get out of here."

"Alicia?" the block chief echoed. "What an unusual name for a Jewish girl. Where are you from?"

"Kielce."

"Alicia from Kielce, with blond curly hair." Her face lighted up.

Now Alicia was sure she had met the woman before.

"I know who you are," the block chief said. "You're Paula Warman's niece. The last time I saw you, you were a little girl. It must have been—oh, 1926. Your mother and aunt often visited us in Krakow. But for some strange reason, we never came to Kielce or Zabiec."

Alicia remembered a pretty girl in a pink linen summer suit saying good-bye to her and Mucia at the railroad station in Krakow—such a long time ago in another world. But she knew now who the block chief was. "You are Eda, Wladek's wife."

"And the usual question: Is anybody left besides you?"

Alicia spread her hands. "Jerry is someplace in Russia, and Jas went to Palestine in 1938."

"I know about Jas. What happened to everybody else?"

"The actions on doctors and Treblinka took care of everybody else. You must be familiar with these stories."

"Beautiful Paula—so witty, smart, and resourceful. They got her also."

"Yes."

Then she told Alicia her story: "At the beginning of the war, I was on the Russian side in Tarnopol, while Wladek was with Polish units somewhere in Russia. I decided to join my parents in Krakow. You know, I was their only child. I was arrested en route and sent to this paradise."

"Like my friend Basia with her parents," Alicia said.

"Is she alive?"

"Yes, she is, but her parents you know." She pointed up. "How about your parents?"

"I learned that they were sent to an extermination camp at Majdanek. So were Wladek's parents and sister."

"Do you know where Wladek is?" Alicia asked.

"I hope that he's with the Russian army, fighting the Germans." She whispered, "It's something that we shouldn't be talking about out loud."

Now Alicia asked, "How come you are serving as a nurse when you are trained as a lawyer?"

"*Sha*. They don't like lawyers in Auschwitz. I pretended to be a nurse. As much as I like having you here, when the doctor comes tomorrow, I must recommend that you be sent to your original blocks. I've seen too many girls leave this place in the wrong direction."

Alicia marveled at how the idea of going to the gas chambers was taken for granted here as run-of-the-mill routine. Almost like going to school or to work in a "normal" world.

On the following day, the doctor came. Before Eda had a chance to speak, the doctor informed her that she had a release for Alicia. She examined her superficially.

"I'm not going without Dana," Alicia said.

"I'll see what I can do."

The other women gathered around them. "How about me, and me?" they asked.

"Girls, girls. I can't discharge everyone. Your turn will come soon." She whispered to Alicia, "Dr. Brazen asked me to get you out of here."

The doctor talked to Eda in her office. Later Eda told Alicia and Dana about the doctor: She was a Czech Jew. She lived in Trans-Olza, a part of Czechoslovakia that Poland had grabbed in 1938. She often came to Krakow to visit her relatives, and Eda knew her from before the war.

Then Eda told them a secret that the doctor had told her: "There was a revolt in the Auschwitz crematoria, and Crematorium III was blown up. The SS is busy catching and punishing the people who were responsible for it." She sighed: "Hangings, torture. I don't know whether to think about the revolt as a useless gesture or as an act of heroism."

Dana was alert now. "I was in the Warsaw uprising. I don't consider it a useless gesture."

Alicia and Dana were getting ready to leave *Kratze*. Alicia cried when she kissed Eda. "I just found a cousin; now I have to leave."

"Let's hope that we meet each other again," Eda said, "if there is ever a world again."

The girls went with the lady doctor to their respective blocks. When Alicia arrived at 3B, Genia was the first person she saw. She pushed Alicia into the little cubicle that served as her quarters for bread distribution. She gave Alicia a big piece of bread. "There's something you must do immediately. Lucia is in a bad situation."

"Is she sick?"

"No, not sick. But the whole model block Eight B is scheduled for transport tomorrow."

Alicia was panic-stricken. "Transport?"

"Take it easy," Genia said. "I am sure it's not for the gas chambers. It's to some other camp in Germany."

Alicia was thinking fast: Lucia had outsmarted herself again. How will she manage among strangers? She was Polish, they were Hungarians. And she, more than anyone else, needed support from her group. After Bella, she was the youngest from Kielce.

"You know what you have to do," Genia said.

"I am going to see Dr. Brazen and ask him to do something to get her back to Three B."

"Go right now before curfew. He has to act fast, because the transport is leaving tomorrow morning. Be careful. God be with you."

Alicia ran toward the fence. What God was Genia talking about? I've got to pray "to whatever gods may be" that I'll find Brazen or Kaplan.

It was an October afternoon, and the days were getting shorter. If the guards find me at dusk, Alicia thought, they will probably shoot me. She was lucky. Dr. Kaplan was standing at the fence waiting for Lucia. Alicia told him the story quickly. Kielce girls, she explained, are like family. We are the only family that Lucia has now and she has to get back to face whatever will happen, with us.

Kaplan told her not to worry. He would visit Margo this evening, and they would get Lucia out by the morning. Alicia surprised herself that, at a moment like this, she was wondering about the relationship between Kaplan and Margo. He sees her in the evenings? Alicia had no more time to speculate. She ran back to 3B and arrived safely before the barracks door closed.

"Thank God you're here," Genia greeted her. "Salka has been asking for you."

"How lucky we all are to have you, Genia, to protect us from Salka."

Next morning, at roll call, Margo herself brought Lucia back. When Alicia waved to them, Margo gave her a cold, contemptuous look. What's the difference if she is a bitch and she thinks she owns this place? She probably wishes that the war will never end. Still, she pulled Lucia from the row of girls waiting to be transported. Alicia often wondered how old Margo was. Once she was told that Margo was nineteen and had arrived at Auschwitz when she was fifteen.

Now Lucia stood near Alicia through the rest of the roll call. "Isn't Kaplan wonderful?" she kept repeating. "By this morning, I had given up all hope of ever being back with you girls."

"Lucia, just, please, don't try to outsmart yourself again. Believe me, you are smart enough."

Usually, Salka would yell if the girls talked at roll call. But this time she pretended not to notice. She was impressed that Margo, her ideal, took a personal interest in Lucia. She didn't know anything about Dr. Kaplan. Since Alicia was Lucia's friend, she wouldn't bother the two girls anymore. From that day on, the girls were able to spend as much time as they wanted talking to the doctors at the fence. Salka would not chase them out from the latrines. Alicia could visit Dana. Through Bronia, she got a few more packages from Basia. Who knows? she thought. If things continue to go as well as they have been, I might be able to get a pass from Salka to visit Basia. They almost wished that they could have waited out the war from where they were.

Transports kept leaving Birkenau. For where? Germany was getting smaller and smaller. Most of the death factories had ceased to function, and there were still too many Jews left alive. The Germans didn't know exactly what to do with them.

Sometime, in the middle of November, it was the turn for 3B.

After roll call that day, they had to clean up their bunks, wash the floors and leave the barracks spic and span. Salka would remain. Would other people be coming here after they were gone? If yes, from where? Part of France was liberated, much of Poland and Hungary as well.

They stood there waiting in front of the barracks. German guards arrived to escort them, probably to the railroad station. Salka waved good-bye. To their amazement, she was crying and wished them good luck.

As they marched, they passed Crematorium III, which was now in charred ruins. It made Alicia feel good. Somebody has actually done something! she exulted.

They entered a building and were told to wait in a big room. It was crowded; there were perhaps two hundred girls altogether. It was getting dark and cold. Alicia wondered why it was so cold. There were so many of them, and each one was giving off body heat. Then she noticed an open window. Through it she could see the setting sun—a fiery red disk. It's going to be a nice day tomorrow, but is it going to be nice for me?

Lucia kept on asking, "What are we waiting for?"

"How should I know? The trains probably haven't arrived yet. We're most likely being sent somewhere in Germany to work."

"Like they sent the doctors?"

"They didn't need so many Jewish doctors," Alicia said. "We're just working slobs. They still need labor."

Alicia had to smile at the thought of what kind of laborers she and Lucia would make.

Suddenly, there was a shrill scream.

"Gas," somebody yelled.

Lucia now was clinging to Alicia for dear life. A strong sense of *deja vu* overcame Alicia. Is this for real now? It was bound to happen eventually. Our luck has run out. There was a familiar cry: "Kielce girls say good-bye." They began kissing each other.

A memory of what Tadek had once told her crossed Alicia's mind: "They make people get in a bus, close all the windows and doors, and let the gas in." Then she started to laugh.

"Have you gone crazy?" Lucia demanded.

"Girls," Alicia said, still laughing, "the window is open."

They noticed Dana shaking a little Radom girl. "Why did you scream? You almost caused a panic."

The girl was whimpering. Finally she said, "I saw a mouse."

Alicia put her arms around shaking Lucia. A woman in charge announced that Dr. Mengele was ready. One by one, the girls would have to pass in front of him, before they would be allowed to go on the train.

So it's a selection, Alicia thought. "Don't put your hand over your heart, Lucia. Pretend that you're one-hundred percent healthy. I know you can act."

Radom girls were generally in worse shape than the Kielce girls. They were thinner. Mrs. Spitz looked fine; maybe she had the best answer: She did not know or care what was going on, she just followed. Bella looked grown up. Mrs. Rothman would pass, hopefully.

They all had to strip naked and put their clothes in a pile. The warm clothes that had saved Alicia during the roll calls were now lying on the floor. The women's only identity was the tattoo on their arms. Whatever they managed to organize in the last few months had to go. They were naked again. They were moving like ghosts, before "god"—Mengele, who was to determine who was going to live.

"They call him Angel of Death," somebody whispered.

A doctor? Alicia thought. Once he took an oath to heal people and prolong their lives.

All the Kielce women passed the selection. Alicia did not know what happened to the others.

They had to pick up new clothes for the transport. After all, there were plenty of clothes in Auschwitz. They even got winter coats.

CHAPTER 15

Ravensbrück, Malchow 1944–45

They boarded cattle trains. Close to two hundred young women were packed like sardines in a space that had previously accommodated eight horses. Some struggled frantically for every square inch. It must have been that way in the trains to Treblinka, only then there were old people and children among the deportees.

"Stay quiet," Alicia told Lucia. "It's the best way to conserve energy."

But Lucia was desperate. She pushed and scratched, and almost bit Alicia. "I can't breathe. My heart can't pump blood very well."

Zosia got mad. "She uses her heart condition," she whispered to Alicia. "Whenever it's convenient for her. When it's time to flirt with men or get extra food, she forgets about it right away."

Alicia barely had the energy to tell Zosia that she remembered how sick Lucia was with rheumatic fever when she was a child.

The Kielce girls made a small space for Alicia and Lucia. Alicia sat sideways, and Lucia sat on top of her legs. On the other side of the train, the women fought, pushing and shoving. One woman fainted and collapsed. The others didn't bother to see how she was; they simply sat on her. The guard announced that he would wait until they reached their destination before he disposed of the dead and disabled.

Alicia urgently needed to empty her bladder. She had to crawl over the bodies of other women to a bucket near the door. And then what? Could she manage to get back to her spot? She reached the bucket, which smelled terrible. As she was urinating, the guard was watching her. At this point she did not care.

She had to fight her way back, nobody wanted to budge, and she was worried that Lucia, in her present state of panic, would not let her in. But Genia had reserved the spot. "For both of you," she said.

The journey stretched out endlessly. Their limbs were cramped, squashed and numb. As always, Alicia wondered if her mother and Henius had survived this kind of trip. Her father was much better off dying quickly.

She spotted Dana, standing with her head down, allowing herself to be pushed. Was it because she didn't care or because she knew it was the best way to survive? Alicia was grateful that Lucia had quieted down. She kept repeating, "Stay still and make your mind a complete blank, and maybe we'll have a chance."

It was difficult for them not to react to what they saw next. A woman, in another group, went berserk. She put her hands around the neck of her neighbor and started strangling her. Women nearby tried to separate them, but to no avail. The victim's face turned purple. She tried to free herself, but she was no match for a woman in rage. The madwoman squeezed harder and harder, cursing horribly.

The guard watched and laughed. The victim finally fell down, her tongue protruding saliva flowing out of her mouth. She was probably dead. The murderess stood with a blank stare, her rage spent. She was not aware of what she had done.

How much or how little does it take to drive a person to murder? At least none of our girls lost control so completely, Alicia thought.

She put her hands over Lucia's eyes. "Don't look," she said. Then she thought, I did it before, once when Wirtz shot Gretchen and her brains spilled all over the floor. And then, when we saw a corpse on an electrified fence in Auschwitz. Maybe being protective of Lucia keeps me human.

The trip took twelve hours. All the Kielce girls survived the horror. Mrs. Spitz still had her vacant stare, and Mrs. Rothman was praying for her son, Jeffie. They arrived at Ravensbrück in the evening; it was dark, drizzly, and cold. The doors opened, the dead were thrown out and the survivors stepped off the train. It was like Auschwitz all over again; the guards with guns and dogs yelled and snapped their whips.

It was a great relief to be able to stretch out. They were surprised that they could walk again. They didn't see or smell smoke coming from anywhere, but it was evening, and they didn't know what had gone on during the day.

The walk helped them realize that they hadn't lost their bodies during the train ride. They arrived at their assigned barrack. It was long and dark, with only one dim bulb overhead. An overpowering feeling of gloom overwhelmed them. Everything seemed cold, musty, and damp. Their block chief was a big, middle-aged woman, who spoke perfect German.

"Are you Jewish?" someone asked her.

"No," she said. "I'm a German political prisoner. I've been here since before the war."

Was she a Communist or a Socialist? It was the first time Alicia met a German political. She wondered what all the years in the concentration camp had done to her. Did she retain the convictions that had sent her here in the first place? She did not hit people. She and her assistant, another political (Alicia thought she was Polish), assigned bunks to the women. Alicia wound up with Lucia, together with four other women. Where was Dana?

Starved and dehydrated, they lined up for rations: bread, water, and soup that was not much more than water. It was too good to believe that they each got a whole little loaf of bread. But then they were told that this was their bread allowance for the week. Alicia and Lucia wondered how to divide their bread into seven parts.

"I wish I could eat the whole thing right now," Alicia told Lucia.

They both looked at Janka. She was eating and eating.

"She's doing it," Lucia said. "What's she going to do for the next six days?"

Janka didn't care; she just kept on eating. When all her bread was gone, she put a blanket over her head and lay there. She's going to try to sleep for the six days, Alicia thought.

The next day was drizzly, but the weather was much milder than in Auschwitz. There were some ugly rumors going around. By now, they knew for sure that there were no gas chambers in Ravensbrück, but the camp had a different reputation. It contained a medical research complex, where the inmates were used as guinea pigs. Alicia didn't know how the women had learned about it.

One evening that week, the German supervisor came to the barracks and spoke to the block chief. They seemed quite friendly. What could a woman from Hitler's youth movement have in common with a political prisoner? One was a Nazi, the other—who knows? The supervisor told the other woman how very bored she was lately. There were practically no male guards left. She asked the block chief to ask the inmates if anyone could sing, dance, or provide some kind of entertainment. The Polish assistant block chief asked the question in Polish.

Out of the blue, Mrs. Spitz, rose and announced, "I can sing."

Her fellow inmates gaped. They hadn't heard her say one word in months. Suddenly, she was her old vibrant self. Her eyes were alive, and she used her arms as she sang in Italian:

> "Un bel di, vedremo
> Le varsi un fil di fumo sull'estremo
> Confin del mare
> E poi la nave appare
> E poi la nave bianca
> [One beautiful morning
> a ship arrives]."

Alicia wondered if Mrs. Spitz imagined herself on the stage of an opera house in Warsaw or Paris, her rags a beautiful evening gown, or perhaps Cio-Cio-San's kimono.

Lucia huddled close to Alicia, and they listened together. For Alicia there was nothing on her mind but the haunting melody. The ship, which Butterfly hoped was bringing back her lover and the father of her child, brought only disappointment and death.

Alicia didn't think about disappointment and death now, she was transfixed by Mrs. Spitz' performance. She didn't feel the bone chill or hunger. All the images that were usually right beneath the surface were now erased. She forgot her mother's pale face, the way she always imagined her in the gas chamber. She forgot her father's face, the way Jankiel described it when he buried him. She forgot the limp bodies of the boys hung right in front of her eyes. She forgot Anne's black and swollen back, and she forgot the smoke and the stench of the crematoria. She just listened.

On the waves of the sound she traveled back in time, back to Zabiec and saw her Grandfather Mark singing—not Butterfly, but "Celeste Aida." If she could only go back there permanently—she, Jerry, Jas, Guta, Paula, and Aunt Yentl, and long before Henius was born, her Grandmother Regina, the peasant boys standing under the opened windows, everybody listening to Radames.

To go back to times when the prospect of death was something remote, theoretical, when life and love were taken for granted and the future held much promise.

Mrs. Spitz finished, took a bow, and the magic was broken. Maybe she realized the gloom, the damp, and the hopelessness. Suddenly, her eyes were dead. She turned inward again, someplace where she couldn't be hurt and where her tragic memories could not reach her. Genia took her arm and led her to her bunk, where she sat down like a mechanical doll. She was Mrs. Spitz again as they all knew her.

The girls gave a sigh of relief; the German supervisor did not notice Mrs. Spitz's vacant stare after she took her final bow. Only mildly interested, she turned around and left.

They stayed in Ravensbrück for two weeks. Then they went with another transport and through the same procedure all over again. Their destination was a work camp attached to a munitions factory in Malchow. The trip was not as bad as the one from Auschwitz to Ravensbrück because it only took two hours.

Again they stripped naked, took showers, and received "new" clothes. As usual, Alicia ended up with ill-fitting clothes and wooden clogs that were heavy but at least didn't pinch her toes. There's no Basia or Dr. Brazen to help me, she thought.

Their new block chief, a Polish Jewish girl, acted like a rational human being. The camp was just being organized. Block chiefs were needed for new arrivals, as well as more workers for the kitchen, the laundry, and the office. At the morning roll call, the German supervisor looked for people to fill these jobs. She noticed Laura, tall and handsome, looking relatively neat. She called her out, and Laura told her that she had been an assistant block chief in Auschwitz. Her German was flawless. The supervisor was impressed and assigned Laura to be chief of a neighboring block. She told her to choose two girls to help with the cleaning and keeping order in the barracks. Alicia hoped that Laura would choose her; everybody wanted an inside job.

Laura chose Rywka and Hela. Alicia did not blame her. Laura needed girls who could scrub floors, straighten out bunks, and occasionally hit other girls.

Zosia befriended Mrs. Lintz, a woman from Silesia, a province of southwestern Poland that bordered Germany. She was an experienced secretary, was fluent in German, typed fast, knew shorthand, and before the war, had been manager of a big office. She became the chief Kapo of Malchow, was in charge of the office, and hired her own help. Zosia became her assistant, and a few other Kielce girls got office jobs.

On the second day after roll call, the majority of the girls had to go to the factory. It was still completely dark when they started marching. They entered thick woods and walked on a narrow path. Walking behind and in front of them, were German armed guards with dogs. Luckily, it wasn't very cold.

The trees looked eerie. Hansel and Gretel must have walked through woods like that, Alicia thought, but they did not have guards with dogs around them.

Lucia was not feeling well and, as usual, leaned on Alicia. Alicia had problems with her feet, and even without Lucia, it would have been hard for her to keep on the narrow path. She stumbled several times.

They passed through a small German town. The burghers looked at them suspiciously, as if they were strange deviants, enemies of the state. The factory was located in the woods beyond the town, probably to camouflage it and thus escape bombing.

The first place they walked into was a big room. At least it was light and warm, and they were able to take off their coats. German women supervisors were all around. They assigned them to tables; on top of each table was a scale. The girls were instructed on how to weigh out specific amounts of gunpowder. That seemed to be their main job.

Alicia could not concentrate on her work; she was in acute discomfort. She had a bladder problem, and she hadn't been to the bathroom since leaving the barracks over one and one half hours ago. One of the women who spoke good German asked the supervisor if they could go to the bathroom. The German said that every three hours a group would be allowed to go.

The three hour wait seemed like an eternity. Finally, at eleven o'clock, ten girls were escorted to the bathroom by a German woman. Somehow, Alicia managed to be in the first group.

One o'clock was their midday break. They went to a large dining hall where they received a bowl of thin soup. Then it was back to work and another bathroom call sometime in the middle of the afternoon. In the evening, it was the same march back to camp.

While in the factory Alicia was able to sneak out to the bathroom bunk in between the calls. One time she was caught by a German supervisor. She was severely beaten and told that if it happened again, she would be shot. There was no point admitting that she had a bladder problem. It was understood that inmates with health problems would be exterminated, one way or another. She decided to drink as little as possible, but that didn't help too much.

One morning, when they were marching to the factory, the guards took them by a different route. They didn't pass the village but kept on going through a thick forest. The women noticed it right away. Lucia was pulling at Alicia's sleeve from the left and Malka—a skinny dark girl always a bundle of nerves—pulled from the right.

"That's it, that's it," Malka kept repeating. "They're taking us to the gas chambers."

There was frost on the hard forest floor; icicles hung from the branches of the trees. Alicia had to concentrate on not slipping. If I fall, she thought, Lucia will fall with me; then we will not have to go to the gas chamber. She looked around at the other women and wondered when she would hear, "Kielce girls let's say good-bye to each other." It turned out that they were only taking a short cut.

One Sunday, the block chief told them that they had to exchange coat sleeves. Every girl was to have a different left sleeve: a blue coat with a green sleeve, a black coat with a brown one, and so on. Thread and scissors were provided. Alicia exchanged sleeves with Lucia. Now I'll really feel like a weird creature, she thought. She was wearing a black ill-fitting coat with a brown sleeve. And on that sleeve was a band with a yellow star.

The girls wondered what the purpose was behind this order. They came to the conclusion that because their tattoos couldn't be seen, something else was needed to alert the burghers that they were different. They'll think we're lepers or some sort of freaks, Alicia thought.

It was the day before Christmas, 1944. As usual, the girls went to the dining hall for the midday break. A Christmas tree was decorated and lighted. Love and peace for all. The German supervisors were standing around, joking and laughing. Even the most brutal one, the woman who beat Alicia, was all smiles. They were commenting on the appearance of the inmates. They were saying that some of the inmates were able to take care of themselves better than others, but that, still, all of them were human refuse and rejects of society.

The girls went for their soup, ladled out by a German cook. The soup was thicker that day, and there were more potatoes. After all, it was the day before Christmas.

The German supervisors kissed and congratulated each other. Was it due only to the Christmas spirit? The women overheard the conversation. Even Alicia, with her limited knowledge of German, understood enough to get upset. According to them, the entire American army was surrounded at Bastogne in the Ardennes, and many prisoners were being taken. "The whole situation on the Western front has changed and 'our great Fuhrer,' " they kept repeating, "is going to lead us to victory after only temporary setbacks. It's going to be a 'Blitzkrieg' all over again like in 1940. We will recapture Paris, and then there will be another 'Dunkirque.' There's even good news from the Eastern front; the Russians aren't going anyplace."

On Christmas Day the factory was closed. The mood in the barracks was bleak. The girls, as usual, concentrated on getting extra food and keeping warm and clean.

In January, nothing was heard anymore about German successes. Alicia's day-to-day existence was becoming unbearable. For the first time since it all began, she doubted that even without being murdered she would live to see the end of the war.

The German winter was not as cold as the Polish, but half-starved and dressed as she was, Alicia was always freezing. The person who helped her most was Genia. She was in charge of the laundry room; by doing favors for the kitchen girls, like having their personal things washed, she always had extra soup to distribute. But there were many hungry Kielce girls, and Alicia often felt that she was at the end of the receiving line. As in Ravensbrück, one small loaf of bread had to last an entire week. It was cold in the barracks; the women stood around iron stoves trying to warm themselves. Alicia's hands and feet were always frozen. It was becoming increasingly difficult to keep clean.

The office was controlled by Mrs. Lintz and Zosia. After the high expectations of late December, the German authorities seemed bored and lethargic again. Some of them were talking about how badly Berlin was bombed.

Lucia convinced Zosia that she would drop dead if she had to march to the factory one more day. Zosia found her a job in the office, even though it was already filled with Kielce girls. Janka also worked there. The women figured that she, with her slovenly habits and tendency toward depression, would never survive the factory. Mrs. Spitz stayed inside the barracks under the pretense of being a *stubenalteste* (barracks elder), the housekeeper. Thirteen-year-old Bella had the job of courier; she carried messages from the office to the block chiefs.

Alicia kept on marching every morning to the factory. Dana was someplace in Malchow but in a different group. Alicia was used to the idea of losing contact with the few of her friends who were not dead: Anne, Basia, Andrew, Saul, and now Dana. She did not think of Chaim as a friend; he was just a fling.

During the morning marches through the icy paths in the forest, Alicia missed Lucia, even though it was easier to walk without her. But having Lucia depend on her somehow forced her to move. Now she would like to lie down under a tree and let everyone pass her by. She figured she would either be shot or freeze to death. Sometimes she heard Pawel's voice. "Keep on plugging, Alicia." Damn you, Pawel, it's easy for you; you've already wound "safe to sea." She kept on moving, following everyone else.

One day at the factory, Alicia developed a toothache. My feet, my bladder, and now my tooth, she thought. It's a good thing I don't have to think about my period. For some reason, then unknown, all the female prisoners had ceased to menstruate. The conviction that she was not going to make it was getting stronger and stronger. The only saving grace was that it was Saturday, and the next day was their day off.

The pain in her mouth was becoming worse. By the time they had to go for the midday meal, her whole face hurt. She hoped that none of the German supervisors would notice that she was in pain.

They entered the dining hall and lined up for the soup, then sat down at long wooden tables. Alicia tried to eat the bread, but chewing was agony. She could barely manage the few potatoes in her soup. She gave her bread to Malka, who was sitting next to her.

Most people considered Malka ugly, but to Alicia her unusual appearance made her attractive. She was well educated and had her Matura. She had a dry wit and at times she could be malicious. In Henrykow, she had lived with a handsome man whom she dominated completely.

Malka looked at Alicia. "Do you know that the right side of your face is swollen?"

Alicia had not realized that it was so noticeable.

"Since tomorrow is Sunday," Malka said, "try to go to the infirmary early in the morning."

There was one doctor in the camp. "I need a dentist," she told Malka.

"You know there's no dentist. The one woman doctor does everything. In the meantime," Malka continued, "try to keep your cheek warm to prevent it from swelling."

Malka kept on talking: "You worry too much about Lucia and her heart condition. She's doing all right. You're in worse shape than she ever was. In Henrykow, while you were starving, she was shacked up with a man who provided for her. Yesterday, I heard her trying to convince Genia that she needs more food than the rest of us, because she's still growing, and she had rheumatic fever. She seems to have her sickness in her pocket and not in her heart; she takes it out whenever she needs food or anything else."

"Lucia is naturally high spirited and sexy. That's why it's hard to believe that she's really sick."

Alicia was thinking about how Malka organized her own food and managed to get it from everybody who had an inside job. She would tell Genia that Zosia did not give her any food, then in the office she claimed that she did not get anything from Genia. To top it off, she would also go to the girls in the kitchen and tell them she was starving. She was able to accumulate four or five bowls of soup and devoured all of them. Alicia wondered how she could compete for available food with Malka and Lucia. According to Darwin, I'll become extinct, she thought. Tonight I don't have to worry about how to divide my bread. I can't eat anyway.

Finally, the work day came to an end, and they all marched back to the barracks.

The toothache kept Alicia awake the whole night. Early Sunday morning she went to the infirmary. It was only six o'clock when she arrived, but the stuffy little room was already packed. Some girls looked quite sick; they were shivering and coughing, and many had skin eruptions. Alicia was afraid that by sitting there she could catch something worse than a toothache.

The doctor started calling the patients by seven o'clock. She had only one helper, a disheveled, zombielike girl, whose main job was to make sure the patients went in one by one.

Alicia recognized the doctor immediately. It was the Czech woman, Eda's friend, whom she met in *Kratze* block at Auschwitz.

The doctor did not look friendly that Sunday morning; she seemed overwhelmed by her job.

When it was Alicia's turn, she knew by the doctor's behavior that it would be of no use to remind her of their previous meeting.

The doctor looked into Alicia's mouth and decided that the molar had to come out. "You will have to hold on to the chair very firmly," she said. "Maybe it would be better if you're tied down." She called her helper, who produced a rope.

Alicia was almost ready to jump off the chair and run out. The doctor guessed her thoughts. "If you want to leave, then go. I can only tell you that if this tooth does not come out, your whole mouth will get infected."

Alicia stayed. "You don't have to tie me. I'll make sure not to cause any problems."

The doctor now looked closer at Alicia and recognized her; she even remembered her name. "You see, Alicia," she said, "I've seen many patients since Auschwitz, under deplorable conditions. I never had the proper medication or equipment to help them, so I had to develop an indifference to human suffering. You are a strong girl, so just hold on. Once this tooth comes out, you'll be all right."

She took a pair of pliers and started pulling. The pain was excruciating, beyond belief. I don't want to faint, Alicia kept repeating to herself; I'd rather die right away. Finally, the rotten tooth came out. There was blood all over. The doctor gave her water and two aspirins, and told her to rinse her mouth well. She put a bandage over Alicia's face and produced from someplace a woolen scarf. She instructed

Alicia to keep her face warm and not to take off the bandage for at least a week. Hopefully, by then, the swelling would be gone.

"May I get a pass to stay out of the factory tomorrow?" Alicia asked.

The doctor shook her head. "I'm sorry. It's only ten o'clock, and already I've given out all the passes I'm allowed. I have many patients who run high temperatures, have bad throat infections and rashes. I can't justify giving out a pass for a tooth extraction. Come tomorrow after work," she suggested. "Maybe I'll be able to do something for you for Tuesday."

"I'll come if I'm still alive."

Alicia ran back to the barracks. Thank God my legs are all right ,she thought, and the boils that I had last winter haven't come back.

In the barracks, the women kept asking her how she was feeling. She couldn't answer; her jaw was sore. She lay down, and thought if she could fall asleep, maybe she would stop feeling sorry for herself.

From her upper bunk she could see the women busy fixing and mending clothes. She knew that they all had hopes of finding their lovers and husbands after the war.

Alicia felt sorry for herself again. If I survive the war, she thought, I will have nobody to look for. As Dana once said, I'll be a strange specimen, who survived against all odds.

Lucia came over with some soup. Alicia was not used to Lucia giving her anything. It was always the other way around. What does she want in return? Maybe I'm not being fair. As if to make up for her thoughts, she told Lucia: "I am sure you'll find Dr. Kaplan after the war."

Alicia tried to drink soup, but the aspirins had upset her stomach. One sip made her feel worse. "Thank you, Lucia," she said. "Maybe later I'll have the soup when my jaw and stomach feel better."

Laura came from her block to visit the Kielce girls. Alicia heard her talking to Zosia, asking for Alicia. How nice of her, Alicia thought; she still remembers me. She felt a little bitter toward Laura. They had shared lives in the Jewish quarters after Treblinka, and they had been friends in Henrykow. Now in Malchow, Laura was a block chief and Alicia worked in the factory. Laura was treating Alicia like a stranger; she belonged to a "higher class."

Laura came to Alicia's bunk. She appeared well-fed and attractive. Her red hair was in a page boy, shoulder length. Even her dark green coat, with the blue sleeve, looked good. The same Laura as ever. She asked Alicia how she was doing.

"It was just a tooth extraction," Alicia told her. "I'll be all right tomorrow."

"I might manage to get a new coat," Laura informed her. "I will give you the one I'm wearing now, and I'll try to get you a dress."

Finally Laura feels sorry for me, Alicia thought. I wish I could take care of myself. then I wouldn't need anyone's pity. But it made her feel good to know that there were still people around who cared for her.

Monday morning Alicia dragged herself to roll call. Genia helped her to make the bunk. The roll calls in Malchow were not as long or as cruel as those in Auschwitz. Alicia had a bandage and the scarf wrapped around her face.

The factory group went on their usual march. As they passed through the German village, the burghers looked at them as always.

I almost feel as bad about myself as they must be thinking of me, Alicia thought. A number of words came to her mind; *pariah, untouchable.*

When they entered the factory, Alicia noticed a mirror in the hall. She glanced at herself and got scared. My mother would have a hard time recognizing me, she thought. She felt like crying. All those doctors around me when I had typhus. Oh, God, I must be going crazy! How can I compare typhus to a tooth extraction? But then, I was important to my parents, my brother, and many other people. It was 1940, and the Germans were winning the war. Now, in 1944, it looks like they're going to be defeated soon. Their December triumph was evidently short-lived.

She clenched her fists; I've got to make it.

The German supervisor approached and scrutinized her. Alicia was scared. I should have taken this bandage off in the factory. The supervisor took out a list from her pocket. "Show me your number," she said.

Alicia gave her a blank stare. For some reason she always believed that pretending not to understand German would be beneficial to her.

Germans like dumb inmates. Not understanding their language meant being stupid.

This time it did not help. The supervisor Fräulein Else, called Malka to translate her instruction to Alicia. Alicia knew very well what Else wanted. She was just stalling for time hoping that the Fräulein would be distracted by something else. It did not happen. Alicia's number, her location in the factory and in the camp were scrupulously placed on the list.

"It's no good to be on that list," Malka warned Alicia.

Alicia did not have to hear it from Malka. She continued weighing.

"Try to talk to Zosia about the list," Malka said.

That evening in the barracks Alicia went to see Zosia. Zosia, as assistant Kapo, had a privileged status. She and a few others had bunks in a special subdivision. There were two non-Jewish girls between them. That, in itself, in a Jewish block, meant special status and an inside job. One of them was a German and had been sent to a concentration camp for prostitution. She had a special type of tattoo to indicate it. The other was Polish and was there for theft. Since the prostitute could not find a man in Malchow, she became a lesbian and slept with the thief.

Zosia was a mother figure to the Kielce girls, and the rumor was that she controlled Mrs. Lintz, the chief Kapo.

"I'm on a list. You'll probably get it in your office by tomorrow," Alicia told her. There was panic in her voice. Zosia looked her over carefully. Alicia had a terrible feeling. Do I look so bad? That damn bandage! Does she think I'm not worth the effort to be saved? I might look like I'm beyond help.

"Don't go to the factory tomorrow," Zosia said. "Report to the office right after roll call. I'll have a job for you inside the camp and don't worry about the list."

Tuesday morning, Alicia did as she was told. Without any typing skills or knowledge of the German language, she realized that her chances of getting a job were slim.

Though Lucia was in the same position, a job had been created for her; she carried papers from desk to desk. No wonder the Radom girls resented the Kielce girls, Alicia thought; the Kielce girls have all the inside jobs. No Germans were around. The inmates seemed to be in control. It looked like an office of the Jewish Council in the Kielce ghetto. Would it serve the same purpose?

Alicia had to wait for Zosia, who was talking to Mrs. Lintz. In the meantime, she spoke with Janka and Lucia and told them how well they looked. When Zosia was free, she came to Alicia. She pointed to a shack across the way, and told her that that's where she would be working.

"What's in there and what am I going to be doing?"

"Somebody in there will tell you," Zosia said.

Alicia went across the yard and knocked at the door. The shack reminded her of a barn in Zabiec. There was no answer. She lifted the door latch and entered. It was dark, there was only one window in the back. As she looked around, her eyes slowly adjusted to the darkness. The little window was filthy, allowing only a small amount of light to pass through. The place was filled with a sort of straw.

"Is anyone here?" she yelled in Polish. A girl came out from the back of the shack. It was Dana.

Alicia became excited. "Dana, I thought I'd lost you. Where have you been?" She ran to her friend, but she could not even kiss her. She tried to laugh, but with a swollen jaw she barely managed a smile. "What a coincidence," she said. "*Kratze* block in Auschwitz all over again, first the doctor and now you. Are you in charge?"

"In charge of what?"

"What are we supposed to be doing here?" Alicia asked.

"I thought you would tell me," Dana answered.

"How did you get this job, whatever it is?"

"Miraculously I found a first cousin in Malchow. She is a block chief. It seems as if, between her and your girls in the office, they cooked up this job especially for us."

Dana now looked at Alicia closely. "You look like hell. What happened to your face?" She herself hadn't changed much since Auschwitz, just a little thinner. "You used to tell me that I'd lost the will to fight. But look at you. I'm the one who should be giving you that speech now. Besides your bandaged face, you look ragged and neglected."

Alicia told her about the tooth extraction and the list, and asked her if she knew what the list was for.

"Oh God, don't you know?" Dana answered. "It's a Ravensbrück list. There was a transport just two weeks ago. As a matter of fact, one of the Kielce girls was in it."

Alicia knew what Ravensbrück meant: hospitals and medical research. "Who was the girl?"

"Not the crazy woman," Dana said, "but the old lady."

"Mrs. Rothman?" Oh, poor Jeffie. If he survives, he'll be all alone, Alicia thought. "Zosia promised that my number would be taken off the list."

"At the rate you're going," Dana answered, "they'll put you on it again. You look like a candidate for a hospital or gas chamber. ⁽⁾

Alicia told Dana about the coat and dress that Laura promised her.

"Make sure you get it and get that thing off your face as soon as possible."

"Since I'm not walking to the factory any more, I'm not exposed to the cold, so it shouldn't be long. I'll be all right soon. In the meantime, I still don't know what our job here is."

"But I know," Dana answered. "We are going to be taking care of ourselves. You have a lot of friends working in the laundry. First thing in the morning, after roll call, try to get a few buckets of hot water. We'll wash ourselves and our underwear. Then, we'll clean our one and only window so we can take advantage of the "beautiful" eastern exposure in the mornings. But most important, we have to get some extra food."

Alicia still couldn't forget Mrs. Rothman. The Kielce girls in the office did not do anything for her. Why should they make an effort for me?

In the evening she asked Zosia again if her number was still on that list.

"I told you not to worry," Zosia said. "I'll take care of it. But you'd better see to it that the German supervisors don't notice you with that bandaged face. At roll call, hide yourself in the middle between the tallest girls. I think Genia has some clothes for you."

Now everybody is feeling sorry for me, Alicia thought.

The next week was the first week of February. February could not be any worse to Alicia than January. The shack was well-insulated, and the straw kept it warm. Alicia took off the bandage and was healing fast now. After they cleaned the little window, they were able to enjoy somewhat of a sunbath in the mornings. Though February's sun was still weak, its rays seemed to concentrate in the shack. Every morning, the girls watched the sunrise. It usually occurred around seven-thirty, just as they entered the shack after roll call. Then the first thing Alicia would do was go to the laundry room for the water. The girls not only kept themselves clean, but they managed to mend their clothes and give themselves haircuts.

Laura kept her promise and got Alicia a new coat. Genia got her a dress. Someone in the laundry room probably had not claimed it. It was a pretty blue dress, too big for Genia but fine for Alicia.

"If only you had decent shoes instead of those wooden boats," Dana told her, "you would be considered well-dressed by camp standards. Fraulein Else would not recognize you anymore, the way you look now. You don't have to worry about the damn list."

Most of the time, Dana and Alicia were hungry. Alicia managed to organize extra food from the luckier Kielce girls. Dana got her share from her cousin, but still it was not enough. Since they didn't have much to do, they talked a lot.

One morning, after watching the sunrise, Alicia said to Dana, "A few weeks ago, I felt that my life would end right here in Malchow. Now I have some hope."

"We might still die of starvation."

"Maybe we'll have our season in the sun," Alicia said. "We will have a time to plant and a time to pluck up what has been planted. Maybe, we'll have a time to laugh and a time to love, too."

"How about a time to mourn and a time to weep, and a time to hate and a time to kill?"

"I will need a time to heal," Alicia answered.

"If I am able to kill all the Germans," Dana said, "then love, laughter, and dance will come."

"Killing all the Germans won't bring our parents back."

"Let's stop these Bible quotations." Dana was eager to change the subject. "Did I ever tell you about my rich relatives in America? They have a house in Westchester and a winter home in Florida."

"Where is Westchester?"

"It's a suburb of New York for only rich people. My aunt belongs to a fancy country club where she plays golf."

"I don't know anything about golf," Alicia said. "I used to play tennis."

"Didn't you see the newsreels showing the Prince of Wales playing golf in Scotland?"

"I probably missed it. But I do remember all the gossip surrounding his romance and abdication. Now it seems so trivial. My Aunt Paula used to say that if she was in England, she could have competed successfully with Mrs. Simpson."

Now they were both laughing. "One thing your Aunt Paula couldn't do was play golf with him," Dana said.

"Yes, but she was a great horsewoman, and they could have ridden together on his famous foxhunts."

The girls forgot their hunger for a few short moments. Then there was a knock at the shack door.

"Look as if you are doing some work," Dana whispered, and went to answer the knock. I'll pretend to be making straw mats, Alicia thought in desperation.

Dana raised the door. Mrs. Lintz walked in with a German supervisor. Thank God it wasn't Else or Berta, but someone new.

Dana threw some strings at Alicia. "*Mach schnell* [hurry up]," she cried.

In spite of her terror, Alicia had a hard time holding back her laughter. Mrs. Lintz asked Dana to explain what they were doing. Dana started talking. Alicia couldn't follow what she was saying, because she used a lot of those long German compounds of nouns strung together. About straw? What long words could she possibly use about straw? The German nodded her head and after a few *jawohls* and *sehr schöne* [yes, yes very nice], they left. Dana gave a big sigh of relief, and both girls sat down.

"What did you tell them?" Alicia asked.

"I don't know."

"It sounded as if you were using fancy words."

"That's the trick," Dana said. "Nobody knew what I was talking about, and they were too embarrassed to admit they didn't understand."

"They might send us both to Ravensbrück when they figure out that you were not making sense."

Dana was sure that they would not. "The German, by saying *jawohl*, gave her approval. Now she has to protect her judgment and not admit a mistake."

"I hope you're right." Alicia said.

"I am. Bureaucrats are the same all over the world. Once they create a job that isn't there, they have to stand by it."

"It looks as if we've just survived another crisis," Alicia said.

Though February 1944 was unseasonably mild, it was cold inside the barracks. There was no wood to feed the iron stove.

Alicia slept on the upper bunk, Lucia on the lower. They often wondered about the luxury of having separate bunks. One especially chilly night, the two girls hovered together in the lower bunk and combined their blankets. They were whispering to each other in the dark. They spoke of their plans for after the war. Lucia wanted to become a doctor, if and when.

"I will write another *War and Peace*, Alicia said jokingly. At least Lucia was not worried about losing her timing, Alicia thought. "How about David Kaplan?"

"I'll try to find him."

"What do you want? Do you want to be a doctor's wife or do you want to be a doctor yourself?"

"I can do both," Lucia assured her.

Alicia was full of wonder. "You missed many years of school, but I believe you'll make up for it," she said. "I was always in such a rush, I thought that losing just one year would be catastrophic. Now Dana and I are both afraid that our timing is gone."

Suddenly, the lights went on. The image of the night in Henrykow, when Zubow brought Anne back, came back to Alicia's mind. What was it this time?

The German supervisor was inspecting the barracks. She had a gun and a whip. The girls moved closer together. When the German came to their bunk, she started hitting them and calling them filthy perverts. She threatened to shoot them unless they separated immediately. Alicia climbed up quickly to her upper berth to avoid a blow, then covered herself with her one ragged blanket. It was hard to figure what the German meant. When she finally understood, she laughed silently to herself. Was lesbianism so common in camps? Were women so desperate for men? She thought about the prostitute and the thief. But Lucia a lesbian? What a joke!

Although still cold, she managed to fall asleep, then a dream came. She was skiing. She was wearing black ski pants and a heavy Scandinavian sweater, the type with the rich design. She wore a matching cap with a pompom, a turtle-neck shirt, and a scarf, to please her mother. Her dark glasses protected her from the brightness of the sun and whiteness of the snow. She was skiing with Mucia, Jas, and Jerry. They were going down gentle slopes in the Swietokrzyski Mountains. Alicia tried to keep up with Jas.

Jerry called to her, "Jas is too good for you—you'll break your neck. Stay back with me and my mother!"

Alicia just turned around and waved to Jerry. "Bye-bye."

Suddenly she was no more in the rolling hills and gentle slopes that she knew so well. The bright, sunny day became overcast, dark and gloomy. There was no Jerry, Jas or Mucia to follow. She was all alone and traveling a steep incline. She could see distant peaks covered with snow. They looked like the Karpathians or the Alps. She was moving fast, and she was scared. And then she heard Anne's voice: "It's good to have family, friends, and a lover, but when the chips are down, sometimes you have to do it alone." The ride became exhilarating again. Even the howling wind and blowing snow felt good.

She woke up. She was cold. Her bladder felt full, and she hoped she could wait until the morning.

She heard Lucia's moans from the lower bunk. She climbed down, touched Lucia's forehead, and realized that it was unusually hot. "Is there anything hurting you?" she whispered.

"My throat."

Alicia was frightened of contracting a sore throat. She and Lucia had huddled together the night before. Whenever things started looking up, something bad happened, and this was apparently it.

Lucia was shivering. "Take it easy," Alicia told her. "The first thing in the morning I'll take you to the doctor." She wished Anne or Laura were here. She placed her own blanket and coat over Lucia and tucked her in. "Just try to keep warm," she kept repeating.

Lucia was still shivering. They were all terrified of sickness and what it could mean to them. Lucia had an additional fear that any kind of infection could further damage her heart.

Alicia tried to reassure her. "The doctor is my friend. She'll take good care of you." Some friend, she thought. Not giving me a medical excuse from the factory when I needed it badly almost cost me my life. She climbed back to her bunk and covered herself with the coat that she had recently got from Laura. She couldn't fall asleep anymore.

In the morning Alicia wrapped Lucia up and rushed her to the doctor's quarters before the German supervisors could spot them. Luckily, early that morning, it was warmer outside than inside, though it was still dark. Thank you, February, for turning out so mild.

When they arrived at the infirmary, the doctor was already up. She seemed to be less harassed. She recognized Alicia right away and asked her about her mouth.

"It's all healed," Alicia told her. "But I'm worried about Lucia. She has a history of rheumatic fever, and now I think she's running a high temperature."

When the doctor read the thermometer, she said, "You're right, it is high. I have a bed ready, I'm going to admit her. You don't have to worry, all my patients were transported to Ravensbrück. It will take a few more weeks before there are enough sick people for another transport."

Alicia was shivering more than Lucia. After all, she almost made Ravensbrück herself. She understood why the doctor was not busy— somebody else was taking care of her patients.

"I'll give your friend some aspirins," the doctor said. "The most important thing is bed rest."

Lucia was crying. "Don't leave me," she kept saying to Alicia.

"You're in good hands," Alicia reassured her. "I must go. There might be another inspection in the shack, and Dana won't be able to cover for me."

Before Alicia left, she asked if she could use the bathroom. There was just one bathroom in the doctor's quarters which had to serve the entire infirmary, and usually a long line stood in front of it. But this day, the little hospital was empty, and Alicia had all the time in the world.

It was a luxury just to sit on a toilet bowl and pee until her bladder was empty. Flushing made her feel almost civilized. There was soap in the soap dish. She picked up a paper towel, took off her dress and sponged herself. She felt refreshed and wonderfully clean.

Should I be happy, she thought, that all those poor sick girls were transported for certain death or to be subjected to torture in the name of science? And yet, somehow, she did not feel guilty about the feeling of well-being that a regular bathroom with soap and water gave her.

She ran across the yard from the infirmary to the shack. As the sun rose, the weather seemed to get warmer. It was almost spring. She lifted the door latch; the sun was pouring through the little window in the back. If only we were not so hungry, she thought, the shack would feel like a resort.

"Did you bring anything to eat?" Dana asked.

"Genia promised me some carrots and potatoes."

"All the privileged people, the ones with the inside jobs, got carrots, potatoes, and soup from the bottom of the keg; the watery top remained for general distribution."

"Oh come on, Dana, everyone is trying to organize extra food to survive."

" 'Organize' is a very nice word, but 'to steal' would be more accurate. Do you remember one woman strangling another in the train for a little space? Fighting for space or food involves the same principle."

"You can't compare organizing extra food to murder."

Dana became pensive. "In what once was called the civilized, world, people fight for money and power. My father did well; he owned a lot of apartment houses in Warsaw, but Warsaw has been leveled to the ground; there's nothing left, and my father is dead. How futile it was to spend all that effort and energy to amass a fortune."

"How could anybody predict?"

"I'll just have to rely on my relatives in America. Hopefully they'll take care of me. Do you have anybody?" Dana asked.

Alicia tried to remember. "My father's two brothers and a sister are in America, but they're not well off. It's not in character for that family to have any money. Besides that, my parents were not much in contact with them. They never liked my mother."

Lately, Alicia didn't have to force herself to get up in the morning to endure another day, not to starve and not to freeze and not to get sick. She was actually looking forward to each day, to the bright sun pouring through the window of the shack and kidding around with Dana.

One day right after roll call, Alicia went to the infirmary again to see Lucia. She trusted Dana's judgment that there would not be another inspection in the shack. Lucia's fever was down, and she was in a better frame of mind. The doctor was right; Lucia needed bed rest. There was something that worried Alicia; two more beds were occupied. The more sick girls, the more chance for a transport. In the meantime, the bathroom and the soap and a chance to sponge herself overshadowed her anxiety.

Then she went to the laundry room to see Genia and left with some soup and more unclaimed clothes.In the shack, Dana was chewing on a piece of bread. Alicia showed her her treasures.

"I'm impressed at how well you have learned to 'organize' things," Dana said.

Alicia noticed that her friend looked worried and preoccupied. "Has anything new happened?" she asked.

"I have some good news about what's happening in the world, but it could be bad news for us."

Alicia was in no mood for bad news.

"A new transport of Polish girls from southwestern Poland arrived a few days ago," Dana continued. "Molly, my cousin the block chief, talked to them, and they know a lot."

Alicia was excited. "What—what did they say?"

"The Russians are finally advancing. They've already taken Warsaw, Kielce, and Krakow."

"But I thought last August, when we were leaving Kielce, we heard Russian artillery."

"You did, but they stopped for half a year. The Poles staged a revolt in the summer of 1944 to liberate Warsaw. They expected help from the approaching Russians. The Russians had a different idea. They wanted the Germans to finish the Poles before they started their final offensive."

"The Russians and the Germans deserve each other," Alicia said, indignantly.

"I have more good news," Dana said. "The Germans are running from Poland. They're in a panic and deadly scared of the Russians—they prefer to take their chances with the Western Allies. Can you imagine the members of the 'Master Race' carrying their possessions on their backs, cold and hungry, running to the Fatherland, which is being pounded by American and English bombs."

"It feels good to hear this," Alicia exclaimed. "Too bad they are not being sent to gas chambers or being transported like cattle as we were."

"Maybe some of them will be grabbed by the Russians and sent to Siberia as slave labor," Dana suggested, eyes glowing. Then sadness came over her. "Some of those Polish girls lived near Auschwitz," she said. "They told Molly what happened there. In the middle of January, in freezing weather, as the Russians were approaching, all the people were taken from the camp, and since there weren't anymore trains available, they went on foot. The Polish girls didn't know where they were going, but probably it was west to relocation camps. The girls heard a lot of shouting."

Alicia thought of her friends left in Auschwitz. Eda, Basia, Dr. Brazen, Dr. Kaplan. "I almost didn't survive those daily marches through the woods to the factory in Malchow, though it only took an hour," she said.

"Molly is the kind of person that, no matter what, will always float to the top—she's a born optimist. But now she's scared."

"It's like in Kielce last August when the Russians were close, and we were deported to Auschwitz," Alicia remembered.

"Only now there is practically no place to deport us. The Allies are advancing fast from the west, the gas chambers are no longer functioning, the guards may just take us to a forest and shoot us all."

"Can you imagine all the women digging graves."

"That's not funny, Alicia."

CHAPTER 16

1945—Malchow, Liberation, Sweden

One day in March, when Alicia came to the infirmary, she found that Lucia was running a fever again. The doctor tried to assure her that it was only a temporary setback, but Lucia looked weak and tired.

She's only eighteen years old, Alicia thought, a girl of that age should be full of pep and energy. "It won't last long," she said. "Just hold on for a few more weeks." If I keep on saying it, maybe I'll believe myself that we'll be alive when the war ends.

"I would like to tell you something," Lucia said. "If I don't make it and you should, then you can either write about it or talk about it."

This was the first time Alicia ever heard Lucia doubting her own survival. "We'll both make it," she insisted. She would never tell Lucia about what had happened in Auschwitz.

"Do you remember that red sweater I was wearing during the selections for Treblinka?" Lucia asked.

Even in the bewilderment of that day, Alicia had noticed the red sweater. Why would Lucia wear a sweater in the terrible heat?

"In the hem and sleeve of that sweater, my mother sewed a lot of jewelry. She never thought that we would be separated; she made me a carrier of the family riches."

Alicia looked at Lucia. Lucia would never admit, not even to herself, that we left our mothers—Alicia thought we were not forcibly separated. She wanted to hear the story.

Lucia continued: "Zubow approached me. He said he had just come back from the railroad station where he'd seen my mother and sister. Mother instructed him, he said, that I should give him all the valuables so he could take them to her. He repeated a few times that it was very important, because it would be harder for them to survive than it would be for me; they would need everything I was holding."

"Did he tell you where you were supposed to be hiding the jewelry?" Alicia asked.

"No, but I was so guilt-stricken—that I had everything and my mother had nothing—that I ripped my sweater off and gave him all I had."

"And I always thought you were smart."

"But at that time," Lucia defended this foolish action, "I hadn't had much experience with Jewish policemen. All I thought about was my poor mother and my little sister."

"So you were left with nothing, just like me. Now I see why you needed a Joseph to take care of you."

"Joseph was very good and kind to me, but I never loved him. After the war, I'm going to look for David Kaplan."

David Kaplan? Did he survive the march from Auschwitz? "First get well and do it fast. I think you've talked enough. You need your rest."

But Lucia kept talking: "How about you? Are you and Chaim going to try to get together?"

Alicia almost responded, "Chaim who?" It seemed to her that he had never had a part in her life. "Oh, no," she told Lucia. "He was like Joseph for you. I did it out of loneliness."

Alicia kissed her friend and left the infirmary. Since it was Friday, the Germans were not around, probably taking a long weekend. It was early, and she decided to go to the laundry room to get some water from Genia. She treasured the piece of soap she had in her pocket, organized from the infirmary. That lousy Zubow, she thought. The same bastard who caught Anne also robbed Lucia on the day that her mother and sister were sent to Treblinka. "Don't be so hard on Your People," Tadek once told her. Zubow is not "My People." *My* people, Jewish and non Jewish, would not behave that way.

She entered the laundry room. Everyone was busy at the scrubbing boards or hand wringing clothes. I could never work here, Alicia thought. At home, they had a laundress come every two weeks to do the heavy wash. I would be helpless here, but these women seemed to know what they were doing.

She looked around but couldn't find Genia. Then she heard a strange noise coming from the back of the laundry room—like somebody whining or moaning. She peeked in. There was a girl lying on a bunk, she had a hot towel wrapped around her stomach. Looking at her closely, Alicia recognized a Kielce girl. After the 1943 action, she was in Ludwikow, therefore Alicia didn't know her well. Her name was Connie, and she was a member of the "click." Her husband, Tarnow, was a powerful policeman of Ludwikow, and Connie had an inside job, supposedly cleaning the barracks. In Auschwitz and Malchow, she did the same.

"What's the matter with you?"

"I've had stomach cramps for almost a week. Genia is hiding me here in the back."

"Shouldn't you go to the infirmary?"

"It could be dangerous. These hot compresses are helping me. If I survive, which I sometimes doubt, I'll owe my life to Genia."

Alicia repeated the same thing she told Lucia: "Don't worry. It will be all over soon, and you'll find your husband, and he'll take care of you."

"My husband?" Connie said. "I don't have any husband."

Alicia was surprised. "But I thought Tarnow was your husband."

"He saved my life by claiming me as his wife, but I didn't love him. I didn't even like him. Every time I slept with him, I hated myself. Even if he just touched me, I felt repulsed. My real husband was gassed in Treblinka."

Alicia wondered why Connie was telling her these things. First Lucia, now Connie. Lucia was her friend, but Alicia barely knew Connie. She had always had privileged status and enough to eat while Alicia was starving.

"You look well lately," Connie told her.

"I'm doing all right. I've survived up to now without sleeping with a policeman and even without speaking German."

"You could not have made it without us, the fighters, who have always taken care of the group."

Alicia smiled. "I appreciate what Zosia and Genia are doing, but I'm not as completely helpless as you think I am." She reminded herself what she came for. I have soap, she thought, I'll get a bucket of hot water, but Dana will kill me unless I organize something to eat. "Do you think I can get some bread and potatoes?" she asked Connie.

"Genia helps many more girls than you. You can't expect too much."

"That's why I came early." She found herself grinning at Connie. "If you want to be mentioned favorably in my future epic novel, you'd better tell me where Genia hides the extra bread."

"Do you really think you'll write a book if we survive?"

"Don't underestimate that clumsy, ungainly *schlepper*, who doesn't know how to scrub floors or make neat bunks."

"I never called you names. Besides, a lot of good pushing and fighting did me. Now I'm in pain and feel like dying."

"You won't die, Connie. After the war a good doctor will find out what's wrong with you. It's probably nothing serious. You're a very attractive woman. You won't have to stay with Tarnow if you dislike him so much. You'll find someone else."

Connie showed Alicia the cupboard where the bread was kept. Alicia dipped Connie's towel in hot water, wrung it out, and placed it on her stomach. Then she went to look for bread.

There were two cupboards against the back wall. Alicia decided to open both.

"Don't take everything," Connie moaned.

Alicia took some bread and put it in her coat pocket. From the other cupboard she swiped two clean sheets and stuffed them inside her panties. She closed both cupboards. I'm learning, she thought. It took me a long time to become a regular "organizer." This war has brought out strange talents in all of us. She picked up the bucket of hot water. She kissed Connie and told her to be careful not to let the Germans discover her hideout.

"Genia will take care of it," Connie said.

When Alicia came to the shack, she threw one clean sheet at Dana. "I have soap and water and—take it easy—I also have bread." She felt good. She put her arms around Dana's waist and started dancing with her.

Dana just shrugged her shoulders. "Not so fast, Alicia. The war isn't over yet. The closer it gets to the end, the more danger we're in."

"Do you have to tell me that, Dana? I feel strong and healthy. All that good food I ate as a child hasn't gone to waste."

"I wish someone had taught you how to sew a button, fix a hem, or peel a potato thin."

That evening, Zosia called Alicia and told her that within the next couple of days, Lucia would have to stop being a patient. A new transport was being planned.

"But she's still running a fever, " Alicia told Zosia, "and the doctor thinks she still needs a lot of bed rest."

"At this time, bed rest must wait until after the war," Zosia said.

The next day, Lucia became the doctor's assistant. Alicia hoped that the good doctor would see to it that Lucia didn't overwork herself.

It was Sunday, in the middle of April. Alicia was sitting on her bunk munching on a carrot. She thought of April as a month of actions.

A German guard walked in, all smiles. "The game is just starting again," he announced. "Our Führer is alive and well, while President Roosevelt is dead." With a malicious smile, he added; "I always thought that his real name was Rosenfeld and that he was Jewish."

Alicia made an effort to listen and to try to understand what he was talking about. The guard was gloating: "Our great German scientists are coming out with miracle weapons. Our rockets are leveling London to the ground. The bombing of Berlin, Hamburg, Dresden, and Cologne will be avenged, and Paris will 'get it' also."

He was really enjoying the fantasizing: "The stupid French will wish that the Germans had stayed in Paris forever. Our poor people from East Prussia, Silesia and east of Oder River, who were expelled from their homes, deprived of all their possessions and abused, will go back and the lousy Poles will be taken to work in Germany. We will make a separate peace with Russia, like in 1939, and have the Western Allies beg us on their knees for a settlement."

After the guard left, Alicia ran to Dana's barracks and told her friend about the death of the American President.

For a while they sat downcast, but then Dana said, "Don't you see, that German is dreaming! No matter who the next president of the United States is, Germany has already lost the war. A democracy does not depend on one person. The vice-president automatically becomes the President."

"I don't remember any other President than Roosevelt," Alicia said.

A few days later, it was still April; Alicia didn't expect anything good to happen. She barely paid attention when Dana tried to tell her about what she heard from Molly. "Wake up, Alicia. Stop dreaming, this is important."

"So, what's happening that's so important?" Alicia said wearily.

"Molly was in the office yesterday when the camp commandant came in and wanted to see the chief Kapo. Mrs. Lintz stepped up, but your Zosia would not let her handle alone whatever it was alone. Mrs. Lintz told the commandant that Zosia was her trusted assistant, and she would take the minutes of his instructions. They went to the inner office."

Alicia's curiosity was raised now. "Okay, Dana, don't make it so dramatic. Just tell me what happened."

"Take it easy, Alicia, I'm coming to that. When the commandant left, Mrs. Lintz and Zosia came out waving a long sheet of paper, and they were arguing. Molly tried to see what was on the paper. She noticed the heading—it was from the Swedish Red Cross. She wondered what such a paper was doing in Zosia's hand. Then she heard Zosia tell Mrs. Lintz that she was glad that she had stopped her from asking the commandant to clarify what he meant by "Polish." Did it mean people from Poland or just Gentile people from Poland? Mrs. Lintz tried to emphasize that it was important to know exactly what the commandant meant. Zosia called her a 'rigid bureaucrat,' a 'Yekie,' and that now was the time to use some imagination. What a scene it must have been," Dana added. "I wish I could have been there."

"You're dramatizing again, Dana. Tell me what else you know about that paper and the Swedish Red Cross."

"Okay, okay," Dana said. "Zosia told Mrs. Lintz that since the commandant wanted a list of all the Polish inmates, which he said he would present to the Swedish Red Cross, she's going to put Kielce and the Radom group at the top. She announced that it can only be for the better to be listed simply as Polish. For all we know, even the Swedish Red Cross doesn't like Jews. Zosia then asked Molly, whom she considered as a representative of the Radom group, what she thought of the idea. Molly agreed that it would be advantageous to associate ourselves with the Gentiles."

"So you see," Alicia said, "you and your Radom girls are always accusing us Kielce girls of robbing you of thick soup, and now Zosia took care of you, hopefully for better things."

"Don't put me in the middle of the argument. I'm not even from Radom. I'm a Warsaw girl," Dana said. "But I do have to give credit to Zosia. She really has some hutzpah."

"Are there many Gentile inmates in Malchow?" Alicia asked.

"There are quite a few blocks of girls from western Poland. When it was "germanized," many Poles were sent to either labor camps or concentration camps."

Alicia was getting excited. "Do you think that the Red Cross will take us back to Poland now that the Russians are there? Hurray, we will be alive and out of Germany."

"I heard rumors that they are going to take us to a neutral country like Sweden. But that sounds too good to be true."

Alicia remembered all the German lies: resettlement east instead of extermination camps; doctors murdered in pits when they believed they were going to work in German hospitals; orchestras playing and children munching chocolate, unaware of their destination—the gas chambers of Auschwitz. The list could go on and on. Are we going to Sweden now? We are not listed as Jewish this time, so maybe there is hope. No death march for us? Would it be possible? As Poles, maybe we have a chance.

It happened on April 20. After roll call, the non-Polish women followed their usual routine. The Polish girls were gathered in a big square. Buses with red crosses painted on the sides were waiting.

Alicia looked around. Where is Dana? She didn't see Lucia either. I want to be near my friends, she thought, but to her chagrin, Malka was standing near her. Not her again!

"The Red Cross signs are a camouflage," Malka whispered, "so we won't resist getting on the buses. They're going to close the windows and gas us."

The German supervisors kept order as usual, with Berte, the woman who once beat Alicia in the factory, yelling and hitting the girls. Nothing has changed, Alicia thought. Would Berte behave like this if we were really being taken by the Red Cross out of Germany? Maybe Malka is right.

Malka said in Alicia's ear, "This is the end."

They started boarding the buses. There was no panic yet but the girls were fidgety. Where are they taking us? It became an automatic reaction to expect poisonous gas or a ride to a cemetery.

Alicia looked at the driver; he was a tall fellow, with a broad, open face and a wide smile. Somehow she knew that he wasn't a German or Ukrainian. What nationality was he?

He told her in English, "Good morning, Miss."

"Where are you from?" Alicia asked in English.

"I'm from Canada. I work for the International Red Cross."

"Where are we going?"

"I'm instructed to drive you to the Danish border."

"And then what?" Alicia asked.

"I'm not supposed to talk," the driver answered, "but I'm quite sure that your final destination is Sweden."

"A neutral country!" Alicia screamed.

It was the magic carpet that she and Anne had once dreamed about, that would take them out of war zones. No airplane, no zeppelin, only a prosaic bus, but a Red Cross bus.

Alicia ran to Zosia and started kissing her, "You've done it—we *are* really going to Sweden."

"I figured it out," Zosia said, "that as long as we were not listed as Jewish, it could only turn out for the good."

"Good?" Alicia said. "This is excellent! They've had no war in Sweden."

To Alicia's delight, she found Dana. They sat together. It was still hard to believe that they were traveling like regular human beings. They were sitting in passenger seats, the windows were half opened, the specter of gas being pumped into the bus was far away from their minds.

As the bus was moving out, Alicia noticed the Czech doctor and Lucia standing in front of the infirmary waving to them.

Alicia was angry at Zosia. She asked her, "How come Lucia is not with us?"

"Believe me I tried, but the doctor would not let her go. She needs her help with the patients."

"The doctor is Czech but Lucia is Polish and a Kielce girl. We should not have left her behind."

"Don't worry, the doctor likes her, and she'll take care of her."

"They're still in Germany while we are going to Sweden."

But as she sat back in her seat near Dana and looked out of the window, she was overwhelmed by the feeling of relief that they were alive and emerging from a nightmare.

They were traveling along the flat country of north Germany, with only weeds and scrub along the road. Far away they saw huge windmills. The country was bare and devastated with no traffic. Some people on foot were carrying heavy rucksacks on their backs. They noticed a soldier on crutches. His uniform was no longer threatening to them. He had a stump instead of one leg. He was probably in his middle teens. Alicia almost forgot that he was a German. He was just a young boy maimed for life, far from home. He should be sitting in a classroom learning, she thought. After school, he should be playing soccer on a beautiful April day. Instead, he was recruited into the army, had his leg blown off, and maybe he had to kill other young men like himself.

"You know," she said to Dana, "if I ever have children, I will not care how they choose to communicate with God, or what language they speak, or if they don't need God at all, as long as they grow up to respect the rights of other people and be able to stand up to tyrants. This poor boy was drafted to an army that tried to invade and subjugate the world."

"He still had more chances than your brother," Dana reminded her.

"Yes, and he's probably no older than my brother would have been." Somehow the desire for vengeance, Jankiel's last cry *'nkume neme'* was gone. Only sadness remained.

"I can't wait until we get to Scandinavia," Dana said. "In June 1938, I went with my parents for a cruise to the Norwegian fjords. It never got dark; there was sunlight for almost twenty-four hours. I was sixteen, and I met an English boy my own age and fell in love. Life looked as bright and carefree as those very long days. The coast was pure magic. We sailed along steep-sided narrow gorges flanked by formidable walls of rock and ice; all human problems seemed petty and insignificant compared to the drama of nature. Nobody had even the slightest premonition of what would come in just a little more than a year. After all, Chamberlain had achieved 'peace in our time' and who cared about Czechoslovakia? The politics and the world situation were far from everyone's mind. Hitler did not exist on that boat. My parents had kosher food reserved for them; they were never ashamed of admitting that they were Jewish, not like other European Jews."

They heard planes overhead. The bus driver stopped at the side of the road and told the women to get out and lie flat in the grass. "Those are Allied planes, but we still have to protect ourselves."

"But you have a Red Cross on your bus!" Alicia protested.

"Yes, but they might think it's a German trick and that there are troops inside the bus."

The girls did what they were instructed to do, lying flat in the tall grass. Alicia's thoughts drifted back to that other trip she took in September of 1939; she was with her mother, brother, Mucia, Jerry, and Sabina. They were driving east trying to escape Hitler's hordes, and there were planes overhead then too, German planes; they had to leave their bus and lie flat alongside the road—and when the pilots spotted them, they flew low and strafed them.

Now it was April 1945, and there were no more German planes, no more ghettos, concentration camps, gas chambers, or crematoria. But also no more mother, father, brother, cousins. Did Jerry and Jas survive? It was good to look up and see American and English planes.

"Stay down," the driver told her.

Alicia thought, death is death, and it doesn't matter if it comes from a German or American bomb.

It took them six hours to get to the Danish border. They came to the little town of Flensburg.

Alicia pinched Dana and said; "It's real. We survived the war, and we're getting out of Germany."

The Germans were still in Denmark, but everybody knew that they were getting out. Danish people came to the railroad station, bringing food and flowers. They kissed and hugged the girls. They all spoke German and English. "They are going. The Germans are leaving. Europe is going to be free again."

Most of the women did not see the flowers and friendly faces; they were too busy grabbing food, gobbling it, and sticking extra bread and cookies in their underwear. They didn't want to be hungry ever again;

it was as if they couldn't believe that food would ever *not* be the biggest problem in their lives.

A big Danish woman kissed Alicia. She told her, "You are all heroines."

"Actually, it was just luck and coincidence that we survived."

She thought about the people who had helped her; Tadek, Mr. X, Genia. . . now it was Zosia putting us on the Polish list. Who knows what would have happened to us in Germany during the last days of the war? She worried again about Lucia.

They boarded the trains that were waiting for them. People kept bringing food up to the last moment. Alicia and Dana got a bottle of milk. They were crying.

They entered the Jutland peninsula. It seemed to them that they were in an enchanted land. The train traveled over long bridges that seemed to stretch forever. They looked at blue waters, at boats, ferries, and rafts, open seas, seagulls, and they were not hungry.

Then sadness came back to Alicia. She thought about her stay in Gdynia with Aunt Paula, about the Baltic beach at Sopot, and visiting Hell's peninsula. The same Baltic, the same seagulls, but no more Mucia. How did all this beauty coexist with the narrow, filthy streets of the ghetto, where only backyards could be used, because we were not worthy of the front streets? How did it coexist with concentration camps and death factories? Why couldn't I have been born a seagull and have wings to fly? But then she reminded herself that in that tight, narrow world, where death was always just around the corner and people were deprived of all human dignity, she had known friendship and love. There was Pawel and Anne—I hope she's alive. Now I have Dana and all the other women. The beauty of the country filled her with hope.

The train made a few stops along the way. It was the same story everywhere: People flocked to the windows with milk and cookies, crying and wishing them luck. The Germans were nowhere to be seen.

Alicia asked the Danish conductor for a map. He explained that they were leaving the Jutland peninsula and were about to cross over a long bridge to Funen Island (Fyn). Now, as the train was moving, they saw many medieval castles.

Dana was falling asleep, but Alicia tried to stay awake. She wanted to remember this trip forever and not to lose any of the details. Then the train entered an intercity ferry. Looking at the map, she knew that they must be leaving Funen and heading toward Zealand Island (Sjaellond). She spoke to the conductor again: "what is our destination?"

"It's Copenhagen," he told her.

The mention of Copenhagen woke Dana up. "Copenhagen!" she exclaimed. "I was there once before. We took a side trip to Elsinore [Helsigör], where Hamlet was supposed to live. In the city, we went to the Tivoli Gardens. You should have seen all the flowers!"

It was late in the afternoon when the train arrived at Copenhagen, but it was still light. The station was right at the harbor."

"I wish we could visit the city," Alicia told Dana.

"We will someday."

They had to board a ferry. Alicia looked at the map: "We really *are* going to Sweden."

They crossed the Öresund, a waterway between Copenhagen and Malmö. The girls were singing, "Hallelujah," thanking heaven that they had survived the war. They arrived in Malmö, late that evening.

The Polish women were welcomed to Sweden by Red Cross volunteers. In comparison with the exuberant Danes, the Swedes appeared stiff, formal, and businesslike. The women missed Danish warmth and joy.

New clothes were issued. The girls got pretty summer dresses and jackets. Swedish ladies have big feet, not like most European Jewish girls, who died in the camps and left their shoes behind. It was no problem for Alicia to find a pair of shoes that fit her. Each received a cosmetic case, lipstick, powder, toothpaste, toothbrush, and a comb. The Swedes were trying to make the group of homeless refugees feel human again.

Mrs. Spitz had been doing much better lately, functioning close to normal. It didn't appear so now. Genia tried to show her the cosmetics, especially the lipstick. But Mrs. Spitz just waved her hand and pushed it away. Her eyes assumed the same vacant expression that the girls knew so well. No Madame Butterfly for her. She was afraid that with lipstick and powder, her terrible thoughts would come back. She could not chance that.

They proceeded to a huge dining hall. The tables were laden with different breads, cold meats, herring, and cheeses. Coffee was served. Some women kept grabbing and hiding herring in their panties.

The next morning, the bureaucracy was set in motion. Everybody had to register, and they were issued provisional identification cards. They were listed as Polish citizens, and they were not asked about their religion.

"We are not *Jude* anymore," Alicia told Dana.

The main thing was that every one of them gave the name and address of relatives that they wanted to contact. Dana was lucky because she knew the exact street number in Westchester County, New York, where her aunt and uncle lived.

Alicia tried to remember the names and addresses of relatives in the United States. She closed her eyes and attempted to visualize a package that her family received from America in 1940 when she was sick with typhus. There it was in black letters, Bertha Knopf, Brooklyn. That was the name Alicia gave, she also listed Jas in Palestine and Jerry, someplace in Russia or Poland.

Most of the Kielce women wanted to find their men in Germany. Out of the eighty women who had boarded the trains to Auschwitz in 1944, all but Mrs. Rothman had survived and they hoped that their husbands and lovers had done just as well. Certainly the men, who were supposed to be stronger than women, should be able to survive.

Laura had uncles in London. She told the girls that they were always in touch with her family in Poland.

The Swedish official told them that many organizations and individuals all over the world were looking for survivors of the concentration camps.

Zosia said to the man, "There are many Jewish organizations, especially in the United States, so maybe it should be mentioned that we are not only Polish, but also Jewish."

The Swede just spread his hands and said, "Polska," and then he continued in German, so the girls could understand him. He explained that there was no column for religion on his forms.

Most of the Gentile girls wanted to be repatriated back to their own country. A few of them, knowing that Russians were occupying Poland, listed relatives in the United States and Canada. The Jewish girls had relatives in America, Palestine, and even as far as Australia and New Zealand.

After all the formalities, the girls went for a walk in the yard. Soldiers were patrolling, and some women, seeing uniforms, became scared.

An officer smiled at Alicia. She smiled back and decided to try English on him. To her surprise, he spoke it perfectly. He told her that he had studied in England for a while, and now he served in the reserves.

Alicia told him that she would try to emigrate to Palestine or to the United States. Then she had an idea; she asked the man for a Swedish-English dictionary and reader, so she could get along while in Sweden.

"Well, maybe I can also help you find a temporary job," he said. "My brother is a university professor in Lund, not too far from here. His wife is expecting a baby. Perhaps you can get a helping with the care of the baby."

After a few days, Alicia got the books, and the man took her name and said that as soon as his sister-in-law gave birth, he would contact her.

The following week, Dana and Alicia got passes to go to the city. It was a bright, sunny spring morning. They entered a little park and sat on a bench. They admired yellow flowers stretching their necks to the sun. They looked at the people around them. There was an old man reading a newspaper, a woman with a cane, a young couple, a woman with a baby in a carriage, and a toddler who was busy chasing pigeons.

Alicia closed her eyes. The sun felt good on her face. It was keeping the flowers alive and was warming the people. In June 1942, the same sun had shone on the flowers in the ghetto garden on Okrzejowa Street, where Mucia lived. The sun didn't care where the flowers grew. Then Alicia thought about the park in Kielce, the path around the pond, and Guta pushing Henius in a baby carriage. She remembered when, a few years later, Henius and Stas took to running around the pond. Guta called to Alicia to watch that they didn't get too close to the water.

Alicia had wanted to rent a boat and take the boys for a row, but her mother protested strongly. "So come with us, Mom," Alicia said.

But Guta said that she was all dressed up and besides she felt that the boats weren't very steady. My poor mother, Alicia thought now, she was always so full of exaggerated fears and only a few years later. . .

She looked at Dana, who was crying. "You told me you were emotionally numb."

"Maybe it's wearing off," Dana answered.

They looked around them again. The old man was no longer reading— he was dozing in the sun. He was probably retired and taking it easy after working hard all his life. Maybe my father and my uncle would be close to their retirement age now, Alicia thought. The baby was sleeping peacefully in his carriage.

Alicia said, "We can't resent these nice people. It's not their fault what happened to us. They were just lucky not to have been born Jewish and that the Germans somehow missed Sweden."

The toddler attracted the girls' attention. His mother was trying to get him out of the park—she probably had plenty of work at home— but the little boy had all the time in the world, and he would not let his mother rush him. He touched the shrubs, looked at the flowers, and ran back and forth, skipping and jumping. The people who were awake smiled at him, and he smiled back.

Alicia said, "He's learning to trust the world and people. He will probably grow up as an outgoing, happy person."

"Stop philosophizing," Dana said. "I know where you're going, even a 'normal' world isn't always a friendly place."

"I wish him just a plain and ordinary life," Alicia said, "to live in his own country, with his family. He should have a proper time for every pursuit under the heavens, and he should never be a displaced person."

"He'll either die from boredom or become an alcoholic and die from cirrhosis of the liver." Both girls laughed. "Now tell me, Alicia, was your life and family in Poland so perfect?"

"Oh no," Alicia said. "I couldn't wait to get out of Poland, but not that way—not via concentration camps."

"My aunt and uncle in America wanted us to join them," Dana said. "But my parents were afraid it would be hard for them to adjust to a new country. I remember a letter in 1938, when my uncle tried to explain that in New York most people are either immigrants or children of immigrants. There are Jewish, Irish, Italian communities, and so on. He tried to convince my father that it wouldn't be hard for him to fit in and make a good living. It is obvious that Sweden is for Swedes."

The young woman finally got her children out of the park. The old man woke up and started reading his paper again. The woman with the cane began to hobble around, and the girls kept looking at the flowers.

"I hope," Alicia said, "that I will never get so enmeshed in the drudgery of daily life that I won't be able to stop and admire the beauty and the miracle of a flower. Is it after Easter, Dana? How about Passover?"

The girls left the park. They walked down a wide street with many fancy shops and restaurants. It looked to them like Warsaw before the war. It seemed like the last six years had never happened. They were back in a regular world. They admired the dresses in the windows, handbags, and shoes. They felt just like everyone else who was walking, talking, and laughing.

"Can you imagine," Alicia said, "all these people never knew the war? While millions were dying, they had peace and prosperity."

They left the boulevard and got to a place that looked like a marketplace. Food still held more interest to them than clothes. They looked at the stands of red apples, green grapes, lemons, oranges and pears. All those forgotten sights. They felt as if they had been whisked from hell straight to paradise.

A heavy Swedish woman was sorting fruit. She looked at the girls. "Polska?" she asked.

Alicia opened her Swedish-English primer. "We have no money," she managed to say in Swedish.

"Folke Bernadotte?" the woman persisted.

"What did she say?" Dana asked.

"I don't quite know. I guess Count Bernadotte brought us here. My friend, the captain, told me that Count Bernadotte the chief of the Swedish Red Cross, negotiated with Himmler for the release of Polish inmates."

Then Alicia explored her book some more. "I think, Dana, that the woman wants to give us fruit even if we don't have money."

Laboriously, she found the Swedish word for apple. Dana pointed to a bunch of grapes. The woman gave them what they wanted and Alicia managed to say *Takso myko* [Thank you].

"Let's pull the same stunt in a bakery. Then it would be nice to invite ourselves to a smorgasbord. Come on Alicia, study your stupid book. They seem to be very impressed with your Swedish."

"We are acting like beggars," Alicia protested.

"What beggars? Just think of how they have been living in a peaceful, normal world while we lived in a hell."

"But they're not responsible for that hell."

"You are mistaken. The whole world is."

"So, we're still organizing," Alicia concluded. The bakery woman gave them four rolls. They each ate one and saved the other two. Alicia thought she would give them to Zosia and Genia.

As they walked through the streets, suddenly Dana started running after a tall, red-haired man. She was yelling in all the languages she knew at the top of her voice, "Stop, stop."

Alicia watched the scene, transfixed. The man turned around and Dana stood embarrassed. She had learned already how to say "excuse me" in Swedish, and then she said in German, "I thought you were somebody else."

The man waved at her and proceeded on his way.

Alicia ran to Dana. "What happened?"

"I think I'm going crazy. I thought it was my Olek. From the back, he looked exactly the same."

"I hope," Alicia said, "that I won't see Pawel in some Swede."

The women could not stay in the Red Cross dormitory indefinitely. More refugees were expected in Sweden. The girls were separated into two groups; one group would be taken to Lund, a university city near Malmö to be housed in a building that had once been used to house Danish children and was called the Danish School. The second group went to a camp in northern Sweden. They were expected to stay there until they found jobs or families to join. Alicia and Dana belonged to the second group.

Once again the girls took a train ride. It was the last day of April. Maybe, the jinx of April was gone. It was a normal regular train ride. They had comfortable seats, there were bathrooms in the back, food was being served. It was easy to forget those other horrible rides:

Kielce–Auschwitz, Auschwitz–Ravensbrück, Ravensbrück–Malchow. To Alicia, April would always be the month her father was murdered.

"I'll sponge off my relatives as long as I can," Dana was saying, "and then hopefully I will find a rich husband. I wouldn't care if I didn't love him or if he was much older, as long as I can travel, eat well, and dress well. I wouldn't want children, they take too much out of women."

"Somehow I don't believe that you would settle for that kind of life. You once were a fighter," said Alicia.

"All the fight is gone from me."

They arrived at Doverstorp. It looked like an enchanted land. It reminded Alicia of Stadion in Kielce, the same kind of pine woods, and hills. There was a beautiful lake on the camp grounds. The girls were housed in barracks, which were once used by boy scouts. The behavior of some of the women didn't change much from the times of the concentration camps. It was painful and embarrassing to watch a group attacking a kitchen for an extra keg of soup. Recriminations went back and forth. Again the Radom girls complained about the Kielce girls and threatened to report them for stealing food and grabbing all the good jobs in concentration camps. The stupid women, Alicia thought, they blame each other for the evil that was done to all of us.

Alicia and Dana found a library. They hadn't seen one since they left Lwow in 1939. They found books in English. Alicia took out poems by Longfellow and complete works by Shakespeare. She was teaching English to a group of girls. She put a poem by Longfellow on the blackboard; "Into each life some rain must fall." "How about a tornado?" she asked the girls.

There were fences around the camp, regular fences, like in Zabiec. The two girls managed to get a pass to visit a nearby town. It was a small provincial town; it was the beginning of May, and the day was warm and sunny. A Swedish housewife invited them for breakfast. The girls looked at the white kitchen, at the pink ruffled curtains on the windows; the coffee was perking on the stove, their hostess was smiling at them. Dana pinched Alicia. "The whole scene is unbelievable."

They drank coffee with milk and sugar, and they ate buttered rolls. The lady told them that she'd ·find some clothes for them. She

produced a trunk with blouses and skirts and even underwear. Alicia
was studying her Swedish primer with the help of the English-
Swedish dictionary. She asked the lady what her name was. It was
Mrs. Olson.

"You are Polish," Mrs. Olson said. "I have an idea of what you
went through. And what is your name?" she asked.

They introduced themselves to Mrs. Olson.

"We are starting to behave like civilized people," Dana remarked
in Polish.

Alicia was still studying her dictionary. She managed to ask in
Swedish: "Do you have an old bathing suit, Mrs. Olson?" She explained to Dana what she was asking for.

"You are a complete nut," Dana told Alicia. "This lady will
probably think that all we are missing are bathing suits."

Mrs. Olson was not surprised at all. "I have a couple of bathing
suits that are barely used. They will probably be too large for you."
She went to her bedroom and came back with two bathing suits.

Alicia thanked her in Swedish, profusely. Mrs. Olson complimented her on how fast she was learning.

The radio was on. There were radios in the camp, one in the office
and one in the library. The girls knew more or less what was going on:
The Russians were in Berlin, Hitler and his mistress had committed
suicide and so had Göring; the Americans, Russians and the British
had met at Torgau on the River Elbe. They heard about the American
General Eisenhower, about Marshal Zhukov and General
Montgomery. But this time, they caught other names in the Swedish
broadcast: "Dachau," "Buchenwald," and "Bergen Belsen." They tried
to figure out what the announcer was saying. Mrs. Olson waved her
hand, as if she was telling them she had enough, then quickly changed
the station to music. Alicia looked again in her dictionary; she asked
her hostess if it was possible to get London on her radio. Mrs. Olson
looked at her carefully; "Are you sure you want to hear it all?" she
asked.

"*Ja so,*" Alicia said, trying to imitate Swedish 'sing-song."

Mrs. Olson smiled at her. This woman, Alicia thought, is not as
simple as she appears to be. Mrs. Olson switched to the English station.

At the end of the broadcast, there was a vivid description of the conditions that the Allied soldiers found in the liberated concentration camps. The inmates were compared to skeletons, barely alive. They had huge deep-set eyes staring out of swollen eye sockets. The soldiers found it hard to believe that these creatures were once ordinary human beings. Most of them were even too weak to pick themselves up and greet the liberating troops. They were described as being beyond saving or any hope of rehabilitation. Alicia and Dana stood there as if made of stone. Kielce men were in these camps. Alicia forgot that some of the men were once policemen, whom she despised. Now she thought about them as husbands and boyfriends of the women who had become her family and only support over the last crucial year in Auschwitz, Ravensbrück, and Malchow. Mrs. Olson didn't understand much English. She must have heard the same story in Swedish. Mercifully, the broadcast was over.

"Would you like me to take you to the movies tomorrow?" Mrs. Olson asked the girls. "There is a very good picture playing. It's American, but the star is a Swedish girl."

"What's her name?" Alicia asked. She was impressed with herself on how good her Swedish was getting.

"Ingrid Bergman," Mrs. Olson said, "and the male star is Charles Boyer. The name of the movie is *Gaslight*."

"Charles Boyer!" Alicia exclaimed. "He was my mother's favorite actor. So was Greta Garbo, another Swedish star."

"I'll write a letter to the camp director, asking permission to take you," Mrs. Olson said.

On their way back to camp, the words of the British announcer came back to them. Alicia thought about her friends in the camps: Anne, Rachel, Ruth, Fanny, Andrew, Saul. . . Had Benjamin and Ira survived in the woods? But she mainly thought about Lucia. Where did she wind up with the Czech doctor?

"We are lucky," Dana said, "that we got out of Germany when we did and landed in a peaceful country where we can start feeling human again."

The next day, Mrs. Olson picked them up at the camp and drove them to the town. The girls were very excited; they hadn't seen a movie in six years. When they walked in, the newsreel was on. They saw American soldiers entering Bergen-Belsen. The pictures fitted the description of the radio announcer they had heard the day before.

"You shouldn't be watching this," Mrs. Olson said. "But I have to. I need to know what some people can inflict on others. You both know it by your own experiences."

As they watched the movie, miraculously the images of the newsreels slipped from their minds. It was like being in a movie in the old Kielce. They admired the beauty of Ingrid Bergman, the deviousness of Charles Boyer, the uprightness of Joseph Cotten, the youth and innocence of the young Angela Lansbury.

The following day, Alicia and Dana went to the lake. Alicia couldn't wait to try on her bathing suit. It was noon, and it was warm under the hot sun. They sat on a rock by the lake, looking at the water. It was so very peaceful and beautiful. Water and sky, so majestic and indifferent to human fate.

"Let's go swimming," Alicia proposed.

"You are crazy. Do you realize how cold a mountain lake is in May?"

"The sun will warm us." Then Alicia noticed a little inlet. "Let's go over there. The water is shallow, and it should be much warmer."

The water in the little inlet was up to their waist and deep enough for swimming. Alicia wandered out to the middle, beyond the shallow water. It was very cold and probably fathoms deep.

Dana yelled at her, "You'll get cramps!" And more soberly, "You survived the war, now you are going to get cramps in your legs, and you'll drown."

"You sound just like my mother," Alicia called back. As soon as she said that, she felt guilty. It's almost like saying that I'm glad my mother is not here, she thought. She slowly swam back to the safety of the inlet and stood there almost crying.

"What's the matter now?" Dana wanted to know. "I'm sorry that I reminded you of your mother."

Alicia looked at the pine forest and watched the sun glistening on the water as it washed off a big rock. This sight did more for her than looking through the fancy stores in Malmö. "Hey-ho, hello." She waved to the trees and to the birds, then she kissed Dana.

"You are nuts again."

"I loved my mother, but I inherited my enthusiasm for living from my Aunt Paula."

"L' Haim," Dana said.

"I feel as if I've recovered from a long illness, and the world is still here waiting for me," Alicia said.

On their way back from the lake, they met Laura. "Have you heard?" she said. "The war in Europe is officially over. The Germans signed an unconditional surrender."

"Hurray," Alicia yelled. She kissed Laura, she never forgot how much Laura had helped her in the past.

"Now if only I could hear from my uncles in London," Laura said. "It would be so good to have a family again. My parents always kept an open house. Sometimes, during the holidays, we had fifty people at the table. My uncles in London were always in contact with us."

"You'll go to London," Alicia said. "You'll be the belle of the ball, and you'll find a handsome doctor."

They joined other women and the Swedish clerks from the office. It was May 8, 1945, VE Day, Victory in Europe Day. There were celebrations in all the big cities of Europe and America; in Paris, in Rome and in London, in Oslo, Amsterdam, and Copenhagen, in New York and San Francisco, in Toronto and in Montreal, in Tel Aviv and Jerusalem, in Moscow and Leningrad, in Warsaw, Budapest, Belgrade, Prague, and Bucharest. Alicia suspected that people liberated by the Russians didn't really have to celebrate too much.

"We will have to start all over in a new world," Dana said.

CHAPTER 17

One morning, Alicia, Dana, and Laura were leaving the library. Clara ran out of the office and excitedly called to Alicia. "There's a letter for you in the office. It's from Palestine. I think it must be from your cousin Jas."

Jas is alive and he found me. Maybe he has heard from Jerry, from the Lublin cousins, from Wladek and Eda.

Alicia was running; it seemed to her she had never run as fast before.

"Don't break your neck," Dana yelled after her.

When she entered the office, there were some other girls standing in line waiting for the mail. She hated them; they were between her and the letter. Finally it was her turn. The letter came through the Red Cross, and it was from Jas. The return address was Tel Aviv. Alicia tore open the envelope and two photographs fell out. She looked at the first one; a group of hatless and disheveled soldiers with their hands behind their heads were following a man with a rifle.

Alicia turned to the back of the photo, and there it was in Jas' handwriting; "March 19, 1945. The sergeant of my company leads the prisoners, members of the 'Herrenvolk [Master Race].' You can only see my shadow."

Jas had taken German prisoners, Alicia thought, thrilled. They certainly didn't look like members of the Master Race. She shivered at the memory of the Germans the way she remembered them: their hats, boots, whips, guns—so proud, so arrogant, owning the world.

She started to read the letter: Jas had served in the British Army since 1941. He mainly saw action in Italy, and reached the rank of major. In September 1944, when the Jewish Brigade was formed, he transferred to it by request.

She thought, Jas could never be one of those able-bodied young Jewish boys who boarded the trains and marched naked on the ramp to the gas chambers. She felt that she herself was growing in self respect because of Jas.

Alicia looked at the other picture, and there was Jas with a young woman and a small child. The woman was nice looking but very short, and Jas, being as tall and straight as ever, was bending down almost halfway to be at her height. The child, a little girl, looked around two years old. Alicia turned the picture and read the explanation: The woman was Jas's wife and the little girl was their daughter. Jas wrote that his wife's name was Ester; she was also from Kielce. She had come to Palestine in the mid thirties and she is a nurse. Alicia kept on reading the letter. Suddenly she stopped reading; she just looked at the letter and began to cry.

"What happened?" Dana asked her.

"Jerry did not make it," Alicia said between sobs. "Jas received a letter from a man who was with Jerry when he died. He died of typhus in a ditch beside a road someplace in the middle of Russia. They had been marching from somewhere trying to join the Polish army. Jerry was too sick to continue. He died in a freezing place, far away from home and family and love."

"I always thought," Alicia sobbed, "that he had a better chance than I." There were no gas chambers in Russia and no medical experiments on humans. There was disease and hunger, but most young people can survive that. But Jerry had succumbed.

"He just joined the roster of all the ones who died," Dana said.

"Stop it, Dana," Alicia cried. "Jerry is not just one of the nameless victims to me. He's a boy I grew up with, my play pal. We dreamed together, read together, got into mischief together, and he was as dear to me as a brother. I counted on him surviving."

Always practical, Dana said, "Does Jas ask about your plans for the future? Is he offering you any help?"

Alicia wiped off her tears. "Let me finish reading."

"Well, at least two of you from your family survived. There are two of us—me and Molly."

Alicia kept on reading the letter. She told Dana that Jas would be forwarding some money and that he wanted to know about her health and plans as soon as possible.

From then on, practically every day, there was mail for someone in the group. Dana heard from her relatives. They wanted to get busy right away to get her and Molly to America. Laura got a letter from her uncles in London. They, too, were eager to send for her.

Through the Red Cross, Alicia got the address of Bertha Knopf in Brooklyn. She sent her a telegram and just wrote that she was the only survivor; father, mother, and brother murdered.

Sweden was accepting more displaced persons, especially sick ones who needed hospital care. Alicia got a letter from a hospital in Malmö; it was from Saul. She sat on the bench with Dana and Laura and read the letter. He came to Sweden from Bergen-Belsen, with tuberculosis. Saul was weak and running a high fever, and it was hard for him to breathe. The pain was constant, and because of stomach problems, he found it difficult to eat. He apologized for his sloppy handwriting, but as he explained, he could hardly muster sufficient energy to press a pen. The letter went on to describe his life from January to April. He arrived at Bergen-Belsen with a transport from Camp Sachsenhausen. There were 760 men in his group. Only six survived. Saul had contracted typhus, and he was in the Bergen "hospital." There were three men to one bunk, all hallucinating because of high fevers. The lice were all over, crawling in all their body cavities; in their mouth, ears, eyes, and so on. They suffered terrible thirst. Everyday, somebody else died, and the orderlies just threw the corpses out to rot. The smell of the "ward" was atrocious, because many patients lay in their own excrement. One of the orderlies saved Saul's life. He was a Kielce man, and he managed to feed Saul and take care of him.

"Who was it?" Dana and Laura asked.

"Oh," Alicia said, "it was Krakower, the one who likes our Clara."

The girls were trying to absorb the horror of the descriptions. Alicia was immune to typhus, since she had once had it. But she was still very scared of lice, almost as much as of gas chambers.

She kept on reading, this time to herself. All of a sudden her face changed, and there was joy. "Listen, girls," she called out. "Anne is alive ane doing well. She worked in the kitchen in Bergen-Belsen. Rachel, Ruth and Fanny are also alright. I hope that all ten of us, tapped by Thomas, survived. I'd like to find out about Lucia."

Laura said something that filled Alicia with sadness: "My sister did not survive."

Why did I have to mention that day when we were tapped? Alicia thought. Will Laura ever forgive me for standing with the nurses, and maybe taking the place of her sister?

Many Kielce women came over: "Does he know anything about our men?"

"Krakower is doing well," Alicia told Clara. And she read to her the paragraph that mentioned him. Clara replied by asking if Saul knew anything about Sid. Alicia was jarred. Surely it should have been Laura who asked after Sid, not jilted Clara. It's like *Midsummer Night's Dream* all over again: Krakower loves her, she loves Sid, but he loves Laura, who still still dreams about her doctor.

The women kept pressing Alicia: "Keep on reading. Who else does he mention?"

"Andrew survived," Alicia said. "He, too, has tuberculosis. He is in a hospital in Germany, and Saul writes that Andrew is in much better shape than he, since he is almost convalescing."

None of the women were interested in Andrew. "Who else? Who else?"

"Before Saul left for Sweden, Chaim visited him," Alicia went on. "He seems to be doing all right."

"Will you try to get together with him?" the girls wanted to know.

Alicia was annoyed. Just a couple of months ago, Lucia had asked her the same question. "No," she said simply.

"He was never in her class," Laura declared.

"Class has nothing to do with it."

More transports of Nazi victims were coming from Germany to Sweden, and the news they brought were generally bleak. Soon the whole scenario unfolded: Kielce men did not do well at all, the policemen and those who resigned from the Jewish police after the selections to Treblinka, with very few exceptions, were dead. Spiegel, Birnbaum, and Zubow were beaten to near death. Oderman, Goldberg, and Tarnow, like many others, died from hunger and disease. Though some of the factory workers of Henrykow and Ludwikow were half starved when they boarded the trains for Auschwitz, they still did much better than the well fed policemen. A few strong and well-built men volunteered for *Sonderkommando*. They had better conditions, more food, and decent clothes. To the Nazis, they represented the prime witnesses of the murders, therefore *Sonderkommandos* were changed every few months. The ones who were discharged from their jobs were taken straight to the gas chambers by the new commandos.

Many men died after the liberation. When the Allied troops entered the camps, they distributed food. The starving men ate voraciously. They couldn't take it in their weakened condition, their stomachs burst, and they died.

Luzer, Zosia's husband, and little Bella's father, survived. They were both Kielce bred and born and they were considered by the boys as decent men. The outsiders from Germany, Austria, Lodz had much less of a chance.

Many survivors like Saul and Andrew came out with chronic sicknesses. Juda, Genia's husband, and Sid survived, being skilled mechanics and electricians.

Alicia heard over and over again that the last days before liberation were the worst. She worried about Lucia. She remembered how many times last winter, during the marches to the factory in Malchow, Lucia was ready to give up.

The women stayed in their bunks crying and crying; it was again like the spring of 1943 when their children were murdered.

Alicia looked at Lola Birnbaum. Once she had hated Lola's husband, but now she felt sorry for the woman. She seemed so tiny and helpless. To Alicia, Birnbaum was a despicable man, but to Lola he was just a husband and a provider and the father of her two murdered children.

Alicia tried to console another woman. She was tall and good looking and so was her dead husband. The rumor was that he had volunteered for *Sonderkommando.* Now his wife said something that made Alicia very mad: "My Louis," she kept repeating, "so handsome and virile, could not make it. But such *nebechs*, puny and sickly like Saul and Andrew, survived."

What a horrible thing to say, Alicia thought. Saul almost died from typhus in Bergen-Belsen; now he had a bad case of tuberculosis. Why should she begrudge him the little life that is left to him? He's only twenty-five, but the way he described his condition, his prospects didn't look too good. At least, unlike Louis, if he recovers he will not dream about the dead bodies he transported from gas chambers to the crematoria.

And there was Dida, the girl who in Henrykow left her husband to sleep with a lover. Both men survived. Dida was ecstatic, and she was ready to join her lover. She completely ignored her husband. But the lover wrote to her that he had met another woman and was no longer interested in renewing the relationship with Dida. She got a letter from her husband who wanted her back. He was in Poland, in Lodz, and he had recovered a factory that belonged to his family before the war.

It didn't take Dida very long to decide to accept her husband's offer. "I don't love him," she admitted to Alicia, "but he is a wealthy man, and he will always take care of me."

There were two sisters, who kept together, supported each other and helped each other survive the camps. The older one was the wife of a policeman, and her husband was now dead. The younger had a lover and he survived. He wrote to her from Germany and asked her to join him, but on one condition; that she leave her sister behind because he didn't like her. The two girls were the only survivors from the whole family. Now the younger one had to choose between her widowed sister and her lover.

Another girl from Kielce, who was too young to know much about life before the war, was unhappy in Sweden. She was a big, healthy good-looking teenager. In Malchow she worked in the laundry with Genia. She became a favorite of Berte, the brutal German supervisor. There were all kinds of rumors about their relationship. The girl fared much better than most of the inmates; she had enough food and clothes. Now, in Doverstorp, she complained that she was better off in Germany than in Sweden.

Alicia sometimes wondered if the women cried about their men or because they were afraid to face the world alone. Hadn't they learned that it is the men who need women to survive? We the girls managed so much better under terrible conditions than they did.

One day, Alicia and Dana came upon Laura, who was deep in thought. She was holding a letter.

"Is it from London?" Alicia asked her.

"I know I shouldn't say it," Laura said, "but I almost wish it was from London. But it's from Germany."

"Who from?"

"From Sid." She seemed befuddled and confused. Even her red

hair wasn't as neatly arranged as usual, her eyes looked troubled.

"Is he all right? Is he healthy?" Alicia asked.

Laura perked up a little. "He's fine. Sid always had good jobs, even in concentration camps."

"Well, then, what's wrong?"

"He wants to come to Sweden," Laura said. "He writes that he's never stopped loving me and that the thoughts of me helped him survive. He wants us to start a new life together."

Alicia almost burst out laughing. All those wailing women, weeping because they had no men to take care of them. And here was Laura, who had a man who certainly would be a good provider, and she had doubts. "You'd better make up your mind soon," she told Laura. "If not, Clara is ready to grab him back. She would leave poor Krakower for Sid anytime."

"I was all set to go to London."

"So why don't you write to your uncles? Maybe they can bring both of you over. Mention to them how talented Sid is, and if he could manage in Germany, he certainly will manage in England. Most important, do you love him?"

Laura put her head in her arms and said, "I don't know."

Later, when Dana and Alicia were alone, they talked about Laura. "I know if it were me and Olek, I wouldn't have any doubts about what to do. The same for you and Pawel."

"But don't you see?" Alicia replied. "Laura had it all planned; rich family, parties, theater, and a professional husband. Now she's afraid she'll become a plain and ordinary housewife before she gets a chance to have some fun."

Dana and Alicia went swimming almost everyday. They also discovered there was an indoor gym in the basement, underneath the library. Alicia was very proud that she could still do hand stands and somersaults. She kept on studying Swedish, and she continued giving English lessons to the girls. Whenever she went to the office to pick up the mail, she practiced her Swedish with the clerks.

Dana and Molly, who was in Lund, received money from their American relatives. Then Alicia got some money from Jas. He wrote her a long letter, insisting that she see a dentist.

Alicia and Dana were now inseparable. They did everything

together. What will I do, Alicia thought, when Dana goes away? I tend to overattach myself to one person. First Pawel, then Anne, and now Dana. I hope that I'll either get to America or Palestine.

Now that Dana and Alicia had some money, they went shopping in town.

Alicia, as usual, got stuck in front of a fruit stand. She was looking at the strawberries, and she almost cried. They were red and shiny and neatly arranged in boxes.

Dana was puzzled. Why should strawberries make Alicia cry?

Alicia said "I haven't seen or eaten strawberries since the summer of 1939, but I've dreamed about them. One afternoon in April last year, I took a nap before roll call. I saw strawberries in my dream but they were not in the boxes. Jerry and I were picking them and eating them. The same day I had that dream, Anne tried to escape. She was brought back by Zubow." All of a sudden, she hugged Dana. "Anne made it," she exclaimed, "and that son of a bitch, Zubow, who caused all that pain and robbed Lucia, did not!"

"To hell with Zubow," Dana said. "Let's buy some strawberries and sit down and eat them."

They sat down on a bench in a little garden. Alicia started eating, but Dana only picked one reluctantly. "Don't you think we should wash them?"

"You remind me of my mother. 'Wash the fruit before you eat it, make sure that your hands are clean,' and on and on."

"Please, don't start crying again."

"My mother doesn't have to worry about germs anymore; Hitler took care of that." But then she shook her head and said, "I'm sure my mother wouldn't want me to mourn for her for the rest of my life, so let's eat."

Dana said, "I used to pull out weeds, brush off the dirt, and chew on the stems and roots. Now, I don't like to eat unwashed strawberries."

The next day, the women were in the office waiting for the mail. Alicia got a heavy letter from Andrew. The return address was a hospital in Germany. He must feel well to write so much, she thought.

Dana received a letter from Molly. "Let's go to the lake, sit on a rock, and read in peace," she suggested.

The girls found their favorite spot at the lake.

Andrew wrote that he was feeling better, wasn't running a fever and was coughing only slightly. He was on a waiting list to get to Sweden, so he could get better medical care. His relatives in the United States were going to try to get a visa for him, but he would have to wait until his illness was arrested before he could emigrate. He would not be admitted to the States with active TB.

He had a lot of information about Kielce people now in occupied Germany: "Benjamin and Ira survived in the woods of Swietokrzyski Mountains. They visited me in the hospital. They appear healthy. They told me that in the last few months of the war they were almost killed by the Polish partisans. They believe that they have a better chance here, in Germany, than in Poland. Benjamin tried to get in touch with Anne, but she didn't want to see or hear from him. He also told me that he was in Kielce, went to his old school, and got copies of his Matura. He is hoping to get to a university in Munich with a scholarship perhaps from a Jewish organization.

"Do you remember Rudek? He was one of your favorite policemen. You were right—it was he who stole your Aryan papers."

Alicja Krystyna Buszewska, that was my name, Alicia reminded herself.

"Rudek bought a little house in the country for a Gentile friend. All he wanted was some food and a place where he and his wife, Litka, could hide. They lived in the cellar from the beginning of 1943 on and were at the mercy of their Gentile friends. In December 1944, when the Russians were at a standstill in the middle of Poland, Rudek's landlords became scared. They suspected that some of their neighbors would report them to the Germans for harboring Jews. They got in touch with partisans. The value of the house was insignificant compared to all the other money that they'd received already from Rudek. One day, the Polish family packed their belongings and left the house. The gang of partisans set fire to it, and the people in the cellar perished in flames."

Alicia was shivering now. Alicja Krystyna Buszewska didn't bring luck to poor Litka. Rudek was so mighty and rich, while I was helpless, with broken glasses, all alone and with no money. I survived, and he didn't. Oh, how are the mighty fallen—Spiegel, Oderman, Rudek. Even Rudek didn't deserve that kind of death!

She continued reading: "The few Kielce doctors who survived the actions up to 1945 did not make it either. Dr. Breitman and medic Rutkowski died in concentration camps. Dr. Brazen collapsed during the January march from Auschwitz, and he was shot. I was in that march myself, I'll tell you about it one day. Basia made it. She is now in Czechoslovakia and married to a Czech doctor."

Alicia sighed with relief, good for Basia.

"Luzer, Juda and Majek Krakower were going back to Poland to claim their property. They expect their wives to join them there. From there, together they would find a country to emigrate to."

Alicia knew that the girls already had this information. Genia and Zosia were very happy, but Clara? Was she still hoping that Laura wouldn't want Sid, and he would come back to her?

"The three miracle children, who were not murdered in Treblinka, or in the following action on children, survived the concentration camps. Bella, like you, is in Sweden with her mother. She's a lucky girl. Her father is alive. Tommy Breslau is in Germany with his mother; old man Breslau did not make it. Shlomo with his father are now in Germany on a waiting list to go to Sweden to join their wife and mother. They are reasonably healthy. Jeffie, the Ludwikow child, wasn't so lucky, he died."

Alicia thought: I always expected Shlomo to make it. Jeffie and his mother were doomed as soon as they boarded the train for Auschwitz.

"You would like to know that your friend Mr. Bloom is alive. Engineers, electricians, mechanics, and plumbers had the best chance. Mr. Bloom has already found a woman, much younger than he, whom he intends to marry."

Alicia was stunned at the news. Mr. Bloom, she thought, must be in his fifties; the last time she saw him, he looked old to her. To Alicia, at twenty three, it was strange that people at that age would marry. Lately, she hadn't known anybody that old. Then she realized that if her mother and aunt had survived, they would be only in their middle forties, and if widows, they could still marry.

Dana looked at Alicia. "You are so absorbed in the letter and so deep in thought."

"Andrew keeps on writing and writing. He seems to know everything about everybody," Alicia said. "I've got to finish reading this letter, and then you must tell me what Molly writes from Lund."

"Tell me what's in the letter that's making you upset?" Dana asked.

Alicia told her friend about Rudek.

"Your friend Andrew seems to be writing about everybody. How come he hasn't mentioned Chaim?" Dana asked.

"Oh, I don't know and I don't really care. What does Molly write?"

"Jobs are available for our girls in Lund. The hospitals are overcrowded with all the sick from Germany, so there are openings for nurses aides and for all kinds of hospital workers. We could also work in factories or as maids."

Alicia grinned: "Those are the only jobs that are open for us poor refugees."

Dana said, "Molly writes something very interesting. She and a group of girls were invited to a dance at the Jewish Center of Malmö and guess what? They just stood there and watched. None of the Swedish Jewish boys would ask a refugee to dance."

Alicia started to laugh. "Don't you remember? The same thing happened to us in Lwow. They made us feel like poor relatives."

Dana finished her letter. "You're right, it's Lwow all over again. Molly came to the conclusion that most of the Swedish Jews don't want to be identified with the bedraggled refugees from concentration camps. There are very few Jews in Sweden, and most of them are completely assimilated. They feel more Swedish than Jewish. Anti-Semitism is almost unknown. The Swedish Jews are afraid that the uncivilized behavior of the new arrivals will bring it up."

Alicia said: "But the Germans were so close to Sweden. They were in Norway, the Netherlands, and Denmark. It's only by a grace of God—or 'whatever gods may be'—that the Swedish Jews weren't in the same position as we. Don't they realize that?"

"But, Alicia, the Germans never came to Sweden, and Swedish Jews feel superior to the rest of their European brethren."

It was time for the girls to go back to their barracks. They had many letters to write.

The following day there was a letter from Anne. It was addressed to both Alicia and Laura. It was a warm and beautiful letter. She

reminded the girls how close they once were in the little hospital in the
Jewish Quarters. She found out that her brother was in Paris; he had
survived the war on Aryan papers. She wrote about the other girls,
Rachel, Fanny, and Ruth. Anne was happy that Andrew and Saul had
survived, but she didn't mention Benjamin, Ira, or Chaim.

Laura was moved by the letter. She told Alicia that she had made
up her mind about Sid. She asked him to come to Sweden and hoped
that both of them would go to England.

Alicia received another letter from Saul, his handwriting much
firmer. His appetite was slowly returning, he said, he was not running a
fever, was in less pain and it was a little easier for him to breathe.
However, he was still bedridden. He wrote that he wanted to break
something to her gently.

Alicia was afraid to read on. Something bad had happened again?
To whom? To Andrew? From the time he wrote his last letter to now?
She kept on reading, then burst out laughing.

"Have you gone nuts?" Dana said. "What's so funny?"

Alicia kept on laughing. Finally she said, "Chaim got married, and
stupid Saul thinks he has to break it to me gently." Then she added
sadly, "I told you I'm not like Laura, who has Sid begging her to
resume their relationship."

Dana shrugged her shoulders. "You wouldn't settle for Chaim,
anyway."

Alicia said, "You're right, Dana, but I'd still feel better if he came
to Doverstorp; then I could tell him to jump in the lake"

Alicia sat quietly for a while and then said, "I understand now how
most of the survivors feel. They are all trying to find another person as
soon as possible, to get married, and to start a new family. It is hard to
face life alone for people like Mr. Bloom, Chaim, and all these women
who lost their men."

The next letter made Alicia very happy. It was from Lucia, she
was in Switzerland. She described the macabre march from Malchow.
They hadn't the vaguest idea where they were going: Lucia, the Czech
doctor, and the patients. Many times they were afraid that the guards
were going to shoot them. Then one day, the guards just disappeared,
and the group was left alone somewhere in the middle of Germany,
terrified of running into German units. Luck was with them, and they

came across an American patrol. At that moment, Lucia wrote, she realized that she had survived the war. But then, the following day, an American soldier tried to rape her.

Alicia started to laugh. She read that part to Dana. "Lucia survived the war without being raped by a German, and then it almost happened to her when she was liberated."

Lucia wrote that eventually the Red Cross took over the group, and she was sent to Switzerland with the children's transport.

Now it was Dana's turn to laugh: "What a child? How many abortions has this child had?"

"Stop it, Dana. I don't think she's had any. Joseph was careful. The important years of Lucia's life were taken away from her, and she deserves all the advantages that she can get. She wrote that she was applying for a scholarship. Do you know what else Lucia wants me to do for her?"

"Maybe you should carry her on your back when you both cross the Alps."

Alicia grinned. "Lucia wants me to help her look for her Auschwitz doctor. She thinks she is still very much in love with him."

"The child wants a man. She probably listed her age as eleven or twelve so she could be sent to Switzerland. I bet that guy is pushing forty."

"Perhaps he was really in love with her," Alicia said.

"I'm just kidding. I'm really very glad that your friend survived, and she deserves every opportunity that she can get."

"You're really a great kid, Dana."

Alicia got another letter from Andrew: "I wrote to you about everybody but myself. One experience last year was especially painful for me. It would probably be healthier to just bury it, forget it, and go on with my life. But certain things don't let themselves be forgotten. There are times, in life-and-death situations that a person comes to grips with his inner core, which otherwise might never be revealed to him. I faced it one day, and I didn't like what I found: I and my cousin Leon were slave laborers in I. G. Farben, a company near Auschwitz."

Alicia remembered that Leon shared a bunk with Andrew at Henrykow. But, unlike Andrew he was shy and did not socialize with the girls.

The letter continued:

> "Leon fell off a ladder, broke his arm, and suffered in-
> ternal injuries. He was sent to a hospital attached to the
> factory. The conditions there were terrible. No linens or
> gowns were available. Naked patients were packed tight-
> ly, one on top of the other; their body heat kept the
> temperature close to 100 degrees. Leon was there for
> three months. By being immobile, he lost the strength in
> his limbs. The majority of the doctors were French in-
> mates, but, under the circumstances, they were all
> stressed out, and to the patients they seemed not much
> better than the Germans.
>
> In late December, I heard rumors about an evacuation.
> I organized a blanket and a cement sack and got Leon
> out of the hospital. You know what was happening to
> patients in those times! In January, in subfreezing
> temperature, we went for the infamous "death march"
> from Auschwitz. First, I carried Leon wrapped in the
> blanket, then I put him in the cement sack to keep him in-
> sulated from the bitter cold. When I couldn't carry him, I
> dragged him. There was shooting going on not far from
> us. The Russians were approaching and firing at the Ger-
> mans. The guards told us to stop; they were afraid that
> we would walk into Russian patrols. When the shooting
> eased up, we were ordered to move again. Leon just lay
> there and refused to be dragged. I pleaded with him, but
> he implored me to leave him be and to follow the others.
> 'Go, go' he repeated over and over. 'Without me, you
> might have a chance.' I kept on begging, but then I left.
>
> Against all odds, Leon survived. He hitched himself to
> a wagon and got to the trains. Now he tells me that if I
> had stayed with him, we might both have been mur-
> dered. But I know that I left him to die. I will have to
> live with that."

Don't be so hard on yourself, Alicia felt like yelling. You did as
much for Leon as was humanly possible and when he refused to go on,
you had no choice but to leave him. No one should be put in that kind

of situation. She thought about Mrs. Spitz, pushing her child to the
transport side, and then losing her mind. And I, Alicia, left my mother
and brother.

May gave way to June. Offers for jobs came to the office. A group
of Kielce girls left for Malmö to work in a hospital. Another group got
jobs in a factory in Lund. Alicia received a letter from her Swedish
friend.

The baby had been born, and Alicia could start working sometime
in the middle of the month. She made plans to leave on the fourteenth,
the day before her birthday.

Dana decided to go to Lund to be with Alicia and Molly. She
didn't need a job; she was getting money regularly from her relatives
in the United States. Laura joined the Lund group. There she could
wait for Sid's arrival and news from her uncles in London.

The camp in Doverstorp was slowly being emptied. Zosia, Genia,
and Clara had their papers processed to go to Poland. The other girls
felt sorry for themselves. Their leaders, who were with them in
Auschwitz, Ravensbrück, and Malchow, who saw to it that none
starved or froze, were now abandoning the group. Their men survived,
and they had property to claim in Poland. From now on these women,
who kept so close together for many horrible months, would be scattered among different jobs, different countries, and different relatives.

As in Tuwim's poem, Alicia thought.

> Everybody will go his own way on crazy mad escapades.
> Wandering in an immense and strange world.

"You don't care," the women told Alicia. "You think you can do it
all by yourself."

One morning in June, as Alicia was leaving her tutoring session,
the girls called her; "You have a visitor in the office." Alicia wondered
who it could be. Her Swedish friend was no place near Doverstorp, and
Jas was in Palestine.

She went to the office. There stood a young man in a military
uniform. The first thing she noticed were the U. S. insignia on his
lapel. His chest was decorated with ribbons and medals. Between the

medals was a bronze star. The man was dark, slim and handsome, but not very tall. He had deep brown eyes.

"Who are you?" she asked in English.

"Oh, you speak English. I speak German if you prefer," he said.

"I speak better English than I do German," she answered. "But who are you?" she repeated.

"I'm Jack Knopf, a lieutenant in the American army; my mother wrote to me from the United States after she found out that you had miraculously survived the war. She sent me your address. I received a few days furlough, and I decided to visit you in Sweden."

So this was her American connection! Alicia became excited. His mother is my father's sister. She felt like kissing and hugging him, but somehow he looked shy to her, and she decided against it.

"I know who you are!" she exclaimed. Our common grandfather told me all about you, about your mother and your brother. I remember that he said you were a rare person who had a job during the depths of the Depression."

Then she became pensive. "Grandfather visited us in Kielce in 1934, and he died shortly afterward. Since then, so many things have happened, so many people were murdered that it's like one hundred lifetimes ago. Tell me, how did you win all these medals?"

"Me?" he said. "I just did what I was supposed to do. But you, Alicia, must have some story to tell. I saw concentration camps in Germany. My mother wrote me that your father, mother, and brother were murdered. Some of our relatives survived in Russia. They went through terrible hardships. Aunt Gnenda from Kotowice died in Russia; she couldn't get insulin for her diabetes."

"One of my cousins perished in Russia and the other survived in Palestine; he was an officer in the British Army," she told him. "I was just lucky. I was with a group of women, and we took care of each other. My friend," Alicia pointed with pride to Dana, "was in the 1943 Warsaw ghetto uprising. She was a messenger from the ghetto to the Polish underground."

Dana stood there listening. Her understanding of English was getting better.

Alicia said, "It's nice to see a Jewish boy and my cousin who fought the Germans. To me, you look like a hero."

Jack seemed embarrassed: "There are many Jewish boys in the American army, I'm just one of them."

A thought crossed Alicia's mind: How would those boys have behaved if they had been in Poland during the war? Policemen? Kapos? She brushed the thought aside.

"I saw heavy fighting last June when we first crossed the Channel," Jack said. "But once I became a lieutenant in the intelligence, it got a little less dangerous."

Dana was very interested. "Military intelligence? That's what I would like to do. It must be exciting!"

"Well, yes and no," he said. "Sometimes it can be disturbing. I grew up and went to school in Germany so I know how to talk to the prisoners. We caught Franz Ziereis, the commandant of Mauthausen. We shot him in the left arm and through the back when he tried to escape. We put him in a hospital in Gusen. Under interrogation, he gave a statement that I translated into English, and believe me it was horrible."

Then he said to Alicia: "Could you tell me some details of what happened to your family. My mother would also like to know."

It was hard for Alicia to talk about everything that happened. She went to the office, took a piece of paper and wrote the story about all the murders, starting with her uncle, then her father, mother, aunt, brother. She put in the dates and details. She wrote about other actions, on doctors, on children and so on. She gave the horrendous statistics about Kielce Jews.

Jack read the story. "Oh, God," he sighed.

Alicia said, "During those years I felt as if He was light years away."

"And you're calling *me* a hero."

"You are, you actively fought," then she added, "You were infinitely better off than we were. You had a gun to shoot at the enemies, you had the U.S. Army and Navy behind you, you had medical units to care for you. We had nobody. All we could do was to try to survive in spite of hunger, cold, disease, and wanton cruelty."

Dana broke in: "Can you tell us about that statement of commandant of Mauthausen?"

Alicia smiled. "Dana is interested in spying and intelligence work. I hope it is not secret?"

"No it's not," Jack said, puzzled. "But why would you want to hear about it? Didn't you have enough?"

"Please, we can take it. I always wanted to know how the Germans would justify themselves."

Jack was still hesitant. "I got sick translating it from the German," he told the girls. "The other men on my team didn't want me to interview the bastard. They were afraid I would strangle him right there in the hospital. Ziereis described the murders, the unspeakable cruelty and sadism. Then he had the nerve to claim that it was not him who ordered it—he was just there as a spectator. He tried to convince us that he attempted to help the prisoners. Then we caught his son, but that will come later. If you still insist, I will read you the excerpts of the statement.

He took out a bunch of closely typed sheets and read it to them.

> By order of Reichsminister Himmler and SS General Dr. Kaltenbrunner, I was to kill all the inmates. All prisoners were to be moved into the Mine at Gusen. Only one entrance was to remain open, and the mine was to be blown up. I did not execute that order. The dynamiting was to be supervised by SS General Wolfram and Ackerman who worked in the Berg Kristall.
>
> By order of SS Capt. Kreisbach, a gas chamber was built in Mauthausen, in the shape of a bathhouse. In this chamber the inmates were gassed. Prisoners were also gassed in an automobile, which commuted between Gusen and Mauthausen. SS Lt. Wassicky placed this car at our disposal. I myself did not gas anyone in this car, but I have driven it.
>
> About the recent killings of 800 prisoners in Gusen, who were killed with axes, clubs, and by drowning, I know nothing, nor did I give any such orders.
>
> Jentsch ordered the following killings; the prisoners were bathed in cold water for three hours, then had to stand outdoors in 12 degrees below zero until they died. Of that, too, I knew nothing.

Kieswetter killed prisoners by injecting gasoline into
their feet at the heel, as well as with injections of 25 percent calcium and Epivan. Dr. Richter performed operations on prisoners, whether they were ill or not, causing
their deaths by removing small portions of their brains.
This involved about a thousand prisoners.

SS General Pohl sent me 6,000 women and children
without my knowing anything about it. These had been
en route for ten days, without any food. These women
were transported in open coal cars, without a roof, in
December 1943 in the severe cold. I had to transport
children to Bergen-Belsen upon orders, I believe that
they all died. I grew quite nervous after that. A transport
of 2,500 prisoners en route from Auschwitz to
Mauthausen was bathed in cold water on the parade
grounds. These prisoners were sent to Gusen, clothed
only in a shirt and drawers. I applied to Berlin for clothing and received the reply that none was available. The
Gauleiter of Oberdauon did not allocate any rations to
me for the newly arrived prisoners and even ordered me
to surrender 50 percent of the potatoes to the civilian
population of Oberdauon.

At Gross-Rosen, prisoners were killed by an SS doctor
who made injections into their hearts.
Commanders Seidler, Schmielewski, and Backmayer
have murdered tattooed prisoners, and had the tattoos cut
out and prepared. From these tattoos they had pictures
made, as well as gloves and slippers.

Jack said, "There's more, but I think we've had enough. I just have
to add that we caught Ziereis's son, and he gave us a statement, too.
You've got to hear this: 'On my fifteenth birthday, my father had forty
prisoners lined up in order to teach me how to shoot. As targets the
prisoners had to remain standing until I hit them, and they dropped
dead.' "

The girls were shaking. Dana asked, "Will you with your team find
all the men that Ziereis mentioned? All those names that he gave you!"

"He claimed that he doesn't know their present whereabouts," Jack
said. "But with some additional drilling. . ."

Dana was all fired up.

My old Dana, Alicia thought, that's her. Not that girl who just wants an easy and lazy life with a rich husband."

"Please, Jack," Dana said. "Maybe I can get a job as your secretary. I would make a perfect Nazi hunter."

She already calls him Jack, Alicia thought. She would sleep with him for a chance to interrogate those bastards.

Jack was unperturbed. "We hope to try them all as war criminals." He smiled at Dana. "Maybe we can use you as a witness."

Alicia exclaimed: "Trials, they don't deserve trials."

"The trials aren't for them—they're for us: to demonstrate the need for the rule of law. Besides, it's important to expose these horrors to the world."

Dana switched to German. "Your cousin here," she said to Jack, "almost found herself the subject of medical experiments last February."

Alicia was annoyed. "You're supposed to practice your English," she told Dana. Then, to Jack, she explained, "I had a swollen face from a tooth infection, and I looked and felt bad, so they put me on a list for Ravensbrück."

"How did you get out of that horrible predicament?"

"Oh, some of our girls worked in the office, they helped."

"When Alicia and I were in Auschwitz," Dana told Jack, "we found ourselves in an isolation block, because we had a skin rash. The next step could have been a hospital where they made experiments on human beings. It would have been much worse than going straight to the gas chambers."

Now I know, Alicia thought, why Dr. Brazen was so anxious to get me out of *Kratze* block. Poor Brazen. I wonder if he knew firsthand about those experiments? He's dead now—I shouldn't speculate about these things. Then she told Jack about Lucia and how worried she was when her friend was bedridden in Malchow.

"Now we've all had enough of horror," Dana said. "Let's go to town."

They went to a little restaurant and ordered smorgasbord. Food, food, food. It tasted so good. Why can't the world always be like this? Smorgasbord, friendly smiling faces, and a veritable hero treating them.

Jack told the girls about his older brother Kurt. He was recruited in 1943, but he was never sent overseas. He was stationed on an island in the Atlantic and worked as a radar technician.

"What's radar?"

Jack tried to explain it to them.

"We're so much behind the times," Alicia lamented. Then she changed the subject: "My grandfather didn't tell me much about his sons in the United States."

Jack said, "Your grandfather didn't talk about his youngest son Hillel, because he was very disappointed in him. Hillel didn't want to go to yeshiva or to a secular school, and he was growing up almost illiterate. So they sent him away to America."

Jack laughed. "Now Hillel is a waiter in a Jewish restaurant on the East Side of New York. He's married and has two sons. The older one is studying to be an accountant; he was classified as 4F because of stomach problems. The younger one is a GI like me and is someplace in France."

"I have so many cousins in the United States!" Alicia marveled. After a while she added, "I wish my father didn't want to go to school. Then he might have been a waiter in America on the East Side of New York. He would be alive today. He became a well-known physician in Poland, but he's dead."

"Well, you are alive, and there's a future for someone like you," Jack comforted her.

He thought for a moment. "You said that I had the support of the United States Army and Navy but, still, when I was fighting in Normandy beachhead last June, I could have been killed or severely wounded. I saw it happen to many of my buddies. But now when I sit here in a nice little restaurant enjoying good food and good company"—he bowed to the girls—"I thank God that I made it."

Alicia wanted to tell him that he also had a country, a mother, and a brother and who knows whom else. But then the miracle that she was alive struck her again. She put her arms around Jack and kissed him.

Jack was embarrassed. Alicia concluded that there was no electricity between him and her, and Dana was amused.

Alicia tried to divert everyone's attention from her outburst. "Tell me about my other uncle," she said to Jack.

Jack was only too glad to be back on solid ground. "He's an insurance salesman in Toronto. He also has two children, a boy and a girl more or less your age."

"Oh, yes," Alicia said, "now I remember. Grandfather gave me the pictures." Then she laughed. "Would you believe that when I was thirteen years old—it would have been 1935—I ran away from home with a girlfriend of mine. We wanted to board a ship and go to America, where I planned to look up my uncles. We made it as far as the port of Gdynia."

Now Dana was laughing. "Your cousin was always crazy," she said to Jack.

"I'll give you the addresses of your uncles, Jack said. "You should write to them. Don't be embarrassed to ask for help. Remember, they were in America while you were in concentration camps. When I get home, I'll contact them and we will try to get you to the United States."

"That would be wonderful," Alicia said. "As I understand, it is almost impossible to get to Palestine. My cousin Jas wrote me, and as he put it, the lousy British don't want to let the Jews in. They don't want to antagonize the Arabs. The irony of it is that the Jews fought by the side of the British while the Arabs were spying for the Germans."

"You have a good command of English. I'm sure you'll do well in the States."

"Maybe I can go to school there and get a meaningful job. Most importantly, I'll have a family.

He took out a large roll of bills, "In the meantime, it is my honor to help you. I have plenty of money."

Alicia tried to hold back the tears. "I don't know when I'll be able to pay you back."

"Don't worry about it. When we're settled in the good old U.S.A., we'll square up the accounts."

"Thank you so much, Jack. It is such a good feeling to know that there are people I can count on, even if they are far across the ocean."

"Nothing is far in this world anymore."

Jack told the girls that he was leaving the next morning and that he would continue his furlough by visiting Brussels and Paris.

"I hope you have a good time," Alicia said wistfully.

"It would be nice to take both of you along to enjoy the sights, but it's too difficult to have your papers processed."

"You did enough for us. So for now, say hello to Le Tour Eiffel and L'Arc de Triomphe from us." Then Alicia was almost ready to cry.

"I'll see you soon in New York," Jack said. They said good-bye at the gates of the camp.

Dana called after him, "Please Jack, catch the murderers."

"We'll try," he said, then waved to them his final good-bye.

Later on, when the girls were alone, Alicia felt sad. She was relieved to switch back to Polish: "I dreamed last night about an ocean voyage to the United States. My mother believed in dreams."

Dana shrugged her shoulders. "Too bad she didn't dream while we were in Lwow of what would happen to us under the German occupation and didn't tell my mother about it. We could all have let the Russians deport us to Siberia instead of going 'home.' "

The next day, the girls went into town for the last time, mainly to say good-bye to Mrs. Olson and to thank her for her kindness. The woman was crying. She tried to give them more clothes, and she kept on repeating how much she was going to miss them.

When they finally left, Dana remarked, "She needed us more than we needed her. We brought a little diversion to her routine. She probably has a very uneventful life."

"Well, we've had enough events in our short lives, Alicia replied. "We could use some monotony for a change."

"You'd soon get very tired of it. Spring and summer wouldn't be too bad. But the fall and winter! Can you imagine Mrs. Olson and other housewives like her during those short days and long nights?"

"They drink coffee, eat cake, and get fat."

Their brief stay in Doverstorp became another chapter of their past. They packed their few belongings and boarded the train that would take them to Lund. Both girls were much better off now than when they first arrived in Sweden. They had money, some clothes, and contact with their relatives. Dana was assured of a visa for the United States, and Alicia hoped to get one soon.

Something else happened that made them feel good about themselves. Like most of the ex-inmates of the concentration camps, they had resumed menstruating. Whatever had happened to them from

Auschwitz on evidently had not affected them permanently. After hearing the statement of the commandant of Mauthausen, they realized how lucky they were to be alive and healthy. They were getting used to traveling comfortably by rail; other trains, the nightmarish trains, seemed like part of a different life. They were out of context, not compatible with present realities.

When they arrived in Lund, Dana joined Molly, who was living with other Polish girls in the Danish School. Laura moved there also. The accommodations were primitive, but after labor and concentration camps, it was heaven.

Alicia, to her pleasant surprise, got letters from her uncles and from Jack's brother, Kurt. They were encouraging letters. They wrote that they are sure that they would be able to get an affidavit for her. Uncle Hillel sent her some money and promised to send more for her passage.

Alicia stayed with the Gustavsons, the Swedish couple. They had a spacious apartment with a tiny maid's room located near the nursery. Alicia even had her own radio. Her main responsibility was to take care of the baby, but she often had to help with the housework as well.

Mr. Gustavson was a professor of economics at the University of Lund. Mrs. Gustavson stayed at home. They were a handsome couple in their thirties; the baby had come to them late in life. Alicia communicated with the man in English and tried Swedish with the lady.

Once Professor Gustavson told Alicia that he could arrange for her to have her tattoo removed. She was amazed. The tattoo didn't bother her at all. "Why should I?" she said. "It's not my shame that it is there. If I had it removed, I would feel that I was absolving the people who put it there from guilt."

Mr. Gustavson asked her something else. he was so embarrassed that he stuttered. "My wife just had a baby. She has always led a sheltered life, and she's quite sensitive. I would appreciate it ,if you wouldn't mention your war experiences or the concentration camps."

Alicia thought: So that's why he wants me to have my tattoo removed! He's afraid it might upset his wife. She promised to be guarded in her speech.

Alicia visited Connie in the hospital. Her pain had subsided. She was sitting at a table, drawing other patients. "If I had paint, I would paint," she told Alicia.

Alicia admired her drawings and thought that Connie had talent.

"My social worker," Connie said, "has applied to a Jewish relief organization, asking for a scholarship for me to go to an art school in Stockholm."

"It would be wonderful if you got it," Alicia said. They never mentioned Tarnower.

Sid arrived. He was assigned to live with other refugees in the Danish School, in the men's section.

"Laura will wait until her wedding night," Dana predicted.

Sid had no problem getting a job right away. The Swedish economy depended heavily on technology. He was one of the few surviving men who was not emaciated and not sick. But he brought the usual horror stories from the camps; one was about Krakower, the hospital orderly in Bergen-Belsen. According to Sid, Krakower strangled patients with his own hands; then he let them lie there for a few days before reporting their death, so that he could collect their rations.

Alicia shuddered as she listened to this story. "But," she said to Sid, "Saul wrote to me that Krakower saved his life."

"Of course. He took care of his friends while getting rid of the others."

Alicia wondered why Sid disliked Krakower so much. After all, he didn't take Clara away from him. It was Sid who left Clara, and then Krakower moved in. Those things were hard to figure out. "Maybe what he did was mercy killing," she said. "He figured that some patients had suffered enough and didn't have a chance. By killing them and giving away their rations, he could save others."

Sid was getting mad. "Krakower decided that people he knew had more right to live than strangers!"

"I am sick and tired of Jews accusing other Jews!" Alicia cried. "As if we created the concentration camps!" Then she told Sid about Ziereis's statement.

Three mornings a week, Alicia took some courses in Swedish and science at the university. The rest of the time, she worked for the Gustavsons, with one day off during the week.

Often, in the evenings the young couple went to the movies or visiting. Alicia would put the baby to sleep, then she studied and ate whatever was available. Saturdays and Sundays, she took the baby to the park, and whenever she could, she studied. Her afternoon off was spent in the university gym, the swimming pool, or with her friends in the Danish School.

Her mail came to the Danish School. One day there was a letter from Lucia. Alicia opened it eagerly. Lucia was going to school, and she liked it. But the other news—Alicia didn't know whether to laugh or cry. Lucia had found Dr. Kaplan, but he was not available for her because he already had two wives. He had survived the war, thinking himself a widower. As he once told the girls, he saw with his own eyes his wife in that fatal line to the gas chambers at Auschwitz; her whole block was going. He told Lucia that he fell in love with her because she reminded him of his wife. After the liberation, he met another woman. He married her and got her pregnant.

Another one who got married in a hurry, Alicia thought. She kept on reading the letter. Dr. Kaplan's first wife was alive. Yes, she was in that line to the gas chamber, but just as it was her turn to enter, the rest of the line was turned back. There was no more room in the gas chamber, so she went back to her block. The day after, her group was sent to a different camp.

That poor woman, Alicia thought. She was literally at death's doorstep. She managed to survive the war. The idea of finding her husband was probably always on her mind, and this kept her going. After the liberation, she found him with another woman expecting his baby. Even if the Germans could not accomplish their goal of killing all European Jews, they certainly messed up the lives of the few who survived. Dr. Kaplan now tried legally to dissolve his first marriage. Then Lucia wrote that she already had a new boyfriend.

On one of her days off in July, Alicia visited Saul in the hospital in Malmö. He was now allowed out of his room. She pushed him in a wheelchair to a park on the hospital's grounds. He was allowed to stay outside for one hour. A lot of people were in the park, enjoying the sun: patients in wheelchairs, visitors, doctors, and nurses. It was a warm July day, but the heat was not oppressive, there was a gentle breeze from the sea. Alicia and Saul sat on a bench and talked. Saul told Alicia about one of the patients in his ward who was an Hasidic

Jew; he insisted on kosher food, but there was no kosher food available
in the hospital, and nobody knew how to prepare it.

"Did he eat kosher food in the German concentration camps?"
Alicia asked.

"You haven't heard the end of the story yet," Saul told her. "He
had a girlfriend he planned to marry when he got well. He wrote to an
Orthodox Jewish organization in England for help. Among other
things, they sent him a wig for the prospective bride to wear as a married woman. As I understand, the wig was very expensive."

Alicia was getting mad: "I don't have any respect for the very Orthodox to spend money on a wig when there's not enough for medication and care for all the sick! With all the ill and dying who came out
of the concentration camps, it's not just ridiculous, to me it's almost
criminal! I respect Jews like my cousin Jas and others in the Jewish
Brigade, who fought the Germans or my American cousin, Jack, who
was in the Normandy invasion. Dana was in the uprising in the Warsaw ghetto."

Saul had different ideas. "Look, Alicia, if not for the Orthodox
Jews, your cousin Jas wouldn't have a Jewish Brigade to join. There
just wouldn't be any Jews. The Orthodox are the ones who preserved
the Jewish identity as people of the Book and of the Law, through all
the centuries of the Diaspora. Now the Nazis are defeated, what was
supposed to be a thousand-year Reich lasted only twelve years. But a
Jewish woman will wear a wig after she gets married and go once a
month to a mikva, as has been done for thousands of years."

"Damn it," Alicia said, "I thought you were a Socialist." After a
while she added, "Jewish identity didn't do me any good. I could give
it to the Orthodox and let them eat their kosher food, and their women
have babies once a year. I wish the six important years of my life had
not been taken away from me."

For some reason Saul laughed. "Alicia," he said, "I don't know
why I don't worry about you. You'll get a visa to the United States and
then some sort of a scholarship."

Now Alicia was laughing, too. "I wish I was as sure of myself as
you seem to be."

"You remember, when I first met you, right after the deportations
to Treblinka? I was lying in traction with my broken leg."

Alicia thought, Rutkowski did a bum job setting his leg. Saul will probably limp the rest of his life. It's ironic that Saul is alive while Rutkowski, with all his wheeling and dealing, didn't make it. Unknown is the will of God, or "whatever gods may be."

"You girls in the little hospital were very good to me," Saul went on. "As a matter of fact, I didn't know which of you to fall in love with. It was Laura or Anne or you. Anne was too formidable for me. Besides, she seemed to have been in love with Benjamin, although I always suspected that he had an eye on Laura. To me, Laura appeared like an angel of mercy. She was so beautiful and kind and had such a way with all those sick boys. Nursing suited her, and everybody loved her. If only she hadn't turned out to be such a snob—first trying to keep company only with doctors and then, when they were gone, with policemen. You, Alicia, looked to me at that time like a helpless little lamb, left with a pack of wolves to be devoured."

"Do you remember when I was a cook? And what a cook I was!"

Saul laughed. "We all joked about it. We tried to help you and we ate the food, which somehow got cooked. But I found out that you were not so helpless at all."

The hour was coming to a close. Alicia looked at Saul. He seemed very tired, and he was so thin. That poor creature, she thought. They ruined his life, and he will never regain his health completely. She decided not to tell him Sid's story about Krakower. Krakower was Saul's friend, and she didn't want to destroy his image of the man. Why talk about it anyway? It should be left between Krakower and his God. "I've got to wheel you back, Saul. You've talked enough, and you must rest now."

"Even if talking exhausts me," by now he was whispering and he was hoarse, "still sitting here in the sun with you and reminiscing acts like a balm for my soul."

"I'll take you back to your ward. Try to take a nap, and remember no matter how unappetizing the food may look to you, try to eat." As she was walking away, she turned around and asked, "You never told me which one of us three you fell in love with?" He was already dozing off, and she didn't disturb him.

CHAPTER 18

1945   Sweden

After her visit with Saul, Alicia took the bus back to Lund and went to the Danish School. She considered the people there "her" people. She enjoyed translating letters that the girls got in English from America and managed to compose love letters in Swedish to those who already had Swedish boyfriends. Sonia was one of them, it did not take her long.

Alicia wished she was writing love letters for herself.

That day, even before Alicia entered the building, Laura met her in the yard waving a letter. "It's from my family in England. I'm sure they still remember how to write Polish, but they want to make themselves important so they wrote in English. Please translate it for me."

Alicia took the letter and tried to go sentence by sentence. As she proceeded, she stopped abruptly. "Let me read the whole thing. It will make it easier for me."

Oh God, what kind of uncles does Laura have? Alicia compared this letter with the ones she had received from her family in the United States and from Jas in Palestine. Those were kind, helpful letters, promising assistance and expressing thanks and wonder that she had survived.

The tone of the letter to Laura was downright nasty. The gist of it was that if the man Laura intended to marry was so capable that he already had a good job, then he should take care of her. They would not consider sending visas to England for both of them.

Alicia wondered how she was going to break this to Laura, who was so intent on having an extended family, uncles, aunts, and cousins as it was before the war. Do her uncles expect her to make a choice between Sid and London? Alicia tried to soften the contents of the letter, but Laura understood it quite well. She just sat there trying to absorb the news.

Alicia did not know what to say. To her Laura looked almost as bad as on the day when the Kielce doctors were taken to the cemetery.

Laura picked herself up. "I've got to make supper for Sid. He will soon be back from work. This is going to be my lot. I'm going to be a housewife in Sweden and die of boredom. Unless, of course, I kill myself first."

Alicia did not take it as a joke. She thought of Mrs. Olson, fat and bored. During the war years in the camps, Laura managed so much better than Alicia. Laura had good jobs, either as a nurse or a block chief, was always neat and well put together. She did not go hungry, while Alicia was often a wreck in threadbare clothes and on the verge of starvation. Now this stupid letter, Alicia thought, has thrown Laura into depression.

"Dana and you will go to the United States," Laura said. "You will go to school while I'll just cook and clean. Sid and I will be here among strangers. Everybody will be leaving for other countries. I thought we were going to be part of a large family in England."

Alicia said: "Come on Laura— family isn't so important. My grandmother didn't speak to her sister, because they'd had arguments over the inheritance from their father. Grandmother wasn't on good terms with her brother from Krakow, either. I hardly knew my father's family, because they didn't like my mother. My father and my uncle were not on speaking terms during the last couple of years before the war. They had arguments over Zabiec. It took the bombs in September of 1939 to force them to make up. In a life-and-death bind, they became friends again. I don't have to tell you about your 'extended family' in London. One person who loves you and you can depend on is worth more than many uncles, aunts, and cousins." After a while, she said, "One guy and a mother and father, of course."

"You're free," Laura insisted.

"Who knows what I'll be free for? You were a wonderful nurse, patients loved you. Why don't you consider a nursing career?"

Laura shrugged her shoulders. "I would have to qualify by Swedish standards. This would mean going back to school and taking millions of tests."

"So do it!" Alicia said.

"I have to cook and take care of Sid," Laura answered.

She's looking for excuses, Alicia thought. "Look at Lucia. She made herself a few years younger, and someone is sending her to school. Heart condition or not, she will become a doctor."

Sid came back from work with wonderful news. His company had offered him a better job starting in September in Stockholm. They would be sending him to school where he would have the opportunity to study for an engineering degree.

Alicia wondered if Laura was happy about the news. She seemed so at the moment, but now Alicia was sure that Laura would never try her wings; she would cook, clean and bear children—would that kind of life satisfy her? Who knew? But at least part of her dream would be fulfilled; she'd have a husband with a university degree.

Alicia decided to spend the night in the Danish School. Between Dana's, Molly's, and Laura's rooms they could always find a place for her to sleep. It was not very comfortable but who wanted to spend a night alone in a maid's room?

Another month passed, and it was August 1945. On August 7, shattering news exploded all over the world. An atomic bomb was dropped on Hiroshima. Alicia's science teacher spent an entire session lecturing about the relationship of mass to energy. He tried to explain to the class how the atomic bomb was constructed.

In the following days, Alicia pored over newspapers. The statistics were slowly coming in; 80,000 people were killed instantly. At ground zero, the epicenter of the blast, everybody and everything was vaporized. The temperature reached several thousand degrees Centigrade. Thousands and thousands of people were burned beyond recognition. Two thirds of the building in the city were completely destroyed. Fire storms were raging all over. Another bomb was released over Nagasaki three days later. Like one big crematorium, she thought, but without gas chambers.

One evening, the Gustavsons came home quite late from visiting with friends. Mr. Gustavson retired to the bedroom right away.

Mrs. Gustavson felt like talking; she had never before tried to confide in Alicia. Any conversations they had were either about the baby or whatever had to be done around the house. "I was disgusted," she said, "and so were the other ladies. We felt neglected and bored with all the talk about the atom bomb."

Alicia was sleepy, but that comment woke her up. Bored by the atom bomb? Appalled, horrified, maybe even impressed, since it was probably the greatest scientific achievement of the century. So many adjectives could be used, but certainly not "bored." A human race can destroy itself with a few devastating bombs, but this lady is bored.

Then Alicia thought about all the incinerated people and almost wished that someone like Mrs. Gustavson had been there. I'm a vindictive bitch, she thought. She's just a silly girl and all those things are beyond her comprehension. She didn't want to hear about concentration camps either. Alicia said, "Men have a nasty habit of wanting to know what's going on in the world."

Mrs. Gustavson said, "I've got to go to sleep, I hope my mother will come tomorrow to take care of the baby and then maybe I'll have a chance to get a manicure and get my hair done."

As usual Alicia spent her day off in the Danish School. Sid wanted to talk to her, he was excited. "Alicia," he said, "you must tell me everything you've learned in your course about the atom." He had some English and German newspapers.

They sat down, and Alicia told him what she knew: First the general theory, then the construction of the bomb, neutrons, the chain reaction, and the critical mass.

Sid caught the term "critical mass." "I read in a German paper," he said, "that they assembled the bomb in the plane just as they flew over Hiroshima, right before they dropped it."

"I bet you would have wanted to be on that plane." As soon as she said it, she realized how it sounded.

Sid didn't react to it as she thought he might. "It must have been very exciting to put the first atomic bomb together."

Oh, my God, Alicia thought. All he seems to be interested in is the scientific and technical aspect of the event. And then a thought occurred to her; the German doctors who used humans as guinea pigs probably felt the same way. What a disgusting comparison!

She groaned. Sid would work for anybody if he could just do his own thing. If the Germans put him to work in the place where they were launching the rockets on London, Sid would work as hard as ever. Maybe some of the rockets that were sent would have killed Laura's obnoxious uncles. Smiling, she said, "I bet if you had the necessary materials, you could make an atom bomb yourself."

Sid answered in a matter-of-fact way, "I would have to know much more about it.

Later on Alicia said to Dana, "Can you imagine all those people killed in Japan?"

"Why should I care?" Dana said. "From what the Americans say, if they didn't drop the two bombs, many more of their soldiers would have been killed. The Japanese are even more stubborn than the Germans. Why should we care about them? Who cared about us?"

"Are you trying to tell me that, because of what happened to us, we will never be able to feel for others?" Alicia demanded. After a moment she added, "Maybe if eighty thousand Germans were vaporized instantly, I would not feel sorry at all."

The next day was a work day for Alicia, first the school, then Gustavsons. In the evening, when the baby was asleep, she picked up her books and started studying.

Studying in Swedish was tedious. She continuously had to resort to a dictionary.

The baby was crying. Alicia changed him, hugged him a little and gave him water from his bottle. She put him back in the crib, sang to him, and he fell back to sleep.

When she returned to the living room, she noticed some fruit in a bowl. She picked up a pear, sat down, and started studying again. Her mood lifted, and it was easier for her to absorb the information. She finished the pear, and mechanically picked up an apple.

The Gustavsons came home, and Alicia retired to her room.

The next morning she took her final exams and thought she had done all right. In the afternoon she went to the Gustavsons. When she came in, Mrs. Gustavson told her that the professor wanted to speak to her in the living room. She always referred to her husband as the "professor."

What did I do? Alicia wondered.

The professor looked very stern and serious. "We decided to count the fruits before we put them out."

"You were babysitting last night, and a few pieces of fruit are missing."

Alicia had to swallow the urge to laugh, because the man looked so solemn and impressed with his own importance. "Occasionally," she admitted easily, "I eat a piece of fruit."

The man was embarrassed. "It's not the way things are done in Sweden. Fruits in the bowl are supposed to stay there."

"In my parents' house," she replied. "the fruits in the bowls were available for all the household members. Nobody ever counted them. When the bowls were empty, they just got refilled."

The professor was now flustered.

Alicia said, "I appreciate your letting me know that you and your wife count the fruits before you put them out."

Between the visits of the regular cleaning woman, Alicia had to vacuum the apartment. Mrs. Gustavson was worried that Alicia was vacuuming too close to the furniture. Once she accused her of scuffing the leg of the table.

Alicia thought about the apartment on Freedom Place, the beautiful credenza in the dining room, the curio cabinet, the mirrors in the salon, the golden curtains. Was my mother also afraid that the maid would scuff the furniture?

Mrs. Gustavson complained that Alicia was spoiling the baby. "Must you pick him up and carry him around everytime he cries? Then he will expect the same from me."

Alicia once said that there was so much misery in the world, at least a little infant should always be happy. She enjoyed cuddling, burping, and changing the little boy. Though he was only two months old, she felt that he recognized her, and he was already smiling. She remembered her brother as an infant. Maybe the Gustavsons will fire me, she thought. I eat too much, I damage their furniture, and I spoil their child. She needed the money she was getting from them; room and board were also important.

The Gustavsons hired another girl as a cook. Alicia and the new girl shared many household chores. Alicia suspected that Mrs.

Gustavson's parents were rich because the professor could not make too much money teaching.

Alicia liked the new girl; she was a simple peasant girl, not very well educated. They ate their meals together. When it came to running the household, the Gustavsons were frugal, nothing was ever wasted. When they had roast beef for supper, the following day they would eat it sliced cold, and the third day the leftovers were mixed with onions, potatoes, and eggs for hash. The two girls knew not to eat too much beef, because it was supposed to last three days. It almost reminded Alicia of getting a weekly ration of one small loaf of bread, which tasted like sawdust.

Food was no longer a problem. Besides eating at the Gustavsons, she ate with Dana and Molly in the Danish School. She was annoyed with them, because they would not accept money from her. She was comparing Dana, who had survived the ghetto and concentration camps, with the Gustavsons who lived in peace but counted the fruit in the bowls.

Alicia hoped that soon she would go to the United States, but at times she had serious doubts about her future. At almost twenty-four, she was penniless and without employable skills. The other girls were seamstresses, typists, while she was just a schoolgirl. Then she remembered that she had worked in her uncle's laboratory helping with urine analysis and looking at slides under a microscope. She had a good science background.

Maybe I'll be able to get a job in a hospital laboratory and go to school at night, she thought. Will the family help me? I hope I won't end up being a maid for people like the Gustavsons, who will watch how much I eat and will not want to look at my tattoo.

Eventually my own family. Husband? Children?

From Dana in New York to Alicia in Sweden:

New York, 25th November, 1945

Dear Alicia,

I miss you. That is why my letter is going to be long, and I hope you will not be bored by it. I can't wait to see you in the United States.

My Aunt Mildred and Uncle Harry treat me and Molly like their two long-lost daughters. I thought they were well off, but now I've come to the conclusion that they are very rich. My father was Mildred's brother and Molly's mother was her sister. There were only the three of them. My aunt met my uncle after the First World War in Poland. He'd had enough of Europe. and he didn't believe in the stability of the new Poland. He had family in New York, they were in banking and investments. My aunt was not happy about leaving Poland, but finally she decided to follow Harry to America. My uncle did well in the twenties. He was one of those rare people who withdrew his money and his client's money just before the crash of 1929. As my aunt still asks, "Was it luck or foresight?"

The depression didn't affect them, and they made a lot of money during the war. They have a big house with a lot of grounds, a beautiful garden, taken care by a professional gardener. A cleaning crew comes regularly to the house. All this just for the two of them. They never had children. They entertain often and have dogs. Now they have me and Molly. Each of us has a separate bedroom with a bathroom.

Aunt Mildred decided that first we must have proper clothes. So she drives us in her big Cadillac (my uncle has a Lincoln Continental) to Manhattan. She parks it in a garage, and we take taxis to wherever we have to go. No subways or buses for yours truly. I heard that New York subways are gloomy. Who wants a gloomy ride? Do you remember the cattle trains with the smell of urine and feces that transported us from one concentration camp to another? Women were ready to kill each other for just a little space; one actually did commit murder. Now the same two girls who traveled in those cars are shopping in Saks Fifth Avenue, Bergdorf Goodman, and Lord and Taylor, where the Rockefellers and Vanderbilts shop.

I have a problem with getting excited about new clothes, but Molly is in paradise. She always loved to dress up. Even in Malchow she was able to scrounge the best that was available. Ha. ha, ha. How does that warehouse in Malchow, with clothes left from murdered people, compare to Lord and Taylor?

Molly is going wild trying on all kinds of outfits, and Aunt Mildred keeps on telling us not to look at the prices. We should just take whatever we like. After a few trips to the stores, Molly now looks like she stepped out of the cover of a fashion magazine, and I don't look so bad myself.

We often go to the theater. That part of being a pampered daughter of rich people I like more than shopping. We usually see musicals. Mildred and Molly agree that we should only see light and happy shows. I would like to see a drama occasionally.

One day we were walking down Broadway loaded with packages. We were planning to get to the garage, where the Cadillac was parked, so we could leave the packages and go for lunch. But whom should we meet walking down the street, but Fela (you remember her), one of the Radom girls. She was walking with an elderly lady (the woman looked much older than our Mildred). Fela was ecstatic to see Molly, and she couldn't get over how beautiful she looked. She said she almost didn't recognize her. They kissed and hugged each other. I got a much cooler reception. After all, I never really belonged to the Radom group, and though I never was in Kielce somehow I was associated with Kielce people. Everybody spoke Yiddish; it seems to be a universal language. Fela looked at the names on our shopping bags and was very much impressed by all the fancy and exclusive Fifth Avenue stores. Their packages were from bargain shops on Union Square. Women who know how to shop can find a good copy of an original design for less than half price.

Mildred asked them to walk with us to the garage to drop off our packages. She then invited us all out to lunch. We were near Rockefeller Center, so we decided to go to the restaurant that faces the skating rink. The restaurant is below street level. We took the elevator down, and it seemed like we were in a fairyland. We admired the skaters in their colorful outfits. The flags of many nations are displayed around the square. Aunt Mildred told us that soon a Christmas tree would be put up there, and that is a wonder of wonders. The food was just marvelous.

Remember how we used to eat in Sweden, as if we couldn't believe our good fortune. We ate fast, so that no one could take it away from us. Lately, I've been trying to eat like a lady. I pick up small morsels and chew them slowly. I guess it's time to take food, shelter, and many good things in life for granted; once I considered it my birthright.

Uncle Harry suggested that Molly and I have skin grafts done over our tattoos. I'm thinking about it. The past just doesn't fit in the present. If I chose to remember it, it should be my prerogative instead of being exposed to ignorant questions.

Beautiful clothes, fancy restaurants—after all, I told you once that's all I would want from life. The six years we spent in an insane and upside down world were like being in a deep hole. I am out of it now, but gravity sometimes still pulls me in. This sounds like your kind of philosophizing, Alicia.

Mildred belongs to many Jewish women's organizations. She wanted me to talk to them about my experiences. I tried once, but I will never do it again. All they seem to be interested is how many times I was raped. They also kept asking about my tattoo.

How could I tell them about Olek being shot right at my side or about my parents boarding the trains to Treblinka, the stench and filth of the Warsaw sewers, and how I hid in the forest like a half starved and hunted animal. Would they understand how it felt to smell burning flesh and watch the smoke from the crematoria of Auschwitz?

Aunt Mildred keeps us busy all the time. We went to the Statue of Liberty, to the Empire State building, the

Bronx Zoo, and many museums. You would enjoy the
Museum of Natural History. We looked at the
dinosaurs. They ruled the earth and then they disappeared like the Jews of Europe. Was there a Hitler for
the dinosaurs? We also went to the Hayden
Planetarium and looked at the stars. I thought about
you as I looked for your distant galaxy, light years
away, where God was during the war.

But all in all I think I will love America. We are not
only going out with Aunt Mildred; sometimes we sit with
uncle Harry and listen to the radio. I understand enough
English to appreciate comedy shows, and they are funny:
Jack Benny, Fred Allen, Fibber McGee and Molly, Bob
Hope, and Eddie Cantor. We listen to Bing Crosby, Al
Jolson, and the Andrews sisters, to name just a few. It
still amazes me from how many different ethnic back-
grounds these people come from. They are Jews, Italians,
Irish, and Anglo-Saxons, and nobody asks them how
they pray to their God. They all achieved fame and fortune, and are protected by the American Constitution and
the Bill of Rights. They have unalienable rights to "life,
liberty and the pursuit of happiness" and these truths are
"self-evident." People here take it for granted, but that
realization brings tears to my eyes. Why couldn't my
parents and your parents? Why did they have to stay in
Poland?

Aunt Mildred sometimes reproaches herself that she
wasn't more aggressive in the thirties trying to bring her
family over. I tried to convince her that they were just too
comfortable in Poland, and they wouldn't have come.
Nobody could envision wholesale murder of innocent
people.

The Jews here are very much concerned about what is
going on in Palestine. The British are turning away ships
carrying people who survived the concentration camps
and now are trying to go to their Homeland. How I
would like to be there and help to smuggle in Jews from
displaced persons camps. I would join Haganah [the underground army] or Irgun or even the Stern Gang. Can

you imagine me blowing up railroads that serve the British Army? I certainly have enough hate accumulated in me to join one of the more extreme groups.

But right now, I am enjoying myself in America, and it helps to have a rich aunt and uncle.

Love Dana

In January 1946, Alicia got another long letter from Dana:

Though Aunt Mildred thinks that we should just be enjoying ourselves for at least one year, neither I nor Molly can see it that way. Molly is working part time in one of my uncle's offices. She knows how to type. She also goes to a business school where she is learning secretarial skills. You remember how resourceful she always was. I give her a couple of years, and then she'll be managing all my uncle's affairs—unless she marries a millionaire along the way. As she puts it, she will not take any ordinary jerk.

You will ask yourself what Dana is doing besides learning how to dress and to behave like a lady. I'm taking a course in photography. I always liked to fool around with cameras. I am also auditing some courses at Columbia, and I hope to become, first a nonmatriculated student and then eventually matriculate for a degree. I will take languages: English, French, and German. But my main interest is Semitic languages: Hebrew and Arabic.

Believe it or not, on occasions I am gainfully employed. I am assistant to a photographer. We go to Bar Mitzvot, weddings, birthdays, and anniversaries. I have contacts with the rich and powerful. Sometimes I feel that I came from another planet, though before the war I was used to their kind of life. But the Dana, wandering through the sewers of Warsaw, is still with me. I met two families who lost sons, one in the battlefields of Normandy and one in the Pacific. Many people made money during the war, but on the other hand, I can imagine all the mothers, sisters, wives, and sweethearts spending sleepless nights worrying about their men and getting terrible telegrams in the morning. But, unlike in Europe and Asia, American cities were never bombed, and I don't have to write to you about what else happened in Europe. Maybe that's why I can't identify with these people. Molly doesn't have this problem. She fits right in.

At one of the Bar Mitzvot, I met a young man, who asked me for a date. He seems like a very nice guy. He's a lawyer. We had dinner a few times, we went to a couple of shows and concerts. I think he is serious about me. Although he is a veteran, he was never overseas. Do you ever think that people who didn't go through what we've been through will always be strangers to us? Restaurants, concerts, movies, theaters. What a life! In the back of my mind I have the feeling that I don't deserve this, as though I hadn't paid dear enough for my survival. See you soon in the old U.S.A.

As always, I love you
Dana

The next letter from Dana came in early May, right after Passover.

Dear Alicia,

My uncle took a couple of weeks off for the holidays and we all drove up to the Catskill Mountains. It's a resort area about two hundred miles north of the city. I would love to have you with me on that ride. Upstate New York is a beautiful country of mountains, forests, lakes, imposing bridges, and golf courses. My uncle's car is very spacious and drives smoothly. It felt like sailing over a calm sea, no bumps or shakes. When we got out of the car after a two-hour ride, we didn't have to stretch. I again thought about that ghastly ride from Auschwitz to Ravensbrück, when we almost lost the feeling in our arms and legs. When I mentioned it to Molly, she shrugged her shoulders and said, "This should give us more reason to enjoy ourselves now."

How right she is. The world is gorgeous. I thought

about our train ride through Denmark and Sweden, and about the trips and cruises I took with my parents before the war. It almost felt the same in my uncle's car but "almost" is the word. The pull of the past is still with me.

Naturally, we are staying in the biggest and one of the most famous of all hotels. The owners are Jews as are most of the guests. It's like a city within a city. Everything here is designed for the enjoyment and entertainment of the guests. You would love it. A lake and a pool are available for swimming; there is boating and fishing. A golfer has a few championship courses to choose from, and there are many tennis courts. People can skate all year around in an indoor skating rink. At night there is dancing until dawn to the music of various bands, along with live entertainment. Many famous comedians and singers perform. The jokes are quite crude, mainly ethnic or dirty sex. It's called the Borsht Circuit. I understand that many successful show people started here. Everything is done to make the guests feel that they deserve the best, and the food is out of this world. I never knew that kosher food could taste so good.

How does this compare to the times when everything was done to make us feel like subhuman, dirty, and filthy freaks? The band with the yellow star, a different colored sleeve sewn to a coat, tattooed, hungry, desperately trying to keep clean, being afraid of getting sick, and deathly frightened that our turn for the gas chamber would soon come. Molly doesn't seem to remember anything. She just enjoys herself. But I, like you, ask myself the question; How come I'm at this beautiful place, while all those other millions. . . ?

People here are not like you and me. You had to be "tapped" by Thomas to be alive now, while they always had unalienable rights. My Uncle Harry must have guessed some of my thoughts. He told me that, though it seems that these people are playing all the time, most of them work very hard during the year. When they have a few days off, they enjoy themselves. He himself is semi-

retired and spends most of his time on the golf course.
It's hard for me to understand how a smart man who is so
shrewd in business can be nuts about a stupid game. It is
the main topic of his conversation. It isn't even a source
of satisfaction for him, because most of the time he is
frustrated and unhappy with his score. "If only I
wouldn't hit the ball in the bunker on the sixteenth hole
or under the tree on the eighteenth hole," he keeps
repeating. "The lousy ball took a bad bounce, and by the
time I got to the green, I was so aggravated that I missed
a short putt."

My aunt says that women should take more interest in
the game, otherwise they could find themselves "golf
widows."

Molly and I, besides taking tennis instructions, also
take golf lessons. According to my aunt it takes years and
years to develop a proper swing. My aunt is the original
founder of the women's golf team at her country club.
She tells me that men make fun of the girls, but then she
assures me that women outscore men and are much more
accurate around the greens. So hurrah for the girls. You
would approve of my aunt.

After a few lessons, my aunt took me and Molly to
play on the golf course. At the beginning it was exciting,
but then I felt silly. I kept asking myself, What am I
doing here chasing the idiotic ball? I still have trouble in
believing in permanency and security in my life. There is
today but what about tomorrow? The gas chambers have
been gone for a long time, but they are too deeply
entrenched in my consciousness, and the fears are still
here. Neither my loving and rich aunt and uncle nor the
American Constitution and the Bill of Rights can give me
back my sense of security.

Life goes on, and I am back in New York photograph-
ing happy people. Slowly I will become an American.
My Uncle Harry explained to me all about baseball. I listen to the radio and can follow it play by play.

One afternoon, Matt took me to Yankee Stadium to
watch a game between the Yankees and the Red Sox.

You really would have enjoyed it. People scream, jump, and boo, they root for the home team and curse the visitors. Their enthusiasm is catching. We ate a lot of what my Uncle Harry calls, *hazerei,* which means hot dogs with mustard and sauerkraut, and drank miserable sodas. But out there, it tasted good. I told Matt that this would be Alicia's kind of fun.

Enough senseless babbling. Write back soon.

Love
Dana

In the middle of August 1946, Alicia in Sweden received another letter from Dana.

New York, 8/15/46

Dear Alicia,

Call me crazy, but lately I am becoming more and more depressed. I thought I was going to make my life here in the United States. It is a great country. People come here with nothing, and if they are lucky and work hard, they become prosperous. There is no rigid class system as in Europe. Young people have the opportunity to be better off than their parents.

And of course there is freedom. It is ideal for Molly but not for me.

Do you remember that morning in Mrs. Olson's kitchen when we drank coffee and ate cake, and the day we saw our first movie? It felt good just to be alive; it was exciting to get a toothbrush, and when we went swimming we were in heaven.

These feelings lasted for a while in America. A visit to a beauty parlor was an event, I loved having someone fussing over me; washing my hair, cutting it and setting it, and getting a manicure. Now everything leaves me cold. It is hard to go through a daily routine unless you can enjoy small everyday pleasures. They probably mean more than bigger events like going to a play or a fancy restaurant.

When Molly hits a golf ball well, she is almost as enthusiastic as Uncle Harry.

Molly and I both passed our driving tests. She was in seventh heaven, and I just thought it would be useful for me to know how to drive. When Molly gets a new dress, she stands in front of the mirror admiring herself. In the morning she makes sure that everything in her outfit matches, and that her hair is done just right. She puts on her makeup with painstaking care. I just go through the motions.

I feel better when I'm working. It is fun to be taking and developing pictures. But even then, in the middle of the day I ask myself, "What am I doing here? Is this for real? Is this going to be my life?"

When I take photographs, I joke and laugh with the people. Though the war affected them in one way or another, I can't expect them to understand what I went through. I pretend to be like them, but it is just an act.

I went with Matt to the Metropolitan Museum of Art. I enjoyed it for a while but there always seems to be something in the back of my mind that interferes with the present. It is like an unresolved problem. Sometimes I believe that I can't go on until I solve it.

That day in the museum, if it was the old Dana standing in front of the masterpieces, she would have appreciated them. Sometimes I think that getting married and having kids would restore me to emotional health. Our common heroine from *War and Peace*, Natasha Rostow, solved her restlessness that way. I know that wouldn't do for me.

It wouldn't be fair to Matt for me to say yes if he proposed to me. Once I thought that I could grow to love him. I like him very much. But I can't imagine myself as a suburban housewife, a house, a station wagon, a couple of kids, driving kids to school, belonging to a parent-teacher organization, playing golf, bridge, just a good middle-class life that I once dreamed of. You were right not believing me when I used to tell you that is all I would want if I survived the war.

As I wrote to you before, I am taking pictures for Bar Mitzvot, weddings, and engagement parties. People here try to show off their wealth and prominence, and some of these affairs are quite extravagant. I guess it has always been this way even when many millions were dying.

I really don't resent these people; even primitive tribes have "rites of passage." But I can't stop thinking about all the Jewish boys in Europe who didn't live long enough to have a Bar Mitzvah. Here, girls who reach thirteen have a coming of age party. It is called Bat Mitzvah—it was unheard of in Europe.

Aunt Mildred suggested that I should find some support group, people who have had experiences similar to mine. There must be plenty in New York. Or I could volunteer in the Veterans' hospital and help disabled men; I understand there are many paraplegics and chronically ill because of the war.

I'm busy enough with my job and going to school, and I don't have either the time or patience for the other activities; they would be good for you or Laura. At this time of my life, I need something more active and immediate. Something that would not leave me much time for brooding.

My aunt and uncle keep asking why I can't be more like Molly and enjoy myself in America. I told them that I simply don't care for what people here do and talk about: furniture, clothes, entertainment, sports, and their ability at the bridge table.

It seems people are always busy with their own pursuits; they rush, and most of the time they don't know why or where.

In Warsaw people sat in cafés and, on one cup of coffee, they discussed politics, philosophy, and literature. It went on for hours. Even in the Warsaw ghetto there were cafés.

In the cafeterias in New York, you have to leave as soon as you finish eating. People don't eat; they just grab food, and then they run. No wonder so many have ulcers.

Entertainment and enjoyment is usually scheduled and organized, and the spontaneity is lacking. Everyone is competing with everyone else: Who can accumulate more money in the shortest possible time? Women never have enough clothes for themselves and their children. I wonder where they put all the junk that they accumulate.

Uncle Harry says that all this shopping brings prosperity to the country and that America is a consumer society.

On a golf course, women who are there supposedly to enjoy themselves don't stop for lunch after nine holes; they grab something fast to eat so they don't lose their turn. The game becomes another high pressure job.

If I am going to press so hard, it will not be to hit a ball well or to show off a beautiful dress. Molly likes that kind of life. She told me that at her work there are many girls who are recent immigrants. But, unlike us, they arrived in America with their families before the war. They are mostly German Jews, and one came here from Switzerland. It gives Molly great satisfaction to be in charge of them, she who came here last. She is thinking about getting a law degree. That's Molly; as I told you once; she will float to the top.

Mildred told me that I shouldn't think of Americans that way. There are many tragedies in ordinary lives; sickness, death, disappointment, failure, broken marriages, loneliness after the children leave. And the war: she understands that the American people were not affected by it as deeply as Europeans, especially the Jews, still thousands of young American boys lost their lives or were maimed for life fighting for the freedom of the world. She told me that I am not alone. Many young people returning to civilian life have a hard time adjusting. I had to agree with her, but what she doesn't understand is that I am not ready for everyday life in a "normal" world. I didn't do enough fighting. Outside of the short stint in the hopeless uprising in the Warsaw Ghetto I, like most of us, was waiting for my turn in the gas chamber or a miracle. I have to prove to myself that the Big God or yours "whatever gods may be" intended for me to survive the war for a purpose.

We the survivors have a restlessness in us. Remember how despondent Laura became when she gave up her dreams of London and settled down with Sid in Sweden. My darling Molly is already Americanized. She will have a skin graft put over her tattoo. It doesn't fit in with her life-style. She has a drive to become a success, both in business and socially. I have to make my own decision and find a way that suits me.

> As always. I love you,
> Dana.

Two weeks later Alicia received another letter from Dana. This time the tone was ecstatic. She wrote that she met a group of young people who are planning to enter Eretz Israel illegally and join Haganah (the underground Jewish army in Palestine).

It didn't take me long to make up my mind to join them. I know I will not be bored. I am going to be with people who feel the way I do. As soon as I made this decision, I felt better. The uneventful, everyday life that we dreamed of is just not for me. My dream is to work for the Intelligence, to be a spy, putting it bluntly. Can you imagine me trying to find out what the British or the Arabs are planning?

It is hard for me to say good-bye to Aunt Mildred. She tried so hard to make me happy and to feel at home. Sorry, Aunt Millie, but the American dream is just not for me. If I remain here, I'll become depressed, slow and lethargic. I have a lot of fighting to do, maybe I'll be back after a few years. You have Molly, I am sure you will have *naches* from her. I have to do what I know is right for me.

I am ready to say goodbye to everybody. To Harry: May all your drives be long and straight. Your fairway shots sail over sand traps and water hazards, may you chip right to the pin and one putt every green.

To Matt: You are a wonderful guy. I will never forget
you, especially for all the fun we had together. But I am
the wrong girl for you. Right now, I'm wrong for any
man. I have to get rid of my rage before I can settle down
to a normal life.

Good-bye to you Molly. Take it easy, slow down a little. I am sure you'll get there.

And finally, to you, Alicia: I love you. You are the
only one who understands me, and you will hear from me
as soon as I know where I am.

Dana

When she was later settled in the United States, Alicia received a
letter from Basia.

Kosice, 30/9/46

Dear Alicia,

I want you to know what has happened to me since we
were in contact in Auschwitz two years ago. Too bad we
didn't see each other; just to look at your face would
have reminded me of the years when we were both growing up. It seems as if it was in a different lifetime with
dreams and expectations. Then Lwow—you, I, and
Dana, it was still a city of lights in 1939, almost like
Paris.

It would be in vain to repeat that we all had a chance to
go to the depths of Russia. Today, our families would
probably be alive. Now, those people from Poland who
spent the war years in Russia, are trying to work themselves back to Poland. From there, they might emigrate to
America or Palestine.

I'd like to mention to you that after you left Lwow, I
saw your cousin Jerry very often. He was so shy, helpless
and lost without his mother. I tried to help him as much
as I could.

People attempted to maneuver themselves from the
deportation to Russia. Jerry did too, but he was such a
nebech that he was one of the first to be put on a train.

We didn't know then that we were best off as far away from the Germans as possible. As I learned later, after a few months in Russia, Jerry had no fight left in him. Hunger and disease got him.

You heard about the evacuation of Auschwitz and the death march in January 1945. Those who survived boarded trains. I don't have to describe to you that journey. We arrived at a womens' camp east of Berlin, not unlike Malchow. We were liberated in April by the Russians. Only then did I realize what I had lost. I had nobody to look for, my parents had no relatives abroad. My entire family had remained in Poland and were murdered. I was twenty-two with no training and no way to make a living. I got my Matura in 1941 in Lwow, but that and sorting clothes in Auschwitz did not train me for a job in the postwar world. I was among strangers. There were no Kielce people, not even Polish people in my group.

In Auschwitz I became friendly with some Slovakian girls, and I learned their language. Not having any better place to go, I followed those girls to Czechoslovakia.

Most of them had somebody. A few had relatives who had survived on Aryan papers. Others had Gentile friends, and some even had Gentile relatives willing to help. I stayed with some nice people, but they were still strangers. I felt so alone that I contemplated suicide.

Then I met my present husband, and my outlook on life changed. He is twelve years older than I, he finished medical school before the war. Ian was in Auschwitz for a few months just before the liberation. His parents managed to survive in hiding. They are quite rich. I feel that I can always rely on him, he's very considerate, and I am safe and secure with him.

I am happy that things worked well for you also.

Love
Basia

Alicia put the letter down, she could not imagine Basia contemplating suicide. Laura maybe, but not Basia. The beautiful, vibrant
girl, adventurous, ready to take chances. All the boys were in love with
her. Now she settled for a man twelve years older than she, on whom
she could rely. Not a word about passion and love. Did Auschwitz do
this to her?

In October, Alicia got a letter from Jas. He had information about
their Krakow and Lublin family: Frania, her two sisters, and brother
survived in Russia and were now in Poland. The older folks, Aunt
Luba, Aunt Yentl, and Luba's husband remained in Lublin and were
murdered in the extermination camp Majdanek. "Cousin Beryl you
remember," Jas wrote. "He was always claiming to be a Communist.
Being in Russia cured him of that disease. He died from typhus. His
wife, Zlata, came to Germany after the war, she had to have both her
legs amputated. They became frozen in Siberia, and gangrene set in.
She committed suicide."

Alicia threw the letter on the table, put her head in her arms and
sighed. She thought about Beryl and how proud Aunt Sura was when
he finished medical school in Italy. Beryl and Zlata, once such a young
and happy couple.

She picked up the letter again. "Grandfather Mark and his wife
died fighting in a bunker in Krakow. Just like our grandfather fighting
to the end."

Jas must be proud of his childhood idol, Alicia thought,

> Wladek and Eda were in Palestine for a short time. He
> arrived through Iran, where he was stationed with Polish
> units. Eda somehow managed to get to Palestine illegally.
> Eda wanted to remain, but Wladek was determined to go
> back to Poland. She joined him reluctantly. He still con-
> siders Poland as his fatherland, *ojczyzna*—my foot.
> More disturbing news: Did you hear about a pogrom in
> Kielce? The pitiful remnant of Kielce Jews, maybe 250,
> came back to claim their prewar property. Some of their
> Gentile ex-neighbors kept on asking them, "How come
> they did not burn you with the others?"
> On July 4, rumors were circulated about the ritual mur-

der of a Christian child. An enraged mob started killing the Jews and rampaging their property. I'm sure there was an economic reason behind the fanatic religious riots. As I was told by a witness, who managed to escape with his life and come to Palestine, the Polish militia and the army just stood there and watched. The rioters did not have guns; they used knives, clubs, axes, hatchets, and so on. Your friend Genia's husband was hidden and saved by a Polish woman. Luckily, Genia was away from Kielce that day. I know that the two of them are planning to come to Palestine. Their relatives in Tel Aviv were frantic, but then very much relieved, on hearing that Juda and Genia were not hurt. So maybe there are still some decent Poles.

I learned some statistics from the papers. Thirty-six people were killed and forty-four were wounded. Out of the forty-four, six died later. Ester Rutkowski, the medic's wife, was one of those killed. Twelve persons were arrested for inciting to riot and for the murders of helpless, unarmed people. Let's hope that they will be punished, but I have my doubts. Perhaps I will have better news in my next letter.

Love,
Jas

Alicia was almost ready to throw the letter away, or at least hide it some place, never to look at it again. She had enough.

She could not get out of her mind all the people who survived Siberia and concentration camps in Germany, but were murdered after the war in Kielce. She thought about Ester Rutkowska, who, after Auschwitz, Ravensbrück, and Malchow, was clubbed to death by hooligans in her own home town.

I can't live forever in a world of "Light Years from God," she decided. I have a life to make for myself in the United States, a job, a school, a man on the horizon.

A few months later Alicia received a letter from Lucia.

Do you still intend to write a book? I would like you to know the story that Dr. Brazen told me in Auschwitz. It is mainly about your uncle, Dr. Peltz. When Dr. Brazen came to Auschwitz in 1942, he was incarcerated in the same block that Dr. Peltz was a year before. The block chief, Herschel, was a man from Kielce. He was sent to Auschwitz early in the occupation, not as a Jew but as a criminal. Before the war Herschel had a reputation as a thief, knifer, and extortionist.

When he was Dr. Brazen's patient, the doctor charged him ridiculously little. He simply was afraid to antagonize the man.

In the middle 1930, Herschel applied to the city council for a permit to own and drive a horse-cab. Dr. Peltz, the only Jew on the council, refused to be intimidated by Herschel, his fellow Jew. He managed to persuade the others not to grant the permit.

In Auschwitz, Herschel was known as a brutal and cruel block chief. Imagine his glee when Dr. Peltz became an inmate of "his block." He made Peltz' life unbearable.

Dr. Peltz could get out from the horrible situation by trying to work with Dr, Mengele. He chose suicide. My father was in a different block. He also killed himself.

Herschel was kind and protective toward Dr. Brazen. He remembered how nice the doctor was to him before the war. Good old Brazen, always the diplomat! Remember how he helped us to survive Auschwitz? Poor guy, he was murdered by a German guard when he collapsed during the march from Auschwitz in January 1945.

Enough of these stories. They seem so unbelievable now! I am very busy in school. Hope to see you sometimes in the future.

Lucia

Mengele, "Angel of Death," Alicia thought. Working with Dr. Mengele? Doing what? No wonder my uncle, and Lucia's father, committed suicide. And Dr. Brazen? What made his living and working in Auschwitz possible for three years?

I should try to write a book, Alicia decided. Part of it would be a tribute to my uncle, that proud man with high principles. But how can I fit writing a book into the hectic routine of my everyday life? Then she heard a voice from a long time ago: "Keep on plugging, Alicia."

Pawel, you again! And Anne: "You can do it!"

In 1948, Alicia heard from Dana: "I am a member of a victorious army. Finally, I am able to laugh and to dance. We have our own country, Israel. I fought for it, and it wasn't hopeless and futile as in the Warsaw ghetto. We Jews did it all by ourselves, the British just left, hoping that the Arabs would finish the job that the Germans set out to do. Now any Jew can come home to Israel."

The Family
1850 - present

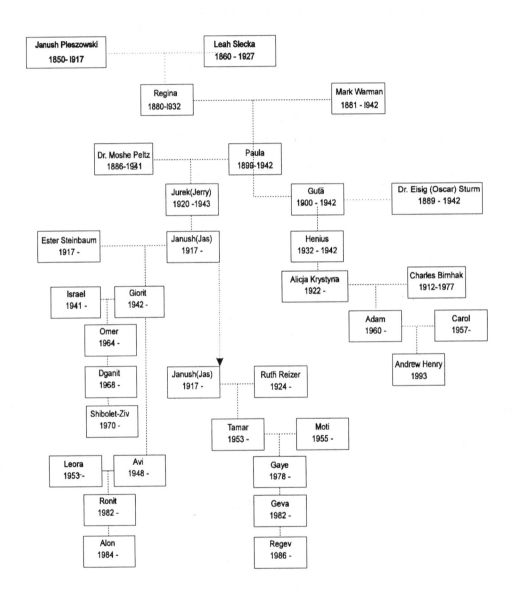

Antimicrobial Susceptibility Testing Protocols

Antimicrobial Susceptibility Testing Protocols

Edited by
Richard Schwalbe
Lynn Steele-Moore
Avery C. Goodwin

CRC Press
Taylor & Francis Group
Boca Raton   London   New York

CRC Press is an imprint of the
Taylor & Francis Group, an **informa** business

Employees of the Department of Health and Human Services who have contributed to the work are not representing the views and opinions of the U.S. government.

CRC Press
Taylor & Francis Group
6000 Broken Sound Parkway NW, Suite 300
Boca Raton, FL 33487-2742

© 2007 by Taylor & Francis Group, LLC
CRC Press is an imprint of Taylor & Francis Group, an Informa business

No claim to original U.S. Government works
Printed in the United States of America on acid-free paper
10 9 8 7 6 5 4 3 2 1

International Standard Book Number-13: 978-0-8247-4100-6 (Hardcover)

Library of Congress Cataloging-in-Publication Data

Antimicrobial susceptibility testing protocols / editors, Richard Schwalbe, Lynn Steele-Moore, and
    Avery C. Goodwin.
      p. ; cm.
    Includes bibliographical references and index.
    ISBN-13: 978-0-8247-4100-6 (alk. paper)
    ISBN-10: 0-8247-4100-5 (alk. paper)
    1. Microbial sensitivity tests. 2. Drug resistance in microorganisms. I. Schwalbe, Richard. II.
Steele-Moore, Lynn. III. Goodwin, Avery C.
    [DNLM: 1. Microbial Sensitivity Tests--methods. 2. Microbial Sensitivity Tests--standards.
3. Anti-Bacterial Agents. 4. Antifungal Agents. 5. Drug Resistance, Fungal. 6. Drug Resistance,
Microbial. QW 25.5.M6 A631 2007]

QR69.A57A63 2007
616.9'041--dc22   2007005182

Visit the Taylor & Francis Web site at
http://www.taylorandfrancis.com

and the CRC Press Web site at
http://www.crcpress.com

Dedication

*This book is dedicated to Dr. Richard Steven Schwalbe,
who passed away September 1, 1998, before our textbook was completed.
All of the contributors to* Antimicrobial Susceptibility Testing Protocols
*respectfully and lovingly present our work as a token of our admiration
to Rick and in the hope that through our efforts we may carry on his
passion and love of susceptibility testing and microbiology.*
l'chaim *my friend . . . I miss you.*

Preface

Recent reports in the lay press describing bacterial resistance to multiple antibiotics serve to emphasize the importance of accurate susceptibility testing. The clinical microbiology laboratory is often a sentinel for detection of drug-resistant microorganisms. Timely notification of susceptibility results to clinicians can result in initiation or alteration of antimicrobial chemotherapy and thus improve patient care. Standardized protocols require continual scrutiny to detect emerging phenotypic resistance patterns.

The aim of *Susceptibility Testing Protocols* is twofold: one is to present a comprehensive, up-to-date procedural manual that can be used by a wide variety of laboratory workers. The second objective is to delineate the role of the clinical microbiology laboratory in integrated patient care. Many protocols that are presented are an extrapolation of procedures approved by the Clinical and Laboratory Standards Institute (CLSI). New procedures that are (at present) nonstandardized are also described.

The first section of this manual addresses the basic susceptibility disciplines that are already in place in many clinical microbiology laboratories. These include disk diffusion, macro- and microbroth dilution, agar dilution, and the gradient method. Step-by-step protocols are provided. Emphasis is placed on optimizing procedures for detection of resistant microorganisms. A chapter is devoted to automated susceptibility testing, introducing the systems that are currently available for purchase, including recent laboratory evaluations, and presents an algorithm that can be followed by laboratory workers who are considering purchasing a new automated system.

The second section is devoted to descriptions of susceptibility protocols that may be performed by a subset of laboratories, whether as reference centers or as part of a research protocol. Specialized protocols such as surveillance procedures for detection of antibiotic-resistant bacteria, serum bactericidal assays, time-kill curves, population analysis, and synergy testing are discussed. Emphasis in this section is on clear descriptions of methods leading to reproducible results.

The final section of this manual includes a series of chapters designed to be used as reference sources. Additional chapters focus on antibiotic development and design, use of an antibiogram, and the interactions of the clinical microbiology laboratory with ancillary areas such as hospital pharmacy, infectious disease personnel, and infection control. A table of antibiotic classes and common "bug–drug" susceptibilities are also included.

This manual is directed to personnel engaged in the laboratory disciplines that perform *in vitro* susceptibility testing, including clinical microbiology, food and agriculture microbiology, pharmaceuticals research, and other applied and basic research environments. It is meant to be used as a bench manual. References are supplied at the end of each chapter to provide additional sources of information to those individuals wishing to pursue a specific topic in greater detail.

Antibacterial Susceptibility Testing Protocols differs from other available sources of information by its scope. Its aim is to combine an updated series of laboratory-based techniques and charts within the context of the role of clinical microbiology in modern medicine.

We would like to acknowledge Debbi Reader Covey for her secretarial assistance and unwavering support. Most of all, we would like to thank Dr. Richard S. Schwalbe for many, many things and for the great person he was.

Lynn Steele-Moore
Avery C. Goodwin, Ph.D.

Editors

Rick Schwalbe was the director of clinical microbiology at the University of Maryland Medical Systems and the director of clinical microbiology and virology at the Veteran's Administration Medical Center in Baltimore, Maryland. He was associate professor of pathology at the University of Maryland School of Medicine. At the time of his death he was president of the Maryland ASM. He served on the editoral board of *Antimicrobial Agents and Chemotherapy* and had over 100 publications.

Lynn Steele-Moore was the manager of Dr. William J. Holloway's Infectious Disease Laboratory at Christiana Care Health Services in Wilmington, Delaware, for 22 years. She currently is employed by the U.S. Food and Drug Administration in Silver Spring, Maryland. Lynn and the late Dr. Richard Schwalbe collaborated on many projects, this text being one of them. Unfortunately, Dr. Schwalbe passed away before the text was completed. However, his contributions can be seen throughout the text with chapters written by many of his friends. We all lovingly dedicate this text to our beloved friend, Rick Schwalbe.

Avery C. Goodwin worked at GlaxoSmithKline on the development of antimicrobial drugs. He is currently employed by the U.S. Food and Drug Administration in Silver Spring, Maryland, as a microbiology reviewer in the Division of Anti-Infective and Ophthalmology Products.

Contributors List

Arthur L. Barry
The Clinical Microbiology Institute
Wilsonville, Oregon

Donna Berg
Christiana Care Health Services
Wilmington, Delaware

Barbara A. Brown-Elliott
The University of Texas Health Center
Tyler, Texas

Cassandra B. Calderón
Select Specialty Hospital
Youngstown, Ohio

Emilia Cantón
La Fe University Hospital
Valencia, Spain

Samuel Cohen
ARUP Laboratories
Salt Lake City, Utah

James D. Dick
Johns Hopkins Medical Institutions
Baltimore, Maryland

Michael Dowzicky
Wyeth Pharmaceuticals
Collegeville, Pennsylvania

Ana Espinel-Ingroff
VCU Medical Center
Richmond, Virginia

Ann Hanlon
Johns Hopkins Medical Institutions
Baltimore, Maryland

Estrella Martin-Mazuelos
Valme University Hospital
Barcelona, Spain

Sophie Michaud
Faculté de Médecine de l'Université de
 Sherbrooke
Sherbrooke, Québec, Canada

Harriette Nadler
Downington, Pennsylvania

Barbara G. Painter
Pharma Microbiology Consult, LLC
Chattanooga, Tennessee

Donald H. Pitkin
Consultant
Mohrsville, Pennsylvania

John H. Powers
National Institute of Health
Bethesda, Maryland

Sadaf Qaiyumi
U.S. Food and Drug Administration
Laurel, Maryland

Nancy T. Rector
BD Diagnostics
Sparks, Maryland

Darcie E. Roe-Carpenter
Barton Memorial Hospital
South Lake Tahoe, California

Beulah Perdue Sabundayo
The Johns Hopkins University School of
 Medicine
Baltimore, Maryland

Sheryl Stuckey
Holy Cross Hospital
Silver Spring, Maryland

Merwyn Taylor
Johns Hopkins Medical Institutions
Baltimore, Maryland

John Thomas
West Virginia University Schools of Medicine
  and Dentistry
Morgantown, West Virginia

Punam Verma
Virginia Mason Medical Center
Seattle, Washington

Audrey Wanger
The University of Texas Medical School
Houston, Texas

Richard J. Wallace, Jr.
The University of Texas Health Center
Tyler, Texas

C. Douglas Webb
Consultant, Anti Infectives
Tybee Island, Georgia

Table of Contents

1 An Overview of the Clinical and Laboratory Standards Institute (CLSI) and Its Impact on Antimicrobial Susceptibility Tests

Arthur L. Barry

CONTENTS

1.1 HISTORICAL PERSPECTIVE

In the middle of the twentieth century, medical technologists and clinical pathologists were expected to maintain expertise in all aspects of the service laboratory; most were poorly trained in diagnostic microbiology. With the widespread use of antimicrobial chemotherapy, the nature of infectious diseases gradually changed and that created new challenges to those concerned with the diagnosis and treatment of infectious diseases. Consequently, clinical laboratories were being asked to perform increasingly sophisticated procedures. To help clinical pathology laboratories meet those new challenges, a number of industries were developed to provide supplies and equipment that laboratorians could no longer make or obtain for themselves. Standardization of methodology was essential for such commercial endeavors to be successful. Performance standards were needed in order for each laboratory to judge the quality of different products. Regulatory agencies were also being asked to monitor the quality of products being sold to diagnostic laboratories. Government agencies were being forced to provide standards for judging the quality of different reagents and equipment; for obvious reasons, laboratory professionals wanted to be involved in writing such standards.

In the mid-1960s a group of interested individuals began discussions that led to the concept of an independent organization that could prepare standards that would be acceptable to everyone using them. This became known as the National Committee for Clinical Laboratory Standards (NCCLS), now called the Clinical and Laboratory Standards Institute (CLSI). The name change (effective January 2005) was felt to be a more accurate representation of the organization. Clinical laboratory standards were to be prepared by committees composed of experts from academia, government, and industry. Once a standard was written and approved by the CLSI council, it was to be published as a proposed standard, and all interested individuals were asked to make written comments or suggestions. After one year of peer review, the subcommittee was asked to respond to all comments and to make appropriate changes or to explain in writing why some suggestions were not accepted. By this process, each standard would be a true consensus document. After the initial review process, each document would be advanced to the status of an approved standard. When important technical changes are needed, the document should be revised and then go through the consensus review process again. Each document is reviewed every three years and either discontinued or revised. In that way, CLSI standards are living documents that are updated as our understanding of the subject improves.

The CLSI was established in 1967–1968, and a small office was established in Los Angeles, California. A part-time secretary helped to solicit individuals who would volunteer to formulate committees that could address specific issues concerning clinical laboratory medicine. Once the first few standards were published and accepted by clinical laboratories, the CLSI support staff was expanded and was eventually moved to Villanova, PA and later to Wayne, PA. CLSI documents are now accepted throughout the world, and regulatory agents often cite CLSI standards as the accepted state of the art.

1.2 DISK DIFFUSION SUSCEPTIBILITY TESTS

The CLSI began by looking for specific areas that would be most benefited by such consensus documents. In the area of microbiology, the antimicrobial disk diffusion susceptibility test was a natural subject. Just before that time, there was a major effort to standardize antimicrobial susceptibility tests on an international level, through the World Health Organization. Sherris and Ericsson coordinated collaborative studies the results of which were published in 1971 [1]. Their extensive labors helped to standardize broth dilution and agar dilution antimicrobial susceptibility tests; microdilution susceptibility tests were not available at that time. Disk diffusion tests had been carefully standardized for use in the Scandinavian countries by Ericsson [2] and for use in the United States by Bauer et al. [3]. With those two methods, many procedural details were carefully controlled and well-defined. A variety of other methods had been advocated, but there was little effort to control important variables such as the inoculum density, agar medium, incubation conditions, etc. The standardized disk tests of Ericsson [2] and of Bauer et al. [3] both involve measuring the diameter of each zone of inhibition and comparing that to minimum inhibitory concentrations (MICs) obtained by agar or broth dilution susceptibility tests.

In the United States, the majority of clinical microbiologists felt that the time required to standardize inoculum densities and to measure zones of inhibition was too difficult for busy clinical laboratories. The most popular method utilized one or more disks for each agent (high- or low-content disks) and simply reported a strain to be susceptible if there was any zone of inhibition and resistant if it grew up to the disk. That was the method that the U.S. Food and Drug Administration (FDA) approved for inclusion in the package insert that was provided in each package of antibiotic disks [4]. A chaotic situation remained because there was no national effort to bring some degree of standardization to the disk diffusion susceptibility test procedure.

In 1968, I was given the honor to chair a CLSI subcommittee on antimicrobial disk susceptibility tests. After interviewing a number of opinion leaders, those that had the foresight to understand the need for standard methodologies were appointed to the subcommittee and serious discussions of methodologic details pursued. In principle, the method of Bauer et al. [3] was accepted by the subcommittee, but a few minor changes were added. Four years later, a document was prepared and given the designation of M2, the second standard written for the Microbiology Area Committee. That document defined the Kirby-Bauer method and the agar overlay modification of that method [5]. Quality control guidelines were also included even though quality control was unknown in clinical microbiology laboratories at that point in time. The M2 document was forwarded to the

CLSI council for review, but it was not approved until 1975. In the interim, the FDA conducted its own survey and concluded that the methods of Bauer et al. [3] and of Barry, Garcia, and Thrupp [5] were preferable, and the package inserts for antibiotic disks were rewritten [4]. With the changes in the FDA's recommendations and publication of the M2 document, CLSI standards were widely accepted within the United States and in many other countries. The M2 document has undergone numerous revisions: it is now in its ninth edition [6].

1.3 OTHER CLSI MICROBIOLOGY DOCUMENTS

Once the M2 document was accepted, other subcommittees were established in order to address additional issues concerning antimicrobial susceptibility tests. Table 1.1 describes the standards that have been developed over the years.

H. Frankel and A. Barry cochaired a subcommittee that provided a reference that manufacturers of dehydrated media could use to help standardize Mueller-Hinton agars (CLSI M6). That ongoing subcommittee has successfully improved the performance of Mueller-Hinton agar sold in the United States.

C. Thornsberry chaired a subcommittee to standardize agar and broth dilution tests of aerobic microorganisms [7]. Broth microdilution methods were being popularized at that time, and the subcommittee was able to standardize that procedure before it was widely used and before inappropriate procedures could be well engrained. Consequently, manufacturers of microdilution trays were given specific standards that their product should meet, and there have been very few problems with commercial panels that were subsequently marketed. This document, M7, is now in its seventh edition.

TABLE 1.1
Overview of CLSI Documents Relating to Antimicrobial Susceptibility Tests

CLSI Designation[a]	General Subject Covered
M2	Disk diffusion tests
M6	Dehydrated Mueller-Hinton agar
M7	Broth agar dilution tests—aerobes
M11	Anaerobic dilution tests
M21	Serum bactericidal test
M23	Guidelines for new drug reviews
M24	Mycobacteria and nocardia
M26	Bactericidal activity
M27	Antifungal tests of yeasts
M31	Veterinary drugs and pathogens
M32	Mueller-Hinton broth
M33	Antiviral agents
M37	M23 for veterinary agents
M38	Antifungal tests of filamentous fungi
M39	Cumulative susceptibility reports
M42	Disk diffusion—aquatic animals
M44	Disk diffusion—yeasts
M45	Dilution and disk—fastidious bacteria
M49	Broth dilution—aquatic animals
M100	Informational supplements for M2 and M7

[a] Each document is assigned a letter (M for microbiology) and a sequential number; this may be followed by a P (proposed), T (tentative), A (approved) or R (report) and by the number of editions, if more than one. Refer to CLSI website (www.clsi.org) for an updated list each year.

V. Sutter chaired a subcommittee that did the same thing for tests of anaerobic bacteria. Initially, that subcommittee limited their document to agar dilution tests of nonfastidious anaerobes. They defined a reference test that was to be used for evaluating other test procedures and anticipated modifications that would permit testing more fastidious species of anaerobes. That document, M11, has now been expanded and has undergone seven revisions [8].

C. Stratton developed the first draft of two documents; one dealt with methods for measuring the bactericidal activity of antibacterial agents and the other concerned the serum bactericidal tests. J. Jorgensen later brought those documents to the status of approved standards (M21). J. Watts developed two documents that deal with issues that are specific for veterinary practice. G. Woods guided the development of a document that defined procedures for susceptibility tests of *Mycobacterium* and related species. J. Galgiani and M. Pfaller have chaired a subcommittee that addressed specific reference methods for testing antifungal agents against yeasts (M27) and against filamentous fungi (M38). R. Hodinka chaired a subcommittee that dealt with methods for testing antiviral agents (herpes simplex virus). The reader is referred to Table 1.1 for document numbers.

The subcommittee for disk diffusion susceptibility tests has now been given responsibility for the documents that dealt with aerobic and anaerobic antibacterial dilution tests of human pathogens. J. Jorgensen and M. Ferraro chaired this subcommittee while it was learning to handle its new responsibilities. W. Novick coordinated the preparation of guidelines that defined the type of information that should be provided by drug manufacturers when applying for inclusion in CLSI tables [9]. The original subcommittee was given responsibility for maintenance of four documents (M2, M7, M11, and M23) since these involve evaluation of the same type of data for selecting interpretive criteria and quality control ranges for each new antibacterial agent. In 1964, Bauer et al. [3] provided interpretive criteria for tests of 20 antimicrobial agents, and 42 years later, the 2006 CLSI document describes criteria for over 90 agents. With this increase in the number of antimicrobial agents, the tables became complex and confusing. J. Hindler and J. Swenson have spearheaded a major effort to make the tables significantly more user-friendly, and their efforts resulted in an important improvement. Because new agents may be added to the tables once or twice a year, revision of the documents every three years is not sufficient. In an attempt to maintain an up-to-date document, an informational supplement is published once a year in January [10]. This supplement contains only the most recent version of the tables, without the text of each standard. Consequently, it can be published without the usual delays required by the peer review process. All new entries in the tables are identified and considered tentative for the first year. If written complaints are received in the first year, the subcommittee will reconsider the issue causing concern.

Although the Microbiology Area Committee has concentrated on issues concerning antimicrobial susceptibility tests, other documents have been prepared and are currently available. Subjects that have been addressed are as follows: blood-borne parasitic diseases, intestinal parasites, quality control of commercial media, fetal bovine serum, protection of laboratory workers from infectious agents, Western blot assay for *B. burgdorferi*, and abbreviated identification of bacteria and yeasts. New documents are in process, including one that addresses PFGE and other methods for bacterial strain typing (see Chapter 15). In all cases, the documents are reviewed on a regular schedule and either withdrawn or revised and updated. Area committees other than microbiology have also been productive in the number of documents that have been published.

1.4 QUALITY CONTROL LIMITS

The most important contribution that was made by these efforts was the selection of quality control (QC) strains and the definition of expected MICs and/or zone diameters for each new antimicrobial agent. The control strains that are currently utilized for different purposes are described in Table 1.2. With these QC strains, laboratories have a way to know whether they are performing the tests appropriately and to monitor the tests that are done on a regular basis. The reader is advised to refer to the most current CLSI documents for an up-to-date list as changes do occur.

TABLE 1.2

Microorganisms Designated for Quality Control of Antimicrobial Susceptibility Tests

Species (ATCC Number)	Purpose and Comments
Escherichia coli (25922)	For dilution and disk tests
Escherichia coli (35218)	For β-lactam/inhibitor combinations
Klebsiella pneumoniae (700603)	For ESBL screening tests
Pseudomonas aeruginosa (27853)	For dilution and disk tests, especially for aminoglycosides vs. *P. aeruginosa*
Enterococcus faecalis (29212)	For dilution tests (vancomycin-S)
Enterococcus faecalis (51299)	Aminoglycoside-resistant control strain
Staphylococcus aureus (29213)	For dilution tests (weak β-lactamase producer)
Staphylococcus aureus (25923)	For disk tests (β-lactamase negative)
Staphylococcus aureus (43300)	For oxacillin dilution tests (MRSA strain)
Streptococcus pneumoniae (49619)	Penicillin intermediate strains for dilution and disk tests of all streptococci
Neisseria gonorrhoeae (49226)	For dilution and disk tests of gonococci
Haemophilus influenzae (49247)	For dilution and disk tests of *H. influenzae* (β-lactamase-negative, ampicillin-R)
Haemophilus influenzae (49766)	Ampicillin-S strain for agents not controlled by 49247
Haemophilus influenzae (10211)	For testing quality of HTM agar or broth
Haemophilus somnus (70025)	For fastidious animal pathogens
Actinobacillus pleuropneumoniae (27090)	For fastidious animal pathogens
Bacteroides fragilis (25285)	For dilution tests of anaerobes
Bacteroides thetaiotaomicron (29741)	For dilution tests of anaerobes
Eubacterium lentum (43055)	For dilution tests of anaerobes
Candida parapsilosis (22019)	For dilution tests of yeasts
Candida krusei (6258)	For dilution tests of yeasts
Aspergillus flavus (204304)	For dilution tests of filamentous fungi
Aspergillus funigatus (204305)	For dilution tests of filamentous fungi

Refer to current CLSI documents for an updated list each year.

Every time a new antimicrobial agent is added to the tables, appropriate multilaboratory collaborative studies must be performed, and the acceptable range of zone diameters or range of MICs is then defined for each QC strain. In general, this range should include at least 95% of all test results, i.e., 1 out of 20 determinations might be just outside of the QC range. If a single determination is out of control by random chance, it should come back into the QC range when repeated. If it remains out of control, some troubleshooting is needed in order to find the problem.

1.5　ROLE OF THE U.S. FOOD AND DRUG ADMINISTRATION (FDA)

As directed by Congress, the FDA has legal responsibility for determining safety and efficacy of new anti-infective agents. When a new drug is released for sale in the U.S., the FDA-approved package insert includes specific guidelines for interpretation of *in vitro* tests and quality control limits for tests performed according to CLSI procedures. The CLSI subcommittee also defines interpretive criteria and QC limits for their tests. Because the two groups actually examine slightly different data, it is not surprising that there are occasional discrepancies between the two. Major efforts are being made to avoid unintended differences, but some minor discrepancies are unavoidable.

The devices division of the FDA also certifies commercial products and monitors the reliability of each. The CLSI does *not* approve or disapprove any commercial product; they only standardize methodology.

The CLSI defines methodologies that can survive the consensus process; they have no regulatory responsibility, but CLSI documents are often cited by agencies that do have such responsibilities.

Many laboratorians feel that they can test only those antimicrobial agents that have interpretive criteria and QC ranges defined in the CLSI tables. Testing and reporting agents that do not have interpretive criteria are the responsibility of the chief microbiologist and such decisions should be made with input from the infectious disease clinicians (see Chapter 17). Clearly, the CLSI has resolved the chaotic situation that existed in the late 1960s, and ongoing activities promise to maintain up-to-date information when it is needed. The area committee for microbiology regularly considers proposals for new projects that may have a substantial impact on the practice of clinical microbiology within the United States.

REFERENCES

1. Ericsson, H.M. and Sherris, J.C. Antibiotic sensitivity testing. Report of an international collaborative study, *Acta Pathol. Microbiol. Scand., Sect. B*, Suppl. 217, 1971.
2. Ericsson, H. The paper disc method for determination of bacterial sensitivity to antibiotics, *J. Clin. Lab. Invest.*, 12, 1–15, 1960.
3. Bauer, A.W., Kirby, W.M.M., Sherris, J.C., and Turck, M. Antibiotic susceptibility testing by a single high content disk method, *Amer. J. Clin. Pathol.*, 45, 492–496, 1966.
4. Wright, W.W. FDA actions on antibiotic susceptibility discs, in *Techniques for Antibiotic Susceptibility Testing*, Balows, A., Ed., Charles C Thomas, Springfield, IL, 1974, 26.
5. Barry, A.L., Garcia, F., and Thrupp, L.D. An improved method for testing the antibiotic susceptibility of rapid growing pathogens, *Amer. J. Clin. Pathol.*, 53, 149–158, 1970.
6. Clinical and Laboratory Standards Institute. Performance standards for antimicrobial disk susceptibility tests, approved standard, M2-A9, 9th ed., CLSI, Wayne, PA, 2006.
7. Clinical and Laboratory Standards Institute. Methods for dilution antimicrobial susceptibility tests for bacteria that grow aerobically, approved standard M7-A7, 7th ed., CLSI, Wayne, PA, 2006.
8. Clinical and Laboratory Standards Institute. Methods for antimicrobial susceptibility testing of anaerobic bacteria, approved standard M11-A6, 7th ed., CLSI, Wayne, PA, 2007.
9. Clinical and Laboratory Standards Institute. Development of *in vitro* susceptibility testing criteria and quality control parameters, approved standard M23-A2, 2nd ed., CLSI, Wayne, PA, 2001.
10. Clinical and Laboratory Standards Institute. Performance standards for antimicrobial susceptibility testing, informational supplement M100-S16, 16th ed., CLSI, Wayne, PA, 2006.

2 Antimicrobial Classifications: Drugs for Bugs

Cassandra B. Calderón and Beulah Perdue Sabundayo

CONTENTS

2.1 INTRODUCTION

Physicians have used drugs for decades to treat infections. However, chemotherapy as a science began with Paul Ehrlich in the late 1800s. Dr. Ehrlich was a German medical scientist who received the Nobel Prize for Physiology of Medicine in 1908. He realized that like human and animal cells, certain bacteria cells colored with certain dyes while others did not. He postulated that it might be possible to make certain dyes, or chemicals, that would kill bacteria while not harming the host organism. He conducted hundreds to thousands of experiments testing dyes against various microorganisms. It wasn't until his 606th experimental compound that he discovered a medically useful drug. This compound, later named *salvarsan*, was arsenic based, and the first treatment for syphilis [1]. In 1889, Vuillemin, a French bacteriologist, suggested using the word *antiobiosis*, meaning "against life," to describe the group of drugs that had action against microorganisms [2]. Selman Waksman, an American microbiologist and the discoverer of streptomycin, later changed this term to *antibiotic* [3]. Many antibiotics have been discovered since then (Table 2.1), but the discovery of penicillin may be one of the most important events in the practice of infectious disease medicine. To date, the U.S. Food and Drug Administration (FDA) has approved 18 antibiotics derived from penicillin and 25 classified as cephalosporins [4,5].

Traditionally, antimicrobial agents have been classified based on their mechanism of action, chemical structure, or spectrum of activity. The primary mode of action is the inhibition of vital steps in the growth or function of the microorganism. These steps include inhibiting bacterial or fungal cell wall synthesis, inhibiting protein synthesis, inhibiting nucleic acid synthesis, or disrupting cell membrane function (Table 2.2) [6].

Antibiotics are often described as "bacteriostatic" or "bactericidal" (Table 2.2). The term bacteriostatic describes a drug that temporarily inhibits the growth of the organism. Once the drug is removed, the organism will resume growth. The term bactericidal describes a drug that causes cell death. For infections that cannot be eradicated by host mechanisms (e.g., endocarditis) or for patients who are immunocompromised (e.g., Acquired Immunodeficiency Syndrome), a bactericidal drug is often required [7].

2.2 ANTIBIOTICS

2.2.1 PENICILLINS

2.2.1.1 Background

Penicillin was first discovered in 1928 by a young Scottish bacteriologist, Alexander Fleming, while studying staphylococcal bacteria at St. Mary's Hospital in London [8–10]. Unlike his

TABLE 2.1
Origin of Antibiotic Classes

Antibiotic Class	Antibiotic(s)	Origin	Discoverer(s)	Year of Discovery
Sulfonamides	Sulfanilamide (not used as an antibiotic)	An azo dye	Paul Gelmo	1908
	Prontosil	An azo dye	Gerhard Domagk	1932
	Sulfanilamide (active component of prontosil)	An azo dye	Trefoul, Nitti, and Bovet	1935
Penicillins	Penicillin	*Penicillium notatum*	Alexander Fleming	1928
			Howard Florey and Ernest Chain	Therapeutic usefulness recorded in 1940
Aminoglycosides	Streptomycin	*Streptomyces griseus* from soil samples	Selman Waksman	1944
	Gentamicin	Micromonospora	Weinstein	1963
Chloramphenicol	Chloramphenicol	*Streptomyces venezuelae* from soil samples collected in Venezuela	John Ehrlich, Q.R. Bartz, R.M. Smith, D.A. Joslyn, and P.R. Burkholder	Published in 1947
Cephalosporins	Cephalothin	*Cephalosporium acremonium* from water samples obtained off the Sardinian coast	Giuseppi Brotzu	1948
Tetracyclines	Chlortetracycline	*Streptomyces aureofaciens* from soil samples collected in Missouri	Benjamin Duggar	1948
Macrolides	Erythromycin	*Streptomyces erythreus* from soil samples collected in the Philippine Archipelago	James McGuire and R.L. Bunch, R.C. Anderson, H.E. Boaz, E.H. Flynn, H.M. Powell, and J.W. Smith.	Recorded in 1952
Glycopeptides	Vancomycin	*Streptomyces orientalis* from soil samples collected in Indonesia and India	McCormick	1956
Lincosamides	Lincomycin	*Streptomyces lincolnensis* from soil samples collected near Lincoln, Nebraska		1962
Fluoroquinolones	Nalidixic acid	A byproduct of chloroquine synthesis	Lesher	1962

Source: Ryan, F. *The Forgotten Plague*, Little, Brown, New York, 1993; Aronson, S.M. *Med Health*, 80(6), 180, 1997; Radetsky, M. *Pediatr Infect Dis J*, 15(9), 811–818, 1996; Thredlekd, D.S., Ed., *Drug Facts and Comparisons*, Facts and Comparisons; St. Louis, 2006; McEvoy, G.K., Ed. *AHFS Drug Information*, American Society of Health-System Pharmacists, Inc., Bethesda, 2006; Jawetz, E., in *Basic and Clinical Pharmacology*, Katzung, B.G., Ed., Appleton and Lange; Norwalk, CT, 1989, pp. 545–552; Woods, G.L. and Washington, J.A., in *Principles and Practices of Infectious Diseases*, Mandell, G.L., Bennett, J.E., and Dolin, R., Eds., Churchill Livingstone, New York, 1995, pp. 169–199.

TABLE 2.2
Antibiotic Mechanisms of Action and Description of Activity

Inhibition of Bacterial Cell Wall Synthesis	Inhibition of Nucleic Acid Synthesis
Penicillins (cidal)[a]	Fluoroquinolones (cidal)
Cephalosporins (cidal)	Rifamycins (cidal)
Carbapenems (cidal)	Sulfonamides (static)
Monobactams (cidal)	Trimethoprim (static)
Glycopeptides (cidal)	Cyclic lipopeptides (cidal)

Inhibition of Protein Synthesis	Inhibition of Cell Membrane Function
Aminoglycosides (cidal)	Amphotericin B
Tetracyclines (static)	Imidazoles (fungistatic)
Glycylcyclines	Triazoles (fungistatic)
Chloramphenicol (static)	Echinocandins
Clindamycin (static)	
Macrolides (static or cidal)	
Ketolides	
Oxazolidinones	
Streptogramins (cidal)	

Source: Thredlekd, D.S., Ed., *Drug Facts and Comparisons*, Facts and Comparisons, St. Louis, 2006; McEvoy, G.K., Ed., *AHFS Drug Information*, American Society of Health-System Pharmacists, Inc., Bethesda, 2006; Jawetz, E. in *Basic and Clinical Pharmacology*, Katzung, B.G., Ed., Appleton and Lange; Norwalk, CT, 1989, pp. 545–552.
[a] cidal = bactericidal; static = bacteriostatic.

associate, who kept a clean and uncluttered laboratory workbench, Fleming was a very untidy person. After returning from a short vacation, Dr. Fleming proceeded to review the petri dishes that he had inoculated. That September day, he noticed something unusual. Some of the culture dishes had been contaminated with a greenish, feathery mold. The contamination wasn't unusual, but the clearing of staphylococcal colonies around the mold was [3]. Alexander Fleming identified the mold as *Penicillium notatum*. He later named his discovery, penicillin, after the mold that produces it [11].

Fleming, who may or may not have fully understood the clinical implications of this discovery, was having difficulty extracting the penicillin from the mold in the purity or quantity that would make it useful. He was also having difficulty raising funds to continue his work. Twelve years later, Howard Florey, an Australian pathologist, Ernest Chain, a German biochemist, and others at Oxford University were given funds to study penicillin and its clinical usefulness in treating infections [3]. They had performed many tests in tissue cultures and animals but never in human volunteers. On January 17,1941, a 50-year-old woman with disseminated breast cancer and not long to live, volunteered to undergo toxicity testing. After receiving the injection of penicillin she complained of a musty taste in her mouth and developed a sudden fever and rigor, but no other ill effects [12].

It was now time for a therapeutic trial of penicillin. In February of 1941, a 43-year-old Oxford policeman was the first to receive penicillin. He was diagnosed with an overwhelming staphylococcal and streptococcal septicemia including multiple facial and lung abscesses and osteomyelitis of his right humerus. Multiple injections of penicillin were administered intravenously and after 5 days, he was afebrile and eating well. Unfortunately, the supply of penicillin ran out, even though it was recovered in his urine, extracted, purified and readministered. The patient deteriorated and died a month later [12].

2.2.1.2 Mechanism of Action

All beta-lactam antibiotics, including penicillins and cephalosporins, are inhibitors of bacterial cell wall synthesis. The antibiotic must first bind to the penicillin-binding protein (PBP) located within the cytoplasmic membrane of the cell wall. Once bound, the antibiotic can cause various effects that eventually lead to cell death, but primarily they inhibit the cross-linking of the peptide chains and thereby, prevent the development of normal peptidoglycan structure. All penicillins are bactericidal [11,13].

2.2.2.3 Chemical Structure

There are 56 beta-lactam antibiotics, all of which contain the four-membered beta-lactam ring. The antibacterial activity of these molecules resides in the ring itself, and cleavage of the ring by bacterial beta-lactamases inactivates the compound. All penicillins are derived from the 6-aminopenicillanic acid nucleus, which consists of a five-membered thiazolidine (penam) ring, a four-membered beta-lactam ring, and a side chain. Manipulations in the side chain result in the formation of other penicillins, which differ in their spectrum of activity, beta-lactamase resistance, and pharmacokinetic properties [11,13].

2.2.2.4 Mechanisms of Resistance

Bacteria have three defense mechanisms against beta-lactam antibiotics: destruction of the antibiotic by beta-lactamases, decreased penetration of the antibiotic to reach the PBP, and decreased affinity of the PBP to the antibiotic [13,14]. Some bacteria, such as *Staphylococcus* species, *Haemophilus influenzae*, gonococci, and most gram-negative enteric rods produce beta-lactamases (penicillinases). These enzymes can break the beta-lactam ring of the antibiotic, rendering it ineffective [13]. To overcome this resistance, some antibiotics are combined with beta-lactamase inhibitors, such as clavulanic acid (ticarcillin/clavulanate and amoxicillin/clavulanate), sulbactam (ampicillin/sulbactam) or tazobactam (piperacillin/tazobactam), to prevent the destruction of the beta-lactam ring. Other penicillins, such as nafcillin, are resistant to beta-lactamase destruction due to the positioning of their side chain [5].

In order for the penicillins to produce their antibacterial effect, they must first bind to the PBPs. Therefore, anything inhibiting or altering the binding of these antibiotics to their receptors can result in the antibiotic being ineffective. Bacteria differ in their number and types of PBPs. Antibiotics differ in their affinity to bind to the PBP. Also, mutations in the PBPs can cause an organism once sensitive to become resistant [13,14].

2.2.2.5 Classification

The penicillins have been divided into categories based on their spectrum of activity (Table 2.3) [13]. The natural penicillins (penicillin G) were the first agents in the penicillin family to be used clinically to treat infections. Shortly after the introduction of penicillin, the emergence of penicillinase-producing staphylococci caused the natural penicillins to be ineffective for these organisms. This led to the development of the penicillinase-resistant penicillins, also known as the *antistaphylococcal penicillins*. Methicillin was the first of this group. The addition of a side chain protected the beta-lactam ring by sterically inhibiting the action of the penicillinase. The need for penicillins with extended activity against gram-negative microorganisms prompted further manipulations of the side chains. This led to the development of three new classes of penicillins: the aminopenicillins, carboxypenicillins, and ureidopenicillins [11,13].

2.2.2.6 Antimicrobial Activity and Therapeutic Uses

The natural penicillins have excellent gram-positive activity and until recently were considered the drug of choice for many infections caused by pneumococci, streptococci, meningococci, and

TABLE 2.3
Penicillins Classifications

Classification/Generic Name	Route of Administration	Penicillinase-Resistant
Natural Penicillins		
Penicillin G	IM,[a] IV, oral	No
Penicillin V	Oral	No
Penicillinase-Resistant Penicillins		
Cloxacillin	Oral	Yes
Dicloxacillin	Oral	Yes
Methicillin	Not available	Yes
Nafcillin	IM, IV, oral	Yes
Oxacillin	IM, IV, oral	Yes
Aminopenicillins		
Amoxicillin	Oral	No
Amoxicillin/clavulanate	Oral	Yes
Ampicillin	Oral	No
Ampicillin/sulbactam	IM, IV	Yes
Bacampicillin	Oral	No
Carboxypenicillins		
Carbenicillin	Oral	No
Ticarcillin	IM, IV	No
Ticarcillin/clavulanate	IM, IV	Yes
Ureidopenicillins and Piperazine		
Mezlocillin	IM, IV	No
Piperacillin	IM, IV	No
Piperacillin/tazobactam	IM, IV	Yes

Source: Thredlekd, D.S., Ed., *Drug Facts and Comparisons*, Facts and Comparisons, St. Louis, 2006; McEvoy, G.K., Ed., *AHFS Drug Information*, American Society of Health-System Pharmacists, Inc., Bethesda, 2006.
[a] IM = intramuscular; IV = intravenous.

non-β-lactamase-producing staphylococci and gonococci. Emerging resistance to these drugs is changing the way these infections are treated [13].

The penicillinase-resistant penicillins, also known, as noted above, as the antistaphylococcal penicillins, have excellent activity against both *Streptococcus* and *Staphylococcus* species (including those strains of penicillinase-producing *Staphylococcus aureus*) but no activity against gram-negative bacteria [4,5,11,13]. They are considered the drugs of choice for the treatment of staphylococcal infections, commonly seen in cellulitis or other skin infections, for example [13].

Aminopenicillins were the first group of penicillin antibiotics to have activity against both gram-positive and gram-negative bacteria. Compared to penicillin G, a natural penicillin, ampicillin has more activity against enterococci, but somewhat less activity against *S. pyogenes, Streptococcus pneumoniae, Neisseria* species, and *Clostridium* species. It also has some activity against gram-negative bacteria such as *Escherichia coli, Proteus mirabilis, Salmonella, Shigella, Listeria,* and non-β-lactamase-producing strains of *H. influenzae* [4,5,11,13]. The emergence of resistant organisms, however, is limiting its use clinically.

Carboxypenicillins have the same antibacterial spectrum of activity as ampicillin, an aminopenicillin, but with greater gram-negative activity. Carbenicillin and ticarcillin are the two drugs in this class. They also have activity against indole-positive *Proteus, Enterobacter, Providencia, Morganella,* and *Pseudomonas aeruginosa*. Unlike the aminopenicillin, ampicillin, carbenicillin and ticarcillin are not very active against enterococci [4,5,11,13].

The ureidopenicillins and piperazine penicillins have the broadest spectrum of activity among the penicillins, covering many gram-positive and gram-negative bacteria. The addition of the ureido group to the penicillin structure produces the antibiotics azlocillin and mezlocillin, whereas the addition of the ureido group and a piperazine side chain produces piperacillin. Their coverage is very similar to that of the carboxypenicillins but with enhanced activity against *P. aeruginosa* [4,5,11,13].

2.2.2.7 Adverse Effect Profile

The major adverse event associated with penicillin use is hypersensitivity reactions, which can range in severity from a mild rash to anaphylactic shock and death. An estimated 1% to 10% of the general population is allergic to penicillins [15]. Although anaphylaxis is more frequent following intravenous therapy, it may also occur with oral use. As with all other orally administered antibiotics, penicillins can cause gastrointestinal disturbances. Symptoms include nausea, vomiting, and diarrhea, and are seen more commonly with ampicillin and amoxicillin than with other penicillins. Hematologic toxicity is rare. Although neutropenia has been documented with all penicillins, it is more common with high doses of penicillin G. Carbenicillin, ticarcillin, and piperacillin have all been associated with thrombocytopenia and/or platelet dysfunction, and are usually reversible upon discontinuation of the medication. Penicillins have caused neurotoxicity, manifested as lethargy, neuromuscular irritability, hallucinations, convulsions, and seizures, when given in large intravenous doses, especially to patients with renal dysfunction. Renal complications, such as interstitial nephritis, are infrequent but are usually associated with high doses of methicillin (Table 2.4) [4,5,13].

2.2.3 Cephalosporins

2.2.3.1 Background

The success seen with the discovery of penicillin lead to the search for other possible antibiotic-producing microorganisms. In 1948, Giuseppi Brotzu, a professor of bacteriology at the University of Cagliari in Sardinia, was studying water samples from a nearby harbor when he observed a clearing of the water surrounding the sewer outlet and suspected it to contain some antibiotic-producing microorganism. Crude filtrate of this water had antibiotic properties that inhibited the growth of *S. aureus in vitro* and was successful in treating some patients. The microorganism in the filtrate was later classified as *Cephalosporium acremonium*, now known as *Acremonium chrysogenum* [11,16]. Brotzu, unable to complete his work, sent a culture of *C. acremonium* to Howard Florey at Oxford University. In 1953, after many exhaustive years of study, they discovered the substance produced by the microorganism possessing the antimicrobial properties, known as cephalosporin C [16,17]. This discovery lead to the formation of the class of antibiotics known as cephalosporins, with cephalothin being the first of many [17].

2.2.3.2 Mechanism of Action

Cephalosporins, like other beta-lactam antibiotics, inhibit peptidoglycan cross-linkage and therefore bacterial cell wall synthesis. Like the penicillins, all cephalosporins are bactericidal [5,11,16].

2.2.3.3 Chemical Structure

The 7-aminocephalosporanic acid nucleus of the cephalosporin is very similar to the 6-aminopenicillanic acid nucleus of the penicillin. In addition to the beta-lactam ring, it has a six-membered dihydrothiazine (cephem) ring, and two side chains. The six-membered cephem ring confers a relative

TABLE 2.4
Adverse Effects Associated with Penicillins

Hypersensitivity Reactions	**Neurologic**
Anaphylaxis	Seizure
Urticaria	Dizziness, paresthesias
Drug fever	Neuromuscular irritability
Gastrointestinal	**Renal**
Nausea and vomiting	Interstitial nephritis
Diarrhea	
Pseudomembranous colitis	
Hematologic	**Miscellaneous**
Hemolytic anemia	Jarisch-Herxheimer reaction
Neutropenia	Skin rash
Thrombocytopenia	Thrombophlebitis
Platelet dysfunction	
Metabolic	
Sodium overload	
Hypokalemia	

Source: Thredlekd, D.S., Ed., *Drug Facts and Comparisons*, Facts and Comparisons, St. Louis, 2006;
McEvoy, G.K., Ed., *AHFS Drug Information*, American Society of Health-System Pharmacists, Inc.,
Bethesda, 2006; Mandell, G.L. and Sande, M.A., in *Goodman and Gilman's The Pharmacological Basis of
Therapeutics*, Goodman Gilman, A., Rall, T.W., Nies, A.S., and Taylor, P., Eds., Pergamon Press, Elmsford,
1990, pp. 1065–1097; Chambers, H.F. and Neu, H.C., in *Principles and Practices of Infectious Diseases*,
Mandell, G.L., Bennett, J.E., and Dolin, R., Eds., Churchill Livingstone; New York, 1995, 233–247.

resistance to certain beta-lactamases compared to the penam ring. Unlike the penicillins, manipulation
of the cephalosporin's structure is allowed in two places versus one, resulting in the formation of
other antibiotics with different spectrums of activity and pharmacokinetic properties [11,16].

2.2.3.4 Mechanisms of Resistance

Like penicillins, bacterial resistance to cephalosporins can be mediated through three major mechanisms: alterations in PBPs, formation of beta-lactamases (cephalosporinases) that inactivate the
drug, or decreased ability of the antibiotics to penetrate the cell wall and reach its PBP [14,16].

2.2.3.5 Classification

Cephalosporins have traditionally been divided into four major groups or "generations" based on
their spectrum of activity [4,5,16]. Refer to Table 2.5 for a listing of antibiotics in this class.

2.2.3.6 Antimicrobial Activity and Therapeutic Uses

First-generation cephalosporins are active against the gram-positive cocci, staphylococci, and streptococci, but not enterococcus species. Among the gram-negative bacteria, *E. coli*, *Klebsiella pneumoniae*, and *P. mirabilis* are usually susceptible. Even though the first-generation cephalosporins have a
broad spectrum of activity and have few side effects, they are rarely the drugs of choice to treat any
infection. However, when penicillins are to be avoided, they are commonly prescribed to treat skin
and skin-structure infections, streptococcal pharyngitis, and community-acquired pneumonia caused

TABLE 2.5
Cephalosporins Classifications

Classification Generic Name	Route of Administration
First Generation	
Cefadroxil	Oral
Cefazolin	IM,[a] IV
Cephalexin	Oral
Cephalothin	Not available
Cephapirin	IM, IV
Cephradine	Oral, IM, IV
Second Generation	
Cefaclor	Oral
Cefamandole	Not available
Cefmetazole	Not available
Cefonicid	IM, IV
Cefotetan	IM, IV
Cefoxitin	IM, IV
Cefprozil	Oral
Cefuroxime	IM, IV, oral
Loracarbef	Oral
Third Generation	
Cefdinir	Oral
Cefixime	Oral
Cefoperazone	IM, IV
Cefotaxime	IM, IV
Cefpodoxime	Oral
Ceftazidime	IM, IV
Ceftibuten	Oral
Ceftizoxime	IM, IV
Ceftriaxone	IM, IV
Fourth Generation	
Cefepime	IM, IV

Source: Thredlekd, D.S., Ed., *Drug Facts and Comparisons*, Facts and Comparisons, St. Louis, 2006; McEvoy, G.K., Ed., *AHFS Drug Information*, American Society of Health-System Pharmacists, Inc., Bethesda, 2006; Mandell, G.L. and Sande, M.A., in *Goodman and Gilman's The Pharmacological Basis of Therapeutics*, Goodman Gilman, A., Rall, T.W., Nies, A.S., and Taylor, P., Eds., Pergamon Press, Elmsford, 1990, pp. 1065–1097; Karchmer, A.W., in *Principles and Practices of Infectious Diseases*, Mandell, G.L., Bennett, J.E., and Dolin, R., Eds., Churchill Livingstone, New York, 1995, pp. 247–264; Moellering, R.C. and Sentochnik, D.E., Cephalosporins, in *Infectious Disease*, Gorbach, S.L., Bartlett, J.G., and Blacklow, N.R., Eds., Lippincott, Williams, & Wilkins, Philadelphia, 1992, pp. 172–182.

[a] IM = intramuscular; IV = intravenous.

by *S. pneumoniae* [5,16]. Cefazolin remains the drug of choice for prophylaxis in most surgical procedures not involving the bowel [5,16,17].

In general, the second-generation cephalosporins are less active against staphylococci and streptococci compared to the first-generation agents but are more active against selected gram-negative bacilli. *Enterobacter, Klebsiella* and indole-positive *Proteus* spp. are usually sensitive, although *P. aeruginosa* is not. Cefoxitin, cefotetan, cefmetazole, and cefamandole all have moderate activity to *Bacteroides fragilis* and can be useful in mixed infections such as peritonitis or diverticulitis. These agents are also commonly prescribed for surgical prophylaxis, especially intraabdominal procedures [17]. Cefuroxime is active against *H. influenzae, Moraxella catarrhalis,* and *S. pneumoniae* and therefore useful in the treatment of bronchitis and community-acquired pneumonia. First- and second-generation oral cephalosporins, such as cefadroxil, cefaclor, and cefprozil, are commonly prescribed in upper respiratory tract infections, such as otitis media, pharyngitis/tonsillitis, and sinusitis [5,16].

Most third-generation cephalosporins have less staphylococcal and streptococcal activity than the first- or second-generation agents, but possess even better activity against gram-negative bacteria, including *P. aeruginosa* and *Enterobacter* spp. These agents were developed to combat nosocomial, multiresistant, gram-negative bacterial infections. Only cefoperazone and ceftazidime have activity against *P. aeruginosa,* and the latter is commonly prescribed in combination to treat such infections. Ceftazidime is also used in immunocompromised patients to treat fever of unknown etiology. The third- and fourth-generation cephalosporins are the only cephalosporins that penetrate the central nervous system and therefore may be used to treat meningitis, depending on the organism [5,16].

The newest generation of cephalosporins represents an attempt to maintain good activity against gram-positive as well as gram-negative organisms, including *P. aeruginosa,* and is designated as fourth-generation cephalosporins [5]. To date only one antimicrobial agent, cefepime, is considered a fourth-generation cephalosporin.

2.2.3.7 Adverse Effect Profile

Oral cephalosporins are generally well tolerated and cause few side effects. Hypersensitivity reactions are the most common side effect and have been reported in less than 5% of patients treated [4]. The most frequently reported side effects to orally administered cephalosporins are nausea, vomiting, and diarrhea. Cephalosporins that contain a methylthiotrazole (MTT) side chain (i.e., cefamandole, cefmetazole, cefoperazone, moxalactam, and cefotetan) have been associated with hypoprothrombinemia and prolonged bleeding [18,19]. These antibiotics are also associated with a disulfiram-like reaction if taken with alcohol or alcohol-containing products (i.e., some cough and cold preparations). This reaction is primarily characterized by rapid onset of flushing, tachycardia, headache, sweating, thirst, nausea, and vomiting (Table 2.6) [18,20].

2.2.4 CARBAPENEMS

Imipenem, meropenem, and ertapenem are beta-lactam antibiotics classified as carbapenems. Like all beta-lactam antibiotics, carbapenems inhibit bacterial cell wall synthesis. Their chemical structure is similar to the penicillins, but with a few modifications. The carbapenems have the broadest antimicrobial spectrum of activity of any beta-lactam antibiotics available to date. They have excellent activity against both aerobic and anaerobic gram-positive and gram-negative bacteria. Among the gram-positive organisms, the carbapenems are active against most strains of methicillin-sensitive *S. aureus* (MSSA) and coagulase-negative staphylococci, *Streptococcus* spp., and *E. faecalis.* The two older carbapenems exhibit excellent activity to the majority of gram-negative bacteria, including troublesome nosocomial pathogens such as *P. aeruginosa.* Ertapenem, on the other hand, has excellent activity against most gram-negative pathogens except *P. aeruginosa.* In cases of documented or suspected infections due to *Pseudomonas* spp., ertapenem should not be used. The carbapenems are also active against most strains of clinically significant anaerobes. Due to their broad spectrum of activity, many clinicians think carbapenems should be reserved for the treatment of mixed bacterial infections and the treatment of resistant aerobic gram-negative bacteria that are not susceptible to other beta-lactam antibiotics [5,21]. The most frequent side effects associated with carbapenem administration are phlebitis, nausea, vomiting, diarrhea, and rash [4,5,21]. Seizures occurred in 1%

TABLE 2.6
Adverse Effects Associated with Cephalosporins

Hypersensitivity Reactions	**Neurologic**
Maculopapular rash	Headache
Anaphylaxis	Insomnia
Urticaria	Seizure
Drug fever	
Pruritus	
Gastrointestinal	**Renal**
Nausea and vomiting	Interstitial nephritis
Diarrhea	
Pseudomembranous colitis	
Biliary sludge	
Hematologic	**Miscellaneous**
Bleeding abnormalities	Disulfiram-like reaction
Platelet dysfunction	Skin rash
Neutropenia	Thrombophlebitis
Leukopenia	

Source: Thredlekd, D.S., Ed., *Drug Facts and Comparisons*, Facts and Comparisons, St. Louis, 2006; McEvoy, G.K., Ed., *AHFS Drug Information*, American Society of Health-System Pharmacists, Inc., Bethesda, 2006; Mandell, G.L. and Sande, M.A., in *Goodman and Gilman's The Pharmacological Basis of Therapeutics*, Goodman Gilman, A., Rall, T.W., Nies, A.S., and Taylor, P., Eds., Pergamon Press, Elmsford, 1990, pp. 1065–1097; Karchmer, A.W., in *Principles and Practices of Infectious Diseases*, Mandell, G.L., Bennett, J.E., and Dolin, R., Eds., Churchill Livingstone, New York, 1995, pp. 247–264; Moellering, R.C. and Sentochnik, D.E., Cephalosporins, in *Infectious Disease*, Gorbach, S.L., Bartlett, J.G., and Blacklow, N.R., Eds., Lippincott, Williams, & Wilkins, Philadelphia, 1992, pp. 172–182; Uri, J.V. and Parks, D.B., Disulfiram-like reaction to certain cephalosporins, *Ther. Drug Monit.* 5(2), 219–224, Jun 1983.

to 3% of treated patients but occurred more commonly in patients with renal insufficiency or underlying central nervous system disease [21,22].

2.2.5 MONOBACTAMS

Aztreonam is a monocyclic beta-lactam antibiotic known as a *monobactam*. Its unique chemical structure is composed solely of the four-membered beta-lactam ring and a side chain. It lacks the five- or six-membered side ring shared by the penicillins and cephalosporins, respectively. Like other beta-lactam antibiotics, aztreonam exerts its bactericidal action by binding to PBPs, disrupting the formation of the peptidoglycan chain and ultimately inhibiting bacterial cell wall synthesis [5,21]. Aztreonam binds primarily to the PBP-3 located on *Enterobacteriaceae, Pseudomonas* spp., and other gram-negative aerobic organisms, but not to the PBPs found on gram-positive bacteria. As a result, aztreonam has a narrow spectrum of activity, limited to gram-negative bacteria [5,11,21]. Aztreonam is well tolerated by most patients and is associated with very few side effects. Patients with a penicillin allergy, as documented through a positive skin test reaction, have received aztreonam with no incidence of anaphylaxis [21,23]. Therefore, due to the lack of cross reactivity, aztreonam is a good alternative for patients who have a serious allergy to penicillin and require treatment. Because it is limited to the treatment of gram-negative infections, it is commonly used in combination with another antimicrobial for empiric therapy [21].

2.2.6 GLYCOPEPTIDES

2.2.6.1 Background

The discovery of penicillins and cephalosporins was very important for the treatment of many infections, but shortly thereafter, microorganisms began to develop resistance. This resistance resulted in many treatment failures and caused the need for more potent antimicrobials. In 1956, McCormick and associates discovered the organism *Streptomyces orientalis*, now called *Nocardia orientalis*, from soil samples gathered in Indonesia and India. This organism produced an active compound called 05856 that had excellent activity against many gram-positive microorganisms [24]. This compound was later named vancomycin, which was derived from the word *vanishes* [25]. The FDA quickly approved it for clinical use in 1958, because of an increase in penicillin-resistant *S. aureus*. In the 1960s, reports of ototoxicity and nephrotoxicity began to appear in the literature, and with the advent of the less toxic semisynthetic penicillins, vancomycin use began to decline. In the early 1970s, *S. aureus*, now resistant to the semisynthetic penicillin, caused a surge in vancomycin use. Today's formulations of vancomycin are virtually void of all impurities, as opposed to the earlier formulation, and the incidence of side effects has decreased [26].

Teicoplanin, a glycopeptide structurally related to vancomycin, was derived from *Actinoplanes teichomyceticus*. It is currently not approved for use in the United States but has been used extensively in Europe [27].

2.2.6.2 Mechanism of Action

Vancomycin inhibits cell wall synthesis via a different mechanism than the beta-lactam antibiotics. Its primary mode of action is inhibition of peptidoglycan formation, which is the major structural component of the bacteria cell wall. Vancomycin is bactericidal to most bacteria except enterococci and tolerant strains of staphylococci, which are inhibited but not killed [5,27].

2.2.6.3 Mechanisms of Resistance

Glycopeptide resistance is categorized on the basis of the minimum inhibitory concentration (MIC) of the organism, and inducibility and transferability of resistance to vancomycin and teicoplanin. VanA is the most common type of resistance, and bacterial strains that possess this phenotype are resistant to both vancomycin and teicoplanin. VanB strains have a lower level of resistance to vancomycin and are susceptible to teicoplanin. VanC strains have low-level vancomycin resistance and are susceptible to teicoplanin [5,14,27].

Vancomycin resistance has been transferred to *S. aureus in vitro*, and clinical isolates with intermediate susceptibility have been reported. In May 1996, the first documented infection with vancomycin (glycopeptide) intermediate resistant *S. aureus* (GISA) was diagnosed in a patient in Japan [28]. In July 1997, the first case of GISA was diagnosed in the United States when a patient receiving continuous ambulatory peritoneal dialysis developed peritonitis. In August 1997, the second case of GISA was diagnosed in the United States [29].

2.2.6.4 Antimicrobial Activity and Therapeutic Uses

The antibacterial spectrum and clinical usefulness of vancomycin are limited to the treatment of gram-positive aerobic and anaerobic bacterial infections. Both (MSSA) and methicillin-resistant strains of *S. aureus* (MRSA) and most strains of coagulase-negative staphylococci are highly susceptible to vancomycin. Streptococci, including *viridans* species and penicillin-sensitive and -resistant pneumococci are susceptible. With the increasing incidence of vancomycin-resistant

TABLE 2.7
Vancomycin Guidelines for Use

Appropriate Use of Vancomycin

Treatment of serious infections due to β-lactam-resistant gram-positive microorganisms

Treatment of infections due to gram-positive organisms in patients with serious allergies to β-lactam antibiotics

Treatment of *C. difficile* colitis that has failed to respond to metronidazole or is severe and potentially life threatening

Endocarditis prophylaxis as recommended by the American Heart Association

Prophylaxis for implantation of prosthetic devices or materials at institutions with high rates of MRSA[a] or MRSE infections

Situations in Which the Use of Vancomycin Should Be Discouraged

Routine surgical prophylaxis

Empiric therapy for febrile neutropenic patients, unless there is evidence of possible gram-positive infection

Treatment in response to a single blood culture positive for coagulase-negative staphylococci

Continued empiric use for presumed infection in the absence of positive cultures

Prophylaxis for infection or colonization of intravascular catheters

Selective decontamination of the GI tract

Eradication of MRSA colonization

Primary treatment of *C. difficile* colitis

Routine prophylaxis for very low birth weight infants

Routine prophylaxis for patients on dialysis

Treatment chosen for dosing convenience in patients with renal failure

Topical application or irrigation

Source: Hospital Infection Control Practices Advisory Committee, *Infect. Control Hosp. Epidemiol.*, 16, 105–113, 1995.
[a] MRSA = methicillin-resistant *S. aureus*; MRSE = methicillin-resistant *S. epidermidis*.

enterococcus (VRE) seen nationwide, many institutions are reviewing vancomycin prescribing patterns. Recently, the Centers for Disease Control and Prevention (CDC) and the Hospital Infection Control Practices Advisory Committee published guidelines for the appropriate use of vancomycin and situations in which the use of vancomycin should be discouraged (Table 2.7) [30].

Vancomycin is poorly absorbed from the gastrointestinal tract, even when the colon is inflamed, and therefore the oral preparation is used only for the treatment of *C. difficile* colitis [5,27].

2.2.6.5 Adverse Effect Profile

The incidence of side effects associated with vancomycin is much less compared with earlier formulations and thought to be due to improved purification techniques. The most frequent adverse effect, the "redman" syndrome, was first described in the 1950s and was associated with a rapid infusion [31]. The syndrome is a nonimmunologic-mediated reaction caused by the release of histamine and is characterized by itching and a flushing of the upper trunk, face, and neck with or without hypotension. This myriad of symptoms may also include chest pain and dyspnea. As a result, it is recommended that vancomycin be infused slowly, over at least an hour in most patients [32]. Ototoxicity associated with vancomycin therapy is relatively uncommon. Reports of ototoxicity from vancomycin reported in the early 1960s were associated with high serum concentrations ranging from 80 to 100 mg/L; the desired peak is usually 25 to 30 mg/L [27,33]. Some experts have concluded that vancomycin may be ototoxic only when given with other ototoxic agents. There have been many retrospective and prospective studies published in the literature evaluating the incidence of vancomycin-induced nephrotoxicity. Nephrotoxicity associated with vancomycin use has been reported at overall rates of 5% to 17% and as high as 35% when combined with an aminoglycoside [34–36]. This phenomenon is usually reversible, and serum creatinine levels return to baseline following dosage adjustment.

2.2.7 STREPTOGRAMINS

Quinupristin-dalfopristin was approved in September 1999 by the FDA's accelerated approval process for the treatment of serious or life-threatening infections associated with vancomycin-resistant *Enterococcus faecium* (VREF) bacteremia. It is the first antibiotic in a new class known as *streptogramins* to be marketed in the United States. Quinupristin-dalfopristin is a synergistic combination in a 30:70 w/w ratio. This combination has been shown to be bacteriostatic against most strains of *E. faecium*, including VREF, but has no activity against *E. faecalis*. It is also active against *S. pyogenes* and MSSA and therefore also indicated for the treatment of complicated skin and skin-structure infections caused by these microorganisms. The most common side effects are infusion-related reactions (e.g., inflammation, pain, edema) followed by arthralgias, myalgias, and nausea [37].

2.2.8 CYCLIC LIPOPEPTIDES

2.2.8.1 Background

Daptomycin (Cubicin) is naturally derived from the fermentation process of *S. roseosporus*. It represents a new class of antibiotics known as *cyclic lipopeptides*. Daptomycin, formerly LY146032, was first discovered by the Eli Lilly Company in the early 1980s, but concerns about skeletal muscle toxicity lead to the voluntary suspension of clinical trials [38]. Today, it is used at lower doses, which allowed for FDA approval in September 2003.

2.2.8.2 Mechanism of Action

The mechanism of action is not fully understood and is unlike any other antibiotic currently on the market. It inserts its lipid tail into the cytoplasmic membrane of gram-positive bacteria with the aid of calcium. This in turn disrupts the functional integrity of the membrane causing a release of intracellular ions. Cell death occurs as the result of widespread dysfunction, primarily disruption of DNA, RNA, and protein synthesis [38]. Daptomycin is only active against gram-positive bacteria because it is unable to penetrate the outer membrane of gram-negative bacteria.

2.2.8.3 Antimicrobial Activity and Therapeutic Uses

In vitro, daptomycin exhibits rapid concentration-dependent bactericidal activity against a variety of gram-positive pathogens, including MRSA, vancomycin-intermediate susceptible *S. aureus,* and vancomycin-resistant enterococci, including *E. faecalis* [39].

Daptomycin was approved by the FDA in September 2003 for the treatment of complicated skin and skin-structure infections caused by susceptible strains of gram-positive organisms, including: *S. aureus* (including methicillin-resistant strains), *S. pyogenes, S. agalactiae, S. dysgalactiae* subspecies *equaisimilis,* and *Enterococcus faecalis* (vancomycin-susceptible strains only) [40]. Daptomycin penetrates poorly into lung tissue and is inactivated by surfactant; therefore, it is not indicated for the treatment of pneumonia.

2.2.8.4 Adverse Effect Profile

Daptomycin is fairly well tolerated when dosed at 4 mg/kg once daily. The most common adverse reactions are gastrointestinal disorders, including constipation, nausea, and diarrhea. But, as discussed previously, earlier studies performed by Eli Lilly showed skeletal muscle toxicity at dosages of 3 or 4 mg/kg twice daily. Two of five subjects receiving the higher dose experienced myalgias and extreme weakness along with elevations in serum creatine phosphokinase levels to >10 times the upper limit of normal [38]. Data suggested these reactions were associated with high trough concentrations and therefore prompted the more recent investigational trials utilizing 4–6 mg/kg once daily. In the more recent Phase 3 complicated skin and skin-structure infections trials, the incidence of elevated creatine phosphokinase levels occurred in 2.8% of the patients receiving daptomycin compared to 1.8% of the control group. Despite the low incidence of myopathy, the manufacturer recommends that patients receiving daptomycin should be monitored for the development of muscle pain, tenderness, or weakness, particularly of the distal extremities, and creatine phosphokinase levels should be monitored weekly [40].

2.2.9 OXAZOLIDINONES

2.2.9.1 Background

Infections due to *E. faecium* and MRSA have been an increasing problem over the past decade, especially in hospitalized and/or immunocompromised individuals. These organisms are inherently resistant to traditional antibiotics, including vancomycin. More recently, MRSA has made its way into the community setting, and in 1989 the first case of vancomycin-resistant *E. faecium* (VREF) was reported in the United States [41,42]. Linezolid represents a new class of antibiotics known as *oxazolidinones* and was approved by the FDA in April 2000.

2.2.9.2 Mechanism of Action

Linezolid inhibits bacterial protein synthesis through a mechanism of action different from that of other antibacterial agents; therefore, cross-resistance between linezolid and other classes of antibiotics is unlikely. Linezolid binds to the 50S subunit on the bacterial ribosome and eventually through a variety of steps prevents protein synthesis. Linezolid is considered to be bacteriostatic against enterococci and staphylococci and bactericidal against the majority of streptococci strains.

2.2.9.3 Antimicrobial Activity and Therapeutic Uses

Linezolid is indicated in the treatment of infections caused by VREF, including bacteremia, nosocomial pneumonia caused by methicillin-susceptible or methicillin-resistant *S. aureus* or penicillin-susceptible strains of *S. pneumoniae*, complicated or uncomplicated skin and skin-structure infections caused by *S. pyogenes,* methicillin-susceptible or methicillin-resistant strains of *S. aureus,* and community-acquired pneumonia caused by penicillin-susceptible strains of *S. pneumoniae*.

2.2.9.4 Adverse Effect Profile

The most commonly reported side effects in patients treated with linezolid were diarrhea, headache, nausea, and vomiting [43].

Not associated with its antimicrobial properties, linezolid is a reversible, nonselective inhibitor of monoamine oxidase. Inhibiting this enzyme can result in decreased metabolism of serotonin. Like the antidepressants, patients receiving linezolid should limit or monitor their intake of tyramine-containing food or beverages to prevent the inadvertent rise of serotonin, possibly leading to serotonin syndrome. Such foods include those that undergo protein changes by aging, fermentation, pickling, or smoking to improve flavor, such as aged cheeses, fermented meats, sauerkraut, tap beer, and red wine. Though not seen in clinical trials, linezolid has the potential to interact with serotonergic agents, such as the antidepressants, and selective serotonin surveillance reuptake inhibitors (SSRIs), causing serotonin syndrome. In postmarketing of linezolid, there have been a limited number of case reports of serotonin syndrome when linezolid was used in conjunction with SSRIs.

2.2.10 AMINOGLYCOSIDES

2.2.10.1 Background

In 1944, Selman Waksman discovered streptomycin, the first aminoglycoside, from soil samples containing *Streptomyces griseus*. Neomycin, kanamycin, tobramycin, and paromomycin are all naturally occurring compounds that were isolated from other *Streptomyces* species. Weinstein produced gentamicin in 1963 from *Micromonospora* spp., while amikacin and netilimicin are semisynthetic derivatives. Aminoglycosides derive their names depending on the sources from which they originated: names ending with *mycin* are derived directly or indirectly from *Streptomyces*, whereas those ending in *micin* are from *Micromonospora* spp. [44,45].

2.2.10.2 Mechanism of Action

Aminoglycosides are bactericidal against susceptible organisms by irreversibly binding to the bacterial ribosome and inhibiting protein synthesis. In order to achieve this, the aminoglycoside must first penetrate the bacteria cell wall. This process requires active transport and passive diffusion. Passive diffusion of an aminoglycoside can be enhanced by the addition of a cell wall synthesis inhibitor, such as a beta-lactam antibiotic, to the antibiotic regimen. Once inside the nucleus of the cell, the aminoglycoside irreversibly binds to the 30S subunit of the bacterial ribosome, disrupts protein synthesis, and eventually causes cell death through leakage of essential bacterial constituents [5,44,45].

2.2.10.3 Mechanisms of Resistance

Three primary mechanisms can result in resistance to the aminoglycosides. First, alterations in active transport or passive diffusion make the drug unable to penetrate the bacterial cell wall and bind to the ribosome. Second, chromosomal mutations result in the drug being unable to bind to the receptor on the 30S subunit of the bacterial ribosome. Third, the microorganism can produce enzymes to inactivate the aminoglycoside [5,14,44,45].

2.2.10.4 Antimicrobial Activity and Therapeutic Uses

Gentamicin, tobramycin, and amikacin have traditionally been used as empiric therapy in the treatment of febrile neutropenic patients and those with severe nosocomial infections because of their excellent activity against enteric gram-negative bacilli. Gentamicin is usually considered the aminoglycoside of choice in most institutions because of its low cost, although in institutions with higher rates of resistance, tobramycin or amikacin may be prescribed more frequently. To decrease the likelihood of resistance formation, aminoglycosides are commonly used in combination for the treatment of serious gram-negative infections, especially those caused by *P. aeruginosa*. Even though aminoglycosides have some limited activity against gram-positive bacteria, they are never used alone for this purpose. They are commonly used in combination with a cell-wall active agent such as a beta-lactam or vancomycin to treat enterococcal, streptococcal, and severe staphylococcal infections [5,44,45]. Aminoglycosides, particularly streptomycin, are used in the treatment of tuberculosis. The CDC recommends streptomycin be added to the drug regimen for the treatment of presumed multidrug-resistant tuberculosis unless the likelihood of resistance to isoniazid or rifampin is low [46]. It is also prescribed when a patient has a contraindication to use or toxicity to another agent.

2.2.10.5 Dosing

Aminoglycosides have traditionally been administered as an intravenous infusion in divided daily doses every 8–12 h, depending on renal function. Currently, once-daily dosing of aminoglycosides is more frequent. The rational for this dosing regimen is to enhance the bactericidal activity of aminoglycosides by maximizing the peak concentration/MIC ratio for the infecting organism. By administering an aminoglycoside as a large single daily dose, a clinician can take advantage of its concentration-dependent bacterial killing, time-dependent toxicity, and a prolonged postantibiotic effect. Data from animal models and clinical trials suggest that once-daily dosing is safe and effective, with no increase in adverse reactions and possibly a decrease in nephrotoxicity and ototoxicity compared with conventional dosing [47].

2.2.10.6 Adverse Effect Profile

All aminoglycosides can cause ototoxicity and nephrotoxicity. Ototoxicity is manifested by both auditory (cochlear damage) and vestibular symptoms. Auditory toxicity is irreversible and characterized by hearing loss, primarily of high frequency tones (those not used in conversation). Tinnitus, nausea, vomiting, and loss of balance may occur and are usually signs of vestibular damage [44,45]. Aminoglycosides have also been associated with the development of nephrotoxicity. The exact mechanism is not clear, and the incidence varies greatly. Nephrotoxicity induced by aminoglycoside use is usually mild and reversible. It occurs more frequently in critically ill patients, in the elderly, in dehydrated patients, in patients receiving other nephrotoxic drugs, and in those with elevated trough concentrations and prolonged therapy. Other risk factors associated with nephrotoxicity include preexisting renal dysfunction, shock, liver dysfunction, and obesity [48]. Serum peak and trough concentrations are commonly monitored for more accurate dosage adjustments and individualized patient dosing. All aminoglycosides may produce neuromuscular blockade. However, this is a rare complication, usually resulting from very rapid intravenous administration. Extra care should be taken when administering this drug to patients who have myasthenia gravis or are receiving neuromuscular-blocking agents (Table 2.8) [49]. Investigators from the CDC have reported an endotoxin-like reaction associated with the administration of intravenous gentamicin. Within 3 h. of receiving a dose, 20 patients at a major medical center in California developed severe shaking chills often accompanied by fever, tachycardia, and/or a decrease in systolic blood pressure. The investigators believe this reaction is associated with an endotoxin present in a particular brand of gentamicin. They explained that with traditional dosing, the endotoxin present in the gentamicin solution is administered in two or three divided doses over 24 h, whereas once-daily dosing delivers larger amounts of endotoxin over a shorter period of time, usually 1 hour. Studies are currently in process to determine the extent of these reactions and to identify their etiology [50].

TABLE 2.8
Adverse Effects Associated with Aminoglycosides

Hypersensitivity	**Neurologic**
Anaphylaxis	Ototoxicity
Rash	Neuromuscular blockade
Urticaria	Muscle twitching
	Peripheral neuropathy
Gastrointestinal	**Renal**
Nausea and vomiting	Nephrotoxicity
Diarrhea	
Hematologic	
Anemia	
Eosinophilia	
Leukopenia	
Thrombocytopenia	

Source: Thredlekd, D.S., Ed., *Drug Facts and Comparisons*, Facts and Comparisons, St. Louis, 2006; McEvoy, G.K., Ed., *AHFS Drug Information*, American Society of Health-System Pharmacists, Inc., Bethesda, 2006; Gilbert, D.N., in *Principles and Practices of Infectious Diseases*, Mandell, G.L., Bennett, J.E., and Dolin, R., Eds., Churchill Livingstone, New York, 1995, pp. 279–306; Sande, M.A. and Mandell, G.L., in *Goodman and Gilman's The Pharmacological Basis of Therapeutics*, Goodman Gilman, A., Rall, T.W., Nies, A.S., and Taylor, P., Eds., Pergamon Press, Elmsford, 1990, pp. 1098–1116; Moore, R.D., Smith, C.R., and Lietman, P.S., *J. Infect. Dis.*, 149, 23–30, 1984; Hakkanen, E., *Acta Neurol. Scan.*, 40, 346–352, 1964; Centers for Disease Control and Prevention, *MMWR*, 47(No. 41), 877–880, 1998.

2.2.11 TETRACYCLINES

2.2.11.1 Background

Benjamin Duggar discovered the first tetracycline, chlortetracycline (Aureomycin®), in 1948 while studying soil samples for antimicrobial properties. These soil samples, collected in Missouri, contained *Streptomyces aureofaciens*. Duggar named the organism and the antibiotic after the Latin word for gold (*aurum*) because of the golden yellow pigment it produced [51]. The second compound, oxytetracycline (Terramycin®), was isolated from *Streptomyces rimosus* in 1950. These two compounds were so similar in structure and clinical importance that they collectively called them *tetracyclines* (*tetra*, Latin for four, and *cyclos*, Latin for rings) [2]. Tetracycline was produced as the result of the catalytic dehalogenation of chlortetracycline in 1953 [52].

2.2.11.2 Mechanism of Action

Tetracyclines reversibly bind to the 30S ribosomal subunit, thereby inhibiting protein synthesis, which is responsible for their bacteriostatic action [5,52,53].

2.2.11.3 Mechanisms of Resistance

Once a microorganism develops resistance to one tetracycline, it generally confers resistance to the entire class of drugs. Resistance occurs more commonly because of chromosomal mutations in the outer membrane of the organisms resulting in a decreased penetration of tetracycline into the cell. Resistance can also occur due to an energy-dependent pumping of the drug out of the cell. Another mechanism, although poorly elucidated, is the biologic or chemical inactivation of tetracyclines by resistant bacteria. Bacteria can produce proteins that interact with the ribosome so that protein synthesis may continue despite the presence of tetracycline within the cell [5,14,52,53].

2.2.11.4 Classification

Tetracyclines are classified based upon their duration of action (Table 2.9) [5].

2.2.11.5 Antimicrobial Activity and Therapeutic Uses

Because of their broad spectrum, tetracyclines are used for a wide variety of infections. They are particularly useful in the treatment of Rocky Mountain spotted fever and are considered the drug of choice for the treatment of early Lyme disease [54]. Tetracyclines are very effective in the treatment of many sexually transmitted diseases. The CDC along with the Public Heath Service recommend doxycycline as the drug of choice for the treatment of lymphogranuloma venereum; nongonococcal urethritis; uncomplicated urethral, endocervical, or rectal *C. trachomatis* infections; pelvic inflammatory disease (with cefoxitin or cefotetan); and epididymitis (with ceftriaxone). Doxycycline may also be used as an alternative for nonpregnant patients with syphilis who report an allergy to penicillin [55]. They are often prescribed as alternative therapy when the drug of choice in not feasible (e.g., allergy to the beta-lactams, sulfas, or quinolones).

2.2.11.6 Adverse Effect Profile

The most common side effect associated with tetracyclines is gastrointestinal related and include epigastric burning, abdominal discomfort, nausea, vomiting, and anorexia. Food may alleviate these symptoms but may also decrease the absorption by up to 50%. Doxycycline may be taken with food with no alterations in absorption. Tetracyclines can cause alterations in the normal bowel flora, causing large bulky stools or diarrhea [56]. Photosensitivity reactions can range from a red rash to blisters on sun-exposed areas and are most common with demeclocycline but may occur with any of the

TABLE 2.9
Tetracyclines Classifications

Classification Generic Name	Route of Administration
Short Acting	
Tetracycline HCl	Oral, IM,[a] IV
Oxytetracycline HCl	Oral, IM
Intermediate Acting	
Demeclocycline	Oral
Long Acting	
Doxycycline hyclate	Oral, IV
Doxycycline calcium	Oral
Doxycycline monohydrate	Oral
Minocycline	IV
Minocycline HCl	Oral

Source: Thredlekd, D.S., Ed., *Drug Facts and Comparisons*, Facts and Comparisons, St. Louis, 2006; McEvoy, G.K., Ed., *AHFS Drug Information*, American Society of Health-System Pharmacists, Inc., Bethesda, 2006; Standiford, H.C., in *Principles and Practices of Infectious Diseases*, Mandell, G.L., Bennett, J.E., and Dolin, R., Eds., Churchill Livingstone, New York, 1995, pp. 306–317; Sande, M.A. and Mandell, G.L., in *Goodman and Gilman's The Pharmacological Basis of Therapeutics*, Goodman Gilman, A., Rall, T.W., Nies, A.S., and Taylor, P., Eds., Pergamon Press, Elmsford, 1990, pp. 1117–1145.
[a] IM = intramuscular; IV = intravenous.

tetracyclines. This reaction can occur within minutes to hours of sun exposure and may persist for 1 to 2 days after discontinuation of the drug [57]. Tetracyclines are usually not recommended for children under 8 years of age because they can cause permanent discoloration of teeth and skeletal bone growth retardation. Hepatotoxicity is rare but often fatal when it occurs (Table 2.10) [5,52].

2.2.12 GLYCYLCYCLINES

2.2.12.1 Background

Emerging antimicrobial resistance has created the need for the development of new antimicrobials that are less likely to be affected by the commonly known mechanisms of resistance formation. Tigecycline is a new broad-spectrum antimicrobial agent that represents the first in its class of semisynthetic glycylcyclines. This drug was specifically designed by Wyeth to overcome the two most common mechanisms of resistance to tetracyclines: efflux pumps and ribosomal protection proteins. By adding a bulky side chain at position 9 of the minocycline molecule, tigecycline is less affected by resistance mutation and has improved activity and tolerability.

2.2.12.2 Mechanism of Action

Like tetracycline, tigecycline also binds to the 30S subunit of the bacterial ribosome to inhibit protein synthesis. The glycylcycline derivatives bind approximately five times more effectively than tetracycline.

2.2.12.3 Antimicrobial Activity and Therapeutic Uses

Tigecycline has activity *in vitro* against many gram-positive organisms including MRSA, glycopeptide-intermediately resistant *S. aureus* (GISA), penicillin-resistant *S. pneumoniae*, and van-

TABLE 2.10
Adverse Effects Associated with Tetracyclines

Hypersensitivity Reactions	Teeth and Bones
Urticaria	Yellow to gray-brown discoloration
Morbilliform rashes	Hypoplasia of the enamel
Exfoliative dermatitis	Bone growth retardation
Anaphylaxis	
Stevens-Johnson syndrome	

Gastrointestinal	Photosensitivity and Hyperpigmentation
Epigastric/abdominal pain	Red rash to blisters
Nausea and vomiting	Pigmentation of nails, skin, and sclera
Anorexia	Discoloration of gums

Hepatic	Miscellaneous
Intrahepatic cholestatis	Vertigo
Jaundice	Systemic lupus erythematous-like syndrome

Source: Thredlekd, D.S., Ed., *Drug Facts and Comparisons*, Facts and Comparisons, St. Louis, 2006; McEvoy, G.K., Ed., *AHFS Drug Information*, American Society of Health-System Pharmacists, Inc., Bethesda, 2006; Standiford, H.C., in *Principles and Practices of Infectious Diseases*, Mandell, G.L., Bennett, J.E., and Dolin, R., Eds., Churchill Livingstone, New York, 1995, pp. 306–317; Sande, M.A. and Mandell, G.L., in *Goodman and Gilman's The Pharmacological Basis of Therapeutics*, Goodman Gilman, A., Rall, T.W., Nies, A.S., and Taylor, P., Eds., Pergamon Press, Elmsford, 1990, pp. 1117–1145; Finegold, S.M., *Am. J. Clin. Nutr.*, 23, 1466–1471, 1970; Frost, P., Weinstein, G.D., and Gomez, E.C., *Arch Derm.*, 105, 681–683, 1972.

comycin-resistant *enterococci* (VRE). It is also active against many gram-negative organisms including *Acinetobacter baumanii*, *Stenotrophomonas maltophilia*, most Enterobacteriaceae, including some strains producing extended-spectrum B-lactamases (ESBLs), and against many atypical bacteria and anaerobes, including *B. fragilis* and *Clostridium perfringes* and *C. difficile*. It does not have clinically significant activity against *P. aeruginosa* or *Proteus* species [58]. Tigecycline is currently FDA approved for the treatment of patients with complicated skin and skin-structure infections and complicated intraabdominal infections caused by susceptible strains.

2.2.12.4 Adverse Effect Profile

Nausea and vomiting appear to be dosed related and are the most common adverse effects associated with tigecycline, occurring in 30% and 20%, respectively. These symptoms usually occur in the first 1 to 2 days of treatment and are more common in women than men. Tigecycline is structurally similar to tetracycline and may cause similar adverse effects, including photosensitivity and discoloration of the teeth if used during tooth development [59].

2.2.13 MACROLIDES

2.2.13.1 Background

In 1952, McGuire and colleagues discovered erythromycin, the prototype and first antibiotic in the class of macrolides. It was isolated from the metabolic products of *Streptomyces erythreus*, originally collected from soil samples obtained in the Philippine archipelago [53]. To date, the FDA has approved azithromycin, clarithromycin, dirthromycin, erythromycin (including many salt forms), and troleandomycin (Table 2.11) [4,5]. A 12–16 membered lactone ring characterizes the chemical structure of macrolides. Azithromycin is a semisynthetic compound that contains a 15-membered

TABLE 2.11
Macrolides

Generic Name	Route of Administration
Azithromycin	Oral, IV[a]
Clarithromycin	Oral
Dirthromycin	Oral
Erythromycin base	Oral
Erythromycin estolate	Oral
Erythromycin stearate	Oral
Erythromycin ethylsuccinate	Oral
Erythromycin lactobionate	IV
Erythromycin gluceptate	IV
Troleandomycin	Oral

Source: Thredlekd, D.S., Ed., *Drug Facts and Comparisons*, Facts and Comparisons, St. Louis, 2006; McEvoy, G.K., Ed., *AHFS Drug Information*, American Society of Health-System Pharmacists, Inc., Bethesda, 2006; Steigbigel, N.H., in *Principles and Practices of Infectious Diseases*, Mandell, G.L., Bennett, J.E., and Dolin, R., Eds., Churchill Livingstone, New York, 1995, pp. 334–346.
[a] IV = intravenous.

structure and is considered the prototype for a new macrolide structure termed azalides; the ketolides, discussed below, have a 14-membered lactone ring.

2.2.13.2 Mechanism of Action

Macrolides penetrate the cell wall of susceptible gram-positive and -negative microorganisms and reversibly bind to the 50S ribosomal subunit, inhibiting RNA-dependent protein synthesis. They are primarily bacteriostatic in nature but can be bactericidal, depending on the microorganism and drug concentration [5,53,60].

2.2.13.3 Antimicrobial Activity and Therapeutic Uses

Macrolides are highly active against many gram-positive organisms and have good activity against some gram-negative organisms, especially those commonly isolated from the respiratory tract. For this reason, they are considered the preferred agent for the treatment of outpatient community-acquired pneumonia, and erythromycin is considered the drug of choice when *Legionella* is suspected [61]. Macrolides are also prescribed for acute bacterial exacerbations of chronic bronchitis. Upper respiratory tract infections, including pharyngitis and tonsillitis, acute maxillary sinusitis, and otitis media, are commonly caused by *S. pyogenes*, *S. pneumoniae*, *H. influenzae*, and *M. catarrhalis* to which macrolides have good activity. They also have good activity against those organisms most commonly implicated in skin and skin-structure infections: methicillin-sensitive *S. aureus*, *S. pyogenes*, and other *Streptococcus* species. *N. gonorrhoeae*, *C. trachomatis*, *Mycoplasma* species, and *Ureaplasma urealyticum,* to which macrolides have good activity, commonly cause sexually transmitted diseases. Erythromycin is considered the drug of choice for treating chlamydial infections in pregnancy, whereas azithromycin is commonly prescribed as a one-time dose for the treatment of *C. trachomatis* in patients in whom compliance is an issue [55]. Clarithromycin combined with omeprazole and/or metronidazole is prescribed for the treatment of *H. pylori*–associated duodenal ulcer disease. The United States Public Health Service recommends a macrolide, usually clarithromycin or azithromycin, be used in combination with other medications for the treatment of *Mycobacterium avium* complex infections. These two macrolides have also been studied as alternative agents for the prevention of *M. avium* complex infections [62].

2.2.13.4 Adverse Effect Profile

The majority of side effects associated with the macrolides are mild and transient, and as a class they are generally well tolerated. The most common complaints involve the gastrointestinal tract and include diarrhea, nausea and vomiting, and abdominal pain. Patients receiving clarithromycin may complain of an abnormal or metallic aftertaste. Hepatotoxicity is a very rare but serious side effect associated primarily with the estolate salt of erythromycin [4,5,53,60].

2.2.14 KETOLIDES

Telithromycin is the first member in a new class of antibiotics known as the *ketolides* approved for use in the United States. This compound, derived from erythromycin A, is very similar in structure to the macrolides but has a ketone bond in the 3-position of the erythronolide ring, instead of the sugar cladinose. Like the macrolides, ketolides inhibit protein synthesis by reversibly binding to the 50S ribosomal subunit of the bacterial ribosome. Their spectrum of activity is similar to the macrolides, except they provide a broader coverage against macrolide-resistant streptococci. They are being developed for respiratory indications, including community-acquired pneumonia, acute bacterial exacerbations of chronic bronchitis, sinusitis, and pharyngitis, especially when resistant *S. pneumoniae* strains may be a concern [63]. The most commonly occurring adverse effects associated with the use of telithromycin were gastrointestinal in nature, including nausea, vomiting, and diarrhea, occurring in 8% to 10% of patients. Visual disturbances (blurred vision, diplopia, and accommodation difficulties) occurred in 0.6% of patients. These reactions more commonly occurred after the first or second dose of the medication and persisted for several hours. Liver abnormalities are currently under review with this medication after a recent paper published in the *Annals of Internal Medicine* described three patients who experienced serious liver toxicity following the administration of telithromycin. On June 29, 2006, the FDA notified healthcare professionals and patients that it had completed its safety review of telithromycin. They concluded that additional warnings about the risk of liver toxicity are required and instructed the manufacturer to revise their package insert.

2.2.15 FLUOROQUINOLONES

2.2.15.1 Background

The fluoroquinolones can be classified into four generations based on their antimicrobial activity. Nalidixic acid, a first-generation fluoroquinolone discovered in 1962, has a narrow gram-negative coverage and limited tissue distribution. Even though it has a very limited place in therapy, it served as the prototype for many other fluoroquinolones [64]. In the 1980s, it was discovered that manipulating the basic structure of nalidixic acid led to agents with a broader spectrum of antibacterial activity, better tissue distribution, and improved pharmacokinetics. These "second-generation" fluoroquinolones include ciprofloxacin, enoxacin, levofloxacin, lomefloxacin, norflox-acin, ofloxacin, and temafloxacin. Temafloxacin was voluntarily withdrawn from the market in 1992 by Abbott Laboratories, because of severe adverse effects, including six deaths, hemolytic anemia, renal and hepatic dysfunction, and hypoglycemia associated with its use in the first three months of marketing [65]. The "third-generation" fluoroquinolones include gatifloxacin, sparflox-acin, moxifloxacin, and grepafloxacin. These agents retain expanded gram-negative and atypical pathogen coverage, as compared to the second generation, but also have improved gram-positive pathogen coverage. On October 27, 1999, grepafloxacin was voluntarily withdrawn from the

TABLE 2.12
Fluoroquinolones Classifications

Classification Generic Name	Route of Administration
First Generation	
Nalidixic acid	Oral
Second Generation	
Ciprofloxacin	Oral, IV[a]
Enoxacin	Oral
Levofloxacin	Oral, IV
Lomefloxacin	Oral
Norfloxacin	Oral
Ofloxacin	Oral, IV
Third Generation	
Gatifloxacin	Oral, IV
Moxifloxacin	Oral
Sparfloxacin	Oral
Fourth Generation	
Trovafloxacin (alatrovafloxacin)	Oral, IV
Gemifloxacin	Oral

Source: Thredlekd, D.S., Ed., *Drug Facts and Comparisons*, Facts and Comparisons, St. Louis, 2006; McEvoy, G.K., Ed., *AHFS Drug Information*, American Society of Health-System Pharmacists, Inc., Bethesda, 2006; Mandell, G.L. and Sande, M.A., in *Goodman and Gilman's The Pharmacological Basis of Therapeutics*, Goodman Gilman, A., Rall, T.W., Nies, A.S., and Taylor, P., Eds., Pergamon Press, Elmsford, 1990, pp. 1047–1064; Hooper, D.C., in *Principles and Practices of Infectious Diseases*, Mandell, G.L., Bennett, J.E., and Dolin, R., Eds., Churchill Livingstone, New York, 1995, pp. 364–376.
[a] IV = intravenous.

market because the pharmaceutical company, GlaxoSmithKline, concluded that the therapeutic benefit was outweighed by the potential cardiac risks, especially given the availability of alternative treatments [66]. The fourth generations of fluoroquinolones have improved gram-positive coverage, maintain gram-negative coverage, and gain anaerobic coverage. This generation includes trovafloxacin, which was approved by the FDA in December 1997, and gemifloxacin, approved April 4, 2003. In June 1999, the FDA issued a public health advisory to all health care professionals that described serious liver injury associated with the use of trovafloxacin. The drug is currently available for use, but the FDA and Pfizer Pharmaceuticals strongly advise it be reserved for patients who meet specific criteria [67]. Since then, two additional fluoroquinolones have been approved by the FDA, moxifloxacin and gatifloxacin (Table 2.12) [4,5]. In May 2006, the FDA in cooperation with Bristol-Myers Squibb (gatifloxacin) mailed a letter to all health care professionals describing serious, sometimes fatal, cases of both hypoglycemia and hyperglycemia. This was prompted by a case-control study published in the *New England Journal of Medicine* that found that the use of gatifloxacin among outpatients was associated with an increased risk of both hypoglycemia and hyperglycemia as found among inpatients [68].

2.2.15.2 Mechanism of Action

The mechanism of action of the fluoroquinolones has not been clearly defined. However, it is clear that they inhibit bacterial DNA synthesis by inhibiting the enzyme DNA gyrase. This enzyme is essential in bacterial replication and is responsible for breaking the superhelical twist of DNA, allowing the incorporation of new DNA and resealing the break [5,69,70].

2.2.15.3 Antimicrobial Activity and Therapeutic Uses

There are currently 12 fluoroquinolones on the market. These agents are considered bactericidal and have a wide range of activity against gram-negative and some gram-positive organisms. Trovafloxacin is the only quinolone with FDA approved labeling for use against anaerobes [4,5]. Among the gram-negative organisms, quinolones have excellent activity against the *Enterobacteriacae* and *H. influenzae*, *N. gonorrhoeae*, *N. meningitidis*, and *M. catarrhalis*. Compared with the other quinolones, ciprofloxacin is more active against pseudomonads and most gram-negative organisms. They also exhibit good, but variable, activity against gram-positive organisms, including methicillin-susceptible *S. aureus* and *S. epidermidis*, but less activity against *Streptococcus* and *Enterococcus* species [4,5,69,70].

Norfloxacin is effective for infections involving the genitourinary and gastrointestinal tracts. It is poorly absorbed and therefore achieves minimal serum levels, and the MICs for most bacteria outside of these two sites preclude it for use in systemic infections. The other fluoroquinolones have been studied extensively as empiric treatment of patients with community-acquired pneumonia. According to recent guidelines from the Infectious Disease Society of America, respiratory fluoroquinolones such as levofloxacin, moxifloxacin, gatifloxacin, or gemifloxacin or a beta-lactam antibiotic with an advanced macrolide (azithromycin or clarithromycin) are considered preferred agents for most patients treated empirically for community-acquired pneumonia [61]. Quinolones have also been used for the treatment of nosocomially acquired pneumonia, bronchitis, sinusitis, and exacerbations of cystic fibrosis.

2.2.15.4 Adverse Effect Profile

The quinolones are generally well tolerated, although the frequency of adverse effects may increase with higher dosage. The most common side effects are gastrointestinal; primarily nausea and diarrhea; however, vomiting, epigastric burning, abdominal cramps, anorexia, and flatulence have been reported. Adverse reactions involving the central nervous system are the second most commonly encountered reaction and occur in 1% to 3% of the patients taking quinolones [70]. Symptoms include tremulousness, headache, dizziness, anxiety, nightmares, and insomnia. As a result of the cartilage damage seen in young animals, the fluoroquinolones are currently not recommended for use in children, pregnant women, or nursing mothers. Moderate to severe phototoxic reactions have occurred in patients exposed to direct or indirect sunlight or artificial ultraviolet light (sunlamps) while taking quinolones. The incidence of this reaction is higher with lomefloxain and fleroxacin compared with the other quinolones [71]. As mentioned earlier reports of hepatotoxicity prompted Pfizer Laboratories to mail "Dear Prescriber Letters," emphasizing the proper use of trovafloxacin for patients with serious infections in which therapy was initially started in the hospital or nursing home [72]. Additional scientific evaluation and analyses to clarify this are ongoing. Other less common adverse effects include cardiovascular, musculoskeletal, renal, hematological, ocular, and respiratory effects.

2.2.16 SULFONAMIDES AND TRIMETHOPRIM

2.2.16.1 Background

In 1932, after many exhaustive experiments, Domagk tested compound Kl-730, a red azo dye, against a streptococcus growing in the test tube and in laboratory mice [73]. The compound had no effect against the streptococcus in the test tube, but when given to the infected mice, they were protected. This compound was named Prontosil rubrum. In 1935, Trefouel and colleagues manipulated Prontosil, breaking the azo bond, and tested the by-products for antibacterial activity. One chemical that was produced was sulfanilamide, which was found to be as potent against streptococcus as Prontosil. They concluded that sulfanilamide was the active component of Prontosil and responsible for the antibacterial effect. Ironically, Gelmo had described sulfanilamide in 1908 while working on his doctoral thesis. He had no idea of its antibacterial properties but was working on the synthesis of dyes (Table 2.1) [69].

Included in the class of sulfonamides are sulfisoxazole, sulfamethoxazole, sulfadiazine, sulfadoxine, sulfasalazine, and sulfapyridine [4,5].

2.2.16.2 Mechanism of Action

The sulfonamides and trimethoprim inhibit the growth of susceptible microorganisms by preventing the formation of nucleic acids, and therefore cell growth. Either drug when used alone is bacteriostatic, but when combined they are bactericidal for susceptible organisms [69,74]. A combination of trimethoprim and a sulfonamide results in a sequential blockade in the folate synthesis pathway in bacteria. Specifically, sulfamethoxazole inhibits the enzyme responsible for the incorporation of para-aminobenzoic acid (PABA) into the precursor of folic acid (dihydrofolic acid), therefore blocking folic acid production in bacteria. Trimethoprim is a potent inhibitor of the enzyme dihydrofolate reductase and interferes with the conversion of folic acid to folinic acid (tetrahydrofolic acid). Folinic acid is necessary in the production of purines, the backbone of both bacterial and mammalian DNA, and therefore inhibition of such results in cell death. Fortunately, mammalian cells can utilize folic acid obtained from the diet, bacteria cells cannot and therefore trimethoprim has little effect on mammalian cells [5,69,74].

2.2.16.3 Antimicrobial Activity and Therapeutic Uses

Trimethoprim-sulfamethoxazole has a wide range of activity against both gram-positive and gram-negative organisms, including *H. influenzae*, *S. pneumoniae*, *S. aureus*, *Salmonella* spp., *Shigella* spp., *Nocardia* spp., *Listeria* spp., *E. coli*, most *Enterobacteriaceae*, and *Pseudomonas* species other than *P. aeruginosa*. It is indicated for a variety of infections involving the genitourinary, gastrointestinal, and respiratory tracts. It is commonly prescribed for urinary tract infections and upper respiratory tract infections (i.e., otitis media, sinusitis, and bronchitis). It is considered the drug of choice for the treatment and prophylaxis of *Pneumocystis carinii* pneumonia and *Toxoplasmosis gondii* [5,69,74].

Sulfadiazine and sulfisoxazole have been shown effective in the treatment of nocardia infections. Sulfasalazine is indicated in the management of mild-to-moderate ulcerative colitis. Topical sulfonamide can be found in a variety of preparations including acne creams, antibacterial eye drops, vaginal creams, and burn creams [74].

2.2.16.4 Adverse Effect Profile

Trimethoprim-sulfamethoxazole is well tolerated by most people. Rashes occur in about 3% of patients who use this product and are usually mild. Severe skin reactions such as Stevens-Johnson syndrome have occurred but are rare. More frequent but less serious side effects include nausea, vomiting, and diarrhea [4,5,74].

2.3 ANTIMYCOBACTERIAL AGENTS

2.3.1 Isoniazid (INH)

Isoniazid, introduced in 1952, is the most active drug for the treatment of tuberculosis and has some activity against the other mycobacterium species. The mechanism of action is not fully understood but is thought to be through inhibition of the mycobacterial cell wall synthesis. It is bactericidal against *M. tuberculosis* when actively growing, but bacteriostatic if the organism is not replicating [75,76]. Peripheral neuropathy, most likely caused by interference with the metabolism of pyridoxine, is associated with isoniazid. Pyridoxine, vitamin B-6, is commonly given to patients to prevent peripheral neuropathy. Isoniazid has also been associated with minor asymptomatic elevations in liver function tests that usually resolve with continued treatment. Though fulminate hepatotoxicity is rare, it may occur at any time, but more likely 4–8 weeks after treatment has begun (Table 2.13) [4,5].

2.3.2 RIFAMPIN, RIFABUTIN, AND RIFAPENTINE

The rifamycins are a class of antibiotics produced by *Streptomyces mediterranei*. First described in the 1960s, there are now three rifamycins currently approved for clinical use in the United States. Rifampin, rifabutin, and, more recently, rifapentine (a long-acting rifamycin) are used primarily for the treatment of mycobacterial infections but are also active against some gram-positive and gram-negative organisms. They inhibit nucleic acid synthesis by binding to DNA-dependent RNA polymerase [5,75,76]. The most common adverse effect is gastrointestinal upset. The rifamycins are excreted in the urine, tears, sweat as well as other body fluids and can cause a red–orange discoloration. Patients should be warned of the discoloration of body fluids and advised of the possibility of discoloration of soft contact lenses. Other reactions include rash, hepatitis, myalgias, arthralgias, and rarely thrombocytopenia and neutropenia. Uveitis is associated with rifabutin and appears to be dose-dependent. Symptoms include acute onset of ocular pain, blurry vision, photophobia, and diminished visual acuity. The patient should be advised to report these symptoms to their health care provider immediately, at which time rifabutin should be discontinued (Table 2.13) [4,5]. Rifabutin, rifapentine, and, to a lesser extent, rifampin are inducers of hepatic microsomal enzymes and therefore have the potential for drug interactions with other medications metabolized through the liver. They may increase the clearance of zidovudine, dapsone, methadone, coumadin, glucocorticoids, estrogens, oral hypoglycemic agents, quinidine,

TABLE 2.13
Antimycobacterial Drugs

Medication	Usual Adult Dosage[a]	Side Effects
Isoniazid	300 mg po qd[b]	Peripheral neuropathy, hepatitis, skin rash, arthralgia, drowsiness, fever
Rifampin	600 mg po qd	Hepatitis, rash, thrombocytopenia, flu-like syndrome, orange-red discoloration
Pyrazinamide	30 mg/kg po qd	Hepatitis, fever, skin rash, arthralgia, hyperuricema, abdominal distress
Ethambutol	15–25 mg/kg po qd	Optic neuritis, skin rash, abdominal distress
Streptomycin	15 mg/kg IM/IV qd	Hearing loss, ataxia, nystagmus, nephrotoxicity
Amikacin	15 mg/kg IV qd	Hearing loss
Ofloxacin	400 mg po q12h	Abdominal distress, headache, anxiety
Ciprofloxacin	750 mg po q12h	Abdominal distress, headache, anxiety

Source: Thredlekd, D.S., Ed., *Drug Facts and Comparisons*, Facts and Comparisons, St. Louis, 2006; McEvoy, G.K., Ed., *AHFS Drug Information*, American Society of Health-System Pharmacists, Inc., Bethesda, 2006; Centers for Disease Control and Prevention, *MMWR*, 42(No. RR-7), 1–7, 1993; Centers for Disease Control and Prevention, *MMWR*, 47, 1998; Alford, R.H. and Wallace, R.J. Jr., in *Principles and Practices of Infectious Diseases*, Mandell, G.L., Bennett, J.E., and Dolin, R., Eds., Churchill Livingstone, New York, 1995, pp. 389–401; Mandell, G.L. and Sande, M.A., in *Goodman and Gilman's The Pharmacological Basis of Therapeutics*, Goodman Gilman, A., Rall, T.W., Nies, A.S., and Taylor, P., Eds., Pergamon Press, Elmsford, 1990, pp. 1146–1181.

[a] Dosages are for adults weighing 60 kg and with normal renal function.

[b] po = by mouth; IM = intramuscular; IV = intravenous; qd = daily; q12h = every 12 h.

verapamil, theophylline, anticonvulsants, cyclosporin, protease inhibitors, and nonnucleoside reverse transcriptase inhibitors [4,5].

2.3.3 Pyrazinamide (PZA)

Pyrazinamide, a synthetic analog of nicotinamide, is bactericidal for *M. tuberculosis*. The most common side effects are nausea and vomiting. The most important adverse reaction to pyrazinamide is liver damage. Hyperuricemia occurs frequently, but acute gout is uncommon. Skin rash and gastrointestinal intolerance are also seen (Table 2.13) [4,5,75,76].

2.3.4 Ethambutol (ETH)

Ethambutol was discovered in 1961 and, at usual doses, is generally considered bacteriostatic against *M. tuberculosis*. It may have bactericidal effects when given at higher doses, but its precise mechanism of action is unknown. Its spectrum of activity is limited to mycobacteria. It has no activity against gram-positive or gram-negative organisms or fungi [5,75,76]. The drug is usually well tolerated with a low frequency of side effects. At higher dosage, retrobulbar neuritis is the most serious side effect of ethambutol. Symptoms include blurred vision, decreased visual acuity, and red–green color blindness (Table 2.13) [4,5].

2.3.5 Antimicrobial Activity and Therapeutic Uses

Tuberculosis must be treated for a long duration as compared with most other infectious diseases; if not, the infection may reoccur, and the patient may develop drug-resistant mycobacteria. Due to the high rates of resistant tuberculosis, it is recommended that all patients receive at least an initial four-drug regimen treatment of isoniazid, rifampin, pyrazinamide, and ethambutol which can later be pared down to a three-drug regimen. (Table 2.14) [46].

The treatment of tuberculosis in persons infected with HIV is complicated by many factors. The risk of drug-resistant tuberculosis is higher among persons with known HIV infection and therefore requires multiple antituberculosis drugs. In addition the concomitant use of rifamycins and protease inhibitors results in potentially harmful drug interactions.

Preventive therapy reduces the risk of developing clinically active tuberculosis in infected persons. Isoniazid is the only antituberculosis drug shown to be effective for preventive therapy. Depending on skin test results, age, and risk categories, it is usually given for 6–12 months in adults and 9 months in children. At least six months of preventive therapy with isoniazid is recommended for adults and children who have abnormal chest radiographs consistent with a past infection of tuberculosis. A 12-month regimen of rifampin alone or in combination with PZA or ethambutol is recommended for people exposed to a patient with INH-resistant *M. tuberculosis* or if the patient has failed treatment. If the index case has documented multidrug resistant tuberculosis, combination therapy with PZA and ofloxacin is recommended [32]. For HIV-infected adults, a nine-month regimen of isoniazid can be administered daily or a two-month regimen of a rifamycin (rifabutin or rifampin) and pyrazinamide can be administered daily. Rifabutin is recommended for patients receiving a protease inhibitor, whereas rifampin is recommended for patients not receiving protease inhibitors. The concurrent administration of rifampin and a protease inhibitor is not recommended [77].

Various treatment regimens for the treatment of disseminated *M. avium* complex (DMAC) infections have been studied. The ideal regimen remains unclear. Azithromycin or clarithromycin, ethambutol, rifabutin, clofazimine, ciprofloxacin, and amikacin are the agents used, usually in combination, for the treatment of DMAC. Rifabutin, clarithromycin, and azithromycin have all been used as prophylactic agents. The U.S. Public Health Service recommends a macrolide, usually azithromycinor, clarithromycin, generally in conjunction with ethambutol, clofazime, ciprofloxacin, or rifabutin, for those patients previously treated for DMAC infections. Prophylaxis should be

TABLE 2.14
Drug Regimens for Culture-Positive Pulmonary Tuberculosis Caused by Drug-Susceptible Organisms

Initial Phase			Continuation Phase			Range of total doses (minimal duration)	Rating* (evidence)† HIV−	Rating* (evidence)† HIV+
Regimen	Drugs	Interval and doses‡ (minimal duration)	Regimen	Drugs	Interval and doses¶ (minimal duration)			
1	INH RHF PZA EMB	Seven days per week for 56 doses (8 wk) or 5 d/wk for 40 doses (8 wk)¶	1a	INH/RIF	Seven days per week for 125 doses (18 wk) or 5 d/wk for 90 doses (18 wk)¶	182–130 (25 wk)	A(I)	A(II)
			1b	INH/RIF	Twice weekly for 38 doses (18 wk)	92–75 (28 wk)	A(I)	A(II)*
			1c*+	INH/RPT	Once weekly for 18 doses (15 wk)	74–58 (26 wk)	B(I)	E(I)
2	INH RIF PZA EMB	Seven days per week for 14 doses (w wk), than twice weekly for 12 doses (8 wk) or 5 d/wk for 10 doses (2 wk),¶ then twice weekly for 12 doses (wk)	2a	INH/RIF	Twice weekly for 36 doses (18 week)	62–58 (26 wk)	A(II)	B(II)*
			2b*+	INH/RPT	Once weekly for 18 doses (18 wk)	44–40 (28 wk)	B(I)	E(I)
3	INH RIF PZA EMB	Three times weekly for 24 doses (8 wk)	3a	INH/RIF	Three times weekly for 54 doses (18 wk)	78 (26 wk)	B(I)	B(II)
4	INH RIF EMB	Seven days per week for 58 doses (8 wk) or 5 d/wk for 40 doses (8 wk)	4a	INH/RIF	Seven days per week for 217 doses (31 wk) or 5 d/wk for 156 doses (31 wk)	273–195 (38 wk)	C(I)	C(II)
			4b	INH/RIF	Twice weekly for 52 doses (31 wk)	115–102 (38 wk)	C(I)	C(II)

Definition of abbreviations: EMB = Ebambutol; INH = Isoniazid; PZA = pyrazinamide; RIF = rifampin; RPT = ribpertine.

* Definitions of evidence ratings: A = preferred; B = acceptable alternative; C = other when A and B cannot be given; E = should never be given.

† Definition of evidence ratings: I = randomized clinical trial; II = data from clinical trials that were not randomized or were conducted in other populations; III = expert opinion.

‡ When DOT is used, drugs may be given 5 days/week and the necessary number of doses adjusted accordingly. Although there are no studies that compare five with seven daily doses, extensive experience indicates this would be an effective practice.

§ Patients with cavitation on initial chest radiograph and positive cultures at completion of 2 months of therapy should receive a 7-month (31 week; either 217 doses [daily] or 62 doses [twice weekly]) continuation phase.

¶ Five-day-a-week administration is always given by DOT. Rating for 5 day/week regimens is AIII.

+ Not recommended for HIV-infected patients with CD_4* cell counts <100 cells/µl.

− Options 1c and 2b should be used only in HIV-negative patients who have negative sputum smears at the time of completion of 2 months of therapy and who do not have cavitation on initial chest radiograph (see text). For patients started on this regimen and found to have a positive culture from the 2-month specimen, treatment should be extended an extra 3 months.

Source: *Treatment of Tuberculosis.* Centers for Disease Control and Prevention (CDC) Morbidity and Mortality Weekly Reports (MMWR) 52(RR11); 1–77, (2003, June 20).

considered for all HIV-infected persons without previous history of DMAC infection who have a CD4+ count of <75 cells/mm^3, although some experts would wait until the CD4+ count is <50 cells/mm^3 [62].

2.4 ANTIVIRAL AGENTS

2.4.1 ANTIRETROVIRAL AGENTS (FUSION INHIBITORS, NUCLEOSIDE AND NUCLEOTIDE REVERSE TRANSCRIPTASE INHIBITORS, NONNUCLEOSIDE REVERSE TRANSCRIPTASE INHIBITORS, AND PROTEASE INHIBITORS)

2.4.1.1 Mechanisms of Action

Targets in the viral replicative cycle that are potentially susceptible to antiviral intervention include entry of the virus into the cell, reverse transcriptase, integrase, protease, and viral maturation and release [78].

Fusion inhibitors directly interfere with host and cellular membrane fusion, thereby preventing entry of HIV-1 into the cell. The HIV-1 envelope contains surface glycoproteins (gp120) and transmembrane glycoproteins (gp41). The initial attachment between virus and cell is the coupling of the viral gp120 subunit to the CD4 cell, resulting in a conformational change that exposes the gp41 fusion peptide and pulls the cell and viral membranes close, allowing fusion and viral entry. Fusion inhibitors bind to a region of gp41, inhibiting apposition and therefore fusion and viral entry [79,80].

Nucleoside reverse transcriptase inhibitors (NRTIs) must be converted to the active triphosphate derivative via a three step process, whereas nucleotide RTIs only require a two step process. The active intracellular moiety causes a 3′ modification, resulting in a missing 3′-hydroxyl group and thereby not allowing the addition of any nucleotides. The ensuing chain termination ultimately stops HIV replication [78].

Nonnucleoside reverse transcriptase inhibitors (NNRTIs) are highly specific, direct, noncompetitive inhibitors of HIV-1 reverse transcriptase. These agents do not require cellular metabolism to be active, are not incorporated into the elongating strand of DNA, and do not cause chain termination [78].

HIV encodes for the protease enzyme that is essential for viral infectivity and the processing of core proteins. The protease cleaves the polyprotein precursors of viral proteins, creating mature virion particles. Protease inhibitors (PIs) compete for the active cleavage site on the protease enzyme, inhibiting the formation of mature core proteins, resulting in the release of noninfectious virion from the host cell [78].

2.4.1.2 Mechanisms of Resistance

HIV resistance to the available antiretroviral agents is inevitable. Highly specific mutations can be transmitted with primary infection and will evolve over time in a patient, particularly in the setting of incomplete viral suppression. There is considerable cross-resistance within the classes of antiretroviral drugs, but cross-resistance between the classes does not occur. The accumulation of mutations results in the expression of amino acid substitutions in the pol gene that encodes for reverse transcriptase and in the viral protease or the gp41 envelope gene associated with resistance to entry inhibitors. Coexpression of multiple and variable substitutions at these positions may occur and are generally associated with higher levels of resistance [81,82].

2.4.1.3 Classification

The antiviral agents used for the treatment of HIV infection are divided into classes based on their mechanism of action (Table 2.15).

TABLE 2.15
Antiretroviral Drugs Classifications

Classification Generic Name (Brand Name)	Route of Administration	Common Adult Dosages[a]
Nucleoside(tide) Reverse Transcriptase Inhibitors		
Zidovudine (Retrovir)	IV,[b] oral	300 mg twice a day
Didanosine (Videx)	Oral	Tablets: 200 mg twice a day
Didanosine EC (Videx EC)		Powder: 250 mg twice a day
		EC capsules: 400 mg once a day
Zalcitabine (Hivid)	Oral	0.75 mg three times a day
Stavudine (Zerit)	Oral	40 mg twice a day
Lamivudine (Epivir)	Oral	300 mg once a day
Abacavir (Ziagen)	Oral	600 mg once a day
Emtricitabine (Emtriva)	Oral	200 mg once a day
Tenofovir (Viread)	Oral	300 mg once a day
Zidovudine/lamivudine (Combivir)	Oral	300 mg/150 mg twice a day
Zidovudine/lamivudine/Abacavir (Trizivir)	Oral	300 mg/150 mg/300 mg twice a day
Lamivudine/abacavir (Epzicom)	Oral	300 mg/600 mg once a day
Emtricitabine/tenofovir (Truvada)	Oral	200 mg/300 mg once a day
Efavirenz/emtricitabine/tenofovir (Atripla)	Oral	600 mg/200 mg/300 mg once a day
Nonnucleoside Reverse Transcriptase Inhibitors		
Nevirapine (Viramune)	Oral	200 mg twice a day
Delavirdine (Rescriptor)	Oral	400 mg three times a day
Efavirenz (Sustiva)	Oral	600 mg once a day
Protease Inhibitors		
Saquinavir (Invirase, Fortovase)	Oral	Invirase: 1000 mg twice a day with ritonavir 100 mg twice a day
Ritonavir (Norvir)	Oral	600 mg twice a day
Indinavir (Crixivan)	Oral	800 mg every 8 h
Nelfinavir (Viracept)	Oral	1250 mg twice a day
Amprenavir (Agenerase)	Oral	1200 mg twice a day
Lopinavir/ritonavir (Kaletra)	Oral	400 mg/100 mg twice a day
Atazanavir (Reyataz)	Oral	400 mg once a day
Fosamprenavir (Lexiva)	Oral	1400 mg twice a day
Tipranavir (Aptivus)	Oral	500 mg twice a day with 200 mg of ritonavir twice a day
Darunavir (Prezista)	Oral	600 mg twice a day with 100 mg of ritonavir twice a day
Fusion Inhibitors		
Enfuvirtide (Fuzeon)	Subcutaneous	90 mg twice a day

Source: Johnson, V.A., Brun-Vezinet, F., Clotet, B. et al. Update of the drug resistance mutations in HIV-1: Fall 2005. *Top. HIV Med.*, 13, 125–131, 2005; Panel on Clinical Practices for Treatment of HIV Infection Convened by the Department of Health and Human Services (DHHS), available at http://www.aidsinfo.org.nih.gov, accessed June 6, 2006.

[a] Dosages are for adults weighing 60 kg, with normal renal and hepatic function and without ritonavir boosting except those that are only FDA approved as such.

[b] IV = intravenous; EC = enteric coated.

2.4.1.4 Antiretroviral Activity and Therapeutic Uses

All drugs in this category are effective against HIV type 1 (HIV-1) [5,6]. In addition, all of the NRTIs and PIs possess activity against HIV type 2 (HIV-2). A select few of these agents also possess activity against hepatitis B virus (HBV), such as lamivudine, emtricitabine, and tenofovir [82,83].

Zidovudine, an NRTI, was the first drug approved by the FDA (1987) for the treatment of HIV and was the only drug available until 1991. Since then, six other nucleoside(tide) reverse transcriptase inhibitors have been added to this class [82,83].

The second class of drugs developed and approved by the FDA, the PIs, was introduced in 1995. There are now ten PIs available for the treatment of HIV infection. These agents, when combined with two NRTIs, revolutionized anti-HIV therapy. Triple combinations of these agents led to what is called "highly active antiretroviral therapy" or "HAART" [82,83].

In 1996, the FDA approved nevirapine, the first drug in the third class of antiviral drugs used for the treatment of HIV. Since then, two other agents have joined the class of NNRTIs, bringing the total to three [82,83]. Triple combinations of an NNRTI with two NRTIS are also referred to as HAART.

The fourth class of anti-HIV drugs introduced to the market was the fusion inhibitors, entering the market in 2003. Enfuvirtide is the only drug from this class that is currently available and can only be given by subcutaneous injection. As such, its use has been limited to salvage therapy when other options are limited [82,83].

Today, there are 22 antiviral agents in four different classifications used for the treatment of HIV infection. Earlier studies demonstrated better clinical utility due to delaying resistance when two NRTIs were combined together for treatment [7]. Current guidelines for the use of these agents are reviewed and updated routinely as new agents and data become available. Currently, recommendations for therapy consist of regimens that combine at least three agents, with the preferred regimens being two NRTIs with either lopinavir/ritonavir (a boosted PI) or efavirenz (NNRTI). Further discussion on the treatment of HIV infection can be found elsewhere [83].

Zidovudine has been shown to be effective in reducing the risk of HIV transmission from mother to infant by about two-thirds [8]. In the trial of the Pediatric AIDS Clinical Trial Group (PACTG) 076, mothers who received zidovudine during the second and third trimester of pregnancy and intravenous zidovudine during delivery, in addition to the infant who received 6 weeks of zidovudine immediately after birth, had a transmission rate of approximately 8%. Those who did not receive this regimen had a transmission rate of about 28% [85]. As a result, it became standard practice to recommend zidovudine treatment to HIV-infected women beyond the first trimester of pregnancy and to the woman's infant for six weeks after birth [86]. Current recommendations have changed to include the use of HAART in all pregnant women. Pregnant women should be evaluated for HAART in much the same way that all other HIV-infected patients are evaluated. The specific regimen that is finally chosen depends upon the risks to the mother and to the fetus [86].

Occupational exposure to HIV may occur in the health care workplace. Introduction of postexposure prophylaxis can greatly reduce the risk of HIV transmission. Current recommendations may involve two to three drugs, two from the NRTIs and potentially one from the PIs (the third drug). The recommendation depends upon the status of the source patient, the severity of the exposure, and the potential for transmission. Therapy should be started within the first 24 h after an exposure to ensure the greatest possibility of preventing transmission and should be continued for 4 weeks [87].

2.4.1.5 Adverse Effect Profile

All the NRTIs share the possibility of lactic acidosis with hepatic steatosis, a rare, but potentially life-threatening toxicity. Most of the NRTIs can cause gastrointestinal complaints like nausea and vomiting and some may cause peripheral neuropathy (didanosine and stavudine). Bone marrow suppression is a concern when using zidovudine, although the frequency is relatively uncommon without the simultaneous use of other potentially bone marrow toxic drugs. Abacavir has the potential to cause a hypersensitivity reaction, resulting in discontinuation of the drug for resolution and does not allow for rechallenges because this may result in serious and sometimes fatal reactions. The NNRTIs as well as the PIs tipranavir, fosamprenavir, and amprenavir are known to cause rash. The NNRTIs and the PIs are also associated with increases in hepatic transaminase levels. The PIs are also known to cause fat redistribution and lipid abnormalities. The PIs are reported to cause hyperglycemia, sometimes leading to the development of diabetes mellitus. The PIs have been associated with gastrointestinal discomfort (nausea, vomiting, and diarrhea). Indinavir is associated with nephrolithiasis; therefore, patients are cautioned to drink at least 1.5 L of fluid, preferably water, per day to decrease this risk (Table 2.16). The most common complaint with enfuvirtide is injection site reactions, occurring in 98% of patients on this drug. Rare cases of pneumonia have also been reported with its use [82,83].

TABLE 2.16
Adverse Effects Associated with Antiretroviral Drugs

Nucleoside and Nucleoside Reverse Transcriptase Inhibitors

Gastrointestinal

Nausea

Vomiting

Diarrhea

Neurologic

Peripheral neuropathy (didanosine, stavudine)

Headache

Hematologic (Primarily Zidovudine)

Anemia

Neutropenia

Miscellaneous

Lactic acidosis with hepatic steatosis

Dyslipidemias (stavudine, zidovudine)

Pancreatitis

Stomatitis

Insomnia

Renal insufficiency (tenofovir)

Rash (abacavir)

Nonnucleoside Reverse Transcriptase Inhibitors

Hypersensitivity Reactions

Rash

Hepatic

Increased transaminase levels

Hepatitis

Miscellaneous

False-positive cannabinoid test (efavirenz)

Teratogenic (efavirenz)

Dyslipidemias

Central Nervous System (Primarily Efavirenz)

Headaches

Dizziness

Somnolence and insomnia

Abnormal dreams

Confusion

Abnormal thinking and impaired concentration

Amnesia

Hallucinations

Euphoria

Protease Inhibitors

Gastrointestinal

Nausea

Vomiting

Diarrhea

Abdominal pain

Dyspepsia

Metabolic

Insulin resistance

Fat redistribution

Dyslipidemias

Renal

Nephrolithiasis (indinavir)

Hepatic

Increased indirect bilirubinemia

Elevated transaminase enzymes

Hepatitis

Hematologic

Thrombocytopenia

Bleeding episodes in patients with hemophilia

Miscellaneous

Headache

Asthenia

Metallic taste and taste perversion

Source: Johnson, V.A., Brun-Vezinet, F., Clotet, B. et al. Update of the drug resistance mutations in HIV-1: Fall 2005. *Top. HIV Med.*, 13, 125–131, 2005; Panel on Clinical Practices for Treatment of HIV Infection Convened by the Department of Health and Human Services (DHHS), available at http://www.aidsinfo.org.nih.gov, accessed June 6, 2006.

2.4.2 Antiviral Drugs

2.4.2.1 Mechanisms of Action

The drugs approved for the treatment of viral infections, other than those for HIV, work by interfering with viral messenger RNA, inhibiting viral DNA synthesis, blocking viral M2 protein ion channels thereby inhibiting viral uncoating and hence viral proliferation, or inducing cellular enzymes that interfere with the synthesis of viral proteins (Table 2.17). Many of these agents must undergo intracellular phosphorylation to their active component in order to be effective [78,88].

2.4.2.2 Mechanisms of Resistance

Viral resistance results from mutations in the viral DNA polymerase gene or by qualitative changes in viral thymidine kinase. Changes in viral RNA segments account for resistance to amantadine and rimantadine. There is cross-resistance between acyclovir, famciclovir, and ganciclovir, and complete cross-resistance between amantadine and rimantadine. Ribavirin shares no cross-resistance with any other drugs in this class. As with the drugs used for the treatment of HIV infection, combination therapy decreases the rate at which resistant viruses emerge during therapy and could potentially lead to decreased dosages and, therefore, decreased risk of adverse events [73].

2.4.2.3 Classification

These agents are classified based on their chemical structure. The chemical structures can be grouped into classes consisting of nucleoside analogs, 10-carbon-ring amines, a nucleotide analog, a pyrophosphate analog, a recombinant protein produced in bacteria, neuraminidase inhibitors, and monoclonal antibodies (Table 2.17) [4,5,88].

2.4.2.4 Antiviral Effects and Therapeutic Uses

The antiviral drugs are effective against a wide variety of viruses (Table 2.18). These agents have been used for the treatment and prevention of many viral infections in both immunocompetent and immunocompromised patients. Some common uses include mucosal, cutaneous, and systemic herpes infections; genital herpes; varicella zoster (shingles) infections; chicken pox; cytomegalovirus (CMV) infections; influenza A; respiratory syncytia virus (RSV); and Kaposi's sarcoma (HHV8) [88,89].

2.4.2.5 Adverse Effect Profile

The most common adverse effects associated with these agents are gastrointestinal in origin. Patients may complain of nausea, vomiting, and/or diarrhea. Headache is also a common complaint. Other potential adverse effects are listed in Table 2.19 [4,5,88,89].

2.5 ANTIFUNGAL AGENTS

2.5.1 Background

Recent advances in antimicrobial therapy, trauma resuscitation, and supportive care in the ICU have decreased mortality but increased the risk of fungal superinfections. Candidemia is the most deadly bloodstream infection, with a mortality rate of approximately 40%. Patients at risk for candidemia and systemic candidiasis include patients with a compromised immune system, have received stem-

TABLE 2.17
Classification of Antiviral Drugs

Classification Generic Name	Mechanism of Action	Route of Administration	Common Adult Dosages[a]
		Nucleoside Analogues	
Acyclovir	DNA chain terminator	IV[b], Oral, Topical	IV: 5–10 mg/kg every 8 hours Oral: 200–800 mg every 4–12 hours
Adefovir	DNA chain terminator	Oral	10 mg daily
Entecavir	DNA chain terminator	Oral	0.5 mg daily
Famciclovir	Inhibits DNA synthesis (Prodrug of penciclovir)	Oral	125–500 mg twice a day
Ganciclovir	Inhibits DNA synthesis	IV, oral	IV: 5 mg/kg twice a day Oral: 1 gram three times a day
Penciclovir	Inhibits DNA synthesis	Topical	1% cream every 2 hours
Ribavirin	Inhibits mRNA	Inhalation, oral	Inh: 6 grams delivered over 18 hours Oral: 500–600 mg twice a day
Valacyclovir	DNA chain terminator (Prodrug of acyclovir)	Oral	500–1000 mg twice a day
Valganciclovir	Inhibits DNA synthesis	Oral	900 mg twice a day for 21 days then 900 mg daily
		Nucleotide Analogue	
Cidofovir	Inhibits DNA synthesis	IV	5 mg/kg every 2 weeks
		Pyrophosphate Analogue	
Foscarnet	Inhibits DNA synthesis	IV	40–60 mg/kg 2–3 times per day
		10-Carbon-Ring Amines	
Amantadine	Inhibits viral uncoating	Oral	100 mg twice a day
Rimantadine	Inhibits viral uncoating	Oral	200 mg once a day
		Recombinant Protein	
Interferon alfa	Inhibits protein synthesis	IM, Sub-Q	5 million units daily or 10 million units three times weekly
Peginterferon alfa-2a	Inhibits protein synthesis	Sub-Q	180 mcg every week with Ribavirin
Peginterferon alfa-2B	Inhibits protein synthesis	Sub-Q	1.5 mcg/kg every week with Ribavirin
		Neuraminidase Inhibitors	
Oseltamivir	Inhibits influenza virus neuraminidase	Oral	75 mg twice a day for 5 days
Zanamivir	Inhibits influenza virus neuraminidase	Inhalation	10 mg twice a day for 5 days
		Monoclonal Antibodies	
Palivizumab	Monoclonal antibody	IM	50–100 mg once a month throughout RSV season

Source: Thredlekd, D.S., Ed., *Drug Facts and Comparisons*, Facts and Comparisons, St. Louis, 2006; McEvoy, G.K., Ed., *AHFS Drug Information*, American Society of Health-System Pharmacists, Inc., Bethesda, 2006; Balfour, H.H., Jr., *N. Engl. J. Med.*, 340, 1255–1268, 1999.

[a] Dosages are for adults weighing 60 kg with normal renal function.

[b] IV = intravenous; IM = intramuscular; sub-Q = subcutaneous.

TABLE 2.18
Antiviral Activity of Antiviral Drugs

Classification	Proven Antiviral Activity	Possible Antiviral Activity
Nucleoside Analogues		
Acyclovir	HSV-1,[a] HSV-2, VZV, CMV	EBV, herpes B (herpes simiae)
Adefovir	Hepatitis B, HIV-1	
Entecavir	Hepatitis B	
Famciclovir	HSV-1, HSV-2, VZV	Hepatitis B
Ganciclovir	CMV	HSV-1, HSV-2, EBV, HHV-8, herpes B
Penciclovir	HSV-1, HSV-2	
Ribavirin	Lassa fever, hantavirus (hemorrhagic fever renal syndrome), Hepatitis C (with interferon alfa)	Respiratory syncytial virus, parainfluenza, influenza A and B, measles, hantavirus (pulmonary syndrome)
Valacyclovir	HSV-1, HSV-2, VZV, CMV	
Valganciclovir	HSV-1, HSV-2, VZV, CMV	
Nucleotide Analogues		
Cidofovir	HSV-1, HSV-2, VZV, CMV	EBV, Adenovirus, HPV, human polymavirus
Pyrophosphate Analogue		
Foscarnet	HSV-1, HSV-2, CMV, VZV	HHV-8, HIV-1
10-Carbon-Ring Amines		
Amantadine	Influenza A	
Rimantadine	Influenza A	
Recombinant Protein		
Interferon alfa	Hepatitis B, Hepatitis C, HHV-8, human papillomavirus	
Peginterferon alfa-2a	Hepatitis B, Hepatitis C	
Peginterferon alfa-2b	Hepatitis B, Hepatitis C	
Neuraminidase Inhibitors		
Oseltamivir	Influenza virus	
Zanamivir	Influenza virus	
Monoclonal Antibodies		
Palivizumab	RSV	

Source: Thredlekd, D.S., Ed., *Drug Facts and Comparisons*, Facts and Comparisons, St. Louis, 2006; McEvoy, G.K., Ed., *AHFS Drug Information*, American Society of Health-System Pharmacists, Inc., Bethesda, 2006; Balfour, H.H., Jr., *N. Engl. J. Med.*, 340, 1255–1268, 1999; Hayden, F.G., in *Principles and Practices of Infectious Diseases*, Mandell, G.L., Bennett, J.E., and Dolin, R., Eds., Churchill Livingstone, New York, 1995, pp. 411–449.

[a] HSV-1 = herpes simplex virus-1; HSV-2 = herpes simplex virus-2; VZV = varicella zoster virus; EBV = Epstein-Barr virus; CMV = cytomegalovirus virus; HHV-8 = human herpes virus 8 (Kaposi's sarcoma).

cell transplants, are receiving chemotherapy, are critically ill in the ICU, have catheters, have recently had surgery, and who are on prolonged antibiotics. To date, the various amphotericin-based products and the azole antifungals have been the mainstay of therapy, but the troublesome side effects and resistance formation have increased the need for improved therapeutic options. More recently a new class of antifungals, the echinocandins, has been FDA approved, including: caspofungin, micafungin, and anidulafungin (Eraxis). The echinocandins were actually first discovered in 1974, as a naturally occurring product derived from *Aspergillus nidulans*. The first echinocandin,

TABLE 2.19
Adverse Effects Associated with Antiviral Drugs (not used for HIV infection)

Gastrointestinal	Central Nervous System (Amantadine, Rimantadine, Interferon Alfa)
Nausea and vomiting	Headaches
Diarrhea	Dizziness
	Insomnia
Hypersensitivity Reactions	Confusion
Rash	Suicide attempts
Worsening of respiratory symptoms (ribavirin)	
Conjunctivitis (ribavirin)	**Hematologic**
	Anemia
Renal	Neutropenia
Increased BUN[a]	
Increased serum creatinine	**Miscellaneous**
Urine protein	Phlebitis
Electrolyte imbalances (foscarnet)	Fever
	Hypotension

Source: Thredlekd, D.S., Ed., *Drug Facts and Comparisons*, Facts and Comparisons, St. Louis, 2006; McEvoy, G.K., Ed., *AHFS Drug Information*, American Society of Health-System Pharmacists, Inc., Bethesda, 2006; Balfour, H.H., Jr., *N. Engl. J. Med.*, 340, 1255–1268, 1999; Hayden, F.G., in *Principles and Practices of Infectious Diseases*, Mandell, G.L., Bennett, J.E., and Dolin, R., Eds., Churchill Livingstone, New York, 1995, pp. 411–449.
[a] BUN = blood urea nitrogen.

cilofugin (Lilly), never made it to the marketplace because early clinical trials were halted due to nephrotoxicity. It was later determined that the nephrotoxicity was related to the vehicle, polyethylene glycol, and not the medication itself.

2.5.2 MECHANISMS OF ACTION

The antifungal agents are grouped according to mechanism of action. The macrolide antifungal agents work by binding to ergosterol in fungal cell membranes, leading to weakening of the membranes and then leakage of the cellular components. This eventually leads to death of the fungal cell. The azole antifungal agents (triazoles and imidazoles) exert their effect by inhibiting the formation of sterols, which alters fungal cellular membranes. When membrane structure is disrupted, there is increased membrane permeability and therefore leakage of essential cell contents and eventually death. The echinocandins specifically target or inhibit the formation of 1,3-β-D-glucan, a key component in the fungal cell wall. Of the miscellaneous agents, flucytosine is taken up by the fungal cell and then it inhibits protein synthesis. Griseofulvin acts by disrupting the cell cycle and possibly by formation of defective DNA, which cannot replicate. Nystatin and terbinafine exert their effect by interfering with the formation of fungal sterols, much like the azole antifungal agents [4,5,90].

2.5.3 MECHANISMS OF RESISTANCE

Mutants with decreased susceptibility (resistance) to the macrolide antifungal agents have been acquired *in vitro*; however, the clinical relevance of such resistance is unknown. Detection of antifungal resistance is difficult. It is unclear if clinical failure is related to fungal resistance or failure on the part of the host because these agents are typically used in immunocompromised patients. Some fungal strains have demonstrated increased MICs to the azole antifungal agents and generally share this potential for resistance with other agents within the class (cross-resistance) [5,90].

2.5.4 CLASSIFICATION

The antifungal agents are classified based on mechanism of action (Table 2.20) [4,5].

TABLE 2.20
Antifungal Drug Classifications

Classification Generic Name	Route of Administration	Common Dosages[a]
Polyene Macrolides		
Amphotericin B deoxycholate (Ampho B)	IV,[b] oral, topical	0.25–1 mg/kg/day
Amphotericin B complex (ABLC)	IV	5 mg/kg/day
Amphotericin B dispersion (ABCD)	IV	3–6 mg/kg/day
Amphotericin B liposomal	IV	3–5 mg/kg/day
Nystatin	Oral, topical	100,000–600,000 units two–four times a day
Azoles (Imidazoles, Triazoles, and Echinocandins)		
Imidazoles		
Butoconazole	Topical	2% cream at bedtime
Clotrimazole	Oral, topical	Oral: 10 mg five times a day
		Topical: 100 mg/500mg/5 grams at bedtime
Econazole	Topical	1% cream twice a day
Ketoconazole	Oral, topical	400 mg oral/2% topical once a day
Miconazole	IV, topical	IV: 200–3600 mg divided three times a day
		Topical: 100 mg/200 mg/2% cream at bedtime
Oxiconazole	Topical	1% cream at bedtime
Sulconazole	Topical	1% solution once a day
Triazoles		
Fluconazole	IV, oral	100–400 mg once a day
Itraconazole	Oral, topical	200 mg once a day
Terconazole	Topical	80 mg/0.4% cream at bedtime
Voriconazole	IV, oral	4–6 mg/kg twice a day
Echinocandins		
Anidulafungin	IV	50–100 mg once a day
Caspofungin	IV	50 mg once a day
Micafungin	IV	50–150 mg once a day
Miscellaneous		
Ciclopirox olamine	Topical	1% cream/lotion twice a day
Flucytosine	Oral	100–150 mg/kg divided four times a day
Griseofulvin	Topical	500 mg–1 gram per day
Haloprogin	Topical	1% cream or solution twice a day
Naftifine	Topical	1% cream twice a day
Terbinafine	Oral	250 mg per day
Tolnaftate	Topical	1% twice a day

Source: Thredlekd, D.S., Ed., *Drug Facts and Comparisons*, Facts and Comparisons, St. Louis, 2006; McEvoy, G.K., Ed., *AHFS Drug Information*, American Society of Health-System Pharmacists, Inc., Bethesda, 2006; Bennett, J.E., in *Principles and Practices of Infectious Diseases*, Mandell, G.L., Bennett, J.E., and Dolin, R., Eds., Churchill Livingstone, New York, 1995, pp. 401–410.

[a] Dosages are for adults weighing 60 kg and having normal renal function.

[b] IV = intravenous.

2.5.5 Antifungal Activity and Therapeutic Uses

The antifungal agents are effective against a wide variety of infections caused by pathogenic fungi (Table 2.21). They are often used for the treatment of invasive, as well as localized fungal infections in immunocompetent and immunocompromised patients such as those with cancers and AIDS (Table 2.22) [90].

TABLE 2.21
Antifungal Activity

Classification	Antifungal Activity
Polyene Macrolides	
(Activity Based on Studies with Amphotericin B Deoxycholate)	
Amphotericin B deoxycholate	*Candida* species, *Cryptococcus neoformans*, *Blastomyces dermatitidis*, *Histoplasma*
Amphotericin B complex	*capsultum*, *Coccidioides immitis*, *Paracoccidioides braziliensis*, *Aspergillus* species, and
Amphotericin B dispersion	mucormycosis caused by *Mucor*, *Phizopus*, *Absidia*, *Entomophthora,* and *Basidiobolus*
Amphotericin B liposomal	Limited activity against protozoa, *Leishmania braziliensis*, and *Naegleria fowleri*
Nystatin	*Candida* species
Azoles	
Imidazoles	
Butoconazole	*Candida* species
Clotrimazole	*Candida* species
Econazole	*Trichophyton rubrum, T. mentagrophytes, T. tonsurans, Microsporum canis, M. audouini, M. gypseum, Epidermophyton floccosum, Candida albicans, Malassezia furfur*
Ketoconazole	*Blastomyces dermatitidis, Candida* species, *Coccidiodes immitis, Histoplasma capsulatum, Paracoccidioides brasiliensis, Phialophora* species, *Trichophyton* species, *Epidermophyton* species, *Microsporum* species, *Malassezia furfur, Cryptococcus neoformans*
Miconazole	*Coccidioides immitis, Candida albicans, Cryptococcus neoformans, Pseudallecheria boydii, Paracoccidioides brasiliensis*
Oxiconazole	*Epidermophyton floccosum, Tricophyton rubrum, T. mentagrophytes*
Sulconazole	*Trichophyton rubrum, T. mentagrophytes, Epidermophyton floccosum, Microsporum canis, Malassezia furfur, Candida albicans*
Triazoles	
Fluconazole	*Candida* species, *Cryptococcus neoformans, Aspergillus flavus, A. fumigatus, Blastomyces dermatitidis, Coccidioides immitis, Histoplasma capsulatum*
Itraconazole	*Blastomyces dermatitidis, Histoplasma capsulatum, Histoplasma duboisii, Aspergillus flavus, A. fumigatus, Candida* species, *Cryptococcus neoformans, Sporothrix schenckii, Trichophyton* species
Terconazole	*Candida* species
Voriconazole	*Aspergillus* spp., *Scedosporium* spp., *Fusarium* spp., *Candida* species, *Cryptococcus neoformans*
Echinocandins	
Anidulafungin	*Aspergillus flavus, A. fumigatus, Candida* species, Pseumocystis
Caspofungin	*Aspergillus flavus, A. fumigatus, Candida* species
Micafungin	*Aspergillus flavus, A. fumigatus, Candida* species
Miscellaneous	
Ciclopirox olamine	*Malassizia furfur, Trichophyton rubrum, T. mentagrophytes, Epidermophyton floccosum, Microsporum canis, Candida albicans*
Flucytosine	*Cryptococcus neoformans, Candida* species

(continued)

TABLE 2.21
Antifungal Activity (continued)

Classification	Antifungal Activity
Griseofulvin	*Microsporum* species, *Epidermophyton* species, *Trichophyton* species
Haloprogin	*Trichophyton rubrum, T. tonsurans, T. mentagrophytes, Microsporum canis, Epidermophyton floccosum, Malassezia furfur*
Naftifine	*Trichophyton rubrum, T. mentagrophytes, T. tonus, Epidermophyton floccosum, Microsporum canis, M audouini, M gypseum, Candida* species
Terbinafine	*Trichophyton rubrum, Trichophyton mentagrophytes, Epidermophyton floccusum, Microsporum gypseum, M. nanum, Trichophyton verrucosum, Candida albicans, Scopulariopsis brevicaulis*
Tolnaftate	*Trichophyton rubrum, T. mentagrophytes, T. tonsurans, Epidermophyton floccusum, Microsporum canis, M. audouini, Malassizia furfur*

Source: Thredlekd, D.S., Ed., *Drug Facts and Comparisons*, Facts and Comparisons, St. Louis, 2006; McEvoy, G.K., Ed., *AHFS Drug Information*, American Society of Health-System Pharmacists, Inc., Bethesda, 2006; Bennett, J.E., in *Principles and Practices of Infectious Diseases*, Mandell, G.L., Bennett, J.E., and Dolin, R., Eds., Churchill Livingstone, New York, 1995, 401–410; Singh, R.M. and Perdue, B.E., *Formulary*, 33, 424–447, 1998.

TABLE 2.22
Antifungal Therapeutic Uses

Infection	Antifungal Agent of Choice	Alternative Antifungal Agents
Aspergillosis	Itraconazole	Amphotericin B
Blastomycosis	Ketoconazole	Amphotericin B, itraconazole
Candidiasis	Clotrimazole	All other agents
Coccidioidomycosis	Amphotericin B	Ketoconazole
Cryptococcosis	Fluconazole	Amphotericin B, flucytosine
Histoplasmosis	Ketoconazole	Amphotericin B, itraconazole
Mucormycosis	Amphotericin B	
Paracoccidioidomycosis	Ketoconazole	Amphotericin B
Sporotrichosis	Itraconazole	Amphotericin B

Source: Thredlekd, D.S., Ed., *Drug Facts and Comparisons*, Facts and Comparisons, St. Louis, 2006; McEvoy, G.K., Ed., *AHFS Drug Information*, American Society of Health-System Pharmacists, Inc., Bethesda, 2006; Bennett, J.E., in *Principles and Practices of Infectious Diseases*, Mandell, G.L., Bennett, J.E., and Dolin, R., Eds., Churchill Livingstone, New York, 1995, 401–410.

Some of these agents have been used together or are proposed for use together. The combination of the amphotericins and the azoles is thought to be potentially antagonistic because the azoles inhibit the product to which the amphotericins bind and exert their effect (ergosterol). Further clinical trials are needed to determine if this effect does indeed happen. Synergism between flucytosine and amphotericin has been reported. As a result, these two agents have often been used together against *Cryptococcus neoformans* [5,90].

The lipid formulations of amphotericin were developed in hopes of decreasing some of the adverse effects of amphotericin B deoxycholate. By incorporating the amphotericin into a lipid product, there is reported to be less uptake by the kidneys and yet greater uptake into other areas such as the reticuloendothelial system (RES). More drug, therefore, may be delivered to the site of infection while decreasing the harmful effects on the kidneys [90,91].

2.5.6 Adverse Effect Profile (Table 2.23)

The amphotericin products are known to cause flulike symptoms, such as fever, chills, malaise, and generalized pain. These agents may also cause nephrotoxicity resulting in increased BUN (blood urea nitrogen) and creatinine concentrations. Electrolyte abnormalities, particularly hypokalemia and hypomagnesemia, are reported as well [4,5,91]. While many of these effects are less common with the lipid products, there is still potential for these effects, particularly with prolonged use, which is often necessary to adequately treat fungal infections [91].

The azoles and other miscellaneous antifungal agents can be divided into topical and systemic drugs when discussing adverse effects. Overall, these agents are well tolerated at usual doses. Using the topical agents may result in localized reactions, such as local irritation, sensitization, itching, burning, erythema, and rashes. Topical agents used for genital fungal infections may also cause dysparuria and/or vulvovaginal burning [4,5,91].

The most common side effect associated with the systemic (oral) use of the azole drugs is gastrointestinal distress. Symptoms include nausea, vomiting, abdominal pain, and diarrhea. Some patients may experience transient increases in liver transaminases. Flucytosine may cause gastrointestinal distress and has been associated with neutropenia and thrombocytopenia in some patients [4,5,91].

TABLE 2.23
Adverse Effects Associated with Antifungal Drugs

Polyene Macrolides

Neurologic	Hepatic
Fever	Bilirubinemia
Headache	Increased AST,[a] ALT, alkaline phosphatase
Gastrointestinal	**Miscellaneous**
Abdominal pain	Chills
Diarrhea	Back pain
Nausea	Rigors
Vomiting	Malaise
Cardiac	Generalized pain
Tachycardia	Anemia
Chest pain	Epistaxis
Renal	Anorexia
Increased serum creatinine concentration	Hypotension
Increase in BUN	Dyspnea
Hypokalemia	Edema
Hypomagnesemia	Cough
	Insomnia
	Multiple organ failure
	Hyperglycemia

Topical Azoles (Imidazoles and Triazoles) and Miscellaneous Agents

Local irritation	Erythema
Sensitization	Rash
Pruritis	Folliculitis
Burning	Pain
Allergic contact dermatitis	Dryness

(continued)

TABLE 2.23
Adverse Effects Associated with Antifungal Drugs (continued)

Systemic Azoles (Imidazoles and Triazoles)

Hepatic

Increased liver enzymes (AST, ALT, alkaline phosphatase)
Bilirubinemia

Dermatologic

Rash
Pruritis
Urticaria
Stevens-Johnson Syndrome (rare)

Endocrine

Gynecomastia
Decreased libido
Impotence
Adrenal insufficiency

Gastrointestinal

Nausea
Vomiting
Diarrhea
Abdominal pain
Flatulence
Dyspepsia

Central Nervous System

Headache
Dizziness
Somnolence
Fever

Echinocandins

Injection site reaction

Phlebitis

Gastrointestinal

Nausea
Vomiting
Diarrhea

Possible Histamine-Mediated Symptoms

Rash
Pruritus
Facial swelling
Vasodilation

Miscellaneous Systemic (Flucytosine and Griseofulvin)

Central Nervous System

Headache
Dizziness
Insomnia

Dermatologic

Urticaria
Rash
Photosensitivity

Hepatic

Increased liver enzymes (AST, ALT, alkaline phosphatase)

Gastrointestinal

Nausea
Vomiting
Diarrhea
Abdominal pain
Flatulence

Hematologic

Anemia
Leukopenia
Pancytopenia
Thrombocytopenia

Source: Thredlekd, D.S., Ed., *Drug Facts and Comparisons*, Facts and Comparisons, St. Louis, 2006; McEvoy, G.K., Ed., *AHFS Drug Information*, American Society of Health-System Pharmacists, Inc., Bethesda, 2006; Bennett, J.E., in *Principles and Practices of Infectious Diseases*, Mandell, G.L., Bennett, J.E., and Dolin, R., Eds., Churchill Livingstone, New York, 1995, pp. 401–410; Singh, R.M. and Perdue, B.E., *Formulary*, 33, 424–447, 1998.

[a] AST = aspartate aminotransferase; ALT = alanine aminotransferase; BUN = blood urea nitrogen.

REFERENCES

1. Ryan, F. *The Forgotten Plague*, Little, Brown, New York, 1993.
2. Aronson, S.M. The naming of antibiotics, *Med. Health*, 80(6), 180, 1997.

3. Radetsky, M. The discovery of penicillin. *Pediatr. Infect. Dis. J.*, 15(9), 811–818, 1996.
4. Thredlekd, D.S., Ed., *Drug Facts and Comparisons*, Facts and Comparisons, St. Louis, 1998.
5. McEvoy, G.K., Ed., *AHFS Drug Information*, American Society of Health-System Pharmacists, Inc., Bethesda, 2006.
6. Jawetz, E. Principles of antimicrobial drug action, in *Basic and Clinical Pharmacology*, Katzung, B.G., Ed., Appleton and Lange, Norwalk, CT, 1989, 545–552.
7. Woods, G.L. and Washington, J.A. The clinician and the microbiology laboratory, in *Principles and Practices of Infectious Diseases*, Mandell, G.L., Bennett, J.E., and Dolin, R., Eds., Churchill Livingstone, New York, 1995, 169–199.
8. Fleming, A. On the antibacterial action of cultures of a penicillium, with special reference to their use in the isolation of B. influenzae, *Br. J. Exp. Pathol.*, 10, 226–236, 1929.
9. Schmidt, J.E. *Medical Discoveries*, Thomas Books, Springfield, IL, 1959.
10. Brooks, G.F., Butel, J.S., and Morse, S.A. *Jawetz, Melnick, & Adelberg's Medical Microbiology*, Appleton & Lange, Stamford, CT, 1998.
11. Mandell, G.L. and Sande, M.A. Penicillins, cephalosporins, and other beta-lactam antibiotics, in *Goodman and Gilman's The Pharmacological Basis of Therapeutics*, Goodman Gilman, A., Rall, T.W., Nies, A.S., and Taylor, P., Eds., Pergamon Press, Elmsford, 1990, 1065–1097.
12. Fletcher, C. First clinical use of penicillin, *Br. Med. J.*, 289, 1721–1723, 1984.
13. Chambers, H.F. and Neu, H.C. Penicillins, in *Principles and Practices of Infectious Diseases*, Mandell, G.L., Bennett, J.E., and Dolin, R., Eds., Churchill Livingstone, New York, 1995, 233–247.
14. Mayer, K.H., Opal, S.M., and Nedeiros, A.A. Mechanisms of antibiotic resistance, in *Principles and Practices of Infectious Diseases*, Mandell, G.L., Bennett, J.E., and Dolin, R., Eds., Churchill Livingstone, New York, 1995, 212–225.
15. Deswarte, R.D. Drug allergy-problems and strategies, *J. Allergy Clin. Immunol.*, 74, 209–221, 1984.
16. Karchmer, A.W. Cephalosporins, in *Principles and Practices of Infectious Diseases*, Mandell, G.L., Bennett, J.E., and Dolin, R., Eds., Churchill Livingstone, New York, 1995, 247–264.
17. ASHP therapeutic guidelines on antimicrobial prophylaxis in surgery, *Clin. Pharm.*, 11, 483–513, 1992.
18. Moellering, R.C. and Sentochnik, D.E. Cephalosporins, in *Infectious Disease*, Gorbach, S.L., Bartlett, J.G., and Blacklow, N.R., Eds., Lippincott, Williams, & Wilkins, Philadelphia, 1992, 172–182.
19. McCloskey, R.V. Spontaneous reports of bleeding: Comparison of N-methylthiotetrazole side chain (MTT) and non-MTT cephalosporins, *J. Infect. Dis.*, 158(6), 1405, Dec. 1988.
20. Uri, J.V. and Parks, D.B. Disulfiram-like reaction to certain cephalosporins, *Ther. Drug Monit.* 5(2), 219–224, Jun 1983.
21. Chambers, H.F. and Neu, H.C. Other B-lactam antibiotics, in *Principles and Practices of Infectious Diseases*, Mandell, G.L., Bennett, J.E., and Dolin, R., Eds., Churchill Livingstone, New York, 1995, 264–272.
22. Schranz, J. Comparisons of seizure incidence and adverse experiences between imipenem and meropenem, *Crit. Care Med.*, 26(8), 1464–1466, Aug. 1998.
23. Saxon, A. Immediate hypersensitivity reactions to beta-lactam antibiotics. *Ann. Intern. Med.*, 107(2), 204–215, 1987.
24. McCormick, M.H., Stark, W.M., Pittenger, G.E., Pittenger, R.C., and McGuire, J.M. Vancomycin, a new antibiotic, *Antibiotics Annual*, 3, 606–611, 1955.
25. Moellering, R.C. Monitoring serum vancomycin levels: Climbing the mountain because it is there? *Clin. Inf. Dis.*, 18, 544–546, 1994.
26. Downs, N.J., Neihart, R.E., Dolezal, J.M., and Hodges, G.R. Mild nephrotoxicity associated with vancomycin use, *Arch. Intern. Med.*, 149, 1777–1781, 1989.
27. Fekety, R. Vancomycin and teicoplanin, in *Principles and Practices of Infectious Diseases*, Mandell, G.L., Bennett, J.E., and Dolin, R., Eds., Churchill Livingstone, New York, 1995, 346–354.
28. Hiramatsu, K., Hanaki, H., Ino, T. et al. Methicillin-resistant *Staphylococcus aureus* clinical strains with reduced vancomycin susceptibility, *J. Antimicrob. Chemother.*, 40, 135–136, 1997.
29. Smith, T.L., Pearson, M.L., Wilcox, K.R. et al. Emergence of vancomycin resistance in *Staphylococcus aureus*, *N. Engl. J. Med.*, 340(7), 493–501, 1999.
30. Hospital Infection Control Practices Advisory Committee. Recommendations for preventing the spread of vancomycin resistance, *Infect. Control Hosp. Epidemiol.*, 16, 105–113, 1995.

31. Wallace, M.R., Mascola, J.R., and Oldfield, E.C. Red man syndrome: Incidence, etiology, and prophylaxis, *J. Infect. Dis.*, 164(6), 1180–1185, Dec. 1991.

32. Schifter, S., Aagaard, M.T., and Jensen, L.J. Adverse reactions to vancomycin, *Lancet*, 2(8453) 499, Aug. 31, 1985.

33. Kucers, A.A. and Bennett, N. Vancomycin, in *The Use of Antibiotics,* J.B. Lippincott, Philadelphia, 1987, 1045–1068.

34. Rybak, M.J., Albrecht, L.M., Boike, S.C., and Chandrasekar, P.H. Nephrotoxicity of vancomycin, alone and with an aminoglycoside, *J. Antimicrob. Chemother.*, 25, 679–687, 1990.

35. Farber, B.F. and Moellering, R.C. Retrospective study of the toxicity preparations of vancomycin from 1974 to 1981, *Antimicrob. Agents Chemother.*, 23, 138–141, 1983.

36. Zimmerman, A.E., Katona, B.G., and Plaisance, K.L. Association of vancomycin serum concentrations with outcomes in patients with gram-positive bacteremia, *Pharmacotherapy*, 15, 85–91, 1995.

37. Anonymous. FDA approves quinupristin-dalfopristin for some vancomycin-resistant infections, *Am. J. Health-Syst. Pharm.*, 56(21), 2174, 1999.

38. Carpenter, C.F. and Chambers, H.F. Daptomycin: Another novel agent for threatening infections due to drug-resistant gram-positive pathogens, *Clin. Infect. Dis.*, 38, 994–1000, 2004.

39. Streir, J.M., Jones, R.N., and Sader, H.S. Daptomycin activity and spectrum: A worldwide sample of 6737 clinical gram-positive organisms, *J. Antimicrob. Chemother.*, VOLUME, 1–6, 2004.

40. Cubicin (daptomycin) package insert. Cubist Pharmaceuticals, Lexington, MA, September 2003.

41. CDC. Public health dispatch: Outbreaks of community-associated methicillin-resistant staphylococcus aureus skin infections-Los Angeles County, California, 2002–2003, *Morbitity and Mortality Weekly Report*, 52, 88, 2003.

42. Murray, B.E. and Nannini, E.C. Glycopeptide, streptogramins and lipopeptide, in *Principles and Practices of Infectious Diseases*, Mandell, G.L., Bennett, J.E., and Dolin, R., Eds., Churchill Livingstone, New York, 1995, 417–425.

43. Anonymous. Linezolid approval brings new treatment option for resistant bacteria, *Am. J. Health-Syst. Pharm.*, 57(11), 1018, 2000.

44. Gilbert, D.N. Aminoglycosides, in *Principles and Practices of Infectious Diseases*, Mandell, G.L., Bennett, J.E., and Dolin, R., Eds., Churchill Livingstone, New York, 1995, 279–306.

45. Sande, M.A. and Mandell, G.L. The aminoglycosides, in *Goodman and Gilman's The Pharmacological Basis of Therapeutics*, Goodman Gilman, A., Rall, T.W., Nies, A.S., and Taylor, P., Eds., Pergamon Press, Elmsford, 1990, 1098–1116.

46. Centers for Disease Control and Prevention. Initial therapy for tuberculosis in the era of multidrug resistance — recommendations of the Advisory Council for the Elimination of Tuberculosis, *Morbitity and Mortality Weekly Report*, 42(No. RR-7), 1–7, 1993.

47. Nicolau, D.P., Freeman, C.D., Belliveau, P.P., Nightingale, C.H., Ross, J.W. et al. Experience with a once-daily aminoglycoside program administered to 2,184 adult patients, *Antimicrob. Agents Chemother.*, 39(3), 650–655, 1995.

48. Moore, R.D., Smith, C.R., and Lietman, P.S. Risk factors for the development of auditory toxicity in patients receiving aminoglycosides, *J. Infect. Dis.*, 149, 23–30, 1984.

49. Hakkanen, E. The aggravating effect of some antibiotics on the neuromuscular blockade in myasthenia gravis, *Acta Neurol. Scan.*, 40, 346–352, 1964.

50. Centers for Disease Control and Prevention. Endotoxin-like reactions associated with intravenous gentamicin — California, 1998, *Morbitity and Mortality Weekly Report*, 47(No. 41), 877–880, 1998.

51. Duggar, B.M. Aureomycin: A product of the continuing search for new antibiotics, *Ann. N. Y. Acad. Sci.*, 51(2), 177–181, 1948.

52. Standiford, H.C. Tetracyclines and chloramphenicol, in *Principles and Practices of Infectious Diseases*, Mandell, G.L., Bennett, J.E., and Dolin, R., Eds., Churchill Livingstone, New York, 1995, 306–317.

53. Sande, M.A. and Mandell, G.L. Tetracyclines, chloramphenicol, erythromycin, and miscellaneous antibacterial agents, in *Goodman and Gilman's The Pharmacological Basis of Therapeutics*, Goodman Gilman, A., Rall, T.W., Nies, A.S., and Taylor, P., Eds., Pergamon Press, Elmsford, 1990, 1117–1145.

54. Steere, A.C., Kevin, R.E., Molley, P.J., Kalish, R.A., Abruha, J.H., Liu, N.Y., and Schmid, C.H. Treatment of Lyme arthritis, *Arthritis Rheum.*, 7, 878–888, 1994.

55. Centers for Disease Control and Prevention. 1998 Guidelines for treatment of sexually transmitted diseases, *Morbitity and Mortality Weekly Report*, 47(No. RR-1), 27–87, 1998.
56. Finegold, S.M. Interaction of antimicrobial therapy and intestinal flora, *Am. J. Clin. Nutr.*, 23, 1466–1471, 1970.
57. Frost, P., Weinstein, G.D., and Gomez, E.C. Phototoxic potential of minocycline and doxycycline, *Arch. Derm.*, 105, 681–683, 1972.
58. Bouchillon, S.K., Hoban, D.J., Johnson, B.M. et al. *In vitro* activity of tigecycline against 3989 gram-negative and gram-positive clinical isolates from the United States Tigecycline Evaluation and Surveillance Trial (TEST Program; 2004), *Diag. Microbiol. Infect. Dis.*, 52, 173–179, 2005.
59. Smith, K.L., McCabe, S.M., and Aeschlimann, J.R. Tigecycline a novel glycylcyclines antibiotic, *Formulary*, (40), 245–252, 2005.
60. Steigbigel, N.H. Macrolides and clindamycin, in *Principles and Practices of Infectious Diseases*, Mandell, G.L., Bennett, J.E., and Dolin, R., Eds., Churchill Livingstone, New York, 1995, 334–346.
61. Mandell, L.A., Bartlett, J.G., Dowell, S.F., File, T.M. Jr., Musher, D.M., & Whitney, C. Update of Practice Guidelines for the Management of Community-Acquired Pneumonia in Immunocompetent Adults. *Clin. Infect. Dis.*, 37, 1405–1433, 2003.
62. USPHS/IDSA Prevention of Opportunistic Infections Working Group. USPHS/IDSA guidelines on opportunistic infections in infected persons with human immunodeficiency virus: Disease-specific recommendations, *Clin. Inf. Dis.*, 30: s29–s65, 2000.
63. Flamm, R.K. and Valdes, J. The new antibacterial class: The ketolides, *Clin. Microbiol. Newsletter*, 22(17), 129–133, 2000.
64. Lesher, G.Y, Froelich, E.J., and Gruetton, D. 1,8-Napthyridine derivative. A new class of chemotherapeutic agents, *J. Med. Pharmacol. Chem.*, 5, 1063–1068, 1962.
65. Adverse effects prompt withdrawal of temafloxacin, *Clin. Pharm.*, 11(9), 747,750, Sep 1992.
66. "Dear Health Care Provider" letter, November 1, 1999, Glaxo Wellcome Inc., available at http://www.fda.gov/medwatch/safety/1999/raxhcp.html, accessed July 17, 2006.
67. Public Health Advisory Food and Drug Administration. Trovan, FDA/Center for Drug Evaluation and Research, Rockville, MD, available at http://www.fda.gov, accessed June 9, 2006.
68. Park-Wyllie, L.Y., Juurlink, D.N., Kopp, A. et al. Outpatient gatifloxacin therapy and dysglycemia in older adults, *N. Engl. J. Med.*, VOLUME, 354, 2006.
69. Mandell, G.L. and Sande, M.A. Sulfonamides, trimethoprim-sulfamethoxazole, quinolones, and agents for urinary tract infections, in *Goodman and Gilman's The Pharmacological Basis of Therapeutics*, Goodman Gilman, A., Rall, T.W., Nies, A.S., and Taylor, P., Eds., Pergamon Press, Elmsford, 1990, 1047–1064.
70. Hooper, D.C. Quinolones, in *Principles and Practices of Infectious Diseases*, Mandell, G.L., Bennett, J.E., and Dolin, R., Eds., Churchill Livingstone, New York, 1995, 364–376.
71. Halkin, H. Adverse effects of the fluoroquinolones, *Rev. Infect. Dis.*, 10 (Suppl 1), S258–S261, 1988.
72. "Dear Health Care Professional," June 10, 1999, Pfizer Inc., available at http://www.fda.gov/cder/news/trovan/trovan-advisory.htm, accessed July 17, 2006.
73. Otten, H. Domagk and the development of the sulphonamides, *J. Antimicrob. Chemother.*, 17, 689–696, 1986.
74. Zinner, S.H. and Mayer, K.H. Sulfonamides and trimethoprim, in *Principles and Practices of Infectious Diseases*, Mandell, G.L., Bennett, J.E., and Dolin, R., Eds., Churchill Livingstone, New York, 1995, 354–364.
75. Alford, R.H. and Wallace, R.J. Jr. Antimycobacterial agents, in *Principles and Practices of Infectious Diseases*, Mandell, G.L., Bennett, J.E., and Dolin, R., Eds., Churchill Livingstone, New York, 1995, 389–401.
76. Mandell, G.L. and Sande, M.A. Drugs used in the chemotherapy of tuberculosis and leprosy, in *Goodman and Gilman's The Pharmacological Basis of Therapeutics*, Goodman Gilman, A., Rall, T.W., Nies, A.S., and Taylor, P., Eds., Pergamon Press, Elmsford, 1990, 1146–1181.
77. American Thoracic Society, Centers for Disease Control and Prevention, and Infectious Diseases Society of America. Treatment of tuberculosis, *Morbitity and Mortality Weekly Report*, 52(RR11), 1–77, 2003.
78. McEvoy, G.K., Snow, E.K., and Kester, L., Eds., *AHFS Drug Information*, American Society of Health-System Pharmacists, Inc., Bethesda, 2006.

79. Altmeyer, R. Virus attachment and entry offer numerous targets for antiviral therapy, *Curr. Pharm. Des.*, 10(30), 3701–3712, 2004.

80. Schols, D. HIV co-receptors as targets of antiviral therapy, *Curr. Top. Med. Chem.*, 4(9), 883–893, 2004.

81. Hirsh, M.S., Brun-Vezinet, F., Clotet, B. et al. Antiretroviral drug resistance testing in adults infected with human immunodeficiency virus type 1: 2003 recommendations of an International AIDS Society-USA panel, *Clin. Infect. Dis.*, 37, 113–128, 2003.

82. Johnson, V.A., Brun-Vezinet, F., Clotet, B. et al. Update of the drug resistance mutations in HIV-1: Fall 2005. *Top. HIV Med.*, 13, 125–131, 2005.

83. Panel on Clinical Practices for Treatment of HIV Infection Convened by the Department of Health and Human Services (DHHS). Guidelines for the use of antiretroviral agents in HIV-1-infected adults and adolescents, May 4, 2006, available at http://www.aidsinfo.org.nih.gov, accessed June 6, 2006.

84. Hammer, S., Katzenstein, D., Hughes, M. et al. A trial comparing nucleoside monotherapy with combination therapy in HIV-infected adults with CD4 counts from 200–500 per cubic millimeter, *N. Engl. J. Med.*, 635, 1081–1090, 1996.

85. Connor, E.M., Sperling, R.S., Gelber, R. et al. Reduction of maternal-infant transmission of human immunodeficiency virus type 1 with zidovudine treatment, *N. Engl. J. Med.*, 331, 1173–1180, 1994.

86. U.S. Department of Health and Human Services. Public Health Services Task Force recommendations for use of antiretroviral drugs in pregnant women for maternal health and interventions to reduce perinatal HIV-1 transmission in the United States, HIV/AIDS Treatment Information Service, Rockville, MD, available at http://www.aidsinfo.org.nih.gov, accessed June 6, 2006.

87. U.S. Public Health Service guidelines for the management of occupational exposure to HIV and recommendations for postexposure prophylaxis, available at http://www.aidsinfo.org.nih.gov, accessed June 5, 2006.

88. Balfour, H.H., Jr. Antiviral drugs, *N. Engl. J. Med.*, 340, 1255–1268, 1999.

89. Hayden, F.G. Antiviral agents, in *Principles and Practices of Infectious Diseases*, Mandell, G.L., Bennett, J.E., and Dolin, R., Eds., Churchill Livingstone, New York, 1995, 411–449.

90. Bennett, J.E. Antifungal agents, in *Principles and Practices of Infectious Diseases*, Mandell, G.L., Bennett, J.E., and Dolin, R., Eds., Churchill Livingstone, New York, 1995, 401–410.

91. Singh, R.M. and Perdue, B.E. Amphotericin B: A class review, *Formulary*, 33, 424–447, 1998.

3 Disk Diffusion Test and Gradient Methodologies

Audrey Wanger

CONTENTS

3.1 INTRODUCTION

3.1.2 HISTORICAL PERSPECTIVE

The earliest methods for assessing the effects of antibiotics on bacteria involved the use of ditches cut into agar plates. Antibiotic solution poured into the ditch was allowed to diffuse out to inhibit the growth of the bacteria streaked perpendicular to the ditch. In 1943, Foster and Woodruff used paper strips impregnated with antibiotics as an alternative source of diffusion [1]. The agar diffusion principles used in the bioassay of penicillin G in plasma were further used to develop the disk diffusion test [2]. Antibiotic reservoirs that initially consisted of antibiotic solutions in agar wells or cylinders were soon replaced by paper disks impregnated with antibiotics.

The results of early diffusion tests were arbitrarily interpreted: the presence of an inhibition zone suggested susceptibility and no zone, resistance. It became obvious at an early stage that many test parameters influenced the inhibition zone size irrespective of the susceptibility of the test organism. Qualitative results were also considered a disadvantage, and multiple disks with a high and a low antibiotic content were then introduced [3]. Categorical interpretations were derived based on the following: zones around both disks were indicative of susceptibility, a zone around the high potency disk only was indicative of intermediate susceptibility, and no zones around either disk was indicative of resistance.

3.1.3 FIRST ATTEMPTS AT STANDARDIZATION

By virtue of its simplicity, the disk diffusion test was rapidly and widely used by many laboratories. However, the lack of standardized procedures gave erroneous and nonreproducible results. In 1954, Ericsson published the first article describing a standardized technique called the *paper disk method* (PDM) for sensitivity testing of bacteria [4]. This technique became the PDM disk diffusion product line manufactured by AB BIODISK, Solna, Sweden, in the mid-1950s. The use of strictly calibrated antibiotic disks (PDM_ASD) together with a specially formulated antibiotic susceptibility test medium (PDM ASM) with controlled levels of thymine, thymidine, and various cations, and the use of a well-defined procedure with prediffusion and lighter inoculum, formed the backbone of this method [5].

Rigorous control of test reagents (PDM disks and media) on a batch to batch basis and the use of a well-defined test procedure made it possible to standardize all components of the PDM method. The zone diameter, an unknown or dependent variable, was then calibrated against reference agar dilution minimum inhibitor concentration (MIC) values (known or independent variable) using regression analysis based on the assumption that there was a linear correlation between zone sizes and MIC values (Figure 3.1).

Information on drug levels, the site of infection, and MIC distributions of biological populations of bacteria were used to select the MIC cutoffs or break points for the PDM method to predict whether bacteria with a certain zone-MIC correlate would respond to therapy with standard dosages. It is surprising that many of the susceptibility-testing principles used today were meticulously defined 50 years ago.

3.1.4 INTERNATIONAL COLLABORATIVE STUDY

In 1961, Ericsson and Sherris in collaboration with the World Health Organization undertook an initiative to define and standardize susceptibility testing on a global level. Experts from 16 countries

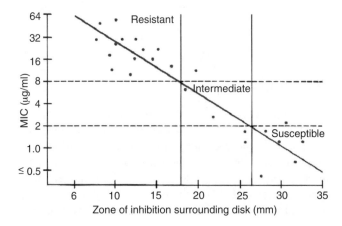

FIGURE 3.1 Example of a regression line demonstrating correlation between disk diffusion zone sizes and MIC values.

stretching from the United States across to Japan contributed to this, which, in its time, was a monumental effort to obtain global consensus on the standardization of susceptibility testing with MIC and disk diffusion methods. The findings and recommendations of this project were published in the *Acta Pathologica et Microbiologica Scandinavica* and titled "Antibiotic sensitivity testing, report from an International Collaborative Study (ICS)" [5]. This comprehensive reference, which has been cited over 5,000 times in the peer reviewed literature, was taken one step further by the Clinical Laboratory Standards Institute (CLSI) formerly NCCLS in the United States to develop specific clinical laboratory standards for antimicrobial susceptibility testing. In the meantime, the Food and Drug Administration (FDA) began its efforts to define the quality specifications of antibiotic disk reagents based on the efforts and findings of Ericsson et al. and to regulate their use for clinical testing [6].

3.1.5 Theory of Inhibition Zones

Despite its simplicity, the disk diffusion test is based on sophisticated physicochemical principles governing the dynamics of diffusion of antibiotics simultaneous to bacterial growth in an agar system. Cooper and Woodman [6] applied the formula for diffusion of neutral particles in gases to the diffusion of antibiotics through agar gels as follows:.

$$X^2 = 4DT\ 2.3(\log M_o/M)$$

where

$\quad\quad X$ = zone radius
$\quad\quad D$ = diffusion coefficient
$\quad\quad T$ = critical time for zone demarcation
$\quad\quad M_o$ = antibiotic concentration at the reservoir
$\quad\quad M$ = critical concentration of antibiotic inhibiting the organism

The critical time T can be further related to the growth characteristics of the test organism and the inoculum factor as follows:

$$T = L + n \log N/N_o$$

where

$\quad\quad L$ = lag period
$\quad\quad n$ = generation time
$\quad\quad N$ = critical mass of cells formed at T
$\quad\quad N_o$ = inoculum density used in the test

Thus, it is clear that many drug- and organism-related variables directly influence the zone size. To obtain meaningful results, as many test variables as possible need to be strictly standardized such that the rate-limiting step influencing the zone size is proportional to the critical concentration of the drug (M) inhibiting the organism relative to its susceptibility or resistance.

3.1.6 The Race between Diffusion and Growth

When an antibiotic disk comes in contact with an inoculated agar surface, the "drug–bug" race begins. Antibiotic molecules diffuse out from the disk into the agar, creating a dynamically changing gradient of antibiotic concentrations, while the test organism starts to divide and growth progresses toward the critical mass. The zone edge is formed at the critical time where the concentration of antibiotic that is just able to inhibit the organism reaches an overwhelming cell mass. At this point, the density of cells is sufficiently high such that the antibiotic in the immediate vicinity can be absorbed, thus maintaining concentrations at subinhibitory levels and enabling the test organism to grow. The critical times of most rapidly growing aerobic and facultative anaerobic bacteria vary between 3 and 6 h and should not be confused with the incubation period needed to achieve visible growth as seen by the naked eye.

Besides molecular properties of the drug such as molecular weight and size, ionic charge, and aqueous solubility, the diffusion coefficient of the drug is also influenced by the viscosity and depth of the agar as well as the assay temperature and incubation conditions. Besides characteristics intrinsic to the organism, growth is affected by the nutritive capacity of the test medium, the density and growth phase of the inoculum, and the incubation temperature [7,8].

3.1.7 NATIONAL VARIANTS OF DISK TESTS

In an attempt to "tame" the disk diffusion test and provide national guidelines, expert groups in several countries began to develop local variants of the disk test. Bauer et al. [9] defined the American version, as we know it today, based on the use of an inoculum density of approximately 10^8 CFU/mL to give semiconfluent growth using Mueller-Hinton agar (MHA) as the test medium. To overcome certain disadvantages of MHA, as observed in the past, e.g., poorer support of growth of gram-positive organisms, higher levels and lot-to-lot variable levels of sulfonamide antagonists, and, in general, significant batch-to-batch reproducibility, European versions opted for the use of other formulations such as PDM ASM (AB BIODISK, Solna, Sweden) and Isosensitest (Oxoid, Basingstoke, UK). A 100-fold lighter inoculum (10^6) (or 1:100 dilution of a 0.5 McFarland turbidity) was also chosen to achieve the so-called ICS inoculum of "dense but not confluent growth." This provided an optical check, and small variations of the lighter inoculum size had less effect on zone sizes than did the heavier inoculum. In the PDM method, Ericsson further implemented a prediffusion period of between 30 and 60 min prior to incubation to allow the gradient to stabilize before growth is initiated.

In the United Kingdom, the Stokes method [10] was introduced in an effort to control the influence of testing variables on the zone size and to improve the reliability of the interpretation of the test result. This technique compares the zone size of the test organism to a few control organisms with known susceptibilities. The test strain is concentrically inoculated in a section adjacent to the control organism on the same agar surface by rota-plating. Different antibiotic disks are then applied at the junction of the test and control. When the zone of the test strain for a certain antibiotic is equivalent to or larger than that of the susceptible control, the result is interpreted as a susceptible category and vice versa for a resistant result. Although the Stokes method is based on a rational assumption, the lack of suitable control strains to represent susceptibility categorization for an increasing number of antibiotics and control strains belonging to different species and with growth rates comparable to those of a wide variety of clinical pathogens have limited its validity and usefulness. Currently, laboratories in the United Kingdom and other former Commonwealth countries are replacing this method with a standardized disk test as described by the BSAC (British Society of Antimicrobial Chemotherapy) [11].

3.1.8 RATIONAL USE OF ANTIBIOTICS

Results of *in vitro* susceptibility tests can at best be used as an educated guess to predict the therapeutic outcome of standard antibiotic dosage regimens in normal patients. Many factors besides the *in vitro* result affect the potential clinical efficacy of a particular antibiotic. These include the pharmacokinetic (PK) properties of the drug such as its absorption, distribution metabolism, elimination, and protein binding and thus the resulting bioavailable drug levels obtained in different fluids and tissues. The pharmacodynamics (PD) or drug effects on the bacteria, such as inhibition of growth (bacteriostatic), killing kinetics of the organism (bactericidal), and postantibiotic effects will equally affect organism eradication and clinical outcome. Host factors, such as the inflammatory response, suppression of normal immune defense mechanisms, site of the infection, and presence of foreign bodies or abscess formation are important factors that will also influence treatment outcome. Thus, susceptibility test results of qualitative methods like the disk diffusion test must be correlated to quantitative reference MIC values in micrograms per milliliter (mg/ml) that are in turn used in different PK/PD models to help optimize antibiotic selection, fine-tune dosage regimens, and minimize resistance selection. Again, these seemingly sophisticated principles were well described by Ericsson in a Ph.D. thesis entitled, "Rational Use of Antibiotics in Hospitals" [12].

The main advantages of disk diffusion testing are the simplicity of use, no requirement for expensive equipment, flexible choice of antibiotics for testing, and cost-effectiveness. The main disadvantage, besides not providing quantitative information, is the amount of technologist time required for setting up the test and for manual reading of zone sizes and consultation with interpretive standards prior to interpretation of results. In many clinical situations, disk diffusion testing and a qualitative interpretation of susceptibility is an acceptable option. In the treatment of most "healthy" patients with, for example, uncomplicated urinary tract infection, the choice of the test method is not critical. In these cases, disk diffusion, break-point agar, or broth dilution systems are equally satisfactory for predicting patient outcome [13].

In critical infections such as endocarditis, meningitis, or osteomyelitis, or in the immunocompromised host, accurate quantitative determination of the exact MIC value is crucial for therapy guidance. In these situations, an MIC value of 0.016 µg/mL has significantly different therapeutic implications than does an MIC of 1 µg/mL in influencing the antibiotic choice and dose relative to factors such as body weight, site of infection, potential drug toxicity, and drug levels [13]. Clinical laboratories usually implement multiple susceptibility test systems and base their choice of test method on patient type, source of specimen, organism species, and expected problems of resistance detection. The need for quantitative methods was emphasized over 30 years ago. Ericsson et al. [5] stated "The basic point of reference should be the MIC determined under reproducible conditions," and the ICS report [5] encouraged "the development and evaluation of new techniques for measuring sensitivity," not just arbitrarily grouping isolates into categories.

3.1.9 Antibiotic Gradient Plate

As early as the 1950s, Bryson and Szybalski [14] recognized the limitations of diffusion methods due to the undefined and unstable gradients generated. For research studies on antibiotic resistance, the selection of bacterial populations with different levels of resistance required a calibrated quantitative gradient. They developed the "wedge plate" method of creating a gradient in an agar plate that would be stable long enough to select out resistant populations of bacteria at defined concentrations of antibiotics in a reproducible manner. A layer of plain agar is poured into a petri dish, preferably square or rectangular in shape, and the agar is allowed to solidify as a slope by placing the plate at an angle. A second layer of agar containing a defined amount of antibiotic is poured on top of the slope and the "sandwich" agar composite is allowed to solidify on a horizontal surface. The drug diffuses vertically downward creating a gradient of antibiotic concentrations across the wedge length of the plate. The concentration gradient is calibrated by calculating the drug concentration in total volume of agar at different sections along the wedge.

3.1.10 Spiral Gradient Plate

The spiral gradient technique [15] uses a diluter-dispenser pump to deposit a continuously diluted bacterial suspension onto an agar surface using a spiral plater. The method was initially developed for the enumeration of bacteria for research and industrial purposes. It was further adapted for dispensing a continuously diluted antibiotic solution as closely spaced concentric rings on an agar surface. After a period of equilibration, an antibiotic gradient is generated with a high concentration in the middle and decreasing progressively toward the rim of the agar plate. In a way, it resembles a "huge" disk diffusion gradient with a concentration maximum in the middle of a circle. After growth of the organism, which is streaked from the center outward like the spokes in a wheel, the distance from the center to the point of inhibition is measured and the inhibiting concentration of the antibiotic can be calculated. Although automated, the technique still requires preparation and quality control of fresh antibiotic solutions, and the stability of the gradients generated is maintained for a relatively short period of time. The technique is useful for research but not for daily use in a clinical laboratory.

3.1.11 ETEST

An innovative gradient technique that combined the principles of both the disk diffusion and agar dilution was developed in Sweden and first presented to the scientific community at the Interscience Conference on Antimicrobial Agents and Chemotherapy (ICAAC) meeting in 1988 [16]. A preformed and predefined gradient of antibiotic concentrations is immobilized in a dry format onto the surface of a plastic strip (Figure 3.2).

The continuous concentration gradient is calibrated across a corresponding MIC range covering 15 twofold dilutions. When applied to the surface of an inoculated agar plate, the antibiotic on the Etest strip is instantaneously transferred to the agar in the form of a stable and continuous gradient directly beneath and in the immediate vicinity of the strip (Figure 3.3).

The stability of the gradient is maintained for up to 18 to 20 hours, which covers the critical times of a wide range of pathogens, from rapid growing aerobic bacteria to slow growing fastidious organisms, including anaerobes and fungi. The stable gradient also provides inoculum tolerance where a 100-fold variation in CFU/mL has minimal effect on the MIC results of homogeneously susceptible strains. This minimizes the inoculum-related day-to-day variability seen in routine susceptibility testing [17]. More importantly, the stable gradient also allows the use of a macromethod with heavier inoculum to optimize the detection of low-level resistance, heteroresistance, and resistant subpopulations.

Etest has been approved by the U.S. FDA since 1991 and is currently cleared for clinical testing of aerobes, anaerobes, pneumococci, streptococci, haemophilus, and gonococci against a wide variety of antibiotics, and for *Candida* spp. against several antifungal agents. Further, it has been extensively validated with over 3,000 international scientific references, more than 1,000 of which

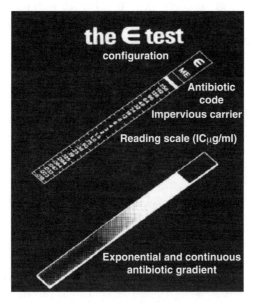

FIGURE 3.2 Configuration of the Etest strip with the antibiotic scale on one side and the predefined gradient on the reverse side.

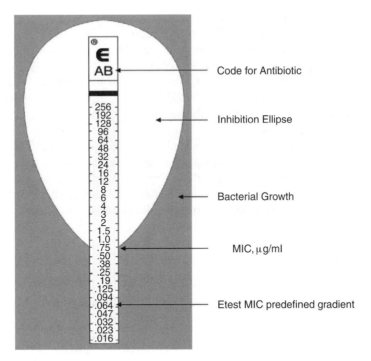

FIGURE 3.3 Schematic diagram of the Etest inhibition ellipse showing the MIC at the intersection of the growth of the organism and the calibrated strip.

have been published in peer-reviewed journals (Etest reference list). These investigations have documented Etest performance to be equivalent to reference MIC methods with a high degree of reproducibility in most laboratory settings.

3.2 PROCEDURE — DISK DIFFUSION

3.2.1 INOCULUM AND INOCULATION

A major source of error in disk diffusion testing is the inoculum variation [18]. In the CLSI (former NCCLS) procedure [19], the inoculum density must be standardized to a final concentration of $1-2 \times 10^8$ CFU/mL. This can be accomplished either by the growth method or direct colony suspension. For the growth method, a loop is used to touch the top of three to five colonies of the same morphological type from an agar plate culture. This is suspended in 4–5 mL of a suitable broth, for example, tryptic soy broth, and incubated at 35°C until it achieves or exceeds the turbidity of a 0.5 McFarland standard (usually 26 h). The turbidity of the actively growing cells when adjusted to the 0.5 McFarland standard using sterile saline will provide an inoculum of approximately 12×10^8 CFU/mL (as initially determined using *E. coli* ATCC 25922 as a reference). The inoculum adjustment can be done visually using a barium sulfate turbidity standard or with a photometric device. Barium sulfate standards must be verified monthly and vigorously agitated before use. Commercially available latex standards (Remel, Lenexa, KS, and Hardy Diagnostics, Santa Monica, CA) with a long shelf life are a practical alternative. The latex suspension should be mixed by inverting gently and not on a vortex mixer.

A more practical alternative is to prepare the inoculum by suspending isolated colonies from an 18–24-h agar plate in broth or saline to a turbidity matching a 0.5 McFarland standard. This is the recommended method for fastidious organisms and for testing staphylococci for the detection of oxacillin resistance. The Prompt (BD Diagnostic Systems, Sparks, MD) inoculum preparation system can also be used to optimize workflow since the organisms are supposedly maintained at the same density for 6 h. However, the system is not suitable for mucoid strains or fastidious organisms since the amount of cell mass absorbed onto the tip of the sampling wand may be insufficient to give the appropriate inoculum density in terms of CFU per milliliter. Furthermore, the inoculum solution contains Tween, a surfactant that can have potential effects on certain organisms, and the diffusion of antibiotics from the disks. Colony counts should be regularly performed to validate that the inoculum density is correct.

The inoculum suspension should be used within 15 min of preparation, and this is particularly important for fastidious organisms that lose their viability rapidly. A sterile cotton swab (not too thin or too tightly spun) is dipped into the suspension and pressed firmly on the inside of the tube to remove excess liquid. The dried surface of the appropriate agar plate is inoculated by streaking the entire surface and repeating it twice, rotating the plate 60° degrees each time to obtain an even distribution of the inoculum. The inoculated plate is allowed to dry with the lid left ajar for no more than 15 min.

3.2.2 Application of Disks

Once the agar plate is completely dry, the different antibiotic disks are applied either manually or with a dispensing apparatus. In general, no more than 12 disks should be placed on a 150-mm agar plate or 5 disks on a 90-mm plate (less for very susceptible organisms, see Figure 3.4).

Optimally, disks should be positioned at a distance of 30 mm apart and no closer than 24 mm apart when measured center to center to minimize overlap of inhibition zones. Most dispenser devices are self-tamping (disks are tapped or pressed onto the agar surface). If applied manually, the disk must be pressed down to make immediate and complete contact with the agar surface. Once in contact with the agar, the disk cannot be moved because of instantaneous diffusion of antibiotics from the disk to the agar.

3.2.3 Incubation and Reading

Agar plates are incubated in an inverted position (agar side up) under conditions appropriate for the test organism (Table 3.1). Plates should not be stacked more than five in a pile to ensure that the plate in the middle reaches incubator temperature within the same time frame as the others.

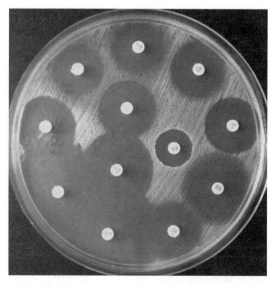

FIGURE 3.4 Kirby-Bauer disk diffusion result for a very susceptible strain of *Staphylococcus* species.

TABLE 3.1
Disk Diffusion Testing Conditions

Organism	Medium[a]	Incubation		
		Temp.	Atmosphere	Duration (hours)
Enterobacteriaceae	MHA	35°C	Ambient	16–18
P. aeruginosa	MHA	35°C	Ambient	16–18
Acinetobacter spp.				
Staphylococcus spp.	MHA	35°C	Ambient	16–18
				24 (oxacillin)
Enterococcus spp.	MHA	35°C	Ambient	16–18
				24 (vancomycin)
Haemophilus spp.	HTM	35°C	5% CO_2	16–18
N. gonorrhoeae	GC	35°C	5% CO_2	20–24
Streptococcus spp. other than *S. pneumoniae*	MHB	35°C	5% CO_2	20–24
S. pneumoniae	MHB	35°C	5% CO_2	20–24

[a] MHA = Mueller-Hinton agar, HTM = *Haemophilus* test medium, GC = gonococcal agar, MHB = Mueller-Hinton + 5% sheep blood agar.

After 16–18 h of incubation for rapidly growing aerobic bacteria, or longer where appropriate for fastidious organisms or specific resistance detection conditions, the agar plate is examined to determine if a semiconfluent and even lawn of growth has been obtained before reading the plate. If individual colonies are seen, the inoculum is too light, and the test should be repeated since zone sizes would be falsely larger. The same holds true for excessively heavy inoculum where zone edges may be very hazy and the zone sizes falsely small.

If the lawn of growth is satisfactory, the zone diameter is read to the nearest millimeter using a ruler or sliding calipers. For MHA (without blood supplements), zone diameters are read from the back of the plate. For blood-containing agar, zone diameters are read from the surface of the agar. The zone margin is identified as the area where no obvious visible growth is seen by the naked eye unless otherwise specified; faint growth or microcolonies detectable only with a magnifying glass or by tilting the plate should be ignored. Although selection of the end point should logically be related to the mode of action of the drug, for example, bactericidal drugs to be read at 100% or complete inhibition of all growth and bacteriostatic drugs at 80% inhibition, such specific recommendations are not provided by the CLSI. The following are highlighted in the CLSI document [19]:

Discrete colonies in an otherwise clear zone should be subcultured, reidentified, and retested.
With *Proteus* spp., the swarming growth within a discernable zone should be ignored.
For streptococci, the zone of growth inhibition should be measured and not the hemolysis seen on blood agar plates.
With trimethoprim and sulphonamides, trailing of growth at the zone edge should be disregarded and the most obvious margin as seen by the naked eye should be read.
Transmitted light should be used to examine oxacillin and vancomycin zones for light growth or microcolonies, both of which are indicative of resistance.

Some examples of different zone edges can be seen in Figure 3.5.

Reading of zone sizes can be automated using a camera-based image analysis systems such as the BIOMIC (Giles Scientific, New York, NY), Aura (Oxoid, Basingstoke, UK), Protozone (Microbiology International, Frederick, MD), and SirScan (i2a, Paris, France). The agar plate is placed into the reader, which is connected to a computer system. The system then reads the different zone

FIGURE 3.5 Examples of different zone edges.

sizes directly from the agar plate and converts the result to a susceptibility category interpretation. Although zone sizes are automatically read, the user can intervene and adjust the results. The BIOMIC system also claims that zone sizes can be converted to MIC equivalents using a database of regression analyses based on the assumption of a linear correlation between the zone size and MIC value. Although a few studies have shown acceptable correlations between zone extrapolated MIC equivalents provided by BIOMIC when compared with reference methods [20,21], accuracy limitations must be recognized. The large standard errors (Sy.x, i.e., variation of y/zone size along each x/MIC value) associated with such linear regression analysis assumptions, combined with the zone size reproducibility of ±3 mm at best, implies that the extrapolated MIC may have an inherent error range of 3 to 4 dilutions. An extrapolated MIC of 4 µg/mL may mean a range of 1 to 16 µg/mL and may potentially incur errors that can vary from minor ones to serious major errors (false resistance) to very major errors (false susceptibility). The use of such MIC extrapolates as substitutes for quantitatively determined real MIC values is questionable especially for critical isolates and for bacterial populations that cluster around interpretive MIC break points.

3.2.4 INTERPRETATION

Zone diameters are converted into different susceptibility categories using the zone/MIC interpretive criteria from the most recent annually published CLSI M100 S series documents for disk diffusion using the appropriate tables for the organism being tested. Organisms are categorized as susceptible, intermediate, or resistant to the antibiotics tested. These categories are defined as follows:

> *Susceptible* — an infection caused by the organism will most probably respond to treatment with a standard dosage of the antibiotic as indicated for use for that infection.
>
> *Intermediate* — these results are usually regarded as indicative of nonuseful therapeutic options similar to the resistant category for treatment purposes. It also serves as a buffer zone to help prevent major categorical errors caused by slight changes in the zone sizes due to the influence of technical variables. However, infections at sites where the antibiotic is likely to be highly concentrated, such as β-lactams in the urinary tract, may respond to therapy.
>
> *Resistant* — the infection is not likely to respond to therapy.

Disk diffusion was initially developed for susceptibility testing of rapidly growing aerobic bacteria, including enterococci, staphylococci, *Enterobacteriaceae*, and *P. aeruginosa*. Modifications have been described by the CLSI for certain fastidious organisms including: *Haemophilus influenzae*, *Neisseria gonorrhoeae*, *Streptococcus pneumoniae*, and *Streptococcus* spp. The inoculum for fastidious organisms should be prepared using the direct inoculation method. In general, these organisms are highly susceptible to most antibiotics tested and therefore, no more than 9 disks should be placed on a large 150-mm agar plate compared to the 12 disks that can be used when testing rapidly growing aerobic organisms. Table 3.1 provides a description of media, inoculum, and incubation conditions recommended.

3.2.5 Special Tests

In certain clinical situations, it may be appropriate to use disk diffusion to screen for certain resistance mechanisms. A single antibiotic can also be used as a group representative to predict susceptibility to agents belonging to the same class. The most commonly used disk screen is the oxacillin 1-μg disk to predict susceptibility of *S. pneumoniae* to β-lactams. All nonsusceptible results by the disk screen must be confirmed by a MIC method. MIC testing of *S. pneumoniae* is recommended as the primary method for sterile body site isolates.

Disks with a higher concentration of either gentamicin or streptomycin can be used to screen enterococci for high-level resistance to aminoglycosides (HLAR) to predict potential synergy or lack thereof between aminoglycosides and penicillin. Enterococci are generally resistant when tested with a standard disk content for aminoglycosides (30-μg disk). However, susceptibility to high-level gentamicin (120 μg) or streptomycin (300 μg) disks predicts potential synergy between that aminoglycoside and penicillin that may contribute to bactericidal effects with drug combination therapy, an important consideration for serious infections.

Two or more of the following disks — cefpodoxime, ceftazidime, aztreonam, cefotaxime, and/or ceftriaxone — can be used to screen strains of *E. coli*, *Klebsiella pneumoniae*, and *K. oxytoca* for the presence of extended spectrum β-lactamase (ESBL). Modified zone size criteria are provided by the CLSI for ESBL screening purposes. Disk diffusion can also be used to confirm the presence of ESBLs by using cefotaxime and ceftazidime disks with and without clavulanic acid. The combination disks initially had to be prepared by hand but are now commercially available (BD Diagnostics, Sparks MD; and Remel, Lenexa, KS). The test principle is based on the fact that most ESBLs will be inhibited by the β-lactamase inhibitor clavulanic acid, hence restoring susceptibility to the cephalosporin. Thus, an increase in zone size in the presence of the inhibitor compared with the cephalosporin alone by 5 mm or more is indicative of an ESBL-producing strain (Figure 3.6). If confirmed, the ESBL-producing strain should be considered and reported to be resistant to all β-lactam antibiotics.

Inducible resistance to clindamycin in gram-positive organisms can be detected by placing a clindamycin and an erythromycin disk 15–20 mm apart and observing for a flattening of the clindamycin zone on the side closest to the erythromycin disk (Figure 3.7) [22]. Detection of a flattened zone correlates with the presence of the *erm* gene and resistance to clindamycin even though it may appear susceptible to clindamycin by routine testing methods.

All organisms not mentioned above are not currently included in the CLSI recommendations for disk diffusion susceptibility testing and should be tested by a MIC method since either the procedure is not applicable or no interpretive criteria have been developed to date. The CLSI guidelines for the use of MHA for aerobic bacteria, unless otherwise specified, and the inoculum described should be strictly followed to achieve acceptable results.

FIGURE 3.6 Detection of ESBLs using ceftazidime and cefotaxime disks plus or minus clavulanic acid.

FIGURE 3.7 D-zone demonstrating inducible resistance to clindamycin.

TABLE 3.2
Disk Diffusion Limitations

Organisms:
  Fastidious, slow growing organisms with the exception of *S. pneumoniae*, *H. influenzae*
Organism/antibiotic combination:
  Viridans streptococci/penicillin
  S. aureus/vancomycin
Antibiotic:
  Vancomycin/enterococci (intermediate results should be confirmed by MIC method)
  Oxacillin/*S. pneumoniae* (intermediate or resistant results should be confirmed by penicillin MIC testing)
Specimen:
  MIC method recommended for testing sterile body site isolates, particularly CSF
Resistance mechanism:
  Inducible beta lactamases
  Heterogeneous resistance
  VISA/h-VISA

The most recent CLSI disk diffusion document, Table 1 and 1A [19], provide suggested groupings of antibiotics that could be tested as primary, secondary, and supplemental panels for aerobes and fastidious organisms, respectively. Disk diffusion testing with a group representative concept can be exemplified by the use of an erythromycin disk to predict susceptibility to all other macrolide antibiotics, including azithromycin and clarithromycin.

Other antibiotic–organism combinations can also be tested, although caution should be taken to avoid combinations specifically contraindicated. The most common contraindications are listed in Table 3.2. If all these disk diffusion testing provisions have been met and problems still occur with the test, for example, quality control results are outside given specifications, the source of possible errors must be investigated and corrective action taken (Table 3.3) [23].

3.2.5.1 Etest

Etest is based on the use of a stable predefined gradient of antibiotic to generate precise MIC values. The gradient immobilized on the plastic strip is placed on an inoculated agar surface to transfer the antibiotic to the agar whereby a stable and continuous gradient is established under and alongside the strip. The stability of this gradient is maintained for up to 20 h. Etest differs from disk diffusion in that it is a preformed and stable gradient applicable for use with a wide range of aerobic and anaerobic organisms, both fastidious and nonfastidious, regardless of varying growth rates and critical times and testing procedures while disk diffusion is only suitable for rapidly growing aerobic bacteria. The key advantages of Etest are that it comprises a stable gradient, is an agar-based method, and can also be used in a macromethod format to optimize detection of antibiotic resistance. Furthermore, molecular properties of the antibiotic do not affect the performance of Etest since the

TABLE 3.3
Disk Diffusion Troubleshooting Guide

Result	Possible Cause(s)	Suggested Resolution
Zones too small	Inoculum too heavy	Use McFarland standard or calibrator to carefully measure inoculum density and perform colony counts
	Agar too thick	Measure agar depth carefully
	Disk expired or inactive	Use new lot of disks or unopened cartridge
	Inoculated plates left too long prior to application of disks	Apply disks within 15 minutes
	Wrong medium for organism	Follow NCCLS guidelines for appropriate choice of media, perform quality control
Zones too large	Inoculum too light	Same as above
	Agar too thin	measure agar depth carefully
	Poor growth (too fastidious, wrong media, not fresh isolate)	check all variables
Single disk out of control	Improper storage of disks	Maintain majority of disk stock at $-20\,^\circ C$, only keep maximum of 1 week supply at $4\,^\circ C$ (be cautious with β-lactams, clavulanic acid containing disks, and imipenem)
	Media pH too low or too high	Particularly effects tetracycline macrolides and clindamycin (CO_2 incubation can decrease pH)
	Cation concentration too low	Especially effects aminoglycosides and *P. aeruginosa*
	Transcription or reading error	Reread or reset the test
Colonies within zone	Mixed population	Reisolate or Gram stain the colonies
Deformation of zone	Disks too close to each other	Place fewer disks on plate (especially with very susceptible organisms)

gradient is preformed and not dependent on diffusion. Thus, large molecules such as vancomycin and lipophilic compounds such as amphotericin that comprise a limitation for disk diffusion testing can be reliably tested with the Etest predefined gradient.

The procedure for inoculum preparation and inoculation of the agar plates is the same as that described for disk diffusion. The plate can also be efficiently streaked using a rota-plater e.g., Retro C80 (AB BIODISK) to obtain an even lawn of growth. After the plate is streaked, it is very important that the agar surface be allowed to dry completely before applying the strips. Etest strips can be applied to the agar surface by using either forceps, a manual single strip applicator, Nema C88, a vacuum-controlled pen, or Simplex C76, or an automatic multiple strip dispenser (Figure 3.8). All applicator devices are available from AB BIODISK.

Up to six strips can be optimally positioned on a large agar plate (150 mm) or one or two on a small agar plate (90 mm). Strips should be applied in an equidistant spoke-wheel pattern with the highest concentration positioned toward the edge of the plate.

The side of the strip carrying the antibiotic gradient must be placed in contact with the agar surface (MIC scale facing upward). Templates provided by AB BIODISK can be used to facilitate the optimal positioning of strips (Figure 3.9).

Because of the immediate release of the antibiotic, the strip cannot be moved once it is in contact with the agar surface. However, if the strip fell with the MIC scale side facing down, it can be picked up, turned over and reapplied correctly. The plate is incubated in an inverted position (agar side up) under conditions appropriate for the organism. Incubation conditions for most organisms are the same as for disk diffusion (Table 3.1). Information on appropriate inoculum, media, and incubation conditions for different organism groups are provided in the product inserts and the Etest Media, Inoculum and Incubation Guide provided by AB BIODISK. Individual

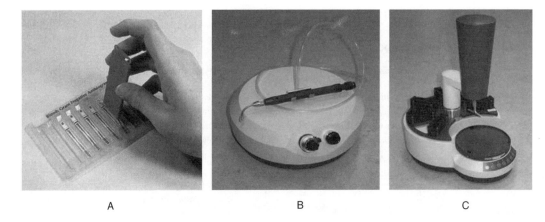

A   B   C

FIGURE 3.8 Methods for application of Etest strips. (A) Applicator tray and manual applicator; (B) Nema C88 vacuum pen; and (C) Simplex C76 automated multistrip dispenser.

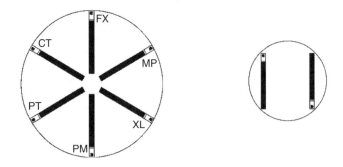

FIGURE 3.9 Templates for application of six or two Etest strips on either a large or small plate, respectively.

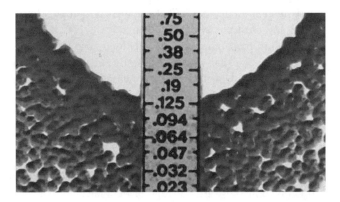

FIGURE 3.10 Example of a clear-cut Etest MIC end point of 0.125 µg/mL.

technical guides and organism-specific application sheets are also available to facilitate the use of Etest. These guides can be downloaded from the AB BIODISK Web site (www.abbiodisk.com) or requested from AB BIODISK directly or the local Etest distributor.

After incubation, a parabolic shaped inhibition zone centered alongside the test strip is seen. The MIC is read at the point where the growth/inhibition margin of the organism intersects the edge of the calibrated strip (Figure 3.10).

MIC endpoints for most antibiotic–organism combinations can be easily read visually. A magnifying glass and/or tilting the plate can be helpful for visualizing microcolonies and hazes or other colonies within the inhibition ellipse when reading the end points of bactericidal drugs and/or when detecting different resistances such as heteroresistance to oxacillin in *S. aureus*.

Specific guidelines are used for reading different types of Etest results depending on the mode of action of the antibiotic or antifungal agent. End points for bacteriostatic drugs are read at 80% inhibition and bactericidal drugs at 100% inhibition. Comprehensive guidelines for reading of an array of end points are provided in Etest reading guides that contain color pictures of a wide range and variety of results for different organisms, drugs, and resistance mechanisms. Incubation of capnophilic organisms such as pneumococci, streptococci, gonococci, and *Haemophilus* spp. is done in 5% CO_2. The resultant acidification and decrease in pH can affect the activity of certain antibiotics such as macrolides. The MIC values of azithromycin and clarithromycin may be increased by one to three dilutions under CO_2 conditions compared with ambient incubation, and MIC interpretive criteria and quality control specifications adjusted for CO_2 according to the manufacturer's instructions should be used whenever appropriate.

Because of the continuous concentration gradient, Etest MIC values can fall in between conventional twofold dilution values. The MIC should be reported as the exact value obtained, for example. 0.38 µg/ml; however, it should be rounded up to the next higher 2-fold dilution value, that is, 0.5 µg/mL (Figure 3.11) before using CLSI interpretive criteria for susceptibility categorization.

A major advantage of Etest is that it can be used as a macromethod because it is "inoculum tolerant" to maximize the detection of resistance mechanisms that may be heterogeneous and expressed at varying levels. A common example of heterogeneous resistance is oxacillin resistance in staphylococci. Laboratories may choose to confirm equivocal oxacillin results from their routine systems using an alternative MIC method such as Etest. Inducible β-lactamases in gram-negative organisms such as *Enterobacter*, *Serratia*, and *Citrobacter* species can also be difficult to detect in standard methods. Resistance to cephalosporins may be falsely reported as susceptible in automated systems, which use a lower inoculum, or falsely resistant if the organism produces excessive filaments. Equally, labile compounds such as imipenem may give unexpected resistant results, in both based methods due to freeze–thaw effects.

Certain antibiotics can be problematic to test with the disk diffusion method because of specific physicochemical properties of the molecule. Glycopeptides such as vancomycin have a high molecular weight (1450) and diffuse very slowly in agar. The limited diffusion and poorly resolved concentration gradient around a vancomycin disk result in only a few millimeter difference in zone size for separating susceptible and resistant strains, thus, results may not be reliable. Because of this limitation, the Centers for Disease Control and Prevention recommends that an MIC method like Etest be used for vancomycin testing with staphylococci for detection of reduced susceptibility

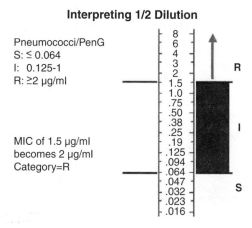

Interpreting 1/2 Dilution

Pneumococci/PenG
S: ≤ 0.064
I: 0.125-1
R: ≥2 µg/ml

MIC of 1.5 µg/ml
becomes 2 µg/ml
Category=R

FIGURE 3.11 Interpretation of Etest half dilution MICs using penicillin MICs for *Streptococcus pneumoniae* as an example.

to vancomycin [24]. Although standardized MIC methods can detect strains with higher level resistance to vancomycin (MICs $\geq 8\mu g/mL$), strains with lower MIC values (4–8 $\mu g/mL$) (intermediate and/or heterogeneously resistant strains) will be better detected using a richer medium like brain–heart infusion agar, a higher inoculum, and extended incubation as described for the Etest macromethod for vancomycin intermediate *S. aureus* (VISA) and hetero-VISA (h-VISA) detection [25, 26]. Hiramatsu [27] first reported that a clinical strain of *S. aureus* (Mu3) heteroresistance to vancomycin (h-VISA) was a precursor strain to the more stable resistant variant Mu50 (VISA), which was associated with clinical failure. More evidence has been generated since then to suggest that the heteroresistant phenotype can be clinically significant in different therapeutic situations. Several studies have demonstrated the limitations of disk diffusion and automated systems for testing of *S. aureus* against vancomycin [28]. Walsh et al. [29] also demonstrated the limitations of most standardized MIC and screening methods for the detection of vancomycin resistance in staphylococci. A modification of the Etest procedure using an inoculum density equivalent to a McFarland 2.0 and brain–heart infusion agar achieved a sensitivity and specificity of 98% when compared with population analysis profiling as the reference method [26]. CLSI also recommends that all enterococci found to have intermediate susceptibility to vancomycin by disk diffusion testing be confirmed with an MIC method. Using a combination of on-scale MIC values to vancomycin and teicoplanin, vancomycin-resistant enterococci (VRE) can also be differentiated into the various phenotypes (*vanA*, *vanB*, and *vanC*).

Unique Etest gradient formats are also available for detecting specific resistance mechanisms such as extended spectrum-lactamases (ESBLs) and metallo-β-lactamases (MBLs). Etest ESBL strips comprise double-sided gradients of either cefotaxime or ceftazidime across seven dilutions on half of the strip and a gradient of the same drug overlaid with a constant concentration of clavulanic acid on the other half. A decrease in MIC of at least three twofold dilutions in the presence of clavulanic acid compared with the parent cephalosporin alone or the presence of a "phantom" or deformed zone along the strip confirms the presence of an ESBL (Figure 3.12 and Figure 3.13).

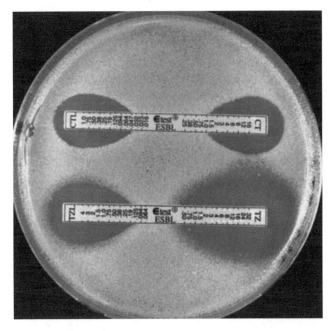

FIGURE 3.12 Positive ESBL result (top, cefotaxime, cefotaxime/clavulanic acid) and negative ESBL result (bottom, ceftazidime, ceftazidime/clavulanic acid) and overall ESBL positive confirmation.

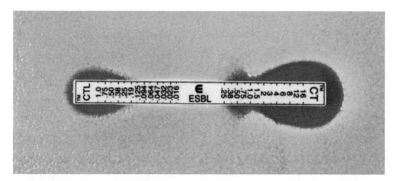

FIGURE 3.13 Deformation of the Etest ellipse demonstrating a positive ESBL result.

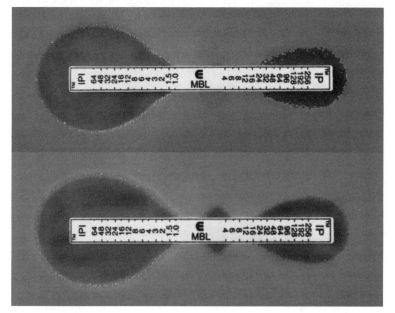

FIGURE 3.14 Positive MBL result (top and bottom) using Etest MBL strips with imipenem CIP and imipenem plus EDTA CIPI.

The Etest MBL strip will be an important tool for tracking the emergence of MBLs in gram-negative aerobic bacteria and also in anaerobes [30]. The MBL strip based on the same configuration as the ESBL strip uses imipenem gradients with and without a zinc chelator EDTA (Figure 3.14). Since MBL enzymes require zinc as an activity cofactor, removing zinc will reduce the activity of the enzyme and restore imipenem activity. Similarly, a decrease in imipenem MIC by at least three dilutions or a deformation of the ellipse or a phantom zone is indicative of a MBL.

Because of the stability of the concentration gradient, Etest can also be used for testing very slow growing organisms, fastidious organisms, and a wide variety of clinically significant organisms that belong to many species. Clinical situations often warrant susceptibility testing of rarely encountered, unusual, and/or opportunistic pathogens for which no CLSI guidelines are available. Scientific references can be used to guide the choice of appropriate media, incubation conditions, and antibiotics to test, and MIC values can be reported to the clinician without providing any interpretations. The electronic version of the Etest reference list that can be provided by AB BIODISK is a useful source of information for these unusual applications. Interaction with the physician is essential to ascertain the necessity for susceptibility testing and which agents to test, and to aid in the understanding of the MIC value itself. Etest can also be applied to susceptibility testing of yeast, molds and mycobacteria. Although mold and microbacteria applications are not cleared for clinical use in the United States by the FDA, equivalence to CLSI and other reference methods has been demonstrated [31,32,34]. The use of a wide concentration range MIC method (15 dilutions) in an agar-based system that provides good growth of most organisms would be advantageous for obtaining quantitative MIC information in difficult clinical situations.

Clinical laboratories must differentiate between CLSI recommendations of reference methods in contrast to the regulatory role of the FDA, which clears the clinical use of commercial test systems. Each commercial manufacturer has to demonstrate that the performance of their product is substantially equivalent to the CLSI reference method, based on comprehensive testing criteria as required by the FDA. CLSI does not "approve" or endorse any commercial test system, and this is clearly outlined in their documents. However, the CLSI also states that alternative methods like the "antibiotic gradient" may be used in place of CLSI reference methods if shown to be substantially equivalent. Additional research applications of Etest include antibiotic combination testing [35], determination of minimum bactericidal concentrations (MBC), kill curve assays, and postantibiotic effect measurements [36].

3.3 QUALITY CONTROL

The correct use and accuracy of any susceptibility test system is dependent on good quality control (QC) practices. Quality of the reagents, media, and testing procedures, and personnel competency must be assessed on a regular basis. It is important that QC data are retained in such a way that deviation trends can be quickly and easily observed. Patient data cannot be released if results for QC strains are out of specification. QC testing should be performed in the same manner and by the same personnel who are testing patient isolates.

3.3.1 QUALITY CONTROL STRAINS: USE AND STORAGE

The CLSI provides guidelines for the selection of QC strains and frequency with which QC should be performed for both disk diffusion and MIC testing [19]. Guidelines for MIC testing should be used for QC of Etest. QC strains chosen for MIC testing should be such that the expected MIC value for the strain falls in the middle of the concentration range for that antibiotic. QC specifications for each Etest reagent are also provided in the product package insert. QC strains can be purchased in a dehydrated form either as Culti-loops (Remel), pellets, or swabs (KWIK-STIK, Hardy Diagnostics, Santa Maria, CA), or lyophilized in multiple unit containers (LYFO-DISK, MicroBioLogics, St. Cloud, MN). After processing according to the manufacturer's instructions, organisms should be maintained on an agar slant, stored at 2–8°C, and can be subcultured weekly for up to 1 month, after which a new QC stock organism should be used. QC organisms can be stored for prolonged periods of time at –70°C in broth (such as brain–heart infusion or brucella) or skim milk. Strains should be subcultured at least twice after the initial rehydration or removal from frozen stocks before being used for QC testing. Testing of QC strains should be performed either on each day of clinical testing for infrequently performed tests or weekly after qualifying an initial 30-day QC specification. CLSI provides flow diagrams for frequency of QC testing, troubleshooting, and corrective action for out-of-control results.

3.3.2 REAGENT HANDLING AND STORAGE

Antibiotic disks are available from several manufacturers (Becton Dickinson, Remel, and Hardy Diagnostics). They should be strictly handled and stored according to the manufacturer's instructions. Short-term (within one week) disks can be stored at 4°C in disk dispensers containing desiccant for day-to-day use. Long-term storage of unopened cartridges should be at –20°C, and

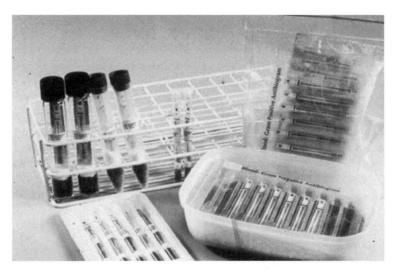

FIGURE 3.15 Examples of different methods to store Etest, e.g., storage tubes, and applicator tray in a Tupperware container.

it is preferable to store all β-lactam antibiotics at –20°C. Packages should be allowed to reach room temperature prior to opening (BBL package insert). Etest is manufactured by AB BIODISK (Solna, Sweden) and is marketed and sold in the United States through their subsidiary in Piscataway, NJ. Etest reagents are provided in packages of 100 strips or 30 for some items. Unopened packages should be stored at –20°C until their expiry date, and the shelf life of most Etset products is longer than 3 years. Prior to use, the package is removed from the freezer and allowed to reach room temperature before opening the package (approximately 30 min if stored at –20°C and longer if stored at –70°C). Once opened, the remaining unused strips from the package must be stored in a storage tube or other airtight container with desiccant. Laboratories may find it convenient to store the Etest strips in an applicator tray with antibiotic selections for specific organism applications. The tray with Etest strips can be stored in a plastic container with desiccant such as a Tupperware box, and can be placed directly in the freezer (Figure 3.15). Strips from opened packages, if appropriately stored at –20°C, have the same expiration date as the unopened package.

3.4 CONCLUSIONS

Disk diffusion is a relatively "inexpensive," easy to use, flexible agar-based method that provides qualitative results for rapidly growing aerobic bacteria. However, disk diffusion is based on the use of a relatively unstable antibiotic concentration gradient generated from a point source diffusion center, that is, the disk. Many *in vitro* variables such as prediffusion, inoculum density, and growth phase, and variations in the agar plate, for example, depth, can directly influence zone sizes and therefore give unreliable results. Larger zones will be obtained with slow growing, fastidious organisms compared with rapidly growing aerobic bacteria directly as a consequence of a longer critical time and not necessarily a lower level of susceptibility. High molecular weight compounds such as vancomycin and polymyxins will not diffuse well in agar and are therefore difficult or inappropriate to test by disk diffusion.

Disk testing is an indirect qualitative method that has to be calibrated against reference MIC methods to generate clinically meaningful zone size–MIC-based interpretive criteria. Like most break-point susceptibility testing methods and broth microdilution systems with limited dilution ranges, the disk method provides categorical results and not quantitative on-scale MIC values. Automated systems, which frequently report results as greater than or less than a numerical value, are just as qualitative as disk diffusion. Disk diffusion is suitable for testing rapidly growing aerobic bacteria isolated from nonsterile body sites. Use of an MIC method and preferably with a wide concentration range would be more appropriate to obtain exact MIC values for isolates from critical patients and critical specimens.

Etest complements disk diffusion testing and other methods currently used for routine susceptibility testing. Since Etest is based on the use of a stable preformed gradient, it can be used for testing a wide range of fastidious and/or slow growing organisms. This is reflected in the FDA clearance of Etest for both gram-positive and gram-negative aerobic bacteria, including gram-negative nonfermenters, anaerobic bacteria, pneumococci, streptococci, gonococci and *Haemophilus*; Etest is the only system cleared for gonococci. It has also been cleared for antifungal testing of *Candida* spp. As a macromethod that is inoculum tolerant, it is suitable for detection of low-level, inducible, or heterogeneous mechanisms of resistance such as penicillin resistance in pneumococci, inducible β-lactamases in gram-negative aerobes, and varcomycin or oxacillin heteroresistance in staphylococci. Treatment of serious life-threatening infections and management of critical patients often require targeted therapy where the choice and dosage have to be optimized using the MIC and PK/PD data. For these situations, Etest is a valuable therapeutic tool that can provide an exact and accurate MIC value for PK/PD-targeted selection of both the antibiotic and the dosage regimen, that is, fine-tuning of therapy for critically ill patients as described in the study by Mohr, Wanger, and Rex [37].

REFERENCES

1. Foster, J.W. and Woodruff, M.B. Microbiological aspects of penicillin; methods of assay, *J. Bacteriol.*, 46, 187–202, 1943.
2. Abraham, E.P., Chain, E., Fletcher, C.M., Florey, H.W., Gardner, A.D., Heatley, N.G., and Jennings, M.A. Further observations on penicillin, *Lancet*, ii, 177–188, 1941.
3. Bauer, A., Roberts, E., and Kirby, W.M.M. *Single Disc Versus Multiple Disc and Plate Dilution Techniques for Antibiotic Sensitivity Testing*, Vol. 1960, Department of Medicine, University of Washington School of Medicine and King County Hospital, Seattle, Washington, 1959.
4. Ericsson, H., Hogman, K., and Wickman, K. A paper disk method for determination of bacterial sensitivity to chemotherapeutic and antibiotic agents, *Scand. J. Clin. Lab. Invest.*, 6, 21, 1954.
5. Ericsson, H., Shems, T., Antibiotic Sensitivity Testing Report of an International Collaborative Study (ICS), Ada Pathologica el Microbiologica Scandinavica, 1971.
6. Cooper, K.E. and Woodman, D. The diffusion of antiseptics through agar gels with special reference to the agar cup assay method of estimating the activity of penicillin, *J. Pathol. Bacteriol.*, 58, 75–84, 1946.
7. Acar, J. and Goldstein, F.W. Disk susceptibility test, in *Antibiotics in Laboratory Medicine*, Lorian, V., Ed.,. Williams & Wilkins, Baltimore, 1996, 1–51.
8. Jorgensen, J., Turnidge, J., and Washington, J. Antibacterial susceptibility tests: Dilution and disk diffusion methods, in *Manual of Clinical Microbiology*, Murray, P.R., Ed., ASM Press, Washington DC, 1999, 1526–1543.
9. Bauer, A., Kirby, W.M.M., Sherris, J.C., and Turch, M. Antibiotic susceptibility testing by a standardized single disk method, *Am. J. Clin. Pathol.*, 45, 493–496, 1966.
10. Stokes, E., and Ridgeway, G.L. Antibiotic sensitivity tests, in *Clinical Microbiology*, 6th ed., Edward Arnold, London, 1987, 204–221.
11. Finch, R.G. The clinical evaluation of antibacterial drugs: Guidelines of the British Society for Antimicrobial Chemotherapy, *Eur. J. Clin. Microbiol. Infect. Dis.*, 9, 542–547, 1990.
12. Ericsson, H., Rational use of antibiotics in hospitals, Ph.D. thesis, *Scand. J. Clin. Lab. Invest.*, 12, 414–422, 1960.
13. Craig, W. *Qualitative Susceptibility Tests Versus Quantitative MIC Tests*, Elsevier Science, New York, 1993.
14. Bryson, V. and Szybalski, W. Microbial selection, *Science*, 116, 45–51, 1952.
15. Schalkowsky, S. Measures of susceptibility from a spiral gradient of drug concentrations, in *Antimicrobial Susceptibility Testing*, Poupard, J., Ed., Plenum Press, New York, 1994, 107–120.

16. Bolmstrom, A., Arvidson, S., Ericsson, M., and Karlsson, A. A novel technique for direct quantitation of antimicrobial susceptibility of microorganisms, Presented at the *Interscience Conference Antimicrobial Agents and Chemotherapy,* Los Angeles, CA, 1988.

17. Washington, J. Current problems in antimicrobial susceptibility testing, *Diag. Microbiol. Infect. Dis.,* 9, 135–138, 1988.

18. Hedges, A. The influence of factors affecting the critical population density of inocula on the determination of bacterial susceptibility to antibiotics by disc diffusion methods, *J. Antimicrob. Chemo.,* 43, 313–316, 1999.

19. CLSI. Performance standards for antimicrobial disk susceptibility tests, approved standard, M2-A8, 8th ed., CLSI, Wayne, PA, 2005.

20. Berke, I. and Tierno, P.M. Comparison of efficacy and cost-effectiveness of BIOMIC VIDEO and Vitek antimicrobial susceptibility test systems for use in the clinical microbiology laboratory, *J. Clin. Microbiol.,* 34, 1980–1984, 1996.

21. Korgenski, E. and Daly, J.A. Evaluation of the BIOMIC video reader system for determining interpretive categories of isolates on the basis of disk diffusion susceptibility results, *J. Clin. Microbiol.,* 36, 302–304, 1998.

22. Jorgensen, J.H., Crawford, S.A., McElmeel, M.L., and Fiebelkorn, K.R. Detection of inducible clindamycin resistance of staphylococci in conjunction with performance of automated broth susceptibility testing, *J. Clin. Microbiol.,* 42, 1800–1802, 2004.

23. Miller, J., Thornsberry, C., and Baker, C.N. Disk diffusion susceptibility test troubleshooting guide, *Lab. Med.,* 15, 183–185, 1984.

24. CDC. Interim guidelines for prevention and control of staphylococcal infection associated with reduced susceptibility to vancomycin, *Morb. Mortal. Wkly. Rep.,* 46, 626–635, 1997.

25. Hubert, S.K., Mohammed, J.M., Fridkin, S.K., Gaynes, R.P., McGowan, J.E., Jr., and Tenover, F.C. Glycopeptide-intermediate *Staphylococcus aureus:* Evaluation of a novel screening method and results of a survey of selected U.S. hospitals, *J. Clin. Microbiol.,* 37, 3590–3593, 1999.

26. Walsh, T.R., Bolmstrom, A., Qwarnstrom, A., Ho, P., Wootton, M., Howe, R.A., MacGowan, A.P., and Diekema, D. Evaluation of current methods for detection of staphylococci with reduced susceptibility to glycopeptides, *J. Clin. Microbiol.,* 39, 2439–2444, 2001.

27. Hiramatsu, K. Vancomycin resistance in staphylococci, *Drug Resist. Updates,* 1, 135–150, 1998.

28. CDC. Vancomycin-resistant *Staphylococcus aureus* — New York, 2004, *Morb. Mortal. Wkly. Rep.,* 53, 322–323, 2004.

29. Walsh, T.R., Bolmstrom, A., Ho, P., Qwarnstrom, A., Wootton, M., Howe, R.A., Bennett, P.M., and MacGowan, A.P. Evaluation of growth conditions in susceptibility testing to discriminate heterovancomycin intermediate *Staphylococcus aureus* (hVISA) and VISAs from methicillin resistant SA (MRSA), *Clin. Microbiol. Infect.,* 6, 84, 2000.

30. Walsh, T.R., Bolmstrom, A., Qwarnstrom, A., and Gales, A. Evaluation of a new Etest for detecting metallo-beta-lactamases in routine clinical testing, *J. Clin. Microbiol.,* 40, 2755–2759, 2002.

31. Espinel-Ingroff, A. A comparison of the Etest with the NCCLS M38-P method for antifungal susceptibility testing of common and emerging pathogenic filamentous fungi, *J. Clin. Microbiol.,* 39, 1360–1367, 2001.

32. Wanger, A. and Mills, K. Etest for susceptibility testing of *Mycobacterium tuberculosis* and *Mycobacterium avium-intracellulare, Diag. Microbiol. Infect. Dis.,* 19, 179–181, 1994.

33. Wanger, A. and Mills, K. Testing of *Mycobacterium tuberculosis* susceptibility to ethambutol, isoniazid, rifampin and streptomycin by using Etest, *J. Clin. Microbiol.,* 34, 1672–1676, 1996.

34. Wanger, A., Mills, K., Nelson, P., and Rex, J. Comparison of Etest and National Committee for Clinical Laboratory Standards broth macrodilution method for antifungal susceptibility testing: enhanced ability to detect amphotericin B-resistant Candida isolates, *Antimicrob. Agents Chemother.,* 39, 2520–2522, 1995.

35. Pankey, G.A. and Ashcraft, D.S. *In vitro* synergy of ciprofloxacin and gatifloxacin against ciprofloxacin-resistant *Pseudomonas aeruginosa, Antimicrob. Agents Chemother.,* 49, 2959–2964, 2005.

36. Bolmstrom, A. Determinations of minimum bactericidal concentrations, kill curves, and postantibiotic effects with the Etest technology, *Diag. Microbiol. Infect. Dis.,* 19, 187–195, 1994.

37. Mohr, J.F., Wanger, A., and Rex, J.H. Pharmacokinetic/pharmacodynamic modeling can help guide targeted antimicrobial therapy for nosocomial gram-negative infections in critically ill patients, *Diag. Microbiol. Infect. Dis.,* 48, 125–130, 2004.

4 Macro- and Microdilution Methods of Antimicrobial Susceptibility Testing

Sadaf Qaiyumi

CONTENTS

4.1 INTRODUCTION

Sensitivity and resistance patterns of microorganisms are constantly changing, and many microorganisms have developed resistance even to the newest antibiotics. Since susceptibility patterns are unpredictable, it is necessary to test isolated pathogens against appropriate antimicrobial agents. The clinical microbiology laboratory plays an important role in assisting physicians in determining an appropriate treatment for an infectious disease. Therefore, once the organism has been isolated and identified from a patient's specimen, it is necessary to determine an antimicrobial susceptibility profile of the isolated organism. With this information, the clinician can choose the appropriate antibiotic to be used in treating the patient.

The lowest concentration of an antibiotic that will inhibit the growth of the organism being tested is known as the minimal inhibitory concentration (MIC). The MIC may assist a physician in deciding the concentration of the antibiotic needed to inhibit the pathogen. The MIC test can be performed on agar or on liquid medium. The traditional method of determining the MIC is with the broth dilution technique, where serial dilutions of antibiotic are incorporated into the broth media in either the wells of microtiter plates or in culture tubes. The concentration of antibiotic used may vary with the antimicrobial, organism identification, and site of infection. Each tube or well contains a different concentration of the antimicrobial agent and is inoculated with a fixed amount of the organism being tested. After appropriate incubation, the lowest concentration showing no visible growth is considered as the MIC. A complete guide to this protocol can be found in the Clinical Laboratory Standards Institute (CLSI) guidelines document M7-A7 [1]. This is a quantitative test, the result of which is expressed in micrograms per milliliter (μg/mL).

In testing for antimicrobial susceptibility, the laboratory must maintain a high level of accuracy and reproducibility in the testing procedures. Because of varying conditions, such as, inoculum size, composition of the culture media, incubation time, temperature, pH, etc., a dilution test may not provide the same end point each time [2]. Generally, the acceptable reproducibility of the test is within a two-fold dilution of the actual end point. There must be a good correlation between the result and the clinical response of the patient. Although, at times, an antimicrobial agent that shows poor *in vitro* activity against a pathogen is used in a patient with good results; the opposite effect may also occur.

4.2 MACROBROTH DILUTION METHOD

The macrobroth dilution method was among the first to be developed and still serves as a reference method. This assay is generally performed in glass test tubes containing a broth volume of >1 mL. Two test tubes containing broth without antimicrobial agent added should be included in each test. One of these tubes should be inoculated with the test organism; the other should be left uninoculated and will serve as a check for media sterility.

4.2.1 PREPARATION OF ANTIBIOTIC SOLUTION

The antibiotic stock solutions should be made to a final concentration of 10 mg/mL or 10 times the highest concentration to be tested and then diluted to an appropriate concentration in broth. It is very important to follow the manufacturer's guidelines when preparing stock solutions of antimicrobial agents. Sterile water is generally used in the preparation of the antibiotic solutions. There are some antibiotics that have limited solubility; therefore, a stock solution of lower concentration should be prepared for such antibiotics. Other antimicrobials require solvents other than water. If such is the case, use a minimal amount of the recommended solvent and make further dilutions with water. For example, rifampin, erythromycin, or chloromphenicol are insoluble in water, but they dissolve readily in 95% ethanol. Therefore, a minimum volume of ethanol should be added dropwise to the antibiotic, until the powder dissolves; the final volume is then brought up in water.

Antibiotic powder obtained from the manufacturer is not always 100% pure. Therefore, prior to making a stock solution, it is important to ensure the potency of each antibiotic. The following formula may be used to determine the amount of antimicrobial needed for the desired volume:

$$\text{Weight (mg)} = \frac{\text{volume (mL)} \times \text{desired concentration (μg/mL)}}{\text{antibiotic potency (μg/mg)}}.$$

Therefore, for 3 mL of 10 mg/mL solution of drug X with 99.4% potency (994 μg/mg)

$$X = \frac{3 \times 10,000}{994}.$$

Weigh out 30.2 mg and dissolve it in 3 mL of sterile distilled water.

Another way to achieve the required concentration is to weigh out the desired amount (or slightly more) of antimicrobial powder and then determine the exact volume of the diluent by using the following formula. It is recommended to weigh 10 mg of the powder or more to improve the accuracy.

$$\text{Volume (mL)} = \frac{\text{weight (mg)} \times \text{potency (μg/mg)}}{\text{concentration (μg/mg)}}.$$

Weigh out drug X (e.g., 10 mg)
Drug purity is 994 μg/mL
Desired concentration is 10,000 μg/mL

$$\text{Volume} = \frac{10 \times 994}{10,000}.$$

Dissolve 10 mg of drug X in 0.994 mL of sterile distilled water to get 10 mg/mL of drug X.

The stock solutions can be further diluted in broth (e.g., Mueller-Hinton) to the highest concentration needed to test the antibiotic by following the formula $M_1V_1 = M_2V_2$. Suppose a working solution of 256 μg/mL is desired in 5 mL. Then

$$M_1V_1 = M_2V_2.$$

$$10,000 \text{ μg/mL} \times V_1 \text{ mL} = 256 \text{ μg/mL} \times 5 \text{ mL}.$$

Therefore, 0.128 mL (128 μl) of the 10,000 μg/mL stock solution should be suspended in 4.872 mL of broth.

Small volumes of the stock solution can be stored at −70°C in freezer vials, without the loss of any activity. Solutions may be stored for up to 6 months unless otherwise indicated in the manufacturer's package insert. Frozen stocks should be thawed the day of use, and any left over is generally discarded.

4.2.2 MUELLER-HINTON BROTH

Mueller-Hinton Broth Cation adjusted is a specially formulated medium for susceptibility testing. It is recommended by the CLSI for testing most commonly encountered aerobic bacteria found in food and clinical samples. The medium demonstrates fairly good batch-to-batch reproducibility for susceptibility testing; it is low in sulfonamide, trimethoprim and tetracycline inhibitors, and yields satisfactory growth of most pathogens.

The amount of divalent cations should be standardized in the Mueller-Hinton broth. The susceptibility testing of antibiotics like aminoglycosides and tetracyclines is greatly affected without the supplementation of these ions. Cation-adjusted Mueller-Hinton broth can be easily purchased from various commercial sources. If the broth does not contain the appropriate concentration of Ca^{2+} and Mg^{2+} (20–25 mg of Ca^{2+}/L and 10–12.5 mg of Mg^{2+}/L), then an adjustment is recommended. For the supplementation of cations in Mueller-Hinton broth, a 10 mg/mL stock solution of $CaCl_2$ and $MgCl_2$ is prepared. Magnesium stock solution is prepared by dissolving 8.36 g $MgCl_2 \cdot 6H_2O$ in 100 mL of deionized water, and calcium stock solution is prepared by adding 3.68 g of $CaCl_2$ to 100 mL of deionized water. The stock solutions should be filtered, sterilized, and chilled before addition to the broth.

Before the addition of cations, it is important to know the cation contents of the Mueller-Hinton broth because unnecessary supplementation may cause false results. If the Mueller-Hinton broth contains no cations, then 2 mL of calcium stock solution and 1 mL of magnesium stock solution can be added to 1 L of cooled Mueller-Hinton broth. The pH of each batch of Mueller-Hinton broth should be checked and must lie between 7.2 and 7.4. Before use, each batch of media should be checked for its ability to support the growth of the most relevant control strains.

4.2.3 PROCEDURE

Label sterile capped 13 × 100 mm test tubes 1 through 11:

a) Pipette 0.5 mL of Mueller-Hinton broth into tubes 2–11.
b) Pipette 0.5 mL of antibiotic solution into tubes 1 and 2.
c) Transfer 0.5 mL from tube 2 to tube 3 and continue through tube 9. Be certain to change pipettes between tubes to prevent carryover of antibiotic.
d) Discard 0.5 mL from tube 9. The tenth tube, which serves as a control, receives no antibiotic.
e) Select 4–5 isolated colonies from an overnight culture and dilute in broth to a trubidity comparable to that of a 0.5 McFarland turbidity standard (approximately 1.0×10^8 CFU/mL). This suspension is further diluted 1:100 (10^6 CFU/mL) with sterile water, 0.85% saline, or broth. Within 15 min of the preparation of this inoculum add 0.5 mL of bacterial broth suspension to each tube except the eleventh (last) tube, which is the broth control tube. The final inoculum concentration of 10^5 CFU/mL is achieved. Note that the final concentration of the antibiotic is now one half of the original concentration in each tube. If there is unavoidable delay in inoculation, the inoculum can be stored at 4°C for up to 2 h. Streak a 10 µl loopful of suspension from the growth control tube onto a sheep blood agar plate (or other appropriate medium) and incubate overnight to check the purity of the test isolate and correct inoculum density. The presence of approximately 50 colonies would indicate an inoculum density of 5×10^5 CFU/mL.

4.2.4 INCUBATION

All assay tubes should be incubated overnight in an ambient air incubator at 35–37°C. During incubation, care should be taken to ensure adequate humidity. With methicillin-resistant staphylococci and vancomycin-resistant enterococci, a 24-h incubation period is recommended.

4.2.5 CONTROL STRAIN

When testing a patient isolate, the corresponding ATCC quality control (QC) organism should be tested concurrently. To consider a test result valid, the MIC of the QC organism must fall within the acceptable limits for quality control strains stated in the CLSI guidelines the M100-S16 document [3].

4.2.6 RESULT INTERPRETATION

The lowest concentration of the antimicrobial agent that will inhibit the growth of the microorganism being tested as detected by lack of visual turbidity, matching with a negative control included with the test, is known as MIC. The MIC of each antimicrobial agent is recorded in microgram per milliliter (mg/mL). Before reading and recording the results obtained with clinical isolates, it is recommended that the tubes be shaken gently before performing a reading. The tubes containing the QC strain should be checked to ensure that their values are within the acceptable range for that antibiotic. In addition, the antibiotic-free growth control tube should be examined for the viability of the test isolate. This is needed to ensure that the culture conditions, such as media, temperature, etc., were suitable for the growth of the organism. The broth control tube included in the assay contains everything except the inoculum of test strains. This control tube should remain clear (no growth). Growth in this tube is an indicator of contamination of one of the components of the test system. In that case, the assay is invalid and should be repeated.

When using an antibiotic such as sulfonamide or trimethoprim, care should be taken in determining the end point because a trailing effect may be observed as a result of drug carryover with the inoculum. Therefore, the MICs of these antimicrobial agents should be interpreted as the end point at which an obvious 80% or more reduction of growth occurs when compared with the growth control tube. A trailing effect is also possible with bacteriostatic drugs such as chloromphenicol and tetracycline.

4.3 MBC DETERMINATION

The minimal bactericidal concentration (MBC) is defined as the lowest concentration of an antibiotic killing the majority (99.9%) of a bacterial inoculum. Since MIC is the ability of inhibitory status, it is possible that if the antibiotic is removed, the microorganism will begin to grow again. In some infections (i.e., evclocaditis), it is necessary to actually kill the microorganism. To determine the ability of the antibiotic to kill the microorganism, a growth test can be performed. This test is referred to as the MBC.

4.3.1 METHOD

Following a broth dilution MIC test, from each tube that shows no growth, remove 50 μL of suspension and spread it onto sheep blood agar plates or other appropriate medium. Incubate the plates overnight at 37°C. The number of colonies growing from each of the test tubes is counted and the number of colonies corresponding to a thousand-fold reduction (as compared to the colony count of the start inoculum) is recorded as the MBC (99.9% killing).

4.3.1.1 Microbroth Dilution Method

The broth dilution method is an adaptation of the broth dilution method using small volumes for routine testing. It utilizes microtiter plastic plates containing 96 wells. The advantage of the system is that it utilizes small volumes of reagents and allows a large number of bacteria to be tested relatively quickly.

4.3.2 WELL VOLUMES

With the exception of those wells acting as drug-free controls, each well should receive either 100 μL or 50 μL of a two-fold dilution series of the antibiotic solution. Each well, except those acting as sterility controls, should then receive either 100 μL or 50 μL of bacterial suspension (containing 10^5 CFU). Note that this protocol results in a final concentration of the antimicrobial agents in the assay wells being twofold lower than in the aliquots added to the wells. Each plate should contain a column of wells that contain no antimicrobial agent (A12–H12). A plate should also include one row containing the full dilution series inoculated with a relevant control strain (A1–A11) and one column inoculated with the sterile 0.9% saline used to prepare the bacterial suspensions (H1–H11).

REFERENCES

1. Clinical and Laboratory Standards Institute. Methods for dilution antimicrobial susceptibility testing for bacteria that grow aerobically. Approved standard M7-A7, Clinical and Laboratory Standards Institute, Wayne, PA, 2006.
2. Turnidge, J.D., Farraro, M. J. and Jorgensen, J.H. *Manual of Clinical Microbiology*, 8th ed., American Society for Microbiology, Washington DC, 2003, 1102–1107.
3. Clinical and Laboratory Standards Institute. Performance standards for antimicrobial susceptibility testing, Sixteenth informational supplement, 2006.

5 Automated Systems: An Overview

Sheryl Stuckey

CONTENTS

5.1 INTRODUCTION

One of the most significant tests performed by the clinical microbiology laboratory for the management of infectious disease is antimicrobial susceptibility testing. Pathogenic organisms that are resistant to frontline antimicrobial agents are constantly emerging, and laboratory technicians and clinicians are more concerned than ever with the resistance patterns of these organisms.

Antimicrobial resistance and the potential of these organisms to acquire resistance dominate the infectious disease arena. In this age of diagnosis-related groups, local medical review policies, managed care health plans (HMOs, IPOs, PPOs, etc.), and budgetary constraints, clinical microbiologists are faced with the challenge of identifying etiological agents quickly, efficiently, accurately, and at a relatively low cost.

Today, a myriad of automated susceptibility testing instruments are incorporated into many institutions. These instruments offer greater sensitivity and speed than manual methods, and aid in the interpretation of antimicrobial susceptibility test endpoints. To alleviate ambiguity, it is important that automated instruments be standardized at regular intervals.

5.2 CONSIDERATIONS IN CHOOSING AN AUTOMATED SYSTEM

Several issues must be considered in determining the appropriate automated instrument for antimicrobial testing:

5.2.1 LABORATORY TEST UTILIZATION

What level and volume of antimicrobial testing do you currently perform, and what is the result turnaround time required by the clinicians you serve? Depending on your staffing level, case mix, and organism antibiogram, if you are doing less than 10 tests per day, the cost of automation may not be warranted. Are your manual results within the acceptable range for accuracy, and do they correspond with patient treatment outcomes? If so, do you need to change?

5.2.2 CASE MIX AND ORGANISM ISOLATION RATES

Is your institution's case mix primarily acute or chronic? If it is acute, do you serve a large percentage of patients for whom infection can be rapidly fatal? Are you isolating significant numbers of multidrug-resistant or difficult to treat pathogens? If you are in an acute setting with potentially high morbidity, limited infection control isolation rooms, or significant numbers of potentially communicable pathogens, the cost savings to the patient and the institution on the treatment side may outweigh the expense of automating the laboratory. However if, on the other hand, you are primarily performing urine cultures and the predominant isolate is a multidrug-susceptible *Escherichia coli*, do you need automation?

5.2.3 ANTIMICROBIAL UTILIZATION AND PRACTICE GUIDELINES

What are the primary antibiotics used by the institution? Consultation with local infectious disease physicians and clinical pharmacy personnel is essential.

Are there clinician practice guidelines in place that require the use of particular agents and/or that forgo the performance of specimen culture? Such guidelines can be a determining factor in whether you need automation because of their impact on test volume.

5.2.3.1 Methodology

Based on the predominant classes of your isolates, will the instrument methodology be compatible with your needs and current reporting options, or will it require extensive training and education of laboratory personnel and clinicians? If you are currently using Kirby-Bauer methodology, you must consider the time and energy involved in learning new methodologies such as broth microdilution. If you are already using broth microdilution, do you require automation of the inoculation process, the reader process, or both? Will automation be labor saving or labor intensive?

5.2.3.2 Instrument Ease of Use

How difficult is the instrument to use? Are frequent calibrations or maintenance checks required? Are the steps to process or troubleshoot tests straightforward? If you must spend significant amounts of time preparing the instrument for processing tests or if downtime of the instrument is frequent and troubleshooting cumbersome, the automation process may cause delays in patient treatment.

5.2.3.3 Instrument Performance

If you test an *E. coli* that is known to be susceptible to a given level of ampicillin, will the instrument accurately interpret the reading, and if not, with what frequency will it fail? What level of failure is acceptable to you, and what level will be acceptable to your risk management department?

5.2.3.4 Instrument Breadth of Line

Can you test all of your common isolates on the instrument? Can you test all of the formulary antibiotics using the automated method? How many times will you have to perform additional testing because of test accuracy problems associated with certain drug versus bug combinations?

5.2.3.5 Instrument Disposables

If cost is a factor, both the supplies and time of automated testing must be taken into account. In addition, the type and number of disposables involved in doing each test should be considered. Each disposable involves some time and expense in its handling, and this can increase labor costs. If reagents are used, you must also consider potential chemical hazards and disposal costs.

5.2.3.6 Instrument Turnaround Time to Result

Once the automated antimicrobial system is inoculated, how quickly do you need or can you get the result? Do you want your results rapidly? If so, what is your definition of rapid? Will speed or accuracy have any measurable effect on patient outcome?

5.2.3.7 Personnel and Regulatory Considerations

Regulatory issues can impact your decision to acquire automation. What are the licensure requirements? Depending on the process you are automating, what is the regulatory complexity of your testing? Given the previous considerations of methodology and ease of use, what level of personnel proficiency and education is required for your testing?

5.3 EVALUATING AN AUTOMATED SYSTEM

Now that you have decided to invest in automated antimicrobial resistance testing, how do you go about evaluating which test system is right for you?

5.3.1 SEARCH FOR REFERENCES

Clinical laboratories may choose among several automated instruments to assist in their routine work. However, before a purchase is made, it is important to obtain written references (journal articles, monographs, research data, etc.) and a list of long-term current and former users. The company representative can assist you with this, but it is important to conduct your own research. You should focus your search on the needs of your particular institution.

5.3.2 CHOICE OF TEST ISOLATES

The key to evaluating your choice of instrumentation is knowing your institution's antibiograms. An antibiogram is the overall antimicrobial susceptibility profile of a bacterial isolate to a battery of antimicrobial agents. Furthermore, it may be useful to take notes of isolation trends that may adversely affect the mix of isolates and their antimicrobial resistance patterns. Below is a list of the types of organisms that should be included in your evaluation:

Common predominant wild type organisms (those naturally occurring in the environment) found in your institution (include the range of possible antimicrobial resistance levels for each antibiotic of interest)

Infrequently isolated wild type organisms seen in your institution

Clinically relevant organisms appropriate for the class of antibiotics of interest (including ≥35 known resistant isolates for each antibiotic tested)

Organisms that the evaluation instrument and any competing instrument under consideration have been noted to have difficulties with interpretation, ease or speed in their interpretation

Quality control organism required for the type of testing

Quality control organisms required by the manufacturer

Finally, care should be taken to avoid wild type isolates from the same source unless there is a significant change in the resistance level beyond the acceptable interpretative standard deviation of the method employed.

5.3.3 PREPARING ISOLATES FOR EVALUATION TESTING

Whenever possible, it is best to prepare evaluation organism sets; this is particularly important when evaluating more than one instrument under consideration so as to remove the possibility of test organism bias. The fairest comparative evaluation of two instruments is to challenge both with the same test isolate. However, this may be difficult to do if careful planning (with regard to the timing of instrument evaluations) is not done prior to the commencement of the evaluation process. Test isolates may be prepared in the following manner:

Perform antimicrobial resistance testing on the isolate using the current system employed by your laboratory; record and maintain the results for future use.

Prepare an 18–24-h broth culture of the isolate in appropriate broth media.

After incubation, subculture the broth to a second broth media and reincubate for at least 18–24 h.

After incubation, subculture the broth to the appropriate solid agar media and incubate at the organism's optimal temperature and atmosphere for at least 18–24 h.

After incubation, use well isolated colonies to prepare a stock culture of the organism using the method employed by your laboratory.

5.3.4 PERFORMING THE EVALUATION

You should obtain the assistance of the manufacturer's personnel (i.e., the clinical applications or technical specialist) for guidance on the use of the automated instrument. Quality control organisms should be used to determine the performance characteristics of the automated instrument and to demonstrate the reproducibility of results. All quality control activities should be recorded.

In order to have a sufficient variety and number of isolates to detect the performance errors of the automated system, it is suggested that you plan to test isolates equivalent in number to at least 5–10% of your normal annual workload or at least a minimum of 100 isolates exclusive of the required quality control organisms.

Isolates from stock cultures should be prepared for testing in accordance with the guidelines of the laboratory (frozen isolates should be subcultured at least twice before testing). Unless the manufacturer's media or organisms preparation requirement dictate otherwise, the same culture and/or inoculum should be used for concurrent testing with the current antimicrobial resistance test method (reference method) and the automated method being evaluated (test method). The manufacturer's instructions should be strictly adhered to during the performance of testing. Upon the completion of testing, the results should be recorded using the system employed by the laboratory for the current test system and that of the manufacturer for the evaluation instrument, and should be maintained for review.

5.3.5 EVALUATION OF RESULTS

Now that you have completed your testing, you must carefully review the results in the context of those factors you considered important in choosing an automated antimicrobial testing system. You can use the test system to challenge data if there are no organisms between the previous reference system results and the current reference system results. It is important to compare your previously maintained reference system results with the current reference system result and look for significant changes that may have resulted from long-term storage and/or repeated subculture of the organism. The test and the reference system must be in categorical agreement (test and reference method achieve the same result) for a given organism versus antibiotic challenge. The degree and frequency of the following errors must be determined by using the challenge data. (When the quality control testing appears to have failed, then the degree and frequency of the following errors must be determined by using the challenge data):

Very major error (test system susceptible/reference system resistant): *false susceptible result*
Major error (test system resistant/reference system susceptible): *false resistant result*
Minor error (test system susceptible or resistant/reference system intermediate)

This review often is the most labor intensive and tiresome of the evaluation process. However, it can be streamlined with a carefully planned evaluation tool that affords easy review and detection of errors and categorical agreement. Figure 5.1 and Figure 5.2 are examples of a simplified evaluation tool.

If your laboratory is accredited or licensed by a body that employs the Clinical Laboratory Standards Institute (CLSI) criteria for evaluation [1], be advised that the CLSI minimum levels of acceptable interpretative error in susceptibility testing are quite restrictive. Very major errors should not exceed 1.5%, major errors should not exceed 3.0%, and overall categorical agreement should equal or exceed 90% for each organism/antibiotic challenge [2]. The following are formulas for calculating these evaluation indices [12]:

$$\text{Very major error rate} = \frac{\text{\# of very major errors}}{\text{total \# of resistant strains}} \times 100$$

$$\text{Major error rate} = \frac{\text{\# of major errors}}{\text{total \# of susceptible strains}} \times 100$$

$$\text{Minor error rate} = \frac{\left(\begin{array}{l} \text{total \# of tests} \\ - \text{\# of very major errors} \\ - \text{\# of major errors} \\ - \text{\# with categorical agreement} \end{array} \right)}{\text{total \# of tests}} \times 100$$

$$\text{\% categorical agreement} = \frac{\text{\# of tests with categorical agreement}}{\text{total number of tests}} \times 100$$

ANTIBIOTIC CHALLENGE: Ampicillin

ISOLATE	REFERENCE SYSTEM	TEST SYSTEM	VERY MAJOR	MAJOR	MINOR	CATEGORICAL AGREEMENT
E. coli 1	R	S	X			
E. coli 2	S	R		X		
E. coli 3	I	R			X	
E. coli 4	S	I			X	
E. coli 5	R	I			X	
E. coli 6	S	S				X
E. coli 7	S	S				X
E. coli 8	I	I				X
E. coli 9	R	R				X
E. coli 10	R	R				X

FIGURE 5.1 Antibiotic challenge: ampicillin.

ANTIBIOTIC CHALLENGE

ISOLATE	REFERENCE SYSTEM	TEST SYSTEM	VERY MAJOR	MAJOR	MINOR	CATEGORICAL AGREEMENT

FIGURE 5.2 Antibiotic challenge

For example, using the chart in Figure 5.2, the rates would be as follows:

$$\text{Very major error rate} = \frac{1 \text{ very major error}}{4 \text{ resistant strains}} \times 100 = 25\%$$

$$\text{Major error rate} = \frac{1 \text{ major error}}{3 \text{ susceptible strains}} \times 100 = 33\%$$

$$\text{Minor error rate} = \frac{\left(\begin{array}{l} 10 \text{ total tests} \\ -\ 1 \text{ very major error} \\ -\ 1 \text{ major error} \\ -\ 5 \text{ with categorical agreement} \end{array}\right)}{10 \text{ total tests}} \times 100 = 30\%$$

$$\%\text{ categorical agreement} = \frac{5 \text{ tests with categorical agreement}}{10 \text{ total tests performed}} \times 100 = 50\%.$$

It is important to keep in mind that some organisms may fail to achieve sufficient growth for interpretation or may fail to grow at all in the automated test system. The number of these organisms should not exceed 10% of the total challenges [4]. Also, antibiotics that lack an intermediate category interpretation can have a one-dilution difference result in a false determination of a very major error or major error. In these cases, there should be >90% agreement within one dilution between the reference system and test system being evaluated [5].

If upon completion of the review of results you find that the performance of the instrument fails to meet the minimum requirements for acceptable testing, then it is important to check your methodology. It is also important to review the technique of the personnel performing the evaluation, calculations, etc., to ensure that no errors have been made.

5.4 THE AUTOMATED SYSTEM ZODIAC

There are three currently available automated instruments capable of generating rapid susceptibility test results: the Dade Microscan system (Dade Behring, West Sacramento, California), the bioMerieux Vitek system (bioMerieux Vitek, Inc., Hazelwood, Missouri), and the Becton Dickinson Phoenix (Becton Dickinson Microbiology Systems, Cockeysville, Maryland). These devices help to facilitate data recording and long-term data storage.

5.4.1 DADE MICROSCAN

The Dade Microscan system [6–8] consists of a large, self-contained incubator and reader that affords the user the possibility of semiautomated (reader only AutoScan-4) and fully automated (incubator/reader Walkaway 40 and Walkaway 96) instrumentation with rapid and/or conventional testing. The system allows for identification and antimicrobial resistance testing, and results may be obtained in as little as 2 to 7 h.

Conventional testing is performed using colorimetric and turbidity readings. Halogen tungsten light passes through one of six colorimetric interference filters specific for the optimal light source for the substrate being read and is focused on a photometer providing a reading. The antimicrobial resistance test reading is determined by detection of changes in the turbidity of each dilution well of the antibiotic. The information is then transferred to a data management computer that determines a biotype, accesses the appropriate database, and produces a list of probable organisms and, based on this identification, the interpretation of the antibiogram for the isolate.

The rapid-testing system utilizes fluorogenic substrates and fluorometric indicators. For identification testing, the presence of preformed enzymes results in changes in the pH of the substrate, causing a decrease or increase in fluorescence that is detected by the instrument. In the case of antimicrobial resistance testing, the substrate is bound to a fluorescent molecule that in the presence of a specific metabolic enzyme will be cleaved, releasing the fluorescence that is detected by the instrument. Identification and interpretation of the antibiogram then proceeds as for conventional testing.

Both the AutoScan-4 and Walkaway 40/96 systems come with data management computer programs that can be used to interpret, store, and report data. In addition, the system includes an expert antibiotic resistance pattern alert system that can be customized to meet the needs of the specific end user, and an antibiotic therapy tracking interface for the pharmacy. These systems also may be interfaced with many current laboratory information systems.

5.4.2 BioMerieux Vitek

5.4.2.1 Vitek Classic

The Vitek "Classic" [9–11] was originally developed for use by the National Aeronautics and Space Administration (NASA) in its space exploration efforts of the 1970s. The original Vitek was highly automated and relatively compact. It was subsequently introduced into the diagnostic microbiology laboratory arena.

Vitek has a modular format consisting of a filler-sealer module, a reader incubator with a capacity for up to 240 test cards, and a computer control module. The system utilizes separate individual small plastic reagent cards containing a variety of substrate or antibiotic wells for identification testing or antimicrobial resistance testing.

Cards are inoculated, sealed, and placed in the reader-incubator. After baseline readings are taken, light emitting diodes and phototransistor detectors scan the cards; a photometer detects changes in light transmission. These readings are transferred to the computer control module, which determines the organism's biotype, identification, and antibiogram.

Like the Microscan instruments, the Vitek system comes with a data management computer for the interpretation, storage, and reporting of data, and can be readily interfaced with several laboratory information systems. In addition, this system pioneered the "expert" system for on-line identification and susceptibility result validation and antimicrobial resistance evaluation. The system uses an inference engine, which, given the probability of certain antimicrobial resistance patterns occurring under certain circumstances, flags anomalies for the user with suggestions to verify or validate the result. This has proven to be a useful tool in some clinical microbiology laboratory settings.

5.4.2.2 Vitek 2

The Vitek 2 [9,13,14] uses fluorogenic technology that allows the instrument to take an optical reading of each test well on the card every 15 min. Each test card is bar coded to avoid the possibility of the clerical errors and unintelligible handwriting that plagued the original Vitek. The Vitek 2 autofills, autoseals, autoincubates, and even autodisposes the test cards upon completion of testing.

5.4.2.3 Vitek 2 Compact

Vitek 2 Compact [9,13,14] was recently introduced by bioMerieux. The system utilizes chromogenic substrates with an "advanced colorimetry" system. The Vitek 2 Compact also makes use of an advanced system that includes an evaluation of the quality of the test. In addition, the system allows connection to bioMerieux's Stellara wireless patient management system that affords integration of laboratory, pharmacy, and other systems to aid the physician in making clinical and therapeutic interventions all from a handheld personal digital assistant (PDA).

5.4.3 Becton Dickinson Phoenix

The Becton Dickinson Phoenix [15–17], with the exception of manual test card inoculation, is a fully automated, fully integrated identification and susceptibility testing system. The Phoenix uses both chromogenic and fluorogenic substrates in the same test card. Using standardized inoculums, panels are manually inoculated and placed in the Phoenix instrument for incubation and reading. Panels are read every 20 min until the testing is completed. Like the other systems, test data is stored in a data management computer, and an "expert" system for reviewing results is included. However, the data management system for the Phoenix is designed to be integrated with other Becton Dickinson microbiology system instrumentation (i.e., blood culture instruments) to provide a total microbiology data management program.

REFERENCES

1. Clinical and Laboratory Standards Institute. Development of *in vitro* susceptibility testing criteria and quality control parameters, approved guideline M23-A2, CLSI, Wayne, PA, 2001.
2. Clinical and Laboratory Standards Institute. Methods for dilution antimicrobial susceptibility tests for bacteria that grow aerobically, approved standard M7-A7, CLSI, Wayne, PA, January 2007.
3. Murray, P.R., Baron, E.J., Jorgensen, J.H., Pfaller, M.A., and Yolken, R.H., Eds., *Manual of Clinical Microbiology*, 8th ed., American Society for Microbiology, Washington, DC, 2003.
4. Clinical and Laboratory Standards Institute. Performance standards for antimicrobial susceptibility testing, 17th informational supplement, *M100-S17*, CLSI, Wayne, PA, January 2007.
5. Jorgensen, J.H. Selection criteria for an antimicrobial susceptibility testing system, *J. Clin. Microbiol.*, 31, 2841–2844, 1993.
6. Product Literature, Dade Microscan, Inc., West Sacramento, CA, 2005.
7. *Walkaway Training Manual*, Dade Microscan, Inc., West Sacramento, CA, 2004.
8. Kelly, M.T. and Leicester, C. Evaluation of the Autoscan Walkaway system for rapid identification and susceptibility testing of gram negative bacilli, *J. Clin. Microbiol.*, 30, 1568–1571, 1992.
9. Product Literature, bioMerieux Vitek, Inc., Hazelwood, MO, 2004.
10. Bourbeau, P.P. and Heiter, B.J. Comparison of Vitek GNI and GNI+ cards for the identification of gram-negative bacteria, *J. Clin. Microbiol.*, 36, 2447–2777, 1998.
11. Doern, G.V., Brueggemann, A.B., Perla, R., Daly, J., Halkias, D., Jones, R.N., and Saubolle, M.A. Multicenter laboratory evaluation of the bioMerieux Vitek antimicrobial susceptibility testing system with 11 antimicrobial agents versus members of the family Enterobacteriaceae and *Pseudomonas aeruginosa*, *J. Clin. Microbiol.*, 35, 2115–2119, 1997.
12. Elder, B.L., Hansen, S.A., Kellogg, J.A., Marsik, F.J., and Zabransky, R.J. *Cumitech 31: Verification and Validation of Procedures in the Clinical Microbiology Laboratory*, American Society for Microbiology, Washington, DC, February 1997.
13. Ligozzi, M., Bernini, C., Bonora, M.G., de Fatima, M., Zuliani, J., and Fontana, R. Evaluation of the VITEK 2 system for identification and antimicrobial susceptibility testing of medically relevant gram-positive cocci, *J. Clin. Microbio.*, 40, 1681–1686, 2002.
14. Funke, G., Monnet, D., deBernardis, C., von Graevenitz, A., and Freney, J. Evaluation of the VITEK 2 system for rapid identification of medically relevant gram-negative rods, *J. Clin. Microbio.*, 36, 1948–1952, 1998.
15. Eigner, U., Schmid, A., Wild, U., Bertsch, D., and Fahr, A.-M. Analysis of the comparative workflow and performance characteristics of the VITEK 2 and Phoenix systems, *J. Clin. Microbio.*, 43, 3829–3834, 2005.
16. Becton Dickinson Microbiology Systems: Product Literature. Cockeysville, MD, 2005.
17. Leverstein-van Hall, M.A., Fluit, A.C., Paaum, A., Box, A.T.A., Brisse, S., and Verhoef, J. Evaluation of the Etest ESBL and the BD Phoenix, VITEK 1, and VITEK 2 automated instruments for detection of extended-spectrum beta-lactamases in multiresistant *Escherichia coli* and *Klebsiella* spp., *J. Clin. Microbio.*, 40, 3703–3711, 2002.

6 Agar Dilution Susceptibility Testing

Ann Hanlon, Merwyn Taylor, and James D. Dick

CONTENTS

6.1 INTRODUCTION

The agar dilution susceptibility-testing method is utilized for the determination of the minimal inhibitory concentration (MIC) of an antimicrobial agent required to inhibit the growth of a microorganism. As with broth dilution susceptibility tests, the agar dilution method provides a quantitative result in the form of an MIC, in contrast to disk diffusion susceptibility tests that result in an indirect measure of susceptibility and provide a qualitative interpretative result. The agar dilution method is the most well-established method for determining antimicrobial susceptibility and is commonly used as the standard or reference method for evaluation of new antimicrobial agents and susceptibility test methods [1–10]. In addition, it offers the convenience of simultaneously testing a number of isolates (32–36), being able to detect mixed cultures or heterogeneous populations, and flexibility in antibiotic selection and concentration range to be tested.

6.2 SIGNIFICANCE

Selection of an appropriate antimicrobial agent should be considered in the context of the microorganism, the antibiotic, and the host [11]. Factors that are involved in this triad include (*a*) the *in vitro* susceptibility of the infecting organism, (*b*) the relative susceptibility of the infecting organism compared to other members of the same species, (*c*) the pharmacokinetic/pharmacodynamic properties of the antibiotic, such as its toxicity, distribution, adsorption, excretion, protein binding, half-life, and postantibiotic effect, (*d*) prior clinical experience of the efficacy of the antibiotic in similar clinical situations, and (*e*) the nature of the pathophysiology underlying the infection in the host and its potential effect on chemotherapy and the immune status of the host. Among these considerations, the concentration of antibiotics required for *in vitro* inhibition or killing can be measured in the clinical laboratory. It is the responsibility of the laboratory to provide the clinician with accurate and appropriate *in vitro* susceptibility information, which, in conjunction with the previously described pharmacologic and host information, can be used to formulate the optimal therapeutic approach for the patients. In addition to direct application in guiding antimicrobial therapy on a patient-by-patient basis, *in vitro* susceptibility information should be capable of and utilized to detect new emerging mechanisms of resistance as well as changing patterns of resistance in a particular location, i.e., ward, institution, or among a particular group of microorganisms.

6.3 AGAR DILUTION PROCEDURE

6.3.1 PREPARATION OF AGAR DILUTION PLATES

6.3.1.1 Media Selection

The basal media used for testing is determined on the basis of the organisms and in some cases the antibiotic to be tested.[1]

- Enterobacteriaceae, nonfermentative gram-negative bacilli, staphylococci, enterococci, nonfastidious bacteria: Mueller-Hinton agar
- Oxacillin/methicillin/nafcillin testing of staphylococci: Mueller-Hinton agar supplemented with 2% (w/v) NaCl
- Streptococci: Mueller-Hinton agar supplemented with 5% (v/v) defibrinated sheep blood (for testing of a sulfonamide, lysed horse blood should be used)
- Neisseria gonorrhoeas: GC base with 1% defined growth supplement (NCCLS, Table 2F-M7-A5, M100-S16)
- Haemophilus: Haemophilus test medium (HTM) (NCCLS, Table 2E-M7-A5, M100-S12)

6.3.1.2 Antibiotic Concentration Range

Choosing the appropriate concentration to test is based on two parameters:

1. Interpretive break points set by NCCLS for both the antibiotic and the organism being tested
2. Quality control organism being utilized

The number of concentrations being tested will vary by the individual laboratory. In addition, it is essential that the interpretive break points be included as well as concentrations that allow for adequate quality control (QC) testing.

---

[1] See NCCLS Table 7-M7-A5; M100-S16 for defined growth supplement and for further information on dilution testing and screening tests for organisms not listed here.

6.3.1.3 Antimicrobial Powders

Pharmaceutical companies will usually supply on request standard antimicrobial reference powder for antibiotics that they market. Some off-patent antibiotics can be obtained from commercial chemical companies.

6.3.1.4 Weighing Antimicrobial Powders

6.3.1.4.1 Potency

Most antibiotics being used for agar dilution are not 100% pure. It is important to know the assay potency of the lot of antibiotic being utilized. Using this information, a standardized solution can be formulated. This information may be found on the vial of the reference powder or may be included in the information enclosed with the drug. The following formula should be used:

$$\text{Weight (mg)} = \frac{\text{volume (mL)} \times \text{concentration (μg/mL)}}{\text{assay potency (μg/mg)}}.$$

EXAMPLE

To prepare 10 mL of a stock solution containing 1,000 μg/mL of a particular antibiotic with a potency of 869 μg/mg, perform the following calculation[1]:

$$\text{Weight (mg)} = \frac{10 \text{ mL} \times 1000 \text{ μg/mL}}{869 \text{ μg/mg}}.$$

$$\text{Weight} = 11.5 \text{ mg}$$

6.3.1.4.2 Weighing

Antimicrobial powders should be weighed on an analytical balance that has been calibrated with National Institute of Standards and Technology weights or other approved reference weights.

6.3.1.5 Preparing Concentrations for Testing

A. Prepare a stock solution of 10,000 μg/mL or 1,000 μg/mL for each antibiotic being tested.
   • Water can be used as a solvent for most antibiotics.
   • Some antibiotics require solvents other than water. It is important to use the minimal amount of solvent needed to solubilize the drug and to use water or another appropriate buffer to make the final stock concentration and dilutions. See the Appendix for a list of buffers.
   • Stock solutions can be stored at 60°C or below for 6 months or more without significant loss of activity with the exception of imipenem and ticarcillin/clavulanate, which can only be stored for 1 month. Quality control should always be performed to verify that no significant deterioration has occurred.
B. Using the stock solution and Table 6.1, the dilution scheme for each antibiotic can be achieved. The reader is also referred to the latest M100 NCCLS document for a scheme for preparing dilutions used in agar dilution.

---

[1] To make a 10,000 μg/mL solution, you can weigh out the same amount of antibiotic and add solvent to a volume of 1.0 mL, or weigh out 10 times as much antibiotic and add solvent to a volume of 10 mL.

TABLE 6.1
Antibiotic Dilution Scheme

Stock Solution	Volume of Stock To Be Added to 1 Liter of Agar (mL)	Final Concentration in Agar (μg/mL)
10,000 μg/mL	25.6	256
	12.8	128
	6.4	64
	3.2	32
	1.6	16
1,000 μg/mL	8	8
	4	4
	2	2
	1	1
100 μg/mL	5	0.5
	1.0	0.1

If you have concentrations of 128 μg/mL and/or 256 μg/mL in your dilution scheme in addition to lower concentrations, always make a 10,000 μg/mL solution and dilute it to a 1,000 μg/mL solution. This way your quality control will be testing your entire dilution scheme.

6.3.1.6 Pouring the Plates

1. Label square or round petri plates for each concentration of antibiotic being tested. Label in such a way that the label can be used to orient the plate, i.e., put the label in the bottom right corner of the square plates or on the bottom edge of round plates.
2. Prepare 1 L of Mueller-Hinton agar or other base media for each concentration of antibiotic being tested per manufacturer's instructions. Before autoclaving the media, add an anti-bubble additive such as Pourite (Compliance Technology, Inc., San Francisco, CA).
3. Cool the media in a water bath to between 45°C and 50°C.
4. Add any supplements to the media, including sheep or horse blood.
5. Take the pH of each batch of media. It should be between 7.2 and 7.4 at room temperature. This should be done once the agar is solidified. This is essential since the potency of some antibiotics will change with the hydrogen ion concentration.
6. Add antibiotic to the liquid agar media.
7. Swirl the flask to mix thoroughly.
8. Pour into the petri plates on a level surface to a depth of 3–4 mm (approximately 40–50 mL/plate).
9. Allow the plates to solidify at room temperature.
10. Store the plates at 2°C–8°C for up to two weeks for routine susceptibility testing (with the exception of imipenem and clavulanate plates, which should be prepared and used within seven days) but no more than five days for reference work. These times are for benchmark purposes.
11. Different antibiotics can be more or less stable, and therefore quality control must be performed on each day of use.

6.3.1.7 Control Plates

In addition to preparing antibiotic dilution plates, it is important to also prepare control plates. These plates consist of only the agar-based media with no antibiotic added. Optimally, a control plate should be made at the beginning of each agar dilution run and at the end to evaluate an organism's ability to grow on the base media, as well as any contamination and antibiotic carryover.

6.3.1.7.1   Testing Isolates Using Agar Dilution Plates

6.3.1.7.1.1   Initial Preparation

1. Remove all concentrations of agar dilution plates and control plates from the refrigerator to allow the plates to come to room temperature and the agar surface to dry. This can be achieved by slightly opening the lids of each plate and allowing them to remain on the bench for 1–2 h.
2. The number of plates of each concentration of antibiotic you will need to test is dependent on the number of isolates being tested and the type of petri plate being used:
Square plates — 36 isolates, including the QC
Round plates — 32 isolates, including the QC
3. Preparing a grid
Each patient isolate and quality control organism needs to be accounted for when setting up an agar dilution run.
A square plate setup is numbered as follows:

1	2	3	4	5	6
7	8	9	10	11	12
13	14	15	16	17	18
19	20	21	22	23	24
25	26	27	28	29	30
31	32	33	34	35	36

A round plate setup is numbered as follows:

	1	2	3	4	
5	6	7	8	9	10
11	12	13	14	15	16
17	18	19	20	21	22
23	24	25	26	27	28
	29	30	31	32	

4. When the plates are dry, close them and arrange the plates so that they are marked as to their correct orientation.

6.3.1.7.1.2   Preparing the Inoculum

1. Growth method
   a. Inoculate 1 mL of Mueller-Hinton broth with a portion of three to five colonies of the organism to be tested. The colonies should be morphologically the same.
   b. Incubate at 35°C for 2–6 h. The growth should reach a turbidity that is equivalent to or greater than a 0.5 McFarland standard.
   c. Adjust the turbidity of the culture using sterile saline to achieve a turbidity equivalent to a 0.5 McFarland standard. This will contain approximately 1.5×10^8 CFU/mL.
2. Direct colony suspension method
   a. This method should be use when testing the following organisms:
   Haemophilus spp.
   N. gonorrhoeae
   Steptococci

Staphylococci when looking for potential methicillin or oxacillin resistance

  b. Isolated colonies for testing should come from 18- to 24-h agar plates. The organism should be grown on nonselective media such as blood agar.
  c. A suspension is made using a portion of three to five colonies that are morphologically similar. Adjust the suspension so that it is equivalent to a 0.5 McFarland standard.

3. Dilution inoculum
  a. Dilute the adjusted suspensions 1:10 in sterile saline. This will give you an inoculum concentration of 10^7 CFU/mL.
  b. Use the diluted suspensions within 15 min of preparation.

6.3.1.7.1.3   Inoculation Agar Dilution Plates

1. Use of a replicator device at this point is helpful. Replicators consist of a block of wells where the organisms go and a transferring head containing metal pins. These pins are usually 3 mm in diameter and transfer 1–2 µl of inoculum on the agar plate creating a 5–8-mm spot. This gives a final inoculum amount on the agar surface of 10^4 CFU/mL.
2. Arrange all tubes containing the diluted suspensions in a rack that corresponds to the grid prepared earlier.
3. Fill the corresponding well in the replicator block half full of the diluted suspension using a sterile transfer pipette. Leave a small portion of the suspension in the pipette and use this to streak an agar plate to be used as a purity check. This plate will also provide fresh isolated colonies from which further testing or repeat testing can be performed.
4. Using the replicator, inoculate the growth control plate.
5. Inoculate each set of antibiotics starting with the lowest concentration.
6. Inoculate a second control plate at the end.

6.3.1.7.1.4   Incubation

1. Allow the plates to sit at room temperature until the inoculum spots have dried, approximately 10 min.
2. Invert the plates and incubate as follows:

Nonfastidious bacteria	16–20 h, 35°C, non-CO_2
Streptococci	20–24 h, 35°C, CO_2 if necessary for growth
Neisseria gonorrheae	20–24 h, 35°C, 5%–7% CO_2
Oxacillin, methicillin, and vancomycin testing of staphylococci	24 h, 33–35°C (do not exceed 35°C), non-CO_2
Vancomycin testing of enterococci	24 h, 35°C, non-CO_2

6.3.1.7.1.5   Determining End Points

1. After the appropriate incubation, check both control plates for growth and any obvious contamination. Any organisms either not growing on the control plate or contaminated should not be read for MICs.
2. Check the purity plates for contamination or mixed cultures. Any plate with more than one morphology of an organism should not be read for MICs.
3. Antibiotic plates should be read for end points on a dark nonreflecting surface.
4. All concentrations of the particular antibiotic being read should be laid out in front of you with the lowest concentration to your left.
5. The MIC is read as the first antibiotic concentration that inhibits the growth of the organism completely. A faint haze caused by the inoculum or a single colony should not be read as growth.

6. Purity should be questioned in the following situations:
   - Greater than one colony on any plate past an obvious endpoint
   - Higher concentrations have growth when lower concentrations have no growth
7. All procedures from 1 through 6 should be repeated by another independent reader.
8. The two readings should be compared to each other, and any discrepancies should be resolved.

6.3.1.7.1.6 Quality Control

Quality control of the agar dilution method of susceptibility testing is important to ensure that all the steps of the procedure result in accurate MICs being reported. In addition to those procedures previously described, the inclusion of four to six control strains on every run adds an additional level of assurance to the susceptibility data.

Quality control isolates should consist of organisms that have MICs that fall into the range of concentrations being tested for each antibiotic. Reference American Type Culture Collection (ATCC) stains that are recommended by NCCLS are as follows:

Enterococcus faecalis	ATCC 29212
Enterococcus faecalis	ATCC 51299
Escherichia coli	ATCC 25922
Escherichia coli	ATCC 35218
Haemophilus influenzae	ATCC 49247
Klebsiella pneumoniae	ATCC 700603
Neisseria gonorrhoeae	ATCC 49226
Pseudomonas aeruginosa	ATCC 27853

Additional control isolates, particularly for gram-positives and nonfastidious gram-negatives, can be selected for inclusion as control organisms. These isolates should be selected on the basis of their reproducibility and as controls for antibiotics that are not controlled by the NCCLS-recommended strains. It is important to assess the accuracy of the standardization of the test inoculum to ensure consistency throughout all the testing. Plate counts should be obtained from a random well in the replicator device on a periodic basis by a conventional pour or spread agar quantitative technique.

6.4 DATA PROCESSING AND ANALYSIS

The rapidly expanding spectrum of antimicrobial agents, microorganisms, and resistance determinants has resulted in the need for computerized processing and analysis of data generated through both identification- and susceptibility-testing systems in large clinical laboratory settings. Automated data analysis permits the integration and evaluation of both species and antibiotic profiles, which are the two essential components for determination of specific resistance determinants not apparent using direct interpretation of a single antibiotic test result. Nonintegrated systems require manual integration of identification and susceptibility data, data evaluation, and decision making, which can result in a significant burden for the bench microbiologist. Many of the automated systems have incorporated "expert systems" into their software to solve this problem; however, laboratories using manual or combinations of automated and manual technologies are still faced with the burden of manually evaluating speciation and susceptibility information prior to final reporting of culture results. The following is a data-processing system used in our laboratory for integration and evaluation of identification- and susceptibility-profile information. The system was designed to accept semiautomated identification and susceptibility data from an agar-based system but is applicable for totally automated, manual–automated, and manual systems that interact with a computerized laboratory information system.

6.4.1 Data-Processing Methodology — Agar Dilution

The agar dilution computer system was designed to support the data entry and processing required to identify and report a microbiology laboratory's results using the agar dilution method. The computer system is composed of three primary components illustrated in Figure 6.1.

These components are the graphical user interface (GUI), data processing unit, and database unit. The GUI provides a framework for technologists to interact with the system. The processing unit accepts data from the GUI, checks it for validity, and applies interpretation rules to it. The database unit stores all the data. The three components are connected to the same network, and it is the shared network connectivity that allows the component to send information to other components.

The first component of the agar dilution computer system is the GUI. The interface is composed of several dialog boxes that technologists use to enter data. The interfaces are used to communicate with various modules contained in the processing unit. Figure 6.2 illustrates the main dialog boxes that are used.

The data entry process begins with the creation of a "RUN." The user interface presents the technologists with a 6×6 grid to enter the isolate identifiers that will be used in the current run. A 6×6 grid was selected as the interface of choice because it reflects the positioning of specimen samples on the dishes and because it is intuitive. The isolate numbers in the 6×6 grid correspond to the positions of the specimen samples. Once the information has been entered, it is transferred to the processing unit. Among other things, the processing unit checks the isolate numbers for validity and transfers the isolate numbers to the database unit where the "RUN" is registered.

After the RUN is created, technologists can enter the biochemical identification reactions for the isolates that have been recorded for that run. The dialog box for the biochemical data entry is similar to that of the RUN setup dialog box. This dialog box also consists of a 6×6 grid, the name of the biochemical substrates tested, and within each cell, drop-down boxes that contain options for that cell. The values entered into the cells are registered with the isolates that have been entered into the corresponding cells of the run and ensure that the technologists enter valid values. Furthermore, by using a dialog box, technologists can enter data in any order and make corrections to data prior to submitting the final results to the processing unit.

Double data entry is used for quality control when registering biochemical results for isolates. When the second technologist enters data, the technologist will be presented with values from the first collection that differ from those just entered. The technologist can override or accept the previous value. To support this feature, the database unit has to be designed to appropriately manage the first and second batch of values, and the processing unit must compare these values when the second technologist enters any data.

The second data entry interface is the susceptibility-reading data entry dialog box. Technologists use this dialog box to enter MIC readings. The susceptibility data entry dialog box is similar to that of the biochemical data entry dialog box. One noticeable difference is that the pull-down selections for the cell differ with the antibiotics that are being processed. The interface communicates with the processing unit to retrieve the allowable options for the cells. This feature ensures that the technologists will only enter allowable values and reduces errors in the system. As in the first interface, double data entry is used for quality control.

FIGURE 6.1 Primary components of an agar dilution computer system.

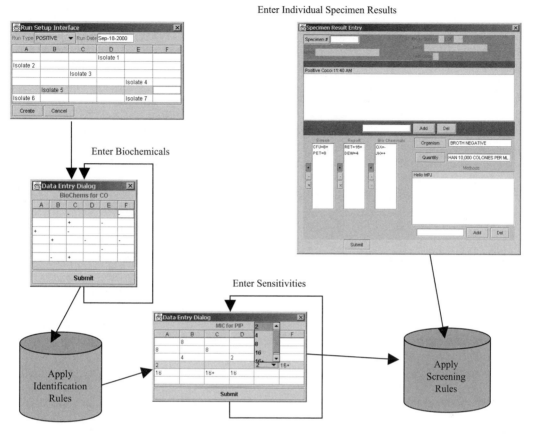

FIGURE 6.2 Agar dilution process and GUI.

The third major interface is the individual specimen results entry dialog box. Technologists use this interface to enter data for isolates of the same specimen. This interface is used to report the identification of organisms that are not identified using the agar method. Using this interface, technologists can enter the organisms that have been identified, the quantity of colonies, the biochemicals used, and the MIC readings. This interface contains shortcuts that reduce the amount of typing required by the technologists. For example, technologists can enter a short three to four letter mnemonic for an organism, and the interface will replace the mnemonic with the organism's name when the organism button is pressed. Since there are over 1,200 organisms that can be entered into the organism text box, this shortcut avoids searching a long list and saves time. If the organism button is pressed and the organism text field does not contain the mnemonic, the technologist is presented with a selection list. This feature is also used for entering quantities, results, and methods.

Technologists enter MIC values in a text box after pressing the "+" button in either the "SCREEN" or "REPORT" list. In the event that an MIC reading was entered in the SCREEN list but it should have been entered in the REPORT list, the interface allows the technologist to move entries from one list to another. This feature makes it easy to recover from mistakes and saves time for the technologists. Removing entries from either list identification is quite intuitive. Technologists simply highlight the entry and press the "=" button. This portion of the interface uses icons that reflect the actions the technologists perform and adds to the intuitive feel of the interface.

The goal of the GUI is to present the technologists with a series of menus and intuitive, easy to use dialog boxes that can be used to navigate through the agar dilution computer system and to enter data. Selection lists are used to minimize errors in data entry. The GUI gets data for the selection lists from the database by sending requests to the processing unit. The processing unit extracts data from the database and passes it along to the GUI. Shortcuts provide efficient options for data entry. Several dialog boxes were designed similarly to ensure consistent interaction with the computer system where appropriate.

6.4.2 PROCESSING UNIT

The processing unit is the component of the computer system that interacts with the GUI. It is an application server that waits for data from the user interface. Therefore, the user interface and the processing unit are individual computer processes that work together. This component has several modules designed specifically for the individual dialog boxes in the GUI. Two of the more important modules are illustrated in Figure 6.2. These modules are the organism identification module and the antibiotic susceptibility screening module.

The organism identification module is invoked after the second collection of biochemical reactions has been entered for the runs. The computer system maintains a list of biochemical patterns and corresponding organisms that are identified by the patterns. This module retrieves the biochemical patterns from the database and compares them to those that have been supplied for individual isolates. If the biochemical results for an individual isolate match those in the biochemical patterns list, the corresponding organism is registered with the isolate.

To improve the efficiency of the search, the identification module keeps the patterns indexed on the first three biochemicals. By searching the first three components of a pattern, the module can quickly narrow down the patterns that may potentially match the technologist's inputs. This feature saves a considerable amount of time since patterns that do not match the biochemical results entered by the technologist can be safely avoided without checking them in their entirety.

The antibiotic screening module is used to determine which antibiotic results should be reported to clinicians and which results should be saved but screened. This module is invoked after the antibiotic susceptibility data has been entered either for isolates that are included in a RUN or for specimens using the specimen result entry dialog. The screening rules are based on the body sources of the specimens, the identified organism, and the antimicrobial agents. This screening information is maintained in the database. One interesting feature of these rules is that they can contain references to classes of organisms as opposed to individual organisms. The database maintains a hierarchy of organisms that can be accessed to resolve individual organisms to their higher level classes. Figure 6.3 contains a sample hierarchy that is used in the system.

Other modules include the organism taxonomy management module and the extensible markup language (XML) parsing module. The organism taxonomy management module provides access to organisms and their subclasses. This information is used in screening rules, and it makes the rule-screening system extremely flexible. Most messages in the computer system are XML-like messages. The XML parsing module is used to transform XML-like messages to structures containing data that can be processed by other modules in the processing unit. The XML-like syntax is a communications standard used by the GUI and the processing unit that allows for the seamless integration of the two units.

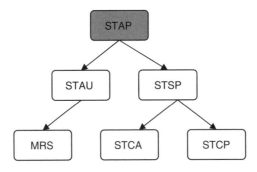

FIGURE 6.3 Portion of organism taxonomy.

6.4.3 Database

The database is an integral part of the agar dilution computer system. It stores the information that is needed to identify organisms, screen antibiotics, supply the user interface with allowable values for selection lists, and manage the data generated by the technologist and the processing modules. Consequently, the database had to be designed to efficiently support these functions. A relational database architecture is used in which data are stored in tables. When necessary, tables may reference one another to link data from one table to that of another.

Figure 6.4 illustrates the subset of the database schema that is used to store the isolate and susceptibility data. The isolate table contains data that is pertinent to the isolate and does not reference the susceptibility data. This is a valid approach because isolates can exist without susceptibility data. The susceptibility table contains information that is pertinent to the MIC values. Since susceptibility readings typically correspond to isolates, the susceptibility table cross-references the isolate table to create a link between isolates and their susceptibility readings.

The biochemical patterns are expressed as XML-like streams. Each pattern is associated with an organism and one or more comments that are to be reported with the organism identification. A typical pattern is expressed as

```
<PATTERN> <PARTIAL ES="+" NA="+" ED="-"/> <FULL
NO="+"SC="+"LC="+"MN="+"ST="+"AB="+"SS="-"/> <PATTERN>
```

The biochemical pattern is partitioned into two components, the partial component and the full component. The partial component is a prefix that is used to index patterns that begin with the same sequence. The full component denotes the remainder of the pattern that is different from other patterns with the same prefix. Both patterns contain mnemonics for the biochemicals that are matched. This information is loaded, parsed, and indexed by the organism identification module.

The antibiotic screening rules are also expressed as XML-like streams. A typical screening rule is expressed as

```
<BODYSOURCE BLOOD/> <ORGANISM ENFM/> <ANTCON> <GT VAN (Vancomycin) =
"64" /> </ANTCON>
```

The preconditions of this rule are (*a*) the body source of the specimen has to be "BLOOD," (*b*) the identified organism should be ENFM (*Enterococcus faecium*) or any of it descendants, and (*c*) the MIC for "VAN" should equal to 64. If the preconditions are all satisfied, the actions for this rule are applied. The actions for a rule are typically expressed as

```
<REPORT TET P-T/> <SCREEN SUL VAN/>
```

In this example, the MIC for TET (tetracycline) will be reported while the MICs for SUL (sulfasoxizole) and VAN will be suppressed from the final report.

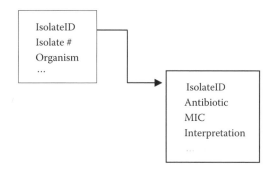

FIGURE 6.4 Isolate and susceptibility tables.

XML tags are used in the biochemical patterns and the antibiotic screening rules to instruct the processing modules on how to construct patterns and rules, respectively. Embedding XML tags in relational tables simplifies the process of amending existing patterns and rules, and provides a flexible framework for adding patterns and rules that are structured differently. This overcomes one of the shortcomings of relational database technology, i.e., changing the structure of the existing data. By adding new tags and embedding tags in different structures, new patterns and rules can be added to the database while avoiding the major task of restructuring the database schema. This design decision makes the agar dilution computer system very flexible.

The database contains an organism taxonomy that was created to allow the antibiotic screening rules to reference classes of organisms. Organism classes can be resolved to individual organisms by traversing the taxonomy. The database contains a table that lists the parent–child relationships that exist among organism classes and organisms. The organism taxonomy table contains three columns, the "super" category, the "sub" category, and the relationship type. For example, PC Aerobe, STAP, and ISA appear in the database and state that STAP is a subclass of PC Aerobe. The processing unit uses the information to build a taxonomy of organisms and provides services that allow the various modules to probe the taxonomy.

Creating a computer system to support agar dilution requires that one carefully consider the design of the user interface, the processing modules, and the storage of data. Ideally, the three components should work together. However, they should not be tightly coupled since a tight coupling among the components creates a less flexible overall system. The user interface should be easy to use and powerful enough to allow the technologists to complete their tasks. The processing unit should contain all the modules that are necessary to complete its tasks and be efficient enough to handle large workloads. The database unit should provide access to data that is presented to users in the GUI, such as selection lists, as well as store the results of all processing modules. Using these design principles should ensure that the computer systems will be flexible and easy to upgrade.

6.5 SUMMARY

The agar dilution antimicrobial testing method is a well-established, standardized technique that is frequently used as a reference for evaluating the accuracy of other susceptibility test methods. The method provides a quantitative result in the form of an MIC to which interpretive criteria can be applied, i.e., susceptible (S), intermediate (I), or resistant (R). MIC data can be utilized directly in conjunction with pharmacokinetic and pharmacodynamic parameters of the antimicrobial agent in optimizing therapy on a case-by-case basis. The method also provides for the simultaneous testing of many isolates (32–36), including control isolates, for each antibiotic and dilution tested. In contrast to broth methods, agar dilution is more amenable to the visual detection of contamination or microbial heterogeneity at the time of testing. Perhaps the greatest advantage of agar dilution susceptibility testing is its flexibility. Since antibiotic-containing plates are most commonly prepared by the user, antibiotics and the concentrations tested are at the laboratory's discretion rather than that of the manufacturer. This permits the user to better correlate their particular antibiotic test battery with those antibiotics being used, i.e., hospital formulary, at their institution. This has the potential for cost savings by not testing unnecessary or nonformulary drugs, which might be included in a commercial antibiotic panel. In addition, since the user is the manufacturer, antibiotic-testing changes can be implemented in a timely manner such as at the time of FDA approval of a new antibiotic. Finally, although the method is labor-intensive, significant cost savings can be realized if it is implemented by a well-trained staff when compared to the cost of commercial susceptibility test systems. The major disadvantages of the agar dilution system are associated with the labor-intensive tasks of preparing and conducting quality control of the antibiotic-containing plates. Additionally, in the absence of a computerized interface for data analysis, the manual evaluation and collating of susceptibility results, particularly when a large number of antibiotics are tested, and of identification information can be time-consuming.

APPENDIX — ANTIBIOTIC BUFFERS

1. Saturated sodium bicarbonate: Add sodium bicarbonate to approximately 5 mL of water until no more will go into solution.
2. 0.025 M KH_2PO_4 buffer, pH 5.5: Dissolve 0.34 g KH_2PO_4 in 100 mL H_2O using a volumetric flask. Adjust to pH 5.5 with approximately 0.07 mL 1 N NaOH.
3. 1 mol/L NaOH: 4 g NaOH + 100 mL H_2O.
4. 0.1 mol/L phosphate buffer, pH 7.0: Prepare the following two solutions in separate 100-mL volumetric flasks:
   A. 2.76 g NaH_2PO_4 + 100 mL H_2O
   B. 2.84 g Na_2HPO_4 + 100 mL H_2O
   In another volumetric flask, add 19.5 mL of solution A and 30.5 mL of solution B. Bring to 100 mL with H_2O.
5. 0.01 mol/L phosphate buffer, pH 7: Prepare the following two solutions in separate 100-mL volumetric flasks:
   0.272 g KH_2PO_4 + 100 mL H_2O
   0.35 g K_2HPO_4 + 100 mL H_2O
   In another volumetric flask, add 19.5 mL of solution A and 30.5 mL of solution B. Bring to 100 mL with H_2O. The pH should be 7.0.
6. 0.1 mol/L KH_2PO_4, pH 4.5: Dissolve 1.362 g of KH_2PO_4 in 100 mL H_2O using a volumetric flask.

REFERENCES

1. Steers, E., Foltz, E.L., and Graves, B.S. An inocula replicating apparatus for routine testing of bacterial susceptibility to antibiotics, *Antibiot. Chemother.*, 9, 307–311, 1959.
2. Ericsson, J.M. and Sherris, J.C. Antibiotic sensitivity testing. Report of an international collaborative study, *Acta Pathol. Microbiol. Scand. Sect. B Suppl.*, 217, 1–90, 1971.
3. Ryan, K.J., Needham, G.M., Dunsmoor, C.L., and Sherris, J.C. Stability of antibiotics and chemotherapeutics in agar plates, *Appl. Microbiol.*, 20, 447–451, 1970.
4. Sherris, J.C., Rashad, A.L., and Lighthart, G.A. Laboratory determination of antibiotic susceptibility to ampicillin and cephalothin, *Ann. N.Y. Acad. Sci.*, 145, 248–265, 1967.
5. Craig, W.A. Qualitative susceptibility tests versus quantitative MIC tests, *Diag. Microbiol. Infect. Dis.*, 16, 231–236, 1993.
6. Tenover, F.C., Swenson, J.M., O'Hara, C.M., and Stocker, S.A. Ability of commercial and reference antimicrobial susceptibility testing methods to detect vancomycin resistance in enterococci, *J. Clin. Microbiol.*, 33, 1524–1527, 1995.
7. Barry, A.L. *The Antimicrobic Susceptibility Test: Principles and Practices*, Lea & Febiger, Philadelphia, 1976.
8. Clinical and Laboratory Standards Institute. Methods for dilution antimicrobial susceptibility test for bacteria that grow aerobically, approval standard M7-A7, 5th ed., National Committee for Clinical Laboratory Standards, Wayne, PA, 2006.
9. Jorgensen, J.H., Turnidge, J.A., and Washington, J.A. Antibacterial susceptibility tests: Dilution and disk diffusion methods, in *Manual of Clinical Microbiology*, Murray, P.R., Baron, E.J., Pffaller, M.A., Tenover, F.C., and Yolken, R.H., Eds., ASM Press, Washington, DC, 1999.
10. Petersdorf, R.G. and Plorde, J.J. The usefulness of *in vitro* sensitivity tests in antibiotic therapy, *Annu. Rev. Med.*, 14, 54–56, 1993.
11. Petersdorf, R.G. and Sherris, J.C. Methods and significance of *in vitro* testing of bacterial sensitivity to drugs, *Am. J. Med.*, 39, 766–779, 1965.

7 Susceptibility-Testing Protocols for Antibiograms and Preventive Surveillance: A Continuum of Data Collection, Analysis, and Presentation

John G. Thomas and Nancy T. Rector

CONTENTS

7.1 INTRODUCTION AND BACKGROUND

7.1.1 ORIGIN

The origin of antibiograms is reflected in the growing emergence of bacterial resistance (Figure 7.1), i.e.,

- Limited resistance development in the 1950s and 1960s
- Penicillin, then methicillin (1970) to *Staphylococcus aureus*
- Resistant *Mycobacterium tuberculosis*
- WHO (World Health Organization) addressed susceptibility testing via the standardization of disk diffusion, i.e., Kirby-Bauer (1973)

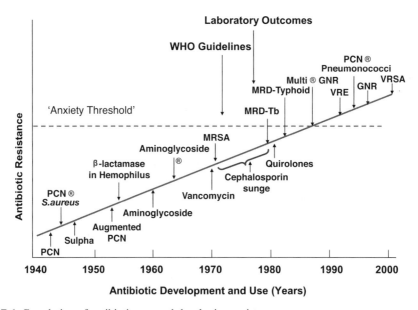

FIGURE 7.1 Correlation of antibiotic use and developing resistance.

7.1.2 History and Review of Antibiograms

- Automation (1970s) required documentation
- Need for new antimicrobials required tracking
- Development of parallel drugs in the same class but with supposedly better activity
- Center for Disease Control (CDC) computer tracking ("Dare-to-Compare") provided free to interested laboratories for data collection and comparison (1970s)
- Differences by geography and institutional type became apparent

7.1.3 Definitions

There are several types of antibiograms, and the following two are most common:

- Cumulative single-dimension antibiogram
- Focused antibiogram

A cumulative single-dimension antibiogram measures the cumulative sensitivity/resistance against a group of antibiotics; one must carefully define exclusive/inclusive criteria for the organisms as well as concentrations of each antibiotic evaluated. One also needs to use consistent interpretations, usually utilizing a consensus oversight organization such as the Clinical and Laboratory Standards Institute (CLSI) formerly NCCLS (National Committee for Clinical Laboratory Standards). Significant differences do occur between countries, because Japan, United Kingdom, Europe, and the United States use different criteria.

The second method, a focused antibiogram, uses a selected subset of information to unmask and eliminate low-frequency data that would be hidden in a standard cumulative antibiogram.

7.2 RELEVANCE OF ANTIBIOGRAMS

7.2.1 Why Are Antibiograms Important?

> The pattern of resistance or sensitivity in a hospital or indeed any environment is the negative imprint of the use of antibiotics in that environment
>
> **Hans M. Ericsson, 1977, Professor of Microbiology**

Table 7.1 tracks this important observation in real terms, while Table 7.2 describes the obvious association with the overuse of antibiotics. Table 7.3 highlights resistance development or loss of susceptibility for intensive care unit (ICU) isolates. Tables 7.4 and 7.5 relate resistance to cost, which in today's economic environment is critical. Table 7.5 emphasizes the importance of "Burden of Disease," generally and specifically, for ventilator associated pneumonia (VAP).

"Preventive surveillance" is another way of defining the benefits of an antibiogram. The word *antibiogram* implies a "static" process, while *preventive surveillance* constitutes active participation and denotes involvement, which is what microbiologists need to do.

7.2.2 How Can Antibiograms Be Used in Patient Care?

- Help in emperic antibiotic selection
- Alert to developing resistance (trends)
- Track outbreaks/epidemiology
- Guide hospital formulary decisions (pharmacy)
- Satisfy regulatory agencies

TABLE 7.1
Concentration (μg/mL) of Anti-Infective Agents That Would Inhibit or Kill Bacteria at Their Discovery and in 1999

Anti-Infective	Bacteria	MIC (μg/mL)	
		At Discovery	1999
Penicillin G	S. pneumonia	0.008	0.1 to >2
	S. aureus	0.1	>128
Ampicillin	K. pneumonia	4	>128
	N. gonorrheae	<0.1	>128
	S. typhi	<1	>128
	H. influenza	<0.1	>128
Trimethoprim/sulfamethoxazole	S. typhi	<2	>128
Erythromycin	S. pyroxenes	<0.1	>128
Ciprofloxacin	MRSA[a]	<1	>16
Isoniazid	M. tuberculosis	<5	>100

[a] MRSA = Methcillin Resistant *Staphylococcus aureus*.

TABLE 7.2
Use of Antibiotics in Hospitals

>30% of all patients receive antibiotics

60% of all antibiotics are administered in the absence of documentation of infection

13%–15% of administered antibiotics are incorrect

70% of antibiotics chosen are the more expensive variety, i.e., an advanced generation antibiotic, when the cheaper antibiotic could be used.

19%–35% of a pharmacy's budget deals with antibiotic use

20% of antibiotics used have complications in their use, e.g., renal toxicity or nosocomial infections

TABLE 7.3
Comparison of Nosocomial Resistance Rates in ICUs by Selected Phenotypes

Antimicrobial-Resistant Pathogen (R-Phenotypes)	% Resistance (1994–1998)	January to May 1999 Numbers	% of Increase in Resistance (1994–1998)	% Resistance (2000–2004)	% of Increase in Resistance (2000–2004
Vancomycin-resistant *Enterococcus*	25.9	58	47	28.5	12
MRSA[a]	54	865	43	59.5	11
Methicillin-resistant CNS	86.7	789	2	89.1	1
Cef3-resistant *E. coli*	3.2	316	23	5.8	0
Cef3-resistant *K. pneumoniae*	8.9	248	−1	20.6	47
Imepenem-resistant *P. aeruginosa*	18.5	298	35	21.1	15
Quinolone-resistant *P. aeruginosa*	23	480	49	29.5	9
Cef3-resistant *P. aeruginosa*	20	490	<1	31.9	20
Cef3-resistant *Enterobacter* spp.	36.4	335	3	31.1	−6

Source: NNIS Report. December 2004.

[a] MRSA = Methcillin Resistant Staphylococcus aurea; CNS = Coagulase Negative Staphylococcus; Cef3 = 3rd Generation Ceflosporin.

TABLE 7.4
Economic Burden of Infectious Diseases

Treatment of non-AIDS STDs	$5.0 billion
Ear infections	$1.2 billion
Intestinal infections (direct costs and lost productivity)	$30.0 billion
Nosocomial infections	$4.5 billion
Antimicrobial resistance	$4.0 billion

Infectious diseases contribute significantly to economic losses and lost productivity in the United States.

TABLE 7.5
Burden of Three Selected Infectious Diseases in the USA

	Hospitalizations	Mortality Rate	Mortality	$ per Patient
Severe sepsis	660,000	23%	150,000	$22,000–70,000
Community acquired	395,000	13%	50,000	
Hospital acquired	265,000	38%	100,000	
Adequate initial Rx[a] (70%)	185,000	28%[a]	51,000	
Inadequate initial Rx[a] (30%)	80,000	62%[a]	49,000	
Pneumonia	1,300,000	9%	115,000	$12,000–22,000
Community acquired	1,000,000	2.4%	24,000	
Hospital acquired	300,000	30%	90,000	
Ventilator associated pneumonia	135,000	45%	61,000	$41,000
Adequate initial Rx[b,c,d,e] (56–75%)	75,000–100,000	10–20%[b,c,d,e]		
Inadequate initial Rx[b,c,d,e] (25–44%)	35,000–60,000	40–60%[b,c,d,e]		

Note: In an average 500-bed hospital, studies indicate that patients with acquired infections will receive inadequate initial antimicrobial therapy XXX per year:
- About 40 with hospital aquired sepsis
- Between 20–30 with ventilator associated pneumonia

[a] The Influence of Inadequate Antimicrobial Treatment of Blood Infections on Patient Outcomes in the ICU Setting. E.H. Ibrahim, G. Sherman, S. Ward, V.J. Fraser, and M.H. Kollef, FCCP. *Chest* 118(1), 9–11, 2000.

[b] Ventilator Associated Pneumonia. J. Chastre and J.V. Fagon, *Am J Respir Crit Care Med.* 165(7):867–903, 2002.

[c] Impact of Invasive and Noninvasive Quantitative Culture Sampling on Outcome of Ventilator-Associated Pneumonia: A Pilot Study. J.M. Sanchez-Nieto, A. Torres, F. Garcia-Cordoba, M. El-Ebiary, A. Carrillo, J. Ruiz, M.L. Nuñez, and M. Niederman. *Am J Respir Crit Care Med.* 157(2):371–376, 1998.

[d] Noninvasive versus Invasive Microbial Investigation in Ventilator-Associated Pneumonia: Evaluation of Outcome. M. Ruiz, A. Torres, S. Ewig, M.A. Marcos, A. Alcón, R. Lledó, M.A. Asenjo, and A. Maldonaldo. *Am J Respir Crit Care Med.* 162(1):119–125, 2000.

[e] Impact of Appropriateness of Initial Antibiotic Therapy on the Outcome of Ventilator-Associated Pneumonia. K. Dupont, H. Mentec, J.P. Sollet, and G. Bleichner. *Intensive Care Med.* 27(2):355–362, 2001.

7.2.3 WHO USES AN ANTIBIOGRAM?

Health care providers, including:

- Physicians
  - Intensivists in intensive care units
- Infection control practitioners
- Pharmacists
- Microbiologists
- Administrators

7.3 PROCEDURE

7.3.1 OVERVIEW OF ANTIBIOGRAM DEVELOPMENT

The process of antibiogram development is a continual interaction of three analytical phases: pre-analytic, analytic, and post-analytic (Figure 7.2). To begin the process, the best starting point is pre-analytic. The first step is data design (I) followed by actual data collection (II). The process then moves into data compilation, using varied types of statistical tools to best exhibit the desired results (III). The post-analytic phase involves the different chart types and presentation methods that best suit the institution and the internal customers (IV). The transition phase between pre-analytic and post-analytic is comparative analysis that brings to light any changes needed to be addressed in the data designing phase for the next cycle of antibiogram design and development.

7.3.2 PREANALYTICAL—DATA DESIGNING

(See checklist for Implementing an Antibiogram, Table 7.6)

7.3.2.1 Data Designing

The antibiogram must fit the surveillance needs of the institution in order to have real value. Several criteria must be identified in order to achieve this goal.

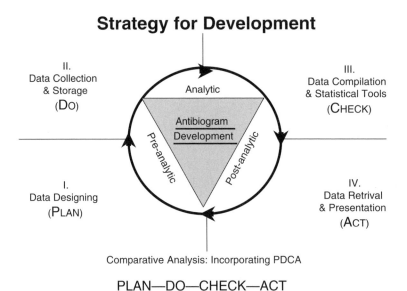

FIGURE 7.2 Overview of designing, implementing, and evaluating an antibiogram.

TABLE 7.6
Checklist for Implementing an Antibiogram

A. Pre-analytical

    1. Identify who the members are of the current P&T/Infection Control committee[a]

        ___Infection control

        ___Pharmacy

        ___Microbiology

        ___Administration

        ___Medical doctor to represent institution specialties

    2. ___Set team goals

    3. ___Perform a team review

    4. ___Assess the current antibiogram

    5. ___Determine frequency of the antibiogram development

    6. ___What is the frame necessary to completely exhibit trending?

    7. What are the desired demographics?

        ___Patient identifier

        ___Patient location

        ___Specimen identifier

        ___Specimen source/type

        ___Organism subset such as Methcillin Resistant *Staphylococcus aureus* (MRSA)/Methcillin Susceptible

        Staphylococcus aureus (MSSA)

        ___Patient age

        ___Institution

        ___Diagnosis

        ___Clinical specialty

        ___Other _____

    8. ___Off-site locations such as geriatric (nursing home)

    9. Choose data type

        ___AST method/result

        ___Formulary list requirements

        ___Drug class

        ___Individual drugs formulary

        ___Antimicrobial agents

        ___Organism identification list

B. Analytical

    10. ___Needs of internal customers

    11. Where is the information?

        ___The Hospital Information System (HIS)

        ___The Laboratory Information System (LIS)

        ___The Instrument Information System (Microbiology ID/AST system)

        ___The Hospital Pharmacy Information System (HPS)

        ___An electronic database

    12. ___Determine the available fields in the institution's computer

C. Post-analytic

    13. ___Patient management (template)

        ___Hospital management (template)

    15. Determine presentation types (tables and figures)

        ___Chart type

        ___Bar graph

        ___Pie chart

        ___Percent

    16. Report type

        ___Traditional

        ___Nontraditional

P&T = Pharmacy and Therapeutics; AST = Antimicrobial and Susceptible Testing; ID/AST = Identification and Antimicrobial and Susceptible Testing.

7.3.2.1.1 Define the Internal Customer

This aspect is dependant on institution type, size, and specialty. Identify who the members are of the current Pharmacy and Therapeutics (P&T) and Infection Control committee. A minimum of a core team is required to successfully cover all areas of involvement. These core team members include infection control, pharmacy, microbiology, and administration. Additional members such as a medical doctor, who represents the institution specialties, can be added if necessary.

7.3.2.1.2 Set Goals

The next set of criteria to be addressed is the team goals. The following points should be considered:

- Surveillance for institution resistance trends: The results of this would fall under the responsibility of the institution team administrative representative.
- Surveillance of formulary functionality within the institution: The pharmacist team member would utilize the antibiogram to evaluate the efficacy and cost-effective nature of the available institution therapies.
- Surveillance of emerging pathogen specifics: The infectious disease physician would participate in the development of the antibiogram to track the incidence of pathogen activity.

7.3.2.1.3 Assess the Team's Needs

Perform a team review and assess the current antibiogram if it exists or discuss the following points with the team for antibiogram development.

Determine frequency of the antibiogram development. Is it a rolling report? What is the time frame necessary to completely exhibit trending? The minimum time frame to best exhibit a trend is 6 months. If data is not available for 6 months, begin assessing data at 3 months.

7.3.2.1.4 Identify the Desired Report Demographics

The primary demographics required in an antibiogram must include:

- Unique patient identification number
- Healthcare facility for institutions with multiple laboratory locations
- *Patient location.* Inpatient vs. outpatient; community vs. noncommunity. (These terms may be used interchangeably.)

The primary specimen information required in an antibiogram must include:

- *Specimen unique identifier*
- *Specimen source/type.* Blood vs. non-blood; urine vs. non-urine. Delineation of specimen source into larger groups is necessary to separate appropriate therapy methods (urinary antimicrobics vs. non-urinary antimicrobics) on the antibiogram chart.

Other institution information:

- Clinical services:
  - ICU (Medical ICU/Surgical ICU)
  - Medical or surgical unit (acute care)
  - Pediatric
  - BMTU (bone marrow transplant unit)
  - ED (emergency department)

Organism subsets such as Methcillin Resistant Staphylococcus Aureus (MRSA)/Methcillin Susceptible Staphylococcus Aureus (MSSA).

Secondary demographics that can be of value in final data assessments are: patient age or gender, institution service such as oncology or the area of specialty treatment within the institution, diagnosis types such as cystic fibrosis, and off-site locations such as geriatric (nursing home).

7.3.2.1.5 Data Type

The choice of data to be exhibited should reflect the needs of the institution.

> *Antimicrobial susceptibility testing (AST) method and result.* Ask the team the following question: Does the medical staff utilize minimum inhibitory concentration (MIC) results? If so, then analysis of MIC results should be displayed on the antibiogram as MIC_{50} or MIC_{90}. If MIC results are not utilized, then use the percent susceptible (S), intermediate (I), or resistant (R) on the antibiogram.
>
> *Routinely calculate the percent susceptible, excluding intermediate.* Exceptions include:
> - combining percent S and I for *Streptococcus pneumoniae*
> - penicillin and ESBLs (extended spectrum β lactamase)
> - penicillin and viridians group *streptococci*
>
> *Please note:* some institutions have chosen to group antibiotic effectiveness by selected categories including: "1st choice," "alternative," "growing resistance," and "don't use."

7.3.2.1.6 Formulary List Requirements

The next step is to discuss the following points with the team to assure the pharmaceutical relevance of the antibiogram:

- Drug class: The antibiogram may be divided into drug classes over a more broad range of antimicrobials if the formulary is not strictly observed by the prescribing physicians
- Individual: Select drugs in use at the institution can be listed.
- Only those antimicrobial agents on formulary should be listed if enforcement of the formulary is required.
- This list may or may not include restricted antimicrobials.
- Do not include combinations with no clinical indication/utility.

7.3.2.1.7 Organism Identification List

This is the last set of data to be discussed within the team.

- Only the most common isolates (15–25) should be listed. These isolates may be different for selected specimens or patient service areas.
- Do not include isolates with very low numbers (<10 isolates).
- For *S. aureus*, provide routine analysis, but include an analysis of oxacillin-resistant subset.

7.3.2.2 Data to Avoid

- Eliminate duplicates by including the "first isolate" for each patient. Duplicate results can skew the data and should be avoided. Parameters should be agreed upon within the team as to what constitutes a "duplicate." A specific time frame and associated specimen type defines a duplicate culture. For example, two blood cultures with the same organism isolate and susceptibility pattern from the same patient within three days would constitute a duplicate culture.
- Inappropriate organism and antimicrobial agent combinations such as *E. coli* and erythromycin should be avoided.
- Known innate resistance patterns such as *P. aeruginosa* and ampicillin, *Enterococcus* spp. and cephalosporins, and *P. mirabilis* and nitrofurantoin should not be part of the antibiogram.

- Organism and antibiotic combinations with no resistance mechanisms described to date such as Vancomycin-resistant *Staphylococcus* spp. or Ceftriaxone-resistant *Haemophilus* spp.
- Isolates from surveillance cultures.

7.3.2.3 Summary of Pre-Analytical Stage

The team members have been chosen and their antibiogram needs explored. With these needs in mind, the design of the antibiogram content is complete. The next stage is the data analysis or *analytic* phase.

7.3.3 ANALYTIC — DATA COLLECTION AND STORAGE

(See checklist for Implementing an Antibiogram, Table 7.6, Part B.)

7.3.3.1 Data Collection Sources

There are several possible sources that depend upon the institution structure and complexity. Larger sized institutions will have more data mining opportunities. A higher level of computerization within the institution will also ease the data mining process. In any case, the data can be retrieved using manual techniques or computerization.

Manual data retrieval will require a larger time obligation, as all laboratory and microbiology records will need to be handled manually. Automated data retrieval will depend greatly on the available computer systems within the institution.

The first step is to look at the needs of the internal customers (team members) and decide what information is necessary to accomplish the team goals. The second step is locating the information? In an institution with a *computerized information* system, the first place to look for the data is the available reports that may be generated from within that system.

The hospital information system (HIS) will generally have patient history and demographics. This system also will have current and historical laboratory patient reports available for data mining either on a manual or electronic basis. Often the HIS has an interface with the laboratory information system (LIS).

The LIS will provide current laboratory testing information through a direct link from the testing instruments. Most LISs are interfaced to the individual instruments that provide actual testing results. In some cases, where the electronic interface is not present, the result and demographic data are entered manually by the technologist performing the test.

The instrument information system (microbiology ID/AST system) will produce printed patient reports (include patient demographic information) or laboratory reports (include the lab result with a patient identifier) or electronically stored reports with accessible data and an available data tracking system. The LIS is the primary generator of patient reports and the instrument data manager usually produces the lab report. It's these lab reports that show the microbiologist more detailed analysis of the patient's actual results, biochemical reactions and MIC/Interpretations that assist the microbiologist in determining the accuracy of the result. The patient result is an LIS striped down version of this showing the physician only the filtered results that are relevant to the patient. ID/AST instrument manufacturers provide software that will generate reports that can be customized to meet the antibiogram needs:

The BD EpiCenter™ Microbiology Data Management System supports the BD Phoenix™ AST/ID system with two expert systems, "pro-active" alerting for microbiologists and other key staff, and extensive epidemiology reporting functionality. Phoenix™ provides both resistance marker confirmation and true doubling MIC dilutions that employs a proprietary redox indicator. Phoenix™ delivers this data to the EpiCenter every 20 minutes. Data are analyzed through the two expert systems resident in EpiCenter. The first of these systems BDXpert™ analyzes data using a "best practice" class CLIS rule set that can be customized by the user. These data are then further refined using the BD EpiCenter EpiCARE™ system. This patent pending "Clinical Applications Rules Editor" provides microbiologists with software that can further expertise the data using specific factors unique to the patient population. These data are linked to the software's "pro-active" alerting systems that can alert the microbiologists, physicians, pharmacists, or infection control staff of sentinel events defined by their institution.

EpiCenter also provides a true multi-user environment enabling the lab, infection control and pharmacy to simultaneously and securely use the software's extensive epidemiology library and reporting tools. The system's library and built-in report design tools empowers users to actively mine data to analyze outbreaks and emerging resistance trends, create customized presentations and then share this information electronically with their colleagues. These tools also provide the ability to routinely monitor events and then use EpiCARE to set up sentinel event alerts. EpiCenter also simultaneously supports BD Bactec™ blood culture systems integrating the microbiology department for improved efficiency. The system integrates seamlessly with the existing LIS eliminating duplicate data entry.

The bioMeriéux VITEK instrument software is configured to detect emerging resistance. The VITEK 2 brings the Advanced Expert System® (AES), which assigns a specific phenotype to each organism tested. This second generation expert system assigns a phenotype to each isolate based on the identification of the organism and the MIC distribution of the antibiotics tested against that organism. The database is comprised of over 2,000 phenotypes and 20,000 MIC distributions. The AES matches the phenotype with the resistance mechanisms known to be associated with that phenotype. This allows for biologic and therapeutic corrections to be made to the microbiology report. AES also allows for the detection of rare phenotypes and phenotypes yet to be described, obviously important in monitoring and reporting emerging antibiotic resistance. The AES is kept current with software upgrades that allow for the incorporation of new phenotypes and resistance mechanisms and the expected distribution of MICs can be modified, as new information becomes available, to insure the detection of known resistance mechanisms if the MIC changes over time. Unlike other expert systems, AES validates all results by assigning them to a known phenotype. This allows users to configure the VITEK 2 as they deem appropriate; for example, a laboratory may choose to "auto-release" those results that AES has found to be fully consistent with a known phenotype. This insures results are released to clinicians in the shortest possible time frame.

VITEK 1 and VITEK 2 therefore detect resistance, including emerging resistance, using several mechanisms. Increased range of dilutions allows for the detection of creeping resistance. Software is used for the generation of antibiograms and MIC trending reports. Expert systems, including the second generation Advanced Expert System, validate results in addition to assigning a phenotype with associated resistance mechanisms to each organism isolated in the laboratory.

The Hospital Pharmacy Information System (HPS) tracks patient demographics, laboratory results and current antimicrobial therapies.

An Electronic Database such as TSN (The Surveillance Network) has accumulated susceptibility and identification statistics from individual institutions and globally to produce resistance statistics. The TSN Database–USA, initiated in 1994 by Focus Technologies, Inc. (formerly MRL, Herndon, Virginia), is a queriable real-time database that electronically assimilates antimicrobial susceptibility testing data and patient demographic data from a network of 270 accredited hospitals in the United States. A laboratory's inclusion in TSN is based on factors such as hospital bed size, patient population, geographic location, and antimicrobial susceptibility testing methods employed. Susceptibility testing of patient isolates is conducted on-site by each participating laboratory as a part of their routine diagnostic testing.[21]

7.3.3.2 What Information?

Specific Infection Control team report parameter needs are delineated in available database fields located in the LIS or ID/AST instrument software. Once team needs are well in hand, the best place to discover data availability is in the LIS or HIS. The available information fields will restrict or enhance data accessibility. The field contains an information packet that identifies a data group or searchable statistic. See the sample with identified fields below.

Collection Date	Specimen Number	Source	Organism	Organism Code	Antibiotic Tested	Susceptibility Code	Result (μg/mL)	Interpretation

This table contains the information accessible to the technologist for data mining.[1] Coding is utilized to prevent transcription inconsistencies with data entered by various individuals.[2]

Next, assess the field information availability. The fields of information may be available but not currently defined or in use. The institution information services contact will address the implementation of needed fields or packets of information to provide team required statistics. An example of this follows: the LIS has a field for patient location, but that particular field is turned off or not in use. The LIS manager may be able to work with the team needs to make that information accessible.

7.3.4 POST-ANALYTIC — RETRIEVING DATA, COMPILATION, AND PRESENTATION

(See checklist for Implementing an Antibiogram, Table 7.6, Part C.)

7.3.4.1 Antibiogram Type

Laboratories historically have created a yearly single dimension cumulative antibiogram for the institution. In the mid-1980's, patient types and specialization expanded, thus it became apparent that institutions needed to unmask potentially infrequent but significant resistant phenotypes and subset the population. Thus, focused antibiograms started to emerge with the number of subsets reflective of the specialization, size and educational commitment of the institutions. This culminated in the organization of two distinct types of focused antibiograms: a) those that deal with the patient management and selection of antimicrobial therapy and b) those that deal with hospital pharmacy and infection control management, where issues of the epidemiology and the evaluation and tracking of selected resistant phenotypes unique to that institution are followed. In describing the options available, a template is created that allows an institution to design and generate, in advance, those sort-parameters for patient management or hospital management to routinely track the antibiotic signatures in their institution.

7.3.4.1.1 Patient Management (Templates)

Specialty organisms: The "other" Microbes, Mycobacteria, Yeast/Moulds
Hospital Pharmacy/Infection Control management by source, service, and by Profession,
    i.e.(School of Dentistry)
Microbial Phenotypic tracking
Hospital epidemiology
Traditional bug/drug format Total vs. Focused and non—traditional format
Specific Example/Recommendations

7.3.4.2 Presentation

Hospital susceptibility/resistance data can be maximized by the method of presentation. Historically, these were tables that listed the focused antibiotic and organism data. Today, aided with software programs, one can maximize the targeted organism antibiotic combinations and measure selected changes visually by expressing data in a variety of manners. Hence, some data is best presented as a bar graph, some as a pie chart and some as percentages, recognizing the statistical validity of the data.

Recently, advances have also been made so that individuals may present both a graphic presentation with an overall signature and the data that corresponds to that in the same table.

7.3.4.2.1 Chart Types
- Bar graph
- Pie chart
- Tabular
- Scientific Examples/Recommendations by organism

7.3.4.2.2 Chart Presentation

As greater susceptibility/resistance data is available and our access to software analysis becomes more convenient, the options grow in presenting these data. Traditional antibiograms including focused, demonstrate time honored formats. However, non-traditional antibiograms are emerging, including susceptibility profiles based on patient disease/DRG, antibiotics organized by mode of action rather than by class, and combinations of bugs/drugs that represent the seven most frequent combinations in the institutions and their total median resistance plotted over years, i.e. tracking the "institution profile."

- Traditional% (Table 7.7)
- Non-traditional (Table 7.8) — Composite of X-microbiology, Y-pharmacy, and Z-costs as a guide. These are usually syndrom focused.

TABLE 7.7
Traditional Data Compilation, Analysis, and Presentation

A. Single Dimension Antibiogram
(Percent resistance or susceptibility): Tracking or preventative surveillance

B. Hospital or community location
IP/OP/hospital location

C. Specimen source
Urine versus non-urine or blood only

D. MIC_{50}/MIC_{90} (selected isolates)

E. Floating 6-month "window"

F. Date of admission
<3 days—community acquired
≥4 days—Nosocomial

G. Organism
S. pneunomiae
MRSA/MRSE
VRE
ESBL
VISA/VRSA
SA: Clindamycin/Eyrthromycin

TABLE 7.8
Nontraditional Data Compilation, Analysis, and Presentation

A. Nonsusceptible histogram (see example)
    (Isolates grouped by mechanisms of resistance)
B. Cumulative Distribution of MICs (see example)
    (Area under the curve)
C. Cross-resistance graphs (MDR = selected phenotypes) (see examples)
    (Positive correlation of selective pressures)
D. Cost per pharmaceutical
    1. Total $/24 hrs
    2. X-Factor, i.e., compared to one common, cheapest drug, i.e.,
       Fraction = antibiotic X ($)/cefazolin ($) cheapest
    3. Rank by cost ($) within a class of antibiotics
    4. Antibiotic usage
       a. Plot R isolates vs. antibiotic usage
       b. Grams of antibiotics per patient day (G/PPD)
E. Tetracycline/erythromycin resistance for representative organisms of various culture sites, e.g., blood, urine, stool,
       respiratory, skin
F. Incidence/disease state (DRG — outcome management)
    (Pulmonary or wound)
G. Trending over time (composite)
    1. Top seven microbes/year and top seven drugs/year
    2. 4 + 1 years comparison (5 years total)
H. Drug comparator (subset): four-quad analysis
I. State antibiogram by geographic regions
J. Comparison of global, national, regional, and institutional data
K. Disease state (clinical antibiogram)
       1. Pulmonary (VAP)
       2. Wound, deep (SICU)
       3. Gastrointestinal tract (GIT)
       4. Skin and soft tissue infections (SSI)
       5. Indwelling medical devices (IMD)

7.3.4.3 Levels of Monitoring

West Virginia University (WVU) provides six levels of monitoring susceptibility programs as described below, usually on a yearly basis. Hospitals of varying size and diversity may need to tailor their needs (Figure 7.3). As described earlier, the primary purpose of antibiograms is five-fold:

1. Provide guidance in selecting empiric therapy.
2. Measure trends in antibiotic resistance patterns.
3. Complement epidemiologic investigations.
4. Satisfy regulatory agencies.
5. Guide hospital formulary discussions.

7.3.4.3.1 Level I

A *generalized antibiogram* illustrates the composite antibiotic susceptibility signature of the entire in-patient population. This does not separate organism-antibiotic combinations by age, hospital service and/or clinics. This establishes a base-line database and allows for generalized trend analysis over a period of time. This is the more traditional manner of summarizing susceptibility data.

Antibiogram Level	Bed Size			Institution Diversity
	≤ 200	200-400	>400	Teaching/University Center
1	+	+	+	+
2		+	+	+
3		+	+	+
4			+	+
5			+	+
6			+	+

FIGURE 7.3 Design of antibiogram complexity versus hospital type.

7.3.4.3.2 Level 2

Recently, *focused antibiograms* have become the method of choice for measuring small changes in susceptibility patterns that may be masked in the "Generalized Antibiogram."[23] In the Focused Antibiogram, selected age groups, clinical presentations, i.e. cystic fibrosis and hospital locations such as ICUs, are separated from the generalized data and "focused" upon for selected bug-drug combinations. It has been found that these reveal hidden trends that may not be evident in the Generalized Format; of particular focus are the ICUs, where concentrated use of cephalosporins is encountered.

7.3.4.3.3 Level 3

Fungal (yeast) susceptibility data is tracked in two ways: 1) MIC distribution for the 6 most common yeast and 2) a yeast Histogram.

7.3.4.3.3.1 Anaerobic Bacteria, Mycobacteria, Virus and Unusual, Fastidious Organisms Susceptibility Profiles

For anaerobic bacteria established national susceptibility profiles have been generated. The CDC does not recommend routine susceptibility testing; in mixed anaerobic infections or for single anaerobic isolates, published guidelines should be used in selecting antimicrobial therapy. However, due to growing resistance, some laboratories assay anaerobes as a "batch," usually once a month.

7.3.4.3.4 Level 4

7.3.4.3.4.1 Miscellaneous Susceptibility Data

The microbiology laboratory sends significant clinical isolates to national reference laboratories for susceptibility testing not routinely performed. These results are collated annually and are available via consultation with the Medical Director. These include mycobacteria, virus, and unusual or fastidious isolates.

7.3.4.3.5 Level 5

7.3.4.3.5.1 Predictable (Established) Susceptibility Patterns; i.e., "Preventative Surveillance"

Stable bug-drug patterns over five years can be used to eliminate routine susceptibility testing, as an example, outpatient urines.

7.3.4.3.6 Level 6

Lastly, by computer analysis, all sensitivities are compared daily to the established patterns or predictable norms of previous isolates via the antibiograms over the past three years. Unusual patterns are highlighted and/or discussed with the attending physician as appropriate on a case/case basis.

7.3.4.4 Examples of Data Compilation

See Figure 7.4.

7.3.4.4.1 Comparative National Data: Surveillance

The use of electronic surveillance and national databases has increased dramatically over the last ten years. There presently are several national databases that allow the participating institutions to download their data on a daily basis and to analyze it in real time. Depending on the national database and its sophistication there is also the potential of searching that database by a variety of parameters in real time. A number of these are described. In addition to the analysis, the real time availability allows for integration of this database into the workflow of both the laboratory and patient management in clinical rounds. This is highlighted (Figure 7.4) describing the partnering of microbiology data, pharmacy data and clinical needs during rounding with medical staff. Further, this database allows one to establish on a routine basis analysis of information provided by the source. Hence, templates can be created and information requested on a routine timely basis as defined by the user.

7.3.4.4.2 Generalized — Electronic, Real Time-International, National, Regional

TSN — Personalized — Multiple Sort Parameters
(Computer Screen/Selection)

7.3.4.4.3 Focused — Retrospective

In contrast to national electronic databases, information can be obtained via participation in national surveys. There are a number of these and they have unique features, recognizing they are static and that their implementation or changing of antibiotic therapy is done based on a yearly summation, not on a daily basis as is the national electronic database. These are dependent on users and their participation in these studies.

- ISS – Merck: ICU gram-negative rods
- SMART – University of Iowa: BSI
- TRUST – Ortho McNiel: URI

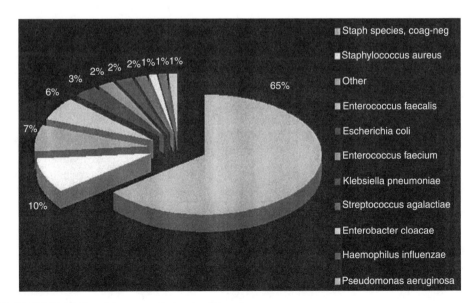

FIGURE 7.4 Example of data compilation (traditional).

7.3.4.5 Electronic Data Collection Devices

Real time use of electronically acquired antibiotic data has been generally tethered to a desktop computer. Recently, with the advance of PDRs (Personal Data Resource), information is available dependent upon network connection/availability. This clearly will have tremendous expansion potential and in the future may present the most realistic mode of acquiring national data, analyzing it and having a return of these data to the user in a real time scenario.

7.4 IMPLEMENTATION/INFORMATION MANAGEMENT/UNLOCKING DATA/MICROECONOMICS

Data is power. As the availability and utilization of susceptibility data grows, its uses, in heretofore-unrecognized scenarios, also grows. This is particularly true in the economic environment that we are presently involved with. It is necessary to routinely run susceptibility patterns on outpatient urine cultures for organisms that have established and stable susceptibility patterns over five years. Can one use a database management that allows for tracking of patterns and predictions based on the stability of those patterns over time? The answer would appear to be yes, given that there is some way of sampling a significant portion to routinely monitor the potential of changes without doing all patients at all times. Antibiograms and the information they provide is an empowerment for the microbiologist. The information held in the antibiograms is unfathomable. Yet its application and its daily use have been very restricted. This should not continue. With the increasing use of electronic surveillance and the availability of immediate recall, antibiograms will be a means by which a laboratory can further prove its value, and to document benefit to patient care via shortening of length of stay and reduced hospitalization costs, i.e. outcomes (Figure 7.5).

Recognizing the importance of Cumulative Antibiograms for Clinical Microbiology, the CLSI in May of 2002, approved guidelines for the tabulation of susceptibility data and provided a second edition in 2006 (Analysis and Prevention of Cumulative Susceptibility Test Data; Approved Guidelines-2nd Edition). This guideline is a consensus document and clearly has as a focus, standardization for hospital reporting. It has both "pros" and "cons" depending upon the institution's previous attempts. One of the major issues discussed during the document development was whether "resistance" or "susceptibility" should be reported. Ultimately, history prevailed, recognizing that most physicians and users have long been accustomed to the term "susceptible". The CLSI standard has

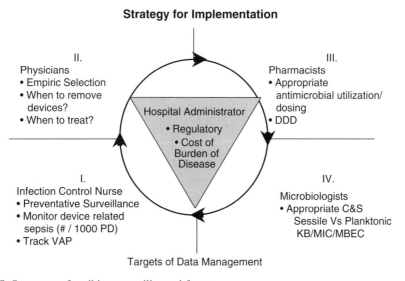

FIGURE 7.5 Summary of antibiogram utility and focus.

several points that need to be considered when producing a Cumulative Antibiogram. The report should be prepared annually. It should establish Susceptible (S) isolates only, not including Intermediate (I) isolates. It should include results from the first isolate of a given species encountered by a patient. It should exclude surveillance isolates, and it should report results for all drugs tested that are appropriate for the species, however, one should not report supplemental drugs that are selectively tested on resistant isolates only. It also clearly defines how frequently repeat isolates from the same patient should be tabulated. Most importantly, a statistical analysis section was added, which focused on the number of isolates needed to define a standard deviation. This was emphasized in "tables," which demonstrated, based on the number of isolates, the range that in fact was represented by that susceptibility result of the institution (see Figure 7.5).

Unfortunately a large proportion of hospitals do not have the capacity to sort by all of these parameters. It is important to note that in our experience, the "first isolates" susceptibilities versus the "total isolates" susceptibilities, including removing duplicated isolates, results in a difference of about 5%.

To facilitate the improved utilization of this incredible data, we have included several options that will guide the user in correctly implementing the steps necessary for accurate and timely antibiotic data (Table 7.6).

7.4.1 TIER I

- Focused Antibiogram: Organism Prevalence ICU
- Focused Antibiogram: % Susceptible ICU
- Relative Resistance
- Relative Resistance Prevalence by Resistance Type
- Trending: Over/Under Analysis

The most frequently used antibiograms are cumulative summaries (usually a year) and have been discussed in detail up to this point. However, with increased resistance of selected patient types and the diversification of hospital organization with "cohorting" by age, disease type and subspecialties, total cumulative antibiograms have limited application. Hence, a number of newer applications of antibiotic data are presented here, focusing particularly on those institutions that are larger than 400-bed and/or teaching and university centers.

The first is a "focused" antibiogram. Antibiotic resistance is sorted by selected parameters, generally the hospital service area, age of the patient, organism, and/or specimen source, i.e. bloods, urines, and respiratory. Focused antibiograms can be tailored to the most prevalent organisms within that service area, and have the advantage of highlighting low frequency resistant phenotypes which may be unrecognized in a standard cumulative antibiogram. Two examples presented here are focused antibiograms for the ICU, which list first, the prevalence within that subset and secondly, the susceptibility of those selected organisms to antimicrobials that would be most useful in dealing with infections in those areas.

The second emerging modification is that of the "Relative Resistant" antibiogram. "Relative Resistance" is based on selected phenotypes and rather than establishing the percent of that individual phenotype, tabulates the percent of that resistant phenotype against the other selected resistant phenotypes (i.e. non-susceptible isolated only); hence, the percentage plot represents a true indication of the frequency of that resistance phenotype within the population tested. This clearly unmasks the most prevalent resistance and can be subset according to hospital location, organism type, age, etc.

Table 7.9 describes Relative Resistance based on eleven important phenotypes and underscores the importance of the frequency of the individual isolate relative to the frequency of all key non-susceptible isolates. Figure 7.6 plots the relative resistance as a visual presentation.

TABLE 7.9
Relative Resistance

Rank	Resistance Type	Total N	N Res	%R	Relative resistance %
1	MRCNS	4,928	3,597	73.0%	62.4
2	MRSA	2,915	1,031	35.4%	17.9
3	CIPRO Res *P. aeruginosa*	1,348	372	27.6%	6.5
4	GENT Res *P. aeruginosa*	1,739	263	15.1%	4.6
5	VAN Res *E. faecium*	273	164	60.1%	2.8
6	IMP Res *P. aeruginosa*	1,339	152	11.4%	2.6
7	CIPRO Res *E. coli*	6,825	71	1.0%	1.2
8	PEN Res *S. pneumoniae*	243	67	27.6%	1.2
9	CAZ Res *K. pneumoniae*	475	43	9.1%	0.7
10	CRO Res *E. coli*	4,916	2	0.0%	0.0
11	LEVO Res *S. pneumoniae*	3	0	0.0%	0.0
		25,004	5,762		37.6

The Relative Resistance is calculated as the % of each resistant phenotype as part of all non-susceptible isolates only. It is a true indicator of the impact of that isolate on the patient population.

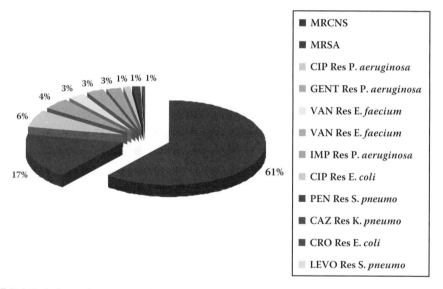

FIGURE 7.6 Relative resistance prevalence.

Another way of demonstrating the change in relative resistance is to plot the selected non-susceptible isolates phenotypes by year (Figure 7.7) and combine this by an "over/under" change as shown in Figure 7.8. Here, a comparison demonstrates that methicillin-resistant CNS decreased in the time period evaluated, whereas gentamicin resistance and imipenem non-susceptible/resistance increased significantly. This idea of trending using the "over/under" analysis is key for selected areas, particularly where cyclical use of antimicrobials may be apparent, as in the ICU; the antibiogram data is focused on a particular service area, with a particular antibiotic, and a particular organism.

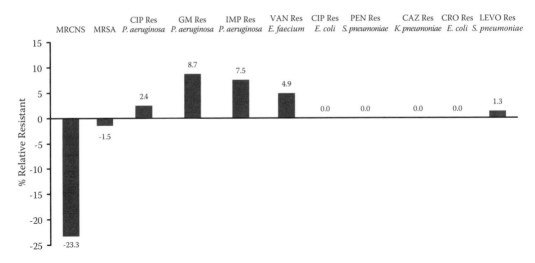

FIGURE 7.7 ICU relative resistance change. Comparing selected non-susceptible isolates (resistant bug-drug phenotypes) for two time periods (2 years apart) for a selected hospital location: ICU.

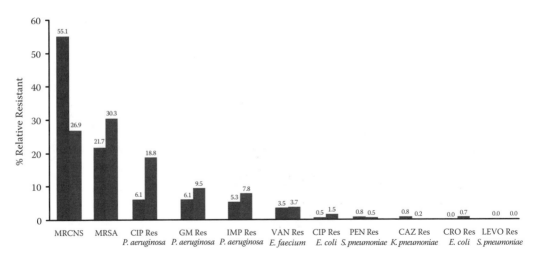

FIGURE 7.8 ICU relative resistance comparison. Plotting (over-under) the % change (increase up or positive; decrease down or negative) of Relative Resistance for the ICU over 2 years. This was used to formulate a resistive formulary in the ICU and implementation of a heterologus or cyclical use of selected antibiotics.

7.4.2 Tier II

- Cumulative Presentation (Figure 7.9)
- Cumulative MIC
- Cumulative Resistance by Mechanism of Resistance
- Cumulative Antibiogram: Cross Resistance

Here the cumulative presentation over a selected period of time, usually a year, may be sorted by a selected characteristic of the antibiotic, particularly emphasizing its mechanisms of resistance. Three examples are shown. First, Cumulative Distribution of MICs tabulates the percent of susceptibility associated with an increasing concentration of the anti-infective. Generally, the organism in the upper left hand corner is more efficacious and is less efficacious as one moves from the upper left to the lower right in the graph.

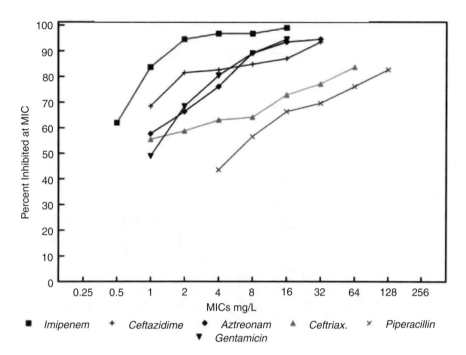

FIGURE 7.9 Cumulative distribution of MICs. Plotting the % susceptible isolates of ascending concentration for each antibiotic (0.25–256 μg/mL). For each antibiotic the MIC$_{50}$ and MIC$_{90}$ can be calculated within a semiquantitative category (S, I, R) or class comparison.

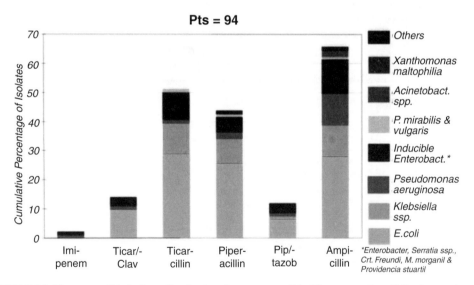

FIGURE 7.10 Nonsusceptible isolates distribution. A non-susceptible Histogram where % Resistance is sorted by mechanism of resistance for selected organisms representing that mechanism. Organisms can be grouped by similar mechanism.

Cumulative "Mechanism of Resistance" is a unique and uncommon presentation: it does however have unique links. The mechanism of resistance is generally defined by the organisms themselves, so that antibiotics with similar mechanisms via selected phenotypes are graphed together (Figure 7.10). This is often referred to as non-susceptible isolate distribution, because the organisms that are plotted are non-susceptible or resistant isolates only.

A unique amplification of mechanisms of resistance is shown in Figure 7.11, which describes the mechanism of resistance, but compared by years. Here, selected non-susceptible isolates are grouped by mechanism of resistance, and changes over time are clearly highlighted.

Cumulative anitbiograms separated by cross-resistance are shown in Figure 7.12. The focus of this antibiogram is multidrug cross-resistance and determines that if a singular phenotype or a

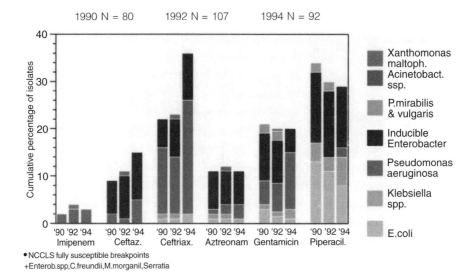

FIGURE 7.11 Resistance distribution by major species group. Tracing by two-year intervals the non-susceptible isolates, grouped by mechanism of action, to selected antibiotics. This highlights the selective pressure of or developing resistance of common pathways.

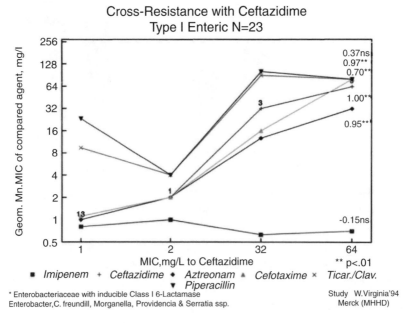

FIGURE 7.12 Cross-resistance with Ceftazidime Type I. The Cross-Resistance Graph emphasizes the MDR problem and potential simultaneous resistance of one drug with other drugs. Here, as ceftazidime resistance increased (higher MIC), a simultaneous increase in MICs was recorded for each other antibiotic, except imipenem

particular antibiotic combination is associated with a simultaneous increase in resistance for another antibiotic.

Shown are the data for ceftazidime MICs, which when measured with other antibiotics, remain stable only for imipenem; all other antibiotics show increasing MIC with higher ceftazidime MICs.

7.4.3 TIER III

- Pharmaconomics (X, Y, Z)
- CAG: Comprehensive Antimicrobial Guide, Integration of % Susceptible, Empiric Selection, and Economics (X, Y, Z)
- Syndrome Approach (X, Y, Z)

Tier 3 represents the amalgamation of the various components involved in patient care and burden of disease. It is an attempt to integrate data from microbiology (represented by X), pharmacy (represented by Y), and cost (represented by Z). One way of integrating data and linking these three features is shown in Figure 7.13, the PharmacoEconomic Form. In cascade fashion, one addresses a susceptibility breakpoint quotient (SBPQ), a serum-inhibitory quotient (SIQ), and finally a cost code, recognizing a 24-hour cost divided by the SIQ. By using the E test, one may illustrate for comparative strips, the antibiotic MIC breakpoint and the zone of inhibition (MIC).

Data are shown prominently in the Comprehensive Antimicrobial Guide shown in Figure 7.14. Here antimicrobials are ranked in efficacy (1–3), based on the features of microbiology susceptibility data, pharmacologics of the antimicrobial, and the cost per 24 hours by the P&T Committee. It avoids the problems of antibiotic percentage comparisons, given that an antibiogram with cumulative percentages only, represents one feature of the three parts. Number 1 is the preferred drug of the institution, number 2 is good coverage, and number 3 is alternative with R representing significant resistance emerging (5-10% change/year).

Figure 7.15 is another attempt at integrating the three features of X, Y and Z, often called the Syndrome Antibiogram. Here, antimicrobials are ranked as either 1) being effective or 2) less effective, but focusing on organisms associated with syndromes, with a simple cost of therapy dollars per day from pharmacy. This is particularly useful when physicians select empiric therapy based on clinical presentation matched to the frequency with which organisms appear within the institution. This can be tailored to the individual hospital, given the geographic differences are noted and reflective also of the type of institutional, its size and patient capabilities. This is a composite presentation, which is simple, but highly effective.

7.4.4 TIER IV

- Other Antibiogram Examples
  - Fungal/Yeast
  - Yeast MICs
  - Dental
- Methods of Distribution (www. etc) - at least 6 methods:
  - Card (Traditional)
  - Electronic (Intra or Internet)
  - PDA (Hand held device)
  - Booklet
  - Path Lab Manual
  - Hard copy always in Front of Patient Chart.

This outlines Antibiograms for organisms or services other than the traditional microbiology laboratory. Here, the focus has recently been on yeast susceptibilities, particularly Candida albicans

WestVirginiaUniversity.
ROBERT C. BYRD HEALTH SCIENCES CENTER

School of Medicine - Department of Pathology

PHARMACOECONOMICS FORM: Linking X, Y and Z

Code Pt_____

1. Organism:_____

2. Source:_____

3. Anti Infective:　　　_____　　　_____　　　_____

	A	B	C
X - MICROBIOLOGY			
4. NCLSI "S" Breakpoint			
5. MIC			
6. S, I, R, Category			
7. MBEC			
8. MBEC/MIC RATIO			
9. Susceptibility Breakpoint Quotient (S-BP/MIC)			
Y - PHARMACY	A	B	C
10. Serum Level (C_{MAX}) / MIC			
11. S I Q (Quotient)			
Z - COST	A	B	C
12. Cost/24 HR Quotient (Life Treating) WVUH ($)			
13. AWP ($)			
14. Cost / SIQ Quotient			
15. Ranking			

FIGURE 7.13 Pharmacoeconomics. The integration of three important factors when selecting antibiotics for hospital formulary: microbiology (X), pharmacy (Y), and costs (Z).

and the other Candida species, given that a number of antifungals are now available. There are now choices that were not available several years ago. In recognizing that most laboratories list C. albicans as one of the five most frequent blood culture isolates in blood cultures, its prevalence is clearly significant. Given that there are several FDA approved commercial antifungal assays, a fungal Antibiogram is important.

Figure 7.16 shows a Fungal Antibiogram for four antifungals: amphotericin B, fluconazole, 5FC and itraconazole. Endpoints for other and newer antifungals are still controversial and are as yet

WVUH Susceptibility Based Antibiotic Guide—All Locations—2005
(N = # of isolates)

GRAM (+) BACTERIA	AMP	NAF	CEFAZ	CFTRI	LEVO	GENT	CLIND	VANC	DOXY	LZD	T/S	SYN
Enterococcus faecalis N=465	1 (99%)	---	---	---	---	1C (69%)	---	2C (97%)	---	3 (100%)	---	---
Enterococcus faecium N=126	RC (12%)	---	---	---	---	1C (75%)	---	RC (32%)	---	1 (100%)	---	1 (97%)
S. aureus All N=787		1 (53%)	2 (53%)	---	---	3C (97%)	2 (85%)	3 (100%)	---	3 (100%)	3 (90%)	3 (100%)
S. aureus MRSA		---	---	---	---	3C (95%)	R (29%)	R (95%)	---	1 (100%)	2 (84%)	2 (100%)
Staphylococcus, coag neg N=623	Frequently a contaminant that rarely needs treatment. If needed, nafcillin first choice if sensitive; vancomycin first choice for methicillin-resistant organism.											
Streptococcus pneumoniae N=80	R (40%)	---	---	1 (91%)	2 (100%)	---	2 (76%)	2 (100%)	3 (65%)	---		

GRAM (-) BACTERIA	AMP/S	P/TZ	CEFAZ	CFTAZ	CFTRI	CEFEP	IMIP	CIPRO	LEVO	GENT/TOB	AMK	AZTR	T/S
Enterobacter aerogenes N=76	---	2 (90%)	---	R (85%)	2C (87%)	3 (99%)	3 (100%)	3 (98%)	3 (99%)	2C (95%)	---	2 (90%)	1 (97%)
Enterobacter cloacae N=149	---	2 (69%)	---	R (87%)	2C (88%)	3 (99%)	3 (100%)	R (84%)	R (85%)	2C (87%)	2C (100%)	R (85%)	1 (84%)
Escherichia coli N=1584	2 (69%)	---	2 (91%)	3 (96%)	3 (98%)	3 (99%)	---	3 (90%)	3 (91%)	1C (95%)	2C (100%)	2 (98%)	1 (84%)
Klebsiella pneumoniae N=367	1 (86%)	---	2 (94%)	3 (96%)	3 (97%)	---	---	---	---	2C (96%)	2C (100%)	2 (97%)	1 (95%)
Proteus mirabilis N=213	1 (92%)	---	2 (91%)	3 (98%)	3 (99%)	---	---	R (59%)	R (71%)	2C (95%)	2C (100%)	2 (98%)	2 (73%)
Pseudomonas aeruginosa N=318?	---	1 (97%)	---	3 (86%)	---	2 (91%)	3 (85%)	R (76%)	R (70%)	G-1C (86%) T-1C (91%)	1C (92%)	2C (69%)	---
Serratia marcescens N=71	---	1 (100%)	---	2 (94%)	1 (96%)	2 (100%)	3 (100%)	---	---	G-2C (83%) T-2C (76%)	2C (100%)	2C (94%)	---
Stenotrophomonas malto. N=56	---	2 (48%) *TC	---	3C (38%)	---	---	---	---	---	---	---	---	1 (93%)

KEY: **1** - WVUH Preferred Choice   **2** - Good Choice   **3** - Alternative or Covering Drug   **R** - Resistance Emerging   **c** - Use Combination Therapy
— Not Routinely Tested or Recommended   **%** - Percent Sensitive   **T/S** -trimethoprim/sulfamethoxazole   ***TC** -Ticarcillin with clavulanic acid

See *Rubyonline for specific data (choose Departments; Pharmacy; References; Antimicrobial Susceptibilities)*

FIGURE 7.14 Susceptibility-based antibiotic guide. Implementation of the X-Y-Z factors into a useable resource. On this CAG (Comprehensive Antibiotic Guide) card (not shown) are listed cost comparisons, empiric selection by source/bug/symptoms segregated by adult and pediatric concentrations.

	Penicillins						Cephalosporins															
	Penicillin	Nafcillin	Ampicillin	Unasyn	Mezlocillin/Piperacillin	Timentin	Ancel, Keflzol	Zinacef	Cefobid	Claforan	Fortaz	Rocephin	Azactam	Primaxin	Clindamycin	Ciprofloxacin	Erythromycin	Tetracycline	Gentamicin/Tobramycin	Bactrim/Septra	Vancomycin	Flagyl
Streptococcus	●	●	●	●	●	●	○	○	○	○		○		●	○		●					○
S. aureus		●	○		●	●	●	○	○			○		●	○	○		○	○	○		●
S. epidemidis		○				○	○															●
Enterococcus			●	●	●									●		○						
H. influenzae			●			●			●	●	●	●	●	●		●			●			
E. coli et al			●	●	●	●	●	●	●	●	●	●	●	●		●			●	●		
Pseudomonas spp.			●	●			●		●		○	●		●								
Bacteroides et al			●	○	●			○				●	●									●
Cost of Therapy ($/day)	33	42	36	56	66	63	21	33	32	39	48	30	64	88	28	60	28	23	38	24	41	28

Legend: Effective ○   Most Effective ●

Syndromes:

Acute sinusitis	Pneumococcus H. influenzae Occasional Staphylococcus	UTI: Community acquired	E. coli et al Proteus
Community adquired pneumonia	Pneumococcus H. influenzae Occasional Staphylococcus E. coli et al	Nosocomial Soft tissue infections	E. coli, Enterococcus Pseudomonas Streptococcus, Staphylococcus occasional E. coli et al
Nosocomial pneumonia	E. coli et al Pseudomonas Staphylococcus	Diabetic/decubital ulcers	Staphylococcus, E coli et al Bacteroides et al (usually polymicrobial)
Biliary infection	E. coli et al Pseudomonas Enterococcus	CNS infections	Meningococcus Pneumococcus H. influenzae
Intraabdominal infection	E. coli et al Bacteroides et al	Endocarditis	Streptococcus, Staphylococcus, Enterococcus
		Bone infection	Staphylococcus occasional GNR

FIGURE 7.15 Syndrome approach. A simplified CAG Card, still highlighting X-Y-Z, but emphasizing syndrome until selected bacteria.

unrecognized, but clearly for the laboratory, measuring an MIC and tracking it is equally as important, given the cost of the various antifungals available. Between the first generation antifungals and the more recent third generation, a cost difference over a hundred fold is not unusual.

The next two figures (Figuress 7.17 and 7.18) list Candida MIC data. A cumulative plot of the MICs for C. albicans and C. galabrata is highlighted, recognizing the considerable concern about the development of resistance and/or intrinsic resistance in question.

Figure 7.19 shows the importance of fungal susceptibility, highlighting an algorithm and the use of PNA-FISH technology to rapidly recognize and detect C. albicans in blood cultures.

Organism		mp B	Fluc	5FC	Itra
Candida albicans	Total Tested	285	287	282	278
	Sus n	283	277	278	256
	Sus %	99%	97%	99%	92%
	S-DD%	0%	2%	1%	5%
	Res %	1%	2%	0%	3%
Candida dubliniensis	Total Tested	4	4	4	4
	Sus n	4	4	4	4
	Sus %	100%	100%	100%	100%
	S-DD%	0%	0%	0%	0%
	Res %	0%	0%	0%	0%
Candida glabrata	Total Tested	100	100	100	98
	Sus n	100	10	98	2
	Sus %	100%	10%	98%	2%
	S-DD%	0%	72%	0%	13%
	Res %	0%	18%	2%	85%
Candida krusei	Total Tested	6	6	6	6
	Sus n	6	1	5	1
	Sus %	100%	17%	83%	17%
	S-DD%	0%	0%	17%	33%
	Res %	0%	83%	0%	50%
Candida lusitaniae	Total Tested	4	4	4	4
	Sus n	4	4	4	2
	Sus %	100%	100%	100%	50%
	S-DD%	0%	0%	0%	50%
	Res %	0%	0%	0%	0%
Candida parapsilosis	Total Tested	59	59	58	59
	Sus n	59	56	58	31
	Sus %	100%	95%	100%	53%
	S-DD%	0%	5%	0%	46%
	Res %	0%	0%	0%	2%
Candida species	Total Tested	2	2	2	2
	Sus n	2	2	2	2
	Sus %	100%	100%	100%	100%
	S-DD%	0%	0%	0%	0%
	Res %	0%	0%	0%	0%
Candida tropicalis	Total Tested	42	43	43	43
	Sus n	43	39	35	16
	Sus %	100%	91%	81%	37%
	S-DD%	0%	9%	0%	58%
	Res %	0%	0%	19%	5%
Cryptococcus neoformans	otal Tested	13	13	13	13
	Sus n	13	13	12	13
	Sus %	100%	100%	92%	100%
	S-DD%	0%	0%	8%	0%
	Res %	0%	0%	0%	0%

FUNGAL ANTIBIOGRAM INTERPRETATION

		INTERPRETATION		
ANTIFUNGAL	MIC	S	SDD*	R
Amphotericin B	μ/ml	≤2	None	>2
5-FC	μ/ml	≤4	8-16	≥32
Fluconazole	μ/ml	≤8	16-32	≥64
Itraconazole	μ/ml	≤0.125	0.25-0.5	≥1
SSD* - Susceptible, but Dose Dependent				

FIGURE 7.16 Fungal antibiogram.

Here based on the antibiograms for yeast, an algorithm has been described which incorporates two parameters: rapid molecular methodology and previous history of resistance within the institution.

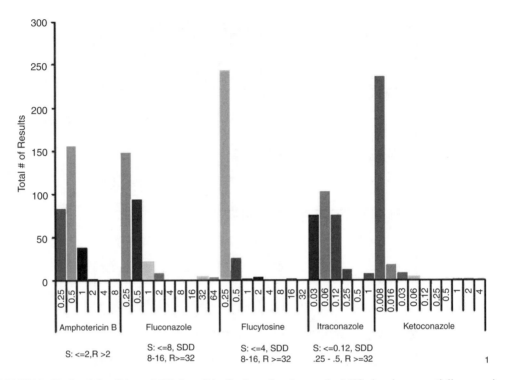

FIGURE 7.17 *Candida albicans* MIC data. Distribution of resistance by MIC showing essentially no resistance for all antifungals.

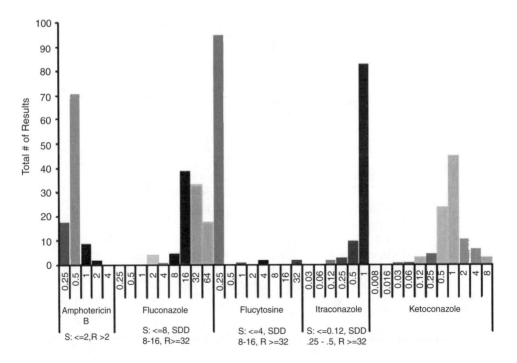

FIGURE 7.18 *Candida glabrata* MIC data. Distribution of resistance by MIC showing essentially no resistance for all antifungals, except significant resistance for fluconazole, itraconazole, and ketoconazole.

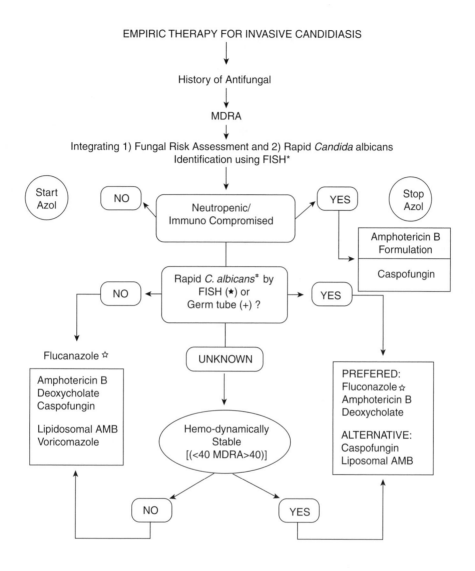

EMPIRIC THERAPY FOR INVASIVE CANDIDIASIS

History of Antifungal

MDRA

Integrating 1) Fungal Risk Assessment and 2) Rapid *Candida* albicans
Identification using FISH*

Start Azol — NO — Neutropenic/ Immuno Compromised — YES — Stop Azol

Amphotericin B Formulation

Caspofungin

NO — Rapid *C. albicans*⁺ by FISH (★) or Germ tube (+) ? — YES

Flucanazole ☆

Amphotericin B
Deoxycholate
Caspofungin

Lipidosomal AMB
Voricomazole

UNKNOWN

PREFERED:
Fluconazole ☆
Amphotericin B
Deoxycholate

ALTERNATIVE:
Caspofungin
Liposomal AMB

Hemo-dynamically
Stable
[(<40 MDRA>40)]

NO   YES

* Candida albicans colonization isolated from: Urine, Tracheal Aspirates, BAL, etc.
★ Fluorescence In situ Hybridization.
☆ Modified by Candida MIC's

FIGURE 7.19 Empiric therapy for invasive candida. An algorithm of treatment integrating antifungal MICs and molecular detection of blood isolates.

Figure 7.20 lists a cumulative antibiogram for isolates recovered in the Oralfacial Microbiological laboratory (Dental) at West Virginia University Hospitals (WVUH). There is growing awareness of the oral-systemic link and of the need for persistent infections to be eradicated by selective therapy. Here the organisms listed are frequent periopathogens, with antibiotics used by the dental community, evaluated using the E-test MIC. The method of Relative Resistance has been utilized for dental isolates and has recently shown that the most frequent resistant phenotype, is ciprofloxacin-resistant gram-negative rods.

Organism	Total n	AMP	CIP	CC	DOX	ERY	MET
Acinobacillus		29%	94%	6%	71%	6%	6%
(n)	17	5	16	1	12	1	1
Bacteroides forsythus		100%	75%	100%	100%	63%	25%
(n)	8	8	6	8	8	5	2
Campylobacter rectus		86%	68%	86%	95%	70%	90%
(n)	79	68	54	68	75	55	71
Campylobacter species		100%	100%	100%	100%	67%	100%
(n)	3	3	3	3	3	2	3
Eikenella corrodens		63%	100%		95%		14%
(n)	93	59	93		88		13
Fusobacterium necrophorum		100%	100%		100%		100%
(n)	1	1	1		1		1
Fusobacterium nucleatum		93%	33%	100%	100%		93%
(n)	27	25	9	27	27		25
Porphyromonas gingivalis		89%	100%	100%	100%	100%	100%
(n)	9	8	9	9	9	9	9
Prevotella intermedia		63%	89%	89%	84%	89%	84%
(n)	19	12	17	17	16	17	16
Prevotella species		78%	44%	89%	89%	78%	56%
(n)	9	7	4	8	8	7	5

FIGURE 7.20 Dental antibiogram. Antibiogram from periodontal isolates detected in the West Virginia Oral-Facial Microbiology Laboratory.

7.5 LIMITATIONS OF DATA, DATA ANALYSIS, AND DATA PRESENTATION

7.5.1 ART vs. AST

The emergence and dissemination of resistance has made it imperative for laboratories to use in vitro tests that can detect resistance. The concept of Antimicrobial Resistance Testing (ART) should replace Antimicrobial Susceptibility Testing (AST). ART requires flexibility in testing systems and current AST methods are often handicapped. This is due to an over emphasis on standardization, not accounting for the diversity and complexity of resistance mechanisms.

7.5.1.1 Limitations of AST

Methods were originally developed when antibiotic resistance was low. Techniques such as disk diffusion, microdilution and rapid automated systems are suited for testing rapidly growing bacteria. They were designed for convenience, rapid turnover of clinical samples and simplification of data handling. Some of the underlying principles of these systems accounts for their limited ability to detect resistance. Because of the unstable antibiotic gradient in a disk test, zone sizes are directly influenced by inoculums and growth rates regardless of susceptibility. This makes the test only useful for screening the susceptibility of rapidly growing aerobes. Microdilution, restricted by volume and limiting nutritive capacity, tends to give false susceptible results. Rapid methods may not detect resistance because many mechanisms are not expressed within the 4-6 hour incubation period used. When using a small inoculum, a necessity in both manual and automated micro-methods, the odds of capturing resistant subpopulations are minimal.

7.5.2 Compilation and Statistical Tools

7.5.2.1 Estimating Resistance

Resistance is measured as a proportion. It is the proportion of organisms that survive a given dosage of a particular antibiotic in a specific place at a certain point in time. We will refer to that proportion as π. Neurobiology laboratories routinely test bacteria in order to establish drug specific resistances and the changes in those resistances over time.

If, in a certain laboratory, five patients are infected with XXXXX in a given month, and if one of those organisms proves resistant to a particular drug then a $1/5 = 20\%$ resistance is reported. Of course, we know that if a larger sample (hypothetically, all XXXXX bacteria) were tested, the proportion of resistant organisms would not be exactly 20%. Another way to view it is to say that value, p=20%, is just an estimate of the actual resistant proportion and that there some amount of uncertainty in the estimate. By way of notation, the sample proportion is indicated by p, in contrast with the true proportion, π.

One way in which uncertainty is expressed is through the standard error of the estimate. Roughly speaking, the standard error of an estimate is the average amount by which the estimate misses the true value (parameter) it is intended to estimate. So, if the standard error is reported to be 4%, that indicates that on average the estimate is "off" by 4%. The standard error is calculated a:

$$SE = p\,(1 - p)/n$$

where n is the sample size.

Another way in which uncertainty is expressed is accomplished by reporting a confidence interval (CI) for the true resistant proportion. A confidence interval is a statement that may take one of three different forms. The first is called a two-sided confidence interval. It is a statement like "we are 95% sure that the interval from 2.7% to 6.8% contains the true resistance". Alternatively, we may use one-sided confidence intervals that lead to statements like "we are 95% sure that resistance is less than 6.6%" or, "we are 95% sure that resistance is at least 3%". The differences in the statements stem from a desire to communicate to the audience the highest likely value of resistance, the lowest likely value of resistance, or a specific range of likely values.

The calculation of confidence intervals is relatively simple. Two-sided intervals are formed from $p + z\,(p(1 - p)/n)$ while one-sided confidence intervals are formed from the same formula using only the "+" sign. Note that the parenthesized term is just the standard error of the estimate. The confidence probability depends on the value of z. While any confidence probability may be used, 95% confidence intervals are almost universally reported. For a 95% two-sided confidence interval, the appropriate value of z is 1.96. For a one-sided interval in which in upper bound is given, $z = 1.645$. For a one-sided interval in which a lower bound is to be given, $z = -1.645$. For example, if 100 XXXXX organisms were tested and 10 of them proved resistant to a particular antibiotic at a certain dosage then, p=10/100=10%. The standard error is given by $0.1(0.9)/100 = 0.03$ so a two-sided 95% confidence interval for π is given by the interval with lower bound .10-1.96 (0.03) or about 0.04. The upper bound is $0.10 + 1.96\,(0.3) = 1.6$. And, we may say we are 95% sure that the true resistance is between 4% and 16%.

When sample sizes are such that np is less than 5, the formula for confidence intervals displayed above may give values that are less accurate than we would like. For circumstances in which np < 5 "exact" confidence interval in the form of either graphs or tables may be obtained from various sources..

Of particular interest is the question of placing bounds on a resistance when no resistant organisms have yet been found. In such cases p – 0 / n. The estimated resistance is zero but it is quite clear that we cannot assert that no X organisms are resistant. In cases where n is small, the problem is particularly important since, for n = 5, if 10% of the organisms are resistant we have a

59% chance that none of our tested organisms will exhibit resistance. In this case we are interested in reporting an upper bound on the proportion of resistant organisms and the sample sizes are often, though not always, small. Suppose that after 100 tests, no organisms have been found to be resistant to a certain dosage of a given antibiotic. We would like to place an upper bound on the proportion of resistant organisms consistent with our experience. One rule of thumb is known as "three-over-n". It approximates the upper bound of a 95% confidence interval by $3/n$. In this case $3/n$ is equal to 0.03, a value that is in good agreement with the exact limit of (approximately) 0.0298 which may be gotten in a much more complex way. A slightly more accurate approximation than $3/n$ may be gotten from $3/(n+1.5)$, which, in this case, yields 0.02955665. The difference in the two approximations is only important for very small sample sizes. The difference in the two approximations is less than _ of one percent so long as $n > 30$.

7.5.2.2 Verification

It is very important to vary antibiotic susceptibility data. One means is to evaluate known bug-drug patterns and antibiotics within a class.

7.5.2.2.1 Data Verification/QA Monitor; Compare these antibiotic patterns
Comparison:

- Gentamicin vs. Tobromycin vs. Amikacin
- Sulfa vs. trimethoprine/sulfamethoxazole (TMP/SMX)
- Oxacillin vs. Cephalosporin

Also, one needs to verify one algorithm a month, as well as check and review the computer print-out.

- Verify algorithms
- Check/Review
- Computer Printout, Monthly.

7.5.2.2.2 Influence of Small Numbers/Data Bases
Also, the laboratory needs to establish criteria for:

- Selected organisms tested, only
- Reflexive testing
- Duplicates
- Low numbers
- Inaccurate Data

7.6 CONCLUSION

In 2002 CLSI issued the first definitive document for preparing and publishing an antibiogram (M-39A, Analysis and Presentation of Cumulative Antimicrobial Susceptibility Test Data; Approved Guidelines). CLSI in 2006 released the second edition of these guidelines (M39-A2 Analysis and Presentation of Cumulative Antimicrobial Susceptibility Test Data; Approved Guideline – Second Edition).

The initial document took a significant first step in standardizing laboratory prepared antibiotic data; it places significant emphasis on verification and validation. It was very specific, however, and has unique key elements: first isolate only selected sub-sets, and >10 isolate criteria. This is one more supporting document for the importance of a well-constructed antibiogram. It is our means of survival and promotion of our values. The current document contains updates to term definitions to include replacing the term "antibiogram" with "cumulative antimicrobial susceptibility test data summary." Updates also include the following areas: Antimicrobial susceptibility test results, Data inclusion/exclusion, Calculations, Reports, Data Review/Quality Assurance and Statistical significance of changes in %S .

7.7 ACKNOWLEDGEMENTS

Ron Masters, MRL/TSN (Focus Technologies, Herndon, VA)

Jerry Hobbs, Associate Professor, West Virginia University, Morgantown, WV

Lindsay Nakaishi, Research Assistant, West Virginia University, Morgantown, WV

7.8 REFERENCES

TRADITIONAL

1. Stratton, CW, et al. Focused microbial surveillance by specific hospital unit as a sensitive means of defining antimicrobial resistance problems, Diag. Microbiol. Infect. Dis., 15, 115-185, 1992.
2. Thomas, J. In search of effective bug-drug combinations, Advance Admin. Lab., 10(5), 28, May 2001.
3. Weinstein, R. Controlling antimicrobial resistance in hospital, infection control and use of antibiotics, Emergin Infec. Dis., 7(2), Special Issue, 2001.
4. Mosser, SA. Antibiograms: Transforming data into knowledge, Clin. Microbiol Newsl., 22(1), 5, 2000.
5. Fradkin, S. et al. Antimicrobial resistance prevalence rates in hospital antibiograms reflect prevalence rates among pathogens associated with hospital acquired infections, Clin. Infect. Dis., 33, 324-330, Aug. 2000.
6. Chan-Tack, K. Changing antibiotic susceptibility sensitivity patterns at a university hospital 1991-1999, South Med. J., 94(6), 619, 2001.
7. Jorgenson, J. et al. Antimicrobial susceptibility testing: Special needs for fastidious organisms in difficult to detect resistant mechanisms, Clin. Infect. Dis., 30, 799, 2000.
8. Slaes, D. et al. Society for Health Care Epidemiology of America and Infectious Disease and Society of American Joint Committee on the Prevention of Antimicrobial Resistance: Guidelines for the prevention of antimicrobial resistance in hospitals. Clin. Infect. Dis., 25, 584, Sep. 1997.
9. Fradkin, S.K. et al. Antimicrobial resistance prevalence rates in hospital antibiograms reflect prevalence rates among pathogens associated with hospital-acquired infections, Clin. Infect. Dis., 33, 324-330, 2001.
10. Fradkin, S.K. et al. Surveillance of antimicrobial use and antimicrobial resistance in US hospitals: Project ICARE Phase 2, Clin. Infect. Dis., 29, 245-252, 1999.
11. Gross, R, et al. Impact of a hospital-based antimicrobial management program on clinical and economic outcomes, Clin. Infect. Dis., 33, 289-295, 2001.
12. Itokazu, G.S., et al. Antimicrobial resistance rates among aerobic gram-negative bacilli recovered from patients in ICU: Evaluations of a national post marketing surveillance program, Clin. Infect. Dis., 23, 779-784, 1996.
13. Namias, S. et al. Incidence and susceptibility of pathogenic bacteria vary between ICU within a single hospital: Implications for empiric antibiotic strategies, J. Trauma, 49, 638-646, 2000.
14. Sahm, D.F. et al. Antimicrobial resistance in key bloodstream bacterial isolates: Electronic surveillance with the Surveillance Network Database-USA, Clin,. Infect. Dis., 29, 259-263, 1999.
15. White, R.L. et al. Effect of removal of duplicate isolates of cumulative susceptibility reports, DMID, 39, 251-256, 2001.

WEB BASED

16. WVUH Microbiology Pocket Handbook, available at http://www.hsc.wvu.edu/som/microguide/. Last accessed 1/1/2007.

17. Center for Biofilm Engineering, available at www.erc.montana.edu Last accessed 1/1/2007.
18. For a discussion of TSN and MRL, see http://www.mrlworld.com/mrlworld/index.html
19. Johns Hopkins, see www.hopkins-abxguide.org Last accessed 1/1/2007.

AVAILABLE TEMPLATES

20. Templates for creating microbiology antibiogram reporta nd pharmacy antibiotic cost charts were available from Roche Laboratories, Inc., 2001.

8 Anaerobe Antimicrobial Susceptibility Testing

Darcie E. Roe-Carpenter

CONTENTS

8.1   INTRODUCTION

It has been well established for many years that anaerobic bacteria can cause medically significant infections [1]. The earliest medical writers have described the distinctive clinical features of tetanus, gas gangrene, and other anaerobic infections. With the discovery of antibiotics and the introduction of agents such as penicillin for prophylaxis and treatment, the incidence of anaerobic infections decreased. Historically, anaerobic infections were treated with antibiotics empirically, so there was little need for routine susceptibility testing. However, with the emergence of the "superbugs" that are resistant to many antimicrobial agents, it is becoming harder to predict the susceptibility of many bacterial species. Although antibiotic resistance in anaerobic bacteria has been increasing, physicians could still choose antibiotics for anaerobic infections empirically from surveillance studies reported in the literature or from data obtained in their own institutions [2]. It is presently much more difficult to predict anaerobe susceptibility patterns based on the literature. An example of this is a report of the antibiograms of anaerobic bacteria from several different hospitals within one metropolitan area. The results of this study showed that there were dramatically different antibiograms between the hospitals and that resistance was based on the use of specific agents at that institution [3].

8.2   RELEVANCE

The current Clinical and Laboratory Standards Institute (CLSI), formerly National Committee for Clinical Laboratory Standards (NCCLS), recommendations for anaerobe susceptibility testing (M11-A7) are as follows [4]. Susceptibility testing should be done to determine patterns of susceptibility or resistance for new agents. Periodic testing in individual hospitals should be done to monitor susceptibility patterns. Testing of anaerobic bacteria from a clinical sample should be done when a pathogen is recovered that is known to be resistant, when therapeutic failure has occurred with the current therapy, when appropriate therapy is critical to patient outcome, with severe infections, when long-term therapy is necessary, or when not enough information is available to make an empirical judgment about the therapy [3,4].

The first guidelines for antibiotic susceptibility testing in anaerobic bacteria were in the CLSI M11-A document, which was a proposed standard in 1979 and became an approved standard in 1985. In the M11-A document, the only procedure described is the modification of the classic agar dilution test for anaerobic bacteria [5]. Wilkins-Chalgren agar was the medium recommended for agar dilution testing in this document. Since the publication of the M11-A document, additional methods have been added: limited agar dilution, Wadsworth agar dilution, broth microdilution procedure, broth macrodilution procedure, and disk elution [6]. It was later demonstrated that the results obtained with the disk elution procedure did not correlate with the agar dilution method, and this procedure was removed from the M11 document [7]. Before the creation of the M11-A4 document, the anaerobe working group did several multicenter studies [8]. The purpose of these studies was to evaluate the best medium for susceptibility testing of a wide range of anaerobic bacteria using the agar dilution procedure. The results of these studies indicated that brucella agar, supplemented with 5% laked sheep blood, vitamin K_1, and hemin, better supports the growth of more fastidious anaerobic species compared with Wilkins-Chalgren agar. Therefore, the CLSI anaerobe working group combined the agar dilution procedure with the Wadsworth agar dilution procedure to create the new procedure that was first described in the M11-A4 document [8]. For broth microdilution, the M11-A4 document had five media formulations that could be used. In addition, these broths could be further supplemented to support the growth of fastidious anaerobic species. The CLSI anaerobe working group completed three studies to optimize the media for the microbroth dilution method, and these results were incorporated into the M11-A6 document [9]. This document lists only one media, brucella broth supplemented with lysed horse blood, hemin, and vitamin K_1, to be used with only *Bacteroides fragilis* group isolates. The CLSI anaerobe working group has made no recommendations for the microbroth dilution method with organisms outside of the *B. fragilis* group. Even though the agar dilution method is the reference method, it is usually performed in research and large clinical laboratories whereas microbroth and the Etest are the methods frequently used by typical clinical laboratories. In 2006, the CLSI anaerobe working group completed a quality control study to add ATCC 700057 *Clostridium difficile* to the approved list of quality control organisms for the agar dilution method. The quality control ranges for this new organism are listed in M11-A7 [4].

8.3 PROCEDURE

8.3.1 AGAR DILUTION — CLSI REFERENCE METHOD

8.3.1.1 Introduction

Agar dilution is the reference method that has been established by the CLSI for susceptibility testing of anaerobic bacteria. This procedure involves making a series of agar plates, each containing a specific concentration of an antimicrobial agent. With the use of a replicating device, up to 36 different isolates can be tested at one time. However, this procedure is very labor intensive and does not lend itself well to daily susceptibility testing by the typical clinical laboratory. This procedure is usually used for periodic testing to monitor resistance in anaerobic bacteria at a facility or for testing a new antimicrobial agent to determine its activity against a wide range of species. This is the gold standard to which all other methods are compared. If any other method can prove its equivalency to this method, it is acceptable for use in the clinical lab. It is not the function of the CLSI to validate every susceptibility method available, so there will always be other methods available that CLSI does not describe or discuss.

8.3.1.2 Materials

1. Media.
   a. Antibiotic sources.
      1) United States Pharmacopeia (USP).
      2) Sigma Chemical Company.
      3) The antimicrobial agent manufacturer.
         - Many antimicrobial agents can be obtained in small amounts from the drug manufacturer at no charge by request through the drug company's customer service department or equivalent department. (Consult the Physicians Desk Reference [PDR] text or your local pharmaceutical representatives for telephone numbers.)
   b. Brucella agar.
      1) Brucella agar is the only medium that should be used for the susceptibility testing of anaerobic bacteria. The media should be made according to the manufacturer's instructions (Becton Dickinson, Remel, Accumedia).
      2) The medium should be supplemented with 1 mL/L of hemin stock solution (5 mg/mL) and 1 mL/L of working vitamin K_1 stock solution (1 mg/mL) before autoclaving or dispensing.

   c. Sterile distilled water.
   d. Laked sheep blood.
     1) Sterile whole defibrinated sheep blood can be purchased from several manufacturers (Remel, PML, Hemostat, Hardy Diagnostics).
       • Sterile laked blood can be purchased from Hardy Diagnostics, PML, and Hemostat.
     2) To prepare laked blood in the laboratory from whole blood, completely freeze the whole sheep blood at –20°C overnight or longer. When the blood is thawed, the red blood cells will lyse and the blood is "laked." The thaw can be done rapidly in a 35°C–37°C water bath or incubator. The thaw can also be done slowly at 2°C–8°C overnight.
     3) Laked blood can be stored in the freezer at –20°C for up to 1 year.
       • Once thawed, laked blood has a 2½-week shelf life at 2°C–8°C and should be labeled with a new expiration date when thawed.
   e. Hemin stock solution (5 mg/mL).
     1) Weigh out 0.5 g of hemin (Sigma # H2250).
     2) Dissolve the hemin powder in 10 mL of 1 mol/L NaOH (ACS certified).
     3) Make sure that the hemin powder is completely dissolved.
       • If the water is added to the hemin solution before it is completely dissolved, the hemin will remain unsuspended.
       • If the hemin will not go into solution in NaOH, the solution can be heated to help dissolve the hemin. *This does not work if it is done after the addition of water.*
     4) Bring the volume of the solution to 100 mL with distilled water.
     5) Make sure that the solution is in a brown bottle or wrapped in foil to protect it from light. Sterilize the hemin solution at 121°C for 15 min.
     6) Cool to room temperature and store at 4°C–8°C.
     7) This solution has a 1-month shelf life and should be labeled with an expiration date when made.
     8) Add 1 mL of the hemin stock solution (5 mg/mL) to 1 L of medium.
   f. Vitamin K_1 solution (10 mg/mL).
     1) Stock solution (10 mg/mL).
      a) Add 0.2 mL of vitamin K_1 solution (3-phytylmenadione, Sigma # V3501) to 20 mL of 95% ethanol.
      b) Mix the ethanol with the vitamin K_1 solution.
      c) Place in a sterile dark bottle and store at 4°C–8°C.
      d) The solution has a 2-year shelf life and should be labeled with an expiration date when made.
       • This solution has not been sterilized; therefore, sterile technique should be used when making this solution.
       • Always inspect the solution for possible contamination before use.
       • Vitamin K_1 can be autoclaved; however, other forms of vitamin K cannot.
     2) Working solution (1 mg/mL).
      a) Add 1 mL of stock vitamin K_1 solution (10 mg/mL) to 9 mL of sterile distilled water.
      b) Place in a sterile dark bottle and store at 4°C–8°C.
      c) This solution has a 1-month shelf life and should be labeled with an expiration date when made.
      d) Add 1 mL of the *working* vitamin K_1 stock solution (1 mg/mL) to 1 L of medium.
       • This solution has not been sterilized; therefore, sterile technique should be used when preparing this solution.
       • Always inspect the solution for contamination before use.
       • Any medium can be autoclaved after the addition of the vitamin K_1.

TABLE 8.1
Antimicrobial Agent Solvents

Antimicrobial Agent	Solvent	Diluent
Amoxicillin, ticarcillin, clavulanic acid	Phosphate buffer, pH 6.0, 0.1 mol/L	Phosphate buffer, pH 6.0, 0.1 mol/L
Ampicillin	Phosphate buffer, pH 8.0, 0.1 mol/L	Phosphate buffer, pH 6.0, 0.1 mol/L
Cefotetan[a]	DMSO[b]	Sterile distilled water
Chloramphenicol	95% ethanol	Sterile distilled water
Metronidazole, opt 80 and tinidazole	DMSO	Sterile distilled water
Metronidazole, opt 80 and tinidazole	DMSO	Sterile distilled water
Niazoxanide and tizoxanide	DMSO	DMSO
Imipenem and Ertapenem	Phosphate buffer, pH 7.2, 0.01 mol/L	Same as solvent
Rifaximin	Methanol	Phosphate buffer, pH 7.4, 0.1 mol/L, + 0.45% SDS
Tilmicosin and tylosin	95% Ethanol	Sterile distilled water

If antibiotic is not listed in the table, the solvent and diluents are sterile distilled water.

[a] All other cephalosporins and cephamycins should be dissolved in phosphate buffer, pH 6.0, 0.1 mol/L, and all further dilutions should be done with sterile distilled water.

[b] DMSO (dimethyl sulfoxide) is potentially toxic. Consult the material safety data sheets (MSDS) available from the product manufacturer before using this material; SDS = sodium dodecyl sulfate.

    g. Brucella broth.
        1) The media should be made according to the manufacturer's instructions (Becton Dickinson, Remel, Accumedia).
        2) The media should be supplemented with 1 mL/L of hemin stock solution (5 mg/mL) and 1 mL/L of working vitamin K_1 stock solution (1 mg/mL) before autoclaving or dispensing of the media.
        3) Dispense into 1–5 mL volumes (depending on how many plates are to be inoculated) if using the direct colony suspension method for preparing inoculum suspensions and 5 mL volumes if using the growth inoculum procedure.
    h. Sterile phosphate buffers at various pHs (Table 8.1).
  2. Supplies.
    a. Test tubes.
      • Any standard laboratory sterile screw cap test tube that holds at least 10 mL can be used for making antibiotic dilutions.
      • Glass tubes with screw caps are needed for making the agar deeps. These test tubes need to be autoclavable and have dimensions greater than 16×150 mm (having at least a 22 mL capacity).
      • It is not recommended to reuse the tubes that were used to make antibiotic dilutions. It is very labor intensive and difficult to clean the glass tubes to ensure that there is no carryover of antibiotics between runs. In addition, it has been shown that some antibiotics (i.e., quinolones) are very efficient at sticking to glass surfaces even after proper cleaning in an automated dishwasher (industrial strength).
    b. Petri dishes.
      • The 32-prong replicator fits a 100×15 mm round petri dish.
      • The 36-prong replicator fits a 100×15 mm square petri dish.
      • A standard 100×15 mm round petri dish has an internal measurement of 87 mm and is 10 mm high. Petri dish manufactures have started making space saver dishes that are now currently being used by media manufacturers. These space saver petri

dishes have an internal dimension of 85 mm and a height of 8 mm. The loss of 2 mm is enough that it makes inoculation of these petri dishes more difficult. The corner isolates in the replicator are inoculated at the extreme edge of the plate and can result in growth that is more difficult to interpret.

c. Pipettes (1-, 5-, 10-, and 25-mL sterile serological pipettes).

d. Pipetting aid for serological pipettes.

e. 0.5 McFarland standard.

   1) Procedure for making McFarland standards [10].

      a) Combine the appropriate amount of $BaCl_2$ and H_2SO_4.

        • For the 0.5 McFarland standard, use 0.5 mL of 0.048 mol/L $BaCl_2$ (1.175% w/v $BaCl_2 \cdot 2H_2O$) and 99.5 mL of 0.18 mol/L H_2SO_4 (1% v/v).

        • For the 1 McFarland standard, use 1 mL of 0.048 mol/L $BaCl_2$ (1.175% w/v $BaCl_2 \cdot 2$ H2O) and 99 mL of 0.18 mol/L H_2SO_4 (1% v/v).

      b) Mix the solutions thoroughly.

      c) Using the same size screw-cap tubes that are to be used for the preparation of bacterial inoculum suspensions, aliquot 4–6 mL into each tube.

      d) Seal the caps with tape or Parafilm.

      e) Store these tubes in the dark at room temperature when not in use.

      f) Mix the standard solution well prior to each use.

        • Manufactured McFarland standards are available from PML and Hardy Diagnostics.

   2) Validation of McFarland standard turbidity.

      a) Absorbency.

        i. Read the optical density of the standard on a spectrophotometer with a 1-cm light path using a matched set of cuvettes.

        ii. The absorbency should be read at 625nm.

          • 0.5 McFarland standard should have a reading of 0.08 to 0.10λ.

          • 1 McFarland standard should have a reading of 0.16 to 0.20λ.

      b) Colony count.

        • The density of a standard can be validated by performing a spread plate colony count on a suspension of *E. coli* ATCC 25923 equivalent to the turbidity of your standard.

        • A 0.5 McFarland standard is considered equivalent to $1–2 \times 10^8$ organisms/mL.

        • A 1 McFarland standard is considered equivalent to 3×10^8 organisms/mL.

        • The density of the McFarland standard being used should be verified monthly by one of these two methods.

   3) Other methods.

      a) Manufactured latex standards.

        • Latex standards have the advantage of a 2-year shelf life and are not light sensitive.

        • Latex standards are available from Remel (Lenexa, KS).

        • Like all standards, the density of latex standards should be verified monthly.

      b) Turbidity meters.

        • Available from Vitek, MicroScan, and Anaerobe Systems.

        • Need to be calibrated with turbidity standards.

        • The frequency of calibration depends on the manufacturer.

f. Sterile swabs.

3. Equipment.

a. Autoclave.

b. Water bath 48°C–50°C.

c. Steers replicator (Figure 8.1).

FIGURE 8.1 Picture of replicator.

- Using a Steer's replicator [11].
  1) Transfer 0.6 mL of each isolate's standardized inoculum to the appropriate individual well of the sterile seed plate.
  2) Move the slide plate to the extreme left, placing the seed plate directly under the inoculating head.
  3) Place the appropriate agar dilution petri dish without a lid in the left-hand position on the slide plate.
  4) Push down on the piston followed by a controlled release; this results in the movement of the inoculating rods in and out of the seed plate.
     - If the release of the inoculating head is not done in a controlled manner, the inoculum may splatter, resulting in cross-contamination of the isolates.
  5) Move the slide plate to the extreme right, placing the inoculating rods directly over the petri dish.
  6) Gently depress the plunger until the inoculating rods rest on the surface of the medium.
     - This will deliver 1–2 µl of the inoculum on the medium per rod.
  7) Controlled release of the pressure results in the inoculating rods rising from the surface of the medium.
     - If the release is not controlled, inoculum splattering on the agar plate will occur.
- The current manufacturer of Steers replicators is CMI-Promex (Pedricktown, NJ). They are available in stainless steel and aluminum, and with 32 prongs for a round plate and 36 prongs for a square plate. The 32-prong pattern offers the advantage of using standard petri dishes. The 36-prong pattern uses a square plate, which is often not a standard order item for most laboratories.

32-prong pattern

	1	2	3	4	
5	6	7	8	9	10
11	12	13	14	15	16
17	18	19	20	21	22
23	24	25	26	27	28
	29	30	31	32	

36-prong pattern

1	2	3	4	5	6
7	8	9	10	11	12
13	14	15	16	17	18
19	20	21	22	23	24
25	26	27	28	29	30
31	32	33	34	35	36

- Steers replicator maintenance.
  a) The replicator should be decontaminated after every use by autoclaving, then cleaned using water, and then reautoclaved to sterilize for the next use.
  b) Soap or any type of disinfectant should not be used to clean the replicator. Residues and the sticking of these agents can affect the results the next time the replicator is used. Only water and scrubbing should be used to clean this instrument.
  c) Repeated autoclaving of the aluminum replicators will result in pitting, which will affect the accuracy of the unit over time. However, the aluminum replicators can be treated, by the process of hard anodizing performed by a metal machinist, to prevent pitting.
  d. Incubator.
  - The incubator should be set for 35°C–37°C.
  - Either the incubator is in an anaerobic chamber or is a non-CO_2 incubator for use with anaerobic jars.
  e. Anaerobic chamber or anaerobic jars.
  - The following are manufacturers of anaerobic systems: Coy, EM, Forma, Microbiology International, Mitsubishi, Oxoid, Plas-Labs, Sheldon Manufacturing, Toucan Technologies.

8.3.1.3 Quality Control

1. Quality control strains:
   - *Bacteroides fragilis* ATCC 25285.
   - *Bacteroides thetaiotaomicron* ATCC 29741.
   - *Eubacterium lentum* ATCC 43055.
   - *Clostridium difficile* ATCC 700057.
2. Frequency of quality control testing.
   - At least two of the above isolates should be tested with every agar dilution run.
   - *E. lentum* is the hardest of the four quality control isolates to grow on agar medium and produces the lightest growth pattern, which makes MIC determination more difficult. *C. difficile* was added as a quality control organism to provide an alternative gram-positive organism to *E. lentum* for agar dilution.
   - All quality control strains should be maintained following procedures described by CLSI [12].
3. Evaluating results.
   - The MIC values for *all* the quality control organisms tested in one run must be within acceptable ranges for the antimicrobial being tested for the results to be considered valid. These ranges are listed in the current CLSI M11 document and in Table 8.2.
   - It is important to keep in mind the function of these quality control organisms, which is to check that the antibiotic concentrations were made properly, meaning the amount

of antibiotic in the agar plate really matches what you think is there. These quality control organisms do not test the quality of the media or the presence of an anaerobic environment.

TABLE 8.2
Quality Control Ranges (μg/mL)(agar dilution)

Antimicrobial Agents	*Bacteroides fragilis* ATCC 25285	*Bacteroides thetaiotaomicron* ATCC 29741	*Clostridium difficile* ATCC 700057	*Eubacterium lentum* ATCC 43055
Amoxicillin/clavulanic acid (2:1)	0.25/0.125–1/0.5	0.5/0.25–2/1	0.25/0.125–1/0.5	—
Ampicillin	16–64	16–64	1–4	—
Ampicillin/sulbactam (2:1)	0.5/0.25–2/1	0.5/0.25–2/1	0.5/0.25–4/2	0.25/0.125–2/1
Cefmetazole	8–32	32–128	—	4–16
Cefoperazone	32–128	32–128	—	32–128
Cefotaxime	8–32	16–64	—	64–256
Cefotetan	4–16	32–128	—	32–128
Cefoxitin	4–16	8–32	—	4–16
Ceftizoxime	—	4–16	—	16–64
Ceftriaxone	32–128	64–256	—	—
Chloramphenicol	2–8	4–16	—	—
Clinafloxacin	0.03–0.125	0.06–0.5	—	0.03–0.125
Clindamycin	0.5–2	2–8	2–8	0.06–0.25
Doripenem	—	—	0.5–4	—
Ertapenem	0.06–0.25	0.25–1	—	0.5–2
Garenoxacin	0.06–0.5	0.25–1	0.5–2	1–4
Imipenem	0.03–0.125	0.06–0.25	—	0.125–0.5
Linezolid	2–8	2–8	1–4	0.5–2
Meropenem	0.03–0.25	0.125–0.5	0.5–4	0.125–1
Metronidazole	0.25–1	0.5–2	0.125–0.5	—
Mezlocillin	16–64	8–32	—	8–32
Moxifloxacin	0.12–0.5	1–4	1–4	0.125–0.5
Nitazoxanide	—	—	0.06–0.5	—
Opt 80	—	—	0.06–0.25	—
Penicillin	8–32 (16–64)[a]	8–32 (16–64)[a]	1–4	—
Piperacillin	2–8	8–32	4–16	8–32
Piperacillin/tazobactam	0.125/4–0.5/4	4/4–16/4	4/4–16/4	4/4–16/4
Ramoplanin	—	—	0.125–0.5	—
Rifaximin	—	—	0.004–0.016	—
Tetracycline	0.125–0.5	8–32	—	—
Ticarcillin	16–64	16–64	16–64	16–64
Ticarcillin/clavulanate	—	0.5/2–2/2	16/2–64/2	16/2–64/2
Tigecycline	—	—	0.125–1	—
Tinidazole	—	—	0.125–0.5	—
Tizoxanide	—	—	0.06–0.5	—
Trovafloxacin	0.06–0.5	0.25–1	—	0.25–1
Tylosin	—	—	0.125–0.5	—
Vancomycin	—	—	0.5–2	—

Values taken from the CLSI M11-A7, 2007 document.

[a] Penicillin units in parentheses are in units/mL.

8.3.1.4 Procedure

1. Plan.

   It is important to completely plan out the entire procedure because it involves many steps over several days. Agar dilution is a very complicated multistep procedure. It is important to have everything ready ahead of time to complete an agar dilution run in a timely manner. It is also important to understand all the steps in the procedure before starting. This procedure can be performed by one person; however, it is significantly more manageable with two people.

   • Determine the number of isolates to be tested, the number of antibiotics to be tested, and the range of concentrations for each antibiotic to be tested.

   • The antibiotic range testing should include at least two dilutions below and two dilutions above the break-point values for that antibiotic. The break points are listed in the current CLSI M11 document and in Table 8.3.

TABLE 8.3
Interpretive Criteria (μg/mL) (break points for agar dilution and broth microdilution)

Antimicrobial Agents	Activity[a]	Susceptible	Intermediate	Resistance
Amoxicillin/clavulanic acid (2:1)	C	4/2	8/4	16/8
Ampicillin	C	0.5	1	2
Ampicillin/sulbactam (2:1)	C	8/4	16/8	32/16
Cefmetazole	C	16	32	64
Cefoperazone	C	16	32	64
Cefotaxime	C	16	32	64
Cefotetan	C	16	32	64
Cefoxitin	C	16	32	64
Ceftizoxime	C	32	64	128
Ceftriaxone	C	16	32	64
Chloramphenicol	S	8	16	32
Clindamycin	S	2	4	8
Ertapenem	C	4	8	16
Imipenem	C	4	8	16
Meropenem	C	4	8	16
Metronidazole	C	8	16	32
Mezlocillin	C	32	64	128
Penicillin	C	0.5	1	2
Piperacillin	C	32	64	128
Piperacillin/tazobactam	C	32/4	64/4	128/4
Tetracycline	C	4	8	16
Ticarcillin	S	32	64	128
Ticarcillin/clavulanate	C	32/2	64/2	128/2
Trovafloxacin	C	2	4	8

Values were taken from the CLSI M11-A7, 2007 document.

[a] bactericidal = C, bacteriostatic = S.

2. Agar dilution plates.
   Prepare the appropriate number of brucella agar deeps. These deeps can be made in advance and stored in the refrigerator for up to 1 month at 2°C–4°C or 1 week at room temperature.
   a. Based on the number of runs to be done and the antibiotics to be tested, calculate the number of agar deeps needed (# runs × number of antibiotic dilutions + controls = # of agar deeps needed).
   b. Calculate the total amount of agar needed (# of agar deeps × 17 mL = total volume needed).
   c. Weigh out the appropriate amount of brucella agar base following the manufacturer's instructions.
   d. Add the appropriate amount of powder and distilled water to a bottle or flask and mix.
   e. Add 1 mL/L of hemin stock solution and 1 mL/L of vitamin K_1 working solution to the liquid medium.
   f. Bring the medium to a full rolling boil for 10 min to ensure that the agar is completely dissolved. The medium will be a consistent color and somewhat translucent; if the media is not homogeneous, boil longer.
      • If the agar is not completely dissolved in the liquid, it will result in agar deeps with different concentrations of agar.
   g. Move hot medium to a 50°C water bath and allow the medium to cool to at least 60°C before dispensing the hot medium.
   h. While leaving the boiled medium in the 50°C water bath, pipette 17 mL ± 0.2 mL of liquid medium into glass or polypropylene test tubes (25.5 mL ± 0.2 mL for square petri dishes).
      • The test tubes do not have to be sterile.
   i. Once all of the medium has been dispensed, cap all of the tubes.
      • The caps do not need to be sterile and should not be put on tightly.
   j. As soon as the tubes have been dispensed, they should be autoclaved at 121°C for 15 min with a slow exhaust.
   k. After autoclaving, allow the tubes to cool and solidify. Once cooled, the tubes should be tightly capped and then can be stored at 4°C for 1 month or at room temperature for 1 week. Tubes should be placed in a 50°C water bath if they are going to be used that day.
   l. If the agar deeps are allowed to solidify, they need to be remelted before use. It is important that the media inside the tube reaches a full boil to ensure that all of the agar is completely melted. The agar deeps are melted by autoclaving at 121°C with a slow exhaust for 3 min or by boiling in a water bath, a steamer, or in a microwave for 3–5 min (time is dependent on the diameter of the tube and the strength of the microwave). Once the medium has reached a full boil, the tubes are transferred to a 50°C water bath and allowed to cool to 50°C before use.
   m. Once the media has cooled to 48°C–50°C, it is ready for the addition of laked sheep blood and antibiotic solutions.
3. Antibiotic stock preparation.
   a. All antibiotic powders should be stored according to their manufacturer's instructions.
   b. All antimicrobial agents are assayed by the manufacturer to determine the units of activity. This difference must be taken into account when making stock solutions.

$$\text{Weight (mg)} = \frac{\text{volume (ml)} \times \text{desired concentration (mg/ml)}}{\text{antibiotic potency (mg/mg)}}$$

c. When possible, more than 100 mg of antimicrobial powder should be weighed out at one time.

d. All stock solutions should be made at the same concentration to minimize confusion. Stock solutions of 2,560 µg/mL work well for most standard susceptibility ranges.

e. The antimicrobial powder should be dissolved in water or other appropriate diluent in a sterile test tube (see Table 8.1). Once the antibiotic is in solution, all further dilutions should be made in water unless otherwise indicated (see Table 8.1).

f. Stock solutions should be aliquoted into volumes necessary for a typical run (approximately 2.5 mL). They should be stored in polypropylene or polyethylene sterile test tubes and frozen at –60°C or lower. Stock solutions should not be stored in frost-free freezers.

g. The stock solutions should be accurately labeled with the antibiotic's name and concentration, preparation date, and an expiration date. The expiration date should be 6 months after the date the stock solution was made or the manufacturer's expiration date for the powder, whichever is earlier.

h. Stock solutions should be discarded at the end of each day and should never be refrozen.

i. Because of the high concentration of antibiotic in the stock solution, sterilizing the solution is not necessary.

j. If using low concentrations of antibiotic or if there is a need to sterilize the antibiotic stock solution, it should be done using a membrane.
   - Paper, asbestos, or sintered filter should not be used since they may bind the antimicrobial agent.
   - If the stock solution is filter sterilized, the absence of adsorption must be documented by appropriate assay procedures. This procedure is not recommended.

4. Antibiotic dilution preparation.
   a. All test tubes should be labeled with the antibiotic's name and appropriate concentration.
   b. Add appropriate amounts of sterile water or proper diluent to each tube (see Figure 8.2).
   c. Add the appropriate amount of the stock solution to the first antibiotic dilution tube.
   d. Continue with the serial dilutions (Figure 8.2).

5. Plate preparation.
   a. Label all the plates with the antibiotic's name, concentration, and run number if appropriate.
   b. Stack plates in an organized fashion starting with the lowest concentration to the highest at the top of the stack.
   c. Remove the melted agar deep from the 50°C water bath, and wipe off the excess water on the outside of the test tube.
   d. Add 1 mL of laked blood to the melted agar deep (1.5 mL for square petri dishes).
   e. Add 2 mL of antibiotic dilution to the melted agar deep (3 mL for square petri dishes). To prepare control plates, add 2 mL of sterile water in place of the antibiotic solution (3 mL for square petri dishes).
   f. Mix by gentle inversion of the test tube three times; turning the tube upside down and back to the upright position counts as one inversion. Try to avoid making any bubbles during this process, and do not shake tubes violently.
   g. Pour the entire volume of media into the appropriate prelabeled sterile petri dish. Rotate petri dish gently to evenly distribute the agar and move any bubbles to the edge. If bubbles still remain in the center of the petri dish, a sterile needle or sterile loop can be used to pop the bubble or move it to the edge. If the bubble is large in size, it is best to try and pop the bubble. This process needs to be done before the agar solidifies.

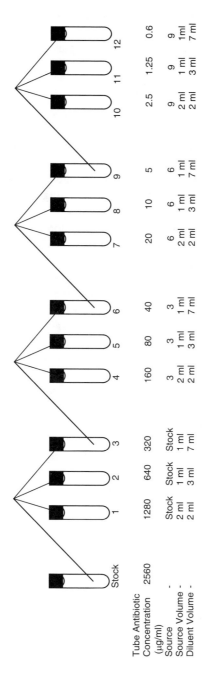

FIGURE 8.2 Tube dilution scheme.

h. Repeat steps c through g for all agar dilution plates needed. Once the plates have solidified (5–10 min), they need to be dried. It is important to make sure that the plates are completely dry before inoculation. This one step will ensure that the inoculum is rapidly absorbed into the agar. This will also help to prevent running of the inoculum spots into one another, which makes the plates hard to read after the incubation. Drying the prepared agar plates can be done in several ways:

1) Let the plates sit overnight at room temperature. *Note:* This cannot be done with less stable antibiotics such as imipenem, meropenem, and any drug combination containing sulbactam or clavulanic acid.

2) Invert (agar side up) and leave the lids ajar in a 35°C incubator for no more than 45 min.

3) Invert and leave the lids ajar in a laminar flow hood or biological safety cabinet for 30–45 min.

- Agar dilution runs can be planned so that the agar plates are prepared several days before they will be used for routine and research testing. This should be avoided if at all possible, especially with antibiotics that are known to be less stable (i.e., imipenem, meropenem, and any drug combination containing sulbactam or clavulanic acid).

- If using agar dilution plates that have been stored at 2°C–4°C, allow them to warm to room temperature on the bench before inoculation. If the plates appear wet, repeat the drying process described in 1), 2), or 3).

- It is not recommended that tubes that were used to make the agar dilution plates or antibiotic dilutions be reused. It is very labor intensive and difficult to clean the glass tubes to ensure that there is no carryover of antibiotics between runs. In addition, it has been shown that some antibiotics (i.e., quinolones) are very efficient at sticking to glass surfaces even after cleaning in an automated dishwasher (industrial strength).

6. Inoculum preparation.
- Make a list of the isolates and quality control organisms to be tested.
- Direct colony suspension.
  a. Inoculum is prepared from pure culture growth on brucella blood agar incubated for 24–72 h at 35°C.
      - Sufficient growth can be obtained at 24 h for rapid growers like *B. fragilis*.
      - Incubation can be 72 h for slow-growing species.
      - Whenever possible, 48-hour plates are preferred.
  b. Lightly touch several colonies of similar colony morphology using a loop or swab.
  c. Suspend the bacteria in brucella broth.
  d. Adjust the turbidity by adding more organism or more brucella broth until the suspension has a density equivalent to a 0.5 McFarland standard.
      - All work done with inoculum preparation can be done on the laboratory bench outside an anaerobic chamber.
      - Inoculum preparation should be done as quickly as possible, and bacterial oxygen exposure should be kept to a minimum. If possible, the preparation of all inocula for one run should be completed within 30 min.
      - If isolates do not grow on the growth control plate on an agar dilution run, those organisms should be repeated with the inoculum preparation done inside of an anaerobic chamber.
      - Not all anaerobic bacteria species grow well on standard agar media. If poor growth is obtained on the growth control plate, the MIC values recorded may not be accurate.

- Isolates that are being tested that were previously frozen must be passed at least twice before susceptibility testing is performed to obtain accurate results.
- Growth method.
  a. Inoculum should come from brucella blood agar plates with 24–72 h growth.
  b. Lightly touch several colonies of similar colony morphology using a loop or swab.
  c. Suspend the bacteria in thioglycolate broth or supplemented brucella broth.
     - If using thioglycollate broth, boil for 5 min before use.
     - One liter of thioglycollate medium should be supplemented with 1 mL hemin stock solution, and 1 mL vitamin K_1 working solution.
     - One or two small marble chips can be added before sterilization. (Marble chips are available from Fisher and VWR.)
  d. Incubate under anaerobic conditions for 6–24 h or until adequate turbidity is achieved.
  e. Adjust the turbidity by adding more broth until the suspension has a density equivalent to a 0.5 McFarland standard.
7. Inoculation of plates.
  a. The agar dilution plates should be organized before the inoculum has been prepared to reduce the amount of time the isolate will be out of an anaerobic environment.
  b. The agar dilution plates should be stamped starting with the bacteristatic antibiotics followed by the bactericidal antibiotics or starting with the least active agent followed by the most active agents (see Table 8.3).
  c. Within the dilution range of one antibiotic, inoculate beginning with the lowest concentration to be tested and move to the highest concentration. Growth control plates should be included at the beginning and end of each antibiotic (see step f further on).
  d. No more than four antimicrobial dilution sets of plates should be used with one replicator. Doing more than four sets increases the chance of antibiotic carryover and contamination of the seed tray of the replicator.
  e. It is also important to note the order that the plates were stamped, for follow-up with contamination or no-growth problems. One option is to label the control plates as follows: end of antibiotic X and start of antibiotic Y.
  f. Four types of control plates should be used with each run: positive growth control plates, negative growth (contamination) control plates, inoculum control plates, and Steers replicator sterility control plate. None of these control plates contains any antibiotics. They should be prepared just like the agar dilution plates but with the addition of 2 mL of water rather than antibiotic. It is not recommended that manufactured plates be used for this purpose.
     1) Positive growth control plates should be placed at the start and end of each antibiotic being tested. These plates are incubated with the agar dilution plates in an anaerobic environment.
        - One plate can serve as the control at the end of one antibiotic and the beginning of a second antibiotic.
        - Using two plates can be more convenient to the workflow if more than one person is reading a set of plates (i.e., each antibiotic dilution can have its own before and after control plates).
        - Using two control plates can reduce the amount of antibiotic carryover within a run.
     2) Negative growth (contamination) control plates should be plated at the start and end of each antibiotic being tested. These plates are incubated in an aerobic incubator.
        - One plate can serve as the control at the end of one antibiotic and the beginning of a second antibiotic.
     3) Inoculum control plates should be done at least once for each replicator run. These plates are stored at 4°C during the incubation period. These plates are very helpful

in determining the difference between wimpy growth of an organism and inoculum dried on the agar with no growth.

    4) A Steers replicator sterility control plate is a plate that is stamped before the inoculator head is introduced into the seed tray with the bacterial suspension. This control plate is not described in the CLSI M11-A7 document [4].

g. Be sure to mark the plates with some indication as to the proper orientation of the plate with regard to the inoculation. This can be done by filling one well in the replicator with diluted india ink or by marking the side on the petri dish with a sharpie to indicate its orientation.

h. The order of inoculation of plates is as follows:
1) Growth control plate
2) Negative growth (contamination) control plate
3) Inoculum control plate.
4) Antibiotic agar dilution set #1
5) Growth control plate(s)
6) Negative growth (contamination) control plates.
7) Antibiotic agar dilution set #2
8) Growth control plate(s)
9) Negative growth (contamination) control plate.
10) Antibiotic agar dilution set #3
11) Positive growth control plate
12) Negative growth (contamination) control plate.

i. Carefully inoculate the agar plates (see sections 8.3.1.2.3 and 8.3.1.4.7 for the procedure).

j. Allow the inoculated plates to remain on the bench with the lids in place until the inoculum has been absorbed into the medium. This should take no longer than 5–10 min. Handle plates as little as possible to avoid running of the inoculum on the plate. Adequate drying of the plates for inoculation will allow absorption to occur. If the plates are wet, it will take significantly longer for the inoculum to be absorbed, which will result in no growth of some isolates or running of the inoculum, creating plates that are difficult to interpret.

k. The appropriate agar dilution plates should be placed as soon as possible into the anaerobic environment that is being used. All anaerobic incubated plates should be in an anaerobic environment within 1 h of inoculum suspension preparation completion. This time is more crucial if anaerobic jars are being used because of the additional time these systems take before anaerobisis is achieved.

8. Incubation.
   a. Agar dilution plates and growth control plates are placed in the anaerobic environment for incubation. Incubation is for 46–48 h at 35°C–37°C.
   b. Negative (contamination) control plates are incubated in an aerobic incubator for 46–48 h at 35°C–37°C (a CO_2 incubator is not required).
   c. Inoculum control plates should be stored at 2°C–8°C until the agar dilution run is to be read.
   d. All plates should be incubated in the inverted position (agar side up).

9. Colony count.
   a. Transfer 0.1 mL from either the replicator block well or the inoculum suspension and add it to 9.9 mL of saline.
   b. Transfer 1 mL from the first tube to a second tube containing 9.9 mL of saline.
   c. Transfer 0.1 mL from the second tube to a third tube containing 9 mL of saline.
   d. Plate 0.1 mL from the third tube onto a brucella blood agar plate (or other medium that adequately supports the growth of the organism being used) and spread it with a

loop or bent glass tube. The plate count should be approximately 10^2 organisms (approximately 100 colonies per plate).

e. Incubate these plates under anaerobic conditions at 35°C–37°C for 48 h.

8.3.1.5 Results

1. Reading.
   a. The agar dilution plates should be read in the order that they were stamped.
      - This is important if a contaminate is found during the run because one can determine the point at which the results are no longer valid.
   b. The agar dilution plates should be read against a dark nonreflecting background.
   c. Record the growth control plate results inoculated at the beginning and end of each set for an antibiotic.
   d. Record a (+) for growth and a (–) for no growth for each isolate on each plate.
   e. The endpoint, i.e., the first (–), is to be read at the point where a *marked* change in growth appears as compared with the growth on the control plate.
   f. Marked change in growth can be a change to a haze, lighter growth, multiple tiny colonies, or a few small colonies. Figure 2 in the M11-A7 document is a good reference for learning how to determine appropriate end points [4]. Determination of end points for anaerobic agar dilution is more difficult than with aerobic bacteria. If performing this procedure for the first time, one should perform the procedure with someone experienced in reading anaerobic agar dilution.
   g. If no growth is seen on the positive growth control plate, no MIC value can be determined for that organism for that antimicrobial agent, even if growth is observed on the antimicrobial agent containing plates.
2. Interpreting.
   - Consult the latest edition of the M11 CLSI document for the appropriate break points for the antimicrobial agents being tested for interpretation of MIC values (Table 8.3).
   - Consult the colored Figure 2 in M11-A7 [4] for assistance in the interpretation of broth microdilution for anaerobes.
3. Reporting.
   MIC values should be reported with their appropriate categorical interpretation: (R) resistant, (I) intermediate, or (S) susceptible. All quality control values for a given antimicrobial agent must be within range to report susceptibility values for that antimicrobial agent.

8.3.1.6 Work Flow

8.3.1.6.1 Before the Run

1. Read the procedure.
2. Check the supplies and order items needed.
3. Prepare the agar deeps.
4. Label the dilution tubes.
5. Add the appropriate amount of water or appropriate diluent to dilution tubes.
6. Label the petri dishes with the appropriate information.
7. Prepare the antibiotic stocks.
8. Autoclave the Steers replicator.
9. Lake the whole sheep blood.
10. Thaw the blood (24 h before the run).
11. Subculture the isolates (48 h before the run).
12. Check the water bath (set to 48°C ± 2°C).

8.3.1.6.2 Day 1

1. Remove antibiotic stocks from the freezer.
2. Warm the blood to room temperature.
3. Prepare antibiotic dilutions.
4. Melt agar deeps.
5. Disinfect the work area.
6. Mix agar deeps + blood + antibiotic, and pour the plates.
7. Dry the plates.
8. Prepare the inoculum.
9. Stamp the plates, and allow the inoculum to be absorbed.
10. Incubate the plates.
11. Disinfect the Steers replicator.

8.3.1.6.3 Day 3

1. Check the growth control plate.
2. Check the negative growth (contamination) control plate.
3. Read the plates, and record the results.

8.3.1.7 Advantages

1. Agar dilution has the ability to test multiple isolates at once.

8.3.1.8 Limitations

1. The agar dilution procedure is not ideal for testing small numbers of isolates.
2. The agar dilution procedure is a very labor intensive procedure and difficult to interpret, even for the experienced microbiologist.
3. The agar dilution procedure requires specialized equipment (Steers replicator).
4. The inoculum is based on the turbidity equivalent 0.5 McFarland standard; however, anaerobic bacteria vary greatly in size and shape, resulting in colony counts that differ from the established $1–2 \times 10^8$ with *E. coli* ATCC 25922 or *B. fragilis* ATCC 25285 [4,13].

8.3.1.9 Conclusions

This is definitely a procedure that should not be attempted without guidance from someone with experience. It is very labor intensive, and the interpretation of the results is difficult for the untrained eye. However, this is the CLSI reference method that all new testing procedures must be compared with.

8.3.2 Microbroth Dilution

8.3.2.1 Introduction

Of the procedures described by the CLSI, this is the most practical one for the clinical microbiology laboratory to use when testing a small number of isolates against a given set of antibiotics. The current CLSI M11-A7 document restricts testing with this method to *B. fragilis* group isolates only [4]. This procedure involves a microtiter tray containing standard twofold dilutions of several antibiotics to be inoculated with one standardized bacterial suspension. These microtiter trays can be prepared fresh, in advance, and frozen or purchased from a manufacturer in either a frozen or lyophilized format (Remel [IDS], PML, TREK [Sensititer — Investigational Use Only]). If using a commercial product, the manufacturer's instructions should be followed.

The procedure described in this chapter is for preparing panels in-house.

8.3.2.2 Materials

1. Media
   a. Antibiotic sources
      1) United States Pharmacopeia (USP)
      2) Sigma Chemical Company
      3) The antimicrobial agent manufacturer
         - Many antimicrobial agents can be obtained in small amounts from the drug manufacturer at no charge by request through the drug company's customer service department or equivalent department. (Consult the PDR or your local pharmaceutical representatives for telephone numbers.)
   b. Agar medium
      1) Brucella blood agar plates supplemented with 5% sheep blood, vitamin K_1, and hemin.
      2) These plates are used to grow isolates for inoculum suspension if using the direct growth method and for purity plates.
   c. Broth medium
      1) Supplemented brucella broth is the only basal medium recommended in the CLSI M11-A7 [4] document. The media should be made following the manufacturer's instructions (Becton Dickinson, Remel, Accumedia).
      2) The media should be supplemented with 1 mL/L of hemin stock solution (5 mg/mL) and 1 mL/L of working vitamin K_1 stock solution (1 mg/mL) before autoclaving or dispensing of the media.
      3) Broth medium should be dispensed in 7.5 mL volumes into screw cap tubes.
      4) As soon as the tubes have been dispensed, they should be autoclaved at 121°C for 15 min with a slow exhaust.
      5) The tubes can be stored at 4°C for 1 month or at room temperature for 1 week.
   d. Sterile distilled water
   e. Laked horse blood
      1) Sterile whole defibrinated horse blood can be purchased from several manufacturers (Remel, PML, Hemostat, Hardy Diagnostics).
         - Sterile laked blood can be purchased from Hardy Diagnostics, PML, and Hemostat.
      2) To prepare laked blood in the laboratory from whole blood, completely freeze the whole horse blood at 20°C overnight or longer. When the blood is thawed, the red blood cells will lyse, and the blood is "laked." With horse blood, the freeze–thaw cycle needs to be repeated five to seven times. The blood then needs to be clarified by centrifuging at 12,000 g for 20 min. Carefully decant the supernatant. The supernatant may need to be centrifuged a second time if it is not free of flocculent material.
      3) Laked blood can be stored in the freezer at 20°C for up to 1 year.
         - Once thawed, laked blood has a $2\frac{1}{2}$-week shelf life at 2°C–8°C and should be labeled with a new expiration date when thawed.
   f. Hemin stock solution (5 mg/mL)
      1) Weigh out 0.5 g of hemin (Sigma # H2250).
      2) Dissolve the hemin powder in 10 mL of 1 mol/L NaOH (ACS certified).
      3) Make sure that the hemin powder is completely dissolved.
         - If the water is added to the solution before the hemin is completely dissolved, the hemin will remain unsuspended.
         - If the hemin will not go into solution in the NaOH, the solution can be heated to help dissolve the hemin. *This does not work if it is done after the addition of water.*
      4) Bring the volume of the solution to 100 mL with distilled water.

5) Make sure that the solution is in a brown bottle or wrapped in foil to protect it from light. Sterilize the hemin solution at 121°C for 15 min.

6) Cool to room temperature and store at 4°C–8°C.

7) This solution has a 1-month self-life and should be labeled with an expiration date when made.

8) Add 1 mL of the hemin stock solution (5 mg/mL) to 1 L of media.

g. Vitamin K_1 solution (10 mg/mL)

1) Stock solution (10 mg/mL)

a) Add 0.2 mL of vitamin K_1 solution (3-phytylmenadione, Sigma # V3501) to 20 mL of 95% ethanol.

b) Mix the ethanol and the vitamin K_1 solution.

c) Place in a sterile dark bottle and store at 4°C–8°C.

d) The solution has a 2-year shelf life and should be labeled with an expiration date when made.

- This solution has not been sterilized; therefore, sterile technique should be used when making this solution.
- Always inspect the solution for possible contamination before use.
- Vitamin K_1 can be autoclaved; however, other forms of vitamin K_1 cannot.

2) Working solution (1 mg/mL)

a) Add 1 mL of stock vitamin K_1 solution (10 mg/mL) to 9 mL of sterile distilled water.

b) Place in a sterile dark bottle and store at 4°C–8°C.

c) This solution has a 1-month shelf life and should be labeled with an expiration date when made.

d) Add 1 mL of the *working* vitamin K_1 stock solution (1 mg/mL) to 1 L of media.

- This solution is not sterilized after making it, and therefore sterile technique should be used.
- Always inspect the solution for possible contamination before use.
- Medium can be autoclaved after the addition of the vitamin K_1.

h. Sterile buffers at various pHs (Table 8.1).

3. Supplies

a. Test tubes

- Any standard laboratory sterile screw cap test tube that holds at least 10 mL can be used for making antibiotic dilutions.
- It is not recommended that the tubes that were used to make antibiotic dilutions be reused. It is very labor intensive and difficult to clean the glass tubes to ensure that there is no carryover of antibiotics between runs. In addition, it has been shown that some antibiotics (i.e., quinolones) are very efficient at sticking to glass surfaces even after proper cleaning in an automated dishwasher (industrial strength).

b. Microtiter trays

- Ninety-six-well microtiter trays are available from the following manufacturers: Evergreen Scientific and Nalgene Nunc International.

c. Pipettes (1-, 5-, 10-, and 25-mL sterile serological pipettes)

d. Pipetting aid for serological pipettes

e. 0.5 McFarland standard (see Section 8.3.1.2 for more details)

f Sterile swabs

g. Sterile cover trays

h. Inoculum reservoirs

4. Equipment

a. Autoclave

b. Water bath 48°C–50°C

c. Replicating device
1) Pipetter (single or multichannel)
2) Disposable multipoint inoculators, available from Dynex Technologies
d. Incubator
- The incubator should be set at 35°C–37°C.
- Either the incubator is in an anaerobic chamber or is a non-CO_2 incubator for use with anaerobic jars.
e. Anaerobic chamber or anaerobic jars
- The following is a list of manufacturers of anaerobic systems: Coy, EM, Forma, Microbiology International, Mitsubishi, Oxoid, Plas-Labs, Sheldon Manufacturing, Toucan Technologies.
f. Freezer (−70°C)
g. Reading device
- Light box
- Mirror reader

8.3.2.3 Quality Control

1. Quality control strains:
   - *Bacteroides fragilis* ATCC 25285
   - *Bacteroides thetaiotaomicron* ATCC 29741
   - *Eubacterium lentum* ATCC 43055
2. Frequency of quality control testing
   - At least one of the above isolates should be tested with every microbroth dilution run. If testing more that 10 isolates, it is recommended to test all three quality control strains.
   - Quality control isolates should be tested following the same procedure used for the clinical isolates.
   - All quality control strains should be maintained following procedures described by the CLSI [12].
   - All three quality control isolates should be tested with each new lot of panels before testing clinical specimens.
3. Evaluating results
   - The MIC values for a quality control organism tested in one run must be within acceptable ranges for the antimicrobial agent being tested with the broth microdilution method. These ranges are listed in the currrent CLSI M11 document and in Table 8.4.
   - It is important to keep in mind the function of these quality control organisms, which is to check that the antibiotic concentrations were made properly, meaning that the amount of antibiotic in the broth microdilution tray really matches what you think is there. These quality control organisms do not test the quality of the media or the anaerobic environment.

8.3.2.4 Procedure

1. Antibiotic stock preparation (see Section 8.3.1.3 for more details)
2. Preparation of trays
   a. Commercially available systems (Dynex Technologies, Inc.) are available to make broth microdilution trays in the laboratory.
   b. Label tubes containing 7.5 mL of the appropriate supplemented broth with the appropriate antibiotic name and antibiotic concentration.
   c. Place the tubes in an organized fashion going from highest to lowest concentration.
   d. Add 0.5 mL laked blood to each broth tube.

TABLE 8.4
Quality Control Ranges (μg/mL)(broth microdilution)

Antimicrobial Agents	*Bacteroides fragilis* ATCC 25285	*Bacteroides thetaiotaomicron* ATCC 29741	*Eubacterium lentum* ATCC 43055
Amoxicillin/clavulanic acid	0.25–1	0.25–1	—
Ampicillin/sulbactam (2:1)	0.5/0.25–2/1	0.5/0.25–2/1	0.5/0.25–2/1
Cefotetan	1–8	16–128	16–64
Cefoxitin	2–8	8–64	2–16
Ceftizoxime	—	—	8–32
Chloramphenicol	4–16	8.32	4–16
Clindamycin	0.5–2	2–8	0.06–0.25
Doripenem	0.12–0.5	0.12–1	—
Doxycycline	—	2–8	2–16
Ertapenem	0.06–0.5	0.5–2	0.5–4
Faropenem	0.015–0.06	0.12–1	0.5–2
Garenoxacin	0.06–0.25	0.25–2	0.5–2
Imipenem	0.03–0.25	0.25–1	0.25–2
Linezolid	2–8	2–8	0.5–2
Meropenem	0.03–0.25	0.06–0.5	0.125–1
Metronidazole	0.25–2	0.5–4	0.125–0.5
Moxifloxacin	0.125–0.5	1–8	0.125–0.5
Penicillin	8–32	8–32	—
Piperacillin	4–16	8–64	8–32
Piperacillin/tazobactam	0.03/4–0.25/4	2/4–16/4	8/4–32/4
Ticarcillin/clavulanate	0.06–0.5	0.5/2–2/2	8/2–32/2
Trovafloxacin	0.125–0.5	0.5–2	0.25–2

Values were taken from the CLSI M11-A7, 2007 document.

e. Add 1 mL of the antibiotic dilution to the broth tube.

f. Mix by gently inverting the test tube three times (turning the tube upside down and back to the upright position counts as one inversion).
   • Try to avoid making any bubbles during this process.
   • Do not shake the tubes violently.

g. Using a dispensing device, transfer 0.1 mL from each of the broth–antibiotic tubes to the appropriate well in each microtiter tray.
   • It is not recommended that volumes smaller than 0.1 mL be used in the microtiter trays because of evaporation.

h. Two wells in the microtiter tray should contain only 0.1 mL of the supplemented broth. These two wells will serve as the positive and negative control wells for the microtiter tray.

i. The prepared trays should be sealed in a plastic bag and placed in a –70°C freezer until needed. Prepared trays should not be stored in a self-defrosting freezer as this type of freezer will shorten the shelf life of the antimicrobial agents in the tray. Prepared trays should not be refrozen after being thawed.

j. The shelf life of the panel is the shortest expiration date on the antibiotics being used or 4–6 months.

k. Appropriate quality control should be done to monitor the performance of the panel throughout the shelf life.

l. Quality control should be performed on each new lot of broth microtiter trays using all three quality control organisms before being used with clinical specimens.

3. Inoculum preparation (see Section 8.3.1.4 for more details)
4. Inoculation of frozen microtiter trays
   a. Remove the number of microtiter test panels to be used from the freezer. Allow the panels to thaw at room temperature.
      • If thawed in a hood unstacked, it will take at least 45 min to thaw. If thawed stacked 4 high with a clean cover tray (cover trays do not need to be sterile), it will take close to 2 h to thaw.
      • Remove the sealing tape as soon as the panels are removed from the freezer, and put a clean cover tray on the top of the panels.
      • Thawed trays should be inoculated and placed in the chamber within 1 h of thawing.
   b. Transfer 3 mL of the adjusted inoculum suspension (equal to a 0.5 McFarland standard) into 27 mL of sterile saline.
   c. Carefully invert the tube several times or vortex to thoroughly mix the suspension (introduce as few bubbles as possible).
   d. Transfer 10 μL of the inoculum to each well of the microtiter tray using a single or multichannel pipette. A multipin inoculator can also be used for this purpose. If using one of these devices, follow the manufacturer's instructions as to what inoculum concentration should be added to the inoculum reservoir.
   e. Inoculated panels should be covered with a tray lid or empty tray.
   f. The microtiter trays should be inoculated and placed into the anaerobic chamber as soon as possible with a maximum total time of 30 min. Panels should not be stacked more that four high. (Stacks higher than four can lead to uneven heat distribution between the panels.)
   g. A purity plate and a negative (contamination) control plate should be prepared for every isolate being tested. If colony counts are being done with an isolate, these plates can serve as the purity plate. Transfer one 10 μL loopful of inoculum from the positive control well and streak for isolated colonies on a brucella agar plate (purity plate) and a tryptic soy agar (TSA) blood agar plate (negative [contamination] control plate).
5. Incubation
   a. Microtiter trays and purity plates should be incubated in an anaerobic environment stacked no more than four high. Incubation is for 46–48 h at 35°C–37°C.
   b. Negative (contamination) control plates should be incubated in an aerobic incubator for 46–48 h at 35°C–37°C. (A CO_2 incubator is not required.)
6. Colony count
   a. Colony counts should be performed periodically to verify the inoculum concentration.
   b. Transfer 10 μL from the positive control well and add it to 10 mL of saline (1:1,000 dilution).
   c. Plate 0.1 mL of the dilution onto a brucella blood agar plate (or other medium that adequately supports the growth of the organism being tested) and spread it with a loop or bent glass tube. The plate count should be approximately 10^2 organisms (approximately 100 colonies per plate).
   d. Incubate these plates under anaerobic conditions at 35°C–37°C for 48 h.

8.3.2.5 Results

1. Reading
   a. Remove the trays and quality control plates from the incubator.
   b. Check the purity plate and evaluate for contamination. If contamination is observed, repeat the test. If no contamination is apparent, continue with reading the panel.
   c. Wipe the bottom of the tray with a damp lint-free tissue to remove any condensation.
   d. Place the tray on a reading device (light box or mirror reader).

   e. The positive control growth well must have good growth.
      • If adequate growth in not achieved in the positive control growth well, the test must be repeated.
      • "Adequate growth" will depend on the species being tested. Isolates that produce small colonies on blood agar plates will usually produce small buttons with the microbroth procedure.
      • If adequate growth is not achieved, consider adding supplements to the medium or performing the entire procedure under anaerobic conditions.
   f. Record a (+) for growth and a (−) for no growth for each well on the microtiter tray.
   g. The end point, that is, the first (−), is to be read at the point where *marked* change in growth appears as compared with the growth in the positive control well.
   h. If no growth is seen in the positive control growth well, MIC values cannot be determined for that isolate for any of the antibiotics tested.
 2. Interpreting
      • Consult the latest edition of the M11 CLSI document for the appropriate break points for antimicrobial agents being tested for interpretation of the MIC values (Table 8.3).
      • Consult the colored Figure 3 in M11-A7 [4] for assistance in the interpretation of broth microdilution for anaerobes.
 3. Reporting
      • MIC values should be reported with their appropriate categorical interpretation: (R) resistant, (I) intermediate, or (S) susceptible. All quality control values for a given antimicrobial agent have to be within range to report susceptibility values for that antimicrobial agent.

8.3.2.6 Work Flow

8.3.2.6.1 *Before the Run*
 1. Read the protocol carefully.
 2. Make sure all the items needed are in stock.
 3. Make or purchase microtiter plates.
 4. Subculture the isolates 48 h before the run.
 5. Check the purity of the isolates.

8.3.2.6.2 *Day 1*
 1. Disinfect a flat, level area where the work is going to be done.
 2. Remove microtiter trays from the freezer, and allow them to thaw at room temperature (30–45 min if they are not stacked, and 2 h if they are in stacks of four or five).
 3. Prepare the inoculum.
 4. Inoculate the trays.
 5. Inoculate the purity plates (anaerobic and aerobic).
 6. Incubate the trays and plates.

8.3.2.6.3 *Day 3*
 1. Read the trays, and record the results.
 2. Check the purity plates.
 3. Check the quality control results.

8.3.2.7 Advantage

 1. The broth microdilution procedure has the flexibility to test any number of isolates desired at one time.
 2. This procedure is easy to perform. If the laboratory prepares the panels in-house, the procedure then becomes a little more complicated and time consuming.

8.3.2.8 Limitations

1. The CLSI M11-A7 document *only* recommends this method with *B. fragilis* group isolates [4]. The procedure has not been validated with other species by the CLSI. Many anaerobic bacterial species do not grow well in broth, even after supplementation.
2. This procedure requires specialized equipment (dispensing equipment) if the panels are going to be prepared by the laboratory.

8.3.2.9 Conclusions

This procedure is easy to perform with minimal labor, especially if manufactured panels are used. Interpretation of the results can be challenging to the untrained eye. This procedure is described and endorsed by the CLSI for *B. fragilis* group isolates only.

8.3.3 ETEST

8.3.3.1 Introduction

Etest (AB Biodisk, Solna, Sweden) is made of a nonporous plastic strip immobilized with a predefined gradient of a given antibiotic on one surface and printed with an MIC scale on the other side. This concept of susceptibility testing was designed by Bolmstrom et al. [14] and was first presented at the ICAAC meeting in 1988.

When the Etest strip is placed on an inoculated agar plate, a continuous, stable, and exponential antibiotic gradient is established along the side of the strip. After incubation, the MIC value (µg/mL) can be read directly from the MIC scale printed on the Etest strip. The resulting MIC is equivalent to the CLSI agar dilution reference values; thus, the MIC interpretive criteria for anaerobic bacteria established by the CLSI in M11-A7 is directly applicable for interpretation of Etest results [4]. This technology is similar to a disk diffusion assay but with a longer stability time for the antibiotic gradient.

8.3.3.2 Materials

1. Etest strips.
   Etest strips can be purchased directly from AB Biodisk or through Remel. Each strip, on average, costs $2.15 and they are sold in packages of 100 strips per antibiotic. The strips are to be stored at –20°C or –70°C. Once a set of strips is removed from the manufacturer's packaging, the unused strips should be stored in an airtight container with a desiccant and returned to –20°C. Etest strips have a shelf life of 2 to 5 years depending on the antibiotic. Etest strips should not be used after the expiration date indicated by the manufacturer. The antibiotics that have obtained FDA clearance for *in vitro* diagnostic use in the United States for anaerobes are listed in Table 8.5. Depending on the antibiotic, the MIC ranges on the Etest strips are either from 0.016–256 µg/mL or 0.002–32 µg/mL, which represents 15 twofold dilutions.
2. A brucella blood agar plate, made in-house or obtained commercially, that meets the following criteria can be used: 4 mm ± 0.5 mm brucella agar with 5% lysed sheep blood supplemented with vitamin K_1 and hemin (either a 90 mm or 150 mm diameter petri dish can be used). These plates should be stored at 2°C–8°C, unless otherwise stated by the manufacturer.
3. Brucella broth is used for making bacterial suspensions. The broth should be in a usable volume, such as 1–5 mL. This broth should be stored at 2°C–8°C.
4. Swabs (sterile, nontoxic).
5. Test tubes (for brucella broth).
6. Pipettes.

TABLE 8.5
Etest Strips with FDA Clearance for Anaerobic Bacteria

Antibiotic	Code
Amoxicillin/clavulanic acid (2/1)	XL
Ampicillin/sulbactam (2/1)	AB
Benzylpenicillin	PG
Cefotaxime	CT
Cefotetan	CN
Cefoxitin	FX
Ceftizoxime	CZ
Clindamycin	CM
Ertapenem	ETP
Imipenem	IM
Meropenem	MP
Metronidazole	MZ
Piperacillin/tazobactam (4 µg/mL)	PTc
Ticarcillin/clavulanic acid	TLc
Tigecycline	TGC

7. Scissors.
8. Forceps or Etest applicator kit.
9. 1 McFarland standard, which can be made following CLSI instructions or purchased from microbiology product manufacturers such as PML, Hardy, or Remel. (See Section 8.3.1.2 for more details.)
10. Air tight storage containers with desiccant (silica gel) for extra Etest strips once the manufacturer's packaging has been opened.
11. Anaerobic system (anaerobic chamber, anaerobic gas generator, or anaerobic bag).
    * The new gas generators made by Oxoid, EM Science, and Mitsubishi can be used for the anaerobic system; however, bicarbonate systems are not recommended for use with Etest because of the time required to generate adequate anaerobiosis.
12. Freezer (–20°C or –70°C) for storage.
13. Vortex.
14. 35°C ambient air or CO_2 incubator (if using anaerobic jars).
15. Etest technical information.
    Etest package insert.
    Etest technical guide no. 1.
    Etest application sheet no. 7.
    Customer information sheet no. 3.
    Etest technical manual.

8.3.3.3 Quality Control

1. Quality control strains:
    * *Bacteroides fragilis* ATCC 25285.
    * *Bacteroides thetaiotaomicron* ATCC 29741.
    * *Eubacterium lentum* ATCC 43055.
    * All quality control strains should be maintained following the procedures described by the CLSI [12].

2. Frequency of quality control testing.
   • Quality control should be run with every new lot of Etest strips.
   • Each antibiotic should be tested within the last 7 days of use if proficiency has been documented following the CLSI procedure of testing for 30 consecutive days. Otherwise, quality control should be done with each occasion of testing.
3. Evaluating the results.
   • AB Biodisk publishes an anaerobe application sheet that lists the quality control ranges for appropriate antimicrobial agents. The values are the same as agar dilution quality control ranges in the current CLSI M11 document (also see Table 8.2).

8.3.3.4 Procedure

1. Obtain a pure culture of the isolate to be tested on a nonselective medium such as brucella blood agar supplemented with vitamin K_1 and hemin.
   • The inoculum should be prepared from plates incubated for 24–72 h, depending on the species being tested.
   • Frozen or lyophilized isolates should be subcultured at least twice prior to susceptibility testing.
2. Remove the strips from the freezer (30 min for –20°C and 60 min for –70°C) before use to allow them to equilibrate to room temperature prior to removing them from the original package or storage container.
3. Using a sterile swab, emulsify enough isolated colonies in sterile brucella broth.
   • If log phase inoculum is desired, add less organism to the broth and allow the suspension to grow until the desired turbidity is acquired (4–6 h).
4. Mix gently to introduce as little oxygen as possible.
5. Adjust the suspension turbidity to be equivalent to a 1 McFarland standard. Add more colonies to increase the turbidity or more broth to decrease the turbidity (photometric devices can also be used to measure the turbidity).
6. The inoculum suspension should be inoculated onto the agar plate within 15 min after preparation. Dip a cotton swab into the bacterial suspension, remove excess liquid by pressing against the test tube wall, and swab the entire surface of a dry agar plate. To cover the entire plate, rotate the plate 120°, swab the entire surface a second time, rotate the plate another 120°, and swab the entire surface for a third time.
   • Make sure that coverage of the inoculum is spread evenly over the entire surface of the plate.
   • A correctly inoculated plate will result in an even lawn of confluent growth.
7. Allow the inoculum to be absorbed completely into the agar (at least 15–20 min). The plate must be completely dry before application of the Etest strip. If moisture is present on the agar surface when the Etest strip is applied, it will affect the performance of the antibiotic gradient. For fastidious anaerobic species, this entire process should be done in an anaerobic chamber.
8. The strip is designed to have the MIC scale facing away from the agar surface and the antibiotic gradient touching the agar surface (you want to be able to see the writing on the strip after applying it to the agar plate). Apply the "E" (highest concentration of antibiotic) at the edge of the petri dish to the agar surface and gently lay down the strip with the lowest concentration end of the strip placed toward the center of the plate. *Once the strip has touched the agar surface, do not move the strip.* If any large bubbles appear under the strip, gently remove the bubbles by pressing on the Etest strip with a forceps or a swab. Small bubbles under the strip will not affect the performance of the Etest strip.

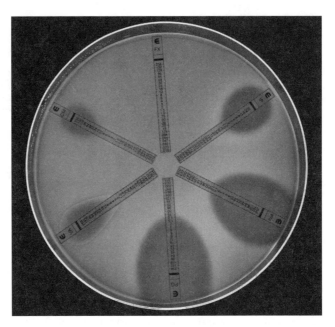

FIGURE 8.3 150-mm Etest picture.

- One to two strips can be placed on a 90-mm plate with opposite orientation to each other (you do not want the "E" on the same side of the plate for two strips since the gradients will overlap).
- Up to six strips can be placed on a 150-mm agar plate in a spoke wheel pattern (Figure 8.3). (Templates are available from AB Biodisk to optimize the positioning of the strips.)
- When using the Etest applicator, refer to the instructions in the product insert.
- Do not remove the Etest strip during any part of the process.

9. Incubate the plate in the inverted position (agar side up) at 35°C in an anaerobic environment (80%–85% N_2, 5%–10% H_2, 5%–10% CO_2) as soon as possible after the placement of Etest strips. (Try to minimize the exposure time of anaerobic bacteria to oxygen as much as possible throughout the working procedure.)
   - Use an anaerobic indicator to verify that anaerobiosis has been achieved (i.e., 1–2 h). Resazurin has a lower redox potential (Eh 450 mV) than methylene blue, making it a more sensitive indicator to the presence of oxygen in an environment.
10. Incubate the plate for 24 h for the *Bacteroides fragilis* group and *Clostridium* spp., with the exception of clindamycin, which requires 48 h. Other fastidious anaerobic species should be incubated for 48–72 h until clear visible growth is seen.

8.3.3.5 Results

1. Reading.
   a. Do not read the results if the incubation exceeds 72 h.
   b. Evaluate the growth of the isolate before reading it. If the lawn of growth appears as no more than a thin haze or if the density of colonies is sparse, do not attempt to read the MIC; reincubate and/or repeat.
   c. Read the MIC where the edge of the inhibition ellipse intersects the MIC scale on the Etest strip (Figure 8.4).
      - Bacteriostatic antimicrobial agents tend to form diffuse edges. These should be read at the so-called 80% inhibition region, that is, the first point of significant inhibition as judged by the naked eye, ignoring the haze and microcolonies.

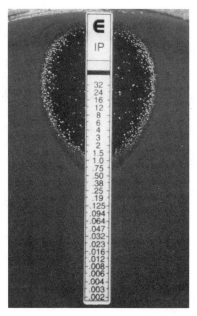

FIGURE 8.4 Close-up of Etest picture.

- Bactericidal antimicrobial agents tend to form sharp edges. With these agents, hazes and isolated colonies are indicative of growth, and the MIC should be read where these are completely inhibited.
- For more detailed descriptions, see the AB Biodisk product insert. AB Biodisk has very useful colored handouts available that show guidelines for interpreting the results.
- If a thin line of growth occurs along the side of the Etest strip within the ellipse, it should not be used to interpret the results; the MIC value is located where the ellipse of growth intersects with the Etest strip.
- If a "lightbulb" shape of inhibition ellipse occurs, read the ellipse at the top of the dip. This is often observed with clindamycin.
- Growth of large colonies within the zone of inhibition is an indication of a mixed culture or two resistant variants, and the test should be repeated with a pure culture.

   d. Do not use hemolysis of the blood in the agar medium as an indication of the MIC; bacterial growth is the only indicator used for interpretation of the MIC value.

   e. If there is complete growth and no zone appears on the plate around a strip, the MIC value is recorded as greater than the highest antibiotic concentration of the strip.

   f. If the inhibition ellipse falls below the lowest value on the strip, the MIC value is recorded as less than the lowest value on the strip.

2. Interpreting.

   a. The MIC results from an Etest strip are based on a continuous gradient; therefore, MIC values between the standard twofold dilution can be obtained. These values can be reported as such, if desired, or rounded up to the next appropriate twofold dilution value, i.e., 0.19 μg/mL becomes 0.25 μg/mL.

   b. To interpret Etest MIC results as susceptible (S), intermediate (I), or resistant (R) categories, always round up the in-between values to the next higher twofold dilution.

- For example, if CLSI break points are S ≤0.064 μg/mL and R ≥0.25 μg/mL, an Etest value of 0.19 μg/mL is rounded up to 0.25 μg/mL and the category is reported as resistant.

   c. Etest MIC values are directly proportional to the CLSI reference agar dilution values. Therefore, CLSI breakpoints are directly applicable to the Etest MIC values. Consult the latest edition of the M11 document for the appropriate agar dilution break points for antimicrobial agents (Table 8.3).

3. Additional considerations.

   a. Clindamycin should not be read before 48 h with any anaerobic bacteria because of delayed expression of inducible resistance genes.

   b. Achievement of an anaerobic environment (Eh 450 mV) early in the incubation time (within the first few hours) is needed when testing metronidazole. MIC values may be falsely elevated if anaerobiosis is incomplete because metronidazole is not sufficiently reduced to its active metabolite. Therefore, the use of bicarbonate anaerobic generators may not be appropriate.

8.3.3.6 Advantages

1. Etest is easy to perform and requires minimal training.
2. Etest can be used for many species, including the more fastidious anaerobic species.
3. Many species of anaerobic bacteria grow better on agar media than broth. Furthermore, contamination can be easily recognized on agar.
4. Etest can be easily set up for a small number of clinical isolates.
5. There is minimal labor involved with Etest as compared with agar dilution if testing a small number of isolates with a small number of antimicrobial agents.
6. Interpretation of the Etest is fairly easy.

8.3.3.7 Limitations

Cost is the most significant limitation; however, if careful consideration is given to which antibiotics to test, for fewer than five strips per isolate, the Etest methodology can be cost effective.

8.3.3.8 Conclusions

The Etest is relatively easy to set up and perform and lends itself well to laboratories that do not test large volumes of clinically significant anaerobes.

8.4 GENERAL CONCLUSIONS

Currently, the gold standard for susceptibility testing for anaerobic bacteria approved by the CLSI is the agar dilution method. This procedure is used typically by research laboratories or large clinical laboratories that can "batch" isolates for large scale research or surveillance studies. This method is very labor intensive and does not lend itself to testing small numbers of clinical isolates. If a manufactured product is proven to be equivalent to the agar dilution procedure, it can be used in the clinical laboratory even though CLSI has not described the use of the product in a document (the CLSI does not endorse products). Of the procedures approved by the CLSI, microbroth dilution is best suited for routine testing in the routine clinical laboratory. It can be used with any number of isolates and is less labor intensive than agar dilution. Microbroth dilution panels can be prepared in bulk and frozen in the laboratory, or they can be purchased from a manufacturer. However, some anaerobic bacterial species do not grow well in broth. If either of the CLSI methods is being used, it is strongly recommended that the most recent CLSI M11 document be viewed. The anaerobe working group has added color figures to help aid in the interpretation of these methods with anaerobes. The other practical method for testing anaerobic bacteria is the Etest. It has similar advantages to the microbroth dilution procedure but is more expensive per antibiotic tested. As antibiotic resistance continues to increase, the need for the clinical laboratory to be able to routinely perform anaerobic susceptibility testing will become more important.

APPENDIX — MANUFACTURERS

AB Biodisk North America Inc.
200 Centennial Avenue
Piscataway, NJ 08854-3910
www.abbiodisk.se
Telephone: 732-457-0408
Fax: 732-457-8980
Product inquires and orders: 800-874-8814

AB Biodisk
Dalvagen 10
S-169 56 Solna
Sweden
www.abbiodisk.se
Telephone: + 46-8-730 07 60
Fax: + 46-8-83 81 58

BD Biosciences
P.O. Box 243
Cockeysville, MD 21030
www.bd.com
Telephone: 410-771-0100
          800-638-8663

CMI-Promex (Steers Replicator)
7 Benjamin Green Road
P.O. Box 418
Pedricktown, NJ 08067
Telephone: 609-351-1000

Coy Laboratory Products, Inc.
14500 Coy Drive
Grass Lake, MI 49137
www.coylab.com
Telephone: 313-475-2200

Dynex Technologies, Inc.
14340 Sullyfield Circle
Chantilly, VA 20151
www.dynextechnologies.com
Telephone: 800-336-4543
          703-631-7800
Fax: 703-631-7816

EM Science
480 S. Democrat Road
Gibbstown, NJ 08027-1297
www.emscience.com
Telephone: 800-222-0342

Evergreen Scientific
2300 E. 49th St.
Los Angeles, CA 90058
Telephone: 213-583-1331

Fisher Scientific Co.
711 Forbes Ave.
Pittsburgh, PA 15219
www.fishersci.com
Telephone: 412-490-8300

Forma Scientific, Inc.
P.O. Box 649
Marietta, OH 45750
www.forma.com
Telephone: 614-374-1851

Gelman Science
600 South Wanger Rd.
Ann Arbor, MI 48103
Telephone: 313-665-0651

Hardy Diagnositics, Inc.
1430 West McCoy Lane
Santa Maria, CA 93455
www.hardydiagnostics.com
Telephone: 805-346-2766
          800-266-2222
Fax: 805-346-2760

Hemostat Laboratories
P.O. Box 790
515 Industrial Way
Dixon, CA 95620
www.hemostat.com
Telephone: 707-678-9594
          800-572-6888

Microbiology International
10242 Little Rock Lane
Frederick, MD 21702
www.microbiology-intl.com
Telephone: 301-662-6835
      800-396-4276
Fax: 301-662-8096

Mitsubichi Gas Chemical America, Inc.
520 Madison Ave. 17th Floor
New York, NY 10022
www.mgc-a.com
Telephone: 212-752-4620
Fax: 212-758-4012

Nalge Nunc International
75 Panorama Creek Dr.
P.O. Box 20365
Rochester, NY 14602
www.nalgenunc.com
Telephone: 800-625-4327

Oxoid, Inc.
800 Proctor Avenue
Ogdensburg, NY 13669
www.oxoid.com
Telephone: 800-567-8378

Plas Labs Inc.
917 East Chilson Street
Lansing, MI 48906
Telephone: 517-372-7177

PML Microbiologicals
27120 SW 95th Ave.
Wilsonville, OR 97070
www.pmlmicro.com
Telephone: 800-628-7014
Customer service: 800-547-0659
Fax: 800-765-4415

Remel (IDS)
12076 Santa Fe Dr.
Lenexa, KS 66215
www.remelinc.com
Telephone: 800-255-6730

Sheldon Manufacturing, Inc.
P.O. Box 627
Cornelius, OR 97113
www.shellab.com
Telephone: 503-640-3000
      800-322-4897
Fax: 503-640-1366

Sigma Chemical Company
P.O. Box 14508
St. Louis, MO 63178
www.sigma-aldrich.com
Telephone: 800-325-3010
Technical Services: 800-325-5832

Toucan Technologies, Inc.
1158 Altadena
Cincinnati, OH 45230
Telephone: 513-232-0200

TREK
previously part of AccuMed International
      (Sensititer)
29299 Clemens Road Suite 1-K
Westlake, OH 44145
www.trekds.com
Telephone: 440-808-0000
      800-871-8909
Fax: 440-346-2760

USP (United States Pharmacopeia)
Customer Service Department
12601 Twinbrook Parkway
Rockville, MD 20852
http://catalog.usp.org
Telephone: 800-227-8772
      800-877-6209

VWR Scientific Products
1310 Goshen Parkway
West Chester, PA 19380
www.vwr.com
Telephone: 610-429-2728

REFERENCES

1. Finegold, S.M. *Anaerobic Bacteria in Human Disease*, Academic Press, New York, 1977.

2. Finegold, S.M. and Wexler, H.M. Present status of therapy for anaerobic infections, *Clin. Infect. Dis.*, 23(Suppl 1), S9–S14, 1996.

3. Hecht, D.W., Osmolski, J.R., and O'Keefe, J.P. Variation in the susceptibility of *Bacteroides fragilis* group isolates from six Chicago hospitals, *Clin. Infect. Dis.*, 16(Suppl 4), S357–S360, 1993.

4. Clinical and Laboratory Standards Institute, M11-A7, Methods for antimicrobial susceptibility testing of anaerobic bacteria, CLSI, Wayne, PA, 2007.

5. Clinical and Laboratory Standards Institute, M11-A, Reference agar dilution procedure for antimicrobial susceptibility testing of anaerobic bacteria, CLSI, Villanova, PA, 1985.

6. Thornsberry, C. Antimicrobial susceptibility testing of anaerobic bacteria: review and update on the national committee for clinical laboratory standards, *Rev. Infect. Dis.*, 12(suppl 2), S218–S222, 1990.

7. Amsterdam, D. and Jones, R.N. Broth-disk elution method for anaerobic susceptibility testing: A simple unreliable test, *Antimicro. Newsl.*, 5, 41–42, 1988.

8. Clinical and Laboratory Standards Institute, M11-A4, Methods for antimicrobial susceptibility testing of anaerobic bacteria, CLSI, Wayne, PA, 1997.

9. Clinical and Laboratory Standards Institute, M11-A6, Methods for antimicrobial susceptibility testing of anaerobic bacteria, CLSI, Wayne, PA, 2004.

10. McFarland, J. Nephelometer: An instrument for estimating the number of bacteria in suspensions used for calculating the opsonic index and for vaccines, *J. Amer. Med. Assoc.*, 14, 1176–1178, 1907.

11. Steers, E., Foltz, E.L., and Graves, B.S. Inocula replicating apparatus for routine testing of bacterial susceptibility to antibiotics, *Antibiot. Chemother.*, 9, 307–311, 1959.

12. Clinical and Laboratory Standards Institute, M7-A7, Methods for dilution antimicrobial susceptibility tests for bacteria that grow aerobically, CLSI, Wayne, PA, 2006.

13. Swenson, J.M. and Thornsberry, C. Preparing inoculum for susceptibility testing of anaerobes, *J. Clin. Micro.*, 19, 321–325, 1984.

14. Bolmstom, S., Arvidson, M., Ericsson, M., and Karlsson, A. A novel technique for direct quantification of antimicrobial susceptibility of microorganisms, Abstract from the Interscience Conference on Antimicrobial Agents and Chemotherapy, poster 1209, Los Angeles, 1988.

9 Antifungal Susceptibility Testing of Yeasts

Ana Espinel-Ingroff and Emilia Cantón

CONTENTS

9.1 INTRODUCTION

Since 1956 and until the introduction of fluconazole in 1990, amphotericin B was the only available antifungal agent for the treatment of severe fungal infections; consequently, there was little need for routine susceptibility testing. Furthermore, the emergence of the AIDS pandemic, modern patient management technologies and therapies such as bone marrow and solid-organ transplants, and the more aggressive use of chemotherapy have resulted in a rapidly expanding number of patients highly susceptible to mycotic infections. With the increased incidence of fungal infections and the parallel development of resistance to established agents, the laboratory's role in the selection of antifungal therapy has gained greater attention. The Clinical and Laboratory Standards Institute (CLSI, formerly NCCLS) has approved standard broth dilution methodologies for susceptibility testing of *Candida* spp. and *Cryptococcus neoformans* to amphotericin B, flucytosine, ketoconazole, fluconazole, itraconazole, voriconazole, and posaconazole [1]. The CLSI antifungal susceptibility testing assays (broth dilution and disk diffusion) and two commercial methods for yeasts are described in this chapter. The endpoints determined by these methods are the minimum inhibitory concentration or the MIC and the inhibition zone diameter (disk testing).

The European Subcommittee on Antifungal Susceptibility Testing (EUCAST) has recently published a standard method for determination of MICs of fermentative yeasts (EUCAST 7.1 document). Although this broth microdilution assay is similar to the CLSI method, medium composition (standard RPMI-1640 supplemented with 2% dextrose), inoculum size (approximately 10^5 CFU/mL), and incubation time (24 h) are quite different; CLSI breakpoints should not be used to interpret EUCAST MICs. Description of this method is not included in this chapter but can be found elsewhere [2].

9.2 RELEVANCE

According to the CLSI recommendations, yeast susceptibility testing should be performed to determine patterns of susceptibility of *Candida* spp. and *C. neoformans* to available antifungal agents by conducting periodic testing in individual medical centers. For a yeast recovered from a clinical sample antifungal susceptibility testing should be performed when a pathogen is recovered from an invasive infection, when therapeutic failure has occurred, in instances where appropriate therapy is critical to the clinical outcome for a patient with a severe life-threatening infection, when long-term therapy is necessary, and when enough information is not available to make an empirical judgment about a therapy [1]. The CLSI M27-A2 document describes broth macro- and microdilution tests. For the development of the M27-A2 document, the Subcommittee on Antifungal Susceptibility Tests conducted several multicenter studies [3–6] to evaluate the best medium, inoculum size, temperature, duration of incubation, and endpoint definition. The test medium recommended is RPMI-1640 broth (RPMI) with [3-(*N*-morpholino)]-propanesulfonic acid (MOPS) buffer. However, this broth does not appear to discriminate between resistant and susceptible strains to amphotericin B, and growth of *C. neoformans* is poor in this medium. The CLSI subcommittee has established breakpoints for fluconazole, itraconazole, voriconazole, and 5-FC (flucytosine), as well as MIC ranges for two American Type Culture Collection (ATCC) quality control strains [1,6–10]. To appreciate the clinical value of the *in vitro* antifungal testing result, one must understand that the predictor value of *in vitro* susceptibility in bacterial infections has been accurately summarized as the "90–60 rule." Infections due to susceptible isolates respond to therapy approximately 90% of the time, whereas infections due to resistant isolates respond approximately 60% of the time. There is now a considerable body of data indicating that standardized antifungal susceptibility testing for *Candida* spp. and some triazoles provides results that have a predictive utility consistent with this rule. However, host factors, rather than azole resistance, can be responsible for clinical failure. For voriconazole, pharmacokinetics and pharmacodynamic parameters (PK/PD) indicate that a 24-h free-drug AUC/MIC (where AUC is the area under the curve) ratio of 20 is predictive of efficacy and recommended doses would produce free-drug AUCs of ~20 mg [11]. Therefore, it can be predicted that current voriconazole recommended dosing regimens could be used successfully to treat patients infected with isolates for which voriconazole MICs are ≤1 mg/mL as determined by the reference method. The PD parameter that predicts efficacy for fluconazole is approximately 25 (AUC/MIC). For itraconazole, an MIC within the susceptible-dose dependent (S-DD) range indicates the need for plasma concentrations >0.5 mg/mL for an optimal response. Actual breakpoints are listed in Table 9.1.

The CLSI group has made no recommendations for other yeasts or yeastlike organisms besides *Candida* spp. and *C. neoformans*. Since the publication of the M27-A document, several additional methods have been developed (CLSI disk test for yeasts and commercial Etest and colorimetric YeastOne methods, among others); however, these methods are not included in the CLSI M27-A2 document.

In Sections 9.3 and 9.4, the design of the CSLI broth macro- and microdilution methods for susceptibility testing of yeasts, respectively, are described. This is followed by descriptions of Etest, the colorimetric YeastOne method, and the disk diffusion method.

TABLE 9.1
(CLSI) MIC Interpretive Criteria (breakpoints [μg/mL])

Antifungal	Susceptible	S-DD[a]	Intermediate	Resistant
Fluconazole[b]	≤8	16–32		≥64
Itraconazole[c]	0.12	0.25–0.5		1
5-FC[d]	≤4		8–16	32
Voriconazole[e]	1	2		4

[a] S-DD, susceptible-dose dependent on achieving maximum dosages or blood level to obtain optimal response, e.g., ≥400 mg/day of fluconazole or ≥0.5 μg/mL of itraconazole blood levels measured by high-pressure liquid chromatography (HPLC).

[b] Based on mucosal infections and limited data from invasive infections [1]. *C. krusei* are intrinsically resistant to fluconazole.

[c] Based on mucosal infections. Breakpoints for invasive infections are not available [1].

[d] Based on historical data and drug pharmacokinetics.

[e] Based on mucosal and invasive infections (Phase III clinical trials) and listed in M27-S2 [7].

9.3 BROTH MACRODILUTION METHOD

9.3.1 INTRODUCTION

The design of the CLSI broth macro- and microdilution methods for susceptibility testing of yeasts is similar to that for antibacterial agents. These procedures involve preparing a series of drug dilutions, each containing a specific concentration of an antifungal agent. If a more practical method should yield results similar to those obtained by using the CLSI methods, it is considered an acceptable method for use in the clinical laboratory. Validation of an alternative method is the responsibility of the laboratory.

9.3.2 MATERIALS

1. Antimicrobial sources:
    a. United States Pharmacopeia (USP).
    b. Sigma Chemical Company.
    c. The antifungal agent manufacturer.
        • Some antifungal agents can be obtained from the drug manufacturer at no charge through the pharmaceutical company's customer service department, or equivalent department, or your local pharmaceutical representatives.
2. Agar media:
    a. Sabouraud dextrose agar (SAB) plates.
    b. CHROMagar plates.
        • SAB plates may be used to grow isolates for inoculum preparation and to validate the density of the inoculum (colony counts). CHROMagar plates can be used to verify the purity of each isolate.
3. Test medium.
    a. RPMI (with glutamine, without bicarbonate, and with a pH indicator) is the broth medium recommended for the susceptibility testing of yeasts. The medium should be buffered with MOPS (0.164 M/L) mol/L. For the composition of the medium, see Table 9.2.
    b. Procedure for making the medium:
        • 10.4 g powdered medium (Sigma catalog # R 6504).
        • 34.53 g MOPS buffer (Sigma catalog # M 3183 or other manufacturer).

TABLE 9.2
Composition of RPMI-1640 Medium

Constituent	mg/L
L-Arginine (free base)	200
L-Aspargine	50
L-Aspartic acid	20
L-Cystine. 2HCl	65.2
L-Glutamic acid	300
Glycine	10
L-Histidine (free base)	15
L-Hydroxypropoline	20
L-Isoleucine	50
L-Leucine	50
L-Lysine. HCl	40
L-Methionine	15
L-Phenylalanine	15
L-Proline	20
L-Serine	30
L-Threonine	20
L-Tryptophan	5
L-Tyrosine. 2Na	28.83
L-Valine	20
Biotin	0.2
D-Pantothenic acid	0.25
Choline chloride	3
Folic acid	1
Myoinositol	35
Niacinamide	1
Para amino benzoic acid	1
Pyridoxine HCl	1
Riboflavin	0.2
Thiamine HCl	1
Vitamin B_{12}	0.005
Calcium nitrate H_2O	100
Potassium chloride	400
Magnesium sulfate (anhydrous)	48.84
Sodium chloride	6,000
Sodium phosphate, dibasic (anhydrous)	800
D-Glucose	2,000
Glutathione, reduced	1
Phenol red, Na	5.3

1) Dissolve the powdered medium in 900 mL distilled water.
2) Add MOPS and stir until dissolved.
3) Adjust the pH to 7.0 at 25°C using 10 mol/L NaOH.
4) Add additional water to bring the medium to a final volume of 1 L.
5) Sterilize by filtration using a 0.22-μm filter, and dispense 100 or 500 mL volumes (depending on the volume needed per run) into sterile glass screw top bottles.
6) Store at 4°C (this solution has a 3-month shelf life, and bottles should be labeled with the preparation and expiration dates).

7) Check the sterility of the medium by incubating five tubes, each containing 2 mL of the medium per liter, at 35°C. In addition, visually inspect the solution for obvious contamination before using it
- The medium can be purchased as a powder (Sigma) or ready to use (Biowhittaker catalog # 04-525F)

4. Sterile saline (8.5 g/L NaCl; 0.85% saline)
5. Supplies:
   a. Test tubes
   - Standard laboratory sterile screw or snap cap test tubes (e.g., 12×75 mm plastic) that hold at least 5 mL can be used for making drug dilutions (13 tubes per antifungal agent and strain) and 16×150 mm tubes for other purposes.
   b. Petri dishes
   - Standard 100×15 mm round petri dishes (two dishes per strain, one with SAB for preparing the inoculum and another to count the number of CFU/mL)
   c. Pipettes (0.1-, 0.25-, 0.5-, 1-, and 5-mL sterile serological pipettes)
   d. Pipetting aid for serological pipettes
   e. Swabs and loops
   f. A 0.5 McFarland standard
      1) Procedure for making McFarland standards [1].
         a) Combine 0.5 mL of 0.048 mol/L $BaCl_2$ (1.175% w/v $BaCl_2$ $2H_2O$) and 99.5 mL of 0.18 mol/L H_2SO_4 (1%v/v)
         b) Mix the solution thoroughly
         c) Using the same size screw-cap tubes that are to be used for the preparation of yeast inoculum suspensions, aliquot 4–6 mL into each tube
         d) Seal the caps with tape or Parafilm®
         e) Store the tubes in the dark at room temperature
         f) Mix the standard solution well prior to each use
            - Commercially available McFarland standards can be obtained from a number of vendors, including PML, Hardy Diagnostics, and Remel
      2) Validation of the McFarland standard turbidity
         a) Absorbance
            - Read the optical density (OD) of the standard on a spectrophotometer with a 1-cm light path using a matched set of cuvettes
            - The absorbance should be read at 530 nm
         b) Colony count
            - The density of the McFarland standard is validated by performing a colony count of a suspension of either *Candida parapsilosis* ATCC 22019, *C. krusei* ATCC 6258, or *C. albicans* ATCC 90028 that is equivalent to the turbidity of the standard
            - The density of the McFarland standard should be verified monthly by the absorbance or colony count method
            - A 0.5 McFarland standard is equivalent to $1–5 \times 10^6$ yeast/mL (the density recommended by the CLSI for the stock inoculum)
      3) Other turbidity standards
         a) Manufactured latex standards
            - Latex standards have a two year shelf life and are not light sensitive
            - Latex standards are available from several manufacturers, including Remel (Lenexa, KS; catalog product # 20-410). The density of latex standards should be verified monthly as described for the McFarland standard
         b) Turbidity meters
            - Available from Vitek and MicroScan Systems

- These should be calibrated with turbidity standards
- The frequency of calibration depends on the manufacturer
6. Equipment:
    a. Autoclave
    b. Water bath (48°C–50°C)
    c. Vortex mixer
    d. Incubator set at 35°C ± 1°C
    e. Spectrophotometer

9.3.3 QUALITY CONTROL

Quality control organisms are used to verify that the antifungal concentrations were prepared properly, but their use does not test the quality of the medium.

1. Quality control strains:
    - *C. parapsilosis* ATCC 22019
    - *C. krusei* ATCC 6258
2. Frequency of quality control testing
    - At least one of the above isolates should be tested with every run and should be performed using the same procedure used for the clinical isolates
    - Quality control strains should be preserved following the procedures described by the CLSI [1]
3. Evaluating quality control MIC results
    - The MIC values for quality control organisms must be within the acceptable ranges for the antifungal agent being tested for the results to be considered valid. These ranges are listed in the current CLSI M27 document and in Table 9.3 and Table 9.4.

9.3.4 PROCEDURE

The purity and viability of the organism should be validated before testing is performed. Isolates that are being tested must be streaked at least twice onto a SAB plate before susceptibility testing is performed to ensure the purity and viability of the test organism.

1. Technical notes.
    - It is important to completely plan out the entire procedure because it involves many steps over several days. It is also important to understand all the steps of the procedure before beginning. The technologist is advised to read and understand the CLSI M27 document before proceeding.

TABLE 9.3
Quality Control MIC Ranges of Antifungal Agents for Broth Macrodilution (48 h)

	MIC Ranges (µg/mL)	
Antifungal	*C. parapsilosis* ATCC 22019	*C. krusei* ATCC 6258
Amphotericin B	0.25–1	0.5–2
Fluconazole	2–8	16–64
Itraconazole	0.06–0.25	0.12–0.5
Ketoconazole	0.06–0.25	0.12–0.5
5-FC[a]	0.12–0.5	4–16

Based on the M27-A method described in [1].

[a] 5-FC = 5-flucytosine.

TABLE 9.4

Quality Control MIC Ranges of Antifungal Agents for Broth Microdilution

| | MIC Ranges (µg/mL) | | | |
| | C. parapsilosis ATCC 22019 | | C. krusei ATCC 6258 | |
Antifungal Agent	24 h	48 h	24 h	48 h
Amphotericin B	0.25–2	0.5–4	0.5–2	1–4
5-FC[a]	0.06–0.25	0.12–0.5	4–16	8–32
Caspofungin	0.25–1	0.5–4	0.12–1	0.25–1
Fluconazole	0.5–4	1–4	8–64	16–128
Itraconazole	0.12–0.5	0.12–0.5	0.12–1	0.25–1
Ketoconazole	0.03–0.25	0.06–0.5	0.12–1	0.25–1
Posaconazole	0.06–0.25	0.06–0.25	0.06–0.5	0.12–1
Ravuconazole	0.016–0.12	0.03–0.25	0.06–0.5	0.25–1
Voriconazole	0.016–0.12	0.03–0.25	0.06–0.5	0.12–1
Anidulafungin	0.25–2	0.5–2	0.03–0.12	0.03–0.12

Based on the M27 method described in [1, 7].

[a]5-FC = 5-flucytosine.

- Determine the number of isolates to be tested, the number of antifungal agents, and the range of concentrations for each antifungal.
- The antifungal range should include drug concentrations that are at least two dilutions below and two dilutions above the breakpoint values for that antifungal. The break points and the concentration ranges are listed in the CLSI M27-A2, CLSI M27-S2 (voriconazole by microdilution method) documents [1,7] and in Table 9.1).

2. Tubes

   a. Based on the number of strains and the antifungal agents to be tested, calculate the number of tubes needed (# strains × number of antifungal dilutions + controls = # of tubes/antifungal).

   b. Calculate the total amount of RPMI needed (# of strains × 12 mL = total volume/strain + 12 mL to prepare antifungal dilutions).

3. Antifungal stock solution preparation

   a. Antifungal powders should be stored according to the manufacturer's instructions. Powders are assayed by the manufacturer to determine the potency of the antifungal agent. This information must be used when making stock solutions as follows:

$$\text{Weight (mg)} = \frac{\text{volume (mL)} \times \text{desired concentration (mg/mL)}}{\text{antifungal potency (mg/mg)}}$$

   b. When possible, at least 10 mg of the antifungal powder should be weighed out at one time.

   c. All stock solutions should be made at the same concentration. Stock solutions of 1,280 µg/mL work well for most standard susceptibility testing ranges for water-soluble agents and 1,600 µg/mL for water-insoluble ones.

   d. The antifungal powder should be dissolved in water or other appropriate solvent as shown in Table 9.5.

   e. Stock solutions should be stored carefully sealed in either glass, polypropylene, or polyethylene sterile tubes at –70°C (or lower) in small aliquot volumes (approximately 1.5 mL). Stock solutions should not be stored in frost-free freezers.

TABLE 9.5
Solvents and Diluents for Preparation of Dilutions of Antifungal Agents

Antifungal Agent[a]	Solvent[b]	Diluent
Amphotericin B	DMSO	RPMI-1640
Itraconazole	DMSO	RPMI-1640
Ketoconazole	DMSO	RPMI-1640
Fluconazole	Water	RPMI-1640
Voriconazole	DMSO	RPMI-1640
Posaconazole	DMSO or PEG200	RPMI-1640
Ravuconazole	DMSO	RPMI-1640
Caspofungin	Water	RPMI-1640
Micafungin	Water	RPMI-1640
Anidulafungin	DMSO	RPMI-1640
5-FC	Water	RPMI-1640

[a] 5-FC = 5-flucytosine.
[b] DMSO = dimethyl sulfoxide; PEG200 = polyethylene glycol, mol. wt. of 200.

f. Stock solutions should be accurately labeled with the antifungal's name and concentration, the amount in the tube, and the preparation and expiration dates (either six months after the stock solution was made or the manufacturer's expiration date for the powder).

g. Stock solutions should be discarded at the end of each day and never refrozen.

h. Because of the high concentration of antifungal in the stock solution, sterilizing the solution is not necessary.

i. If there is a need to sterilize the antifungal stock solution, it should be done using a membrane such as a 0.22-μm membrane.
  - Paper, asbestos, or sintered glass filters should not be used because they may bind to the agent.
  - Filter sterilization is not recommended because the antifungal agent may be retained in the filter.

4. Drug dilution preparation.

a. Preparation of water-soluble antifungal agents (fluconazole, 5-FC, caspofungin, micafugin). (Figure 9.1) [12].

  1) Label 10 (16 × 150 mm) tubes 2–11 with the antifungal name and the appropriate concentration.

  2) Add appropriate amounts of sterile RPMI to each tube (see Figure 9.1 and M27-A2) as follows:
    - Add 1 mL of RPMI to tubes 2 and 11.
    - Add 0.5 mL of RPMI to tubes 3, 5, and 8.
    - Add 0.75 mL of RPMI to tubes 6 and 9.
    - Add 1.5 mL of RPMI to tube 4.
    - Add 1.75 mL of RPMI to tubes 7 and 10.

  3) Add 1 mL of the stock solution (1,280 μg/mL) to the first antifungal dilution tube (tube 2).

  4) Transfer from tube 2, 0.5 mL to tubes 3 and 4.

  5) Transfer from tube 4, 0.5 mL to tube 5 and 0.25 mL to tubes 6 and 7.

  6) Transfer from tube 7, 0.5 mL to tube 8 and 0.25 mL to tubes 9 and 10.

  7) Transfer from tube 10, 1 mL to tube 11.

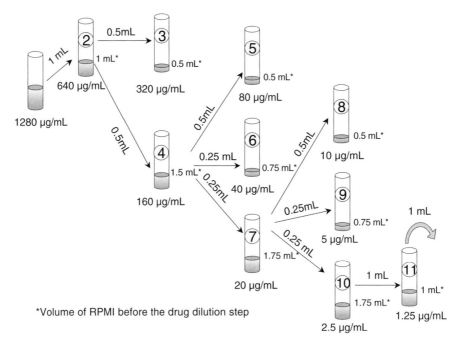

FIGURE 9.1 Scheme to perform the dilutions of water-soluble antifungal agents.

8) Finally, discard 1 mL from tube 11.
- Vortex each tube before the dilution step.
- Notice that when dilutions have been prepared, each tube contains 1 mL.
- Nine sets of MIC tubes may be prepared with these volumes.

b. Preparation of MIC tubes for water-soluble agents (Figure 9.2) [12].
1) Place the tubes containing the drug dilutions (1 mL each) in an organized fashion, going from the highest to the lowest drug concentration.
2) Label rows of 10 tubes (12 × 75 mm) with the final drug concentrations (64–0.12 µg/mL).
3) Dispense 0.1 mL from each drug dilution tube into the bottom of each corresponding MIC tube using a repetitive or reservoir pipette with a syringe of 1 mL.
- Beginning with the lowest concentration, the same tip can be used.
4) Close the tubes with screw caps (plastic or metal caps), and store them at –70°C for up 6 months.
5) On the day of the test, allow the tubes to thaw at room temperature before inoculation (about 1 h). Each tube is inoculated with 0.9 mL of the corresponding diluted inoculum.

c. Preparation of antifungal dilutions for water-insoluble agents (Figure 9.3) [12].
- The dilutions of water-insoluble antifungal agents (amphotericin B, itraconazole, ketoconazole, posaconazole, ravuconazole, voriconazole, and anidulafungin) must be prepared by using a solvent such as dimethyl sulfoxide (DMSO) (see Table 9.5).
- It is important to prepare the stock solution and drug dilutions in the solvent (follow the scheme of the dilution and instructions below) to avoid dilution artifacts that can result from the precipitation of a compound of low solubility (e.g., itraconazole) in aqueous media, thereby producing erroneous drug dilutions.
1) All the test tubes should be labeled with the antifungal's name and the appropriate concentration as described here for the broth macrodilution method.

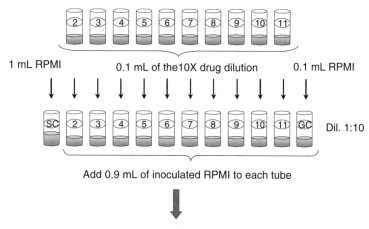

FIGURE 9.2 Preparation of MIC tubes for water-soluble antifungal agents.

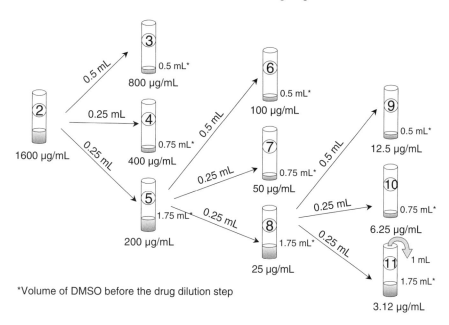

FIGURE 9.3 Scheme to perform the dilutions of water-insoluble antifungal agents.

2) Add the appropriate amounts of DMSO to each labeled tube 3–11 (see Figure 9.3 and M27-A2 [12]) as follows:
- Add 0.5 mL of DMSO to tubes 3, 6, and 9.
- Add 0.75 mL of DMSO to tubes 4, 7, and 10.
- Add 1.75 mL of DMSO to tubes 5, 8, and 11.

3) Label the stock solution tube (1,600 µg/mL) as tube 2.

4) Transfer from tube 2, 0.5 mL to tube 3 and 0.25 mL to tubes 4 and 5.

5) Transfer from tube 5, 0.5 mL to tube 6 and 0.25 mL to tubes 7 and 8.

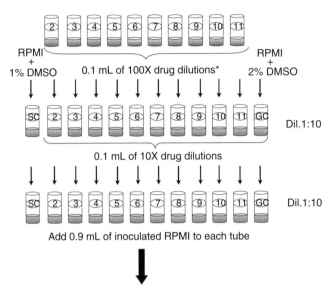

FIGURE 9.4 Preparation of MIC tubes for water-insoluble antifungal agents.

      6) Transfer from tube 8, 0.5 mL to tube 9 and 0.25 mL to tubes 10 and 11.
      7) Finally, discard 1 mL from tube 11.
- Vortex each tube before the dilution step.
- Notice that when dilutions have been prepared, all tubes contain 1 mL.

   d. Preparation of MIC tubes for water-insoluble antifungal agents (Figure 9.4) [12].
      1) Place the tubes containing the drug dilutions (1 mL) in an organized fashion, from the highest to the lowest drug concentration and label rows of 10 tubes (12×75 mm) with the final drug concentrations (16–0.03 μg/mL).
      2) Prepare a 1:10 dilution by mixing 0.9 mL of RPMI with 0.1 mL from each drug concentration, and mix well with a vortex mixer.
      3) Nine sets of MIC tubes may be prepared with these volumes.
      4) Dispense 0.1 mL from each concentration into the bottom of each sterile plastic test tube (12×75 mm), using a repetitive or reservoir pipette with a syringe of 1 mL.
- Beginning with the lowest concentration, the same tip can be used for all the test tubes.
      5) Close the tubes with plastic or metal screw caps, and store them at –70°C for up to 6 months.
      6) On the day of the test, allow the tubes to thaw at room temperature before inoculation (about 1 h). Each tube is inoculated with 0.9 mL of the corresponding inoculum. When inoculated, the final concentration of DMSO is 1%.
  5. Inoculum preparation.
- Direct colony suspension (Figure 9.5) [12].
- The inoculum is prepared from pure cultures grown on SAB at 35°C for 24 h (*Candida* spp.) and 72 h (*C. neoformans*).

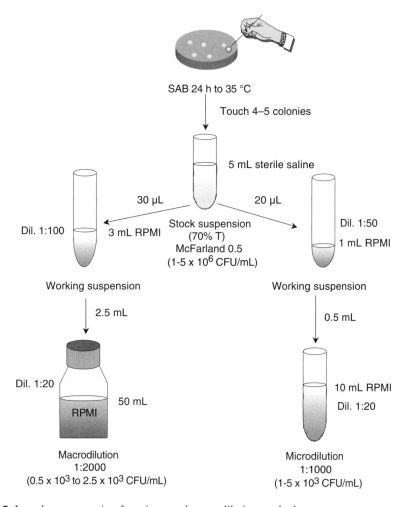

FIGURE 9.5 Inoculum preparation for micro- and macrodilution methods.

    a. Lightly touch five colonies (at least 1 mm-diameter) of similar morphology using a loop or swab.

    b. Suspend the yeast cells in 5 mL of sterile 0.85% NaCl, and mix the cell suspension using a vortex mixer for 15–20 s.

    c. Adjust the turbidity of the inoculum to the density of a 0.5 McFarland standard at 530 nm wavelength. This procedure yields a yeast stock suspension of $1–5 \times 10^6$ cells/mL.

    d. Prepare the working suspension by making a 1:100 dilution of the stock suspension followed by a 1:20 dilution with RPMI, which results in 5×10^2 to 2.5×10^3 CFU/mL.

       • Vortex each tube before the dilution step.

       • If possible, the preparation of inocula for one run should be completed within 30 minutes, otherwise, the suspensions may be held at 2°C–8°C for up to 2 h.

  6. Inoculation of the tubes.

    a. The drug concentration tubes should be organized before the preparation of the inocula in ascending order.

    b. Include two tubes, for positive (growth control) and negative (sterility) controls.

    c. Calculate the volume of the standardized inoculum–broth suspension needed for each isolate, including the growth control tubes (for example, for one antifungal agent and yeast, 10 mL of inoculated RPMI are needed), at the desired final concentration (5×10^2 to 2.5×10^3 CFU/mL).

- Begin inoculating the lowest drug concentration to be tested and move to the highest concentration.

d. The two control tubes contain 0.1 mL of RPMI (or the solvent) rather than the antifungal and either 0.9 mL of the diluted inoculum (growth control) or 0.9 mL of RPMI (sterility control).
- The growth control tube ensures that the inoculum is viable and actively growing, and indicates the 100% growth of the isolate.
- The negative control tube provides evidence of medium sterility.
- The inoculum control plate confirms that the inoculum is properly standardized.

e. Inoculum control plates should be prepared for each strain on either SAB or CHRO-Magar medium. The latter medium can determine both the purity and the density of the inoculum.
1) Remove 10 μL from the growth control tube to a CHROMagar plate or SAB before the incubation step.
2) Incubate for 24–48 h at 35°C, and count the CFUs (5–25 CFUs).

7. Incubation.
- MIC tubes and growth control plates and tubes are incubated in an aerobic incubator without CO_2 at 35°C for 48 h (*Candida* spp.) to 72 h (*C. neoformans*). The 24-h MIC results may also be obtained, and the tubes are then immediately reincubated [13,14].

9.3.5 MACRODILUTION MIC DEFINITIONS

9.3.5.1 MIC Definition for Azoles, echinocandins, and 5-FC

The MIC is the lowest concentration of the antifungal agent that produces an 80% (see Section 9.3.4) or more growth inhibition (light turbidity or optically clear) as visually compared with the growth control after 48 h (or 24 h for echinocandins) of incubation.

For the azoles (fluconazole, itraconazole, ketoconazole, posaconazole, ravuconazole, and voriconazole) and echinocandins, there is usually a slight turbidity at concentrations above the MIC (mostly with *C. albicans* and *C. tropicalis*). This is known as the *trailing effect.*

9.3.5.2 MIC Definition for Amphotericin B

The MIC is the lowest drug concentration that prevents any discernible growth (optically clear) after 48 h of incubation.

9.3.6 BROTH MACRODILUTION RESULTS

9.3.6.1 Reading

The tubes should be shaken manually before reading to homogenize the turbidity.

Compare the amount of growth in the growth-control tubes with the amount of growth in each MIC tube. The 80% turbidity can be estimated by diluting 1:5 the contents of the growth control tube (0.2 mL plus 0.8 mL of medium). For this 1:5 dilution, use the negative control tube.

9.3.6.2 Interpretation

For the interpretation of MIC values, consult the latest edition of the CLSI M27 and M27-S2 (voriconazole by the microdilution method) documents [1,7] for the appropriate breakpoints for the antifungal agent being tested (also see Table 9.1).

9.3.6.3 Reporting

Quality control values for a given antifungal agent must be within range to report susceptibility values for that agent. MIC values should be reported with their appropriate categorical interpretation: resistant (R), intermediate (I), susceptible dose dependent (S-DD), or susceptible (S).

9.3.7 ADVANTAGES

1. Since susceptibility testing is not an assay that must be performed for all yeasts, the broth macrodilution has the advantage of testing only a single isolate and agent.
2. This procedure does not require specialized equipment.
3. The macrodilution procedure may give a less subjective measurement of the growth inhibition than does the microdilution method described in Section 9.4.

9.3.8 LIMITATIONS

1. The macrodilution procedure cannot be used for *Malassezia* spp. isolates because some of these species require oil overlay for growth.
2. The macrodilution procedure is not an ideal method for routine testing or for testing multiple isolates because it is labor-intensive and technically demanding.
3. Even for an experienced microbiologist, it is difficult to interpret MICs by this procedure because of the trailing growth of azoles.
4. *C. neoformans* isolates do not grow well in RPMI and must be read after 72 h of incubation.
5. Amphotericin B resistance is not well detected by this method.
6. Breakpoints are only available for fluconazole, itraconazole, 5-FC, and voriconazole against *Candida* spp.

9.3.9 CONCLUSIONS

This procedure should be attempted only with the guidance of an experienced individual; if an alternative method is chosen, its results should match those of the CLSI standard.

9.4 BROTH MICRODILUTION METHOD

9.4.1 INTRODUCTION

Of the two procedures described by the CLSI, the broth microdilution method is the most practical one for use in the clinical laboratory or for use when testing a large number of isolates against a given set of antifungal agents. This procedure involves a microtiter tray containing standard twofold dilutions of antifungal agents to be inoculated with standardized yeast suspensions. Each microtiter tray can be prepared with several antifungal agents or with only a single agent. The latter is the procedure described in this chapter.

9.4.2 MATERIALS

1. Antimicrobial sources (refer to Section 9.3.2)
2. Agar media (refer to Section 9.3.2)
3. Test medium, RPMI-1640 and sterile saline (refer to Section 9.3.2).
4. Supplies
   The same supplies listed under the broth macrodilution method are needed (refer to Section 9.3.2), plus the following items.

a. Microtiter trays
  • Sterile 96 U-shaped-well microtiter trays (M27-A2 document [1]) are available from a number of manufacturers, including Dynatech and Nalgene Nunc International.
  b. Micropipettes (single and multichannel) and sterile tips for 100-μL volumes
5. Equipment.
  a. Reading devices
  • Mirror reader or plate reader

9.4.3 QUALITY CONTROL

1. Quality control strains:
  • *C. parapsilosis* ATCC 22019
  • *C. krusei* ATCC 6258
2. Frequency of quality control testing
  • See instructions under the broth macrodilution method, and, in addition, test one of these isolates with each new lot of microdilution trays prior to testing clinical specimens.
3. Evaluating quality control MIC results
  • As for the broth macrodilution method, the MIC values for a quality control organism tested must be within acceptable ranges for the antifungal agent being tested. These ranges are listed in the current CLSI M27 and M27-S documents and in Table 9.4.

9.4.4 PROCEDURE

1. Antifungal stock preparation (see the broth macrodilution method in Section 9.3.4).
2. Preparation of water-soluble antifungal agents (Figure 9.1) [12].
  a. Water-soluble antifungal agents
    1) Label 10 (16 × 150 mm) tubes 2–11
    2) Add the appropriate amounts of sterile RPMI to each tube as follows:
      • Add 1 mL of RPMI to tubes 2 and 11.
      • Add 0.5 mL of RPMI to tubes 3, 5, and 8.
      • Add 0.75 mL of RPMI to tubes 6 and 9.
      • Add 1.5 mL of RPMI to tube 4.
      • Add 1.75 mL of RPMI to tubes 7 and 10.
    3) Add 1 mL of the stock solution (1,280 µg/mL) to the first antifungal dilution tube (tube 2).
    4) Transfer from tube 2, 0.5 mL to tubes 3 and 4.
    5) Transfer from tube 4, 0.5 mL to tube 5 and 0.25 mL to tubes 6 and 7.
    6) Transfer from tube 7, 0.5 mL to tube 8 and 0.25 mL to tubes 9 and 10.
    7) Transfer from tube 10, 1 mL to tube 11.
    8) Finally, discard 1 mL from tube 11.
      • Vortex each tube before the dilution step.
      • Notice that when dilutions have been prepared, each tube contains 1 mL.
  b. Preparation of microdilution trays for water-soluble antifungal agents (Figure 9.6) [12].
    1) Place tubes containing the drug dilutions (1 mL each) in an organized fashion, going from the highest to the lowest drug concentration.
    2) Prepare a 1:5 dilution by adding 4 mL of RPMI to the drug dilution tubes, and mix each tube well with a vortex mixer.

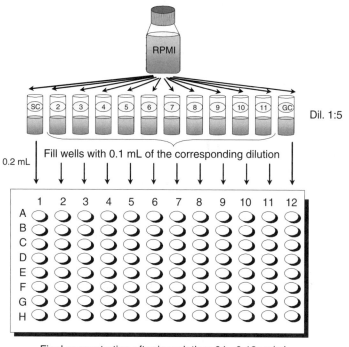

Add 4 mL RPMI to the antifungal dilution tubes

RPMI

SC 2 3 4 5 6 7 8 9 10 11 GC   Dil. 1:5

Fill wells with 0.1 mL of the corresponding dilution

0.2 mL

	1	2	3	4	5	6	7	8	9	10	11	12
A												
B												
C												
D												
E												
F												
G												
H												

Final concentration after inoculation: 64 –0.12 µg/mL

SC: sterility control
GC: growth control

Trays are now ready for the inoculation step.

FIGURE 9.6 Preparation of microdilution trays for water-soluble antifungal agents.

3) Using a dispensing device, transfer 0.1 mL from each of the drug dilution tubes to the appropriate wells of each microtiter tray (Figure 9.6) [12].
- The concentration of the antifungal agent in each well is 2 times the concentration needed after this step.
- It is not recommended to use volumes smaller than 0.1 mL because the medium can evaporate during the incubation step.
4) Add 0.2 mL of RPMI to the wells in column 1 and 0.1 mL to the wells in column 12. These wells will serve as the negative (sterility) and positive (growth control) control wells, respectively.
5) The prepared tray should be sealed in a plastic bag and placed at –70°C until needed. Prepared trays should not be stored in a self-defrosting freezer as this type of freezer will shorten the shelf life of the antifungal agent in the tray. Prepared trays should not be refrozen after being thawed.
6) The shelf life of the tray is the expiration date of the antifungal being used or 6 months, whichever one comes first.
c. Preparation of water-insoluble antifungal agents (Figure 9.3) [12].
- The dilutions of water-insoluble antifungal agents (amphotericin B, itraconazole, ketoconazole, posaconazole, ravuconazole, voriconazole, and anidulafungin) must be prepared by using a solvent such as DMSO or another appropriate solvent (Table 9.5).
- It is important to prepare the stock solution and drug dilutions in the solvent (follow the scheme of dilution and instructions below) to avoid dilution artifacts that can

result from the precipitation of a compound of low solubility (e.g., itraconazole) in aqueous media, thereby producing erroneous drug dilutions.

1) Label 9 (12 × 75 mm) tubes 3–11.
2) Add the appropriate amounts of DMSO to each tube as follows:
   - Add 0.5 mL of DMSO to tubes 3, 6, and 9.
   - Add 0.75 mL of DMSO to tubes 4, 7, and 10.
   - Add 1.75 mL of DMSO to tubes 5, 8, and 11.
3) Label the stock solution tube (1,600 µg/mL) as tube 2.
4) Transfer from tube 2, 0.5 mL to tube 3 and 0.25 mL to tubes 4 and 5.
5) Transfer from tube 5, 0.5 mL to tube 6 and 0.25 mL to tubes 7 and 8.
6) Transfer from tube 8, 0.5 mL to tube 9 and 0.25 mL to tubes 10 and 11.
7) Finally, discard 1 mL from tube 11.
   - Vortex each tube before the dilution step.
   - Notice that when dilutions have been prepared, all tubes contain 1 mL.

d. Preparation of microdilution trays for water-insoluble antifungal agents (Figure 9.7) [12].
   1) Place the tubes containing the drug dilutions (1 mL) in an organized fashion, from the highest to the lowest drug concentration. Label a row of ten tubes with the final drug concentrations.
   2) Prepare a 1:50 dilution by mixing 4.9 mL of RPMI with 0.1 mL from each drug dilution tube, and mix well with a vortex mixer.

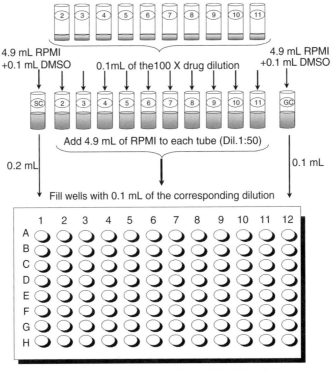

FIGURE 9.7 Preparation of microdilution trays for water-insoluble antifungal agents.

3) Using a dispensing device, transfer 0.1 mL from each of the final drug dilution tubes to the appropriate well in each microtiter tray.
4) Add 0.2 mL of RPMI plus 2% DMSO (or the solvent used) to column 1 of the microtiter tray and 0.1 mL of RPMI plus 2% DMSO (or the solvent that was used) to column 12. These two wells will serve as the negative (sterility control) and positive (growth control) control wells, respectively.
   • The concentration of the antifungal agents in the wells is now 2 times the concentration needed.
   • The concentration of DMSO in the wells is now 2%
   • It is not recommended to use volumes smaller than 0.1 mL because the medium can evaporate during the incubation step
   • The prepared trays should be sealed and stored in a plastic bag at −70°C as described above for water-soluble agents.
3. Inoculum preparation
   a. Prepare the stock inoculum suspension as described above under the broth macrodilution method (see Section 9.3.4 and Figure 9.5).
   b. Prepare the working suspension by making a 1:50 dilution, and further diluting 1:20 with the medium to obtain two times the test inoculum concentration ($1–5 \times 10^3$ CFU/mL). Mix with a vortex mixer before the dilution step.
4. Inoculation of the microtiter trays
   a. Allow the microdilution trays to thaw at room temperature under a hood. It will take approximately 2 h to thaw if they are stacked four trays high or 45 min if unstacked.
   b. Remove the sealing tape as soon as the panels are taken from the freezer and cover them with a clean lid to avoid contamination.
   c. Thawed trays should be inoculated within 1 h of thawing.
   d. Fill each row of the microtiter tray from wells 2–12 with 0.1 mL of the working inoculum suspension (well mixed with a vortex mixer) using a single or a multichannel pipette. If using another device, follow the manufacturer's instructions as to what inoculum concentration should be added to the inoculum reservoir.
      • Eight clinical isolates or seven isolates and one of the quality control isolates can be tested in one tray.
   e. A purity control agar plate should be prepared for every isolate being tested. Colony count plates can also serve as the purity control. For colony counts, transfer 10 μL of inoculum to an agar plate (CHROMagar or SAB) from the positive control well before the incubation step and streak for isolated colonies. The CFU per plate must range from 5–30.
5. Incubation
   Microtiter trays and purity agar plates should be incubated in an aerobic environment stacked no more than four high at 35°C for 46–48 h for *Candida* spp. and 72 h for *C. neoformans*.

9.4.5 MICRODILUTION MIC DEFINITIONS

9.4.5.1 Microdilution MICs of Azoles and 5-FC

The MIC is the lowest concentration of the antifungal agent that substantially inhibits growth (about half, or 50%, or less growth than in the growth control) of the organism as detected visually after 24 h (caspofungin and other echinocandins) or 48 h of incubation.

For azoles, echinocandins, and 5-FC, there is slight turbidity at concentrations above the MIC (trailing effect), mainly for *C. albicans* and *C. tropicalis*.

9.4.5.2 Microdilution MICs of Amphotericin B

The MIC is the lowest drug concentration that prevents any discernible growth (optically clear) after 48 h of incubation.

9.4.6 BROTH MICRODILUTION RESULTS

9.4.6.1 Reading

It is important to disperse (or homogenize) the growth in each well by pipetting, vortexing, or stirring before reading. This step is helpful for strains that have abundant trailing growth at 48 h.

1. Visual reading
   a. Remove the trays and colony count and/or purity plates from the incubator.
   b. Check the purity plate. If contamination is observed, purify the isolate and repeat the MIC procedure. If no contamination is apparent, read the MIC trays.
   c. Place the tray on a reading device (light box, concave mirror reader, or plate reader).
   d. The growth control well must have sufficient growth.
      - If adequate growth is not achieved, the test must be repeated. Adequate growth will depend on the species being tested. Isolates that produce small colonies on agar plates will usually produce small buttons in the microdilution trays.
   e. Determine the MIC endpoint as described in Sections 9.4.5.1 and 9.4.5.2 (Table 9.6).
2. Spectrophotometric reading
   - This procedure is not included in the CLSI document, but sometimes it is helpful; it has been demonstrated that it provides results that are similar to those obtained by visual reading [13].
   a. Set the spectrophotometer at 405 nm and determine the optical density (OD) of each well.
      - Similar results are obtained using 450-, 492-, 550-, or 600-nm filters.
   b. Before reading, agitate the trays to ensure a uniform turbidity. The agitation can be made by either pipetting or with a microtiter shaker.
   c. Subtract the OD of the blank (uninoculated wells, column 1 wells) from the OD of the inoculated wells.
   d. The MIC is the lowest drug concentration that produces a ≥50% growth reduction for azoles and 5-FC and ≥95% growth reduction for amphotericin B.
      - Caution: With some brands of microtiter plates, bubbles may appear after incubation that will preclude an accurate MIC determination by this method. Burst the bubbles with a heated insuline needle to prevent these erroneous results. Alternatively, the Greiner-Bio-One microtiter plates (reference # 650180) will also prevent this problem.

9.4.6.2 Interpretation

See the description for the broth macrodilution method (Table 9.1).

9.4.6.3 Reporting

See the description for the broth macrodilution method.

Although the CLSI recommends reading after 48 h incubation, some species have sufficient growth at 24 h. Because it has been reported that reading at 24 h correlates with *in vivo* results in animal models [14,15], it is recommended to read MICs at both 24 and 48 h to establish the incubation time that better correlates with *in vivo* results. It has been demonstrated that the 24-h results correlate well with the 48-h endpoints [14,15].

9.4.7 ADVANTAGES

1. The broth microdilution procedure can test a number of isolates at one time.
2. This procedure is easy to perform and requires less space in the laboratory freezer and incubator than does the broth macrodilution procedure.
3. It does not require specialized equipment.

TABLE 9.6
Summary of M27-A2 Methods

Test Medium	RPMI-1640 with glutamine, without bicarbonate, and with a pH indicator
pH	6.9–7.1
Buffer	[3-(*N*-morpholino)]-propanesulfonic acid (MOPS) at a concentration of 0.164 mol/L (34.53 g/L)
Inoculum size	0.5–2.5 × 10³ CFU/mL
Duration and temperature of incubation[a]	*Candida* spp., 48 h at 35°C *C. neoformans,* 72 h at 35°C
Concentrations to be assayed	Fluconazole and 5-FC[a]: 64–0.06 µg/mL Amphotericin B, itraconazole, ketoconazole, posaconazole, ravuconazole, caspofungin, anidulafungin, micafungin, and voriconazole: 16–0.03 µg/mL
MIC definition: For macrodilution method[b]	Amphotericin B: The lowest drug concentration that prevents any discernible growth (clear tubes) after 48 h of incubation Azoles, echinocandins, and 5-FC: The lowest drug concentration that produces an 80% of growth reduction as compared with the growth control after 48 or 24 h of incubation
MIC definition: For microdilution method	Amphotericin B: The lowest drug concentration that prevents any discernible growth (clear wells) after 48 h of incubation Azoles, echinocandins, and 5-FC: The lowest drug concentration that produces a prominent reduction of growth (50%) as compared with the growth control after 48 or 24 h of incubation
Break points	Fluconazole: S ≤ 8 µg/mL, S-DD 16–32 µg/mL, R ≥ 64 µg/mL Itraconazole: S ≤ 0.12 µg/mL, S-DD 0.25–0.5 µg/mL, R ≥ 1 µg/mL Voriconazole: S ≤ 1 µg/mL, S-DD 2 µg/mL, R ≥ 4 µg/mL 5-FC: S ≤ 4 µg/mL, I 8–16 µg/mL, R ≥ 32 µg/mL
Quality control strains	*C. krusei* ATCC6258 and *C. parapsilosis* ATCC22019

[a] 5-FC = 5-flucytosine; S = susceptible; S-DD = susceptible-dose dependent; R = resistant.
[b] For caspofungin, micafungin, and anidulafungin (not described yet in CLSI documents), MICs could be obtained at 24 h (50% or more growth inhibition).

9.4.8 LIMITATIONS

1. The CLSI M27 document recommends this method only for *Candida* spp. and *C. neoformans* [1]; it has not been validated for other yeast species.
2. *C. neoformans* isolates do not grow well in RPMI and must be read after 72 h of incubation.
3. Amphotericin B resistance is not well detected by this method.
4. Azole MICs are difficult to interpret due to trailing growth.
5. Breakpoints are only available for fluconazole, itraconazole, 5-FC, and voriconazole against *Candida*. spp.

9.4.9 CONCLUSIONS

The CLSI microdilution procedure is easy to perform with minimal labor. The interpretation of MIC results can be challenging to the untrained eye. This procedure is described by the CLSI for *Candida* spp. and *C. neoformans* isolates only.

9.5 ETEST

9.5.1 INTRODUCTION

Etest (AB Biodisk, Solna, Sweden) is a nonporous plastic strip immobilized with a predefined gradient of a given antimicrobial agent on one side and printed with an MIC scale on the other side. When the Etest strip is placed on an inoculated agar plate, a continuous, stable, and exponential antimicrobial gradient is established along the side of the strip. After incubation, the MIC value (µg/mL) can be read directly from the MIC scale printed on the Etest strip. If the resulting MIC is equivalent to the CLSI reference values, the CLSI criteria for yeasts are directly applicable for interpretation of Etest results [1]. This technology is similar to a disk diffusion assay but with a longer stability time for the antimicrobial gradient.

9.5.2 MATERIALS

1. Etest strips can be purchased directly from AB Biodisk or through Remel. Strips (approximate cost ≥$2 per strip) are sold in packages of 100 strips per antifungal agent and are stored at –20°C or –70°C (see Table 9.7 for Etest drug dilution ranges). Once a set of strips is removed from the manufacturer's package, the unused strips should be stored in an airtight container with a desiccant and returned to –20°C. Etest strips should not be used after the expiration date indicated by the manufacturer.

2. Plates consisting of RPMI-1640 supplemented with 2% glucose and 1.5% agar, prepared in-house or obtained commercially (Remel or others), that have an agar depth of 4 mm ± 0.5 mm can be used. Plates should be stored at 2°C–8°C. Modified casitone agar or antibiotic medium 3 (AM3) agar can also be used [16] as recommended by the manufacturer in the Etest technical guide No. 4.

3. Saline solution for making yeast suspensions

4. Swabs (sterile, nontoxic)

5. Test tubes (for inoculum preparation)

6. Pipettes

7. Scissors

8. Forceps or Etest applicator kit

9. A 0.5 McFarland standard (this can be made following CLSI instructions or purchased from microbiology product manufacturers such as PML, Hardy, or Remel).

10. Airtight storage containers with desiccant (silica gel) for extra Etest strips once the manufacturer's packaging has been opened. These storage containers are available from AB Biodisk and Remel.

11. Freezer (–20°C or –70°C) for storage.

12. Vortex mixer

13. 35°C ambient air incubator

14. Etest technical information
    - E-test package insert
    - E-test technical guide No. 4

TABLE 9.7
E-Test Strips

Antifungal	Code	Concentrations (µg/mL)
Amphotericin B	AP	0.002–32
Fluconazole	FL	0.016–256
Itraconazole	IT	0.002–32
Flucytosine	FC	0.002–32
Ketoconazole	KE	0.002–32
Voriconazole	VO	0.002–32
Caspofungin	CAS	0.002–32
Posaconazole	POS	0.002–32

- E-test application sheet EAS 006
- Customer information sheet No. 5, for preparation of the media

9.5.3 QUALITY CONTROL

1. Quality control strains:
   - *C. parapsilosis* ATCC 22019.
   - *C. krusei* ATCC 6258.
   - All quality control strains should be maintained following procedures described by CLSI [1].
2. Frequency of quality control testing.
   - A quality control organism should be run for every new lot of Etest strips prior to use.
   - Each antifungal agent should have quality control testing within the last 7 days of use, following the CLSI procedure for testing during 30 consecutive days [1]. Otherwise, quality control should be conducted on each occasion that testing is performed.
3. Evaluating results.
   - The E-test antifungal application sheet lists the quality control ranges for antifungal agents. These values are not included in the CLSI M27-A2 document.

9.5.4 PROCEDURE

1. Obtain a pure culture of the isolate to be tested on a nonselective medium as described for the CLSI methods.
   - The inoculum should be prepared from 24 h (*Candida* spp.) and 48–72 h (*C. neoformans*) cultures as described for the CLSI methods.
   - Frozen or lyophilized isolates should be subcultured at least twice prior to susceptibility testing.
2. Remove the strips from the original package or storage container from the freezer 30 (–20°C) or 60 min (–70°C) before use to allow them to equilibrate at room temperature.
3. Emulsify five or more isolated colonies in saline by using a sterile swab.
4. Vortex for 15 s
5. Adjust the suspension turbidity to a 0.5 McFarland standard for *Candida* spp. and to a 1 McFarland standard for *C. neoformans*. Add more colonies to increase the turbidity or more saline to decrease the turbidity (photometric devices can also be used to measure the turbidity).
6. The inoculum suspension should be inoculated onto the agar plate within 15 min after preparation. Dispense 150 μL to the center of a 90-mm plate or 400 μL to a 150-mm plate. Swab carefully to obtain an even growth over the entire surface of the agar in three different directions.
   - Make sure that the inoculum is spread evenly over the entire surface of the plate. A correctly inoculated plate will have an even lawn of confluent growth.
   - Plates can be inoculated automatically with the AB-Biodisk spiral autoinoculator CR10.
7. Allow the inoculum to be absorbed completely into the agar (at least 15–20 min). The plate must be completely dry before the application of the Etest strip. If moisture is present on the agar surface when the Etest strip is applied, it will affect the performance of the antifungal gradient.
8. The strip is designed to have the MIC scale facing away from the agar surface and the antifungal gradient touching the agar surface (you should be able to see the writing on the strip after applying it to the agar plate). Apply the "E" labeled area of the strip (highest concentration of antifungal) at the edge of the Petri dish to the agar surface and gently place the end of the strip with the lowest toward the center of the plate. *Once the strip*

has touched the agar surface do not move the strip. If any large bubbles appear under the strip, gently remove the bubbles by pressing on the Etest strip with a forceps or a swab. Small bubbles under the strip will not affect the performance of the Etest strip.

- One to two strips can be placed on a 90-mm plate with opposite orientation to each other (you do not want the "E" end of the strip on the same side of the plate for two strips, i.e., the gradients will overlap).
- Up to six strips can be placed on a 150-mm agar plate in a spoke wheel pattern. (Templates are available from AB Biodisk to optimize the positioning of the strips.)
- When using the Etest applicator, refer to the instructions in the product insert.
- Do not remove the Etest strip during any part of the process.

9. Incubate the plate in the inverted position (agar side up) at 35°C in an aerobic environment as soon as possible after the placement of Etest strips.

10. Incubate the plate until growth is clearly seen (24–48 h for the *Candida* spp. and 48–72 h for *C. neoformans*) with the exception of amphotericin B, which requires at least 48 h for *Candida* spp. and 48 to 72 h for *C. neoformans*.

9.5.5 ETEST RESULTS

9.5.5.1 Reading

1. Evaluate the growth of the isolate before reading. If the lawn of growth appears as a thin haze or if the density of colonies is sparse, do not attempt to read the MIC, reincubate the plate and/or repeat the test validating the inoculum size.

2. Read the MIC where the edge of the inhibition ellipse intersects the MIC scale on the Etest strip (use of the technical guide No. 4 for endpoint selection is highly recommended).
   - Fungistatic antifungal agents, such as azoles, tend to form diffuse edges. These should be read at the so-called 80% inhibition region, for example, the first point of significant inhibition as judged by the naked eye, ignoring the haze and microcolonies. However, if large colonies are detected inside the ellipse, the MIC should be read where these large colonies are inhibited.
   - Fungicidal agents such as amphotericin B tend to form sharp edges. With these agents, hazes and any isolated colonies inside the ellipse are indicative of growth, and the MIC should be read where these are completely inhibited.
   - If a thin line of growth occurs along the side of the Etest strip within the ellipse, it should not be used for interpretation because the MIC is where the ellipse of growth intersects with the Etest strip.
   - If there is complete growth and no zone appears on the plate around a strip, the MIC value is recorded as greater than the highest antifungal concentration of the strip.
   - If the inhibition ellipse does not fall above the lowest value on the strip, the MIC value is recorded as less than the lowest value on the strip.

9.5.5.2 Interpreting

1. Etest MICs are based on a continuous gradient; therefore, MIC values between the standard two-fold dilution schema can be obtained. These values can be reported as such, if desired, or rounded up to the next appropriate twofold dilution value. for example, 0.19 µg/mL becomes 0.25 µg/mL.

2. To interpret Etest MIC results as susceptible, intermediate, susceptible-dose dependent, or resistant categories, always round up the in-between values to the next higher twofold dilution.
   - For example, the CLSI fluconazole breakpoint for resistant is ≥64 µg/mL. An Etest value of 48 µg/mL is rounded up to 64 µg/mL, and the category is reported as resistant.

3. Etest MIC values are directly proportional to the CLSI reference dilution values. Therefore, CLSI breakpoints are directly applicable to the Etest MIC values. Consult the most
   current M27 and M27-S documents for the appropriate breakpoints for antifungal agents
   (or see Table 9.1).

9.5.5.3 Additional Considerations

Amphotericin B should not be read before 48 h.

9.5.6 ADVANTAGES

1. Etest is easy to perform and requires minimal training for test performance, however,
   end points can be difficult to determine for the azoles against *Candida* spp.
2. Contamination can be easily recognized.
3. Etest can be easily set up for a small number of clinical isolates.
4. There is minimum labor involved with Etest as compared with broth dilution methods.
5. It is an adequate method to detect potentially resistant strains to amphotericin B [17].

9.5.7 LIMITATIONS

1. Cost is the most significant limitation. Careful consideration should be given to which
   antifungal agents to test because the Etest methodology can be cost effective for fewer
   than five strips per isolate.
2. Agreement between Etest and M27 results is species and antifungal agent dependent.
   The lowest correlation is for the combinations: *C. glabrata* and fluconazole; *C. tropicalis*,
   fluconazole, and itraconazole; and *C. neoformans* and amphotericin B [18].
3. Etest is not suitable for *C. neoformans*.

9.6 SENSITITRE YEASTONE COLORIMETRIC METHOD

9.6.1 INTRODUCTION

The Sensititre YeastOne colorimetric antifungal panel (TREK International, Westlake, OH) consists
of a disposable tray that contains individual wells dried in serial twofold dilutions of up to six
established antifungal agents in RPMI-1640 medium supplemented with 1.5% dextrose. The wells
also contain the color indicator alamar blue. In the United States, antifungal agents included in the
FDA-approved panel are fluconazole, itraconazole, and 5-FC. Panels for other antifungal agents are
also available (amphotericin B, ketoconazole, voriconazole, and caspofungin). In Europe, antifungal
agents included are amphotericin B, fluconazole, itraconazole, ketoconazole, 5-FC, voriconazole, and
caspofungin. A high degree of intra- and interlaboratory reproducibility of MIC endpoints has been
demonstrated with this method [19]. Reading of the azoles and 5-FC is performed at 24 h and for
amphotericin B at 48 h. The agreement with the CLSI M27 method for azoles and 5-FC ranged
between 92–100% and for yeast species other than *C. albicans* from 87–90%. For amphotericin B,
the agreement ranged from 92–99%. The exception is *C. neoformans* with a 76% agreement [19].

9.6.2 MATERIALS

1. Yeast susceptibility test panels.
2. Sensititre yeast-susceptibility inoculum broth.
3. Autoclaved demineralized water (5 mL volumes).
4. Panel layout template.
5. Manual worksheet.

6. Plate seals.
7. Plate view-box light or mirror type.
8. A 0.5 McFarland turbidity standard.
9. SAB plates.
10. Sterile wooden applicator sticks or a loop.
11. Non-CO$_2$ incubator set at 35°C.
12. Vortex mixer.
13. 20-μL pipette.
14. Multichannel pipette for 100-μL volumes.
15. Disposable pipette tips.

9.6.3 QUALITY CONTROL

1. Quality control strains:
   • *C. parapsilosis* ATCC 22019.
   • *C. krusei* ATCC 6258.
   • Quality control strains should be preserved following procedures described for the CLSI methods [1].
2. Frequency of quality control testing.
   • Quality control should be run in parallel with every run. The ranges of the quality control MIC results are the same as those listed in the M27-S2 [7] (or see Table 9.4). The Sensititre YeastOne package insert also provides the acceptable ranges for the antifungal agent being tested.

9.6.4 PROCEDURE

1. Remove the panels to be used from storage. Panels should not be used if the desiccant is not present or if the integrity of the packing is compromised.
2. The inoculum should be prepared from 24 h (*Candida* spp.) or 48–72 h (*C. neoformans*) cultures as described for the CLSI method. Prepare a working suspension (1.1–8 × 10^3 cells/mL) by adding 20 μL of the stock yeast suspension to 11 mL of YeastOne inoculum broth.
3. Panels can be inoculated manually using a pipetting device or automatically with the Sensititre autoinoculator. Fill each well of the Sensititre panel with 100 μL of the working suspension. The excess of the working suspension can be used to inoculate SAB or CHROMagar plates to check purity and ensure inoculum density.
4 Cover the inoculated plates with the plate seals.
5. Place the plates in a stack of no more than three panels high.
6. Incubate panels for 24–48 h at 35°C in a non-CO$_2$ incubator and read either after 24 h (*Candida* spp. and azole agents) or 48 h (*Candida* spp. and amphotericin B). *C. neoformans* requires 48–72 h of incubation.

9.6.5 SENSITITRE YEASTONE MIC RESULTS

1. The MIC of azoles and 5-FC is the lowest concentration of antifungal solution changing from red to purple (prominent growth inhibition) or blue (no growth) after 24–72 h of incubation.
2. The MIC of amphotericin B is the lowest concentration of antifungal solution changing from red (growth) to blue (no growth) after 48 h of incubation.
3. Reading
   Panels may be read visually by using a view box and in normal laboratory lighting.
   If the growth control well is red, the endpoints for antifungal agents can be interpreted. If after incubation the well is only weakly purple, reincubate for several additional hours until it turns red. Do not read the turbidity in Sensititre YeastOne panels.

4. Interpreting and reporting Sensititre YeastOne MIC results
   As the agreement with the M27-A2 broth microdilution method is >90% [19], CLSI MIC
   interpretations can be applied (Table 9.1).

9.6.6 ADVANTAGES

1. Sensititre YeastOne is easy to perform and requires minimal training for test performance.
2. Sensititre YeastOne can be easily set up for a small number of clinical isolates.
3. Interpretation of the MIC is more objective.
4. Sensititre YeastOne panels are stored at room temperature.

9.6.7 LIMITATIONS

1. This method is suitable for *Candida* spp. and other rapid growing yeast species; it is not
   suitable for *C. neoformans* [19].
2. It does not discriminate well between amphotericin B-resistant and -susceptible strains.
3. Breakpoints are only available for fluconazole, itraconazole, 5-FC, and voriconazole.

9.6.8 CONCLUSIONS

The Sensititre YeastOne procedure is easy to perform with minimal labor. The interpretation of
MIC results is more objective.

9.7 DISK DIFFUSION METHOD (CLSI M44-A DOCUMENT)

9.7.1 INTRODUCTION

To make antifungal susceptibility testing more readily available to clinical microbiology laboratories,
the CLSI has proposed a standardized disk diffusion method for susceptibility testing of *Candida*
spp. to the triazoles, fluconazole, voriconazole, and poraconazole [20]. The subcommittee has only
established zone interpretative criteria (break points) for fluconazole and voriconazole (Table 9.8)
and quality control parameters for fluconazole, voriconazole, and posaconazole (Table 9.9) [20,21,
CLSI annual meeting minutes, 2006]. Therefore, the clinical relevance for other than fluconazole
and voriconazole drug–organism combinations is uncertain. The design of the disk diffusion method
for yeasts is similar to that for bacteria using the same medium (Mueller–Hinton agar) supplemented
with glucose and methylene blue dye (Table 9.8, Table 9.9, and Table 9.10).

9.7.2 MATERIALS

1. Autoclave
2. Water bath (48–50°C)
3. Refrigerator
4. Non–frost-free freezer (–14°C or below)
5. Incubator set at 35°C ± 1°C with ambient air
6. Metric vernier calliper
7. Vortex mixer
8. Swabs (sterile, nontoxic)
9. Test tubes (for inoculum preparation)
10. Plastic or glass petri dishes (150-mm or 90–100-mm diameter)
11. Saline solution
12. Pipettes
13. Forceps or disk-dispensing apparatus
14. A McFarland 0.5 turbidity standard. (Can be made following CLSI recommendations or
    purchased from a product manufacturer such as, PML, Hardy, or Remel.)

TABLE 9.8
Inhibition Zone Diameter Interpretative Standards and Equivalent MIC Break Points for
Candida **spp.**

Antifungal Agent	Disk content	Zone Diameter (Nearest Whole mm)			Equivalent MIC Break Points (µg/mL)		
		R[a]	S-DD	S	R	S-DD	S
Fluconazole	25 µg	≤14	15–18	≥19	≥64	16–32	≤8
Voriconazole[b]	1 µg	≤13	14–16	≥17	≥4	2	≤1

[a] S = susceptible; S-DD = susceptible-dose dependent; R = resistant.
[b] Listed in the CLSI M27-S2 and M44-51 documents [7,21].

TABLE 9.9
Recommended Quality Control Inhibition Zone Diameter (mm) Ranges

Antifungal Agent	Disk Content	*C. krusei* ATCC 6258	*C. parapsilosis* ATCC 22019	*C. albicans* ATCC 90028	*C. tropicalis* ATCC 750
Fluconazole	25 µg	—[a]	22–33	28–39	26–37
Voriconazole	1 µg	16–25	28–37	31–42	—
Posaconazole[b]	5 µg	23–31	25–36	24–34	23–33

[a] Quality control ranges have not been established for these strain and antifungal combinations because of their extensive interlaboratory variability during initial quality control studies.
[b] CLSI annual meeting minutes, January 2006.

TABLE 9.10
Summary of M44-4 Document

Test Medium	Mueller–Hinton agar + 2% glucose +0.5 µg/mL methylene blue
pH	7.2–7.4
Inoculum size	0.5 McFarland standard and swab plates
Duration and temperature of incubation	35°C for 20 to 24 h
	Some strains of *C. glabrata* and *C. krusei* often require 48 h.
Disk content	Fluconazole 25 µg
	Voriconazole 1 µg
	Posaconazole 5 µg
Measurement of zone inhibition	Measure to the nearest whole millimeter at the point at which there is prominent reduction in growth
Breakpoints	Fluconazole: R ≤ 14 mm; S-DD 15–18 mm; S ≥ 19 mm
	Voriconazole: R ≤ 13 mm; SDD 14–16 mm; S ≥ 17 mm
Quality control strains (zone inhibition)	*C. parapsilosis* ATCC 22019 (fluconazole: 22–33 mm; voriconazole: 28–37 mm; posaconazole: 25–36 mm)
	C. krusei ATCC 6258 (voriconazole: 16–25 mm; posaconazole: 23–31 mm)
	C. albicans ATCC 90028 (fluconazole: 28–39 mm; voriconazole: 31–42 mm; posaconazole: 24–34 mm)
	C. tropicalis ATCC 750 (fluconazole: 26–37 mm; posaconazole: 23–33 mm)

CLSI annual meeting minutes, 2006 and references 20, 21.

9.7.3 ANTIFUNGAL DISKS

1. Source and disk content
   - Fluconazole 25 μg (Pfizer Inc., Becton Dickinson, BBL).
   - Voriconazole 1 μg (Pfizer Inc.).
   - Posaconazole 5 μg (Schering-Plough Corporation, Becton Dickinson, BBL).
2. Storage of antifungal disks
   Cartridges containing commercially prepared paper disks for susceptibility testing are generally packaged to ensure appropriate anhydrous conditions. Disks should be stored as follows:
   a. Refrigerate the containers at 8°C or below, or freeze at –14°C or below in a non–frost-free freezer until needed. The disk may retain greater stability if stored frozen until the day of use.
   b. Remove the unopened disk containers from the refrigerator or freezer 1–2 h before use to equilibrate them to room temperature before opening. This procedure minimizes the amount of condensation that occurs when warm air contacts the cold disk.
   c. Once a cartridge of disks has been removed from its sealed packing, it should be placed in a tightly sealed, desiccated container.
   d. Disks should be discarded on the expiration date, or if the diameter range of the quality control strains is not within the established range, or if the problem cannot be attributed to another faulty methodology.

9.7.4 TEST MEDIUM

1. Mueller-Hinton agar plus 2% glucose and 0.5 μg/mL methylene blue dye (pH 7.2–7.4). The addition of glucose provides suitable growth for most commonly encountered yeast pathogens. The addition of methylene blue dye enhances the zone edge definition.
   This medium is considered the best medium for routine susceptibility testing of yeasts for the following reasons:
   - There is not much variation.
   - It shows acceptable batch-to-batch reproducibility.
   - It is readily available.
   - The base medium can easily be supplemented either pre- or postproduction to contain the final concentration of 2% glucose and 0.5 μg/mL methylene blue dye.
   Check the suitability of any new batch of Mueller-Hinton medium by following CLSI document M6 recommendations or by the expected inhibition zones for quality control isolates because some batches will not support adequate growth of some organisms. Therefore, zones obtained by a disk diffusion test will be usually larger than expected and may exceed the acceptable quality control limits.
2. Procedure to prepare the medium.
   The medium can be prepared and poured as the complete medium with supplements (glucose and methylene blue) or the supplements can be added to commercially prepared Mueller-Hinton agar plates. The latter technique enables the use of routine Mueller-Hinton agar plates from the bacteriology laboratory.
   a. Glucose stock solution (0.4 g/mL):
      - 40 g glucose and 100 mL distilled water.
      - Heat gently and mix to dissolve.
   b. Methylene blue dye (Merck) solution (5 μg/mL):
      - 0.1 g methylene blue and 20 mL distilled water.
      - Warm gently until the dye is dissolved, but do not overheat.

   c. Glucose-methylene blue (GMB) stock solution:
- Add 200 μL of methylene blue dye solution to 100 mL of the glucose stock solution.
- Dispense GMB stock solution into bottles or individual-use small vials containing 3.5 mL aliquots for 150-mm plates or 1.5 mL aliquots for 90–100-mm plates.
- Autoclave for 25 min at 121°C followed by slow exhaust.
- Store at room temperature (maximum a year) and handle aseptically.

   d. Preparation of supplemented Mueller-Hinton agar:

Prepare Mueller-Hinton agar from a commercially available dehydrated Mueller-Hinton agar base following the manufacturer's instructions.

1) Add 100 μL of the methylene blue dye per liter of Mueller-Hinton agar.
2) Add 20 g of glucose per liter of Mueller-Hinton agar.
3) Autoclave as directed by the manufacturer's instructions.
4) After autoclaving, allow it to cool in a 45–50°C water bath.
5) Pour the medium into glass or plastic petri dishes on a level, horizontal surface to give a uniform depth of approximately 4 mm; the corresponding volumes are 67–70 mL of medium for 150-mm diameter plates and 28–30 mL for 100-mm diameter plates.
6) Allow the medium to cool at room temperature, and store it at refrigerator temperature (2–8°C). Although the plates can be used the same day of preparation, it is better to use them the following day to obtain sharper edges of growth.
7) A representative sample of each batch of plates (5%) should be examined for sterility by incubating at 30–35°C for 24 h.
8) Plates should be used within seven days after preparation, unless adequate precautions have been taken to minimize drying of the agar.

   e. Supplementation of commercially prepared Mueller-Hinton agar with glucose and methylene blue:

Commercially prepared Mueller-Hinton agar is identical to that utilized by the bacteriology laboratory for performing Kirby-Bauer disk diffusion tests for bacteria. These plates can be obtained from a variety of manufacturers.

a) Pour 3.5 mL of GMB supplement onto the surface of a 150-mm plate with a 70-mL fill or 1.5 mL onto a 90–100-mm plate with a 30-mL fill.
b) Spread the supplement evenly on the agar with a sterile spreader or sterile bent glass rod.
c) Allow the GMB solution to absorb completely at room temperature or in the refrigerator before inoculating the plate. The time required for the agar to absorb the solution depends on the humidity of the plate (16–18 h). It is advisable to prepare supplemented plates the day before performing the test to allow absorption of the solution overnight in the refrigerator.

9.7.5 Quality Control

A quality control culture can be used to monitor the precision (reproducibility) and accuracy of the disk diffusion test. An unexplained result suggests a change in the organism's inherent susceptibility, and a fresh culture of the control strain should be obtained.

1. Quality control strains:
   - *C. parapsilosis* ATCC 22019
   - *C. krusei* ATCC 6258
   - *C. albicans* ATCC 90028
   - *C. tropicalis* ATCC 750
- All quality control strains should be maintained following procedures described by CLSI [1,20].

2. Frequency of quality control testing:
   - A quality control organism should be run for each new lot of medium and prior to using each lot of antifungal disks.
   - At least one of the above isolates should be tested with every run, and testing should be performed using the same procedure used for the clinical isolates. If satisfactory performance is documented, quality control testing may be conducted weekly.
3. Evaluating quality control disk results:
   The inhibition zone values for the quality control organisms must be within the acceptable ranges for the antifungal agent being tested for the results to be considered valid. These ranges are listed in the current CLSI M44-A [20,21, CLSI annual meeting minutes, 2006] document and in Table 9.9.

9.7.6 PROCEDURE

1. Obtain a pure culture of the isolate to be tested on a nonselective medium as described for CLSI microdilution methods.
2. Remove the disks from the original package or storage container from the refrigerator or the freezer (−14°C or below) 1–2 h before use and allow them to equilibrate at room temperature.
3. If a disk-dispensing apparatus is used, the apparatus should be warmed at room temperature before opening. When not in use, the dispensing apparatus (containing the disks) should always be refrigerated, fitted with a tight cover, and stored with an adequate desiccant.
4. Remove the supplemented Mueller-Hinton agar plates from the refrigerator and equilibrate them at room temperature. If excess surface moisture is present, place the plates in an incubator (35°C) or a laminar flow hood at room temperature (with the lids ajar) until the excess surface moisture has evaporated (10–30 min). The agar surface should be moist, but the petri dish covers and agar surface should be free of droplets of moisture when the plates are inoculated.
5. Inoculum preparation — direct colony suspension method.
   a Lightly touch five colonies (at least 1-mm diameter) of similar morphology using a loop or swab.
   b. Suspend the yeast cells in 5 mL of sterile 0.85% NaCl, and mix the cell suspension using a vortex mixer for 15 s.
   c. Adjust the turbidity of the inoculum to the density of a 0.5 of McFarland standard with a spectrophotometer at 530 nm wavelength. This procedure yields a yeast stock suspension of $1–5 \times 10^6$ cells per mL and should produce semiconfluent growth with most *Candida* spp. isolates.
      - The preparation of the inocula for one run should be completed within 15 min.
      - Never use undiluted overnight broth culture or other unstandardized inocula.
6. Inoculation and incubation of test plates
   a. Dip a sterile cotton swab into the well mixed with a vortex mixer-adjusted suspension, and rotate several times and press firmly on the inside wall of the tube above the fluid level. This will remove excess inoculum from the swab.
   b. Streak the swab carefully over the entire sterile agar surface to obtain an even growth in three different directions. Finally, swab the rim of the agar.
      - A correctly inoculated plate will have an even growth.
      - Plates can also be inoculated with a rotary plate inoculator.
   c. Leave the lids ajar for 3–5 min, but no more than 15 min, to allow for any excess surface moisture to be absorbed before applying the drug-impregnated disks.

7. Application of disks to inoculated agar plates and incubation.
   a. Dispense the predetermined battery of disks onto the surface of the inoculated agar plate, and press down each disk to ensure its complete contact with the agar surface.
   b. Disks must be distributed no closer than 24 mm from center to center.
      * No more than 5 disks should be placed on a 100-mm plate.
      * Up to 12 disks can be placed on a 150-mm plate.
   c. Once the disk has touched the agar surface, do not move the disk.
   d. Place the plates in the inverted position in an incubator set at 35°C in an aerobic environment within 15 min of the placement of the disks.
   e. Incubate the plates for 18–24 h.
8. Reading and interpretation of results
   a. Examine the plates after 20–24 h of incubation. If the plate was satisfactorily streaked and the inoculum was correct, the resulting zones of inhibition around the disk will be uniformly circular, and there will be a semiconfluent lawn of growth.
   b. Hold the plate a few inches above a black, nonreflecting background that is illuminated with reflecting light.
   c. Measure the zone diameter to the nearest whole millimeter at the point at which there is a prominent reduction in growth.
      * Reading is subjective, and experience results in greater accuracy.
      * The presence of pinpoint microcolonies at the zone edge or large colonies within an inhibition zone should be ignored.
   d. If insufficient growth occurs after 24-h incubation, reincubate the plates and read them at 48 h.

9.7.7 DISK DIFFUSION RESULTS

Disk diffusion inhibition zone diameters correlate inversely with MIC results by standard dilution tests. Table 9.8 lists the MIC breakpoint correlates that correspond to the inhibition zone diameter interpretative criteria. These MIC correlates were based on inhibition zones diameters versus MIC comparisons and are generally identical to MIC interpretative criteria defined in the CLSI documents M27 and M27-S [1,7].

9.7.8 ADVANTAGES

1. The disk diffusion test is easy to perform and requires minimal training for test performance; however, the endpoints can be difficult to determine.
2. Contamination can be easily recognized.
3. The disk diffusion test can be easily set up for a small number of clinical isolates.
4. There is minimum labor involved as compared with the standard broth dilution methods.
5. It is cost-effective for routine testing.
6. The disk diffusion test usually provides qualitative results 24 h sooner than the standard broth dilution methods.
7. It is a good method to use as a routine screening procedure to test fluconazole against *Candida* spp.

9.7.9 LIMITATIONS

1. The method has been standardized for *Candida* species and two antifungal agents only.
2. The inhibition zone measurement is subjective.
3. Zone interpretative criteria (breakpoints) are available only for fluconazole and voriconazole.
4. Quality control parameters are available only for fluconazole, voriconazole, and posaconazole.

5. *C. krusei* and *C. glabrata* and sometimes *C. parapsilosis* strains may require 48 h of incubation [22].

6. Comparisons of this method with the approved M27 methods are scarce for agents other than fluconazole and voriconazole [22].

9.7.10 CONCLUSIONS

The disk diffusion method is an easy method for routine testing of fluconazole, voriconazole, and posaconazole in microbiology laboratories because it requires the same technology and medium used for bacteria testing. The medium only requires a supplementation with glucose and methylene blue dye; both reagents are easily available. Reports correlating disk diffusion results with M27-A methods have concluded that the disk diffusion methodology does not adequately separate fluconazole-resistant from -susceptible dose-dependent isolates [22–27]. Therefore, MIC determination may be needed for those strains that have intermediate or resistant zones by the diffusion method.

9.8 GENERAL CONCLUSIONS

Currently, the gold standard for susceptibility testing of yeasts to antifungal agents is the CLSI broth microdilution methodology [1], but the simpler CLSI disk methodology is also available for three triazoles, fluconazole, posaconazole, and voriconazole. Research or large clinical laboratories that can "batch" isolates for large-scale research or surveillance studies use CLSI procedures (disk and broth dilution) [27]. The CLSI broth dilution methodology is labor intensive and does not lend itself to testing small numbers of clinical isolates. However, of the two procedures approved by the CLSI, the broth microbroth dilution is better suited and less labor intensive than the broth macrodilution method for testing in the routine clinical laboratory. Broth microdilution trays can be prepared in bulk and stored frozen. If a commercial method is proven to be equivalent to the CLSI broth dilution procedure, that method can be used in the clinical laboratory. The colorimetric method has similar advantages to the broth microdilution procedure. The most suitable method for the discrimination between susceptible and resistant strains to amphotericin B is the Etest [17]. However, endpoints are difficult to determine. As antifungal resistance continues to increase, the need for the clinical laboratory to routinely perform yeast susceptibility testing is becoming more important. Other methods have also been evaluated [28]. For a summary of CLSI broth dilution methods, see Tables 9.9 and 9.10 for disk diffusion method (CLSI M44-A).

REFERENCES

1. Clinical and Laboratory Standards Institute. Reference method for broth dilution antifungal susceptibility testing of yeasts, approved standard M27-A2, vol. 22, no. 15, 2nd ed., CLSI Document. Clinical and Laboratory Standards Institute, Villanova, PA, 2002.

2. Rodriguez-Tudela, J.L., Barchiesi, F., Bille, J. et al. Method for the determination of minimum inhibitory concentration (MIC) by broth dilution of fermentative yeasts, *Clin. Microbiol. Infect.*, 9, I–VIII, 2003.

3. Pfaller, M.A., Buschelman, M.G., Bale, M.J. et al. Multicenter evaluation of four methods of yeast inoculum preparation, *J. Clin. Microbiol.*, 26, 1437–1441, 1988.

4. Pfaller, M.A., Rinaldi, M.G., Galgiani, J.N. et al. Collaborative investigation of variables in susceptibility testing of yeasts, *Antimicrob. Agents Chemother.*, 34, 1648–1654, 1990.

5. Espinel-Ingroff, A., Kish, C.W., Jr., Kerkering, T.M. et al. Collaborative comparison of broth macro- and microdilution antifungal tests, *J. Clin. Microbiol.*, 30, 3138–3145, 1992.

6. Fromtling, R.A., Galgiani, J.N., Pfaller, M.A. et al. Multicenter evaluation of broth macrodilution antifungal susceptibility test for yeasts, *Antimicrob. Agents Chemother.*, 37, 39–45, 1993.

7. Clinical and Laboratory Standards Institute. Quality control minimal inhibitory concentration (MIC) limits for broth microdilution and MIC interpretive breakpoints, approved standard M27-S2, 2nd ed., Clinical and Laboratory Standards Institute, Villanova, PA, 2006.

8. Pfaller, M.A., Bale, M., Buschelman, B. et al. Quality control guidelines for National Committee for Clinical Laboratory Standards recommended broth macrodilution testing of amphotericin B, fluconazole, and flucytosine, *J. Clin. Microbiol.*, 33, 1104–1107, 1995.

9. Rex, J.H., Pfaller, M.A., Lancaster, M. et al. Quality control guidelines for National Committee for Clinical Laboratory Standards recommended broth macrodilution testing of ketoconazole and itraconazole, *J. Clin Microbiol.*, 34, 816–817, 1996.

10. Barry, A.L., Pfaller, M.A., Brown, S.D. et al. Quality control limits for broth microdilution susceptibility tests of ten antifungal agents, *J. Clin. Microbiol.*, 38, 3457–3459, 2000.

11. Andes, D., Marchillo, K., Stamstad, T., and Conklin, R. *In vivo* pharmacokinetics and pharmacodynamics of a new triazole, voriconazole, in a murine candidiasis model, *Antimicrob. Agents Chemother.*, 47, 3165–3169, 2003.

12. Cantón, E., Martín-Mazuelo, E., and Espinel Ingroff, A. Pruebas de sensibilidad antifúngica, in *Guia Práctica de Identificación y Diagnóstico en Micología Clínica*, Pemán, J., Martín-Mazuelo, E., and Rubio-Calvo, M.C., Eds., *Bilbao, Revista Iberoamericana de Micología*, 2001, 15.1–15.13.

13. Rex, J.H., Nelson, P.W., Paetznick, V.L. et al. Optimizing the correlation between results of testing *in vitro* and in therapeutic outcome *in vivo* for fluconazole by testing critical isolates in a murine model of invasive candidiasis, *Antimicrob. Agents Chemother.*, 42, 129–134, 1998.

14. Espinel-Ingroff, A., Barchiesi, F., Cuenca-Estrella, M. et al. Comparison of visual 24 h and spectrophotometric 48 h MICs to CLSI microdilution MICs of fluconazole, itraconazole, posaconazole, and voriconazole for Candida spp.: A collaborative study, *J. Clin. Microbiol.*, 41, 4535–4540, 2005.

15. Lozano-Chiu, M., Arikan, S., Paetznick, V.L. et al. Optimizing voriconazole susceptibility testing of *Candida*: effects of incubation time, endpoint rule, species of *Candida,* and level of fluconazole susceptibility, *J. Clin Microbiol.*, 37, 2755–2759, 1999.

16. Espinel-Ingroff, A., Pfaller, M., Erwin, M.E. et al. Interlaboratory evaluation of the Etest method for antifungal susceptibility testing of pathogenic yeasts for five antifungal agents by using casitone agar and solidified RPMI-1640 medium with 2% dextrose, *J. Clin. Microbiol.*, 36, 198–202, 1996.

17. Wanger, A., Mills, K., Nelson, P.W. et al. Comparison of Etest and National Committee for Clinical Laboratory Standards broth macrodilution method for antifungal susceptibility testing: Enhanced ability to detect amphotericin B-resistant *Candida* isolates, *Antimicrob. Agents Chemother.*, 39, 2520–2522, 1995.

18. Martín Mazuelos, E., Gutiérrez, M.J., Aller, A.I., et al. A comparative evaluation of E-test and microdilution broth method for fluconazole and itraconazole susceptibility testing of *Candida* species, *J. Antimicrob. Chemother.*, 43, 477–481, 2000.

19. Espinel-Ingroff, A., Pfaller, M., Messer, S.A. et al. Multicenter comparison of the Sensititre YeastOne colorimetric antifungal panel with the National Committee for Clinical Laboratory Standards M27-A reference method for testing clinical isolates of common and emerging *Candida* spp. and *Cryptococcus* spp., and other yeast and yeast-like organisms, *J. Clin. Microbiol.*, 37, 591–595, 1999.

20. Clinical and Laboratory Standards Institute. Method for antifungal disk diffusion susceptibility testing of yeasts; approved guideline M44-A, Clinical and Laboratory Standards Institute, Villanova, PA, 2004.

21. Clinical and Laboratory Standards Institute. Zone diameter interpretive standards and corresponding minimal inhibitory concentration (MIC) interpretive breakpoints, supplement M44-S1, Clinical and Laboratory Standards Institute, Wayne, PA, 2006.

22. Barry, A.L., Pfaller, M., Rennie, R.P. et al. Precision and accuracy of fluconazole susceptibility testing by broth microdilution, Etest, and disk diffusion methods, *Antimicrob. Agents Chemother.*, 46, 1781–1784, 2002.

23. Barry, A.L. and Brown, S.D. Fluconazole disk diffusion procedure for determining susceptibility of *Candida* species, *J. Clin. Microbiol.*, 34, 2154–2157, 1996.

24. Cantón, E., Pemán, J., Carrillo-Muñoz, A. et al. Fluconazol susceptibility of bloodstream *Candida* sp. isolates as determined by National Committee for Clinical Laboratory standards Methods M27-A and two other methods, *J. Clin. Microbiol.*, 37, 2197–2200, 1999.

25. Lee, S., Fung, C., Lee, N. et al. Fluconazole disk diffusion test with methylene-blue and glucose-enriched Mueller-Hinton agar for determining susceptibility of *Candida* species, *J. Clin. Microbiol.* 39, 1615–1617, 2001.

26. Meis, J., Petrou, M., Ellis, D. et al. A global evaluation of the susceptibility of *Candida* species to fluconazole by disk diffusion, *Diag. Microbiol. Infect. Dis.*, 36, 215–223, 2000.
27. Pfaller, M.A., Boyken, L., Messer, S. et al. Comparison of results of voriconazole disk diffusion testing for *Candida* species with results from a central reference laboratory in the ARTEMIS global antifungal surveillance program, *J. Clin. Microbiol.*, 43, 5208–5213, 2005.
28. Espinel–Ingroff, A. Antifungal susceptibility methods and their potential clinical relevance, *Lab. Med.*, 33, 626–631, 2002.

APPENDIX — MANUFACTURERS

AB Biodisk North America Inc.
200 Centennial Avenue
Piscataway, NJ 08854-3910
www.abbiodisk.com
Telephone: 732-457-0408
Fax: 732-457-8980
Product inquires and orders: 800-874-8814

AB Biodisk
Dalvagen 10
S-169 56 Solna
Sweden
Etest@abbiodiskna.com
www.abbiodisk.com
Telephone: +46-8-730-07-60
Fax: +46-8-83-81-58

Angus Biochemicals Inc.
2236 Liberty Dr.
Niagara Falls, NY 14304-3796
Telephone: 716-283-1434
Fax: 716-283-1770

BD Biosciences
P.O. Box 243
Cockeysville, MD 21030
www.bd.com
Telephone: 410-771-0100
800-638-8663

CMI-Promex (Steers Replicator)
7 Benjamin Green Road
P.O. Box 418
Pedricktown, NJ 08067
Telephone: 609-351-1000

Coy Laboratory Products, Inc.
14500 Coy Drive
Grass Lake, MI 49137
www.coylab.com
Telephone: 313-475-2200

Dynex Technologies, Inc.
14340 Sullyfield Circle
Chantilly, VA 20151
www.dynextechnologies.com
Telephone: 703-631-7800
800-336-4543
Fax: 703-631-7816

EM Science
480 S. Democrat Road
Gibbstown, NJ 08027-1297
www.emscience.com
Telephone: 800-222-0342

Evergreen Scientific
2300 E. 49th St.
Los Angeles, CA 90058
Telephone: 213-583-1331

Fisher Scientific Co.
711 Forbes Ave.
Pittsburgh, PA 15219
www.fishersci.com
Telephone: 412-490-8300

Forma Scientific, Inc.
P.O. Box 649
Marietta, OH 45750
www.forma.com
Telephone: 614-374-1851

Gelman Science
600 South Wanger Rd.
Ann Arbor, MI 48103
Telephone: 313-665-0651

Hardy Diagnostics, Inc.
1430 West McCoy Lane
Santa Maria, CA 93455
www.hardydiagnostics.com
Telephone: 805-346-2766
800-266-2222
Fax: 805-346-2760

Hemostat Laboratories
P.O. Box 790
515 Industrial Way
Dixon, CA 95620
www.hemostat.com
Telephone: 707-678-9594
    800-572-6888

Microbiology International
10242 Little Rock Lane
Frederick, MD 21702
www.microbiology-intl.com
Telephone: 301-662-6835
    800-396-4276
Fax: 301-662-8096

Mitsubishi Gas Chemical America, Inc.
520 Madison Ave. 17th Floor
New York, NY 10022
www.mgc-a.com
Telephone: 212-752-4620
Fax : 212-758-4012

Nalgene Nunc International
75 Panorama Creek Dr.
P.O. Box 20365
Rochester, NY 14602
www.nalgenunc.com
Telephone: 800-625-4327

Oxoid, Inc.
800 Proctor Avenue
Ogdensburg, NY 13669
www.oxoid.com
Telephone: 800-567-8378

Plas Labs Inc.
917 East Chilson Street
Lansing, MI 48906
Telephone: 517-372-7177

PML Microbiologicals
27120 SW 95th Ave.
Wilsonville, OR 97070
www.pmlmicro.com
Telephone: 800-628-7014
Fax: 1-800-765-4415
Customer service: 800-547-0659

Remel (IDS)
12076 Santa Fe Dr.
Lenexa, KS 66215
www.remelinc.com
Telephone: 800-255-6730

Sheldon Manufacturing, Inc.
P.O. Box 627
Cornelius, OR 97113
www.shellab.com
Telephone: 503-640-3000
    800-322-4897
Fax: 503-640-1366

Sigma Chemical Company
P.O. Box 14508
St. Louis, MO 63178
www.sigma-aldrich.com
Telephone: 800-325-3010
Technical Services: 800-325-5832

Toucan Technologies, Inc.
1158 Altadena
Cincinnati, OH 45230
Telephone: 513-232-0200

TREK
29299 Clemens Road, Suite 1-K
Westlake, OH 44145
www.trekds.com
Telephone: 440-808-0000
    800-871-8909
Fax: 440-346-2760

USP (United States Pharmacopeia)
Customer Service Department
12601 Twinbrook Parkway
Rockville, MD 20852
http://catalog.usp.org
Telephone: 800-227-8772
800-877-6209

VWR Scientific Products
1310 Goshen Parkway
West Chester, PA 19380
www.vwr.com
Telephone: 610-429-2728

10 Antifungal Susceptibility Testing of Filamentous Fungi

Ana Espinel-Ingroff and Emilia Cantón

CONTENTS

10.1 CLSI PROCEDURES FOR FILAMENTOUS FUNGI

10.1.1 Introduction

The laboratory's role in guiding the selection of antifungal therapy has gained greater attention because of the increased incidence of fungal infections, the development of new antifungal agents, and the description of resistance to itraconazole and amphotericin B among *Aspergillus* spp. and other important emerging molds. The Clinical and Laboratory Standards Institute (CLSI) Subcommittee on Antifungal Susceptibility Tests has developed a reproducible reference testing methodology (M38-A document) for antifungal susceptibility testing of filamentous fungi (molds) [1]. CLSI procedures for molds and comparable commercial methods are described in this chapter; the end point is the minimum inhibitory concentration or the MIC.

10.2 RELEVANCE

Mold susceptibility testing should be performed to determine the susceptibility of common molds that cause invasive infections (*Aspergillus* spp., *Fusarium* spp., *Rhizopus arrhizus*, and other zygomycetes, *Pseudallescheria boydii* [*Scedosporium apiospermum*], and the mycelial form of *Sporothrix schenckii*) and other opportunistic pathogenic molds to itraconazole, voriconazole, posaconazole, ravuconazole, and amphotericin B as well as the new echinocandins, caspofungin, micafungin, and anidulafungin. Determination of the antifungal susceptibility endpoints for the echinocandins is not described in the CLSI document, but it is described later in this chapter. CLSI methodology has not been evaluated for the yeast forms of dimorphic fungi, such as *Blastomyces dermatitidis*, *Coccidioides immitis*, *Histoplasma capsulatum* variety *capsulatum*, *Penicillium marneffei*, or *S. schenckii*. Susceptibility testing could also be performed to determine patterns of susceptibility by conducting periodic batch surveys to establish antibiograms within an institution when the pathogen is recovered from an invasive infection due to a mold, when the utility of the antifungal agent is uncertain, when monitoring resistance development during therapy, and when testing new pathogens and new drugs. Because interpretative breakpoints are not available for any species of filamentous fungi versus any antifungal agent, the clinical relevance of susceptibility testing for molds remains uncertain. For the development of the M38-A document, the Subcommittee on Antifungal Susceptibility Tests conducted multicenter studies [2–5] to evaluate the best medium, inoculum size, temperature, duration of incubation, and end-point definition; quality control MIC limits for a mold isolate have also been established. The test medium recommended is RPMI-1640 broth (RPMI) with [3-(*N*-morpholino)]-propanesulfonic acid (MOPS) buffer. Since the publication of the proposed CLSI document (M38-A) for molds, alternative methods have been developed (Etest, colorimetric, etc.); however, these methods are not described in the CLSI M38-A document. The CLSI group is currently evaluating a disk diffusion assay for mold testing; reference testing conditions also have been identified for testing dermatophytes (briefly described in Section 10.7).

The CLSI broth macro- and microdilution methods for susceptibility testing of molds involve preparing a series of drug dilutions, each containing a specific concentration of an antifungal agent. If a more practical method should yield results similar to those obtained using CLSI methods, it is considered an acceptable method for use in the clinical laboratory. Validation of an alternative method is the responsibility of the laboratory.

- Caution: Because the risk of producing aerosols is present, all steps in testing molds must be performed in a class IIA or IIB biological safety cabinet.

10.3 BROTH MICRODILUTION METHOD

10.3.1 INTRODUCTION

The design of the CLSI broth microdilution method for susceptibility testing of molds is similar to that for yeasts. It is an easier and more economical method than the broth macrodilution method.

The purity and viability of the organism should be validated before any testing is performed.

1. Technical notes.
   - It is important to completely plan out the entire procedure since it involves many steps over several days. It is also important to understand all the steps of the procedure before beginning. The technologist is advised to read and understand the CLSI M38-A document before proceeding.
   - Determine the number of isolates to be tested, the number of antifungal agents, and the range of concentrations for each antifungal (Table 10.5).

10.3.2 MATERIALS

1. Antimicrobial sources:
   a. United States Pharmacopeia (USP)
   b. Sigma Chemical Company
   c. The antifungal agent manufacturer
      - Some antifungal agents can be obtained from the drug manufacturer at no charge through the pharmaceutical company's customer service department or equivalent department or from your local pharmaceutical representatives.
2. Agar media:
   a. Sabouraud dextrose agar (SAB) plates
   b. Potato dextrose agar slant tubes
      - SAB plates should be used to determine the viable number of CFU per milliliter (inoculum density validation) and potato dextrose agar plates should be used to induce conidium and sporangiospore formation.
3. Test medium
   a. RPMI-1640 (with glutamine, without bicarbonate, and with a pH indicator) is the medium recommended for the susceptibility testing of filamentous fungi. The medium should be buffered with MOPS (0.164 mol/L). For the composition of the medium, see Table 10.1.
   b. Procedure for making RPMI-1640 medium:
      - 10.4 g powdered RPMI-1640 medium (Sigma catalog # R 6504).
      - 34.53 g MOPS buffer (Sigma catalog # M 3183 or other manufacturer).
      1) Dissolve powdered medium in 900 mL of distilled water.
      2) Add MOPS, and stir until dissolved.
      3) Adjust the pH to 7.0 at 25°C using 10 or 1 mol/L sodium hydroxide while stirring.
      4) Add additional water to bring the medium to a final volume of 1 L.

TABLE 10.1
Composition of RPMI 1640 Medium

Constituent	mg/L
L-Arginine (free base)	200
L-Aspargine	50
L-Aspartic acid	20
L-Cystine.2HCl	65.2
L-Glutamic acid	300
Glycine	10
L-Histidine (free base)	15
L-Hydroxyproline	20
L-Isoleucine	50
L-Leucine	50
L-Lysine.HCl	40
L-Methionine	15
L-Phenylalanine	15
L-Proline	20
L-Serine	30
L-Threonine	20
L-Tryptophan	5
L-Tyrosine.2Na	28.83
L-Valine	20
Biotin	0.2
D-Pantothenic	0.25
Choline chloride	3
Folic acid	1
Myo-inositol	35
Niacinamide	1
PABA[a]	1
Pyridoxine HCl	1
Riboflavin	0.2
Thiamine HCl	1
Vitamin B_{12}	0.005
Calcium nitrate $\times$ H_2O	100
Potassium chloride	400
Magnesium sulfate (anhydrous)	48.84
Sodium chloride	6,000
Sodium phosphate, dibasic (anhydrous)	800
D-Glucose	2,000
Glutathione, reduced	1
Phenol red Na	5.3

[a] PABA (Para amino benzoic acid)

5) Sterilize by filtration using a 0.22-μm filter, and dispense into 100 or 500 mL volumes (depending on the volume needed per run) into sterile glass screw-top bottles.
6) Store at 4°C (this solution has a three-month shelf life and bottles should be labeled with the preparation and expiration dates).
7) Check the sterility of the medium by incubating five tubes, each containing 2 mL of the medium per liter, at 35°C. In addition, visually inspect the solution for obvious contamination before using it.
   • The medium can be purchased as a powder (Sigma) or ready to use (Biowhittaker catalog # 04525).

4. Sterile saline (8.5 g/L NaCl; 0.85% saline).
5. Tween 20.
6. Supplies
   a. Test tubes
      - Standard laboratory sterile screw- or snap-cap test tubes (e.g., 12×75 mm and 16×150 mm plastic) that hold at least 5 mL
   b. Petri dishes
      - Standard 100×15 mm round petri dishes (one dish per strain)
   c. Pipettes (0.1-, 0.25-, 0.5-, 1-, and 5-mL sterile serological pipettes)
   d. Pipetting aids for serological pipettes
   e. Swabs and loops
   f. Microtiter trays
      - Sterile 96 U-shaped-well microtiter trays (M38-A document) are available from a number of manufacturers, including Dynatech and Nalgene Nunc International.
   g. Micropipettes (single and multichannel) and sterile tips for 100-μL volumes
   h. A 0.5 McFarland standard
      1) Procedure for making McFarland standards [1].
         a) Combine 0.5 mL of 0.048 mol/L $BaCl_2$ (1.175% w/v $BaCl_2$ 2 H_2O) and 99.5 mL of 0.18 mol/L (0.36 N) H_2SO_4 (1%v/v).
         b) Mix the solution thoroughly
         c) Using the same size screw-cap tubes that are to be used for the preparation of conidial inoculum suspensions, aliquot 4–6 mL into each tube.
         d) Seal the caps with tape or Parafilm®. Store the tubes in the dark at room temperature
         e) Vigorously agitate the standard solution on a vortex mixer prior to each use
         f) Replace standards or validate densities three months after their preparation
            - Commercially available McFarland standards can be obtained from a number of vendors, including PML, Hardy Diagnostics, and Remel.
      2) Validation of the McFarland standard turbidity
         a) Absorbance
            i) Read the optical density (OD) of the standard on a spectrophotometer with a 1-cm light path using a matched set of cuvettes
            ii) The absorbance should be read at 625 nm (OD should be 0.08 to 0.10)
         b) Colony count
            - The density of the McFarland standard is validated by performing a colony count of a conidial suspension of either reference isolate *Aspergillus flavus* American Type Culture Collection (ATCC) 204304 or quality control isolate *Paecilomyces variotii* ATCC MYA-3630 (2) that is equivalent to the turbidity of the standard
            - The density of the McFarland standard should be verified monthly by the absorbance or colony count method.
            - A 0.5 McFarland standard is equivalent to $0.4–5 \times 10^6$ conidia or sporangiospores per mL (density recommended by the CLSI for the stock inoculum).
      3) Other turbidity standards
         a) Manufactured latex standards
            - Latex standards have a two-year shelf life and are not light sensitive
            - Latex standards are available from Remel (Lenexa, KS; catalog # 20-410) as well as other manufacturers. The density of latex standards should be verified monthly as described for the McFarland standard.
         b) Turbidity meters
            - Available from Vitek and MicroScan Systems
            - Turbidity meters should be calibrated using turbidity standards.
            - The frequency of calibration depends on the manufacturer.

7. Equipment
   a. Biological safety cabinet (class IIA or IIB)
   b. Autoclave
   c. Water bath (48°C–50°C)
   d. Vortex mixer
   e. Incubator set at 35°C ± 1°C
   f. Reading devices
      • A concave mirror reader or plate reader

10.3.3 QUALITY CONTROL

Quality control organisms are used to verify that the antifungal concentrations were made properly, but their use does not test the quality of the media. Recently, one mold isolate (*Paecilomyces variotii* ATCC MYA-3630) has been selected for quality control purposes, and several other molds have been selected as reference strains [2]. The yeast quality control strains [6] and the reference molds listed here and in Table 10.2 can also be used.

1. Quality control strains
   • *Paecilomyces variotii* ATCC MYA-3630
   • *Candida parapsilosis* ATCC 22019
   • *C. krusei* ATCC 6258
2. Reference strains
   • *Aspergillus flavus* ATCC 204304
   • *Aspergillus fumigatus* ATCC MYA-3631
   • *Aspergillus fumigatus* ATCC MYA-3626
   • *Aspergillus fumigatus* ATCC MYA-3627
   • *Aspergillus terreus* ATCC MYA-3633
   • *Fusarium moniliforme* ATCC MYA-3629
   • *Scedosporium apiospermum* ATCC MYA-3635
3. Frequency of quality control or reference testing
   • At least one of the above isolates should be included each time testing is performed using the same procedure as for the clinical isolates.
   • Quality control and reference strains should be preserved following the procedures described by the CLSI [1].
4. Evaluating quality control MIC results
   • MIC values for quality control organisms must be within the acceptable ranges for the antifungal agent being tested for the results to be considered valid. These ranges are listed in the current CLSI M38-A document and in Table 10.2.

10.3.4 PROCEDURE

1. Drug dilutions
   a. Antifungal stock solution preparation
      1) Antifungal powders should be stored according to the manufacturer's instructions. Powders are assayed by the manufacturer to determine the potency of the antifungal agent. This information must be taken into account when making stock solutions as follows:

$$\text{Weight (mg)} = \frac{\text{volume (mL)} \times \text{desired concentration (mg/mL)}}{\text{antifungal potency (mg/mg)}}$$

TABLE 10.2
Quality Control (QC) and Reference MIC Ranges of Antifungal Agents for M38-A Microdilution and Macrodilution Methods

QC Isolates	Antifungal Agent[a]	MIC Range (μg/mL)[b]		
		48 h, Macrodilution	24 h, Microdilution	48 h, Microdilution
P. variotii ATCC MYA-3630	Amphotericin B	NA	NA	1.0–4.0
	Itraconazole	NA	NA	0.06–0.5
	Posaconazole	NA	NA	0.03–0.25
	Voriconazole	NA	NA	0.015–0.12
C. parapsilosis ATCC 22019	Amphotericin B	0.25–1.0	0.25–2.0	0.5–4.0
	Fluconazole	2.0–8.0	0.5–4.0	1.0–4.0
	Itraconazole	0.06–0.25	0.12–0.5	0.12–0.5
	Ketoconazole	0.06–0.25	0.03–0.25	0.06–0.5
	Posaconazole	NA	0.06–0.25	0.06–0.25
	Ravuconazole	NA	0.016–0.12	0.03–0.25
	Voriconazole	NA	0.016–0.12	0.03–0.25
	Flucytosine	0.12–0.50	0.06–0.25	0.12–0.5
	Caspofungin	NA	0.25–1.0	0.5–4.0
	Anidulafungin[a]	NA	0.25–2.0	0.5–2.0
C. krusei ATCC 6258	Amphotericin B	0.25–2.0	0.5–2.0	1.0–4.0
	Fluconazole	16–64	8.0–64	16–128
	Itraconazole	0.12–0.5	0.12–1.0	0.25–1.0
	Ketoconazole	0.12–0.5	0.12–1.0	0.25–1.0
	Posaconazole	NA	0.06–0.5	0.12–1.0
	Ravuconazole	NA	0.06–0.5	0.25–1.0
	Voriconazole	NA	0.06–0.5	0.12–1.0
	Flucytosine	4.0–16	4.0–16	8.0–32
	Caspofungin	NA	0.12–1.0	0.25–1.0
	Anidulafungin	NA	0.03–0.12	0.03–0.12

(continued)

TABLE 10.2
Quality Control (QC) and Reference MIC Ranges of Antifungal Agents for M38-A Microdilution and Macrodilution Methods (continued)

QC or Reference Isolates	Antifungal Agent[a]	MIC Range (μg/mL)[b]		
		48 h, Macrodilution	24 h, Microdilution	48 h, Microdilution
A. flavus ATCC 204304	Amphotericin B	NA	NA	0.5–4.0
	Itraconazole	NA	NA	0.25–0.5
	Posaconazole	NA	NA	0.06–0.5
	Ravuconazole	NA	NA	0.5–4.0
	Voriconazole	NA	NA	0.5–4.0
A. flavus ATCC MYA-3631	Amphotericin B	NA	NA	1.0–8.0
	Posaconazole	NA	NA	0.12–1.0
	Voriconazole	NA	NA	0.5–2.0
A. fumigatus ATCC MYA-3626	Amphotericin B	NA	NA	0.5–4.0
	Itraconazole	NA	NA	0.25–2.0
	Voriconazole	NA	NA	0.25–1.0
A. fumigatus ATCC MYA-3627	Amphotericin B	NA	NA	0.5–4.0
	Itraconazole	NA	NA	≥16
	Voriconazole	NA	NA	0.25–1.0
A. terreus ATCC MYA-3633	Amphotericin B	NA	NA	2.0–8.0
	Voriconazole	NA	NA	0.25–1.0
F. moniliforme ATCC MYA-3629	Amphotericin B	NA	NA	2.0–8.0
	Itraconazole	NA	NA	>16
	Posaconazole	NA	NA	0.5–2.0
	Voriconazole	NA	NA	1.0–4.0
S. apiospermum ATCC MYA-3635	Amphotericin B	NA	NA	4.0–16
	Posaconazole	NA	NA	1.0–4.0
	Voriconazole	NA	NA	0.5–2.0

[a] Caspofungin and anidulafungin are not described in the M38-A document; however, they will be in the M38-A2 document.

[b] Most MIC ranges have been obtained by the microdilution method [2,6]; incubation times for molds are 24 h (Aspergillus spp. and Fusarium spp.) and 48 h for S. apiospermum.

TABLE 10.3
Solvents and Diluents for Preparation of Dilutions of Antifungal Agents

Antifungal agent[a]	Solvent[b]	Diluent
Amphotericin B	DMSO	RPMI-1640
Itraconazole	DMSO	RPMI-1640
Ketoconazole	DMSO	RPMI-1640
Fluconazole	Water	RPMI-1640
Voriconazole	DMSO	RPMI-1640
Posaconazole	DMSO or PEG200	RPMI-1640
Ravuconazole	DMSO	RPMI-1640
Caspofungin	Water	RPMI-1640
Micafungin	Water	RPMI-1640
Anidulafungin	DMSO	RPMI-1640
5-FC	Water	RPMI-1640

[a] 5-FC = 5-flucytosine.
[b] DMSO = dimethyl sulfoxide; PEG200 = polyethylene glycol, mol. wt. of 200.

2) When possible, at least 10 mg of the antifungal powder should be weighed out at one time.

3) All stock solutions should be made at the same concentration. Stock solutions of 1,280 µg/mL work well for most standard susceptibility testing ranges of water-soluble agents and 1,600 µg/mL for water-insoluble ones.

4) The antifungal powder should be dissolved in water or other appropriate diluent as shown in Table 10.3.

5) Stock solutions should be stored carefully sealed in either glass, polypropylene, or polyethylene sterile tubes at −70°C (or lower) in small aliquot volumes (approximately 1.5 mL). Stock solutions should not be stored in frost-free freezers.

6) Stock solutions should be accurately labeled with the antifungal agent's name, concentration, amount in tube, and the preparation and expiration dates (either six months after the stock solution was made or the manufacturer's expiration date for the powder).

7) Stock solutions should be discarded at the end of each day and are never refrozen.

8) Because of the high concentration of antifungal in the stock solution, sterilizing the solution is not necessary.

9) If there is a need to sterilize the antifungal stock solution, it should be done using a membrane such as 0.22-μm membrane.

10) Paper, asbestos, or sintered glass filters should not be used because they may bind to the agent.
   • Filter sterilization is not recommended because the antifungal agent may be retained in the filter.

b. Drug dilution preparation

1) Preparation of water-soluble antifungal agents (Figure 10.1) [7]

   a) Label 10 (16 × 150 mm) tubes 2–11.

   b) Add the appropriate amounts of sterile RPMI to each tube as follows:
   • Add 1 mL of RPMI to tubes 2 and 11.
   • Add 0.5 mL of RPMI to tubes 3, 5, and 8.
   • Add 0.75 mL of RPMI to tubes 6 and 9.
   • Add 1.5 mL of RPMI to tube 4.
   • Add 1.75 mL of RPMI to tubes 7 and 10.

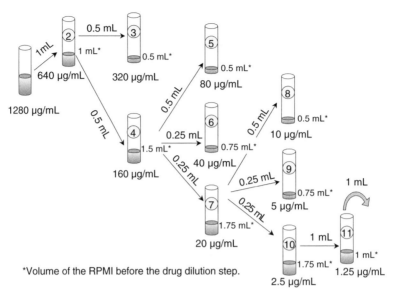

*Volume of the RPMI before the drug dilution step.

FIGURE 10.1 Scheme to perform the dilutions of water-soluble antifungal agents.

    c) Add 1 mL of the stock solution (1,280 μg/mL) to the first antifungal dilution tube (tube 2)

    d) Transfer from tube 2, 0.5 mL to tubes 3 and 4

    e) Transfer from tube 4, 0.5 mL to tube 5 and 0.25 mL to tubes 6 and 7

    f) Transfer from tube 7, 0.5 mL to tube 8 and 0.25 mL to tubes 9 and 10

    g) Transfer from tube 10, 1 mL to tube 11

    h) Finally, discard 1 mL from tube 11

- Notice that when the dilutions have been prepared, each tube contains 1 mL.
- Mix well with a vortex mixer before each dilution step.

2) Preparation of microdilution trays for water-soluble antifungal agents (Figure 10.2) [7].

    a) Place the tubes containing the drug dilutions (1 mL each) in an organized fashion, going from the highest to the lowest drug concentration.

    b) Prepare a 1:5 dilution by adding 4 mL of RPMI to each drug dilution tube and mix well with a vortex mixer

    c) Using a dispensing device, transfer 0.1 mL from each of the drug dilution tubes to the appropriate wells of each microtiter tray; mix well before performing the dispensing step

- The concentration of the antifungal agent in each well is 2 times the concentration needed after this step.
- It is not recommended to use volumes smaller than 0.1 mL because the medium can evaporate during the incubation step.

    d) Add 0.2 mL of RPMI to the wells in column 1 and 0.1 mL to wells in column 12. These wells will serve as the negative (sterility) and positive (growth) control wells, respectively.

    e) The prepared tray should be sealed in a plastic bag and placed at –70°C until needed. Prepared trays should not be stored in a self-defrosting freezer as this type of freezer will shorten the shelf life of the antifungal agent in the tray. Prepared trays should not be refrozen after being thawed

    f) The shelf life of the tray is the expiration date of the antifungal being used or 6 months, whichever comes first

3) Preparation of water-insoluble antifungal agents (Figure 10.3) [7].

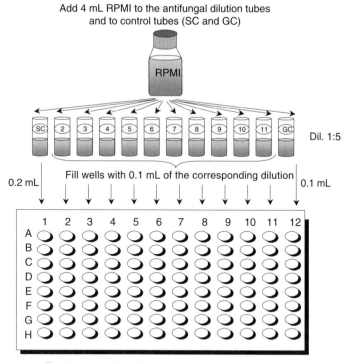

FIGURE 10.2 Preparation of microdilution trays for water-soluble antifungal agents.

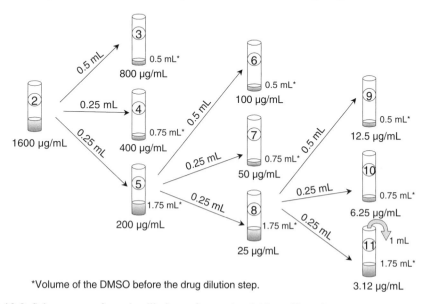

FIGURE 10.3 Scheme to perform the dilutions of water-insoluble antifungal agents.

- The dilutions of water-insoluble antifungal agents (amphotericin B, itraconazole, ketoconazole, posaconazole, ravuconazole, voriconazole, and anidulafungin) must be prepared by using dimethyl sulfoxide (DMSO) or some other appropriate solvent (Table 10.3).

- It is important to prepare the stock solution and drug dilutions in the solvent (follow the scheme of dilution and instructions outlined here) to avoid dilution artifacts that can result from the precipitation of a compound of low solubility (e.g., itraconazole) in aqueous media, thereby producing erroneous drug dilutions.

a) Label 9 (12 × 75 mm) tubes 3–11.

b) Add appropriate amounts of DMSO to each tube as follows:
   - Add 0.5 mL of DMSO to tubes 3, 6, and 9
   - Add 0.75 mL of DMSO to tubes 4, 7, and 10
   - Add 1.75 mL of DMSO to tubes 5, 8, and 11

c) Label the stock solution tube (1,600 µg/mL) as tube 2

d) Transfer from tube 2, 0.5 mL to tube 3 and 0.25 mL to tubes 4 and 5

e) Transfer from tube 5, 0.5 mL to tube 6 and 0.25 mL to tubes 7 and 8

f) Transfer from tube 8, 0.5 mL to tube 9 and 0.25 mL to tubes 10 and 11

g) Finally, discard 1 mL from tube 11
   - Notice that when dilutions have been prepared, all the tubes contain 1 mL
   - Mix well with a vortex mixer before the transfer step

4) Preparation of microdilution trays for water-insoluble antifungal agents (Figure 10.4) [7].

a) Place the tubes containing the drug dilutions (1 mL) in an organized fashion, from the highest to the lowest drug concentration and label a row of 10 tubes with the appropriate drug concentration.

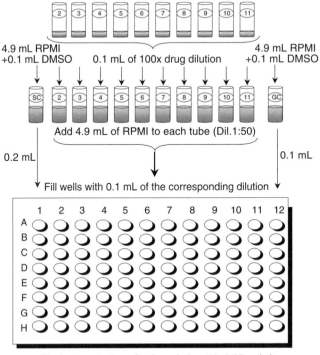

Final concentration after inoculation: 16–0.03 µg/mL

SC: sterility control (Tube 1)
GC: growth control (Tube12)
Trays are now ready for the inoculation step.

FIGURE 10.4 Preparation of microdilution trays for water-insoluble antifungal agents.

b) Prepare a 1:50 dilution by mixing 4.9 mL of RPMI with 0.1 mL from each drug dilution tube; mix well with a vortex mixer.

c) Using a dispensing device, transfer 0.1 mL from each of the final drug dilution tubes to the appropriate well in each microtiter tray.

d) Add 0.2 mL of RPMI plus 2% DMSO (or the solvent that was used) to column 1 of the microtiter tray and 0.1 mL of RPMI plus 2% DMSO (or the solvent that was used) to column 12. These two wells will serve as the negative (sterility) and positive (growth control) control wells, respectively, for the microtiter tray.

e) The concentration of the antifungal agents in the wells is now 2 times the concentration needed.

f) The concentration of DMSO in the wells is now 2%.

g) Follow steps e) and f) (preparation of microdilution trays for water-soluble agents) for storage of prepared microdilution trays.

2. Inoculum preparation (Figure 10.5) [7]

a. For *Aspergillus* spp., *R. arrhizus*, *S. apiospermum*, and *S. schenckii*, inoculum must be prepared from a conidium or sporangiospore suspension obtained from 7-day cultures grown on potato dextrose agar at 35°C. *Fusarium* spp. should be grown on potato dextrose agar for 48–72 h at 35°C and then at 25°C–28°C until day 7. Some isolates need longer incubation (more than 7 days) to produce conidia.

b. Recover conidia by wetting a loop with Tween 20 and transfer the loopful of conidia into 3 mL of sterile saline.

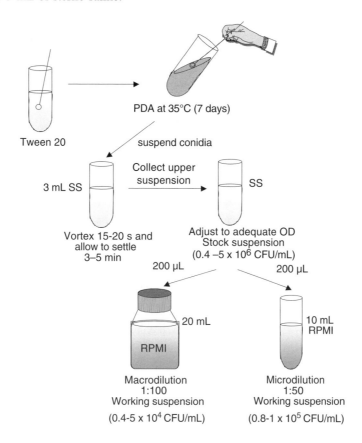

SS: saline solution

FIGURE 10.5 Inoculum preparation of molds for micro- and macrodilution methods.

   c. Vortex the conidia suspension vigorously for 15–20 s to prevent clumping of the spores. (Caution: Remove the cap carefully as liquid adhering to the cap may produce aerosols upon opening).

   d. Allow the heavy particles to settle for 3–5 min and then transfer the upper suspension to a sterile tube and adjust using a spectrophotometer (530 nm) to the optical density (OD) that yields a stock suspension of $0.4–5 \times 10^6$ viable conidia or sporangiospores per milliliter. The OD at which the inoculum must be adjusted will depend on the size of conidia. Table 10.4 shows the OD for some species and the corresponding CFU/mL [1, 8].

   e. Prepare a working suspension by diluting 1:50 of the conidia stock suspension in the standard medium; mix well with a vortex mixer. Inoculum suspensions of *S. apiospermum* may require a lower (50%) dilution factor. The 1:50 inoculum dilutions will correspond to double the density needed (approximately $0.4–5 \times 10^4$ CFU/mL).

   f. Check or verify the final inoculum size by plating 10 μL of a 1:20 dilution of working suspension onto SAB plates (approximately 4–50 colonies per plate).

   g. Incubate plates at 35°C (or 28°C–30°C) and observe daily for the presence of fungal colonies.

      • Colonies should be counted as soon as possible after growth becomes visible (24 h or less for *R. arrhizus* to 5 days for *S. apiospermum*).

3. Inoculation of microtiter trays.

   a. Allow the microtiter trays to thaw at room temperature; it will take approximately 2 h to thaw if they are stacked four trays high or 45 min if unstacked under a hood.

   b. Remove the sealing tape as soon as the trays are taken from the freezer and cover them with a clean lid.

TABLE 10.4

Optical Density (OD) Range and Inoculum Sizes for Common and Uncommon Molds

Species	OD Range (%T)[a]	10^6 CFU/mL Range
A. nidulans	0.09–0.11 (80–82)	1.1–2
A. flavus	0.09–0.11 (80–82)	0.4–4
A. fumigatus	0.09–0.11 (80–82)	0.6–5
A. terreus	0.09–0.11 (80–82)	0.9–5
Bipolaris hawaiiensis	0.2–0.3	0.07–0.4
B. spicifera	0.2–0.3	0.3–3
Cladophialophora bantiana	0.15–0.17 (68–70)	0.4–3.1
Dactilaria constricta	0.15–0.17 (68–70)	0.4–1
Fusarium oxysporum	0.15–0.17 (68–70)	0.8–5
F. solani	0.15–0.17 (68–70)	0.5–5.9
Paecilomyces lilacinus	0.09–0.13	0.8–2.3
P. variotii	0.09–0.11 (80–82)	ND
Scedosporium apiospernum	0.15–0.17	0.4–3.2
R. arrhizus	0.15–0.17	0.4–2.6
S. prolificans	0.15–0.17	0.6–1.7
S. schenckii	0.09–0.11	
Trichoderma longibrachiatum	0.09–0.11	0.7–2.3
Wangiella dermatitidis	0.15–0.17	1.2–3.7

[a] %T = percent transmission.

Based on Refs. 4 and 8.

  c. Thawed trays should be inoculated within 1 h of thawing
  d. Fill each row of the microtiter tray from wells 2–12 with 0.1 mL of the working inoculum suspension using a single or a multichannel pipette; mix well with a vortex mixer before dispensing. If using another device, follow the manufacturer's instructions as to what inoculum concentration should be added to the inoculum reservoir
     • Eight clinical isolates or seven isolates and one of the quality control or reference isolates can be tested in one tray. The GC ensures that the isolate is viable and indicates the 100% growth of the isolate.
4. Incubation
  MIC trays are incubated without agitation in an aerobic incubator without CO_2 at 35°C for 46–50 h for most of the opportunistic molds (*Aspergillus* spp., *Fusarium* spp., and *S. schenkii*). *Rhizopus* spp. and other zygomycetes will require 21–26 h of incubation, and *S. apiospermum* and *S. prolificans* 70–74 h. Stack trays no more than three high.
5. Microdilution MIC definitions
  a. MIC definition for itraconazole, the new triazoles (voriconazole, ravuconazole and posaconazole), and amphotericin B (MICs of 5-FC [5-flucytosine] and ketoconazole can also be determined by this methodology) is as follows:
     • The MIC is the lowest drug concentration that prevents any discernible growth (optically clear) as detected visually.
6. Reading
  a. Visual reading
     1) Remove the trays from the incubator.
     2) Place the tray on a reading device (light box, concave mirror reader, or plate reader).
     3) The growth control well must have sufficient growth.
     4) If adequate growth is not present, the trays must be reincubated. Adequate growth will depend on the species being tested.
     5) Determine the MIC endpoint, using the definition described above.
     6) MICs for quality control isolates should be within the established limits (Table 10.3) [2,6]
  b. Spectrophotometric reading
     • This procedure is not included in the CLSI documents, but sometimes it is helpful.
     1) Set the spectrophotometer at 405 nm, and determine the OD of each well.
     2) The use of 450-, 492-, 550-, or 600-nm filters gives similar results.
     3) Do not agitate the trays before reading them.
     4) Subtract the OD of the blank (uninoculated column 1 wells) from the OD of the inoculated wells.
     5) The MIC is the lowest drug concentration that produces ≥95% growth reduction both for azoles and amphotericin B.
        • Caution: With some brands of the microtiter plates, bubbles may appear after incubation that will preclude an accurate MIC determination or OD reading. Use of the Greiner-Bio-One microtiter plates (reference # 650180) will avoid this problem. Burst the bubbles with a heated needle.

10.3.5 Interpretation of the Results

Interpretative breakpoints have not been established for molds. The clinical relevance of testing this group of fungal pathogens remains uncertain. Nevertheless, preliminary data indicate that high itraconazole MICs (>8 µg/mL) are associated with clinical resistance to this agent [9,10] when the MICs are determined by the M-38-A microdilution method [1]. For the new triazole antifungal agents, data indicating a correlation between MICs and clinical outcome of treatment are not yet available. The same applies to amphotericin B. However, correlation between clinical outcome and amphotericin B MIC results suggests that MICs >2 μg/mL are associated with treatment failure and MICs below 2 μg/mL with clinical response [11].

Trailing endpoints with amphotericin B, itraconazole, posaconazole, ravuconazole, and voriconazole against *Aspergillus* spp. and most other opportunistic pathogenic molds are not usually encountered. Such a pattern may reflect clinically relevant drug resistance [9,10].

10.3.6 ADVANTAGES

1. The broth microdilution procedure can test several isolates in the same microtiter tray.
2. Microtiter plates can be prepared in advance and stored at –70°C for 6 months.
3. This procedure is easy to perform and requires less space in the laboratory freezer and incubator than does the macrodilution procedure.
4. It does not require specialized equipment.
5. It is the optimal standard procedure to detect azole resistance in *Aspergillus* spp. [5].

10.3.7 LIMITATIONS

1. The method has only been standardized for conidium-forming molds with azoles and amphotericin B. It has not been evaluated for the yeast forms of dimorphic fungi, such as *B. dermatitidis, C. immitis, H. capsulatum* variety *capsulatum, P. marneffei*, or *S. schenckii*.
2. Breakpoints are not yet available.
3. The OD for preparation of inocula varies with the species to be tested.
4. There is a risk that drug dilutions in the microdilution trays could dry out when testing slow-growing molds.

10.3.8 CONCLUSIONS

This procedure requires the utilization of a biological safety cabinet and should be attempted only with the guidance of an experienced individual; if an easier method is chosen, its results should match those of the CLSI standard. The medium, inoculum size, time and temperature of incubation can affect the MICs for filamentous fungi. The RPMI medium yields reproducible results and facilitates the detection of itraconazole and amphotericin B resistant strains. The minimum effective concentration (MEC) is a more reliable susceptibility end point to evaluate the echinocandins (see Section 10.3.10); although testing conditions for this class of antifungal agents are not described in the CLSI M38-A document.

10.3.9 MINIMUM FUNGICIDAL (OR LETHAL) ACTIVITY

The M38-A document does not describe testing conditions for the determination of minimum fungicidal (or lethal) concentrations (MFCs). It has been demonstrated that the MFC may be a better predictor of therapeutic failure than the MIC in disseminated trichosporosis [12,13]. A CLSI collaborative study has identified certain testing conditions for determining the MFCs of azoles (itraconazole, posaconazole, voriconazole and ravuconazole) and amphotericin B [14]. These testing conditions are:

1. MFC determination.
   a. Subculture 20 μL from each MIC well that showed complete inhibition (100% or an optically clear well) after 72 h of incubation onto SAB plates.
      • Do not agitate the well prior to removal of the specified volumes.
   b. Subculture 20 μL from the growth control well (drug-free medium) onto SAB plates.
      • Do not agitate the well prior to removal of the specified volumes.
   c. Incubate the plates at 35°C until growth is seen in the growth control subculture (usually before 48 h).

2. MFC definition.

The MFC is the lowest drug concentration that shows either no growth or fewer than three colonies to obtain an approximately 99–99.5% killing activity.

3. Additional considerations

a. The clinical relevance of the MFC needs to be established.

b. Preliminary data suggest that the poor *in vitro* fungicidal activity of amphotericin B appears to correspond to the refractory nature of *A. terreus* infections to amphotericin B therapy [15].

c. The method has good reproducibility for azoles and amphotericin B (91%–98% to 96%–100%, respectively) [8].

10.3.10 BROTH MICRODILUTION ALTERNATIVE APPROACH FOR MOLDS VERSUS THE ECHINOCANDINS: EVALUATION OF MORPHOLOGIC CHANGES

Trailing growth is not a problem when testing azoles against most molds. However, when testing the echinocandins, most *Aspergillus* isolates show trailing growth and conventional MIC determination could categorize these trailing isolates as resistant. A more careful examination of microdilution wells reveals the presence of compact, round microcolonies. Under microscopic examination, these micro-colonies correspond to significant morphologic alterations. The hyphae grow abnormally as short, highly branched filaments with swollen germ tubes. The concentration of drug producing these morphologic changes is defined as the minimum effective concentration (MEC) to distinguish it from conventional MICs. A multicenter study has demonstrated that caspofungin MECs were reliable end points in 14 of 17 laboratories [16]; similar results were obtained in another study in the 8 laboratories that participated in the study when evaluating anidulafungin against a variety of mold species.[1]

MICs and MECs of the echinocandins are usually <1.0 μg/mL for *Aspergillus* spp. but higher for other molds (MECs and MICs >8 μg/mL). However, MICs <1.0 μg/mL have been reported for some isolates of the dimorphic fungi, *Phialophora* spp. and *S. apiospermum*. MEC methodology will be introduced in the revised M38-A2 CLSI document.

10.4. BROTH MACRODILUTION PROCEDURE

10.4.1 INTRODUCTION

The design of the CLSI broth macrodilution method is similar to that for yeasts with some variation. This method has been assayed by a number of laboratories and has been found to correlate well with the microdilution method [3,4]. It is a practical method for use in the clinical laboratory when testing slow-growing fungi that require a long incubation time (more than 72 h).

1. Technical notes.

   • It is important to completely plan out the entire procedure since it involves many steps over several days. It is also important to understand all the steps of the procedure before beginning. The technologist is advised to read and understand the CLSI M38-A document before proceeding.

   • Determine the number of isolates to be tested, the number of antifungal agents, and the range of concentrations for each antifungal.

   • The concentration ranges for drugs are the same as for yeast susceptibility testing (see Table 10.5).

---

[1] Espinel-Ingroff, A., Ghannoum, M., Manauathu, E., et al. ICAAC poster M-1605, 2005.

TABLE 10.5
Summary of M38-A Method

Test medium	RPMI 1640 with glutamine, without bicarbonate and with a pH indicator
pH	6.9–7.1
Buffer	[3-(N-morpholino)]-propanesulfonic acid (MOPS) at a concentration of 0.164 mol/L (34.53 g/L)
Inoculum size	$0.4–5 \times 10^4$ CFU/mL
Duration and temperature of incubation	*Rhizopus* spp.: 21–26 h at 35°C
	Aspergillus spp., *Fusarium* spp., *S. schenckii*: 46–50 h at 35°C
	S. apiospermum: 70–74 h at 35°C
Concentrations to be assayed	Amphotericin B, itraconazole, voriconazole, posaconazole, ravuconazole: 16–0.03 μg/mL
MIC definition	Amphotericin B, itraconazole, voriconazole, posaconazole, ravuconazole: the lowest drug concentration that prevents any discernible growth (clear tubes) after 48 to 72 h of incubation; echinacandins, MEC determination at 24 to 48 h
Breakpoints	Not established for molds
Quality control strains	*P. variotii* ATCC MYA-3630
	Candida krusei ATCC6258 and *C. parapsilosis* ATCC22019
Reference strains	*Aspergillus flavus* ATCC 204304 and others listed in Table 10.2

10.4.2 MATERIALS

1. Antimicrobial source (refer to Section 10.3.2)
2. Agar media (refer to Section 10.3.2)
3. Test medium is RPMI 1640 medium (refer to Section 10.3.2 for medium preparation)
4. Sterile saline (8.5 g/L NaCl; 0.85% saline)
5. Tween 20
6. Supplies
   - The same supplies listed in Section 10.3.2 are needed with the exception of microtiter trays and multichannel micropipettes.
7. Equipment
   - The same equipment listed in Section 10.3.2 is needed with the exception of the microdilution plate reader.

10.4.3 QUALITY CONTROL

Quality control organisms verify that the antifungal concentrations were made properly, but they do not test the quality of the media. *Paecilomyces variotii* ATCC MYA-3630 has been selected for quality control purposes, and several other molds have been selected as reference strains [2]. The yeast quality control strains [6] described in Chapter 9 or the reference molds listed here and in Table 10.2 can also be utilized; however, most quality control data have been obtained by the microdilution method.

1. Quality control strains
   - *Paecilomyces variotii* ATCC MYA-3630.
   - *Candida parapsilosis* ATCC 22019.
   - *C. krusei* ATCC 6258.
2. Reference strains
   - *Aspergillus flavus* ATCC 204304.
   - *Aspergillus fumigatus* ATCC MYA-3631.
   - *Aspergillus fumigatus* ATCC MYA-3626.
   - *Aspergillus fumigatus* ATCC MYA-3627.

- *Aspergillus terreus* ATCC MYA-3633.
- *Fusarium moniliforme* ATCC MYA-3629.
- *Scedosporium apiospermum* ATCC MYA-3635.

3. Frequency of quality control or reference testing.
   - At least one of the above isolates should be included each time testing is performed using the same procedure used for the clinical isolates.
   - Quality control and reference strains should be preserved following procedures described by the CLSI [1].
   - See instructions given in in Section 10.10.4 under "Inoculation of MIC tubes" for a description of how to perform the inoculations. In addition, test one of these isolates with each new lot of macrodilution tubes before testing clinical specimens.

4. Evaluating quality control and reference strain MIC results.
   - The MIC values for a quality control or reference organism tested must be within acceptable ranges for the antifungal agent being tested. These ranges are listed in Table 10.2 [2,6].

10.4.4 Procedure

1. Tubes
   a. Based on the number of strains and the antifungal agents to be tested, calculate the number of tubes needed (# strains × number of antifungal dilutions + controls = # of tubes per antifungal).
   b. Calculate the total amount of RPMI needed (# of strains × 12 mL = total volume per strain plus 12 mL to prepare antifungal agent dilutions).

2. Drug dilutions
   a. Antifungal stock solution preparation (see Section 10.3.4).
   b. Drug dilution preparation
      1) Preparation of the water-soluble antifungal agents (Figure 10.6) [7].
         a) Label 10 (16 × 150 mm) tubes 2–11.

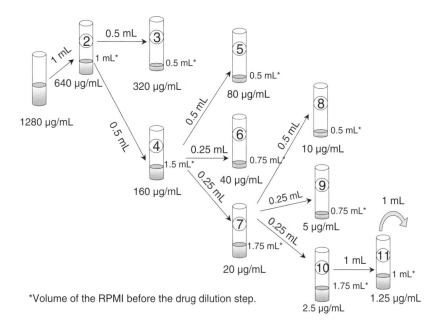

*Volume of the RPMI before the drug dilution step.

FIGURE 10.6 Scheme to perform the dilutions of water-soluble antifungal agents.

b) Add the appropriate amounts of sterile RPMI to each tube as follows:
- Add 1 mL of RPMI to tubes 2 and 11.
- Add 0.5 mL of RPMI to tubes 3, 5, and 8.
- Add 0.75 mL of RPMI to tubes 6 and 9.
- Add 1.5 mL of RPMI to tube 4.
- Add 1.75 mL of RPMI to tubes 7 and 10.

c) Add 1 mL of the stock solution (1,280 µg/mL) to the first antifungal dilution tube (tube 2)

d) Transfer from tube 2, 0.5 mL to tubes 3 and 4

e) Transfer from tube 4, 0.5 mL to tube 5 and 0.25 mL to tubes 6 and 7

f) Transfer from tube 7, 0.5 mL to tube 8 and 0.25 mL to tubes 9 and 10.

g) Transfer from tube 10, 1 mL to tube 11

h) Finally, discard 1 mL from tube 11
- Notice that when dilutions have been prepared, each tube contains 1 mL.
- Mix well with a vortex mixer before each transfer or dilution step.

1) Preparation of MIC tubes for water-soluble agents (Figure 10.7) [7].

a) Place the tubes containing the drug dilutions (1 mL each) in an organized fashion, going from the highest to the lowest drug concentration
- Nine sets of MIC tubes may be prepared with these volumes.

b) Label the rows of 10 tubes (12 × 75 mm) with the final drug concentrations (64 to 0.12 µg/mL)

c) Dispense 0.1 mL from each drug dilution tube into the bottom of each corresponding MIC tube using a repetitive or reservoir pipette with a syringe of 1 mL; mix well before dispensing
- Beginning with the lowest concentration, the same tip can be used throughout.
- Mix well with a vortex mixer before each dispensing step.

d) Close the tubes with screw caps (plastic or metal caps), and store them at −70°C for up 6 months

e) On the day of the test, allow the tubes to thaw at room temperature before inoculation (about 1 h). Each tube is inoculated with 0.9 mL of the corresponding diluted inoculum

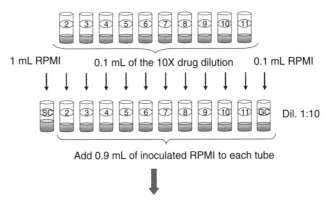

1 mL RPMI   0.1 mL of the 10X drug dilution   0.1 mL RPMI

Add 0.9 mL of inoculated RPMI to each tube

Final concentration after inoculation:
64–0.12 µg/mL

SC: sterility control (Tube 1)
GC: growth control (Tube 12)

FIGURE 10.7 Preparation of MIC tubes for water-soluble antifungal agents.

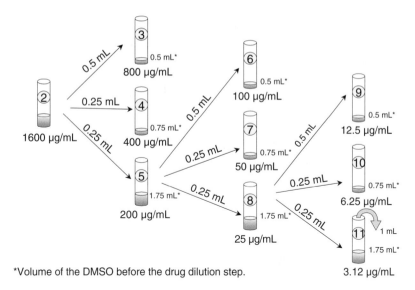

*Volume of the DMSO before the drug dilution step.

FIGURE 10.8 Scheme to perform the dilutions of water-insoluble antifungal agents.

2) Preparation of the water-insoluble antifungal agents (Figure 10.8) [7].
   - The dilutions of water-insoluble antifungal agents (amphotericin B, itraconazole, anidulafungin, ketoconazole, posaconazole, ravuconazole, and voriconazole) must be prepared by using a solvent such as DMSO or other appropriate solvent (Table 10.3).
   - It is important to prepare the stock solution and drug dilution in the solvent (follow the scheme of dilutions and instructions here) to avoid dilution artifacts that can result from the precipitation of a compound of low solubility (e.g., itraconazole) in aqueous media, thereby producing erroneous drug dilutions.
   a) Label 10 (12 × 75 mm) tubes 3–11.
   b) Add appropriate amounts of DMSO to each tube as follows:
      - Add 0.5 mL of DMSO to tubes 3, 6, and 9.
      - Add 0.75 mL of DMSO to tubes 4, 7, and 10.
      - Add 1.75 mL of DMSO to tubes 5, 8, and 11.
   c) Label the stock solution tube (1,600 µg/mL) as tube 2.
   d) Transfer from tube 2, 0.5 mL to tube 3 and 0.25 mL to tubes 4 and 5.
   e) Transfer from tube 5, 0.5 mL to tube 6 and 0.25 mL to tubes 7 and 8.
   f) Transfer from tube 8, 0.5 mL to tube 9 and 0.25 mL to tubes 10 and 11.
   g) Finally, discard 1 mL from tube 11.
      - Notice that when dilutions have been prepared, all the tubes contain 1 mL.
      - Mix well with a vortex mixer before each transfer step.
3) Preparation of MIC tubes for water-insoluble antifungal agents (Figure 10.9) [7].
   a) Place tubes containing the drug dilutions (1mL) in an organized fashion, from the highest to the lowest drug concentration and label rows of 10 tubes (12 × 75 mm) with the final drug concentrations (16 to 0.03 µg/mL).
   b) Prepare a 1:10 dilution by mixing 0.9 mL of RPMI with 0.1 mL from each drug concentration, and mix well with a vortex mixer.
   c) Nine sets of MIC tubes may be prepared with these volumes.
   d) Dispense 0.1 mL from each concentration into the bottom of each sterile 12 × 75 mm plastic test tube, using a repetitive or reservoir pipette with a syringe of 1 mL.
   e) Beginning with the lowest concentration, the same tip can be used throughout.

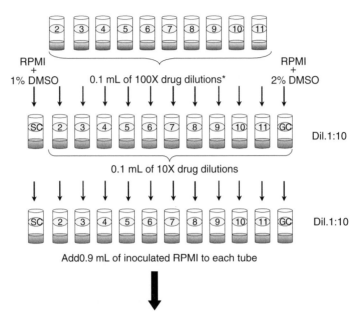

*Add 0.9 ml of RPMI to each tube for the 1:10 dilution
SC: sterility control (Tube 1)
GC: growth control (Tube 12)

FIGURE 10.9 Preparation of MIC tubes for water-insoluble antifungal agents.

       f) Mix well with a vortex mixer before each dispensing step.

       g) Close the tubes with screw caps (plastic or metal caps), and store them at –70°C for up to 6 months.

       h) On the day of the test, allow the tubes to thaw at room temperature before the inoculation (about 1 h). Each tube is inoculated with 0.9 mL of the corresponding inoculum, and the final concentration of DMSO is 1%.

3. Inoculum preparation (Figure 10.10) [7]

    a. For *Aspergillus* spp., *R. arrhizus*, *S. apiospermum*, and *S. schenckii*, inoculum must be prepared from a conidium or sporangiospore suspension obtained from 7-day cultures grown on potato dextrose agar at 35°C. *Fusarium* spp. should be grown on potato dextrose agar for 48–72 h at 35°C and then at 25°C–28°C until day 7. Some isolates need longer incubation (more than 7 days) to produce conidia.

    b. Recover conidia by wetting a loop with Tween 20 and transfer the loopful of conidia into 3 mL of sterile saline.

    c. Vortex the conidia suspension vigorously for 15–20 s to prevent clumping of the spores. (Caution: Remove the cap carefully as liquid adhering to the cap may produce aerosols upon opening).

    d. Allow the heavy particles to settle for 3–5 min, and then transfer the upper suspension to a sterile tube and adjust using a spectrophotometer (530 nm) to the OD that yields a stock suspension of $0.4–5 \times 10^6$ viable conidia or sporangiospores per milliliter. The OD at which the inoculum must be adjusted will depend on the size of conidia. Table 10.4 shows the OD for some species and the corresponding CFU per milliliter [1,8].

    e. Prepare a working suspension by diluting 1:100 the conidia stock suspension in the test medium. Inoculum suspensions of *S. apiospermum* may require a lower (50%)

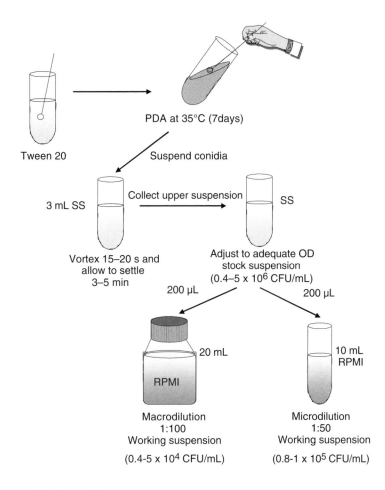

SS: saline solution

FIGURE 10.10 Inoculum preparation for micro- and macrodilution methods.

dilution factor. The 1:100 inoculum dilutions will correspond to the density needed (approximately 0.4–5×10^4 CFU/mL).

f. Check or verify the final inoculum size by plating 10 μL of a 1:20 dilution of working suspension onto SAB plates (approximately 4–50 colonies per plate).

g. Incubate SAB plates at 35°C (or 28°C–30°C) and observe daily for the presence of fungal colonies.
   • Colonies should be counted as soon as possible after growth becomes visible (24 h or less for *R. arrhizus* to 5 days for *S. apiospermun*).

4. Inoculation of MIC tubes

   a. Allow the MIC tubes to thaw at room temperature; it will take approximately 1 h to thaw.

   b. Thawed MIC tubes should be inoculated within 1 h of thawing.

   c. The drug concentration tubes should be organized before the preparation of the inocula in ascending order.

   d. Include two tubes, for positive (growth control) and negative (sterility) controls per isolate.

   e. Calculate the volume of standardized inoculum-broth suspension needed for each isolate, including the growth control tubes (for example, for one antifungal agent and mold, 10 mL of inoculated RPMI are needed), at the desired final concentration (0.4–5×10^4 CFU/mL).

- Begin inoculating the lowest drug concentration to be tested and move to the highest concentration.
  f. The two control tubes contain 0.1 mL of RPMI (or solvent) rather than the antifungal and either 0.9 mL of the diluted inoculum (growth control) or 0.9 mL of RPMI (sterility control).
     - The growth control tube ensures that the inoculum is viable and actively growing and indicates 100% growth of the isolate.
     - The negative control tube provides evidence of medium sterility.
  g. Add 0.9 mL of the working suspension to the MIC tubes with the antifungal agent; mix this suspension well with a vortex mixer before the inoculation step.
5. Incubation.
   - MIC tubes are incubated at 35°C (without agitation) in an aerobic incubator and observed for the presence or absence of visible growth. The incubation time depends on the species. Most opportunistic filamentous fungi (*Aspergillus* spp., *Fusarium* spp., and *S. schenkii*) require 46–50 h of incubation, while *Rhizopus* spp. require 21–26 h and *S. apiospermum*, 70–74 h.
6. Reading
   a. Visual reading
      1) Remove MIC tubes from the incubator.
      2) The growth control tube must have sufficient growth.
      3) If adequate growth is not present, the tubes must be reincubated. Adequate growth will depend on the species being tested.
      4) Determine the MIC end point as described here.
      5) MICs for quality control isolates should be within established ranges (Table 10.3) [2,6].
7. Macrodilution MIC definition and interpretation
   The MIC definition for itraconazole, the new triazoles (voriconazole, ravuconazole and posaconazole), and amphotericin B (MICs of 5-FC and ketoconazole can also be determined by this methodology) is as follows:
   - The MIC is the lowest drug concentration that prevents any discernible growth (optically clear) as detected visually.
   - Interpretative breakpoints have not been established for molds. The clinical relevance of testing this group of fungal pathogens remains uncertain.

10.4.5 ADVANTAGES

1. Since susceptibility testing is not an assay that must be performed for all filamentous fungi, the broth macrodilution has the advantage of testing only a single isolate and agent.
2. It does not require specialized equipment.
3. It is the best method for slower growing organisms or for testing those fungi that require more than 72 h of incubation to produce enough growth for MIC determination. As with the microdilution method, there is a risk of evaporation and thus may yield erroneous MIC results.

10.4.6 LIMITATIONS

1. The method has only been standardized for conidium-forming molds. It has not been used in the yeast forms of dimorphic fungi such as *B. dermatitidis*, *C. immitis*, *H. capsulatum* variety *capsulatum*, *P. marneffei*, or *S. schenckii*.
2. Broth macrodilution is not an ideal method for routine testing or for testing multiple isolates because it is labor-intensive and technically demanding.

3. The incubation period is variable, depending on the type of fungal species involved. Nevertheless, most pathogenic filamentous fungi show enough growth after 48–72 h of incubation.

4. Breakpoints are not yet available. There is a need to document *in vitro* versus *in vivo* correlations.

5. The OD for inoculum densities varies with the species to be tested.

10.4.7 CONCLUSIONS

This procedure should be attempted only with the guidance of an experienced individual; if an easier method is chosen, its results should match those of the CLSI standard. MICs for filamentous fungi can be affected by varying the conditions outlined here. Careful attention must be given to the OD required for each mold species and each spectrophotometer. The RPMI medium provides good reproducibility and allows the detection of itraconazole resistant strains. For a summary of CLSI methods, see Table 10.5.

10.5 ETEST PROCEDURE

10.5.1 INTRODUCTION

Etest (AB Biodisk, Solna, Sweden) is a nonporous plastic strip immobilized with a predefined gradient of a given antimicrobial on one side and printed with an MIC scale on the other side. When the Etest strip is placed on an inoculated agar plate, a continuous, stable, and exponential antimicrobial gradient is established along the side of the strip. After incubation, the MIC value (μg/mL) can be read directly from the MIC scale printed on the Etest strip. This technology is similar to a disk diffusion assay but with a longer stability time for the antimicrobial gradient. The equivalency of the resulting MIC with the CLSI reference values has not been well established. Preliminary results show that the correlation improves if the Etest MICs are read after 24 h of incubation rather than after 48 h or when sufficient growth is visible [17].

10.5.2 MATERIALS

1. Etest strips can be purchased directly from AB Biodisk or through Remel (Table 10.6). Strips (approximate cost ≥$2/strip) are sold in packages of 100 strips per antifungal agent and are stored at –20°C or –70°C. Once a set of strips is removed from the manufacturer's package, the unused strips should be stored in an airtight container with a desiccant and returned to –20°C. Etest strips should not be used after the expiration date indicated by the manufacturer.

TABLE 10.6
E-Test Strips for Fungi and Concentration Ranges

Antifungal	Code	Concentrations (μg/mL)
Amphotericin B	AP	0.002–32
Fluconazole	FL	0.016–256
Itraconazole	IT	0.002–32
Flucytosine	FC	0.002–32
Ketoconazole	KE	0.002–32
Voriconazole	VO	0.002–32
Posaconazole	PO	0.002–32
Caspofungin	CS	0.002–32

2. Plates consisting of RPMI-1640 supplemented with 2% glucose and 1.5% agar, prepared in-house or obtained commercially (Remel or others), that have a depth of 4 mm ± 0.5 mm can be used. Plates should be stored at 2°C–8°C. Modified casitone agar or antibiotic medium 3 (AM3) agar can also be used [17] as recommended by the manufacturer.
3. Saline solution for making conidium suspensions
4. Swabs (sterile, nontoxic)
5. Test tubes (for inoculum preparation)
6. Pipettes
7. Scissors
8. Forceps or Etest applicator kit
9. A 0.5 McFarland standard (this can be made following CLSI instructions or purchased from microbiology product manufacturers such as PML, Hardy, or Remel).
10. Airtight storage containers with desiccant (silica gel) for extra Etest strips once the manufacturer's packaging has been opened. Storage containers may be purchased from AB Biodisk or Remel.
11. Freezer (–20°C or –70°C) for storage
12. Vortex mixer
13. 35°C ambient air incubator
14. Etest technical information
   • Etest package insert
   • Etest technical guide No. 10
   • Etest application sheet EAS 012
   • Customer information sheet (CIS) No. 5 for preparation of the media

10.5.3 QUALITY CONTROL

1. Quality control strains:
   • *C. parapsilosis* ATCC 22019
   • *C. krusei* ATCC 6258
   • *P. variotii* ATCC 22319
   • All quality control strains should be maintained following the procedures described by CLSI [1].
2. Frequency of quality control testing
   • A quality control organism should be run with every new lot of Etest strips prior to their use.
   • Each antifungal agent should have quality control testing for 30 consecutive days [1]. Otherwise, quality control should be conducted on each occasion that testing is performed.
3. Evaluating the results
   • The Etest antifungal application sheet EAS 012 lists the quality control ranges for appropriate antifungal agents (also see Table 10.7); *P. variotii* ATCC MYA-3630 isolate has not been evaluated by the Etest.
   • These values are not included in the CLSI M38-A document.

10.5.4 PROCEDURE

   • Caution: All steps in the testing of molds must be performed in a class IIA or IIB biological safety cabinet.
1. Remove the strips from the freezer 30 min (–20°C) or 60 min (–70°C) before use from the original package or storage container to allow them to equilibrate at room temperature.

TABLE 10.7
Quality Control MIC Ranges (μg/mL) of Antifungal
Agents for the Etest Method against Molds

Antifungal agent	*Candida parapsilosis* ATCC 22019	*Paecilomyces variotii* ATCC 22319
Amphotericin B	0.25–2	0.24–1
Itraconazole	0.064–0.25	0.032–1
Ketoconazole	0.032–0.125	0.064–0.5

Based on Etest application sheet EAS 012.

2. Use mature growth from SAB or potato dextrose agar slants, 5–7 days, depending on the genus.
3. Carefully pour 1 mL of sterile saline over the growth, and homogenize the conidia and hyphal particles into suspension using a Pasteur pipette.
4. Pipette out the suspension, and transfer to a sterile screw cap tube (13×100 mm).
5. Vortex gently for 15 s, and allow the particles to settle for 15 minutes.
6. Adjust the turbidity of the supernatant to a 0.5 McFarland standard or correct the percent transmission at 530 nm to obtain colony counts of approximately 10^6 CFU/mL (see Table 10.4). Add more conidia to increase the turbidity or more saline to decrease the turbidity (photometric devices can also be used to measure the turbidity).
7. Dip a swab into the inoculum suspension and streak the whole surface of the plate carefully in three different directions to obtain an even growth; mix well before the inoculation step.
   - Make sure that the inoculum is spread evenly over the entire surface of the plate. A correctly inoculated plate will have an even lawn of confluent growth.
   - Plates can be inoculated automatically with the AB–Biodisk spiral autoinoculator CR10.
8. Allow the inoculum to be absorbed completely into the agar (at least 15–20 min). The plate must be completely dry before the application of the Etest strip. If moisture is present on the agar surface when the Etest strip is applied, it will affect the performance of the antifungal gradient.
9. The strip is designed to have the MIC scale facing away from the agar surface and the antifungal gradient touching the agar surface (you should be able to see the writing on the strip after applying it to the agar plate). Apply the "E" labeled area of the strip (highest concentration of antifungal) at the edge of the petri dish to the agar surface and gently lay down the strip with the lowest concentration end of the strip placed toward the center of the plate. *Once the strip has touched the agar surface do not move the strip.* If any large bubbles appear under the strip, gently remove the bubbles by pressing on the Etest strip with a forceps or a swab. Small bubbles under the strip will not affect the performance of the Etest strip.
   - One to two strips can be placed on a 90-mm plate with opposite orientation to each other (you do not want the "E" end of the strip on the same side of the plate for two strips, that is, the gradients will overlap).
   - Up to six strips can be placed on a 150-mm agar plate in a spoke wheel pattern. (Templates are available from AB Biodisk to optimize the positioning of the strips.)
   - When using the Etest applicator, refer to the instructions in the product insert.
   - Do not remove the Etest strip during any part of the process.
10. Incubate the plate, in plastic bags, in the inverted position (agar side up) at 35°C in an aerobic, non-CO_2 environment.

11. Incubate the plate until growth is clearly seen (24–72 h for most Zygomycetes) [17]. Incubation conditions are genus-dependent, for example, *Fusarium* spp. are incubated at 35°C for 24–48 h followed by room temperature (approximately 25°C) for 24–48 h. For slow-growing clinical isolates, extend the incubation time as needed and inspect the plates daily.

10.5.5 ETEST RESULTS

1. Reading
   a. Evaluate the growth of the isolate before reading, and read as soon as possible. Reading times are species-dependent, for example, *Rhizopus* spp. for 16–24 h and *Aspergillus* spp. for 24–48 h. A longer incubation gives overgrowth.
   b. Make the first reading at 16–24 h and the second at 48 h. Slow-growing isolates may require up to 72 h or longer before sufficient growth is obtained.
   c. Read the MIC where the edge of the inhibition ellipse intersects the MIC scale on the Etest strip (use the technical guide No. 10 for endpoint selection assistance).
   d. Ignore filaments bending over into the ellipse; they are usually caused by overgrowth when incubation is prolonged.
   e. If there is complete growth and no zone appears on the plate around a strip, the MIC value is recorded as greater than the highest antifungal concentration of the strip.
   f. If the inhibition ellipse does not fall below the lowest value on the strip, the MIC value is recorded as less than the lowest value on the strip.
2. Interpreting
   a. Etest MICs are based on a continuous gradient; therefore, MIC values between the standard twofold dilutions can be obtained. These values can be reported as such, if desired, or rounded up to the next appropriate twofold dilution value, for example, 0.19 µg/mL becomes 0.25 µg/mL.
   b. Because CLSI interpretative criteria are not available, only report the MIC values.

10.5.6 ADVANTAGES

1. Etest is easy to perform and requires minimal training for test performance.
2. Contamination can be easily recognized.
3. Etest can be easily set up for a small number of clinical isolates.
4. There is minimum labor involved with Etest as compared with broth dilution methods.
5. The Etest methodology is cost-effective for two antifungal agents.
6. Etest is a flexible methodology because the antifungal agent, medium, incubation time, and inoculum size can be adapted to each organism.
7. Itraconazole *in vitro* resistant strains may be distinguished by the Etest method [17].

10.5.7 LIMITATIONS

1. The cost is the most significant limitation. Careful consideration should be given to which antifungal agents are tested because for fewer than two strips per isolate, the Etest methodology can be cost-effective.
2. A low level of reproducibility has been reported: 67% for amphotericin B and 87% for itraconazole [18].
3. End points can be difficult to determine.
4. The agreement between Etest and M38-A results is dependent on the species, antifungal agent, and incubation time; results are usually comparable (for example, using itraconazole, from 83.3% for *Aspergillus nidulans* to >90% for other species). For amphotericin B,

the lowest agreement is for *F. solani* (70%) and *A. flavus* (75%) and the highest is for *A. niger* (100%) [19].

5. Amphotericin B MIC values can substantially change from 24 to 48 h of incubation for some strains.

6. Etest strips are not U.S. FDA approved for mold testing at this time.

10.5.8 ADDITIONAL CONSIDERATIONS

1. The inhibition ellipses of amphotericin B can be narrower than those of voriconazole and itraconazole.

2. The MIC values obtained by the Etest method are generally higher than those obtained by the M38-A method.

   For amphotericin B, itraconazole, and posaconazole, the agreement improves if Etest MICs are determined at 24 h [18,19] or as soon as sufficient growth allows it (before 48 h) [17]. Major discrepancies between amphotericin B MICs determined by the Etest at 48 h and M38-A have been reported for *Aspergillus* spp. and *F. solani* [17].

3. For voriconazole, the agreement is less dependent on the incubation time (24 or 48 h) [19].

10.5.9 CONCLUSIONS

The Etest is easy to perform. However, the changes in MIC values from 24 to 48 h warrant further evaluation to identify optimal conditions for its use and to establish which results (24 vs. 48 h) correlate better with *in vivo* results. Reproducibility studies are also needed.

10.6 SENSITITRE YEASTONE COLORIMETRIC METHOD

10.6.1 INTRODUCTION

The Sensititre YeastOne colorimetric antifungal plate (TREK International, Westlake, OH) consists of a disposable tray that contains dried serial twofold dilutions of seven (in Europe) or three (in the United States) established antifungal agents in RPMI-1640 medium supplemented with 1.5% dextrose in individual wells. The wells also contain the color indicator Almar blue (TREK). YeastOne panels have been evaluated with filamentous fungi [18,20–24]. Good intra- and interlaboratory reproducibility of MIC endpoints has been demonstrated with this method [18,19], for example, using *Aspergillus* spp., 83–93% for itraconazole and >93% for amphotericin B after 24 and 48 h of incubation [18]. Agreement (within ±2 $\log_2$ dilutions) with the CLSI M38-A method for itraconazole is poor (84.6%); however, it is better with amphotericin B (99.6%) [18]. In the United States, the FDA has approved this panel only for yeast testing for three antifungal agents. In Europe, antifungal agents included in the panel are amphotericin B, fluconazole, itraconazole, ketoconazole, 5-FC, caspofungin, and voriconazole.

10.6.2 MATERIALS

1. YeastOne susceptibility test panels
2. YeastOne susceptibility inoculum broth
3. Autoclaved demineralized water (5-mL volumes)
4. Panel layout template
5. Manual worksheet
6. Plate seals
7. Plate viewbox light or mirror type
8. A 0.5 McFarland turbidity standard
9. SAB plates

10. Sterile wooden applicator sticks or a loop
11. Non-CO_2 incubator set at 35°C
12. Vortex mixer
13. 20-μL pipette
14. Multichannel pipette for 100-μL volumes
15. Disposable pipette tips

10.6.3 QUALITY CONTROL

1. Quality control strains:
   - *C. parapsilosis* ATCC 22019
   - *C. krusei* ATCC 6258
   - *P. variotii* ATCC MYA-3630
   - Quality control strains should be preserved following the procedures described by CLSI [1].
2. Frequency of quality control testing
   - Quality control should be run in parallel with every run. The MIC ranges are the same as those in the M38-A document (see Table 10.2). Quality control strains confirm the potency of the antifungal agent dilutions. YeastOne provides the acceptable ranges for the antifungal being tested [1], but the *P. variotii* ATCC MYA-3630 isolate has not been evaluated by the YeastOne method.

10.6.4 PROCEDURE

1. Remove the panels to be used from storage. Panels should not be used if the desiccant is not present or if the integrity of the packing is compromised.
2. The inoculum should be prepared as described for the microdilution method (see Section 10.3.4) in TREK demineralized water.
3. Prepare a working suspension by adding 20 μL of the stock suspension to 11 mL of YeastOne inoculum broth.
4. Panels can be inoculated manually using a pipetting device or automatically with the Sensititre autoinoculator. Fill each well of the Sensititre panel with 100 μL of the working suspension. The excess of the working suspension should be used to inoculate SAB plates to check the inoculum density.
5. Cover the inoculated panels with the panel seals.
6. Stack the panels no more than three high.
7. Incubate the panels for 24–72 h at 35°C in a non-CO_2 incubator, and read when the control well (A1) is red.

10.6.5 YEASTONE MIC RESULTS FOR MOLDS

1. The MIC of azoles, 5-FC, and amphotericin B is the lowest concentration of antifungal solution changing from red (growth) to blue (no growth) after 48 h of incubation.
2. Reading.
   Panels may be read visually by using a view box and in normal laboratory lighting.
   If the growth control well is red, the end points for antifungal agents can be interpreted. If after incubation the well is only weakly purple, reincubate for several additional hours until it turns red. *Do not read the turbidity in Sensititre YeastOne panels.*
3. Interpreting and reporting YeastOne MIC results.
   As no CLSI interpretative criteria are available (see the microdilution method), only report MIC values.

10.6.6 ADVANTAGES

1. YeastOne is easy to perform and requires minimal training for test performance.
2. YeastOne can be easily set up for a small number of clinical isolates.
3. This method discriminated well two itraconazole-resistant strains [23].
4. Panels are stored at room temperature.

10.6.7 LIMITATIONS

1. Low reproducibility MIC values and low agreement with the M38-A method for itraconazole have been reported [18].
2. Breakpoints are not available.
3. There is only limited experience with this method for mold testing.

10.6.8 CONCLUSIONS

The YeastOne procedure is easy to perform with minimal labor and compares well with M38-A for amphotericin B, voriconazole, and posaconazole [24]. Other uses and the clinical relevance of results by the panel are yet to be determined.

10.7 BROTH MICRODILUTION METHOD FOR DERMATOPHYTES

The M38-A broth microdilution method has also been successfully adapted, with minor modifications, to the testing of dermatophytes [25]. These modifications include the use of oatmeal agar for inoculum preparation when testing *Tricophyton rubrum* to induce conidium formation and incubation at 35°C for 4–5 days for MIC determination (80% growth inhibition end points). Two isolates of *Trichophyton* spp. have been selected as reference strains by the subcommittee for testing this group of fungi.

10.8 CONCLUSIONS

Currently, the gold standard for susceptibility testing for molds is the CLSI M38-A broth dilution methodology [1]. This methodology is used typically by research laboratories or large clinical laboratories that can "batch" isolates for large-scale research or surveillance studies. The CLSI methods are labor intensive and do not lend themselves well to testing small numbers of clinical isolates. If a commercial product is proven to be equivalent to the broth dilution procedure, it can be used in the clinical laboratory even though CLSI does not describe alternative methods. Of the two procedures approved by the CLSI, the microdilution method is best suited for routine testing in the clinical laboratory. It can be used with any number of isolates and is less labor intensive than is the broth macrodilution method. Broth microdilution panels can be prepared in bulk and frozen. For molds that require more than 72 h of incubation to achieve visual growth, the macrodilution method is a more suitable procedure. Other alternative methods for testing molds are the colorimetric (YeastOne and others) and Etest procedures; reproducibility and agreement with the M38-A are controversial for these tests. At the present time, the M38-A is a reproducible method that discriminates azole-resistant strains, but the overall relevance of *in vitro* results with clinical outcomes (breakpoint development) is not yet established [26]. As antifungal resistance continues to increase, the need for the clinical laboratory to routinely perform mold susceptibility testing has become more important. For a summary of CLSI methods, see Table 10.5.

REFERENCES

1. Clinical and Laboratory Standards Institute. Reference method for broth dilution antifungal suscep-tibility testing of filamentous fungi, approved standard M38-A, vol. 22, no. 16, Clinical and Laboratory Standards Institute, Wayne, PA, 2002.

2. Espinel-Ingroff, A., Fothergill, A., Ghannoum, M. et al. Quality control and reference guidelines for CLSI broth microdilution susceptibility method (M38-A document) of amphotericin B, itraconazole, posaconazole and voriconazole, J. Clin. Microbiol., 41, 5243–5246, 2005.

3. Espinel-Ingroff, A., Dawson K., Pfaller, M. et al. Comparative and collaborative evaluation of stan-darization of antifungal susceptibility testing for filamentous fungi, Antimicrob. Agents Chemother., 39, 314–319, 1995.

4. Espinel-Ingroff, A., Bartlett, M., Bowden, R. et al. Multicenter evaluation of proposed standardization procedure for antifungal susceptibility testing for filamentous fungi, J. Clin. Microbiol., 35, 139–143, 1997.

5. Espinel-Ingroff, A., Bartlett, M., Chaturvedi, V. et al. Optimal susceptibility testing conditions for detection of azole resistance in Aspergillus spp. NCCLS collaborative evaluation, Antimicrob. Agents Chemother., 45, 1828–1835, 2001.

6. Clinical and Laboratory Standards Institute. Quality control minimal inhibitory concentration (MIC) limits for broth microdilution and MIC interpretive breakpoints, supplement M27-S2, Clinical and Laboratory Standards Institute Wayne, PA, 2006.

7. Cantón, E., Martín-Mazuelo, E., and Espinel-Ingroff, A. Pruebas de sensibilidad antifúngica, in Guia Práctica de Identificación y Diagnóstico en Micología Clínica, Pemán, J., Martín-Mazuelo, E.., Rubio-Calvo, M.C., Eds., Bilbao, Revista Iberoamericana de Micología, 2001, 15.1–15.13.

8. Espinel-Ingroff, A., Chatuvedi, V., Fothergill, A. et al. Optimal testing conditions for determining MICs and minimum fungicidal concentrations of new and established antifungal agents for uncommon molds: NCCLS collaborative study, J. Clin. Microbiol., 40, 3776–3781, 2002.

9. Denning, D.W., Venkateswarlu, K., Oskley, K.L. et al. Itraconazole resistance in Aspergillus fumigatus. Antimicrob. Agents Chemother., 41, 1364–1368, 1997.

10. Denning, D.W., Radford, S.A., Oakley, K.L. et al. Correlation between in-vitro susceptibility testing to itraconazole and in-vivo outcome of Aspergillus fumigatus infection, J. Antimicrob. Chemother., 40, 401–414, 1997.

11. Lass-Florl, C., Kofler, G., Krospshofer, G. et al. In vitro testing of susceptibility to amphotericin B is a reliable predictor of clinical outcome in invasive aspergillosis, J. Antimicrobiol. Chemother., 42, 497–502, 1998.

12. Walsh, T.J., Melcher, G.P., Rinaldi, M.G. et al. Trichosporn beigelii, an emerging pathogen resistant to amphotericin, J. Clin. Microbiol., 28, 1616–1622, 1990.

13. Walsh, T.J., Lee, J.W., Melcher, G.P., et al. Experimental disseminated trichosporosis in persistently granulocytopenic rabbits: implications for pathogenesis, diagnosis, and treatment of an emerging opportunistic infection, J. Infect. Dis., 166, 121–133, 1992.

14. Espinel–Ingroff, A., Fotherhill, A., Peter, J., et al. Testing conditions for determination of minimum fungicidal concentrations of new and established antifungal agents for Aspergillus spp.: NCCLS collaborative study, J. Clin. Microbiol., 40, 3204–3208, 2002.

15. Iwe, P.C., Rupp, M.E., Langnas, A.N. et al. Invasive pulmonary aspergillosis due to Aspergillus terreus: 12 year experience and review of the literature, Clin. Infect. Dis., 26, 1092–1097, 1998.

16. Odds, F.C., Motyl, M., Andrade, R. et al. Interlaboratory comparison of results of susceptibility testing with caspofungin against Candida and Aspergillus species, J. Clin. Microbiol., 42, 3475–3482, 2004.

17. Espinel-Ingroff, A. Comparison of the Etest with the NCCLS M38-P method for antifungal susceptibility testing of common and emerging pathogenic filamentous fungi, J. Clin. Microbiol., 39, 1360–1367, 2001.

18. Meletiadis, J., Mouton, J.W., Meis, J.F.G.M., et al. Comparison of the Etest and the sensititre colo-rimetric methods with the NCCLS proposed standard for antifungal susceptibility testing of Aspergillus species, J. Clin. Microbiol., 40, 2876–2885, 2002.

19. Espinel-Ingroff, A. and Rezusta, A. E-test method for testing susceptibilities of Aspergillus spp. to the new triazoles voriconazole and posaconazole and to established antifungal agents: Comparison with NCCLS broth microdilution method, J. Clin. Microbiol., 40, 2101–2107, 2002.

20. Espinel-Ingroff, A., Bartlett, M., Bowden, R. et al. Multicenter evaluation of proposed standardized procedure for antifungal susceptibility testing of filamentous fungi, J. Clin. Microbiol., 35, 139–143, 1997.

21. Castro, C., Serrano, M.C., Flores, B., et al. Comparison of the Sensititre YeastOne colorimetric antifungal panel with a modified NCCLS M38-A method to determine the activity of voriconazole against clinical isolates of *Aspergillus* spp., *J. Clin. Microbiol.*, 42, 4358–4360, 2004.
22. Linares, M.J., Charriel, G., Solis, F., Rodriguez, F., Ibarra, A., and Casal, M. Susceptibility of filamentous fungi to voriconazole tested by two microdilution methods, *J. Clin. Microbiol.*, 43, 250–253, 2005.
23. Martín-Mazuelos, E., Pemán, J., Valverde, A. et al. Comparison of the Sensititre YeastOne colorimetric antifungal panel and Etest with the NCCLS M38-A method to determine the activity of amphotericin B and itraconazole against clinical isolates of *Aspergillus* spp., *J. Antimicrob. Chemother.*, 52, 365–370, 2003.
24. Espinel-Ingroff, A. Comparison of three commercial (Etest, YeastOne and Neosensitabs tablets) and disk diffusion (modified M44-A) assays with reference (CLSI M38-A and M27-A2 microdilution) MICs for testing Zygomycetes, *Aspergillus* spp., *Candida* spp., and *Cryptococcus neoformans,* with posaconazole, *J. Clin. Microbiol.*, 44, 3616–3622.
25. Ghannoum, M.A., Chaturvedi, V., Espinel-Ingroff, A. et al. Intra- and interlaboratory study of a method for testing the antifungal susceptibilities of dermatophytes, *J. Clin. Microbiol.*, 42, 2977–2979, 2004.
26. Espinel-Ingroff, A. Utility of mould susceptibility testing, *Current Opinions Infect. Dis.*, 16, 527–532, 2003.

11 Susceptibility Testing of Mycobacteria

Barbara A. Brown-Elliott, Samuel Cohen,
and Richard J. Wallace, Jr.

CONTENTS

11.1 INTRODUCTION

This chapter reviews the principles and procedures of mycobacterial susceptibility testing for the nontuberculous mycobacteria (NTM), including *Mycobacterium avium* complex (MAC) and the rapidly growing mycobacteria (RGM). A review of the advances in susceptibility testing of the M. tuberculosis complex (*M. tuberculosis*, *M. bovis*, *M. africanum*, *M. bovis BCG*, and *M. canettii*) is also included. Conventional methodology using critical concentrations in agar proportion method is discussed along with newer methods, including broth-based systems such as BACTEC 460 TB and MGIT 960, (Becton Dickinson Biosciences, Sparks, MD), ESPII system (Trek Diagnostic Systems, Westlake, OH), and the BacT/ALERT 3D System (bioMérieux, Durham, NC).

11.2 PRINCIPLES OF *MYCOBACTERIUM TUBERCULOSIS* COMPLEX SUSCEPTIBILITY TESTING

Mycobacteriology susceptibility testing should be performed by experienced technologists who process enough specimens and see enough positive cultures to handle them promptly and correctly. The American Thoracic Society (ATS) has recommended that laboratories culture at least 20 specimens per week to maintain proficiency as well as continuing and frequent performance of test procedures [1]. Problems such as contamination, mixed cultures, slow growth, or improbable results should be recognized by the technologist. Some of the media is expensive and has a relatively short shelf life, a consideration for laboratories that do minimal mycobacterial susceptibility testing. The laboratory must have quality control strains to cover all species tested, and the strains must be stored and subcultured appropriately [2]. The laboratory director or supervisor must be willing and able to provide consultation and feedback to physicians and public health officials, and technologists must troubleshoot problems in a timely manner. In this era of overnight air courier service and electronic communication, patients may be better served when small, localized laboratories send their clinical specimens to a reference laboratory that is specialized in the identification and susceptibility testing of Mycobacterium species.

When is susceptibility testing warranted? As recently as the mid-1980s, susceptibility testing of *M. tuberculosis* complex initial isolates in the United States was not recommended unless a "high probability of drug resistance is expected" [3]. Issues such as HIV, homelessness, prison conditions, and immigration changed the official position on susceptibility testing of initial *M. tuberculosis* complex isolates, making it mandatory in the United States [4]. The recent Clinical Laboratory and Standards Institute (CLSI, formerly The National Committee for Clinical Laboratory Standards, NCCLS) M24-A document [2] states that susceptibility testing should be performed on the first isolate of *M. tuberculosis* complex cultured from a patient sample. Testing should be repeated if the patients fail to convert to negative after 3 months of therapy or there is evidence of failure to respond to therapy.

Until the development of streptomycin and *p*-amino salicylic acid (PAS), there were no drugs to treat tuberculosis. Other agents such as isoniazid (INH) were subsequently introduced. Subsequently, drug resistance began to develop and the need to detect drug resistance became evident. Eventually, international committees (i.e., International Working Groups for Mycobacteria Taxonomy, IWGMT) met to set standards for susceptibility testing and to define drug-susceptible and drug-resistant *M. tuberculosis* complex so that the results of testing could be interpreted consistently.

"Susceptible" strains are defined as "those that have never been exposed to the main antituberculosis drugs ("wild" strains) and respond to these drugs, generally in a uniform manner" [5]. The definition was based on *in vitro* studies showing that growth of such strains was inhibited by a narrow range of concentrations of drugs such as INH, PAS, and streptomycin. The goal of susceptibility testing was to determine whether a patient's isolate conformed to the pattern of wild strains and if so treat with a standard regimen that generally provided a cure. The *critical concentration* was close to the lowest concentration that inhibited the growth of wild strains in culture medium. When an isolate did not conform to the pattern of wild strains it was considered *resistant*. According to IWGMT, "resistance is defined as a decrease in sensitivity of sufficient degree to be reasonably certain that the strain is different from a sample of wild strains of human type that have never come into contact with the drug" [6]. This historic definition of susceptibility and resistance applies only to isolates of the *M. tuberculosis* complex. Testing of the nontuberculous mycobacteria utilizes definitions more in-line with those used by the CLSI for bacterial species. An unanswered question with this definition is whether mutations that confer minor changes in the minimum inhibitory concentrations (MICs) that are still within achievable serum levels (e.g., isolates resistant to 0.1 μg/mL but susceptible to 1.0 μg/mL of INH) will still respond to therapy with that drug.

We now know that most resistance to the antituberculous drugs relates to mutations in the genes that encode for one or more enzymes that are inhibited by the drug. These mutations generally interfere with the binding of the drug such that it no longer inhibits the enzymes. Specific enzyme systems inhibited include catalase-peroxidase (KatG gene for INH), DNA-dependent RNA polymerase (rpo β gene for rifampin), arabinose transferases (emb CAB operon for ethambutol), and pyrazinamidase (pncA gene for pyrazinamide). Other resistance relates to mutations in the ribosomal RNA genes that encode protein synthesis (e.g., streptomycin, amikacin).

Today, the goal of susceptibility testing of *M. tuberculosis* complex isolates remains to differentiate resistant from wild strains so that the physician is able to make informed choices about chemotherapy. Because of the continued significant incidence of resistant strains in the United States, including multiple drug resistant (MDR-TB) strains, defined as strains resistant to two or more of the primary antituberculosis agents (isoniazid and rifampin), the laboratory is under increased pressure to provide rapid susceptibility results so that patients infected with these strains can be placed on individualized treatment regimens designed to exclude the drugs to which the isolate is resistant. This was emphasized in the early 1990s outbreak of MDR-TB in New York City in which delays in obtaining susceptibility results almost certainly contributed to poor patient outcomes, especially among HIV-infected patients [7,8].

Current therapy for suspected or proven disease due to *M. tuberculosis* complex generally involves administering four drugs until drug susceptibility reports are available. In the United States, these drugs are isoniazid, rifampin, pyrazinamide, and ethambutol. In countries outside the United States, streptomycin is sometimes used in place of ethambutol, primarily for cost reasons. If the isolate is found to be susceptible, the ethambutol (or streptomycin) is discontinued. Pyrazinamide is discontinued after 2 months, and therapy is continued with isoniazid and rifampin for the remaining 4 months.

This 6-month regimen is currently the approved regimen (by the ATS and CDC) for treating tuberculosis disease in the United States [9] and it is referred to as the *standard short course therapy*. Patients whose isolates are resistant to one or more of these primary drugs may then be treated with one or more secondary drugs that include amikacin, streptomycin, ethionamide, cycloserine, and the fluorinated quinolones such as ofloxacin or levofloxacin. Recent studies suggest that some of the newer fluoroquinolones, such as moxifloxacin, may have better activity against *M. tuberculosis* complex as well as other *Mycobacterium* species [10].

There are two types of drug resistance as detected in clinical isolates; *Primary* or *initial* drug resistance occurs when the patient has been infected with a strain that is already resistant to one or more drugs; *Acquired* drug resistance stems from the proliferation of naturally occurring resistant mutants when they have been exposed to a drug during suboptimal or inadequate chemotherapy. Patient's noncompliance with the treatment regimen also leads to acquired resistance. Clinical trials with some of the first antituberculosis drugs, especially streptomycin, showed the inability of monotherapy to prevent the emergence of resistance to the administered drug. It then became clear that multidrug regimens were necessary to obviate acquired (mutational) drug resistance and to successfully treat tuberculosis. Therefore, by using multiple agents with different targets of activity, one can minimize the emergence of resistance. Consequently, it is standard practice to test at least the four primary drugs, also called *first-line drugs*: isoniazid, rifampin, ethambutol, and pyrazinamide (PZA). Streptomycin, once considered a first-line drug, is rarely used in the United States except when treating patients with drug resistant isolates.

For susceptibility testing of *M. tuberculosis* complex, qualitative assays are standard. These may be performed in a broth-based system (e.g., BACTEC MGIT 960 system [11–13]) or by an agar proportion method using Middlebrook 7H10 or 7H11 agar plates (Table 11.1) [12,14–16]. If testing is performed by the agar proportion method, one may choose to perform susceptibility testing to both the primary and the secondary agents (e.g., aminoglycosides, capreomycin, cycloserine) at the same time. Performing both simultaneously may be more cost effective and improve turnaround time for results. The agar proportion method may be accomplished easily using commercially available plates (REMEL, Lenexa, KS; Hardy Diagnostics, Santa Maria, CA), or preparing them in-house.

The Centers for Disease Control and Prevention (CDC) recommends that laboratories work toward the goal of reporting first-line susceptibility results within 15–30 days from receipt of the initial clinical specimen [4]. Ideally, susceptibility results should be available within 7–14 days following the isolation and identification of *M. tuberculosis* complex from a clinical specimen. This is generally possible only if primary isolation and susceptibility testing is performed using a broth culture system and if the initial specimen is acid-fast bacillus (AFB) smear positive. Timely laboratory results allow changing the short-course standard regimen if indicated and preclude the physician's prescribing drugs to which the isolate is resistant. A short description of the various methods for performing susceptibility testing for *M. tuberculosis* complex is listed here.

TABLE 11.1
Comparison of Mycobacterial Growth Indicator Tube, BACTEC 460 TB, and Conventional Method of Proportion Antimycobacterial Susceptibility Testing

MGIT[a]	BACTEC 460 TB	LJMOP	7H10MOP	Reference
	Mean Time to Reporting for AST (Days)			
6.2	Not given	21	8	22
5.38[b]/7.9	7.33			24, 25
4	4.2–6.9[c]		13.7–21[b]	11
5		16		13
5.58/5.47[d]	7.4			23
	4–8		21	31, 32
	Mean Detection Time for Mycobacteria			
10	10			24, 25
	8.3		19.4	11
	5.2 (NTM)		17.8 (NTM)	
12.5		19.5		13
	Radiometric Instrumentation Requiredd			
No	Yes	No	No	
No	Yes	No	No	

Note: Unless specified, data refers to testing of *M. tuberculosis*.

[a] MGIT = mycobacterial growth indicator tube; MOP = method of proportion; AST = antimycobacterial susceptibility testing; LJ = Löwenstein-Jensen; 7H10 = Middlebrook 7H10 agar.

[b] Includes *M. tuberculosis* or nontuberculous mycobacteria.

[c] Range given; no mean turnaround time is available.

[d] Testing of ethambutol and streptomycin, respectively.

11.2.1 BROTH-BASED SYSTEMS [17]

1. BACTEC 460TB (Becton Dickinson Biosciences [BD], Sparks, MD). The radiometric qualitative susceptibility test in the BACTEC 460 TB system is a broth-based, FDA-approved method [12,15,16,18]. This system is a rapid and highly reliable method for susceptibility testing of *M. tuberculosis* complex. With this system, growth in the presence of the drug is compared with that in a drug-free culture representing 1% of the bacterial population. The BACTEC procedure for drug susceptibility testing of mycobacteria is based on the same principle employed in the conventional agar method. The main difference is that a liquid medium is used and instead of counting colonies, the growth is monitored radiometrically. The critical proportion for resistance is read as 1% for all antituberculous agents. This means that if ≥1% of the test mycobacterial population is resistant, the isolate is considered resistant. Results are based on the radiometric growth index (GI) as a measure of radiolabeled CO_2 generated by the multiplying organisms. Currently, five drugs—streptomycin, isoniazid, rifampin, ethambutol (SIRE) and PZA—are recommended for this method. This method has been used to test other agents (e.g., levofloxacin and others) in laboratories that have validated its reliability. The short comings of the method are: There is limited experience with testing of second-line drugs, it utilizes radiolabeled substrate and the disposal of the vials may be problematic, and finally, the instrument used to monitor the vial is "old"—parts are not readily available and the manufacturer has been phasing out its use. Therefore, over the past 5–10 years, BD has developed a nonradiolabeled broth system that will address these shortcomings. Susceptibility testing including PZA with BACTEC is rapid and reliable [19,20].

2. BACTEC MGIT 960 system (Becton Dickinson [BD] Biosciences, Sparks, MD). This nonradiometric system for susceptibility testing of *M. tuberculosis* complex is FDA approved for testing SIRE and PZA [16,18,21–25]. The tubes contain enriched 7H9 broth with an O_2-sensitive fluorescence sensor indicating microbial growth. Positivity is indicated by a bright orange fluorescence on the bottom of the tube and an orange reflection at the meniscus; negative tubes show little or no fluorescence [13]. A fully automated MGIT 960 instrument allows for the continuous monitoring of positive tubes [21]. Macondo and colleagues [22] reported that the MGIT 960 could be used as an alternative to the BACTEC 460TB system for rifampin and isoniazid; however, they, like previous investigators [23], reported discrepancies with streptomycin and ethambutol, which gave impetus to additional studies [21,22]. Since then, multiple studies have demonstrated that the BACTEC 460TB and the MGIT 960 have equivalent sensitivity and reliability when performing susceptibility testing for the primary agents and PZA [18,23–26]. Recently, a multicenter validation study of the MGIT 960 technique for susceptibility testing of the second-line drugs and newer agents has been published [27].

3. *ESP*II system (Trek Diagnostics Inc., Westlake, OH). The *ESP*II (an FDA approved method) combines a liquid culture media, a growth supplement, and specific antibiotics with a detection system that automatically incubates and continuously monitors culture bottles. Sponges in the bottles provide growth support and increase the surface area exposed to headspace oxygen. The technology for the *ESP*II is based upon detection of headspace pressure changes within a sealed bottle. These pressure changes are the result

of gas consumption or gas production due to mycobacterial growth. Susceptibility testing of *M. tuberculosis* complex isolates is performed by inoculating a suspension of organisms into five ESP Mycoculture bottles supplemented with ESP Myco GS and one of the four primary drugs. One control bottle without drug is also inoculated. An ESP connector is attached to each bottle to establish a closed system enabling the bottles to be monitored on the ESP instrument. A hydrophobic membrane in the connector prevents aerosols released into the laboratory. Bergmann and Woods reported the *ESP*II system as a rapid and reliable method for susceptibility testing of *M. tuberculosis* complex [28]. A similar study by LaBombardi and Lukowski concluded the ESP was in agreement with the agar reference method [29]. However, both authors indicated that susceptibility results for ethambutol and streptomycin may be discrepant and need further study [29]. Ruiz, Zerolo, and Casal reported good agreement with the BACTEC 460TB for testing rifampin, isoniazid, streptomycin, and ethambutol with the lowest agreement between the two methods (88.6%) for isoniazid [30]. LaBombardi also showed that the PZA results were reliable [20].

4. The BacT/ALERT system (bioMérieux Inc., Durham, NC). The system is a rapid, sensitive, fully automated method continuously monitored for growth and detection of mycobacteria. Recently, investigators have studied the potential of the system for antimycobacterial susceptibility testing of *M. tuberculosis* complex. They found correlation of sensitivity with the BACTEC 460 TB system for isoniazid, ethambutol, streptomycin, and rifampin of 96%, 100%, 78%, and 92%, respectively [31–33]. Brunello and Fontana reported the median turn around time was 8.5 days (range of 5–11 days) for the MB/BacT versus 6 days (range of 4–8 days) for the BACTEC 460 TB system [32] while other investigators reported a range of 2.5–10.7 days with a 7 day average for the MB/BacT compared to 21 days by agar proportion [31]. The authors stated, however, that further development was necessary to improve the sensitivity of drug resistance. Thus, the BacT/ALERT 3D system for susceptibility testing of mycobacteria is not available currently.

11.2.2 AGAR-BASED SYSTEMS

Agar-based tests are carried out in quadrant Petri dishes in which one quadrant contains drug-free medium while the other quadrants contain antituberculosis drugs incorporated at the critical concentrations (Table 11.2) [2]. The CLSI M24-A previously recommended 7H10 agar or 7H11 (which is 7H10 supplemented with casein hydrolysate to promote better growth of drug-resistant strains) [2]. The critical concentration of some of the drugs is different for 7H10 and 7H11 media (see Table 11.2) [2]. With these media, "susceptible" is defined as less than 1% growth in the presence of the drug compared to the number of colonies on the drug-free control [3,34]. Two types of susceptibility testing are possible on agar plates: the "direct" test in which an AFB smear-positive specimen concentrate is inoculated directly onto the plates and the "indirect" test in which a previously grown culture is inoculated onto the media. Plates for this assay can be made in-house or purchased from a commercial source. When preparing plates, this can be accomplished using specially designated elution disks or by adding diluted antibiotic solutions that are made from purchased powder (Table 11.4). Results of direct and indirect tests are reported as the percent of bacteria resistant to each drug. When there is no growth in the presence of the drug, the result "zero percent resistant" indicates the strain is fully susceptible [34].

TABLE 11.2
Drugs for *M. tuberculosis* Complex Susceptibility Testing, with Recommended Test Concentrations in Middlebrook Agar

	Concentrations (µg/mL)	
	7H10 Agar	7H11 Agar
Primary Drugs		
Ethambutol (EMB)	5.0	7.5[a]
Isoniazid (INH)	0.2	0.2
	1.0	1.0
Rifampin[b] (RMP)	1.0	0.2
Pyrazinamide (PZA)	NR[c]	NR
Secondary Drugs[d]		
Capreomycin	10.0	10.0
Ethionamide	5.0	10.0
Ethambutol	10.0	10.0
Kanamycin[e]	5.0	6.0
Ofloxacin[f]	2.0	2.0
p-Aminosalicylic acid	2.0	8.0
Rifabutin[g]	0.5	0.5
Streptomycin	2.0	2.0
	10.0	10.0

Source: Woods, G.L., et al. Susceptibility testing of mycobacteria, nocardiae, and other aerobic actinomycetes, approved standard, M24-A, NCCLS, Wayne, PA, 2003.

[a] Data supporting equivalency with 7H10 (5.0 µg/mL) are limited.

[b] Rifampin is the class agent for rifapentine.

[c] NR = not recommended.

[d] All secondary drugs should be tested on isolates of *M. tuberculosis* complex that are resistant to rifampin or resistant to any two primary drugs. Testing cycloserine is not recommended due to technical problems.

[e] Kanamycin is the class agent for amikacin.

[f] Ofloxacin is the class agent for the older fluoroquinolones (ciprofloxacin and ofloxacin) but not moxifloxacin.

[g] Some investigators have included a higher concentration, usually 1.0–2.0 µg/mL.

11.3 SUSCEPTIBILITY TESTING FOR *MYCOBACTERIUM TUBERCULOSIS* COMPLEX

11.3.1 Procedure 1: Qualitative Radiometric Drug Susceptibility Testing for *M. tuberculosis* [15,35]

1. Principle.
   Susceptibility testing for the four first-line drugs—isoniazid, streptomycin, rifampin, and ethambutol—can be performed as a qualitative test in the BACTEC 460 TB system. This broth-based susceptibility method is based on the proportion method, testing a "critical concentration" of the drug, just as in the direct and indirect agar plate proportion methods. In this test, the radiometric growth index in the presence of the critical concentration is compared with that representing 1% of the bacterial population in the 1:100 control. At the end of the test, if the change in GI of a drug containing vial is greater than that of the 1:100 control, the isolate is considered to be resistant to that drug. If the change in GI of a drug-containing vial is less than that of the 1:100 control, the isolate is susceptible.

2. Specimen.
   A 7H12 broth culture ("seed culture") grown to GI of 500 or greater, or a smooth suspension of a *M. tuberculosis* complex culture is adjusted to the density of a 1 McFarland standard

3. Reagents, media, and supplies.
   See the manufacturer's suggestions.

4. Procedure.
   See the manufacturer's technical procedure manual [15,35].

5. Reporting and calculations.
   See the manufacturer's technical procedure manual [15].

6. Quality control [15,35].

7. Limitations.
   This test is limited to qualitative results. Percent resistant cannot be determined from GI values.

8. Method validation [3,15,35].

11.3.2 PROCEDURE 2: PYRAZINAMIDE SUSCEPTIBILITY

1. Principle.
   Pyrazinamide, one of the first-line drugs, is more active at an acidic rather than at neutral pH. It is necessary, therefore, to test this drug at low pH (5.9–6.0) to obtain accurate results. Agar-based methods such as the agar proportion method have not proved satisfactory because of the failure of many isolates to grow at an acidic pH. Susceptibility testing of PZA in the BACTEC 460 TB system has proven to be satisfactory and as of 2003 was considered the reference method [2]. The procedures in the manufacturer's technical procedure manual should be followed carefully [36,37]. More recently, a study by Piersimoni et al. evaluated current nonradiometric detection systems as an option for replacing the BACTEC 460 TB radiometric method. The authors concluded that although all of the currently available systems were acceptable, the BACTEC MGIT 960 appeared to be the most reliable option [17].

2. Specimen.
   A 7H12 broth culture grown to GI of 500 or greater ("seed culture") or a smooth suspension of a *M. tuberculosis* complex culture adjusted to the density of a 1 McFarland standard.

3. Reagents, media, and supplies.
   See the manufacturer's technical procedure manual [36].

4. Procedures.
   See the manufacturer's technical procedure manual [36].

5. Reporting and calculations.
   The categories for reporting PZA resistance include "susceptible," "resistant," or "borderline" [2].

6. Quality control.
   See the manufacturer's technical procedure manual [36].

7. Expected values.
   See the manufacturer's technical procedure manual [36].

8 Limitations.
   See the manufacturer's technical procedure manual [36].

9. Method validation.
   See the manufacturer's technical procedure manual [36].

Isolates that yield uninterpretable results in the BACTEC PZA test system should be retested with and without polyoxyethylene stearate (POES), which has been reported to cause inhibition of growth of some isolates [38].

11.3.3 PROCEDURE 3: DIRECT DRUG SUSCEPTIBILITY TEST IN 7H10 OR 7H11 AGAR PLATES

1. Principle.

   This test determines the percentage of drug resistant organisms in the patient's specimen by inoculating a concentrated specimen directly onto 7H11 agar plates containing various antituberculous drugs (see Table 11.3). It is preferentially performed on specimens from known or suspected TB patients.

2. Specimen.

   Digested, decontaminated specimen concentrate

   > If the concentrated specimen is AFB negative by smear examination ($200-400 \times$ magnification), it should be inoculated undiluted. The following dilutions are necessary if the specimen is smear-positive:
   >
   > Up to 25 AFB per field—dilutions 1 and 0.1.
   > From 50 to 250 AFB per field—dilutions 1 and 100 (1:100).
   > Greater than 250 per field—dilutions 100 and 1000 (1:100 and 1:1000).
   > *Note:* If <5 AFB seen per field, increase the inoculum to 0.2mL.

TABLE 11.3
Stock, Working, and Final Concentrations of Antituberculous Drug Solutions for Middlebrook 7H10 Agar Medium

Antimicrobial Agent	Solvent	Working Concentration (µg/mL) for 7H10 Agar	Volume to Add to 200 mL of 7H10 Agar	Final Concentration of Drug in 7H10 Agar
		First-Line Agents		
Ethambutol	SDW[a]	1,000	1.0	5.0
			2.0	10.0
Isoniazid	SDW	200	0.2	0.2
			1.0	1.0
Rifampin	DMSO	1,000	0.2	1.0
		Second-Line Agents		
Capreomycin	SDW	1,000	2.0	10.0
Ethionamide	DMSO	1,000	1.0	5.0
Kanamycin	SDW	1,000	1.0	5.0
Ofloxacin	SDW	200	2.0	2.0
Rifabutin	Methanol	100	1.0	0.5
Streptomycin sulfate	SDW	1,000	0.4	2.0
			2.0	10.0
p-Aminosalicylic acid	SDW	1,000	0.4	2.0

Source: Woods, G.L., et al. Susceptibility testing of mycobacteria, nocardiae, and other aerobic actinomycetes, approved standard, M24-A, NCCLS, Wayne, PA, pp. 34–35, 2003.

[a] SDW = sterile distilled water; DMSO = dimethyl sulfoxide (should not be filter sterilized using synthetic filters; solutions made in DMSO should be left at room temperature in the dark for 30 minutes for self-sterilization; personal communication, author, SC).

Calculate the weight based on potency if less than 100%.

Sterilize stock solutions by filtration through 0.22-μm pore membrane, and dispense into sterile vial before freezing. Thaw the vials to room temperature, and use immediately. The excess should be discarded and never refrozen!

3. Procedure.
   a. At the same time the media for primary isolation is being inoculated, inoculate 0.1 mL of the specimen (diluted as above if necessary) on each quadrant of a set of labeled drug susceptibility plates. Tilt plates gently to spread the inoculum. Allow plates to stand for 1 hour under the hood for absorption of the inoculum. If there are only a few AFB on the smear, the quadrants can be inoculated with 0.2 mL each and left under the hood to dry.
   b. Place the plates top-side up individually into CO_2-permeable polyethylene bags and seal the bags. Incubate in the CO_2 incubator at 37°C. Check the growth appearance, at 1, 2, 3, and 6 weeks of incubation. Read at 3 weeks if the growth is adequate.
   c. Remove the plates from the incubator and leave upside down (agar-side up) at room temperature until the condensate disappears from the cover. Examine the plates macroscopically and with a dissecting microscope. Record the number of colonies on each quadrant onto a laboratory worksheet.
4. Reporting and calculations.
   Calculate the percentages of bacteria resistant to the various drug concentrations based on the number of colonies in the drug-free control and the number in the drug-containing quadrants.

$$\text{Percent resistant} = \frac{\text{number of colonies in drug-containing quadrant}}{\text{number of colonies in the drug-free control quadrant}} \times 100$$

   Most laboratory computer systems can be programmed to perform the calculations and print a report showing the percent resistant for each drug.
5. Quality control.
   Each day of testing, inoculate a set of plates with the CLSI (NCCLS) quality control *M. tuberculosis* strain American Type Culture Collection (ATCC) 27294 (H37Rv) [2].
6. Expected values.
   Colony counts should be within the expected range for the test to be valid. Thus, precise quantitation may be difficult when direct testing is performed.
7. Limitations.
   The test is valid only when there is no contaminant overgrowth and there are >50 colonies on the drug-free controls. A comment should be noted in the laboratory report about the limited validity of the results if:
   a. Sufficient growth in the drug-free controls did not appear within 3 weeks of incubation.
   b. There are fewer than 50 colonies per drug-free quadrant.
      State that the drug susceptibility test should be repeated as an indirect test. In case of heavy contamination, request a repeat specimen. If there is no growth on the control plates, perform an indirect susceptibility test from the primary isolate if positive.
8. Method validation [3,14].
   Validate by performing the indirect susceptibility test, colony count of the control quadrant, and by use of ATCC reference quality control strains.

11.3.4 Procedure 4: Indirect Drug Susceptibility Test in 7H10 or 7H11 Agar Plates

1. Principle.
   This test shows the percentage of drug resistant organisms for *M. tuberculosis* complex isolates. The indirect test may be performed if the results of the direct test are not valid due to contamination, insufficient numbers of colonies in the drug-free quadrants, or insufficient growth after 3 weeks of incubation. The preparation of this inoculum is critical because variations in the number of AFB in the suspension can alter the test interpretation [34].

2. Specimen.

The following cultures can be used:

a. A suspension made from surface of the medium (L-J, 7H10, 7H11, etc.). Primary cultures, rather than subcultures, should be used when available.

b. A BACTEC 12B vial at GI of 500 or greater [15,35].

c. Isolates from other continuous monitoring systems (see the manufacturers' guidelines) [15].

d. 7H9 broth at the optical density equal to a 1 McFarland standard.

3. Procedure.

a. If the only culture available contains only a few colonies on solid media, use these colonies to inoculate 7H12 (BACTEC 12B) or 7H9 broth. Incubate the 12B vial until the GI is 500 or greater, or the growth in the 7H9 broth is equal to a McFarland 1 standard.

b. If there is sufficient growth on solid media, prepare a 7H9 suspension made directly from the culture. Lightly inoculate a sterile tube containing four to five small glass beads and 5 mL of 7H9 broth. Incubate the tube at 37°C for a total of 48–72 hours or until the turbidity in the tube matches that of a 1 McFarland standard. Inside a biological safety cabinet (BSC), vortex the tube vigorously, twice daily (in the AM and PM) to facilitate smooth bacterial suspension.

c. Dilute the bacterial suspension to 10^2 (1:100) and 10^4 (1:10,000) in serial 1:10 dilutions made in the 4.5 mL blanks. The plates must be inoculated the same day the dilutions are made.

d. BACTEC 12B vials can be used directly, undiluted, if the GI is 500 or 10^2 and 10^4 if GI is 999. Store the vials at room temperature (22°C–24°C) if the test cannot be done the same day the desired GI is reached. Do not refrigerate.

e. Inoculate each quadrant of a set of labeled plates with 0.1 mL of the bacterial suspension. Tilt the plates for even distribution of the inoculum, and allow them to stand under the hood for 1 hour to allow the inoculum to be absorbed.

f. Place the plates, agar side up, individually into CO_2-permeable polyethylene bags and seal the bags. Incubate in the CO_2 incubator at 37°C. Check the growth appearance, at 1, 2, and 3 weeks of incubation. Discard the plates that do not grow adequately within 3 weeks of incubation. (Hold plates for up to three additional weeks if the organism growth is suspected to be dysgonic as in some multiple drug-resistant strains. If there is still inadequate growth, repeat the test.)

g. Read at 3 weeks if the growth is adequate. Count the number of colonies in each quadrant and record the results on a laboratory worksheet as above for the direct test.

4. Reporting and calculations.

As for the direct test, calculate the report percent resistant for each drug.

5. Quality control.

Each day of testing, inoculate a set of plates with the CLSI recommended *M. tuberculosis* ATCC 27294 [2].

6. Expected values.

N/A.

7. Limitations.

Results of the direct and indirect test for the same drug-resistant isolate may not agree. Selection at the time of subculture may change the proportion of the drug-resistant subpopulations within the culture as a whole. Sometimes a direct susceptibility from a relapsed patient may show greater susceptibility because the raw specimen originated in a recently broken down cavity that has been protected from drugs and therefore does not contain the acquired resistant populations in areas of the lung that have been previously accessible.

8. Method validations [3,34].

    The indirect test is currently the "gold standard" for tuberculosis susceptibility testing. However, the current trend is to perform broth susceptibility testing for first-line agents.

11.4 PRINCIPLES OF ANTIMYCOBACTERIAL SUSCEPTIBILITY TESTING OF NONTUBERCULOUS MYCOBACTERIA

Just as mycobacterial susceptibility testing for the *M. tuberculosis* complex should be performed by experienced technologists, so also should susceptibility testing of the nontuberculous mycobacteria be performed by qualified laboratories. Many of the recommendations that are made for laboratories that test *M. tuberculosis* complex should be followed by laboratories that test isolates of NTM. Problems such as contamination, mixed cultures, unusual growth rates, or aberrant results should also be recognized.

To answer the question of when it is necessary to perform susceptibility testing of NTM, the laboratory must consider the type of specimen, number of positive cultures, and the clinical setting. The ATS and the CLSI have published diagnostic recommendations that should be followed in determining whether or not an isolate is clinically significant and thus requires susceptibility testing [1,2,9].

For instance, the CLSI recommendation is not to perform susceptibility testing on respiratory isolates of *M. gordonae* unless recovered from multiple samples [2]. Most experts agree that *M. gordonae* is rarely, if ever, a respiratory pathogen [2,9]. For some species of the rapidly growing mycobacteria in respiratory samples (e.g., *M. fortuitum* group, *M. mucogenicum* and pigmented rapid growers), this advisement is also true. Because many of the species are common environmental organisms, the physician must evaluate the situation carefully. However, susceptibility testing is indicated for any NTM considered clinically significant from blood, tissue, and skin and soft tissue sources. The likelihood that the NTM is a pathogen is increased when the isolate is recovered from multiple specimens in large numbers or in a specimen that is smear positive for AFB. Clinical failure to eradicate the NTM from almost any site (except respiratory) after 6 months of appropriate antimicrobial therapy emphasizes the need to confirm species identification and perform repeat susceptibility testing [1,2,9]. For respiratory specimens, the ATS (2006) recommends reliance on specific criteria for determining clinical significance of the NTM [9]. At least two positive sputum cultures or one culture positive bronchial wash or lavage usually confirm clinical significance of the isolate. Single positive sputum cultures (e.g., one of three or four) that are AFB smear negative and grown only in the broth medium and not solid agar are likely to be clinically insignificant [9].

The MIC value obtained when performing susceptibility testing with NTM indicates the concentration of agent necessary to inhibit the growth of the NTM. The MIC, however, does not represent an "absolute value." The "true" MIC is a specific value somewhere between the lowest test concentration that inhibits the organism's growth (that is, the MIC reading) and the next lower test concentration [2].

MICs are generally derived from serial two-fold dilutions indexed to base 1 (e.g., 1, 2, 4, 8, 16, etc.) although other dilution schemes may provide MICs between these values. When there is inhibition of growth at the lowest concentration, the true MIC can not be determined and must be reported as "less than or equal to the lowest MIC."

MIC results are typically reported as "susceptible," "intermediate," or "resistant" [2]. The "susceptible" category implies that an infection can be effectively treated with the dosage of the antimicrobial agent recommended for that type of infection and species of NTM unless otherwise contraindicated. The "intermediate" category includes isolates with MICs that approach attainable blood and tissue levels and for which response rate may be slower than for susceptible isolates. This category also allows for small, uncontrolled technical factors that might cause large discrepancies in interpretations, especially with narrow pharmacotoxicity margins. Finally, the "resistant" category contains those isolates that are not inhibited by the usual achievable systemic concentrations of the agent [2]. Note that these definitions are in agreement with other CLSI definitions for susceptibility of bacterial species, and quite different from the definition of resistance used for MTB.

Preparation of microtiter panels may be time consuming, may require considerable experience, and may be an expensive undertaking for the average laboratory , especially if the number of NTM isolates seen is low. Thus, many laboratories choose to use a reference laboratory for testing isolates of NTM. Only recently have the methods for testing NTM been approved by the CLSI [2]. Laboratory quality control should include the CLSI recommended isolates to be tested, and the strains must be stored and subcultured appropriately [2]. Panels are now available commercially; however, these should be used by technologists experienced in working with nontuberculous mycobacteria.

11.4.1 Rapidly Growing Mycobacteria (RGM)

1. Introduction.
   Four different methods have been used for susceptibility testing of the RGM. These methods include agar disk diffusion, broth microdilution, E-test, and agar disk elution. Each method has advantages and disadvantages, but until recently, none has been compared in multicenter trials or been standardized by the CLSI. Recently, following publication of a multicenter trial [39], members of the Antimycobacterial Susceptibility Subcommittee of the CLSI recommended the determination of MICs by the broth microdilution as the "gold standard" for susceptibility testing of the RGM [2].

   Details of the broth microdilution MIC follow this brief review of the following nonstandardized methods (2a–c).
2. Methods.
   a. *Agar disk diffusion.* This method applies the Bauer-Kirby technique of bacterial susceptibility testing to the susceptibility testing of RGM. This method has not been recommended for several years due to major technical problems such as interpretation of "partial zones" and lack of validation of the newer drugs (e.g., fluoroquinolones, clarithromycin, imipenem and linezolid) against an MIC method. Although its major advantage is the simplicity of the procedure, the problems outweigh the advantages, and this method can only be recommended as a "screening tool" prior to the performance of broth MICs, as a taxonomic aid, or as a supplement to broth microdilution. As an adjuvant to broth microdilution, it allows for rapid recognition of bacterial contamination, for recognition of mixed susceptible/resistant organism populations (presence of double zones), and for crude assessment of the validity of results obtained by broth microdilution. Disk diffusion should not be used as the sole testing method for NTM in the laboratory.
   b. *Agar disk elution.* This method is used most often by laboratories who test limited numbers of isolates infrequently. This method uses commercial susceptibility disks from which the drug is eluted into the Middlebrook enrichment into the OADC (oleic acid-albumin-dextrose-catalase) and mixed with molten agar to produce specific final drug concentrations. Interpretation of the results is similar to the proportion method. This method is not practical and is not recommended for the following reasons: (1) tedious preparation of the plates, (2) difficulty in the adjustment of inoculum to avoid too heavy suspensions resulting in "overinoculation", (3) lack of validation studies with MICs for the newer antimicrobials such as the fluoroquinolones, imipenem, clarithromycin and linezolid, (4) some desired concentrations are not practically attainable due to the amount of drug in the commercial disk, and (5) "trailing endpoints" (seen by the appearance of "microcolonies") especially with the macrolides [40]. Moreover, this method is also considered a nonstandardized method for testing of the RGM.

TABLE 11.4
Drugs and Drug Concentrations for Agar Disk Elution Susceptibility Testing of *Mycobacterium tuberculosis* Complex

Antimycobacterial Agent	Disk Content (µg)	Final Drug Concentration in Well (µg/mL)
Control		0
Rifampin	5	1.0
Isoniazid	1	0.2
Isoniazid	5	1.0
Ethambutol	25	5.0

Source: Woods, G.L., et al. Susceptibility testing of mycobacteria, nocardiae, and other aerobic actinomycetes, approved standard, M24-A, CLSI, Wayne, PA, 2003, pp. 1–71.

The use of a six-well tissue culture plates (round instead of square wells) is recommended for this method; 5 mL of Middlebrook 7H10 agar is added to each well.
The control well contains no disks.

c. *E-test.* The E-test (AB Biodisk) or gradient diffusion combines the simplicity of the agar diffusion method with an exponential gradient of antimicrobials to produce MIC results. However, a recent interlaboratory study by members of the Subcommittee on Antimycobacterial Susceptibility Testing of the CLSI showed that interpretation and reproducibility of the E-test MICs with the RGM were difficult. Trailing endpoints and diffuse elliptical edges made determination of precise MICs difficult with several drugs, including ciprofloxacin, clarithromycin, imipenem, and cefoxitin. No break points utilizing this method were established and no control strains could be suggested since no standard RGM strain exhibited reproducible MICs for all of the drugs tested. Thus, the CLSI determined that further studies were needed before a recommendation for adopting its use for susceptibility testing of the RGM could be made [41]. In addition, E-test is not a cost effective method when one considers testing multiple agents for a given isolate. However, the E-test is an appealing alternative when the laboratory is asked to perform susceptibility testing for an agent not found on a standard panel (e.g., tigecycline) or when new and/or investigational agents become available.

d. *Broth microdilution MIC.* This method is currently the CLSI recommended susceptibility procedure for testing the RGM and is described below [2,42].

The procedure described in this section is intended for the susceptibility testing of RGM based on studies that have included *Mycobacterium fortuitum* group (*M. fortuitum*, *M. peregrinum*, and the former *M. fortuitum* third biovariant complex that includes species such as *M. porcinum*, *M. houstonense*, and *M. senegalense*), *M. chelonae* complex (defined as strains including formerly *M. chelonae* subsp. *chelonae* and other novel species that have similar 16S gene sequences but are currently uncertain if they can be identified by conventional methods), and *M. abscessus* [39,43–54]. They should also apply to other species such as *M. mucogenicum*, *M. smegmatis* group (*M. smegmatis*, *M. wolinskyi*, and *M. goodii*) and clinically significant pigmented RGM.

Most RGM species will grow well in unsupplemented, cation-adjusted Muller-Hinton broth (CAMHB). However, on rare occasion, supplementation with OADC may be necessary to support the growth of some isolates. When supplementation is added, it should be disclosed by stating that "susceptibility testing was performed by non-CLSI standardized methodology."

1) Specimen. Suspensions are prepared from viable RGM colonies on solid media that has been incubated at 28°C–30°C in ambient air. An alternative option is to subculture isolates in 7H9 or CAMHB, incubate the tube at 28°C–30°C for 24–48 hours, and use this suspension to inoculate MIC panels.

2) Procedure.

   a) Sweep the confluent portion of growth with a sterile loop or swab, and transfer the colonies to 4.5 mL of sterile water containing glass beads until the turbidity matches the density of a 0.5 McFarland standard. (If large clumps remain, allow them to settle and use the supernatant for the inoculum suspension.)

   b) Vortex suspensions vigorously for 15–30 seconds or invert 8–10 times to mix.

      i. Freeze-dried panels [2].

         (a) Prepare the standardized inoculum to match the 0.5 McFarland standard as described previously.

         (b) Transfer 50 μL of the standardized suspension into a 10 mL tube of CAMHB and mix well by vortexing and/or inverting the tube several times.

         (c) Pour the broth suspension into a sterile trough.

         (d) Transfer 100 μL of broth suspension into each well of the 96 well plate and inoculate the plate using a multichannel pipettor with sterile pipette tips.

         (e) A periodic check of the colony count should be performed by sampling the positive control well. Isolates should have an inoculum of 5×10^5 CFU/mL (range 1×10^5 to 1×10^6).

         (f) Cover wells with plastic lid or adhesive seal. If using an adhesive seal, press all wells firmly to assure adequate sealing and avoid creasing of the seal.

         (g) Incubate aerobically at 30°C in a non-CO_2 incubator for 72 hours. Check for growth at 72 hours and if inadequate, reincubate up to 5 days.

         (h) Test results are best read using a viewer that displays the underside of the wells.

            (i) It is not necessary to remove the adhesive seal for reading when the plate is read from the bottom.

            (ii) Read the growth control well first. If the control well does not exhibit satisfactory growth (see previous discussion), the plates should be reincubated an additional 24 hours.

            (iii) Growth appears as turbidity or as a button of cells at the bottom of a well. The growth control (no drug) well should always be used as the reference for interpreting growth patterns in the plate.

      ii. RGM plates containing antimicrobials in broth.

         (a) Alternatively, if inoculating prepared RGM plates containing antimicrobials in 100 μL of broth, the volume of standardized suspension to be added to 36 mL of water diluent to obtain a final organism concentration of $1–5 \times 10^5$ CFU/mL ($1–5 \times 10^4$ CFU per well in 0.1 mL volume) is calculated. The volume depends on the delivery system that is being used. For example, when using a disposable plastic multi-pronged inoculating device that delivers 0.01 mL (10 μL) per well, the inoculum is prepared as follows [2,42]:

            (i) Prepare 0.5 McFarland suspension (approximately $1–5 \times 10^8$ CFU/mL) and invert or vortex to mix.

            (ii) Add 0.5 mL of the 0.5 McFarland standardized suspension to 4.5 mL of water diluent (1:10 dilution) = $1–5 \times 10^7$ CFU/mL, and vortex.

> (iii) Add 4 mL from previous step to 36 mL of water diluent (1:10 dilution) = $1-5 \times 10^6$ CFU/mL.
>
> (iv) Prongs deliver 0.01 mL into 0.1 mL in well (1:10 dilution) = $1-5 \times 10^5$ CFU/mL or 1.5×10^4 per well.

3. Reagents, media, and supplies.
   a. Mueller–Hinton broth aliquots, stored at ambient temperature.
   b. Microtiter panels.
   c. Sterile pipette troughs.
   d. Multi (8 or 12) channel pipettor.
   e. Sterile pipette tips.
   f. Sterile water blanks, 4.5 mL tubes.
   g. 0.5 McFarland ($BaSO_4$) turbidity standard.

4. Reading, reporting, and interpretation of MIC values for RGM.

   At 72 hours, trays are examined for growth. If the growth is sufficient (i.e., at least 2+ based on the following criteria: ± growth = few flecks in bottom of the well; 1+ = light growth in the well; 2+ = moderate growth for the particular species in the well; 3+ to 4+ = readily visible button in the bottom of the well, maximum growth seen for the RGM), MICs are recorded (see Figure 11.1). Otherwise, trays are reincubated and read

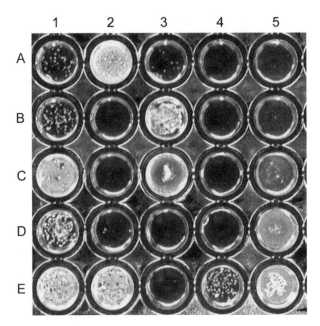

FIGURE 11.1 Legend:
   1E Control growth (4+)
   3A ± Few countable colonies; no turbidity (also wells 5B and 2D are ±)
   5C ± Few countable colonies, hazy turbidity (also well 3E is ±)
   5D 1+ Definite haze or turbidity
   5E 2+ Definite turbidity and "clumpy" growth
   1B 2+ Moderate countable colonies; slight turbidity
   1D 3+ Heavy colonial growth
   4E 3+ Heavy growth, turbidity
   1C 4+ Heavy confluent growth comparable to control (also wells 2A and 2E are 4+)
Wells 4A, 5A, 2B, 4B, 4C, 3D, and 4D are all negative.
Source: Woods, G.L., et al. Susceptibility testing of mycobacteria, nocardiae, and other aerobic actinomycetes, approved standard, M24-A, NCCLS, Wayne, PA, 2003, p. 28.

TABLE 11.5

Antimicrobial Agents and MIC Break Points Using Broth Microdilution for Rapidly Growing Mycobacteria

Antimicrobial Agent	MIC Break Points (µg/mL)		
	Susceptible	Intermediate	Resistant
Amikacin	≤16	32	≥64
Cefoxitin	≤16	32–64	≥128
Ciprofloxacin	≤1	2	≥4
Clarithromycin[a]	≤2	4	≥8
Doxycycline/Minocycline[b]	≤1	2–8	≥16
Imipenem	≤4	8	≥16
Linezolid	≤8	16	≥32
Sulfamethoxazole[c]	≤32		≥64
Tobramycin	≤4	8	≥16
Trimethoprim/Sulfamethoxazole[b,c]			

Source: Woods, G.L., et al. Susceptibility testing of mycobacteria, nocardiae, and other aerobic actinomycetes, approved standard, M24-A, CLSI, Wayne, PA, 2003, p. 40.

[a] Isolates of *M. fortuitum* group with a trailing endpoint should be considered resistant. Recent studies suggest this trailing reflects the presence of an inducible erythromycin (macrolide) methylase (erm) gene that confers macrolide resistance [Nash, K.A., et al. *J. Antimicrob. Chemother.,* 55, 170, 2005]. Results for *M. chelonae* and *M. abscessus* should be read at 3 days. Clarithromycin is the class agent for the newer macrolides.

[b] No CLSI standardized break points have been proposed yet. These break points are based on the authors' (BBE, SC, RJW) personal experience with RGM. Break points given for TMP/SMX are the closest value to the sulfamethoxazole value.

[c] MIC is 80% inhibition of growth.

daily thereafter (for up to 5 days) until growth is sufficient. For all antibiotics recommended by the CLSI for susceptibility testing except sulfonamides, the MIC is recorded as the lowest concentration of drug that inhibits macroscopic growth [2].

Sulfonamide MICs are read at 80% inhibition of growth compared to the growth control well (Table 11.5) [2].

5. Quality control and proficiency testing.

M. peregrinum ATCC 700686 (preferred) or *Staphylococcus aureus* ATCC 29213 and/or *Enterococcus faecalis* ATCC 29212 [2,55].

If plates are prepared in-house, susceptibility testing should be validated by performing the MIC on a series of isolates with known MICs. For laboratories that encounter RGM only rarely, referral to an established reference laboratory is recommended. Currently, no proficiency testing program from the College of American Pathologists (CAP) regularly includes these organisms in their program, although the CDC performance evaluation does include at least one NTM in each shipment. Therefore, the best alternative is comparison of the test results with those from an established reference laboratory on initial validation and at regular intervals thereafter to evaluate performance proficiency.

6. Expected values. See Table 11.6 for acceptable MIC ranges.

7. Notes.

   a. When testing isolates of *M. chelonae* complex and *M. abscessus*, incubation for 4–5 days is sometimes necessary to obtain sufficient growth.

   b. Given the known temporal instability of imipenem, the frequent need for prolonged incubation, and the modal MICs (i.e., 8–16 µg/mL) being at the resistance break point, imipenem MICs tend to result in major category changes of susceptibility for

TABLE 11.6
Recommended Quality Control Strains and Their Ranges of MICs (μg/mL) for Testing Rapidly Growing Mycobacteria

Antimicrobial Agent	MIC range(μg/mL)		
	Mycobacterium peregrinum ATCC 700686 (Modal Value)[a]	*Staphylococcus aureus* ATCC 29213	*Enterococcus faecalis* ATCC 29212[b]
Amikacin	≤1–4 (1)	1–4	64–256
Cefoxitin[c]	16–32 (16)	1–4	
Ciprofloxacin	≤0.12–0.5 (1.125)	0.12–0.5	0.25–2
Clarithromycin	≤0.06–0.5 (0.25)	0.12–0.5	
Doxycycline	0.12–0.5 (0.25)	0.12–0.5	2–8
Minocycline[d]	≤0.5	0.15–0.5	1–4
Imipenem	2–16 (8)	0.015–0.06	0.5–2
Linezolid[c]	≤2–4 (1)	1–4	1–4
Sulfamethoxazole	≤1–4 (1)	32–128	
Tobramycin	4–8 (4)	0.12–1	8–32
Trimethoprim/Sulfamethoxazole[e] (TMP/SMX)	≤0.5/9.5	≤0.5/9.5	≤0.5/9.5

Source: Woods, G.L., et al. Susceptibility testing of mycobacteria, nocardiae, and other aerobic actinomycetes, approved standard, M24-A, NCCLS, Wayne, PA, 2003, p. 41.

[a] Unpublished data, Wallace, R.J.W., et al.

[b] Clinical and Laboratory Standards Institute. Performance Standards for Antimicrobials Susceptibility Testing, 16th Informational Supplement. CLSI document M100-S16, 2006, CLSI, Wayne, PA.

[c] Revision of break points proposed for *M. peregrinum* ATCC 700686: 4–32 μg/mL for cefoxitin and 1–8 μg/mL for linezolid [Holliday, N., et al. 105th ASM General Meeting, Atlanta, GA, June 5–9, 2005, C-020].

[d] No CLSI standardized break point has been established for *M. peregrinum* ATCC 700686. Personal communication from authors (BBE, SC, RJW).

[e] No CLSI standardized break point has not been established for *M. peregrinum* ATCC 700686. Personal communication from authors (BBE, RJW).

M. chelonae/M. abscessus group. Imipenem categorization (susceptible, intermediate, or resistant) is not reproducible for the *M. abscessus/chelonae* groups because the modal MIC is at the intermediate break point, and hence CLSI recommends not reporting MICs currently for these species [2]. The drug may be clinically useful, however, and the other useful beta lactam (cefoxitin) is often not available. Hence, imipenem may be reported with a disclaimer in situations such as these. All other groups of the RGM, including isolates of the *M. fortuitum* group, *M. mucogenicum*, and the *M. smegmatis* group are intermediate or susceptible *in vitro* to imipenem and have not shown problems with reproducibility; therefore, imipenem MICs should be reported for these species.

c. Because tobramycin is the aminoglycoside of choice only for isolates of *M. chelonae* complex, tobramycin MICs are reported for this species but not for other RGM [2].

d. Testing of antimicrobials other than those recommended by the CLSI may be desired, especially when encountering multidrug resistant isolates. (For example, the new 8 methoxy-fluoroquinolones, such as moxifloxacin and the new glycylcycline, tigecycline, may be useful to test since they may be used as part of a treatment regimen, and susceptibility to these agents is not be predicted by ciprofloxacin, levofloxacin, or the tetracyclines (including doxycycline or minocycline) [56,57]. For laboratory testing of these agents, currently the recommendation is to use the CLSI bacterial break points provided in the CLSI documents [55], Supplemental Tables, until further studies have been done with the RGM [2,55]. The laboratory should note that these drugs have not yet been validated or approved by the CLSI for use with mycobacteria.

   e. For linezolid, the proposed CLSI break points for the RGM are ≤8 μg/mL, susceptible; 16 μg/mL, intermediate; and ≥32 μg/mL, resistant (Table 11.5).

8. Limitations.

   a. The control well must show sufficient growth in order to interpret reading of the drug wells. This is especially important when reading the MICs of sulfonamides. Because sulfonamide susceptibility is read as 80% inhibition, insufficient growth in the wells can be misinterpreted and the MIC may be read as lower than the expected value. This may also be true for some newer antimicrobials such as linezolid and tigecycline for which data is sparse. The positive control well may also be used to perform colony counts to ensure the inoculum is appropriate.

   b. The purity or negative control well, if present, should show no growth.

   c. Skipped wells occur occasionally that may indicate a pipetting or some other technical or procedural error. The first well in which there is no growth after the last well with growth should be regarded as the MIC. If skipped wells occur more than once in the plate or at the break point concentration, the MIC determination should be repeated.

   d. If bacterial contamination occurs in the wells, the MIC should be repeated. On a rare occasion, when one or two wells are contaminated with bacteria but the purity check plate is pure and the contaminated wells do not interfere with reading the MICs, the contaminated wells may be ignored.

   e. Initial transfers of isolates into broth and preparation of dilutions into panels should be performed within 30 minutes.

   f. Plates containing high concentrations of doxycycline or minocycline (≥32 μg/mL) may show a precipitate after incubation. To avoid this problem, these wells (≥32 μg/mL) should be reconstituted with 5 μL of sterile distilled water before broth is added.

9. Method validation.

A multicenter CLSI study of broth microdilution MICs with RGM was conducted to assess the interlaboratory reproducibility of the method against eight antimicrobials including amikacin, cefoxitin, ciprofloxacin, clarithromycin, doxycycline, imipenem, sulfamethoxazole, and tobramycin. The recent interpretative guidelines were based on the data obtained from this study [2,39].

11.4.2 SLOWLY GROWING NTM: *MYCOBACTERIUM AVIUM* COMPLEX

1. Principle.

The only antimicrobials for which a correlation between *in vitro* susceptibility tests for MAC and clinical response has been demonstrated in controlled clinical trials are the macrolides (clarithromycin and azithromycin) [58–61]. Therefore, routine susceptibility testing should be performed for these drugs only. Furthermore, since clarithromycin and azithromycin are cross-susceptible and cross-resistant, clarithromycin may serve as the "class agent" for both drugs so that it should be necessary to test clarithromycin only [2].

   Recently, the CLSI recommended susceptibility testing of macrolides (clarithromycin or azithromycin) with MAC using a broth-based method, either macrodilution or microdilution (Table 11.7). However, since solubility in microvolumes may be a problem with azithromycin, macrodilution is the preferred method when testing this agent. As for the RGM, the broth microdilution MIC panels may be purchased commercially as freeze-dried or frozen or they may be prepared in-house.

TABLE 11.7

Susceptibility and Resistance Break Points for Macrolide Testing in Broth against *Mycobacterium avium* **Complex**

Drug	Method	pH	Broth[a]	Susceptible	Intermediate	Resistant
				Break Points MIC (µg/mL)		
Clarithromycin	BACTEC 460 TB or broth microdilution	6.8	12 B or CAMHB[a]	<16	32	≥64
	BACTEC 460 TB	7.3–7.4	12 B	≤4	8–16	≥32
	Broth microdilution	7.3–7.4	CAMHB	≤8	16	≥32
Azithromycin	BACTEC 460 TB	6.8	12 B	≤128	256	≥512

Source: Woods, G.L., et al. Susceptibility testing of mycobacteria, nocardiae, and other aerobic actinomycetes, approved standard, M24-A, CLSI, Wayne, PA, 2003, p. 37.

[a] CAMHB = cation-adjusted Mueller-Hinton broth plus oleic acid-albumin-dextrose-catalase (OADC) Middlebrook 7H9 broth (pH corrected to 7.3–7.4 with 1 mol/L KOH). [Brown, B.A., Wallace, R.J., Jr., and Onyi, G. *Antimicrob. Agents Chemother.*, 36, 1987, 1992].

2. Specimen.

Inoculum is prepared as for the RGM broth microdilution. Care should be taken to pick transparent colony-types when present as they tend to be more drug resistant than the pigmented colonies [61].

3. Reagents, media, and supplies.

Broth microdilution.

a. Sterile water, 4.5 mL tube.

b. Mueller-Hinton broth (CAMHB, 10 mL) with 5% OADC.

c. Sterile pipette trough.

d. Microtiter panel with drug.

e. Sterile pipette tips.

Broth macrodilution (see the manufacturer's procedure manual).

a. BACTEC 12B medium.

b. BACTEC diluting fluid.

c. Sterile pipette tips.

4. Drug concentrations.

a. Broth microdilution. For clarithromycin, the minimum range of concentrations (doubling dilutions) is 1–64 µg/mL; the optimum range is 0.25–256 µg/mL [2].

b. BACTEC 460 TB macrodilution. For clarithromycin, concentrations of 2, 4, 8, 16, 32, and 64 µg/mL are proposed. Alternately, testing only 4, 16, and 64 µg/mL in BACTEC 12B medium at pH 6.8 or 4, 8, and 32 µg/mL in 12B medium at pH 7.3–7.4 may provide adequate data for patient management and be more cost effective. For azithromycin, the optimal concentrations for testing patient isolates by the radiometric macrodilution method are 16, 32, 64, 128, 256, and 512 µg/mL. However, testing only 32, 128, and 512 µg/mL may provide adequate data for patient management and be more cost effective [2].

When using the radiometric macrodilution method, the concentrations of clarithromycin and azithromycin used for quality control differ from those used to test patient isolates. Clarithromycin quality control concentrations are 1, 2, and 4 µg/mL at pH 6.8 and 0.5, 1, and 2 µg/mL at pH 7.3–7.4 when using 12B medium. For azithromycin, they are 8, 16, and 32 µg/mL in 12B medium (pH 6.8) [2,61].

5. Procedure.

   Broth microdilution.

   a. Inoculate a tube of sterile demineralized water with several colonies from the primary agar plate. Adjust the organism suspension to a 0.5 McFarland standard. Vortex for 15–30 seconds.

   b. Transfer 50 μl of the organism suspension to 10 mL of Mueller Hinton broth (CAMHB with 5% OADC). Vortex. Once the final inoculum has been prepared, the plate must be inoculated within 30 minutes to prevent organism overgrowth (it is recommended to streak an agar plate from the final inoculum to act as a purity check).

   c. Transfer 100 μl of inoculated broth to each well of the plate. A final organism density of approximately 1×105 CFU/mL is recommended for testing.

   d. Place the plastic lid on the plate or if using plates with adhesive seals, apply the adhesive seal. After applying the seal, *press firmly* and carefully to ensure adequate sealing and prevent creasing of the seal.

   e. Incubate aerobically at 35°C–37°C for 7 days. If growth in the control well is 1+ or less, reincubate and read again at 14 days.

6. Reading and reporting of results.

   Test results are best read using a viewer that displays the underside of the wells.

   a. It is not necessary to remove the adhesive seal or lid for reading when the plate is read from the bottom.

   b. Read the growth control well first. If the control well does not exhibit satisfactory growth (2+ or greater), the plates should be reincubated until satisfactory growth appears (up to 2 weeks for most slowly growing NTM). However, some fastidious species may require longer incubation times, and note should be made if this occurs as some results may be invalidated by lengthy incubation.

   c. Growth appears as turbidity or as a button of cells at the bottom of a well. The growth control well should always be used as the reference for interpreting growth patterns in the plate.

   d. The MIC is recorded as the lowest concentration of antimicrobial that inhibits macroscopic growth.

   e. MIC values and an interpretation should be reported as "susceptible," "intermediate," or "resistant." Break points are provided in Table 11.7.

   f. For an isolate with an "intermediate" level of susceptibility to one of the macrolides, a comment should be added to the report of the susceptibility result, indicating that the isolate should be monitored for possible emerging macrolide resistance. Additional testing of other isolates may also be warranted.

   g. Trailing endpoints with macrolides and isolates of MAC should be disregarded.

7. Quality control.

   M. avium ATCC 700898 is recommended for quality control of broth dilution testing of MAC [2].

8. Expected value.

   See Table 11.8.

9. Notes.

   a. Procedures for alkalization of 12B broth can be found in the CLSI, M24-A, 2003, Appendix E, p. 5 [2].

   b. W orking quality control cultures of MAC should be subcultured weekly or each time testing is performed (if done less often than weekly).

   c. For storage, stock cultures should be maintained at *less than* 20°C in an appropriate culture medium although the working culture may be stored at ambient temperatures for up to 1 month.

TABLE 11.8
Quality Control of Ranges of MICs for *M. avium* ATCC 700898

Drug	Media pH	Acceptable MIC Range (μg/mL)
Clarithromycin	6.8	0.5–2
	7.3–7.4	1–4
Azithromycin	6.8	8–32

Source: Woods, G.L., et al. Susceptibility testing of mycobacteria, nocardiae, and other aerobic actinomycetes, approved standard, M24-A, CLSI, Wayne, PA, 2003, pp. 22–23.

d. The interpretive criteria for MAC are based in part on a monotherapy clarithromycin trial of disseminated disease in humans [58]. Untreated MAC isolates are uniformly susceptible to macrolides, but macrolide resistance develops within a few months with monotherapy and may also occasionally occur in combination therapy. This resistance correlates with clinical relapse and the emergence of a base pair mutation at the adenine at position 2058 or 2059 in the 23S ribosomal RNA macrolide binding site. Untreated strains of MAC that always have adenine at these two positions ("wild type") should always be macrolide susceptible [62].

e. While testing first-line antituberculous agents with MAC is not recommended, testing of newer antimicrobials such as moxifloxacin and/or linezolid may be reasonable especially for isolates that are macrolide resistant or are from patients who failed therapy with standard drugs since it is not yet known if these predict clinical outcome (results of testing the antituberculous drugs rifampin and ethambutol do not and hence are not tested). These drugs should be tested using a broth microdilution method and established bacterial break points as described in the CLSI Supplemental Tables [55] until further studies with MAC are available. For linezolid, the break points as proposed in the CLSI document for the RGM may be used [2].

f. The status of testing aminoglycosides such as amikacin and streptomycin against isolates of MAC has not been addressed by the CLSI. If MICs are requested for either of these agents, each laboratory must validate their method and results and appropriate quality control must be performed.

11.4.3 BACTEC 460 DRUG SUSCEPTIBILITY FOR NONTUBERCULOUS MYCOBACTERIA

1. Principle.

The BACTEC 460 radiometric susceptibility test is based on the modified proportion method in that when >1% of a test population is resistant to the drug, the culture is considered resistant. The inoculum in the control is adjusted 100-fold less as compared to the inoculum in the drug vial to achieve 1% proportion.

Studies have shown that if the appropriate inoculum is used, susceptibility testing of NTM including MAC, *M. kansasii* (except streptomycin), and *M. marinum* correlates well with conventional drug susceptibility testing.

Generally, in 12B medium, the NTM show greater susceptibility to streptomycin, rifampin, and ethambutol than when tested by the proportion method on 7H10 agar and are resistant to the concentrations of INH used for testing of *M. tuberculosis*. Susceptibility with NTM has been reported by multiple investigators with antituberculosis drugs as well as newer agents [35,60,63,64,66–69].

2. Specimen.

Due to the more rapid growth of the NTM, the drug susceptibility testing in the BACTEC 460 uses a more dilute inoculum so that the GI in the control vial reaches about 30 in 4–8 days [15,35].

3. Reagents, media, and supplies.
   a. BACTEC 460 12B medium.
   b. BACTEC diluting fluid.
   c. McFarland standards.

4. Procedure.
   a. Set up the test with an actively growing culture in 12B medium. The original culture may be growing on solid or liquid medium. In 12B medium, the GI should be >500. If it is in another broth, the turbidity should approximate a 1 McFarland standard. If from solid medium, make the suspension in BACTEC diluting fluid with the turbidity approximately equal to a 1 McFarland standard.
   b. Subculture 0.1 mL into a 12B medium vial. Incubate and test daily on the BACTEC 460 instrument. Once the GI reaches 999 (usually within 1–3 days), use as the inoculum for testing as follows:
      1) *M. kansasii*. Prepare 1:20 dilution by mixing 0.5 mL culture with 9.5 mL BACTEC diluting fluid.
      2) *M. avium complex*. Prepare a 1:100 dilution by mixing 0.1 mL into 9.9 mL BACTEC diluting fluid.
      3) *RGM*. Prepare a 1:1000 dilution in BACTEC diluting fluid.
   c. Inoculate 0.1 mL of the diluted culture into the drug containing 12B vial. For the control, dilute again 1:100 and inoculate 0.1 mL into the 12B vial without antimicrobial. Test the vial daily until the GI of the control vial >30 (4–10 days). If GI 30 is achieved in <3 days, do not interpret the results.

5. Reading and reporting results.

Interpretations are made as for *M. tuberculosis* susceptibility tests. The radiometric method using BACTEC 460 is accurate and reliable [15,35] for susceptibility testing of MAC. See previous sections for information regarding other commercial systems (i.e., MGIT, ESP, etc.)

6. Quality control [2,15,17,35].

Quality control must be validated for each species of NTM as susceptibility with NTM other than MAC is currently nonstandardized [2].

7. Expected results.
   a. Compared to testing on solid media, drug susceptibility tests performed by the BACTEC method usually yields more susceptible results to streptomycin, rifampin, and ethambutol.
   b. Variation in drug susceptibility levels with the same species of NTM, especially MAC, is not uncommon.

8. Limitations.

See the manufacturer's technical procedure manual [15,35].

The clinical efficacy (i.e., reproducibility, correlation with the agar method of proportion, and relationship to clinical outcome) of the antituberculosis drugs with NTM in BACTEC 460 susceptibility testing has not been fully determined [2,15,35].

11.4.4 SLOWLY GROWING NTM: *MYCOBACTERIUM KANSASII*

1. Modified proportion method in Middlebrook 7H10 or 7H11 agar [2].
   a. Drug to be tested routinely:
      1) Rifampin only.

b. Additional agents to test against RMP resistant *M. kansasii:*
   1) Rifabutin.
   2) Ethambutol.
   3) Isoniazid.
   4) Streptomycin.
   5) Clarithromycin.
   6) Amikacin.
   7) Ciprofloxacin.
   8) Trimethoprim-sulfamethoxazole or sulfamethoxazole.
   9) Linerolod
c. Agar proportion method of preparation of drug medium.
   1) 7H10 or 7H11 agar prepared from dehydrated base as recommended by manufacturer.
   2) After the agar is autoclaved and cooled to 50°C–60°C in a water bath, add OAD or OADC supplement (warmed to room temperature) and the appropriate antimycobacterial agent.
   3) The antituberculous agent is then added to plastic quadrant petri plates, so that three quadrants contain different concentrations of one or more of the agents to be tested and one quadrant in each plate is filled with 7H10 agar medium without drug (growth control quadrant).
   4) For the agar dilution method, thaw a tube of frozen stock of drug and dilute with sterile distilled water to yield a working concentration (usually 200–10,000 μg/mL). To achieve the final concentration (see Table 11.3), add the appropriate volume of working solution to sterile 7H10 agar (cooled to 50°C–60°C) to reach a volume of 180 mL.
   5) Mix the agar thoroughly with OAD or OADC (20 mL for 200 mL total volume) and the antituberculous drug solution.
   6) Dispense 5 mL amounts into labeled quadrants of a series of sterile plastic petri plates, reserving one quadrant for 7H10 medium without any added drug.
   7) Dry the plates thoroughly (preferably under a laminar flow hood for several hours or overnight) with the lids partially removed.
   8) After drying, store in sealed plastic bags in the refrigerator (protected from light) for no more than 28 days.
   9) To test several samples of each batch of plates for sterility by incubating at 35°C for 48 hours; discard these test samples.
d. Preparation of inoculum for the agar proportion method.
   1) Scrape colonies (not more than 4–5 weeks old) from surface of medium, taking care not to remove medium.
   2) Transfer the mycobacterial mass to a sterile 16 × 125 mm screw-cap tube containing 3-mm glass beads and Middlebrook 7H9 broth.
   3) Emulsify the growth and vortex for 1–2 minutes.
   4) Allow the tube to stand for >30 minutes (less than 4 hours) to allow large particles to settle.
   5) Withdraw the supernatant suspension and transfer into another sterile glass tube.
   6) Adjust the broth to a 1 McFarland standard density.
e. Inoculation and incubation of media.
   1) Prepare 10^{-2} and 10^{-4} dilutions of the standardized suspensions in sterile water, sterile saline, or 7H9 broth.
   2) Inoculate 0.1 mL of the 10^{-2} dilution onto the control quadrant and onto each of the drug containing quadrants.
   3) Inoculate 0.1 mL of the 10^{-4} dilution in the same fashion.

4) Allow the plates to remain at room temperature until the inoculum (three drops each quadrant) spots are absorbed and dry.

5) Seal the plates in CO_2 permeable polyethylene bags.

6) Incubate the plates medium-side down at $37°C \pm 2°C$ in CO_2 or ambient air. (Incubation in CO_2 is not necessary for growth of *M. kansasii*. Do not incubate in CO_2 when testing macrolides.)

7) Examine plates carefully at the end of 7 days. If growth in the control well is 1+ or less, reincubate an additional 7 days.

f. Interpretation.

1) MICs to INH, RMP, EMB for untreated strains generally fall within a narrow range, and mutational resistance to INH and EMB are only seen in association with RMP resistance. Hence, routine susceptibility testing to agents other than RMP is not recommended by the CLSI [2,68,70–72].

2) The critical concentrations of RMP (1 μg/mL) and EMB (5 μg/mL) used to test *M. tuberculosis* also inhibit untreated (wild) strains of *M. kansasii* [2].

3) MICs for INH for wild strains of *M. kansasii* range from 0.5 to 5 μg/mL so that the standard MTB critical concentration of 0.2 μg/mL in 7H10 agar shows resistance and the 1.0 μg/mL concentration gives variable results. Thus susceptibility testing of INH at either of these concentrations is not recommended [2,69].

4) Isolates susceptible to rifampin are also susceptible to rifabutin.

5) For isolates resistant to RMP (1 μg/mL), secondary agents should be tested (see Table 11.9).

g. Quality control strains and expected ranges [2].

1) *M. kansasii* ATCC 12478 (RMP ≤1 μg/mL)

2) *M. marinum* ATCC 927 (RMP ≤0.25–1 μg/mL)

3) *Enterococcus faecalis* ATCC 29212 (RMP ≤0.5–4 μg/mL)

Note: Either or all three of the above strains may be used until a standardized reference strain is CLSI approved and available for testing.

The strain(s) should be tested weekly or each time the test is performed, if less often than weekly.

2. Agar disk elution method of preparation of drug medium (see agar proportion method for additional details) [2,40,73].

a. Dispense the commercially prepared antimycobacterial agent disks aseptically into each well of a 6-round well tissue culture plate.

b. Prepare the 7H10 agar with OAD or OADC supplement. Dispense 5 mL of this medium into each well overlaying the disk and keeping the disk centered. Allow to solidify at room temperature.

c. Before use, dry plates as in step 7) for the agar proportion method and store as in step 5) to 6) for the agar proportion method.

d. Examine sample plates as in step 7) of agar proportion method.

3. Broth microdilution MIC method.

a. Inoculate a tube of sterile demineralized water with three to five colonies from the primary agar plate. Adjust organism suspension to a 0.5 McFarland standard. Invert 8 to 10 times to mix or vortex 15 to 30 seconds.

b. Transfer 50 μl of the organism suspension to 10 mL of CAMHB (with 5% OADC). Invert 8 to 10 times to mix. Once the final inoculum has been prepared, the plate must be inoculated within 30 minutes to prevent organism overgrowth. It is recommended to streak a noninhibitory agar plate (such as blood, tryptic soy agar, etc.) from the final inoculum to act as a purity check).

c. Transfer 100 μl of inoculated broth to each well of the plate. A final organism density of approximately 5×10^5 CFU/mL is recommended for testing.

TABLE 11.9
Proposed Antimycobacterial Agents, Resistance Break Points, Media, and Methodology for Testing *M. kansasii*

Antimycobacterial Drugs	Intermediate and Resistance Break Points (µg/mL)	7H10/7H11 Agar Proportion or Agar Disk Elution	BACTEC 460 TB	Broth Microdilution (MHB + 5% OADC[a] or 7H9)
		Test Medium and Methodology		
	Primary Test Drug			
Rifampin[b]	1	(+)		(+)
	2		(+)	
	Secondary Test Drugs			
Ethambutol	5	(+)	(+)	
	4			(+)
Isoniazid	2–4			(+)
Rifabutinb[a]	2	(+)		(+)
Streptomycin	10	(+)	(+)	
	4–8		(+)	
Antibacterial Drugs				
Amikacin	32			(+)
Ciprofloxacin[c]	2			(+)
Clarithromycin[d]	16	(+)	(+)	(+)
Linezolid	16			(+)
Moxifloxacin[e]	2			(+)
Sulfamethoxazole[b]	32			(+)
Trimethoprim/Sulfamethoxazole	2/38			(+)

Source: Woods, G.L., et al. Susceptibility testing of mycobacteria, nocardiae, and other aerobic actinomycetes, approved standard, M24-A, NCCLS, Wayne, PA, 2003, p. 38.

[a] MHB + OADC = cation-adjusted Mueller-Hinton broth + 5% oleic acid-albumin-dextrose-catalase.

[b] No intermediate break point.

[c] Class agent for older fluoroquinolones (ciprofloxacin, ofloxacin, levofloxacin). Ciprofloxacin is not as active in vitro as moxifloxacin; thus, it cannot be used to predict susceptibility to moxifloxacin.

[d] Class agent for macrolides (clarithromycin, azithromycin, roxithromycin) [Woods, G.L., et al. NCCLS, 2003].

[e] The CLSI has not yet addressed the susceptibility break points for slowly growing nontuberculous mycobacteria other than MAC to moxifloxacin. Therefore, break points used here are bacterial break points [CLSI. Sixteenth Informational Supplement, M100-S16, 2006].

      d. Place the lid on top of the plate, or if using adhesive seals, apply the seal. After applying the seal, press firmly and carefully to assure adequate sealing and prevent creasing of the seal.

      e. Incubate aerobically at 35°C–37°C. Read and interpret results as described earlier for broth microdilution method for MAC. Read at 7 days; if not readable, reincubate and read at 14 days.

4. Reading and reporting of results. Test results are best read using a viewer that displays the underside of the wells, and does not require removal of the adhesive seal.

5. Quality control. See the discussion of quality control and expected ranges for the agar proportion method.)

6. Expected values. See Table 11.9.

TABLE 11.10
Proposed Antimycobacterial Agents, Resistance Break Points, and Methodology for Susceptibility Testing of *Mycobacterium marinum*

	Resistance Break Point (µg/mL)	7H10 Agar Proportion	Agar Disk Elution	Broth Microdilution
Antimycobacterial Drugs				
Ethambutol	5	(+)	(+)	
	4			(+)
Rifampin	1	(+)	(+)	(+)
Antibacterial Drugs				
Amikacin	12		(+)	
	32			(+)
Clarithromycin[a]	16			(+)
Doxycycline/Minocycline	6		(+)	
	4			(+)
Sulfamethoxazole	20		(+)	
	32			(+)
Trimethoprim sulfamethoxazole	2/32			(+)

Note: Routine susceptibility is not recommended [Woods, G.L., et al. NCCLS, Wayne, PA, 2003, p. 39].

[a] Class agent for macrolides (clarithromycin, azithromycin, roxithromycin).

11.4.5 SLOWLY GROWING NTM: *M. MARINUM*

Generally, routine MICs are not required as there is little variability in susceptibility to antimicrobial agents and the number of organisms present at the infected site is low. Thus there is little risk for the development of mutational resistance. Unless a patient fails therapy, or is intolerant of antibiotics, the CLSI recommends not performing susceptibility testing on isolates of *M. marinum* [2].

1. Methodology. See *M. kansasii* except that incubation temperature requires 28°C–30°C and the incubation period is 7 days) [2,73].
2. Drugs to be tested in cases of therapy failure (Table 11.10):
   a. Rifampin.
   b. Ethambutol.
   c. Doxycycline/Minocycline.
   d. Clarithromycin.
   e. Amikacin.
   f. Trimethoprim sulfamethoxazole or sulfamethoxazole.

11.4.6 SLOWLY GROWING NTM: MISCELLANEOUS (*M. TERRAE* COMPLEX, *M. XENOPI*, *M. SIMIAE*, *M. MALMOENSE*, ETC.)

Follow guidelines for other primary and secondary drugs for *M. kansasii*. Too few isolates from each of these species have been tested to recommend a specific method for these species [2,66,74].

11.4.7 Susceptibility Testing of *Mycobacterium haemophilum*

1. Currently there is no CLSI standardized method of susceptibility testing for *M. haemophilum*.
2. Methods of susceptibility testing which have been previously reported include the broth microdilution MIC method, E-test, and agar disk elution [75–80]. For any of these methods, supplementation with ferric ammonium citrate or hemin is necessary to support growth. Incubation may require 2–3 weeks for adequate growth.
3. In-house validation of the method should be established as a quality control measure. Currently, no optimal reference strain is available for quality control of susceptibility testing of *M. haemophilum*.

11.4.8 Susceptibility Testing of Other Fastidious Species (*M. genavense, M. ulcerans*)

Currently there is no CLSI standardized method of susceptibility testing for these fastidious NTM. Too little is known about these species to make recommendations for susceptibility testing.

1. *M. genavense* requires more than 6 weeks using the radiometric system [81–83].
2. *M. ulcerans* requires incubation for 4–6 weeks [2,65,84].
3. Currently no optimal reference strain is available for quality control of susceptibility testing of these species.

REFERENCES

1. Wallace, R.J., Jr. et al. American Thoracic Society Statement: Diagnosis and treatment of disease caused by nontuberculous mycobacteria, *Am. Respir. Crit. Care Med.* 156, S1, 1997.
2. Woods, G.L., et al. Susceptibility testing of mycobacteria, nocardiae, and other aerobic actinomycetes, approved standard, M24-A, NCCLS, Wayne, PA, 2003, pp. 1–71.
3. Heifets, L.B. *Drug Susceptibility in the Chemotherapy of Mmycobacterial Infections*, CRC Press, Boca Raton, FL, 1991, pp.18–28, 97–99, and 106–115.
4. Tenover, F.C., et al. The resurgence of tuberculosis: Is your laboratory ready? *J. Clin. Microbiol.*, 31, 767, 1993.
5. Canetti, G., et al. Advances in techniques of testing mycobacterial drug sensitivity tests in tuberculosis programmes, *Bull. WHO*, 41, 21, 1969.
6. Canetti, G., et al. Mycobacteria: Laboratory methods for testing drugs sensitivity and resistance, *Bull. WHO*, 29, 565, 1963.
7. Moss, A.R., et al. A city-wide outbreak of a multiple-drug-resistant strain of *Mycobacterium tuberculosis* in New York, *Int. J. Tuberc. Lung Dis.*, 1, 115, 1997.
8. Park, M.M., et al. Outcome of MDR-TB patients, 1983–1993, *Am. J. Respir. Crit. Care Med.*, 153, 317, 1996.
9. Griffith, D.E., et al. Diagnosis, treatment and prevention of nontuberculous mycobacterial diseases, *Am. J. Resp. Crit. Care Med.*, Supplement (in press), 2006.
10. Gillespie, S.H., et al. Early bactericidal activity of a moxifloxacin and isoniazid combination in smear-positive pulmonary tuberculosis, *J. Antimicrob. Chemother.*, 56, 1169, 2005.
11. Roberts, G.D., et al. Evaluation of the BACTEC radiometric method for recovery of mycobacteria and drug susceptibility testing of *Mycobacterium tuberculosis* from acid-fast smear-positive specimens, *J. Clin. Microbiol.*, 18, 689, 1983.
12. Siddiqi, S.H., Hawkin, J.E.D., and Laszlo, A. Interlaboratory drug susceptibility testing of *Mycobacterium tuberculosis* by a radiometric procedure and two conventional methods, *J. Clin. Microbiol.*, 22, 919, 1985.
13. Palaci, M., et al. Evaluation of mycobacteria growth indicator tube for recovery and drug susceptibility testing of *Mycobacterium tuberculosis* isolates from respiratory specimens, *J. Clin. Microbiol.*, 34, 762, 1996.

14. Kent, P.T. and Kubica, G.P. *A Guide for the Level III Laboratory*, Centers for Disease Control, Atlanta, GA, 1985, p. 166.

15. Siddiqi, S.H. *BACTEC® 460 TB System Product and Procedure Manual*, Becton Dickinson Diagnostic Instrument Systems, Sparks, MD, 1995, Sec. IV, pp. 1–22.

16. Pfyffer, G., et al. Multicenter laboratory validation of susceptibility testing of *M. tuberculosis* against classical second-line and newer antimicrobial drugs by using the radiometric BACTEC 460 technique and the proportion method with solid media, *J. Clin. Microbiol.*, 37, 3179, 1999.

17. Piersimoni, C., et al. Current perspective on drug susceptibility testing of *Mycobacterium tuberculosis* complex: The automated nonradiometric systems, *J. Clin. Microbiol.*, 44, 20, 2006.

18. Tortoli, E., et al. Evaluation of automated BACTEC MGIT 960 system for testing susceptibility of *Mycobacterium tuberculosis* to four major antituberculous drugs: Comparison with the radiometric BACTEC 460 TB method and the agar plate method of proportion, *J. Clin. Microbiol.*, 40, 607, 2002.

19. Miller, M.A., et al. Testing of susceptibility of *Mycobacterium tuberculosis* to pyrazinamide: Comparison of Bactec method with pyrazinamidase assay, *J. Clin. Microbiol.*, 33, 2468, 1995.

20. LaBombardi, V.J. Comparison of the ESP and BACTEC systems for testing susceptibilities of *Mycobacterium tuberculosis* complex isolates to pyrazinamide, *J. Clin. Microbiol.*, 40, 2238, 2002.

21. Bemer, P., et al. Multicenter evaluation of fully automated BACTEC mycobacteria growth indicator tube 960 system for susceptibility testing of *Mycobacterium tuberculosis*, *J. Clin. Microbiol.*, 40, 150, 2002.

22. Macondo, E.A., et al. Rapid susceptibility testing of *Mycobacterium tuberculosis* by the mycobacteria growth indicator tube (MGIT AST SIRE), *Clin. Microbiol. Infect.*, 6, 361, 2000.

23. Bergmann, J.S. and Woods, G.L. Reliability of mycobacteria growth indicator tube for testing susceptibility of *Mycobacterium tuberculosis* to ethambutol and streptomycin, *J. Clin. Microbiol.*, 35, 3325, 1997.

24. Ardito, F., et al. Comparison of the mycobacteria growth indicator tube with radiometric and solid culture for isolation of mycobacteria from clinical specimens and susceptibility testing of *Mycobacterium tuberculosis*, *Microbiologica*, 23, 151, 2000.

25. Ardito, F., et al. Evaluation of BACTEC mycobacteria growth indicator tube (MGIT 960) automated system for drug susceptibility testing of *Mycobacterium tuberculosis*, *J. Clin. Microbiol.*, 39, 4440, 2001.

26. Pfyffer, G.E., Palicova, F., and Rüsch-Gerdes, S. Testing of susceptibility of *Mycobacterium tuberculosis* to pyrazinamide with the nonradiometric BACTEC MGIT 960 system, *J. Clin. Microbiol.*, 40, 1670, 2002.

27. Rüsch-Gerdes, S., et al. Multicenter laboratory validation of the BACTEC MGIT 960 technique for testing susceptibilities of *Mycobacterium tuberculosis* to classical second-line drugs and newer antimicrobials, *J. Clin. Microbiol.*, 44, 688, 2006.

28. Bergmann, J.S. and Woods, G.L. Evaluation of the ESP Culture System II for testing susceptibilities of Mycobacterium tuberculosis isolates to four primary antituberculous drugs, *J. Clin. Microbiol.*, 36, 2940, 1998.

29. LaBombardi, V.J. and Lukowski, C. Anti-tubercular susceptibility testing using the DIFCO ESP Myco System, presented at the 97th ASM General Meeting, Miami Beach, FL, May 4-8, 1997, U-75, p. 556.

30. Ruiz, P., Zerolo, F.J., and Casal, M.J. Comparison of susceptibility testing of *Mycobacterium tuberculosis* using ESP Culture System II with that using the BACTEC method, *J. Clin. Microbiol.*, 38, 4663, 2000.

31. Díaz-Infantes, M., et al. Evaluation of the MB/BacT Mycobacterium detection system for susceptibility testing of *Mycobacterium tuberculosis*, *J. Clin. Microbiol.*, 38, 1988, 2000.

32. Brunello, F. and Fontana, R. Reliability of the MB/BacT system for testing susceptibility of *Mycobacterium tuberculosis* complex isolates to antituberculous drugs, *J. Clin. Microbiol.*, 38, 872, 2000.

33. Ängeby, K.A.K., et al. Evaluation of the BacT/ALERT 3D system for recovery and drug susceptibility testing of *Mycobacterium tuberculosis*, *Clin. Microbiol. Infect.*, 9, 1148, 2003.

34. Heifets, L.B. Qualitative and quantitative drug-susceptibility tests in mycobacteriology, *Am. Rev. Respir. Dis.*, 137, 1217, 1988.

35. Siddiqi, S. BACTEC MGIT 960 SIRE. Nonradioactive susceptibility testing for *Mycobacterium tuberculosis*, in *Clinical Microbiology Procedures Handbook*, 2nd ed., Isenberg, H.D., Ed., ASM, Washington, DC, 2004, pp. 7.8.5.1–7.8.5.5.

36. Siddiqi, S.H. *BACTEC 460 TB System Product and Procedure Manual*, Becton Dickinson Diagnostic Instrument Systems, Sparks, MD, 1995, Sec. VI., pp.1–7.

37. Siddiqi, S. BACTEC MGIT 960 PZA. Susceptibility testing for *Mycobacterium tuberculosis*, in *Clinical Microbiology Procedures Handbook*, 2nd ed., Isenberg, H.D., Ed., ASM, Washington, DC, 2004, pp. 7.8.6.1–7.8.6.4.

38. Miller, M.A., et al. Growth inhibition of *Mycobacterium tuberculosis* by polyoxyethylene stearate present in the BACTEC pyrazinamide susceptibility test, *J. Clin. Microbiol.*, 34, 84, 1996.

39. Woods, G.L., et al. Multisite reproducibility of results obtained by the broth microdilution method for susceptibility testing of *Mycobacterium abscessus, Mycobacterium chelonae*, and *Mycobacterium fortuitum, J. Clin. Microbiol.*, 37, 1676, 1999.

40. Brown, B.A., Swenson, J.M., and Wallace, R.J., Jr. Agar disk elution test for rapidly growing mycobacteria, in *Clinical Microbiology Procedures Handbook*, Isenberg, H.D., Ed., American Society for Microbiology, Washington, DC, 1992, p. 5.10.11.

41. Woods, G.L., et al. Multisite reproducibility of Etest for susceptibility testing of *Mycobacterium abscessus, Mycobacterium chelonae,* and *Mycobacterium fortuitum, J. Clin. Microbiol.*, 38, 656, 2000.

42. Brown, B.A., Swenson, J.M., and Wallace, R.J., Jr. Broth microdilution MIC test for rapidly growing mycobacteria, in *Clinical Microbiology Procedures Handbook*, Isenberg, H.D., Ed., American Society for Microbiology, Washington, DC, 1992, p. 5.11.1.

43. Brown, B.A., et al.. Activities of four macrolides, including clarithromycin, against *Mycobacterium fortuitum, Mycobacterium chelonae*, and *M. chelonae*-like organisms, *Antimicrob. Agents Chemother.*, 36, 180, 1992.

44. Wallace, R.J., Jr., et al. Activities of ciprofloxacin and ofloxacin against rapidly growing mycobacteria with demonstration of acquired resistance following single-drug therapy, *Antimicrob. Agents Chemother.*, 34, 65, 1990.

45. Wallace, R.J., Jr., Brown, B.A., and Onyi, G.O. Susceptibilities of *Mycobacterium fortuitum* biovar *fortuitum* and the two subgroups of *Mycobacterium chelonae* to imipenem, cefmetazole, cefoxitin, and amoxicillin-clavulanic acid, *Antimicrob. Agents Chemother.*, 35, 773, 1991.

46. Wallace, R.J., Jr., Brown, B.A., and Onyi, G.O. Skin, soft tissue, and bone infections due to *Mycobacterium chelonae chelonae*: Importance of prior corticosteroid therapy, frequency of disseminated infections, and resistance to oral antimicrobials other than clarithromycin, *J. Infect. Dis.*, 166, 405, 1992.

47. Wallace, R.J., Jr., et al. Activities of linezolid against rapidly growing mycobacteria, *Antimicrob. Agents Chemother.*, 45, 764, 2001.

48. Wallace, R.J. Jr. et al. Human disease due to *Mycobacterium smegmatis*, *J. Infect. Dis.*, 158, 52, 1988.

49. Wallace, R.J., Jr., et al. Clinical significance, biochemical features, and susceptibility patterns of sporadic isolates of the *Mycobacterium chelonae*-like organism, *J. Clin. Microbiol.*, 31, 3231, 1993.

50. Wallace, R.J., Jr., et al. Treatment of non-pulmonary infections due to *Mycobacterium fortuitum* and *Mycobacterium chelonei* on the basis of *in vitro* susceptibilities, *J. Infect. Dis.*, 152 ,500, 1985.

51. Swenson, J.M., et al. Antimicrobial susceptibility of five subgroups of *Mycobacterium fortuitum* and *Mycobacterium chelonae*, *Antimicrob. Agents Chemother.*, 28, 807, 1985.

52. Swenson, J.M., Thornsberry, C., and Silcox, V.A. Rapidly growing mycobacteria: testing of susceptibility to 34 antimicrobial agents by broth microdilution, *Antimicrob. Agents Chemother.*, 22, 186, 1982.

53. Brown, B.A., et al. Description of *Mycobacterium wolinskyi* and *Mycobacterium goodii*, two new rapidly growing species related to *Mycobacterium smegmatis* and associated with human wound infections: A cooperative study from the International Working Group on Mycobacterial Taxonomy, *Int. J. Syst. Bacteriol.*, 49, 1493, 1999.

54. Brown-Elliott, B.A., and Wallace, R.J., Jr. Clinical and taxonomic status of pathogenic nonpigmented or late-pigmenting rapidly growing mycobacteria, *Clin. Microbiol. Rev.*, 15, 716, 2002.

55. CLSI. Performance standards for antimicrobial susceptibility testing. Sixteenth Informational Supplement, M100-S16, 2006.

56. Brown-Elliott, B.A., et al. Comparison of *in vitro* activities of gatifloxacin and ciprofloxacin against four taxa of rapidly growing mycobacteria, *Antimicrob. Agents Chemother.*, 46, 3283, 2002.

57. Wallace, R.J., Jr., et al. Comparison of the *in vitro* activity of the glycylcycline tigecycline (formerly GAR-936) with those of tetracycline, minocycline, and doxycycline against isolates of nontuberculous mycobacteria, *Antimicrob. Agents. Chemother.*, 46, 3164, 2002.

58. Chaisson, R.E., et al. and the AIDS Clinical Trial Group Protocol 157 Study Team. Clarithromycin therapy for bacteremic *Mycobacterium avium* complex disease. A randomized, double-blind, dose ranging study in patients with AIDS, *Ann. Intern. Med.*, 121, 905, 1994.

59. Heifets, L. Susceptibility testing of *Mycobacterium avium* complex isolates, *Antimicrob. Agents Chemother.*, 40, 1759, 1996.

60. Shafran, S.D., et al. Does *in vitro* susceptibility to rifabutin and ethambutol predict the response to treatment of *Mycobacterium avium* complex bacteremia with rifabutin, ethambutol, and clarithromycin? *Clin. Infect. Dis.*, 27, 1401, 1998.

61. Inderlied, C.B. Microbiology and minimum inhibitory concentration testing for *Mycobacterium avium* complex prophylaxis, *Am. J. Med.*, 102, 2, 1997.

62. Meier, A., et al. Molecular mechanisms of clarithromycin resistance in *Mycobacterium avium*: Observation of multiple 23S rDNA mutations in a clonal population, *J. Infect. Dis.*, 174, 354, 1996.

63. Heifets, L.B., et al. PZA is not active *in vitro* against *M. avium* complex, *Am. Rev. Resp. Dis.*, 134, 1287, 1986.

64. Brown, B.A., Wallace, R.J., Jr., and Onyi, G. Activities of clarithromycin against eight slowly growing species of nontuberculous mycobacteria, determined by using a broth microdilution MIC system, *Antimicrob. Agents Chemother.*, 36, 1987, 1992.

65. Portaels, F., et al. *In vitro* susceptibility of *Mycobacterium ulcerans* to clarithromycin, *Antimicrob. Agents Chemother.*, 42, 2070, 1998.

66. Hoffner, S.E., Hjelm, U., and Källenius, G. Susceptibility of *Mycobacterium malmoense* to antibacterial drugs and drug combinations, *Antimicrob. Agents Chemother.*, 37, 1285, 1993.

67. Siddiqi, S.H., Heifets, L.B., and Cynamon, M.H. Rapid broth microdilution methods for determination of MICs for *Mycobacterium avium* isolates, *J. Clin. Microbiol.*, 31, 2332, 1993.

68. Steadham, J.E., Stall, S.K., and Simmank, J.L. Use of the BACTEC system for drug susceptibility testing of *Mycobacterium tuberculosis*, *M. kansasii*, and *M. avium* complex, *Diagn. Microbiol. Infect. Dis.*, 3, 33, 1985.

69. Biehle, J., and Cavalieri, S.J. *In vitro* susceptibility of *Mycobacterium kansasii* to clarithromycin, *Antimicrob. Agents Chemother.*, 36, 2039, 1992.

70. Wallace, R.J., Jr., et al. Rifampin-resistant *Mycobacterium kansasii*, *Clin. Infect. Dis.*, 18, 736, 1994.

71. Ahn, C.H., et al. Sulfonamide-containing regimens for disease caused by rifampin-resistant *Mycobacterium kansasii*, *Am. Rev. Respir. Dis.*, 135, 10, 1987.

72. Hawkins, J.E., and Gross, W.M. Radiometric drug susceptibility testing of *Mycobacterium kansasii* and *M. marinum,* presented at the 24th Interscience Conference on Antimicrobial Agents and Chemotherapy, Washington, DC, 1200, 303, 1984.

73. Stone, M.S., et al. An agar disk elution method for clinical susceptibility testing of *Mycobacterium marinum* and the *Mycobacterium fortuitum*-complex to sulfonamides and antibiotics, *Antimicrob. Agents Chemother.*, 24, 486, 1983.

74. Wallace, R.J., Jr., et al. Susceptibility testing of slowly growing mycobacteria by a microdilution MIC method with 7H9 broth, *J. Clin. Microbiol.*, 24, 976, 1986.

75. Bernard, E.M., et al. Activities of antimicrobial agents against clinical isolates of *Mycobacterium haemophilum*, *Antimicrob. Agents Chemother.*, 37, 2323, 1993.

76. Kiehn, T.E., and White, M. *Mycobacterium haemophilum*: An emerging pathogen, *Eur. J. Clin. Microbiol. Infect. Dis.*, 13, 925, 1994.

77. McBride, M.E., et al. Diagnostic and therapeutic considerations for cutaneous *Mycobacterium haemophilum* infections, *Arch. Dermatol.*, 127, 276, 1991.

78. Thibert, L., Lebel, F., and Martineau, B. Two cases of *Mycobacterium haemophilum* infection in Canada, *J. Clin. Microbiol.*, 28, 621, 1990.

79. Saubolle, M.A., et al. *Mycobacterium haemophilum*: Microbiology and expanding clinical and geographic spectra of disease in humans, *Clin. Microbiol. Rev.*, 9, 435, 1996.

80. Straus, W.L., et al. Clinical and epidemiologic characteristics of *Mycobacterium haemophilum*, an emerging pathogen in immunocompromised patients, *Ann. Intern. Med.*, 120, 118, 1994.

81. Böttger, E.C., Hischel, B., and Coyle, M.B. *Mycobacterium genavense* sp. nov, *Intern. J. Syst. Bacteriol.*, 43, 841, 1993.

82. Wald, A., et al. Infection with a fastidious mycobacterium resembling *Mycobacterium simiae* in seven patients with AIDS, *Ann. Intern. Med.*, 117, 586, 1992.

83. Carlson, L.D.C., Wallis, C.K., and Coyle, M.B. Standardized BACTEC method to measure clarithromycin susceptibility of *Mycobacterium genavense*, *J. Clin. Microbiol.*, 36, 748, 1998.

84. MacCallum, P., et al. A new mycobacterial infection in man, *J. Pathol. Bacteriol.*, 60, 93, 1948.

85. Nash, K.A., et al. Molecular basis of intrinsic macrolide resistance in clinical isolates of *Mycobacterium fortuitum*, *J. Antimicrob. Chemother.*, 55, 170, 2005.
86. Holliday, N., et al. *Mycobacterium peregrinum* ATCC 700686 susceptibility testing: A multi site evaluation to establish microbroth dilution quality control (QC) ranges for 5 antimicrobial agents, presented at 105th ASM General Meeting, Atlanta, GA, June 5–9, 2005, C-020.

12 Methods for Determining Bactericidal Activity and Antimicrobial Interactions: Synergy Testing, Time-Kill Curves, and Population Analysis

Punam Verma

CONTENTS

12.1 CLINICAL RATIONALE

It is common to use antibiotic combinations in the practice of today's clinical medicine. Antimicrobial combinations are used for a number of reasons: expansion of antimicrobial spectrum, minimization of drug toxicity, minimization of antimicrobial resistance, and antimicrobial synergism [1–3]. Combination therapy has become the empirical choice to treat severe bacterial infections until the etiologic agent has been established. Antimicrobial combinations are also used to treat polymicrobial infections when treatment with a single agent may be inadequate. Increased failure rates have been reported with the use of a single agent to treat serious infections such as acute bacterial endocarditis, osteomyelitis, or septic shock. Reduction in antimicrobial dosage-related toxicity might also be theoretically achieved by antimicrobial combinations, permitting the use of drugs at lower doses than if the drugs were administered independently [1–3]. In practice, this is almost impossible to accomplish because drug levels attained in the blood cannot predict the achievable levels at the infected site. Combination therapy may also avert or delay the emergence of antibiotic-resistant subpopulations. This tactic has been used in the treatment of tuberculosis because the use of monotherapy inevitably results in the development of resistance. With escalating numbers of immunocompromised patients in recent years and concurrent documented cases of endocarditis, meningitis, and osteomyelitis there may be a pressing need to achieve bacterial killing or cidal activity with an antimicrobial agent(s). Routine susceptibility tests used in a clinical microbiology laboratory usually measure inhibitory activity of a single antimicrobial agent. This information is sufficient in most clinical situations to curtail the spread of the etiologic agent and augments the activity of the host immune system to eradicate the agent, achieving clinical cure [1–4]. In cases of clinical failure, anticipation of clinical failure due to immunosuppression or other underlying conditions requiring multidrug prophylaxis, the clinician in concert with the infectious disease specialist might wish to revisit the complex role of polyantimicrobial therapy. Obtaining meaningful information about the interaction of antimicrobials in combination, singly or in synergy may require *in vitro* testing in the clinical laboratory. Determination of frank resistance, susceptibility, identification of resistant clones, antagonism, synergism, and resistance attributable to genotypic induction need to be assessed by sensitive laboratory methods. Assessment of drug interactions in the laboratory is, because of its very complexity and sensitivity, an expensive and time consuming approach to therapy. Approaching the issues involved necessitates the use of consulting specialists to provide advice on the proper assays to be performed, their timing, and ultimate usefulness [4]. It cannot be stressed enough that proper performance of many assays discussed in this chapter needs highly trained and certified laboratory personnel under the direction of a clinical microbiologist trained in the interpretation of these specialized testing results.

12.2 METHODS FOR ASSESSING DRUG INTERACTIONS

12.2.1 CHECKERBOARD TITRATION

12.2.1.1 Principle

Checkerboard titration is one of the most frequently used techniques to assess drug interactions. The term *checkerboard* arises from the pattern that is generated by the multiple dilutions of the two antimicrobial agents that are being tested [1]. The range of concentrations tested for each antimicrobial agent is four to five dilutions lower than the minimal inhibitory concentration (MIC) and at least two dilutions higher than the MIC (if antagonism is suspected). Twofold dilutions of each antimicrobial agent are used. Tubes are arranged in a column and row format. Each row has a constant amount of one drug and twofold doubling dilutions of the second drug. In other words, the first row has doubling dilutions of drug A and the columns have twofold doubling dilutions of the second drug. Each tube has a unique combination of the two antimicrobial agents being tested [1]. Historically, this test was performed in an array of tubes using broth macrodilution that was cumbersome, time consuming, and costly. Testing is now most often performed utilizing microtiter trays. If testing is desired using broth macrodilution, the assay is performed using a limited series of tubes. The results are calculated mathematically and expressed in terms of a fractional inhibitory concentration (FIC) index equal to the sum of the FICs for each drug. The FIC for a drug is defined as the MIC of the drug in combination divided by the MIC of the drug used alone. If the FIC index is ≤0.5, the antimicrobial combination is interpreted as being synergistic; between 1 and 4 as indifferent; and >4 as antagonistic. Isobolograms can also be used to represent these interactions [1,2,5].

12.2.1.2 Specimen

Test organisms must be in pure culture and may be removed from trypticase soy agar plates with or without 5–7% sheep blood. Test organisms should be 18–24-h old, and if taken from frozen stocks, must be consecutively subcultured twice before testing.

12.2.1.3 Materials

12.2.1.3.1 Broth Microdilution Method

12.2.1.3.1.1 Media and Reagents

1. Cation-supplemented Mueller-Hinton broth (CSMHB)
2. Trypticase soy agar with or without 5% sheep blood
3. Sterile 0.85% sodium chloride
4. Sterile stock antibiotic solutions (frozen)

12.2.1.3.1.2 Supplies

1. Sterile 75×12 mm, and 17×100 mm glass or plastic tubes
2. Sterile microtiter plates, 96 wells (U bottom)
3. 0.5 McFarland turbidity standard
4. Sterile 1-, 5-, and 10-mL disposable pipettes
5. Pipette bulb or automatic pipette device
6. Sterile cotton-tipped swabs
7. Tray-sealing tape
8. Plastic storage bags

12.2.1.3.1.3 Equipment

1. Vortex mixer
2. Multichannel pipette, 50 μL capacity with sterile tips
3. 100-μL adjustable micropipette with sterile tips
4. 1-μL and 10-μL calibrated loops
5. Plate viewer
6. 35°C $\pm$ 2°C ambient-air incubator (or other growth conditions as required by some organisms)

12.2.1.3.2 Broth Macrodilution Method

12.2.1.3.2.1 Media and Reagents

1. Cation-supplemented Mueller-Hinton broth
2. Trypticase soy agar with 5% sheep blood (BAP)
3. Sterile 0.85% sodium chloride
4. Sterile stock antibiotic solutions (frozen)

12.2.1.3.2.2 Supplies

1. Sterile 75×12 mm, and 17×100 mm capped glass tubes
2. Sterile polypropylene 50-mL screw-capped tubes
3. 0.5 McFarland turbidity standard
4. Sterile 1-, 5-, and 10-mL disposable pipettes
5. Pipette bulb or automatic pipette device
6. Sterile cotton-tipped swabs

12.2.1.3.2.3. Equipment

1. Vortex mixer
2. Multichannel pipette 50 μL capacity with sterile tips
3. 100-μL adjustable micropipette with sterile tips

4. 1- and 10-μL calibrated loops
5. 35°C ± 2°C ambient-air incubator (or other growth conditions as required by some organisms)

12.2.1.4 Quality Control

1. Choose appropriate quality control strains depending on the antimicrobial agent being tested. The quality control strain should be susceptible to the antimicrobial agent being tested.
2. The following quality control strains are recommended:
   a. *Escherichia coli* ATCC 25922.
   b. *Pseudomonas aeruginosa* ATCC 27853.
   c. *Staphylococcus aureus* ATCC 29213.
   d. *Enterococcus faecalis* ATCC 29212.
3. Quality control strains must be tested in parallel with the clinical isolate following the same procedure.
4. The growth control should show 3+ to 4+ turbidity.
5. The sterility control should show no growth.
6. The inoculum control should show 75–150 colonies with no contaminating organisms.
7. Acceptable results:
   a. The growth medium supports the growth of control and test organisms.
   b. MIC values obtained for quality control strains should be within published limits for the individual antimicrobial agent.
   c. The growth, inoculum, and sterility controls should show appropriate results.
8. If unacceptable results are obtained, repeat the quality control testing. If unacceptable results are obtained when the test is repeated, inform a supervisor and determine the reason for the failure. *Do not* report any patient results if the quality control results are unacceptable.

12.2.1.5 Procedure

12.2.1.5.1 Broth Microdilution Method

12.2.1.5.1.1 Preparation of Checkerboard Microdilution Panels

1. Determine the MIC of individual antibiotics for the test isolate.
2. Construct a panel configuration by completing the worksheet as shown in Appendix 12.1 in the following manner:
   a. Place the MIC value of antibiotic A in Cell A7 of the worksheet.
   b. Place the MIC value of antibiotic B in cell E1 of the worksheet.
   c. Complete the worksheet by following the example shown in Appendix 12.2.
3. Determine the number of combination panels to prepare: one for each isolate, two for the quality control isolates, and one for the dilution of the second antibiotic.
4. Prepare sufficient quantities of antimicrobial solutions. The initial concentration should be four times the desired concentration in the first well for each drug. For example, if the initial concentration for antibiotic A is 512 μg/mL and for antibiotic B is 64 μg/mL, then it is necessary to start with a concentration of 2,048 μg/mL for antibiotic A and 256 μg/mL for antibiotic B.
5. For each panel, the following quantities of antibiotic solutions will be required:
   a. Antibiotic A: 16 wells × 0.05 mL = 0.8 mL.
   b. Antibiotic B: 24 wells × 0.05 mL = 1.2 mL.

6. For one isolate:
    a. Prepare two panels; one is for the combination drug panel (panel 1) and the other (panel 2) is used for making antimicrobial dilutions for the second antibiotic (antibiotic B).
        1) For panel 1:
            a) Dispense 50 μL of sterile CSMHB into every well except those of column 1 and column 12.
            b) Add 50 μL of sterile CSMHB to G12.
            c) Add 50 μL of antibiotic solution A to wells A12–G12 and wells A11–H11.
            d) Dilute serially from column 11 to column 2.
            e) Discard 50 μL from column 2.
            f) Take 50 μL from B1–B11 from panel 2 and dispense it in the corresponding row of panel 1.
            g) Repeat step f for the next higher concentration.
        2) For panel 2:
            a) Dispense 100 μL of CSMHB into every well except those of row A and row H.
            b) Add 100 μL of antibiotic solution B to H1–H11 and G1–G12.
            c) Dilute serially from row G to row B.
            d) Discard 100 μL from each well in row B (the final volume in each well is 100 μL [0.1 mL]).
7. Prepared panels can be used immediately or can be stored at –70°C for up to 6 months. If the panels are to be used later, the trays should be covered with lids or sealed with tape and placed in sealed plastic bags.

12.2.1.5.1.2 Preparation of Inoculum

1. Select 3 to 5 colonies of the same morphologic type from a fresh (18–24 h) agar plate culture.
2. Touch the top of the colonies using a sterile loop or swab and transfer the test inoculum to 5 mL of sterile CSMHB.
3. Incubate at 35°C until the turbidity matches that of a 0.5 McFarland standard (1.5×10^8 CFU/mL).
4. A total of at least 4.8 mL of diluted inoculum is required for one panel (50 μL $\times$ 96 wells = 4.8 mL). Include sufficient excess volume for the reservoir.
5. Add 0.1 mL of the adjusted inoculum suspension from step 3 to 9.9 mL of sterile CSMHB (1:100 dilution) to achieve approximately 10^6 CFU/mL.

12.2.1.5.1.3 Inoculation and Incubation of Checkerboard Panel

1. Using a multichannel pipette, add 50 μL of diluted inoculum to every well except H12.
2. Add 50 μL of diluted inoculum to growth control well A1.
3. Using a 0.001-mL (1-μL) calibrated loop, inoculate a purity plate by subculturing 0.001 mL of inoculum from the reservoir onto a blood agar plate.
4. Prepare an inoculum count verification plate as follows:
    a. Add 50 μL of diluted inoculum to 0.45 mL of sterile 0.85% saline (dilution 10^{-1}).
    b. Transfer 0.1 mL from dilution 10^{-1} to 0.9 mL of sterile 0.85% saline and vortex well (dilution 10^{-2}).
    c. Transfer 0.1 mL from dilution 10^{-2} to 0.9 mL of sterile 0.85% saline and vortex well (dilution 10^{-3}).
    d. Plate 0.1 mL of dilution 10^{-3} onto a blood agar plate and spread for quantitation by streaking in several directions with a sterile loop or by using a sterile bent glass rod to spread the inoculum evenly.
5. Place the trays in plastic bags. Incubate at 35°C $\pm$ 2°C for 16–20 h.
6. Incubate purity and inoculum verification plates at 35°C $\pm$ 2°C for 16–20 h.

12.2.1.5.1.4   Reading MIC Panels

1. Examine the growth control well for organism viability. The growth control well should show heavy turbidity.
2. Examine the purity plate, and verify that the culture is not mixed. If it is mixed, repeat the test.
3. Count the number of colonies on the inoculum verification plates. The number of colonies should be between 75 and 150.
4. Record growth or no growth with the aid of a viewing device for all the wells on the worksheet.
5. Record the MIC results for antibiotic A from wells A2–A12.
6. Record the MIC results for antibiotic B from wells B–H in column 1.

12.2.1.5.2 Broth Macrodilution Method

12.2.1.5.2.1   Preparing Broth Macrodilution Limited Checkerboard

1. Determine the MIC of individual antibiotics for the test isolate by using the broth macrodilution methodology.
2. Use the template as shown in Appendix 12.3 to determine the concentrations and number of tubes needed for synergy testing.
3. Prepare sufficient quantities of antimicrobial solutions. The initial concentrations are four times the desired concentrations as shown in Appendix 12.3.
4. Calculate the volumes of individual concentrations of antibiotics needed for each organism (0.5 mL of each antibiotic concentration is required per tube).
5. Aliquot the antibiotic solutions into the desired tubes.
   a. Dispense 0.5 mL of antibiotic A to the appropriate tubes.
   b. Dispense 0.5 mL of antibiotic B to the appropriate tubes.
   c. The tubes now contain twice the desired concentration of the antibiotic solution.
   c. Dispense 1 mL of CSMHB to the growth control tube and the sterility control tube.
6. The prepared antibiotic concentration, growth control, and sterility control tubes can be capped and stored at –70°C for up to 6 months.

12.2.1.5.2.2   Preparation of Inoculum

1. Using a sterile loop or swab, transfer 3–5 colonies of the bacterial isolate to 5 mL of sterile CSMHB.
2. Incubate at 35°C until turbidity equivalent to a 0.5 McFarland standard is achieved (1.5×10^8 CFU/mL).
3. Make a 1:100 dilution of the standardized suspension. (Add 0.25 mL of standard suspension to 25 mL of CSMHB to achieve 1.5×10^6 CFU/mL.)
4. Mix by inverting five or six times, or gently vortex the suspension.
5. Using a sterile serologic pipette, add 1 mL of the organism suspension to each tube (7.5×10^5 CFU/mL; antibiotic concentration is diluted 1:2). Make sure that organisms are inoculated below the fluid meniscus without touching the tube sides with the pipette.
6. Prepare an inoculum count verification plate as follows:
   a. Add 0.1 mL from the growth control tube to 0.9 mL of sterile 0.85% saline (dilution 10^{-1}).
   b. Transfer 0.1 mL from dilution 10^{-1} to 0.9 mL of sterile 0.85% saline and vortex well (dilution 10^{-2}).
   c. Transfer 0.1 mL from dilution 10^{-2} to 0.9 mL of sterile 0.85% saline and vortex well (dilution 10^{-3}).
   d. Plate 0.1 mL of dilution 10^{-3} onto a blood agar plate and spread for quantitation by streaking in several directions with a sterile loop or by using a sterile bent glass rod to spread the inoculum evenly.

7. Incubate the tubes at 35°C ± 2°C for 16–20 h in an ambient air incubator.
8. Incubate the purity and inoculum verification plates at 35°C ± 2°C for 16–20 h in an ambient air incubator.

12.2.1.5.2.3   Reading and Recording the Results

1. Examine the growth control tube for organism viability. The growth control tube should show heavy turbidity.
2. Examine the purity plate, and verify that the culture is not mixed. If it is mixed, repeat the test.
3. Count the number of colonies on the inoculum verification plates. The number of colonies should be between 75 and 150.
4. Record growth or no growth for all the tubes on the worksheet as shown in Appendix 12.3.
5. Record the MIC results for antibiotic A.
6. Record the MIC results for antibiotic B.

12.2.1.5.3   Calculations

1. Calculate the FIC for each antibiotic as follows:

$$\text{FIC for antibiotic A} = \frac{\text{MIC of antibiotic A in combination}}{\text{MIC of antibiotic A alone}}$$

$$\text{FIC for antibiotic B} = \frac{\text{MIC of antibiotic B in combination}}{\text{MIC of antibiotic B alone}}$$

2. Calculate the summation of FIC (ΣFIC) index for each combination as follows:

$$\Sigma \text{FIC} = \text{FIC for antibiotic A} + \text{FIC for antibiotic B}$$

12.2.1.5.4   Interpretation

1. If acceptable quality control parameters are obtained, interpret and record each ΣFIC. Interpretation of the summation is as follows:
   Synergism = ΣFIC is ≤0.5.
   Antagonism = ΣFIC is >0.5 and ≤4.
   Indifference = ΣFIC is >4.
2. Report results in terms of the organism tested, single antibiotic MICs, and interpretation of the summation of the FIC index, that is, synergism, antagonism, or indifference.

12.2.1.6   Limitations

This technique is usually used in a research setting and is not standardized completely [1,2,5]. There are significant flaws in the methodology. First, it does not examine bactericidal activity. Second, the FIC index calculation assumes a linear dose–response curve for all antimicrobial agents. Because this method only provides all-or-none responses (growth or no growth), it is incapable of measuring the graded responses necessary to define dose–response curves. Third, it provides a static view of the antimicrobial interaction since the results are examined only at one time interval. Results obtained by the checkerboard method may disagree with time-kill methods because each method measures different parameters [1,2,5–9].

12.2.2 SYNERGY TESTING BY DISK DIFFUSION TESTING

12.2.2.1 Principle

Qualitative measurement of drug interaction can be performed using the disk diffusion method. The advantages of this technique are ease of performance in a clinical laboratory and utilization of commercially available antimicrobial-impregnated disks and media. This technique utilizes the same inoculum and Mueller-Hinton agar as routine Bauer-Kirby susceptibility testing. Disks impregnated with individual antimicrobial agents are placed at a distance equal to the sum of the zone radii of inhibition of drugs when tested separately. After overnight incubation, the interface of zone of inhibition is examined. Synergism shows an enhancement or bridging at or near the junction of the two zones of inhibition, or inhibition of growth only due to the combined effects of both antimicrobial agents. Truncation of zones near the junction of the two zones represents antagonism. An indifferent antimicrobial combination shows no change. Refer to Figure 12.1 for examples. Antagonism is best studied by this methodology [1,2,5].

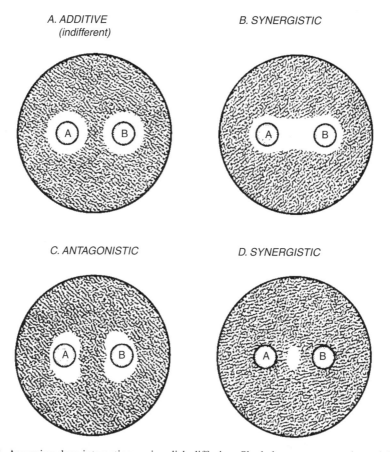

FIGURE 12.1 Assessing drug interactions using disk-diffusion. Shaded areas represent bacterial growth and clear areas represent zones of inhibition. (Adapted and reprinted with permission from Eliopoulos, G.M. and Moellering, R.C., Jr. *Antibiotics in Laboratory Medicine*, Lorain, V., Ed., Williams Wilkins, Baltimore, 1996, figure 9.10, p. 344.)

12.2.2.2 Specimen

Refer to section 12.2.1.2.

12.2.2.3 Materials

12.2.2.3.1 Media and Reagents

1. Mueller-Hinton agar medium
2. Sterile cation-supplemented Mueller-Hinton broth
3. Antimicrobial disks

12.2.2.3.2 Supplies

1. Sterile cotton-tipped swabs
2. Biohazard waste bag
3. 0.5 McFarland turbidity standard
4. 13 × 100 mm test tubes with snap caps
5. Test tube racks
6. Millimeter ruler
7. Sterile transfer pipette
8. Forceps
9. Inoculating loop or needle

12.2.2.3.3 Equipment

1. 35°C ± 2°C ambient-air incubator (or other growth conditions as required by some organisms)
2. Incandescent light
3. Vortex mixer

12.2.2.4 Quality Control

1. Choose the appropriate quality control strains depending on the antimicrobial being tested. The quality control strain should be susceptible to the antimicrobial agent being tested.
2. The following quality control strains are recommended:
   a. *E. coli* ATCC 25922.
   b. *P. aeruginosa* ATCC 27853.
   c. *S. aureus* ATCC 29213.
   d. *E. faecalis* ATCC 29212.
3. Quality control strains must be tested in parallel with the clinical isolate following the same procedure.
4. The zone measurements for a given antimicrobial for a specific quality control strain should be within limits published by Clinical and Laboratory Standards Institute (CLSI) (refer to the current M100 document).
5. Acceptable results:
   a. The growth medium supports the growth of control and test organisms.
   b. The zone measurements obtained for quality control strains should be within published limits for the individual antimicrobial agent.
   c. The culture is not mixed with contaminants. If it is mixed, repeat the test.
6. If unacceptable results are obtained, repeat the quality control testing. If unacceptable results are obtained when the test is repeated, inform a supervisor and determine the reason for failure. *Do not* report any patient results if the quality control results are unacceptable.

12.2.2.5 Procedure

1. Allow the agar and antimicrobial disks to warm to room temperature.
2. Inoculum preparation:
   a. Using a sterile loop or swab, transfer three to five colonies of the bacterial isolate to 5 mL of sterile CSMHB.
   b. Incubate at 35°C until a turbidity that is equivalent to a 0.5 McFarland standard is achieved (1.5×10^8 CFU/mL).
3. Inoculation of agar plate:
   a. Dip a sterile cotton-tipped swab into the inoculum within 15 min after adjusting the turbidity of the inoculum suspension, and rotate it several times.
   b. Remove excess inoculum by pressing the swab against the wall of the tube above the liquid.
   c. Streak the swab over the entire agar surface three times, rotating the plate approximately 60° each time to ensure even distribution of inoculum.
   d. Finally, swab the rim of the agar.
   e. Allow the inoculated plate to stand for 3–15 min before the application of the disks.
4. Application of the disks to inoculated agar plates:
   a. Using a sterile forceps, place disks separated by a distance equal to the sum of the zone of radii for each disk tested separately.
   b. Press down each disk to ensure complete contact with the agar surface.
   c. Do not move a disk once it has made contact with the agar surface.
5. Incubation:
   a. Incubate inoculated plates at 35°C ± 2°C for 16–18 h in an ambient air incubator.
   b. Invert plates (lids facing down), and do not stack more than five high.
6. Reading the plates:
   a. Examine plates for a confluent lawn of growth. Read the plates only if the growth is confluent or nearly confluent.
   b. Observe the interface of the zones of inhibition.

12.2.2.6 Interpretation

If the quality control is within limits, record the pattern of the zones of inhibition as follows (see Figure 12.1):

1. Indifference: Two independent circles
2. Synergism: Enhancement or bridging at or near the junction of the two zones of inhibition or inhibition of growth only due to the combined effects of both antibiotics A and B.
3. Antagonism: Truncation of zones is observed near the junction of the two zones.

12.2.2.7 Limitations

This methodology yields only qualitative information about the antimicrobial agent combination. Using this technique, it may be difficult to distinguish indifferent from synergistic interaction [1,2,5].

12.2.3 Time-Kill Curves

12.2.3.1 Background

The killing effect of an antimicrobial agent can be expressed as the rate of killing by a fixed concentration of drug under controlled conditions [1,4,10,11]. This rate is determined by measuring the number of viable bacteria at various time intervals. The resulting graphic depiction is known as a *time-kill curve*. Historically, time-kill curves have been used in the evaluation of new drugs. It is rarely used to guide chemotherapy in an individual patient. Both concentration-dependent and time-dependent bactericidal activities of antimicrobial agents can be studied using time-kill curves. Time-kill curves may be used to verify the presence of persisters, paradoxical effect, and tolerence [4]. They are also used to determine synergy between two or more antimicrobial agents. Several studies have shown that results obtained for synergy testing by the checkerboard method may differ from the time-kill method [6,8,9,12]. The reason for this discrepancy is that in the checkerboard methodology results are examined only at one time interval whereas killing curves measure changes over time. Time-kill curve results correlate best with cure in animal models. A steep negative slope of the curve indicates a faster rate of decline of survivors. The rate of decline of survivors at different concentrations of antimicrobial agent provides more information than the concentration at which 99.9% killing of the final inoculum occurs.

Because of the selection of resistant mutants, antimicrobial degradation, or unaffected bacterial cells, colony counts may increase after initial reduction in organism numbers [1,2,4,10]. The important aspect of this unexplained rebound effect is to isolate the survivors, determine the MIC, and make a determination whether a resistant clone has been selected as a result of selective pressure. Determination of whether the antimicrobial agent has been inactivated versus selection of resistant mutants may be determined by filter sterilization of the original antimicrobial containing broth and performance of MIC determinations of a known ATCC strain with a defined MIC value. If antibiotic degradation has occurred, the MIC value for the known ATCC strain will increase. If resistant subpopulations have been selected, the MIC of the survivors will be several-fold higher than the parent strain.

Various published protocols exist for this methodology including a CLSI protocol, but none have been standardized [4,10]. The protocol described here is a recommendation only.

12.2.3.2 Principle

Time-kill curves are used to study the efficacy of an antimicrobial agent to a particular bacterial isolate [1]. A standardized inoculum of the bacterial isolate is grown in the presence and absence of the antimicrobial agent. Viable cells are counted by performing serial dilutions on an aliquot removed at different time intervals. The results are plotted on semilog paper with the time intervals on the abscissa (x axis) and the number of survivors on the ordinate (y axis). Bactericidal activity can be determined from a time-kill curve if a greater than 3 $\log_{10}$-fold decrease in the number of survivors is noted. This is equivalent to 99.9% killing of the inoculum [1,10]. Time-kill curves can also be used to study drug interactions. Synergy is defined as a ≥ 2 $\log_{10}$(CFU/mL)-fold decrease by the combination compared with the most active single agent. Antagonism is defined as a ≥ 2 $\log_{10}$(CFU/mL)-fold increase by the combination compared with the most active single agent [1,10].

12.2.3.3 Specimen

Refer to section 12.2.1.2.

12.2.3.4 Materials

12.2.3.4.1 Media and Reagents

1. Cation-supplemented Mueller-Hinton broth
2. Trypticase soy agar with 5% sheep blood
3. Sterile 0.85% sodium chloride
4. Sterile stock antibiotic solutions (frozen)

12.2.3.4.2 Supplies

1. Sterile 75 × 12 mm and 17 × 100 mm capped tubes
2. Sterile polypropylene 50-mL screw-capped tubes
3. 0.5 McFarland turbidity standard
4. Sterile 1-, 5-, and 10-mL disposable pipettes
5. Pipette bulb or automatic pipette device
6. Sterile cotton-tipped swabs

12.2.3.4.3 Equipment

1. Vortex mixer
2. 100-μL adjustable micropipette with sterile tips
3. 1-μL and 10-μL calibrated loops
4. 35°C ± 2°C ambient-air incubator (or other growth conditions as required by some organisms)

12.2.3.5 Quality Control

1. Choose appropriate quality control strains depending on the antimicrobial being tested. The quality control strain should be susceptible to the antimicrobial agent being tested.
2. The following quality control strains are recommended:
   a. *E. coli* ATCC 25922
   b. *P. aeruginosa* ATCC 27853
   c. *S. aureus* ATCC 29213
   d. *E. faecalis* ATCC 29212
3. Quality control strains must be tested in parallel with the clinical isolate following the same procedure.
4. Growth control should show 3+ to 4+ turbidity.
5. Sterility control should show no growth.
6. Inoculum control should show 75–150 colonies with no contaminating organisms.
7. Acceptable results:
   a. The growth medium supports the growth of control and test organisms.
   b. MIC values obtained for quality control strains should be within published limits for the individual antimicrobial agent.
   c. Growth, inoculum, and sterility controls show appropriate results.
8. If unacceptable results are obtained, repeat the quality control testing. If unacceptable results are obtained when the test is repeated, inform a supervisor and determine the reason for failure. *Do not* report any patient results if the quality control results are unacceptable.

12.2.3.6 Procedure

1. Time-kill curve for determining bactericidal activity
   a. Preparation of antimicrobial agent concentrations:
      1) Determine the MIC of the antimicrobial agent for the test isolate.
      2) Test several concentrations of antimicrobial agent, usually multiples of the MIC, for example, 1×, 2×, and 4× the MIC.
      3) Determine the number and quantity of antimicrobial agents that will be needed.
      4) Calculate the volume of antimicrobial agent stock solution needed for the assay.
      5) Preparation of working antibiotic concentrations:
         a) Dispense 9.9 mL of CSMHB to sterile 50-mL tubes for each antimicrobial concentration to be tested.

      b) Add 100 μL of 100-fold-concentrated antimicrobial agent to achieve the final working concentration.

      c) Mix by using a vortex.

    6) Dispense 10 mL of CSMHB to the growth and sterility control tubes.

    7) Perform a limited broth macrodilution MIC for the quality control strain.

  b. Preparation of inoculum:

    1) Using a sterile loop or swab, transfer three to five colonies of the bacterial isolate to 5 mL of sterile CSMHB.

    2) Incubate at 35°C until a turbidity that is equivalent to a 0.5 McFarland standard is achieved (1.5×10^8 CFU/mL).

    3) Make a 1:100 dilution of a standardized suspension. (Add 0.1 mL of the standard suspension to 9.9 mL of CSMHB to achieve 1.5×10^6 CFU/mL.)

    4) Mix by inverting five or six times or gently vortex the suspension.

  c. Inoculation and incubation:

    1) Using a sterile serologic pipette, add 1 mL of organism suspension to each tube (7.5×10^5 CFU/mL). Make sure that organisms are inoculated below the fluid meniscus without touching the tube sides with the pipette.

    2) Mix gently by inverting several times.

    3) Remove 10 μL of the above suspension using a calibrated loop, and streak for isolation on a blood agar plate.

    4) Remove another 100-μL aliquot from each tube, and return the tubes to the 35°C ± 2°C incubator.

    5) Perform a 10-fold serial dilution from 10^{-1}–10^{-7} on the aliquot removed as follows:

      a) Take 7 tubes and label them from 1–7.

      b) Add 100 μL of saline to each tube.

      c) Remove a 100-μL aliquot, and add it to the tube marked as 1.

      d) Mix using a pipettor, aspirate 100 μL, and add it to the tube marked as 2.

      e) Repeat steps c and d.

      f) Remove 100 μL from tube number 7.

      g) Spot 10 μL each of the 10^{-2} to 10^{-7} dilutions (in duplicate) as shown in Figure 12.2 onto a single blood agar plate.

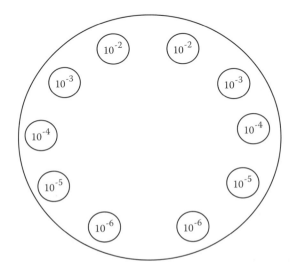

FIGURE 12.2 Spot inoculation of serial dilutions on agar plate for colony enumeration. (Adapted and reprinted with permission from Eliopoulos, G.M. and Moellering, R.C., Jr. in *Antibiotics in Laboratory Medicine*, Lorain, V., Ed., Williams Wilkins, Baltimore, 1996, figure 9.5, p. 339.)

6) Incubate the plates at 35°C for 48 h.

7) Repeat sampling (steps b–f) at 4, 6, 8, and 24 h.

d. Reading and recording the results:

1) Count viable colonies from those dilutions containing 5–50 CFU.

2) Multiply colony counts with the dilution factor to obtain CFU per milliliter.

3) Tabulate the results as CFU per milliliter (mean; y axis) versus time (x axis) on semilog paper (CFU per milliliter can be converted to $\log_{10}$ values, e.g., $\log_{10}$ 2.5×10^7 Å 7.4).

4) Determine the antimicrobial agent concentration that shows a 3 $\log_{10}$(CFU/mL)-fold decrease when compared with the growth control.

5) Determine the time when the 3 $\log_{10}$(CFU/mL)-fold decrease occurs when compared with the growth control. Refer to Appendix 12.5.

2. Time-kill curves for determining antimicrobial agent interactions.

a. Preparation of antimicrobial agent concentrations:

1) Determine the MIC of the antimicrobial agent for the test isolate.

2) Use the template as shown in Appendix 12.5 to determine the concentrations and number of tubes needed for this assay.

3) Calculate the volumes of individual antimicrobial agent stock solution needed for each organism tested.

4) Preparation of working antibiotic concentrations:

a) Dispense 9.8 mL of CSMHB to sterile 50-mL tubes for each antimicrobial concentration to be tested.

b) Add 100 μL of each 100-fold-concentrated antimicrobial agent to achieve the final working concentration.

c) Mix by using a vortex.

5) Dispense 10 mL of CSMHB to the growth and sterility control tubes.

6) Perform a limited broth macrodilution MIC for the quality control strain.

b. Preparation of inoculum:

1) Using a sterile loop or swab, transfer three to five colonies of the bacterial isolate to 5 mL of sterile CSMHB.

2) Incubate at 35°C until turbidity equivalent to a 0.5 McFarland standard is achieved (1.5×10^8 CFU/mL).

3) Make a 1:100 dilution of standardized suspension. (Add 0.1 mL of standard suspension to 9.9 mL of CSMHB to achieve 1.5×10^6 CFU/mL.)

4) Mix by inverting five or six times, or gently vortex the suspension.

c. Inoculation and incubation.

1) Using a sterile serologic pipette, add 1 mL of the organism suspension to each tube (7.5×10^5 CFU/mL). Make sure that organisms are inoculated below the fluid meniscus without touching the tube sides with the pipette.

2) Mix gently by inverting several times.

3) Remove 10 μL of the above suspension using a calibrated loop and streak for isolation on a blood agar plate.

4) Remove another 100-μL aliquot from each tube and return the tubes to the 35°C ± 2°C incubator.

5) Perform 10-fold serial dilutions from 10^{-1} to 10^{-7} on the aliquot removed as follows:

a) Label seven tubes as 1–7.

b) Add 100 μL of saline to each tube.

c) Remove a 100-μL aliquot, and add it to the tube marked as 1.

d) Mix using a pipettor, aspirate 100 μL, and add it to the tube marked as 2.

e) Repeat steps c and d.

f) Remove 100 μL from tube number 7.

      g) Spot 10 μL each of the 10^{-2} to 10^{-7} dilutions (in duplicate) as shown in Appendix 12.5 onto a single blood agar plate.

    6) Incubate the plates at 35°C for 48 h.

    7) Repeat sampling (steps b–f) at 4, 6, 8, and 24 h.

  d. Reading and recording the results:

    1) Count viable colonies from those dilutions containing 5–50 CFU.

    2) Multiply the colony counts with the dilution factor to obtain CFU per milliliter.

    3) Tabulate results as CFU per milliliter (mean; y axis) versus time (x axis) on semilog paper (CFU milliliter can be converted to $\log_{10}$ values, for example, $\log_{10} 2.5 \times 10^7$ Å 7.4).

    4) Determine the antimicrobial agent combination that shows a 2 $\log_{10}$ (CFU/mL)-fold decrease (synergy) and increase (antagonism) when compared with the most active single agent.

    5) Determine the time at which the 2 $\log_{10}$ (CFU/mL)-fold decrease (synergy) and increase (antagonism) occurs when compared with the most active single agent.

12.2.3.7 Interpretation

1. Time-kill curve for determining bactericidal activity in the presence of an antimicrobial agent.

$$\text{Bactericidal activity absent} = <3 \log_{10} \text{ (CFU/mL) decrease}$$

2. Time-kill curve for determining antimicrobial interactions by a combination relative to the most active single antimicrobial agent.

$$\text{Antagonism} = \geq 2 \log_{10} \text{ (CFU/mL) increase}$$

12.2.3.8 Limitations

This technique is cumbersome and laborious, and therefore only a few drug combination concentrations can be effectively tested. The concentrations of the antimicrobial agent combination tested should be carefully planned and should be those that are achievable at the infected site. Based on the time-kill curve, if one suspects inactivation of antimicrobial agent or selection of resistant mutants, then appropriate testing must be performed to confirm this. For antimicrobial agents that exhibit concentration-dependent killing, organisms may be killed faster at concentrations greater than the MIC, requiring sampling at shorter time intervals [1,2,4,10].

12.2.4 POPULATION ANALYSIS

12.2.4.1 Principle

Population analysis is employed to determine the mechanism of phenotypic resistance and bactericidal activity of a given bacterial isolate. A checkerboard is created with serial dilutions of inoculum on the ordinate (y axis) and serial dilutions of the antimicrobial agent on the abscissa (x axis). A pour-plate agar procedure is performed, and colonies are counted after incubation. Results are tabulated as CFU per milliliter versus concentration of antimicrobial agent. If the isolate expresses homogeneous resistance, then a steep decline in the number of survivors will be noted and no growth will be seen at a concentration above the MIC. If the test isolate consists of a heterogeneous population, then a subpopulation of survivors will be seen at increasing concentrations of antimicrobial agent [13,14]. Similar to time-kill curves, an antimicrobial is said to have bactericidal activity if a ≥ 3 $\log_{10}$(CFU/mL)-fold decrease at a given antimicrobial concentration is obtained when compared with counts obtained on plates without antibiotic.

12.2.4.2 Specimen

Refer to section 12.2.1.2.

12.2.4.3 Materials

12.2.4.3.1 Media and Reagents
   a. Cation-supplemented Mueller-Hinton broth
   b. Cation-supplemented Mueller-Hinton agar
   c. Brain–heart infusion (BHI) broth
   d. Trypticase soy agar with 5% sheep blood
   e. Sterile 0.85% sodium chloride
   f. Sterile stock antibiotic solutions (frozen)

12.2.4.3.2 Supplies
   a. Sterile 75×12 mm and 17×100 mm capped tubes
   b. Sterile polypropylene 50-mL screw-capped tubes
   c. Sterile Erlenmeyer flasks
   d. Sterile 100-mm petri dishes
   e. 0.5 McFarland turbidity standard
   f. Sterile 1-, 5-, and 10-mL disposable pipettes
   g. Pipette bulb or automatic pipette device
   h. Sterile cotton-tipped swabs
   i. Semilog paper

12.2.4.3.3 Equipment
   a. Vortex mixer
   b. Orbital shaker incubator, $35°C \pm 2°C$
   c. Spectrophotometer with appropriate filters
   d. $35°C \pm 2°C$ ambient-air incubator (or other growth conditions as required by some organisms)

12.2.4.4 Quality Control

Refer to section 12.2.3.4.

12.2.4.5 Procedure

12.2.4.5.1 Preparation of Inoculum

1. Grow the isolates in Brain Heart Infusion (BHI) broth and incubate overnight in an orbital shaker at 35°C.
2. Adjust the turbidity with fresh BHI broth until it is equivalent to a 0.5 McFarland standard.
3. Return the flasks to the orbital shaker, and incubate further at 35°C until the culture is grown to an absorbance of 0.5–0.55 optical density (OD) units at 620 nm.

4. Prepare serial dilutions from 10^{-1} to 10^{-8} of the inoculum as follows:
   a. Assemble eight 50-mL polypropylene tubes.
   b. Label the tubes from 1–8
   c. Using a 25-mL disposable pipette, dispense 18 mL of sterile saline in each tube.
   d. Add 2 mL of inoculum to tube 1.
   e. Vortex.
   f. Using a sterile disposable pipette, transfer 2 mL from tube 1 to tube 2.
   g. Vortex.
   h. Repeat steps f and g to dilute from tube 2 to tube 8.
   i. Discard 2 mL from tube 8 (final volume in each tube is 18 mL).

12.2.4.5.2 Preparation of Antimicrobial Dilutions in Melted Agar

1. Assemble 13 50-mL polypropylene tubes for each culture dilution to be tested.
2. Label the tubes with twofold increasing concentrations of the antibiotic.
3. Place the tubes in a test tube rack.
4. Place the rack in a water bath at 50°C.
5. Using a 25-mL sterile disposable pipette, dispense 14 mL of melted BHI agar cooled to 50°C into all the tubes except tube 2 (64 µg/mL).
6. Dispense 28 mL of melted BHI agar to tube 2 (64 µg/mL).
7. Add 1.9 mL of prepared antibiotic stock solution (1,028 µg/mL) to the tube marked 128 µg/mL.
8. Add 3.8 mL of prepared antibiotic stock solution to the tube marked 64 µg/mL.
9. Vortex.
10. Using a 25-mL sterile disposable pipette, transfer 14 mL of melted agar from tube 2 (64 µg/mL) into tube 3 (32 µg/mL).
11. Vortex.
12. Repeat steps 10–11 to dilute serially from tube 3 to tube 12.
13. Discard 14 mL of melted agar from tube 12.
14. The final concentrations of antimicrobial agent in this series will be from 128 µg/mL to 0.06 µg/mL after the addition of the inoculum.

12.2.4.5.3 Inoculation and Incubation

1. With the agar still melted, add 1 mL of the culture from each serial dilution to each tube in the twofold increasing antimicrobial concentration series.
2. Mix by either gently inverting the tube or by drawing solution back and forth into the pipette six to eight times without causing air bubbles or splashes.
3. Pour the mixture into 100-mm empty sterile petri dishes.
4. Allow the agar to solidify at room temperature.
5. Incubate plates at 35°C for 48 h.

12.2.4.5.4 Reading and Recording the Results

1. After incubation, count the number of colonies at each concentration.
2. Tabulate the results as CFU per milliliter versus concentration of antimicrobial agent on semilog graph paper.
3. Determine the antimicrobial agent concentration that shows a [3 $\log_{10}$ (CFU/mL0]-fold decrease when compared with the growth control.
4. Determine the slope of the curve if the mechanism of phenotypic resistance is being elucidated.

12.2.4.6 Interpretation

1. Bactericidal activity at a given antimicrobial concentration relative to the control.

$$\text{Bactericidal activity} = \geq 3\log_{10}\text{CFU/mL decrease}$$

$$\text{Bactericidal activity} = < 3\log_{10}\text{CFU/mL decrease}$$

2. Expression of phenotypic resistance.
   a. Homogeneous: A steep negative slope
   b. Heterogeneous: A gradual slope indicating the presence of a subpopulation at higher concentration of the antibiotic

12.2.4.7 Limitations

The limitations of this assay are similar to those noted for time-kill curves.

APPENDIX 12.1 — WORKSHEET TEMPLATE FOR BROTH MICRODILUTION CHECKERBOARD PANEL

	1	2	3	4	5	6	7	8	9	10	11	12
A	Growth control	$\frac{1}{32}$ MIC	$\frac{1}{16}$ MIC	$\frac{1}{8}$ MIC	$\frac{1}{4}$ MIC	$\frac{1}{2}$ MIC	Enter MIC for antibiotic A	2× MIC	4× MIC	8× MIC	16× MIC	32× MIC
B	$\frac{1}{8}$ MIC for antibiotic B											
C	$\frac{1}{4}$ MIC for antibiotic B											
D	$\frac{1}{2}$ MIC for antibiotic B											
E	Enter MIC for antibiotic B											
F	2× MIC for antibiotic B											
G	4× MIC for antibiotic B											
H	8× MIC for antibiotic B											Sterility control

APPENDIX 12.2 — EXAMPLE OF A BROTH MICRODILUTION CHECKERBOARD PANEL

	1	2	3	4	5	6	7	8	9	10	11	12
A	GC	A 0.5	A 1	A 2	A 4	A 8	A 16	A 32	A 64	A 128	A 256	A 512
B	B1	A 0.5 + B1	A 1 + B 1	A 2 + B 1	A 4 + B 1	A 8 + B 1	A 16 + B 1	A 32 + B 1	A 64 + B 1	A 128 + B 1	A 256 + B 1	A 512 + B 1
C	B2	A 0.5 + B2	A 1 + B 2	A 2 + B 2	A 4 + B 2	A 8 + B 2	A 16 + B 2	A 32 + B 2	A 64 + B 2	A 128 + B 2	A 256 + B 2	A 512 + B 2
D	B4	A 0.5 + B4	A 1 + B 4	A 2 + B 4	A 4 + B 4	A 8 + B 4	A 16 + B 4	A 32 + B 4	A 64 + B 4	A 128 + B 4	A 256 + B 4	A 512 + B 4
E	B8	A 0.5 + B8	A 1 + B 8	A 2 + B 8	A 4 + B 8	A 8 + B 8	A 16 + B 8	A 32 + B 8	A 64 + B 8	A 128 + B 8	A 256 + B 8	A 512 + B 8
F	B16	A 0.5 + B16	A 1 + B 16	A 2 + B 16	A 4 + B 16	A 8 + B 16	A 16 + B 16	A 32 + B 16	A 64 + B 16	A 128 + B 16	A 256 + B 16	A 512 + B 16
G	B32	A 0.5 + B32	A 1 + B 32	A 2 + B 32	A 4 + B 32	A 8 + B 32	A 16 + B 32	A 32 + B 32	A 64 + B 32	A 128 + B 32	A 256 + B 32	A 512 + B 32
H	B64	A 0.5 + B64	A 1 + B 64	A 2 + B 64	A 4 + B 64	A 8 + B 64	A 16 + B 64	A 32 + B 64	A 64 + B 64	A 128 + B 64	A 256 + B 64	BC

(Adapted and reprinted with permission from Moody, J.A. Synergism testing: Broth microdilution checkerboard and broth macrodilution methods, in *Clinical Procedures Handbook*, Isenberg, H.D., Ed., ASM Press, Washington, DC, 1992, Appendix 3, p. 5.18.16.)

APPENDIX 12.3 — WORKSHEET TEMPLATE FOR BROTH MACRODILUTION LIMITED-SERIES CHECKERBOARD FORMAT

		DRUG A				
		1/8 MIC	¼ MIC	½ MIC	MIC	2 X MIC
DRUG B	1/8 MIC	SYN (1/8 MIC A+ 1/8 MIC B)				ANT (2 MIC A+ 1/8 MIC B)
	¼ MIC		SYN (1/4 MIC A+ 1/4 MIC B)			ANT (2 MIC A+ 1/4 MIC B)
	½ MIC			SYN (1/2 MIC A+ 1/2 MIC B)		ANT (2 MIC A+ 1/2 MIC B)
	MIC					ANT (2 MIC A+ MIC B)
	2 X MIC	ANT (1/8 MIC A+ 2 MIC B)	ANT (1/4 MIC A+ 2 MIC B)	ANT (1/2 MIC A+ 2 MIC B)	ANT (MIC A+ 2 MIC B)	

The concentrations in shaded boxes are tested. Concentrations designated as SYN and ANT are tested for synergism and antagonism, respectively. (Adapted and reprinted with permission from Moody, J.A. Synergism testing: Broth microdilution checkerboard and broth macrodilution methods, in *Clinical Procedures Handbook*, Isenberg, H.D., Ed., ASM Press, Washington, DC, 1992, Appendix 8, p. 5.18.19.)

APPENDIX 12.4 — EXAMPLE OF TIME-KILL CURVE SHOWING
SYNERGISM AND ANTAGONISM

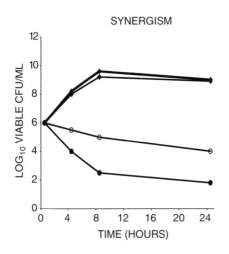 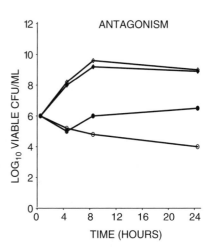

Symbols: ◇, growth control; ◆, agent A; ○, agent B; ●, agent A+B. (Adapted and reprinted with permission from Eliopoulos, G.M. and Moellering, R.C., Jr. Antimicrobial combinations, in *Antibiotics in Laboratory Medicine*, Lorain, V., Ed., Williams Wilkins, Baltimore, 1996, figure 9.6, p. 340.)

APPENDIX 12.5 — RESULTS OF CHECKERBOARD REPRESENTED AS ISOBOLOGRAMS

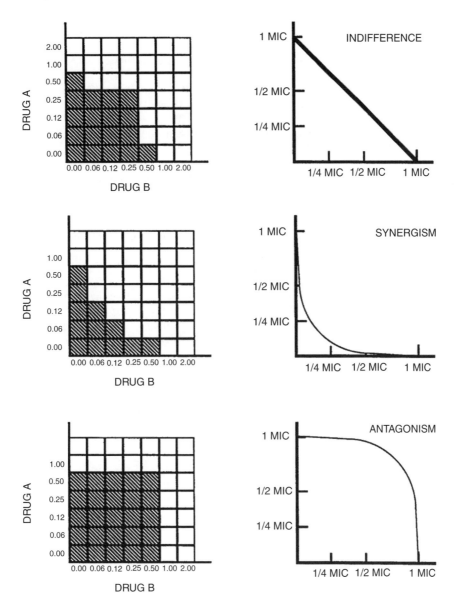

(Adapted and reprinted with permission from Eliopoulos, G.M. and Moellering, R.C., Jr. Antimicrobial combinations, in *Antibiotics in Laboratory Medicine*, Lorain, V., Ed., Williams Wilkins, Baltimore, 1996, figure 9.2, p. 335.)

REFERENCES

1. Eliopoulos, G.M. and Moellering, R.C., Jr. Antimicrobial combinations, in *Antibiotics in Laboratory Medicine*, Lorain, V., Ed., Williams Wilkins Co., Baltimore, 1996, pp. 330–396.

2. Eliopoulos, G.M. and Eliopoulos, C.T. Antibiotic combinations: Should they be tested? *Clin. Microbiol. Rev.*, 1, 139–156, 1988.

3. King, T.C., Schlessinger, D., and Krogstad, D.J. The assement of antimicrobial combinations, *Rev. Infect. Dis.*, 3, 627–631, 1981.

4. National Committee for Clinical Laboratory Standards. Methods for determining bactericidal activity of antimicrobial agents, approved guideline, M26-A, vol. 19, no. 18, National Committee for Clinical Laboratory Standards, Villanova, PA, 1999, 1–30.

5. Moody, J.A. Synergism testing: Broth microdilution checkerboard and broth macrodilution methods, in *Clinical Procedures Handbook*, Isenberg, H.D., Ed., ASM Press, Washington, DC, 1992, pp. 5.18.1–5.18.28.

6. Norden, C.W., Wentzel, H., Keleti, E. Comparison of techniques for measurement of *in vitro* antibiotic synergism, *J. Infect. Dis.*, 140, 629–633, 1979.

7. Eliopoulos, G.M. and Moellering, R.C., Jr. Antibiotic synergism and antimicrobial combinations in clinical infections, *Rev. Infect. Dis.*, 4, 282–293, 1982.

8. Greenwood, D. Correlations between methods for the measurement of antibiotic synergy, *J. Infect. Dis.*, 143, 757, 1981.

9. Moellering, R.C., Jr. Antimicrobial synergism—An elusive concept, *J. Infect. Dis.*, 140, 639–641, 1979.

10. Knapp, C. and Moody, J.A. Tests to assess bactericidial activity, in *Clinical Procedures Handbook*, Isenberg, H.D., Ed., ASM Press, Washington, DC, 1992, pp. 5.16.1–5.16.33.

11. Berenbaum, M.C. Synergy assessment with growth curves, *J. Infect. Dis.*, 150, 304, 1984.

12. Ryan, R.W. and Tilton, R.C. Methological variation in antibiotic synergy tests against enterococci, *J. Clin. Microbiol.*, 13, 73–75, 1981.

13. Hartman, B.J. and Tomasz, A. Expression of methicillin resistance in heterogeneous strains of *Staphylococcus aureus*, *Antimicrob. Agents Chemother.*, 28, 85–92, 1986.

14. Schwaaalbe, R.S., Ritz, W.J., Verma, P.R., Barranco, E.A., and Gilligan, P.H. Selection of Varicomycin resistance in clinical isolates of *Staphyloccus hemolyhcus*. *J. Infect. Dis.* 161, 45–51, 1990.

13 Serum Bactericidal Testing

Harriette Nadler and Michael Dowzicky

CONTENTS

13.1 INTRODUCTION

A procedure for determining serum inhibitory titers (SITs) was developed by Schlichter and MacLean to provide guidance for the treatment of certain serious bacterial infections, such as endocarditis [1]. As more became known about the pharmacodynamic requirements (effect of drug against infecting organism) for successful treatment of endocarditis (*bactericidal* rather than *bacteriostatic* activity), the test procedure was modified by Fisher to enable determination of bactericidal end points, hence, the serum bactericidal titer (SBT) test [2].

There are very few clinical situations warranting conducting a SBT. Routine susceptibility tests, such as the minimum inhibitory concentration (MIC) test, are most often adequate in guiding therapy since the patient's success depends largely on the patient's own defense mechanisms that ultimately kill and eradicate infecting pathogens reduced in number by antibiotic agents. However, in certain clinical circumstances where host defenses are compromised or sites are difficult to penetrate and bactericidal activity is required, it may be necessary to make a quantitative assessment of this effect. Bactericidal antibiotics most often tested have included the β-lactam agents and aminoglycosides. Quinolones, glycopeptides, streptogramins, and glycylcyclines, may also be assayed for bactericidal activity. The antimicrobic–organism combination most frequently assayed has been staphylococci and β-lactam agents because of lack of reproducibility and hence often artificially diminished killing observed with such assays [3]. It is not advisable to conduct an SBT on fastidious microorganisms, that is, isolates that will not grow in Mueller-Hinton broth with 24-h incubation.

When precise assessments of bactericidal activity are needed, the individual pharmacokinetics of the patient must be addressed (the patient's absorption and elimination of the antibiotic and the binding of the drug to serum proteins). The SBT test uniquely incorporates both pharmacodynamic (intrinsic drug activity) and pharmacokinetic therapeutic considerations. The SBT test measures the interaction of pathogen, drug(s), and patient. This is most important when assaying a highly serum protein–bound drug, for example, nafcillin or ceftriaxone. The SBT also determines the effect of interactions with other drugs administered simultaneously with the antibiotic or when the dosing regimen is altered.

The SBT is a variation of the broth dilution MIC test and is intended only for aerobic organisms that grow well after overnight incubation in cation-adjusted Mueller-Hinton broth (CAMHB). Rather than an antibiotic solution, samples of the patient's serum taken at the beginning (trough) and at the end (peak) of the dosing interval are diluted serially in twofold dilutions. After inoculation of the patient's organism and incubation at 35°C, tubes with no visible growth are subcultured for colony counts. The SIT is useful to guide selection of samples for subculture. The SBT may then be defined as the greatest dilution of the patient's serum that kills ≥99.9%, that is, ≥3 log_{10} (CFU/mL), of the inoculum. For this reason, the *interim inoculum size* used to inoculate the serum dilutions may be estimated by comparison of actively growing cultures with the 0.5 McFarland turbidity standard. However, the *final inoculum size* must be confirmed by a colony count for interpretation of killing end points.

Bactericidal activity determined by SBTs correlates with estimates based on minimum bactericidal concentrations (MBCs) assessed in conjunction with drug assays in blood provided that the SBTs and MBCs were determined in a physiological diluent such as CAMHB [4]. The SBT is more convenient to conduct than the two other procedures and has the additional capability of measuring the impact of drug interactions.

Determination of bactericidal activity reflects the intrinsic activity of the specific antimicrobial and microorganism being studied, but also depends on the procedures and test conditions used. Both SBTs and MBCs are methodologically dependent. Results obtained may vary with inoculum size, growth phase of the inoculum, choice of medium, volume of broth subcultured for colony counts, and extent of physical contact between the organism and drug [5]. SBTs may also vary with the accuracy of patient sample collection.

The two test conditions with the most impact on end points and interpretations include extent of contact between organisms and drug within the test system as well as the inoculum size and proportion of rapidly growing cells within the inoculum. Splashing of organisms and adherence to the test tube surface above the meniscus may lead to bacterial escape from drug action and hence invalid test results. Adherence may be minimized by the use of acid-washed borosilicate test tubes, rather than polypropylene plastic tubes. Optimal bactericidal activity of most antibiotics can be achieved with mid-logarithmic phase (rapidly growing), rather than stationary phase (slowly growing), cultures (Figure 13.1).

Mid-logarithmic phase inocula are optimally prepared in a flask, beaker, or bottle, and incubated in a shaker-incubator for up to 6 h for staphylococci and <6 h for gram-negative rods. It is equally important that final inocula contain the correct inoculum size both in terms of the concentration of

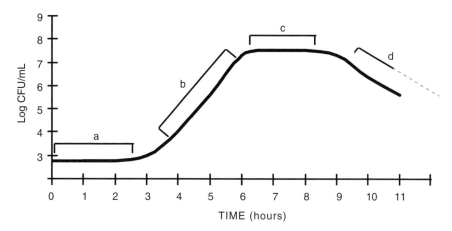

FIGURE 13.1 Bacterial growth curve. a) Lag Phase; b) Logarithmic Phase; c) Stationary Phase; d) Death Phase. Source: Clinical and Laboratory Standards Institute, M26-A, pg. 4, 1999

organisms per milliliter of broth and the absolute number of organisms in the test system to permit expression of resistance mechanisms or selection of mutants.

Results of both SBTs and MBCs are also subject to the influence of biological phenomena characteristic of certain antimicrobic–organism combinations tested such as the laboratory-induced tolerance of organisms to bactericidal activity of β-lactam agents (reduction in rapidity and magnitude of bactericidal activity of penicillins or cephalsporins) or are dependent on test conditions used (laboratory-induced resistance development during conduct of the test). Variability in SBT results can be minimized if a standardized methodology [6,7] is consistently followed, and results may be more relevant to the situation of human infection if a physiologic diluent with at least 50% serum supplement is used.

The use of human serum may, however, be problematic because of the presence of complement and other antibiotic-neutralizing activity that may negatively affect organism survival. Pooled human serum may offer advantages over use of serum from a single donor. These challenges may be overcome by the use of an ultrafiltrate of the patient's serum [7]. Ultrafiltration separates the free antimicrobial agent present and allows the use of CAMHB as the diluent.

Although the SBT procedure has been used for almost 50 years, standardization efforts have been made only in the last decade — 1992 and 1999 — by the Clinical and Laboratory Standards Institute (CLSI) formerly NCCLS [6,7]. Differences in test methodology from laboratory to laboratory have led to poor reproducibility and difficult result interpretation. Furthermore, a drug's capability in eradicating bacteria, when considered alone, has not been adequately predictive of successful treatment of patients. Other drug attributes beyond intrinsic bactericidal activity such as the postantibiotic effect (growth inhibitory effects determined after drug removal) and growth inhibitory effects at sub-MIC concentrations may also influence bacteriologic response. Difficulties in SBT interpretation have been further compounded by the effect of serious underlying diseases, the degree of heart or major organ failure, and the intensity of medical management on the outcome of infection treatment. Hence the clinical value of the SBT has been controversial.

Major indications for performing the SBT include endocarditis, osteomyelitis, or infections in seriously immunocompromised patients [7–10]. The SBT allows an estimate of bactericidal activity at only two specified time points, the beginning and the end of the dosing interval. If additional information is desirable, especially for newly introduced antibiotics, research parameters, such as the area-under-the-bactericidal-titer-curve and serum bactericidal rate, may also be determined [6,7]. These parameters will further describe the rapidity, magnitude, and duration of bactericidal activity, and should only be conducted by experienced laboratory personnel having special expertise in medical microbiology.

13.2 APPROPRIATE TIMING, COLLECTION, AND HANDLING OF SERUM SPECIMENS

It is of great value to have an initial consultation with the ordering physician at the time of the SBT order and determine its clinical value and potential limitations. Inherent in the design of the SBT is the use of the patient's serum to represent the physiologic concentration of the antimicrobial agent being tested. The details on the collection and handling of serum specimens must be followed for the SBT to be of any clinical value.

13.2.1 TIMING OF SERUM SPECIMENS

Generally, *peak* (maximal theoretical drug concentration) and *trough* (lowest theoretical drug concentration) samples are obtained and assayed for the serum bactericidal test. The optimal timing of samples for obtaining a peak level varies by drug and route of administration; therefore, the product labeling should be consulted to select the optimal sampling times [11]. A general guideline for obtaining a peak serum sample is as follows:

- Sixty minutes after completion of a 30-min intravenous infusion.
- Sixty minutes after giving an intramuscular dose.
- Ninety minutes after an oral dose [6,7,12,13].
- If more than one antibiotic is being used, then 60 min after giving the second antibiotic [7].

This timing is used to ensure that peak levels are obtained approximately 30–60 min after the antimicrobial agent has had a chance to be absorbed and/or distributed. The trough level is obtained immediately before the next dose.

13.2.2 COLLECTION AND HANDLING OF SPECIMENS

To avoid possible contamination from the skin, collect the serum sample aseptically. Because of the short half-lives of some antimicrobial agents, the timing of the collection is crucial, and the time the antimicrobial agent was given to the patient should be confirmed and documented. The following steps to ensure this process are recommended:

- Record the time that the previous dose was given.
- Record the time that the current dose was given or will be given.
- Record the duration of the infusion when obtaining peak levels for IV administered agents.

To ensure proper collection, the above information must be recorded on the laboratory requisition slip or entered into the computerized order process system by the appropriate persons (medications nurse or phlebotomist) [6,7].

After the specimen has been collected the following guidelines are recommended:

- The serum must be separated rapidly from the red blood cells to avoid hemolysis and subsequent interference with the assay.
- If a delay of more than 2 h in performing the SBT is expected, the serum collected from the specimen must be frozen.
- When submitting the serum sample for SBT testing to a reference laboratory, it must be placed in a sterile *plastic* vial and shipped in a frozen state on dry ice.

Of special note is the need for strict adherence to the pharmaceutical manufacturer's guidelines [11] for the maximum storage periods of the antibiotic in frozen human serum prior to testing to avoid degradation of the drug [5–7].

13.3 PROCEDURES

13.3.1 Isolate Preparation for Storage and Subsequent Retrieval Prior to SBT Test

- The patient's isolate must be stored frozen prior to the performance of the SBT procedure. The isolate may be kept frozen at −70°C in trypticase soy broth or in a glycerol (5–10%) suspension of a subculture from a trypticase soy agar plate or slant.
- It is necessary to subculture the isolate three times before testing to ensure that the organism has an optimal growth and metabolic status before performing the drug exposure [7].

13.3.2 Serum Dilution Procedure

The SBT method is a variation of the MIC broth dilution test, and many of the precautions used to control the variables in the MIC test are applicable to the serum dilution procedure (see Chapter 4, Macro- and Microdilution Methods of Antimicrobial Susceptibility Testing).

13.3.2.1 Broth Medium

13.3.2.1.1 Broth and Supplements

- Many different broths have been used as diluents in the SBT test, that is, trypticase soy or brain–heart infusion, but cation adjusted Mueller-Hinto broth (CAMHB) is the most commonly used for isolates that do not have special growth requirements [14]. One advantage of CAMHB is that the Ca^{2+} and Mg^{2+} will approximate that found in serum, thereby facilitating closer approximation of the pH and osmolality of the serum. In addition, CAMHB conforms to the CLSI-recommended MIC procedure, especially for the testing of aminoglycosides against *Pseudomonas aeruginosa* and of tetracyclines versus all bacteria [15]. The use of salt-containing diluents must be avoided *when* testing staphylococci and β-lactam agents.
- For highly protein-bound drugs, for example, ceftriaxone and nafcillin, it is advisable that CAMHB combined with pooled human serum (at least a 1:1 ratio) be used as the diluent in the SBT [6,7,16]. Some of the key advantages of using human serum as part of the diluent are that it mimics more closely the physiological environment in the bloodstream of humans and allows one to assess the role of serum protein binding in the final results. It should be noted that for antimicrobial agents that are known to have relatively little protein binding (<90%, e.g., gentamicin and vancomycin), CAMHB alone can be used as the diluent [6,7,17,18].
- An ultrafiltrate of the patient's own serum (instead of pooled human serum) may also be used as a diluent but the process of ultrafiltration may not be practical in a small laboratory. Ultrafiltration separates the free antimicrobial agent present, avoids the interfering substances, that is, complement, that may be in pooled serum, and allows the use of CAMHB as the diluent.

13.3.2.1.2 Diluent Monitoring

The chemical and performance characteristics of both the CAMHB and human serum must be monitored:

- The pH of each batch of CAMHB should be checked when the medium is prepared; the pH should be between 7.2 and 7.4.
- MIC and MBC characteristics using the CAMHB alone and the combination of CAMHB and pooled human serum should be evaluated periodically (monthly) with a standard set of quality control microorganisms and with an antibiotic from each major class. Select an ATCC quality control organism that most closely resembles the species of the test organism [6,7,14].

  Pooled human serum can be obtained from commercial sources or from volunteers (outdated blood bank blood). This pooled human serum must have its quality confirmed like any other reagent in the clinical microbiology laboratory. It is critical to determine the presence of β-lactamase activity in the pooled human serum because these enzymes will neutralize some antimicrobial agents, for example, β-lactam agents [6,7].

- The serum from volunteers needs to be screened for hepatitis B virus antigen and for antibodies to HIV-1.
- The pooled human serum from either source (commercial preparation or volunteers) may be heated to 56°C for 1 h upon receipt. This inactivates any HIV, hepatitis B antigen, and complement that may be present and also ensures the safety of the laboratory staff performing the SBT test.
- The serum should then be adjusted with 0.1 mol/L NaOH or 0.1 mol/L HCl to a pH of 7.2 to 7.4. After this pH adjustment, the serum should be run through a 0.80-μm filter and a 0.22-μm filter.

Before using it, the pooled human serum should be tested for the presence of β-lactamase activity by using a cefinase disk (Becton Dickinson, Cockeysville, MD); drop serum on a test strip or disk and wait for a color change by 30 min. In addition, the serum should be screened for antimicrobial activity by putting 20 μL of the pooled human serum on blank paper disks, placing the disks onto nutrient agar that has been seeded with *Bacillus subtilis* ATCC 6633, and looking for zones of inhibition after incubation at 35°C for 24 h.

13.3.2.2 Dilution Procedure

Serum bactericidal titers can be determined by either:

- Macrodilution method (1–2 mL in each test tube).
- Microdilution method (100 μl in each microliter well).

In this chapter as in Chapter 4, we focus on the broth macrodilution SBT procedure.

- The macrodilution method allows for a larger volume of inoculum to be delivered, i.e., 10-fold more (absolute numbers of) microorganisms in each tube as compared with each tray well (microdilution method), and greater surface area for growth. This provides optimal growth and testing conditions to measure killing activity of most antibiotics [19–21].
- The broth microdilution method has been found by some workers to be more reproducible than the broth macrodilution method for SBT testing, especially for staphylococci tested against β-lactam agents; however, it can be difficult to determine 99.9% killing of the final inoculum because of the low absolute number of microorganisms in each tray well. Close adherence to the details of the broth macrodilution method can increase the reproducibility of the test method [22,23].

13.3.2.2.1 Macrodilution Method

The macrodilution method should be performed in sterile 13×100 mm acid-treated borosilicate glass test tubes. Bacteria adhere to the sides of plastic tubes. The procedure is as follows (Figure 13.2):

- Add 1.0 mL of pooled human serum:CAMHB (1:1 ratio) to tubes 2 through 10.
- Add 1.0 mL of the patient's serum to each of the first two tubes.
- Make serial twofold dilutions of the serum from tubes 2 through 9 with a calibrated semiautomatic pipette, leaving a volume of 1.0 mL in each tube.
- Add 1.0 mL of CAMHB to each tube to yield a final volume of 2.0 mL in each tube.
- Tube 10 is a growth control tube.

Mix each transfer by flushing the pipette two or three times without splashing the sides of the tubes or creating air bubbles, and discarding the excess 1.0 mL in the pipette from the tube 9 transfer. There is no need to change pipette tips during the serial transfer because the concentration is being decreased during serial dilution and the *between-sample* contamination should be very small.

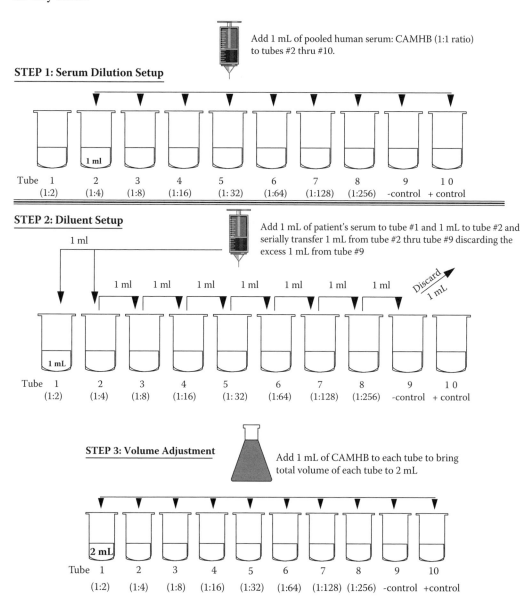

FIGURE 13.2 General serum bactericidal activity setup (macrodilution method).

13.3.3 PREPARATION OF INOCULUM

The patient's isolate is used to prepare the inoculum. It is critical that proper preparation of the standardized inoculum be achieved because variations in the density of the inoculum may affect the end points by several-fold. The procedure is as follows (see Figure 13.3):

STEP 1: Inoculum Setup

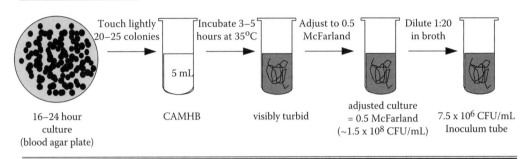

STEP 2: Inoculum Delivery

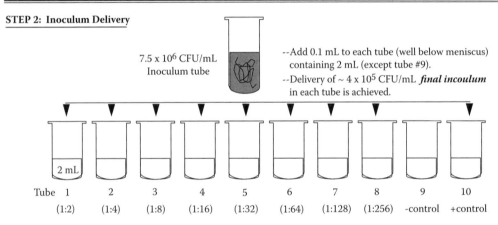

STEP 3: Verify Final Inoculum Size

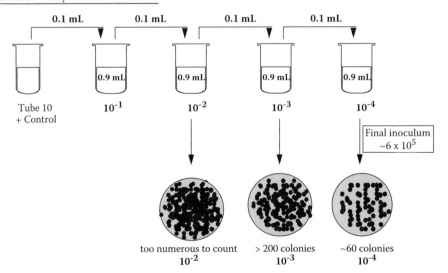

FIGURE 13.3 Inoculum preparation delivery.

- Touch lightly five to ten colonies of one single morphological type from a subculture plate (blood agar media) that has been incubated between 16–24 h. This addresses the possibility of heterogeneously distributed resistance among colonies.
- Place into *prewarmed* (35°C) enrichment broth containing 5.0 mL of CAMHB or trypticase soy broth. *Note:* Avoid the use of cultures that have recently undergone a change in test condition, for example, temperature shift or a change from agar to broth medium.
- Incubate this bacterial suspension until visibly turbid (usually takes no longer than 6 h at 35°C); for staphylococci and gram-negative rods, it may require less time, but for methicillin-resistant *Staphylococcus aureus* (MRSA) (slow growing), it may require a little more time.
- Adjust the turbidity of the actively growing culture (log phase) to the density of a 0.5 MacFarland standard.
- Dilute the adjusted culture in broth so that each tube contains ~5×10^5 CFU/mL (final inoculum), that is, an interim inoculum size estimated to be within the appropriate size. *Important exception:* when testing enterococci, the traditional inoculum is ~5×10^6 CFU/mL [10].

The dilution procedure to follow to obtain this final inoculum depends on the final volume of culture medium in each tube. For example, if 2 mL is the final desired volume in each tube, and the inoculum used is 0.1 mL, the following procedure is followed:

- Dilute the adjusted culture (~1.5×10^8 CFU/mL) 1:20 (one part of organism suspension and nineteen parts of broth) to yield ~7.5×10^6 CFU/mL.
- Since 0.1 mL of this suspension is inoculated into 2 mL of broth, the final inoculum in each tube will be ~4×10^5 CFU/mL.
- To verify the final inoculum size, one must serially dilute at 10^2, 10^3, and 10^4 dilutions of the positive growth control tube (tube 10) and spread the withdrawn aliquot (10 μL) onto agar surfaces, e.g., Mueller-Hinton (using a sterile loop). Colonies present after overnight incubation are counted and recorded on the laboratory worksheet. If pinpoint colonies are observed at 18–20 h, reincubate until colonies are more visible, allowing adequate time for colonies to grow (Figure 13.3).

13.3.4 INOCULATING BROTH

13.3.4.1 Macrodilution method

- The serum dilutions, as detailed in Section 13.3.2.2, should be done at the start of the preparation and incubation of the inoculum.
- Once this is completed, take 0.1 mL of the final inoculum and release beneath the meniscus of the serum dilution in tubes 1–8 and 10. Mix by flushing the pipette two to three times without splashing the sides of the tubes or creating air bubbles. *Do not vortex or agitate the tubes.*
- Once the inoculation is completed, the final range of dilutions will be from 1:2 to 1:256 in tubes 1–8, respectively; the negative control will be in tube 9, and the positive control will be in tube 10. Alternatively, in lieu of a negative control in tube 9, an additional dilution can be made, expanding the range to 1:512.

13.3.5 INCUBATION

- For the macrodilution method, incubate the test tubes at 35°C in air (or CO_2 if required) to ensure adequate growth of the patient's isolate.

- Macrodilution tubes should be incubated for 20 h, vortexed, reincubated and then vortexed (4 s) again before sampling at 24 h.

13.3.6 ENDPOINT DETERMINATION

- Antibiotic carryover can be determined by streaking the sample just subcultured across the surface of a prewarmed agar plate and then allowing the inoculated plates to sit 20 min at room temperature to ensure antimicrobial absorption into the agar.
- Cross-streak this inoculum over the entire surface, and after 24 h of incubation look for inhibition of colony growth at the site of the initial streak [24]. Antibiotic carryover is extremely important to determine when testing staphylococci and β-lactams.

13.3.6.1 Determination of Macrodilution Endpoints

- Using a 0.01-mL (10-μL) calibrated pipettor, subculture each clear test tube onto an agar plate surface.
- Streak the broth subcultures throughout the agar plate. Because of the inherent variability of performing colony counts, it is advisable to prepare duplicate subcultures onto solid media to determine the endpoints.
- The number of colonies grown after 48 h of incubation is used to determine the lethal endpoint (≥99.9% kill) (Figure 13.4). The SBT is considered the highest titer of serum that prevented growth and also reduced the inoculum by ≥99.9%. Survivors at lower titers (usually having higher concentrations of drug) are ignored as long as they number below 0.1% of the original inoculum count. These are accounted for by their rejection values (Table 13.1).

  Rejection values are determined by considering the final inoculum size, single versus duplicate sampling, pipetting error, and the Poisson distribution of sample responses. For example, if the final inoculum is ~6×10^5 CFU/mL, the dilution having fewer than 29 colonies is the lethal endpoint. It is this dilution that demonstrates ≥99.9% killing of the final inoculum and is the serum bactericidal titer.

After 24 hour incubation of tubes:

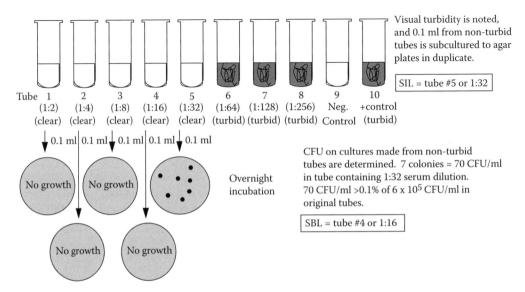

FIGURE 13.4 Determination of serum inhibitory (SIL) and bactericidal (SBL) end points.

TABLE 13.1
Rejection Values and Calculated Sensitivity and Specificity for Each Initial Concentration on the Basis of Duplicate Samples

Final Inoculum (CFU/mL)	Rejection[a]	Sensitivity(%)	Specificity (%)
1×10^5	4	77	97
2×10^5	8	89	99
3×10^5	15	99	99
4×10^5	20	99	99
5×10^5	25	99	99
6×10^5	29	99	99
7×10^5	33	99	99
8×10^5	38	99	99
9×10^5	42	99	99
1×10^6	47	99	99
2×10^6	91	99	99
3×10^6	136	99	99
4×10^6	182	99	99
5×10^6	227	99	99
6×10^6	273	99	99
7×10^6	318	99	99
8×10^6	364	99	99
9×10^6	409	99	99
1×10^7	455	99	99

Source: Clinical and Laboratory Standards Institute, M26-A, 1999, p. 4.

Note: The sum of colonies from duplicate samples was equal to or less than the rejection value; the antibiotic was declared lethal.

[a] Number of colonies.

13.4 RESULT INTERPRETATION AND REPORTING

Every test for bactericidal activity should be interpreted by someone knowledgeable in infectious diseases and bactericidal testing.

As a general guideline, it has been suggested that peak serum SBTs of 16 to 32 were frequently associated with more favorable clinical outcomes in patients with endocarditis and neutropenia [7,22,23]. More specifically, a SBT of 16 indicates that there will be some bactericidal activity in the serum for at least four half-lives of the drug(s) being tested. Since the precise interpretation of the SBTs has been very conroversial, the interpretation of the results must be customized for the individual patient and the patient's treatment regimen by the supervisory microbiologist or chief laboratory technologist in concert with the attending physician. SBTs will not accurately and reproducibly predict either favorable or unfavorable patient outcome. However, they will document whether therapeutic concentrations are present and if bactericidal activity is achieved.

The assessment of antibiotic combinations becomes important in infected immunocompromised patients, for example, neutropenic patients and activity of the combination can be assessed by use of the SBT.

The SBT has been reported to be useful in certain cases for patients with skeletal infections, for example, osteomyelitis and suppurative arthritis, although, in this situation, some workers have indicated that trough, rather than peak, SBTs (2 or greater) are more predictive of patient outcome [25]. Some workers have used the SBT for patients with meningitis. However, there is little information to evaluate clinical utility in that situation.

The SBT cannot be used to define what dosage regimens are ineffective. If the patient response is favorable, the dosage regimen need not be altered. In addition, an arbitrary SBT should not be targeted because there is a likelihood of increased toxicity, and surgical intervention may be indicated despite the observation of high SBTs.

13.5 TROUBLESHOOTING AND INDICATIONS FOR RETESTING AND PHYSICIAN CONSULTATION

13.5.1 CONSULTATIONS

It is suggested that the attending physician be consulted when retesting of the patient's isolate becomes necessary. Consultation with the nursing staff may also be warranted to ensure proper serum sample collection in association with drug dosing. In addition, it is highly recommended that the supervisory laboratory scientist discuss the interpretation of the final SBT results with the physician.

13.5.2 LABORATORY OBSERVATIONS

1. *Overestimated* bactericidal activity, for example, no growth in low and nearly all high dilutions:
   - Question of inadequate inoculum size or excess drug potency; recheck methods used for preparation.
   - Question of *neutralizing activity* within pooled or donor serum used for diluent; recheck source and qualification testing of serum.
2. *Underestimated* bactericidal activity, for example, growth in low and high dilution(s) or initial decrease followed by increase:
   - Question of drug inactivation during storage or handling of serum; recheck serum collection, serum sample labels (peak versus trough), and serum dilution procedures. If loss of drug potency is strongly suspected, especially for 24-h determinations, it is advisable to contact the manufacturer. The telephone numbers may be obtained from the Physicians' Desk Reference [11]. It is important to be aware of drugs that are more easily degraded during laboratory storage and testing, for example, carbapenems and streptogramins. The reader may refer to Chapter 2, Antimicrobial Classifications: Drugs for Bugs, for a list of drugs by class.
   - Question of excess bacterial inoculum size or stationary, rather than logarithmic, growth; recheck method for preparation. *Note:* McFarland standards need periodic replacement and may become contaminated; they may thus become an invalid guide for inoculum adjustment.
   - Question of inadequate contact between organisms and drug and/or splashing of inoculum above the broth mixture; recheck methodology used to inoculate serum dilutions and determine if dilutions were vortexed at 20 h and again at 24 h.
   - Question of selection of resistant mutants from test population during procedures; check for increase in MIC. This is a common observation with some drug classes, for example, aminoglycosides.
3. *Skip* tubes (low dilutions with growth followed by interim dilution(s) without growth and then followed by the higher dilution(s) with recurrence of growth).
   - Question of error during addition of bacterial inoculum or dilution of serum; recheck procedures.
4. *Growth in highest*, but not lowest, dilutions beyond the SIT or growth inhibitory end point.
   - This is a common observation when testing cell wall-active agents, for example, penicillins, cephalosporins, and carbapenems, and can be ignored for staphylococci; however, it must be considered if it occurs with gram-negative rods, for example,

Enterobacter spp. or *P. aeruginosa*. At the higher concentrations of cell wall active agents, protein synthesis may be substantially diminished so that the drug's lethal effect cannot be expressed because it depends upon rapid growth and cell wall turnover.

5. *Discrepancies* between quality control strain and patient isolates when bactericidal activity is expected:
   - It is advisable to repeat the testing.
   - Notify laboratory supervisory personnel.
6. *Poor growth* in many dilutions:
   - It is advisable to optimize growth of the patient's isolate in broth, with supplements as needed, before repeating the SBT. *Note:* Organisms from patients already undergoing antibacterial treatment may be damaged and require repeated subculture in nutritionally rich or hypertonic (sucrose-enriched) broth [6,7].

13.5.3 TERMS ASSOCIATED WITH BACTERICIDAL TESTING

See Table 13.2 [10].

TABLE 13.2
Terms Associated with Bactericidal Testing

MIC: Minimum inhibitory concentration; the lowest concentration of an antimicrobial agent that inhibits growth as determined visually after a standard incubation period (usually 18–24 h).

MBC (MLC): Minimum bactericidal concentration (minimum lethal concentration); the lowest concentration of an antibacterial agent that causes at least a 3 $\log_{10}$ reduction in the number of surviving cells (as compared with the initial, preincubation density) following 22–24 h incubation.

SIT: Serum inhibitory titer; the highest dilution (or titer) of a serum sample taken from a patient receiving antimicrobial therapy that inhibits visible growth after incubation (usually 22–24 h).

SBT: Serum bactericidal titer; the highest dilution (or titer) of a serum sample taken from a patient receiving antimicrobial therapy that causes at least a 3 $\log_{10}$ reduction in the number of surviving cells (as compared to the initial density) following 22–24 h incubation. This test has also been referred to as the serum dilution test, or as the Schlichter test.

Paradoxical effect (eagle phenomenon): The phenomenon in which an unexplained, increasing number of surviving cells (indicating decreasing bactericidal activity) is seen as the antimicrobial concentration increases above the MBC or SBT.

Skip tubes: The phenomenon in which one or more tube dilutions are seen to be free of bacterial growth (or contain densities ≥3 $\log_{10}$ lower than the initial inoculum) that are followed by one or more tubes containing higher concentrations of antimicrobial agents that contain surviving bacterial densities with a <3 $\log_{10}$ reduction.

Tolerance: The phenomenon in which normally bactericidal agents (e.g., B-lactams, vancomycin) appear to have reduced or absent bactericidal activity against selected bacterial strains.

ACKNOWLEDGEMENTS

We acknowledge the technical assistance of Michael Pease.

REFERENCES

1. Schlichter J.G. and MacLean, H. A method of determining the effective therapeutic level in the treatment of subacute endocarditis with penicillin: A preliminary report, *Amer. Heart J.*, 34, 209–211, 1947.
2. Fisher, A.M. A method for the determination of antibacterial potency of serum during therapy of acute infections. A preliminary report, *Bull. Johns Hopkins Hosp.*, 90, 313–320, 1952.
3. Taylor, P.C., Schoenknecht, F.D., Sherris, J.C., and Linner, E.C. Determination of minimum bactericidal concentrations of oxacillin for *Staphylococcus aureus*: Influence and significance of technical factors, *Antimicrob. Agents Chemother.*, 23, 142–150, 1983.

4. Stratton, C.W., Weinstein, M., and Reller, L.B. Correlation of serum bactericidal activity with antimicrobial agent level and minimal bactericidal concentration, *J. Infect. Dis.*, 145, 160–168, 1982.

5. Stratton, C.W. Serum bactericidal test, *Clin. Microbiol. Rev.*, 1, 1579–1580, 1988.

6. Clinical and Laboratory Standards Institute. Methodology for the serum bactericidal test, tentative standard, M21-T document, Clinical and Laboratory Standards Institute, Wayne, PA, 1992.

7. Clinical and Laboratory Standards Institute. Methodology for the serum bactericidal test, approved standard, M21-A document, Clinical and Laboratory Standards Institute, Wayne, PA, 1999

8. Wolfson, J.S. and Swarts, M.N. Serum bactericidal rate as a measure of antibiotic interactions, *New Engl. J. Med.*, 213, 968–975, 1985.

9. Klastersky, J., Daneau, D., Swings, G., and Weerts, D. Antibacterial activity in serum and urine as a therapeutic guide in bacterial infections, *J. Infect. Dis.*, 129, 187–193, 1974.

10. Peterson, L.R. and Collins, S.M. Bactericidal testing for infectious disease therapy: The why and how to measure if we kill the bugs, *Clin. Micro. Newsletter*, 22, 153–157, 2000.

11. Physicians' Desk Reference, 61st ed., Thompson Corporation, Toronto, 2007.

12. Weinstein, M., Stratton, C., Hawley, H.B., Ackley, A., and Reller, B. Multicenter collaborative evaluation of a standardized serum bactericidal test as a predictor of therapeutic efficacy in acute and chronic osteomyelitis, *Amer. J. Med.*, 83, 218–222, 1987.

13. Anhalt, J.P. and Washington, J.W., II. Bactericidal tests, in *Laboratory Procedures in Clinical Microbiology*, 2nd ed., Washington, J.A., Ed., Springer-Verlag, New York, 1985, 431–745.

14. Pien, F.D. and Vosti, K.L. Variation in performance of the serum bactericidal test, *Antimicrob. Agents Chemother.*, 6, 330–333, 1974.

15. Clinical and Laboratory Standards Institute. Methodology for dilution antimicrobial susceptibility tests for bacteria that grow aerobically, 5th ed., approved standard, M7-A7 document, Clinical and Laboratory Standards Institute, Wayne, PA, 2007.

16. Stratton, C.W. and Reller, L.B. Serum dilution test for bactericidal activity, selection of a physiologic diluent, *J. Infect. Dis.*, 136, 187–195, 1977.

17. Leggett, J., Wolz, S., and Craig, W. Use of serum ultrafiltrate in the serum dilution test, *J. Infect. Dis.*, 160, 616–623, 1989.

18. Hyatt, J.M., McKinnon, P.S., Zimmer, G.S., and Schentag, J.J. The importance of pharmacokinetic/pharmacodynamic surrogate markers to outcome, *Clin. Pharmacokinetic Concepts*, 28(2), 143–160, 1995.

19. Woolfrey, B.F., Lally, R.T., and Tait, K.R. Influence of technical factor variations on serum inhibitions and bactericidal titers, *J. Clin. Microbiol.*, 23, 997–1000, 1986.

20. Pearson, R.D., Steigbigel, R.T., Davis, H.T., and Chapman, S.W. Method for reliable determination of minimal lethal antibiotic concentrations, *Antimicrob. Agents Chemother.*, 18, 699–708, 1980.

21. Stratton, C. and Reller, B. Serum dilution test for bactericidal activity: Selection of a physiologic diluent, *J. Infect. Dis.*, 136(2), 187–195, 1977.

22. Weinstein, M.P., Stratton, C.W., and Hawley, H.B. Multicenter collaborative evaluation of a standardized serum bactericidal test as a predictor of therapeutic osteomyelitis, *Amer. J. Med.*, 83, 218–222, 1987.

23. Sculier, J.P. and Llasterskyu, J. Significance of serum bactericidal activity in gram negative bacillary bacteremia in patients with and without granulocytopenia, *Amer. J. Med.*, 76, 429–435, 1984.

24. Pelletier, L.L. and Baker, C.B. Oxacillin, cephalothin, and vancomycin tube macrodilution MBC result reproducibility and equivalence to MIC results for methicillin-susceptible and reputedly tolerant *Staphylococcus aureus* isolates, *Antimicrob. Agents Chemother.*, 32, 374–377, 1988.

25. Norden, C., Gillespie, W.J., and Nade, S. *Infections in Bones and Joints*, Blackwell Scientific Publications, Oxford, UK, 1994.

14 Bioassay Methods for Antimicrobial and Antifungal Agents

Donald H. Pitkin and Estrella Martin-Mazuelos

CONTENTS

14.1 INTRODUCTION

The concentrations of antimicrobial agents in human body fluids were originally determined to support toxicological, pharmacological, and pharmacokinetic studies related to regulatory requirements [1–4].

In the 1960s investigators began to determine the antimicrobial concentrations in body fluids from patients treated with drugs that have a narrow therapeutic range, such as aminoglycosides or vancomycin. The concentrations were monitored to minimize occurrence of possible concentration associated toxicity, including nephrotoxicity and ototoxicity [5–9].

Once the importance of antimicrobial agent concentrations in body fluids was established, it was demonstrated that both efficiency and toxicity of antimicrobial agents were related to drug concentration and its duration in body fluids. The importance of determining antibiotic concentrations in body fluids is now widely accepted [2,9–13]. Determinations of antimicrobial agent concentrations in patients receiving drugs with a narrow therapeutic range are made to avoid underdosing, with the likelihood of a poor therapeutic outcome, and to avoid overdosing, with the likelihood of concentration related toxicity [7,8]. Peak concentrations are monitored to ensure therapeutic efficacy and to avoid a large overdose [13,14]. Determinations of antimicrobial agent concentrations in serum are also used to evaluate the pharmacokinetic profile of a new antimicrobial agent.

Rapid, commercially available methods for the accurate quantification of antimicrobial agent concentrations in serum and other biological fluids were developed because of the need to correlate drug concentrations with therapeutic effectiveness and drug induced adverse events [1,2,15–17]. In the 1960s and 1970s, efforts to develop assays centered on microbiological assay systems for the major classes of antibiotics. Since then, substantial technological advances have provided a variety of alternative methods to replace the tedious and time-consuming bioassay, radioenzymatic assay, and radioimmunoassay methods [2,14–18]. However, bioassays remain an important component of modern therapy in many clinical settings.

14.2 CLINICAL SPECIMENS

14.2.1 OVERVIEW

Blood, serum, plasma, urine, and cerebrospinal fluid are commonly assayed for their concentration of antimicrobial agents. Serum is the most frequently assayed body fluid. The use of universal or standard precautions, to prevent exposure of the laboratory worker to infection, is advised when working with clinical specimens.

Proper specimen collection, accurate documentation of the time and route of drug administration, the dose administered, sampling times, and a list of other medications given to the patient are vital to the interpretation of assay results. Improper handling and storage of collected specimens may influence assay results. The effects of handling and storage conditions on the stability of the antimicrobial should be known. Antimicrobial agents must remain stable while specimens are processed and during storage prior to assay. If any procedure is performed incorrectly, the resulting data may be invalid and require additional patient specimens. Repeated testing consumes time and resources, and is unnecessarily discomforting and stressful to the patient.

When biological fluids are assayed, the determination of antimicrobial content may be influenced by factors such as serum protein binding, abnormal serum protein or serum biochemical profiles, specimen availability, and the diluent used to prepare the standard response line [11,19–21].

14.2.2 SPECIMEN COLLECTION TIMES

The appropriate postdose interval(s) to collect specimens of serum or other body fluids are dependent on the intent of the study, the route of drug administration, and the body fluid collected. A study to determine the pharmacokinetic properties of a new intravenously administered antimicrobial agent requires a completely different set of sampling intervals than does a study to routinely monitor peak and trough concentrations of the drug. Drugs administered intravenously, intramuscularly, and orally will each have unique sampling interval requirements [22–24]. Drugs administered intramuscularly or orally achieve their peak concentration later than an intravenously administered drug. The solubility of drug at the site of administration is a major variable in the time required to reach peak concentration. Poorly soluble drugs will take longer to reach their peak concentration, and the peak concentration achieved will be less than that of drugs with greater solubility [22,24].

Appropriate times for sample collections for routine monitoring of antimicrobial concentrations for toxicity and efficacy are when peak and trough concentrations of the antibiotic are present. Peak and trough concentrations are defined as the highest (peak) and the lowest (trough) concentration of drug achieved during the dosage interval. The timing of samples for trough concentrations is independent of the route of administration. Trough samples should be obtained immediately prior to administration of the next dose.

Determination of the peak concentration of an antimicrobial in serum may be important if efficacy is concentration dependent, for example, aminoglycosides or fluoroquinolones. It can also be important for drugs that have adverse reactions associated with high concentrations of drug in serum, such as, 5-flucytosine (5-FC) or chloramphenicol.

The steady state concentration of an antimicrobial may be measured 4–8 h after initiating a continuous intravenous infusion; for example, after administration of a β-lactam antibiotic that has a short half-life [25].

Urine specimens are usually obtained as pools containing all of the urine voided by the patient during a specified time interval. The total volume of urine in the pool must be documented and the volume made known to the laboratory to determine the amount of drug excreted. Thoroughly clean urine collection containers after use to eliminate specimen cross-contamination.

14.2.3 SPECIMEN PROCESSING AND STORAGE

Specimens should be processed without delay to prevent possible loss of antimicrobial agent potency. Prior to processing, specimens can be stored at 2°C–8°C.

14.2.3.1. Plasma

Collect the patient's blood in a tube containing a suitable anticoagulant. Plasma must be separated from the red blood cells. Centrifuge the blood specimen using conditions that permit separation of cells and plasma. Decant the plasma into a sterile container and label. If the expected concentration of antimicrobial in the plasma is greater than the highest concentration on the standard response line, dilute the specimen with plasma prior to assay. Do not dilute plasma specimens with serum; the diluted sample may clot.

14.2.3.2 Serum

Collect the patient's blood in a tube without any anticoagulant. Serum is separated from blood cells after the blood has clotted and clot retraction has occurred. Permit clot retraction to occur in a refrigerator, 2°C–8°C, for several hours. If the expected concentration of antimicrobial in the serum is greater than the highest concentration on the standard response line, dilute the specimen with serum. Do not dilute serum specimens with plasma as the diluted sample may clot.

14.2.3.3 Cerebral Spinal Fluid (CSF)

Specimens of CSF should be free from obvious contamination with blood. Contamination with blood is evidenced by the presence of a pink to red color. The assay of CSF samples contaminated with blood will provide unreliable data on the content of drug in the CSF. Assays of CSF specimens pose significant challenges to the analyst. The limited specimen volume available minimizes the number of replicate determinations that can be made and the volume available for each estimate. Assay formats that require small sample volumes are preferred. The difficulty in obtaining drug-free CSF affects the preparation of a standard response line. Preparation of the standard response line using serum diluted with an aqueous diluent to a protein content similar to that of the CSF specimen is a potential alternative. The serum protein content of the diluent is particularly important for drugs such as ceftriaxone that are highly bound to serum proteins.

14.2.3.4 Urine

Urine collection containers should be kept cold, for example, in an ice bath, during the collection interval to minimize loss of bioactivity. It is important to record the total volume of urine collected during each collection interval. Mix the total volume collected and submit a labeled aliquot to the laboratory for analysis.

Processed specimens that are assayed the same day they are collected may be stored at 2°C–8°C until they are assayed. Store all other processed specimens at –70°C to –80°C. Some antimicrobials are stable at –20°C; however, others such as imipenem require colder storage temperatures to ensure multiple day stability. Urine specimens containing certain antimicrobials, including imipenem, should be diluted in the buffer suggested by their manufacturer to ensure stability in the frozen state. Frozen specimens must be completely thawed and mixed before they are assayed.

14.3 BIOASSAY METHODS

14.3.1 OVERVIEW

Most, if not all, of the bioassays run in a clinical laboratory to determine antimicrobial concentrations in body fluids are based on agar diffusion methods. The assays measure the total antimicrobial activity in the specimen to which the indicator organism responds. The presence of more than one antimicrobial in a specimen will invalidate the results unless the analyst takes special precautions to suppress the activity of the interfering antimicrobial agent(s) that are present.

The antimicrobial activity is measured by determining the diameter, in millimeters, of the zone of no indicator organism growth that surrounds the tested material. The clarity of the edge of the zone of inhibition is a critical variable in obtaining reproducible results. Subtle changes in the inoculum colony forming units per milliliter (CFU/mL), media composition, media pH, depth of agar in the petri dish, and duration of incubation can have pronounced effects on inhibition zone size and edge clarity [27–29].

Bioassays are quantified by comparing the response of the indicator organism to an unknown concentration of a known antimicrobial agent in the sample to the responses produced by known concentrations of the same antimicrobial agent in a standard response line.

In a clinical laboratory, any organism that is inhibited by the antimicrobial agent can be used as an indicator and any media that supports growth of the indicator can be used. The concentrations of antimicrobial used to prepare the standard response line will vary with the antimicrobial agent, indicator organism, assay media, incubation conditions, and type of sample. The choice of indicator organism and growth media may, to a large extent, be varied to suit the required assay sensitivity and the needs of the laboratory.

The analyst must then determine the antimicrobial concentrations to use in preparing the standard response line. Determine the standard response line concentrations using data obtained in a preliminary assay. In preliminary assays, use widely separated concentrations of the antimicrobial, for example, 0.25, 1, 2.5, 10, 25, and 100 µg/mL. A plot of logarithm of the concentration against linear inhibition zone diameter should form a straight line without obvious deviations. Deviations in linearity of a response line are most likely to occur at concentration range extremes unless technical errors were made during preparation of the solutions, during application of the solutions to the assay plates, or measurement of zone diameters. The concentration range chosen must encompass the range of concentrations expected in the sample or dilution of the sample. When determining the drug concentrations for the standard response line, it is generally appropriate to avoid concentrations that produce small (<13 mm) or large (>27 mm) zones of inhibition. When calculating the drug concentration in a specimen, do not extrapolate the concentration using inhibition zones with a diameter that exceeds the boundaries of the standard response line. The response may not be linear.

The standard response line concentrations suggested in the U.S. Pharmacopeia and the Code of Federal Regulations Title 21 relate to bioassays of drug substances in aqueous solution and were intended for assays of dosage forms. The standard response line concentrations required for assays of clinical specimens, particularly those of blood, serum, or plasma, may not be the same as those for a drug substance in an aqueous environment. The concentrations required are often greater.

Development of inhibition zones with a clearly defined edge is a critical requirement for all bioassays. Poorly defined inhibition zone edges make it essentially impossible to run a reproducible bioassay. The analyst should run a preliminary trial of any new bioassay before using the assay to analyze clinical samples [20,21,30]. A trial run provides training for the analyst and permits subtle changes to be incorporated into the final procedure before clinical specimens are tested. The results of the trial assay will show the quality and sizes of the inhibition zone diameters and the assay sensitivity. Microbiological bioassays are labor intensive and slow, and have a low degree of specificity, but they require only a minimal amount of specialized equipment.

Aminoglycosides and glycopeptide antimicrobials, such as gentamicin and vancomycin, respectively, produce standard response lines with a steep slope, i.e., only a small difference in response is obtained for relatively large differences in concentration. Doubling the concentration of aminoglycoside or vancomycin may change the zone diameter by only 0.5–1.5 mm. Consistent and accurate measurement of zone diameters is mandatory. A change of only 0.2 mm in the average zone diameter may change an assayed concentration value by 15%. Replicate zones of inhibition should have zone diameters that are almost the same size. Large differences in replicate zone diameters, >1 or 1.5 mm for assays using a 6.3-mm disk, suggest technical errors may have occurred.

Bioassays should only be run by well trained technical staff. Strict control of analytical technique is necessary to minimize the likelihood of errors. Sequential carryover errors may occur when serial dilutions are used to produce standard response line concentrations. Standard response line preparation schema should minimize use of serial dilutions. Control samples of known antimicrobial content stored under the same conditions as the specimens should be tested with each batch of assays to evaluate assay quality and accuracy. Antibacterial bioassays typically have a sensitivity in the range of 0.1 to 5 µg/mL [3,30].

14.3.2 Assay Formats

Bioassays can be broadly classified into two formats: the self-contained and the internally normalized assay. All bioassays should be validated and written procedures strictly followed to ensure production of reproducible data.

14.3.2.1 Self-Contained Assay

In the self-contained assay, each assay dish includes a complete standard response line and sample(s). Assays can be run in a 90-mm petri dish with a two-point standard response line, two zones of each material on each plate. The statistical power of this assay format is low. Now that more powerful assay formats have been developed it is infrequently used and is not recommended.

Alternately, use a 150-mm petri dish with a five-point standard response line and a single sample, one zone of each material on each plate. Replicate estimates of each response are run on separate assay plates. Corrections for interplate variation in responses are not to be made using this assay format. Each of these assays can be run using a single layer of nutritive agar seeded with inoculum or on a plate containing two layers of nutritive agar, the unseeded bottom layer and an overlaid seeded top layer of nutritive agar. Preparation of uniform assay plates is mandatory and preparation of uniform two-layer plates requires extensive practice.

Assays run in the Nunc square dish, 295 mm [24,28,29], are a modification of the self-contained assay. In this modification, multiple replicates of each standard response line concentration and multiple samples are tested in a single plate. Tested materials may be applied using a matrix of eight materials in each of eight columns (8×8 matrix) or nine materials using a 9×9 application matrix. Each standard concentration and each sample is randomly assigned to a specified unique location in each column. Replication of each tested material is contained in a single dish; therefore, interplate variation in response is eliminated as a variable. Accurate placement of each solution in the correct location is necessary. Use of a template for placement of solutions and identification of zones is recommended.

14.3.2.2 Internally Normalized Assay

In the internally normalized bioassay using 90-mm petri dishes, each dish alternately contains three replicates of a single concentration of one standard or three replicates of one sample and three replicates of a solution common to all plates [31]. The solution common to all plates is frequently, but is not required to be, the midpoint of the standard response line. Additional replicate values for each standard and sample are on separate plates. Each standard response line concentration or sample is typically replicated on each of 3 or 4 plates to provide 9 to 12 estimates of the "true response." Petri dishes of 150-mm diameter may also be used with an adjustment of agar volume based on the relative surface areas of the two plate sizes. The 150-mm petri dish format reduces the likelihood of zone overlap or interference when large, >27 mm, adjacent zones are produced.

The process of normalizing the responses of the common solution across all assay dishes and applying the correction to each set of plates containing a standard response line concentration or sample eliminates interplate variation in standard and sample responses.

14.3.3 INDICATOR ORGANISM

The CFR Title 21 and current edition of the U.S. Pharmacopeia list suitable indicator organisms for assaying specimens containing most common single antimicrobial agents (Table 14.1). Spores of *Bacillus subtilis* ATCC 6633, or cells of *Staphylococcus aureus* 6538P (ATCC 29737), *S. epidermidis* ATCC 12228, *Enterococcus faecalis* ATCC 10541, or *Micrococcus luteus* ATCC 9341 are often used to assay antimicrobials active against gram-positive organisms. *Escherichia coli* ATCC 10536, *Klebsiella pneumoniae* ATCC 10031, and *Pseudomonas aeruginosa* ATCC 25619 are often used for antimicrobials active against gram-negative organisms.

The presence of multiple antimicrobial agents or combination drugs, such as a β-lactam antibiotic plus a β-lactamase inhibitor, may require selection of an alternate indicator organism. Assays of specimens containing multiple antimicrobial agents require the analyst to modify the media or sample by the addition of agents to selectively inactivate or remove the interfering

TABLE 14.1
Microbiological Assay Methods: Indicator Organism Inocula

Test Organism[a]	Method[b]/Media[b]	Incubation (hr/C°)	Suggested Dilution	Storage Period[c]
A-*Staphylococcus aureus* ATCC 6538P	1/1	24/32–35	1:20	1 week
B-*Micrococcus luteus* ATCC 7468	1/1	24/32–35	1:30	2 weeks
C-*Micrococcus luteus* ATCC 9341	1/1	24/32–35	1:40	2 weeks
D-*Staphyloccocus epidermidis* ATCC 12228	1/1	24/32–35	1:14	1 week
E-*Saccharomyces cerevisiae* ATCC 9763	6/19 or 7/19	48/29–31	1:30	4 weeks
F-*Bordetella bronchiiseptica* ATCC 4617	1/1	24/32–35	1:20	2 weeks
H-*Bacillus subtilis* ATCC 6633	1/1	24/32–35	e	1 month
or	2/32	5–7 days/32–35		6 months
I-*Klebsiella pneumoniae* ATCC 10031	1/1	24/36–37.5	1:25	1 week
J-*Escherichia coli* ATCC 10536	1/1	24/32–35	1:20	2 weeks
K-*Enterococcus faecium* ATCC 10541	5/...	24/36–37.5	/4/	1 week
T-*Saccharomyces cerevisiae* ATCC 2601 Cerevisiae[d]	7/3	48/29–31	1:30	4 weeks
W-*Pseudomonas aeruginosa* ATCC 25619	1/1	24/36–37.5	1:25	2 weeks
Y-*Pseudomonas aeruginosa* ATCC 29336	9/36	24/36–37.5	1:50	1 week
Paecilomyces variotii ATCC 36257	10/3	24–48/29–31	1:1	1 day
Crysosporium pruinosum ATCC 36374 (5-flucytosine resistant)	10/3	24–48/29–31	1:1	1 day
Saccharomyces cerevisiae ATCC 36375	6/19[f]	48/29–31	e	2 days
Candida tropicalis ATCC 13803	6/19[f]	24–48/29–31	e	2–5 days

Test organism letters A through K correspond to those used in Kirshbaum, A. and Arret, B. *J. Pharm. Sci.*, 56(4), 512, 1967.

... No media suggested

[a] Organisms are available from American Type Culture Collection, 12301 Parklawn Dr., Rockville, MD 20852.

[b] Methods are defined in Table 14.2, and media are defined in Table 14.3.

[c] Storage temperature 2°C–8°C.

[d] If the antibiotic to be tested is paromomycin, the dilution factor is 1:25.

[e] Determine dilution with test plates.

[f] Yeast morphology agar may be used. (Hulsewede, W. *Int. J. Med. Microbiol. Virol. Parasitol. Infect. Dis.*, 281, 513–518, 1994.)

antimicrobial agents. A β-lactamase preparation such as the mixed β-lactamase from *Bacillus cereus* that contains both a serine active site β-lactamase and a zinc dependent β-lactamase can inactivate most available β-lactam antibiotics, with the possible exception of the monobactam aztreonam. This enzyme preparation is commercially available under the name of Genzyme®. Addition of 1% w/v cellulose phosphate or 3% to 5% w/v sodium polyanethol sulfonate (Sigma Chemical Co) to the media will suppress activities due to aminoglycosides. Adjustment of assay media pH will enhance or suppress activity of an antimicrobial whose activity is pH dependent. Differences in sensitivity to heat can be used to separate activities of some antimicrobial agents; β-lactam antibiotics are heat sensitive while aminoglycosides are considerably more heat resistant. The presence of urea and bilirubin in serum may interfere with bioassays, especially the determination of aminoglycoside concentrations [7]. Specimen dilution with normal human serum may resolve the interference if the concentration of antimicrobial in the specimen is sufficient to permit specimen dilution. Use of an indicator organism that does not respond to the interfering antimicrobial is another alternative. The chosen indicator organism must respond to concentrations of the antibiotic of interest that are expected to be present in the sample. Suitable control samples must be tested in parallel with the specimens to verify assay accuracy and selectivity when testing samples containing multiple antimicrobials.

14.3.4 INOCULUM

The inocula for most one-layer bioassays will contain $2–10 \times 10^5$ CFU/mL of nutritive agar. The inocula for two-layer bioassays generally contain a larger number of CFU per milliliter of nutritive agar than the inocula for a single-layer assay. It may contain as many as 1×10^8 CFU/mL of seeded agar (Table 14.2). Use inoculum cells in mid to late log phase of growth for the rapid determination of antibiotic concentrations. Spores of *B. subtilis* ATCC 6633 provide a readily available inoculum inhibited by many antibiotics, have a long shelf life, and are commercially available from media manufacturers. The spores may lack adequate sensitivity or produce unacceptable inhibition zone edges when used as an indicator for some assays.

14.3.5 CULTURE MEDIA

A universal culture media for bioassays does not exist. The CFR currently lists more than 17 media for bioassays (Table 14.3) [3]. The choice of media depends on the antibiotic assayed, the indicator microorganism, and pH requirements.

The volume of media to add to each petri dish is a variable [28,29] (Table 14.3 and Table 14.4). Small volumes enhance assay sensitivity while large volumes may clarify zone edge definition. Petri dishes of 90-mm diameter, for the single-layer assay format, may contain 7–25 mL of nutritive agar, depending on the required sensitivity and inhibition zone quality. Volumes of 10–15 mL of nutritive agar per plate frequently produce acceptable results. For two-layer assay plates, use 20 mL of sterile base agar and overlay with 3–5 mL of seeded nutritive agar. The relative temperatures of the solidified base layer and molten seeded agar overlay are important variables when preparing two-layer plates. A uniform thickness of seeded overlay cannot be obtained if the base layer is too cold. The seeded layer must be uniformly distributed on the surface of the base layer, and each plate must be overlaid with the same volume of seeded agar to provide interplate consistency.

Petri dishes of 150-mm diameter for the single-layer assay format may contain 15–50 mL of nutritive agar. Volumes of 25–30 mL of nutritive agar per dish frequently produce acceptable results. For two-layer assay plates, use 40 mL of sterile base agar and overlay with 7–8 mL of seeded agar following the same precautions as used for the smaller plate size.

The Nunc 295-mm square plates require 200–300 mL of seeded nutritive agar for one-layer plates. These plates are not recommended for two-layer assays because of the difficulty in evenly spreading the thin layer of seeded agar over the sterile base layer in a large plate.

14.3.6 ANTIBIOTIC STANDARDS

The antimicrobial agent used to prepare the standard response line must be prepared from a reference powder of known potency (purity). The use of a therapeutic preparation of an antimicrobial agent is not recommended because many therapeutic preparations contain antimicrobially inactive excipients. Each lot of antibiotic has its own potency [3]. Small amounts of reference grade antimicrobial can be obtained from the drug manufacturer, the U.S. Pharmacopia, or Sigma Chemical Company among other sources. Stock reference solutions of high concentration should be prepared using the reference powder. Equilibrate the temperature of a reference standard powder to room temperature before opening the container to minimize adsorption of moisture. Dissolve the powder in the recommended diluents, and store small volumes of the stock reference solution at the temperature recommended by the manufacturer, or as listed in the CFR (Table 14.5 and Table 14.6), or as suggested by the Clinical and Laboratory Standards Institute (CLSI) [31]. Stock reference solutions prepared from a reference powder can frequently be stored at $-70°C$ for up to 3 months [3]. Do not refreeze a stock reference solution once it is thawed. During preparation of the stock reference solution, the analyst must take into consideration the potency of the antimicrobial. Some antimicrobials, especially some of the

TABLE 14.2
Microbiological Assay Methods: Preparation of Indicator Organism

Method 1

Maintain organisms on agar slants containing 10 mL of the appropriate medium. Incubate the slants at 32°C–35°C for 24 h. Using 3 mL of sterile U.S.P. saline, wash the growth from the agar slant onto a large agar surface, such as a Roux bottle, containing 250 mL of the appropriate medium. Spread the suspension of organisms over the entire surface of the Roux bottle with the aid of sterile glass beads. Incubate the Roux bottle at 32°C–35°C. Wash the resulting growth from the agar surface with 50 mL of sterile U.S.P. saline.

Standardization of suspension: Determine the dilution factor that will give 25% light transmission at a wavelength of 580 mυ using a suitable photoelectric colorimeter and a 13-mm diameter test tube as an absorption cell. It may be necessary to adjust the suspension. Determine the amount of suspension to be added to each 100 mL of agar or nutrient broth by the use of test plates or test broth. Store the test organism suspension under refrigeration.

Method 2

Proceed as directed in method 1.

Standardization of the suspension: Centrifuge and decant the supernatant liquid, resuspend the sediment with 50–70 mL of sterile U.S.P. saline, and heat the suspension for 30 min at 70°C. Use test plates to assure the viability of the spores and to determine the amount of spore suspension to be added to each 100 mL of agar. Maintain the spore suspension under refrigeration.

Method 3

Proceed as directed in method 1.

Standardization of the suspension: Heat the suspension for 30 min at 70°C, wash the spore suspension three times with 25–50 mL of sterile distilled water, resuspend the organisms in 50–70 mL of sterile distilled water and heat-shock again for 30 min at 70°C. Use test plates to assure the viability of the spores and to determine the amount of spore suspension to be added to each 100 mL of agar. Maintain the spore suspension under refrigeration.

Method 4

Maintain the test organisms in 100-mL quantities of nutrient broth (Medium 3). For the test, prepare a fresh subculture by transferring a loopful of the stock culture to 100 mL of the same nutrient broth and incubate for 16–18 h at 37°C. Store this broth culture under refrigeration.

Method 5

Maintain the test organisms on agar slants containing 10 mL of the appropriate medium. Incubate the slants at 32°C–35°C for 24 h. Inoculate 100 mL of nutrient broth-Medium 13. Incubate for 16–18 hours at 37°C.

Standardization of the suspension: Follow the directions for method 1.

Method 6

Proceed as directed in method 1, except incubate the slants at 30°C for 24 h and incubate the Roux bottle at 30°C for 48 h.

Method 7

Maintain organisms on agar slants containing 10 mL of the appropriate medium and transfer to a fresh slant about once a week. Incubate the slants at 37°C for 48 h. Using 3 mL of sterile U.S.P. saline, wash the growth from the agar slant into a 500-mL Erlenmeyer flask containing 100 mL of medium 34 and 50 g of glass beads. Agitate the culture by rotation at a speed of 130 cpm and a radius of 3.5 cm at 27°C for 5 days. Determine the amount of suspension to be added to each 100 mL of agar by the use of test plates. Store the test organism suspension under refrigeration.

Method 8

Proceed as directed in method 1, except incubate the slant and Roux bottle at 37°C and wash the resulting growth from the agar surface with 50 mL of Medium 37.

Method 9

Proceed as directed in method 1, except standardize to 80%–90% light transmission at 360 mυ.

TABLE 14.3
Microbiological Assay Methods: Culture Media

Medium 1
Peptone: 6.0 g
Pancreatic digest of casein: 4.0 g
Yeast extract: 3.0 g
Beef extract: 1.5 g
Dextrose: 1.0 g
Agar: 15.0 g
Distilled water, q.s: 1,000 mL
pH 6.5–6.6 after sterilization

Medium 2
Peptone: 6.0 g
Yeast extract: 3.0 g
Beef extract: 1.5 g
Agar: 15.0 g
Distilled water, q.s: 1,000 mL
pH 6.5–6.6 after sterilization

Medium 3
Peptone: 5.0 g
Yeast extract: 1.5 g
Beef extract: 1.5 g
Sodium chloride: 3.5 g
Dextrose: 1.0 g
Dipotassium phosphate: 3.68 g
Potassium dihydrogen phosphate: 1.32 g
Distilled water, q.s: 1,000 mL
pH 6.95–7.05 after sterilization

Medium 4
Peptone: 6.0 g
Yeast extract: 3.0 g
Beef extract: 1.5 g
Dextrose: 1.0 g
Agar: 15.0 g
Distilled water, q.s: 1,000 mL
pH 6.5–6.6 after sterilization

Medium 5
Medium 5 is the same as medium 2, except adjust the final pH to 7.8–8.0 after sterilization.

Medium 8
Medium 8 is the same as medium 2, except adjust the final pH to 5.8–6.0 after sterilization.

Medium 9
Pancreatic digest of casein: 17.0 g
Papaic digest of soybean: 3.0 g
Sodium chloride: 5.0 g
Dipotassium phosphate: 2.5 g
Dextrose: 2.5 g
Agar: 20.0 g
Distilled water, q.s: 1,000 mL
pH 7.2–7.3 after sterilization

(continued)

TABLE 14.3
Microbiological Assay Methods: Culture Media (continued)

Medium 11
Medium 11 is the same as medium 1, except adjust the final pH to 7.8–8.0 after sterilization.

Medium 13
Peptone: 10.0 g
Dextrose: 20.0 g
Distilled water, q.s: 1,000 mL
pH 5.6–5.7 after sterilization

Medium 19
Peptone: 9.4 g
Yeast extract: 4.7 g
Beef extract: 2.4 g
Sodium chloride: 10.0 g
Dextrose: 10.0 g
Agar: 23.5 g
Distilled water, q.s: 1,000 mL
pH 6.0–6.2 after sterilization

Medium 32
Prepare as medium 1, except add 300 mg of hydrated manganese sulfate to each liter of medium.

Medium 34
Glycerol: 10.0 g
Peptone: 10.0 g
Beef extract: 10.0 g
Sodium chloride: 3.0 g
Distilled water, q.s.: 1,000 mL
pH 7.0 after sterilization

Medium 35
Same as medium 34, except add 17.0 g of agar to each liter of medium.

Medium 36
Pancreatic digest of casein: 15.0 g
Papaic digest of soybean: 5.0 g
Sodium chloride: 5.0 g
Agar: 15.0 g
Distilled water, q.s: 1,000 mL
pH 7.3 after sterilization

Medium 37
Pancreatic digest of casein: 17.0 g
Soybean peptone: 3.0 g
Dextrose: 2.5 g
Sodium chloride: 5.0 g
Dipotassium phosphate: 2.5 g
Distilled water, q.s.: 1,000 mL
pH 7.3 after sterilization

Medium 38
Peptone: 15.0 g
Papaic digest of soybean meal: 5.0 g

(continued)

TABLE 14.3
Microbiological Assay Methods: Culture Media (continued)

Sodium chloride: 4.0 g
Sodium sulfite: 0.2 g
L-Cystine: 0.7 g
Dextrose: 5.5 g
Agar: 15.0 g
Distilled water, q.s.: 1,000 mL
pH 7.0 after sterilization

Description of media: Medium numbers 1, 2, 3, 4, 5, 8, 9, 10, 11, and 13 correspond to those used in Grove, D.C. and Randall, W.A. *Assay Methods of Antibiotics*, Medical Encyclopedia, Inc., New York, 1955, p. 220. Medium numbers 18 through 21 correspond to those used in Kirshbaum, A. and Arret, B. *J. Pharm. Sci.*, 56(4), 512, 1967.

newer quinolone antibiotics, are light sensitive. These antimicrobials must be handled under conditions of low light intensity and stored in containers shielded from light.

The final dilutions of the stock reference solution that are used to prepare the standard response line concentrations are made in the same body fluid as the sample that will be assayed, when possible. For example, for the determination of antibiotic levels in blood, the final dilutions of each standard response line concentration should be made using blood as the diluent. Plasma samples are diluted in plasma, and serum samples are diluted in serum [24]. Urine samples may be diluted in drug-free urine if available [1] or 1% phosphate buffer pH 6–7. Standards used to assay CSF samples may require dilution in an aqueous dilution of serum to mimic the concentration of plasma proteins in the CSF because of difficulty in obtaining drug-free CSF and its scarcity. When the antibiotic is diluted in a liquid that is different than that of the test sample, large errors in the results may occur because of the pH or content of serum proteins [1].

Bioassays should include at least three concentrations to generate the standard response line and a minimum of five concentrations is recommended. Suggested standard response line concentrations for aqueous specimens may be found in the CFR or U.S. Pharmacopeia [3]. Each laboratory may prefer to develop its own standard response line concentrations based on available indicator organisms, antimicrobials of interest, and type of specimens tested. It is critical that the antibiotic standards be free of other antimicrobial substances.

14.3.7 APPLICATION OF TEST MATERIALS TO ASSAY PLATES

Solutions of antimicrobial agents can be applied to assay plates using filter paper disks (Schleicher & Schuell 740 E) of 6.25-mm or 12.5-mm diameter. The smaller disk readily adsorbs 20 μL of liquid. The larger disk readily adsorbs 80 μL of liquid. The liquid can be placed on disks using a micropipette, changing the pipette tip between solutions of higher concentration. Alternatively, disks can be carefully dipped into the liquid and the excess volume drained off (or place the disk on a screen to dry), before applying the disk to an assay plate. Application of the same absorbable volume of liquid to each disk, not the absolute volume applied, is critical.

Wells of consistent size, usually 6–9-mm in diameter, are cut into the agar surface of assay plates with a cutting tool such as a cork borer attached to a suction device to remove the agar plug. A well cutter with adjustable well spacing can be custom made to simplify and standardize the procedure. Cut the wells without causing fissures to develop around the well. A cutter sharpened (beveled) on the inner surface, rather than the outer surface, may be easier to use. The solution volume added to each well must be the same, but the absolute volume applied will vary with the well diameter and agar depth.

TABLE 14.4
Microbiological Assay Methods: Preparation of Agar Diffusion Assay Plates

Antimicrobial Agent	Media to Be Used Listed by Medium Number		mL of Media to Be Used in the Base and Seed Layers		Test Organism	Suggested Volume of Standardized Inoculum to Be Added to Each mL (mL)	Incubation Temperature (°C)
	Base Layer	Seed Layer	Base Layer	Seed Layer			
Amoxicillin	11	11	21	4	C	0.5	32–35
Amphotericin B	None	19	None	8	E	1.0	29–31
Ampicillin	11	11	21	4	C	0.5	32–35
Bacitracin	2	1	21	4	B	0.3	32–35
Bacitracin	2	1	21	4	L	0.3	32–35
Carbenicillin	9	10	21	4	W	0.5[a]	36–37.5
Cefactor	2	1	21	5	A	0.05	36–37.5
Cefadroxil	2	1	21	4	A	0.05	36–37.5
Cefamandole	2	1	21	5	A	0.06	36–37.5
Cefazolin	2	1	21	4	A	0.05	32–35
Cefotaxime	2	1	21	5	A	0.1	36–37.5
Cefoxitin	2	1	21	5	A	0.1	36–37.5
Cephalexin	2	1	21	4	A	0.05	32–35
Cephaloglycin	2	1	21	4	A	0.2	32–35
Cephaloridine	2	1	21	4	A	0.1	32–35
Cephalothin	2	1	21	4	A	0.1	32–35
Cephapirin	2	1	21	4	A	0.08	32–35
Cephradine	2	1	21	4	A	0.05	32–35
Clindamycin	11	11	21	4	C	1.5	36–37.5
Cloxacillin	2	1	21	4	A	0.1	32–35
Colistimethate, sodium	9	10	21	4	F	0.1	36–37.5
Colistin	9	10	21	4	F	0.1	36–37.5
Cyclacillin	11	11	21	4	C	0.5	36–37.5
Dactinomycin	5	5	10	4	H		36–37.5
Dicloxacillin	2	1	21	4	A	0.1	32–35
Dihydrostreptomycin	5	5	21	4	H	b	36–37.5
Erythromycin	11	11	21	4	C	1.5	32–35

(continued)

TABLE 14.4
Microbiological Assay Methods: Preparation of Agar Diffusion Assay Plates (continued)

Antimicrobial Agent	Media to Be Used Listed by Medium Number		mL of Media to Be Used in the Base and Seed Layers		Test Organism	Suggested Volume of Standardized Inoculum to Be Added to Each mL (mL)	Incubation Temperature (°C)
	Base Layer	Seed Layer	Base Layer	Seed Layer			
Gentamicin	11	11	21	4	D	0.03	36–37.5
Kanamycin B	5	5	21	4	H	b	36–37.5
Methicillin	2	1	21	4	A	0.3	32–35
Nafcillin	2	1	21	4	A	0.3	32–35
Natamycin	None	19	None	8	E	0.8	29–31
Neomycin	11	11	21	4	A	0.4	32–35
Neomycin	11	11	21	4	D	1.0	36–37.5
Netilmicin	11	11	20	5	D	0.25	36–37.5
Novobiocin	2	1	21	4	D	4.0	34–36
Nystatin	None	19	None	8	T	1.0	29–31
Oleandomycin	11	11	21	4	D	1.0	36–37.5
Oxacillin	2	1	21	4	A	0.3	32–35
Paromomycin	11	11	21	4	D	2.0	36–37.5
Penicillin G	2	1	21	4	A	1.0	32–35
Penicillin V	2	1	21	4	A	1.0	32–35
Polymyxin B	9	10	21	4	F	0.1	36–37.5
Rifampin	2	2	21	4	H	0.1	29–31
Sisomicin	11	11	21	4	D	0.03	36–37.5
Streptomycin	5	5	21	4	H	b	36–37.5
Ticarcillin	38	38	21	4	Y	1.5	36–37.5
Vancomycin	8	8	10	4	H	b	36–37.5

[a] Use dilution of the suspension that gives 25% light transmission in lieu of the stock suspension.
[b] Determine the amount of the inoculum by the use of test plates.

TABLE 14.5
Microbiological Assay Methods: Solutions

Solution 1: 1% potassium phosphate buffer, pH 6.0
Dibasic potassium phosphate: 2.0 g
Monobasic potassium phosphate: 8.0 g
Distilled water, q.s.[a]: 1,000 mL
Adjust with 18 N phosphoric acid or 10 N potassium hydroxide to yield a pH 5.95–6.05 after sterilization.

Solution 3: 0.1 M potassium phosphate buffer, pH 8.0
Dibasic potassium phosphate: 16.73 g
Monobasic potassium phosphate: 0.523 g
Distilled water, q.s: 1,000 mL
Adjust with 18 N phosphoric acid or 10 N potassium hydroxide to yield a pH 7.9–8.1 after sterilization.

Solution 4: 0.1 M potassium phosphate buffer, pH 4.5
Monobasic potassium phosphate: 13.6 g
Distilled water, q.s: 1,000 mL
Adjust with 18 N phosphoric acid or 10 N potassium hydroxide to yield a pH 4.45–4.55 after sterilization.

Solution 6: 10% potassium phosphate buffer, pH 6.0
Dibasic potassium phosphate: 20.0 g
Monobasic potassium phosphate: 80.0 g
Distilled water, q.s: 1,000 mL
Adjust with 18 N phosphoric acid or 10 N potassium hydroxide to yield a pH 5.95–6.05 after sterilization.

Solution 10: 0.2 M potassium phosphate buffer, pH 10.5
Dibasic potassium phosphate: 35.0 g
10 N potassium hydroxide: 2.0 mL
Distilled water, q.s: 1,000 mL
Adjust with 18 N phosphoric acid or 10 N potassium hydroxide to yield a pH 10.4–10.6 after sterilization.

Solution 12: 10% potassium phosphate buffer, pH 7.0
Monobasic potassium phosphate: 100.0 g
Distilled water, q.s: 1,000 mL
Adjust with 18 N phosphoric acid or 10 N potassium hydroxide to yield a pH 6.95–7.05 after sterilization.

Solution 14: 2% sodium bicarbonate solution
Sodium bicarbonate: 20.0 g
Distilled water, q.s: 1,000 mL
Prepare daily.

Solution 16: 0.1 M potassium phosphate buffer, pH 7.0
Dibasic potassium phosphate: 13.6 g
Monobasic potassium phosphate: 4.0 g
Distilled water, q.s.: 1,000 mL
Adjust with 18 N phosphoric acid or 10 N potassium hydroxide to yield a pH 6.8–7.2 after sterilization.

Solution numbers 1, 3, 4, and 6 correspond to those in Grove, D.C. and Randall, W.A. *Assay Methods of Antibiotics,* Medical Encyclopedia, Inc., New York, 1955, p. 222.

[a] q.s. = dilute to volume.

Stainless steel or glazed ceramic penicylinders can be placed on the inoculated agar surface of assay plates. Fill the cylinders with individual solutions. Each cylinder will hold at least 100 μL. Penicylinders must seat firmly on the agar surface, and all movement of the cylinders must be prevented after they are filled to prevent leakage of the solutions. Cylinders that leak produce

TABLE 14.6
Microbiological Assay Methods: Example of Agar Diffusion Assay Standard Response Lines for Aqueous Protein Free Specimens[a]

Antibiotic	Initial Solvent (Number)	Subsequent Diluent (µg/mL)	Stock Solution Concentration	Standard Response Line (µg/mL)	Storage Time at 2–8°C
Amoxicillin	3	DW	1,000	0.064, 0.08, 0.1, 0.125, 0.156	1 week
Amphotericin B	DMSO	DMSO	1,000	0.64, 0.8, 1, 1.25, 1.56	Use immediately
Ampicillin	DW	DW	1,000	0.064, 0.8, 0.1, 0.125, 0.156	1 week
Bacitracin zinc	0.01 N HCl		100 units	0.64, 0.8, 1, 1.25, 1.56	Use immediately
Carbenicillin	1	1	1,000	12.8, 16, 20, 25, 31.2	2 weeks
Cefaclor	1	1	1,000	3.2, 4, 5, 6.25, 7.81	1 day
Cefadroxil	1	1	1,000	12.8, 16, 20, 25, 31.2	Use same day
Cefamandole	3	1	1,000	1.28, 1.6, 2, 2.5, 3.12	1 day
Cefazolin	1	1	1,000	0.64, 0.8, 1, 1.25, 1.56	5 days
Cefotaxime	1	1	1,000	6.4, 8, 10, 12.5, 15.6	Use same day
Cefoxitin	1	1	1,000	12.8, 16, 2, 25, 31.2	Use same day
Cephalexin	1	1	1,000	12.8, 16, 20, 25, 31.2	1 week
Cephaloglycin	DW	DW	100	6.4, 8, 10, 12.5, 15.6	1 week
Cephaloridine	1	1	1,000	0.64, 0.8, 1, 1.25, 1.56	5 days
Cephalothin	1	1	1,000	0.64, 0.8, 1, 1.25, 1.56	5 days
Cephapirin	1	1	1,000	0.64, 0.8, 1, 1.25, 1.56	3 days
Cephradine	1	1	1,000	6.4, 8, 10, 12.5, 15.6	5 days
Chloramphenicol	EtOH	EtOH	1,000	4, 6, 8, 12, 16	1 week
Clindamycin	DW	DW	1,000	0.64, 0.8, 1, 1.25, 1.56	1 month
Cloxacillin	1	1	1,000	3.2, 4, 5, 6.25, 7.81	1 week
Colistimethate	6	6	1,000	0.64, 0.8, 1, 1.25, 1.56	Use same day
Colistin	6	6	1,000	0.64, 0.8, 1, 1.25, 1.56	2 weeks
Cyclacillin	DW	DW	1,000	0.64, 0.8, 1, 1.25, 1.56	1 day

Dactinomycin	3		1,000	0.5, 0.71, 1, 1.41, 2	3 months
Dicloxacillin	1		1,000	3.2, 4, 5, 6.25, 7.81	1 week
Dihydro-streptomycin	3		1,000	0.64, 0.8, 1, 1.25, 1.56	30 days
Erythromycin	3	3	1,000	0.64, 0.8, 1, 1.25, 1.56	2 weeks
5-Flucytosine	DMSO	DMSO	1,000	5, 7.5, 15, 25, 50, 75, 100	Use same day
Gentamicin	3	1	1,000	0.064, 0.08, 0.1, 0.125, 0.156	1 month
Itraconazole	DMSO	DMSO	1,000	0.25, 0.75, 2, 6, 15, 25	Use same day
Kanamycin B	3	1	1,000	0.64, 0.8, 1, 1.25, 1.56	1 month
Methicillin	1	1	1,000	6.4, 8, 10, 12.5, 15.6	4 days
Nafcillin	1	1	1,000	1.28, 1.6, 2, 2.5, 3.12	2
Neomycin	3	3	1,000	0.64, 0.8, 1, 1.25, 1.56	2 weeks
If test organism D is used					
If test organism A is used				6.4, 8, 10, 12.5, 15	
Netilmicin[b]	3	1	1,000	0.064, 0.08, 0.1, 0.125, 0.156	1 week
Novobiocin	3	3	1,000	0.32, 0.4, 0.5, 0.625,	5 days
or EtOH		6		0.781	
Nystatin[c] (Use red low actinic glassware)	DMF	6	1,000 units	12.8, 16, 20, 25, 31.2	Use same day
Oleandomycin ethyl alcohol	3	1	1,000	3.2, 4, 5, 6.25, 7.81	30 days
Oxacillin	1	1	1,000	3.2, 4, 5, 6.25, 7.81	3 days
Penicillin G or V	1 units	1	1,000	0.64, 0.8, 1, 1.25, 1.56	4 days
Polymyxin B[a]	6 units	DW	1,000	6.4, 8, 10, 12.5, 15.6	2 weeks
Rifampin	MeOH	DW (stir)	1,000	3.2, 4, 5, 6.25, 7.81	1 day
Streptomycin	3	1	1,000	0.64, 0.8, 1, 1.25, 1.56	30 days
Sisomicin[c]	3	1	1,000	0.064, 0.08, 0.1, 0.125, 0.156	2 weeks
Ticarcillin	1	1	1,000	3.2, 4, 5, 6.25, 7.81	1 day
Vancomycin	DW	DW	1,000	6.4, 8, 10, 12.5, 15.6	1 week

DW = distilled water, HCl = hydrochloric acid, MeOH = methyl alcohol, EtOH = ethyl alcohol, DMSO = dimethylsulfoxide, DMF = dimethylformamide.

[a] Additional suggestions can be found in the current edition of the U.S. Pharmacopeia.

[b] Working standard should be stored below 20°C under an atmosphere of nitrogen. Netilmicin sulfate and sisomicin are hygroscopic and care should be exercised during weighing.

[c] For assay of nystatin pastilles, use 80% aqueous dimethylformamide as the initial solvent and as diluent for all dilutions where dimethylformamide is required.

erratically shaped and sized inhibition zones that invalidate the zone diameters on the plate. The cylinders must be thoroughly decontaminated, cleaned, and rinsed between uses to prevent cross-contamination. Decontaminate and clean cylinders by immersion in water containing a glassware cleaner and autoclave for 15 min. Rinse cylinders thoroughly with tap water followed by distilled water to remove the cleaner. Periodically it may be necessary to clean the cylinders with 6 N nitric acid followed by thorough rinsing to remove protein buildup.

14.3.8 INCUBATION

Incubate assay plates at a temperature suitable for growth of the indicator organism. Use an incubator that maintains a closely controlled, uniformly distributed temperature. Minimize the temperature variation in the incubator because small differences in the incubator temperature can influence zone diameters. A water jacketed incubator maintains a more uniform temperature than does a flowing air incubator and may vibrate less. Vibration during incubation is a particular concern for assays with penicylinders. The duration of incubation depends on the growth rate of the indicator organism. Incubate assay plates in stacks no more than four high to minimize temperature variation within the stack.

14.3.9 ZONE DIAMETER MEASUREMENT

The diameter of zones of inhibition is determined to the nearest 0.1 mm using calipers, a Fisher-Lilly zone reader, or other similar device. Repeated measurements of individual zone diameters on a set of plates using a Fisher Lilly zone reader can be expected to vary by <0.2 mm on average. Consistent variation in excess of 0.2 mm for repeated measurements suggests that the zone edge definition is poor, the zone reader permits slack movement of the measurement scale, or operator variability may be influencing the results. Computerized image analyzers are available that enable the analyst to record images of each assay plate for subsequent analysis. Discrimination in locating the zone edges is a critical variable in computerized image analysis.

14.3.10 CALCULATIONS

14.3.10.1 Self-Contained Assays

There is a linear relationship between the diameter of the zone of inhibition, in millimeters, and the logarithm of the concentration of solutions used to prepare the standard response line. A plot of the resulting data should be a straight line [24,28,29].

Compute the average zone diameter for each standard response line concentration using data from all replicate plates. Compute the average zone diameter for the sample.

Using two- or three-cycle semilogarithmic graph paper, plot the logarithm of the standard response line concentrations against the average zone diameter for each concentration. Fit a line to the plotted points using a least squares regression statistical analysis [24,30]. Determine the sample concentration that corresponds to the average zone diameter of the sample. Multiply the determined sample concentration by any specimen dilutions that were made.

14.3.10.2 Internally Normalized Assays

Compute the average zone diameter of each standard response line concentration using data from all replicate plates. Compute the average zone diameter of the common solution on each set of replicate plates. Compute the overall average zone diameter for the common solution on all assay plates in all sets. Compute the average zone diameter for each sample. For each set of replicate plates, compare the computed average response produced by the common solution in that set of plates to the computed overall (all plates) response produced by the common solution. Normalize the response of the common solution on each set of replicate plates. Normalize the response of the unique solution on each set of replicate plates using the same correction required to normalize the response of the common solution on those plates. For example, if the overall common solution response was 20.0 mm and common solution response for a set of replicate plates was 19.8 mm, add 0.2 mm to the average response of the common solution and add 0.2 mm to the average response of the unique solution on those plates.

Plot the logarithm of the standard response line concentrations against the averaged and normalized zone diameter for each concentration on two- or three-cycle semi-logarithmic graph paper. Fit a line of least squares to the plotted points. Determine the sample concentration that corresponds to the averaged and normalized zone diameter of the sample. Multiply the determined sample concentration by any specimen dilution that was made.

Bioassays frequently are less reproducible and have a greater standard deviation between replicate assays than assays based on physical or chemical parameters. Typical agar diffusion assays have a standard deviation of about 10%; however, bioassays with a standard deviation of 5%–6% are reported [32].

14.3.11 ANTIFUNGAL AGENTS

The concentration of antifungal agents in body fluids can be assayed following the same general principles that apply to bioassay of antibacterial agents. However, the value of determining blood levels for antifungal agents other than 5-flucytosine (5-FC) is questionable. The differences between the two types of assays include: the type of indicator organism, inoculum CFU per milliliter, the growth and assay media, temperature, and duration of the incubation, and frequently the solvent used to solubilize the reference standard [33,34].

Bioassays of multiple antifungal agents in a single specimen are typically run using intrinsically resistant organisms or organisms that have developed decreased susceptibility during therapy or by selective inactivation. Examples of selective inhibition include heat inactivation of amphotericin B, 90°C for 30–45 min, in the presence of 5-FC, or addition of 0.05% cytosine to the assay medium to suppress the activity of 5-FC in the presence of amphotericin B [1,18,35,42]. Antifungal agent concentrations can also be determined using high performance liquid chromatography (HPLC) [18,35–38].

The clinical implications of specific antifungal agent concentrations have not yet been as clearly established as they have for many antibacterial agents. Interpretation of assay results is best made by laboratory personnel in consultation with local infectious disease and pharmacy staff [40–42].

14.4 ALTERNATIVE ASSAYS

14.4.1 TURBIDIMETRIC BIOASSAY

The term *turbidity* is used to define any technique that depends upon the change in bacterial mass after incubation in liquid medium and that is used to quantify the amount of antibiotic in a solution. The change in bacterial mass is inversely proportional to the amount of antibiotic present. The change in bacterial mass is measured photometrically after the cells are killed. The cells are killed by heating the culture to at least 80°C for several minutes or by addition of 0.5 mL of 12% formalin for every 10 mL of culture volume [28]. The photometric measurements can be automated and the resulting computer file, if secure, saved as raw data.

The photometric data can be plotted as percent transmission, optical density, or other data algorithm as a function of concentration of antimicrobial, or equivalently, dilution of a reference sample. Turbidimetric assays have the capability of rapidly testing a large number of samples. Using a log phase inoculum, turbidimetric antibacterial assays often require <4 h of incubation [30] (Table 14.7).

TABLE 14.7
Microbiological Assay Methods: Examples of Turbidimetric Assay Conditions for Aqueous Specimens

Antibiotic	Incubation Temperature (C°)	Test Organism[a]	Media	Volume per 100 mL of Media
Amikacin	36–37.5	A	3	0.1
Candicidin	27–29	E	13	0.2
Capreomycin	36–37.5	I	3	0.05
Chloramphenicol	36–37.5	J	3	0.7
Chlor-tetracycline	36–37.5	A	3	0.1
Cycloserine	36–37.5	A	3	0.4
Dihydro-streptomycin	36–37.5	I	3	0.1
Gramicidin	36–37.5	K	3	1.0
Kanamycin	36–37.5	A	3	0.2
Lincomycin	36–37.5	A	3	0.1
Oxytetracycline	36–37.5	A	3	0.1
Spectinomycin	36–37.5	J	3	0.1
Streptomycin	36–37.5	I	3	0.1
Tetracycline	36–37.5	A	3	0.1
Tobramycin	36–37.5	A	3	0.15

[a] Refer to Table 14.1 for abbreviation description.

The standard response line for a turbidimetric assay typically spans a reduced range of concentrations relative to agar diffusion assays. The plotted standard response line is evaluated point to point without fitting the data to a straight line. The standard response line may or may not be a straight line (Table 14.8). Each rack of assays must contain its own replicated set of standard concentrations and samples. Inclusion of a "known unknown" as the first and last sets of tubes of a turbidimetric assay permits the analyst to monitor and correct for possible changes in indicator organism growth (assay drift) during the assay. Assays can be highly reproducible when a replicated parallel line assay format is employed, incubation temperatures are closely controlled, ±0.1°C, and readings are made using a sensitive photometer. The standard deviation of the replicate assays is typically <4% [24,28,30]. Automated commercially available laboratory instrumentation for running turbidimetric assays following these principles has been developed [28,29]. Use of a validated computer program to analyze the data is recommended because of the large amount of data generated.

Turbidimetric assays are infrequently used to determine the antimicrobial content of clinical specimens; the automated equipment and computer programs are expensive and require highly trained operators. Turbidimetric bioassays are more likely to be used in a quality control or research environment.

14.4.2 Assays Based on Physical or Chemical Methods

14.4.2.1 Overview

Historically, about 75%–85% of all antimicrobial concentrations in clinical specimens were determined by microbiological assays. These assays have frequently been replaced by more rapid, sensitive, and accurate nonmicrobiological assays [1,2,9,10]. Currently there are a number of chemical or physical methods available to determine the level of antimicrobial agents in body fluids. The choice of method(s) depends on the antimicrobial agent, type of specimen, and laboratory resources available at the institution where the assay is performed [1,2,4,5,11–18,26] (Table 14.9).

TABLE 14.8
Microbiological Assay Methods: Examples of Turbidimetric Assay Standard Response Lines for Aqueous Specimens

Antibiotic (1 mg/mL)	Initial Solvent	Diluent Solvent	Final Antibiotic Concentration (µg/mL)	Storage at 2–8°C
Amikacin	DW	DW	8, 8.9, 10, 11.2, 12.5	2 weeks
Candicidin[a]	DMSO	DW	0.03, 0.043, 0.06, .08, .085, 0.12	Use same day
Capreomycin	DW	DW	80, 89, 100, 112, 125	7 days
Chloramphenicol	EtOH	DW	2, 2.24, 2.5, 2.8, 3.12	1 month
Chlor-tetracycline	0.01 N HCl	DW	0.048, 0.054, 0.06, 0.067, 0.075	4 days
Cycloserine	DW	DW	40, 44.5, 50, 56, 62.5	1 month
Dihydro-streptomycin	DW	DW	24, 26.8, 30, 33.5, 37.5	30 days
Doxycycline	0.1 N HCl	DW	0.08, 0.089, 0.1, 0.112, 0.125	5 days
Gramicidin	EtOH U.S.P.	EtOH	0.032, 0.0356, 0.04, 0.0448, 0.05	30 days
Kanamycin	DW	DW	8, 8.9, 10, 11.2, 12.5	1 month
Lincomycin	DW	DW	0.4, 0.447, 0.5, 0.559, 0.625	1 month
Oxytetracycline	0.1 N HCl	DW	0.192, 0.215, 0.24, 0.268, 0.3	4 days
Spectinomycin	DW	DW	24, 26.8, 30, 33.5, 37.5	1 month
Streptomycin	DW	DW	24, 26.7, 30, 33.5, 37.5	30 days
Tetracycline	0.1 N HCl	DW	0.192, 0.215, 0.24, 0.268, 0.3	1 day
Tobramycin	DW	DW	2, 2.236, 2.5, 2.795, 3.125	2 weeks

DW = distilled water, HCl = hydrochloric acid, EtOH = ethyl alcohol, DMSO = dimethylsulfoxide.

The gramicidin working standard and the gramicidin standard response line concentrations are used for the assay of tyrothricin.

[a] Use sterile equipment for all stages of this assay.

TABLE 14.9
Antimicrobial Assay Methods

Assay	Sensitivity (µg/mL)	Specificity	Time Required	Sample Size	Advantages	Disadvantages
RIA	0.1	Metabolite	2–4 h	50–200 µL	Sensitive, specific	Radioactive waste, costly reagents, and equipment
EMIT	1–2	Highly specific	10 min	<100 µL	Rapid, specific	Low sensitivity, expensive reagents
FPI	0.3–2	Highly specific	10–30 min	50 µL	Automated, sensitive, specific, rapid	Costly reagents and equipment
HPLC	0.1	Highly specific	30–60 min	<1 mL	Sensitive, specific, rapid, versatile	Expensive equipment, technically difficult
Bioassay	0.1–5	Low, other antibiotics may interfere	4–48 h	1–3 mL	Simple, versatile, inexpensive	Poor sensitivity, specificity, speed, and precision

RIA: Radioimmune assay; EMIT: enzyme multiplied immunoassay; FPI fluorometric assay; HPLC: high performance liquid chromatography.

14.4.2.2 High Performance Liquid Chromatography (HPLC)

This technique is specific and sensitive and can be used to assay many classes of antimicrobial agents. HPLC methods have the capability to separate parent drug from metabolites or breakdown products. HPLC is the method of choice for many antimicrobial agents that contain aβ-lactam ring. Separation of the antimicrobial agent from the surrounding biological fluid using organic solvents may be necessary. The disadvantages of HPLC methods include costly equipment, the need for highly trained technologists, and the need to dispose of used solvents. HPLC units are often dedicated to a single function or antimicrobial agent. These factors restrict use of HPLC methods in many laboratories.

14.4.2.3 Fluorometry

Fluorometric methods are accurate, sensitive, highly specific, and can be automated. The disadvantages of fluorometric methods include cost of equipment and specimens are often tested in batches. These tests are frequently used to assay aminoglycoside and glycopeptide concentrations.

14.4.2.4 Radioenzymatic Assay (RIA)

RIA assays have greater sensitivity and specificity, and are more rapidly completed than bioassays. They are infrequently used in clinical laboratories because of the cost of equipment and supplies, and the use of radioisotopes.

14.4.2.5 Enzyme Multiplied Immunoassay Technique (EMIT)

EMIT assays have greater specificity than bioassays; however, they are less sensitive and require expensive reagents. They are not often used in clinical laboratories in the United States.

14.5 INTERPRETATION OF ASSAY RESULTS

The interpretation of the importance of a given antimicrobial concentration is a complex undertaking. Several variables must be considered in addition to the antimicrobial agent and its absolute concentration. The variables include: the type of specimen tested, patient related physiological variables that modify drug disposition or excretion, interactions with concomitant medications, and possible interference caused by metabolic or breakdown products of the antimicrobial. An example of an interference due to drug metabolism is the effect of hydroxyitraconazole on the bioassay for itraconazole.

The concentration of an antimicrobial agent that is acceptable in a urine specimen is unlikely to be acceptable in CSF or serum specimens. The concentration of an antimicrobial agent in serum that has a high probability of producing a therapeutic success can be predicted using the highest minimum inhibitory concentration (MIC) for that antimicrobial that defines a fully susceptible organism of the type causing the infection. Following this rationale, the therapeutic levels of several antimicrobials are presented (Table 14.10).

14.6 GENERIC AGAR DIFFUSION BIOASSAY PROTOCOL

14.6.1 Equipment Needed

1. Flat and level bench top.
2. Analytical balance capable of accurately weighing to at least four decimal places to weigh reference antimicrobial agents.
3. General purpose laboratory weighing scale to weigh chemicals and powdered media.

TABLE 14.10
Therapeutic Ranges, µg/mL, for Selected Antimicrobial Agents

Antimicrobial Agent	Organism Group	Therapeutic Range[a]
β-Lactams		
Ampicillin	*Enterobacteriaceae*	≤8
	Enterococcus spp.	≤8
	Staphylococcus spp.	≤0.25
Methicillin	*Staphylococcus* spp.	≤8
Nafcillin	*Staphylococcus aureus*	≤2
Oxacillin	*Staphylococcus aureus*	≤2
Penicillin	*Staphylococcus* spp.	≤0.12
	Enterococcus spp.	≤8
Most cephalosporins	*Staphylococcus aureus*	≤8
Carbapenems	*Staphylococcus* spp.	
Imipenem		≤4
Meropenem		≤4
Ertapenem		≤2
Glycopeptides		
Teicoplanin		≤8
Vancomycin		≤4
Aminoglycosides		
Amikacin		≤16
Gentamicin	*Enterococcus* spp.	≤500
	Other organisms	≤4
Kanamycin		≤16
Netilmicin		≤8
Tobramycin		≤4
Macrolides		
Azithromycin		≤2
Clarithromycin		≤2
Erythromycin		≤0.5
Other Classes		
Tetracycline		≤4
Most fluoroquinolones		≤1
Ciprofloxacin		≤1
Chloramphenicol		≤8
Clindamycin		≤0.5
Rifampin		≤1

[a] The therapeutic ranges are based upon CLSI document M100-S16 fully susceptible category MIC values. [Clinical and Laboratory Standards Institute (formerly NCCLS). Performance standards for antimicrobial susceptibility testing. document M100-S16, Clinical and Laboratory Standards Institute, Wayne, PA, January 2006.]

4. Turbidity standards or photometer to standardize the inoculum.
5. Autoclave to sterilize media and buffers and to decontaminate waste.
6. Appropriate nutritive agar(s) for the inoculum and the assay plates.
7. Appropriate indicator organism(s).
8. Incubators controlled to the desired temperatures.
9. Appropriate antimicrobial reference standard of known potency.

10. Appropriate solvent for reference standard and sterile diluent to prepare standard response line concentrations and if necessary to dilute specimens.
11. Sterile petri dishes of the appropriate diameter or sterile Nunc plates.
12. S & S disks of appropriate diameter, well cutter with attached vacuum source, or penicylinders.
13. Water bath controlled to 45°C–48°C; if *B. subtilis* ATCC 6633 spore suspension is used as the indicator organism, the temperature can be higher, 50°C–55°C.
14. Volumetric flasks of sizes 10, 20, and 25 mL.
15. New disposable 16–18 × 125–175-mm glass tubes for samples.
16. Sterile serological pipettes of assorted sizes.
17. Adjustable micropipette with sterile tips to apply samples or forceps to hold disks while dipping and draining.
18. Calipers or a Fisher-Lilly or equivalent zone reader.
19. Gloves, lab coat, safety glasses, marker pen, paper, semilogarithmic graph paper, pen, and calculator or computer.

14.6.2 PROCEDURE FOR AN INTERNALLY NORMALIZED BIOASSAY

14.6.2.1 Assumptions

1. Use 90-mm petri dishes; 10 mL per plate of nutritive agar seeded with 2×10^5 CFU/mL of *B. subtilis* spores using a *B. subtilis* spore suspension containing 2×10^8 CFU/mL.
2. Use a 5-point standard response line with 4 assay plates (12 values) per concentration.
3. The stock reference solution contains 1.0 mg/mL of drug potency and the standard response line concentrations are 1, 1.5, 2.5, 4, and 9 μg/mL. The midpoint of the standard response line, 2.5 μg/mL, is the internal reference (common) solution. The reference powder has a potency of 90% = 900 μg/mg or mg/g and is soluble in 1% pH 6 phosphate buffer. Apply 20 μL to each 6.3-mm (1/4-in.) S&S 740E disk.
4. Five urine samples require testing. Four urine samples do not require dilution and one has been determined in a screening assay to require a dilution of 1:50 before it is assayed.
5. Each sample is tested on 4 assay plates (12 values). Apply 20 μL of a solution to each 6.3-mm (1/4-in.) S&S 740E disk.

    Note: For samples that are screened for antimicrobial activity: the change in zone diameter produced by halving the drug concentration of the standard is the same millimeter change in zone diameter that a 1:2 dilution of the sample will produce. For example, if 2 μg/mL of standard produces an 18-mm zone of inhibition and 1 μg/mL of standard produces a 15-mm zone diameter; a 1:2 dilution of the specimen would reduce the zone diameter by 18 mm – 15 mm = 3 mm. A dilution of 1:8 is mathematically equivalent to three consecutive 1:2 dilutions. A 1:8 dilution of the specimen (1 part specimen + 7 parts diluent) would reduce the zone of inhibition about 3 mm × 3 dilutions = 9 mm. Zones of inhibition whose size is limited by diffusion, typically zones with a diameter exceeding 40 mm, may not closely follow this example. A 1:2 dilution of such a specimen may reduce the zone diameter by less than the calculated number of millimeters.

14.6.2.2 Protocol

1. Inoculate the indicator organism on the surface of an appropriate agar growth medium and incubate. Harvest the resulting bacterial growth using a minimal volume of sterile pH 6–7 phosphate buffer or sterile 0.9% saline in the mid to late log phase of growth. Prolonged incubation, 5–7 days, may be required if spores are required. Standardize the cell density using McFarland barium sulfate turbidity standards or a photometer [3,23].

This step is not necessary if a stock *B. subtilis* spore suspension containing a known number of CFU per milliliter of spores is the indicator and the desired spore concentration in the seeded agar is known. Determine the number of spores in a spore suspension by means of a standard plate count. *Bacillus subtilis* spore suspensions can be kept at 2°C–8°C for several months before use.

2. Determine which bioassay format and size of assay plate will be used (internally normalized assay with 90-mm petri dishes).

3. Determine the number of plates required and prepare a few extras ($20 + 20 + 5 = 45$).

4. Calculate the amount of agar required ($10 \times 45 = 450$ mL).

5. Prepare an amount of suitable nutritive agar for all assay plates following manufacturer's directions. Include a 10%–15% overage to account for losses during autoclaving and provide a small surplus. If agar is prepared in an Erlenmeyer flask, fill the flask to no more than 65% of capacity ($450 + 50 = 500$ mL, prepare the agar in a 1-L flask).

6. Autoclave the nutritive agar following manufacturer's directions. Place the autoclaved agar in the temperature-controlled water bath for at least 1 h before use to permit temperature equilibration of the agar. Do not hold melted and cooled agar in the water bath longer than necessary. Excessive heat can damage the nutrient qualities of media.

7. Add the inoculum to the autoclaved and cooled agar then mix thoroughly without formation of air bubbles (500 mL $\times 2 \times 10^5$ CFU/mL $= 1 \times 10^8$ total CFU required/2×10^8 CFU/mL of spore suspension; use 0.5 mL of spore suspension per 500 mL agar).

8. Dispense the desired volume of seeded (inoculated and mixed) agar into each assay plate on a flat and level bench top or in a biosafety hood. Dispense the seeded agar with a Cornwall dispensing syringe or other automated dispenser to minimize plate-to-plate variation in the volume dispensed and to minimize bubble formation. Use of a serological pipette to dispense seeded agar may cause variation in the volume dispensed and increase bubble formation. Bubbles should be avoided; break any bubbles that develop by rapidly sweeping the surface of the agar plate with a small flame or by sweeping to the side using a pipette. Do not overheat the agar as the indicator may be damaged. Bubbles can interfere with zone formation and size determination.

9. Allow the agar to harden in each assay plate; then dry the surface by partially opening the plate lid for 20–30 min. The moist plates may be placed in a biosafety cabinet with the exhaust fan operating to dry. Do not dry plates in an incubator.

10. Prepare reference stock solution at a concentration of 1.0 mg/mL of potency. To prepare a 100 mL volume of reference stock solution: (1 mg $\times 100$ mL)/0.9 potency $= 111.1$ mg of reference powder and 100 mL of solvent are required. Dissolve the powder in the solvent. A low power sonic cleaning bath is a useful aid when dissolving a poorly soluble powder.

11. Prepare standard response line concentrations using the reference stock solution as the starting material. Mix all solutions thoroughly before use.

    10 μg/mL = 0.25 mL stock solution at 1,000 μg/mL diluted to volume in a 25-mL volumetric flask with diluent.

    9 μg/mL = 9.0 mL of 10 μg/mL diluted to volume with diluent in a 10-mL volumetric flask.

    4 μg/mL = 4.0 mL of 10 μg/mL diluted to volume with diluent in a 10-mL volumetric flask.

    1.5 μg/mL = 1.5 mL of 10 μg/mL diluted to volume with diluent in a 10-mL volumetric flask.

    1.0 μg/mL = 1.0 mL of 10 μg/mL diluted to volume with diluent in a 10-mL volumetric flask.

12. Prepare the internal reference (common solution).

    2.5 μg/mL = 5.0 mL of 10 μg/mL diluted to volume with diluent in a 20-mL volumetric flask.

    Note: Tubes or small flasks may be used instead of volumetric flasks. When using tubes or small flasks, determine the volume of diluent to add by subtracting the volume of reference stock solution used from the total volume required. For example, to prepare the 10-μg/mL stock solution, add 24.75 mL of diluent to the 0.25 mL of reference stock solution.

13. Label each solution as it is prepared. Place all solutions for assay in an ice bath or refrigerator until they are assayed. The reference stock solution should be labeled, dated, assigned an expiration date, and small aliquots stored at the appropriate temperature.

14. Place aliquots of the four urine samples that do not require dilution in separate tubes and label.

15. Place 200 μL of the urine that requires dilution in a tube and add 9.8 mL of the diluent, 1% phosphate buffer pH 6.0, mix thoroughly, and label.

16. Place six disks, equally spaced, approximately 12–14 mm from the edge of an assay plate and place a mark on the edge of the plate to indicate the location of disk number 1. The same disk numbering sequence, either clockwise or counterclockwise from the starting point (disk number 1), should be used on all plates and by all analysts.

17. Place 20 μL of the common solution on disks 1, 3, and 5.

18. Place 20 μL of one standard response line concentration on disks 2, 4, and 6.

19. Replace the lid on the plate and repeat steps 16 to18 three times.

20. Repeat steps 16 to 19 using each of the remaining standard response line concentrations.

21. For each sample, repeat steps 16 to 19 replacing the standard response line concentration with one of the samples.

22. Place all plates in the temperature controlled incubator with the agar side down in stacks of no more than four plates, for 16–18 h.

23. Remove plates from the incubator.

24. Verify the zero and full scale readings on the caliper or zone reader.

25. Determine the diameter of each zone of inhibition to the nearest 0.1 mm.

26. Compute the average zone diameter for each material on each set on four replicate assay plates.

27. Compute the overall overage zone diameter of the common solution on all assay plates; this is the normalized average common solution zone diameter.

28. Normalize the average zone diameter of the common solution on each set of four plates and in like manner normalize the zone diameter of the standard or sample on these plates.

29. Plot the logarithm of the concentration versus linear normalized average zone diameter of all standards and the common solution; fit a standard response line to the data using the method of least squares.

30. Determine the concentration of each sample using the normalized average sample zone diameter and the standard response line. Multiply the resulting concentration by the sample dilution. In this generic assay, the sample dilution of 4 of the urine specimens is 1 and the dilution of the remaining sample is 50.

   Note: All calculations may be done manually, using a calculator, or computer. As a rule of thumb, consider excluding as an outlier from the standard response line any single point that is located more than about 0.6–0.7 mm from the line of best fit. A statistical test for outlying data can be used to verify the correctness of the decision to omit the data point.

REFERENCES

1. Klassen, M. and Edberg, S.C. Measurement of antibiotics in human body fluids: techniques and significance, in Lorian, V., Ed. *Antibiotics in Laboratory Medicine*, 4th ed. Williams & Wilkins, Baltimore, 1996, 230–295.

2. Ostergaard, B.E., Lakatua D., and Rotschafer, J.C. Assays for antimicrobial agents in body fluids, in Murray, P.R., Baron, E.J., Pfaller, M.A., Tenover, F.C., and Yolken, R.H., Eds., *Manual of Clinical Microbiology*, 6th ed. American Society for Microbiology, Washington, DC, 1995, 1428–1434.

3. Code of Federal Regulations (CFR) Title 21, Volume 5, Sections 300 to 499, Subsection 436. U.S. Government Printing Office, April 1, 1998.

4. Edberg, S.C. and Chu, A. Determining antibiotic levels in the blood. *Am. J. Med. Technol.,* 41, 99–105, 1975.

5. Sabath, L.D., Casey, J.I., Ruch, P.A., Stumpf, L.L., and Finland, M. Rapid micro-assay for circulating nephrotoxic antibiotics. *Antimicrob. Agents Chemother.,* 5, 83–90, 1971.

6. Carling, D.C., Idelson, B.A., Casano, A.A., Alexander, E.A., and McCabe, W.R. Nephrotoxicity associated with cephalotin administration. *Arch. Int. Med.,* 135, 797–801, 1975.

7. Kaye, D., Levinson, M.E., and Labovitz, E.D. The unpredictability of serum concentrations of gentamicin: pharmacokinetics of gentamicin in patients with normal and abnormal renal function. *J. Infect. Dis.,* 130, 150–154, 1974.

8. Noone, P., Parson, T.M.C., Pattison, J.R., Slack, R.C.B., Garfield-Davies, D., and Hughes, K. Experience in monitoring gentamicin therapy during treatment of serious gram-negative sepsis. *Brit. Med. J.,* 1, 474–481, 1974.

9. Noone, P., Parson, T.M.C., Pattison, J.R., and Slack, R.C.B., Assay of gentamicin. *Lancet* 1, 49–50, 1973.

10. Edberg, S.C., Young, L.S., and Barry, A.L. Therapeutic drug monitoring of antimicrobial agents, in *Cumitech 20.* American Society for Microbiology, Washington DC, 1984, 1–20.

11. Martinez, L., and Perea, E.J. Fundamentos del tratamiento antimicrobiano, in Perea, E.J., Ed., *Enfermedades Infecciosas* 2nd ed. DOYMA S.A., 1992.

12. Garrod, L.P., Lambert, H.P., and O'Grady, F. *Antibiotics and Chemotherapy.* Churchill Livingstone, Edinburgh, 1973.

13. Rouan, M.C. Antibiotic monitoring in body fluids (review). *J. Chromatogr.,* 340, 361–400, 1985.

14. Gilbert, D.N. Aminoglycosides, in Mandell, G.L., Bennett, J., and Dolin, R., Eds., *Principles and Practice of Infectious Diseases,* 4th ed. Churchill Livingstone, New York, 1995, 279–306.

15. Liberman, D.F., Fitzgerald, J., and Robertson, R.G. Rapid disk test for determining clindamycin serum levels. *Antimicrob. Agents Chemother.,* 5, 458–461, 1974.

16. Noone, P., Pattison, J.R., and Slack, R.B.C. Rapid antibiotic assay. *Lancet,* 1, 49–50, 1973.

17. Sabath, L.D., Casey, J.I., Ruch, P.A., Stumpff, L.L., and Finland, M. Rapid microassay of gentamicin, kanamycin, neomycin, streptomycin, and vancomycin in serum or plasma. *J. Lab. Clin. Med.,* 78, 457–463, 1971.

18. Hulsewede, W. Comparison of high performance liquid chromatography and bioassay for the determination of 5-fluorcytosine in serum. *Int. J. Med. Microbiol. Virol. Parasitol. Infect. Dis.,* 281, 513–518, 1994.

19. Baer, D.M. and Paulson, R.A. The effect of hyperlipidemia on therapeutic drug assays. *Ther. Drug Monit.,* 9, 72–77, 1987.

20. Pitkin, D.H., Actor, P., and Weisbach, J.A. Serum protein binding alterations of selected cephalosporin antibiotics by fatty acids and their derivatives. *J. Pharmaceut. Sci.,* 69, 354–356, 1980.

21. Smith, S.E. and Rawlins, M.D. *Variability in Human Drug Response.* Redwood Press, Trowbridge Wiltshire, England, 1973.

22. Ritschel, W.A. *Handbook of Basic Pharmacokinetics.* 1st ed. Drug Intelligence Press, Hamilton, IL, 1976.

23. Sawada, Y., Hanano, M., Sugiyama, Y., and Iga, T. Prediction of the disposition of β-lactam antibiotics in humans from pharmacokinetic parameters in animals. *J. Pharmocokin. Biopharmaceut.,* 12, 241–260, 1984.

24. Hewitt, W. *Microbiological Assay.* Academic Press, New York, 1977.

25. Wade, J.D., Shimpff, S.C., Newman, K.A., Fortner, C.L., Moody, M.R., Young, V.M., and Wiernik, P.H. Potential of mezlocillin as empiric single agent therapy in febrile granulocytopenic cancer patients. *Antimicrob. Agents Chemother.,* 18, 299–306, 1980.

26. Kallner, A. and Tryding, N. Laboratory tests to evaluate drug administration. *Scand. J. Clin. Lab. Invest.* Suppl., 195, 19–21, 1989.

27. Yamada, Y., Sasaki, J., Matsuzaki, T., and Shiiki, K. Influence of medium and diluent pH and diffusion time on antibiotic assay. *Exp. Clin. Med.* 6, 23–33, 1981.

28. Kabanaugh, F., Ed., *Analytical Microbiology.* Vol. 1. Academic Press, New York, 1963.

29. Kabanaugh, F., Ed., *Analytical Microbiology.* Vol. 2. Academic Press, New York, 1972.

30. Arret, B., Johnson, D.P., and Kirshbarum, A. Outline of detail for microbiological assays of antibiotics: second revision. *J. Pharm. Sci.* 60, 1689–1694, 1971.

31. Clinical and Laboratory Standards Institute. Document M100-S16, CLSI, Wayne, PA, 2006.

32. Pitkin, D., Actor, P., Holl, W., Post, W., and Weisbach, J. Semiautomated turbidimetric microbiological assay for determination of cefazolin. *Antimicrob. Agents Chemother.* 5, 223–227, 1974.

33. McGinnis, M.R. and Rinaldi, M.G. Antifungal drugs: mechanism of action, drug resistance, susceptibility testing and assays of activity in biological fluids, in Lorian, V., Ed., *Antibiotics in Laboratory Medicine*, 4th ed. Williams & Wilkins, Baltimore, 1996.

34. Law, D., Moore, C.B., and Denning, D.W. Bioassay for serum itraconazole concentrations using hydroxyitraconazole standards. *Antimicrob. Agents Chemother.* 38, 1651–1666, 1994.

35. McGinnis, M.R. *Laboratory Handbook of Medical Mycology.* Academic Press, New York, 1980.

36. Hulsewede, J.W. and Dermouni, H. Serum level determination of fluconazole by high-performance liquid chromatography and bioassay. *Zbl. Bakteriol.* 283, 492–496, 1996.

37. Rex, J.H., Hanson, L.H., Amantea, M.A., Stevens, D.A., and Bennett, J.E. Standardization of a fluconazole bioassay and correlation of results to those obtained by high-pressure liquid chromatography. *Antimicrob. Agents Chemother.* 35, 846–850, 1991.

38. Clearly, J.D., Chapman, S.W., Hardin, C.T., and Rinaldi, M.G. Amphotericin B enzyme-linked immunoassay for clinical use: comparison with bioassay and HPLC. *Ann. Pharmacother.* 31, 39–44, 1997.

39 Anaissie, E., Kontoyiannis, D.P., Huls, C., Vartivarian, S., Karl, C., Prince, R.A., Bosso, J., and Bodey, G.P. Safety, plasma concentrations, and efficacy of high-dose fluconazole in invasive mold infections. *J. Inf. Dis.* 1972, 599–602, 1995.

40. Rex, J.H., Nelson, P.W., Paetznick, V.L., Lozano-Chiu, M., Espinel-Ingroff, A., and Anaissie, E. Optimizing the correlation between results of testing *in vitro* and therapeutic outcome *in vivo* for fluconazole by testing critical isolates in a murine model of invasive candidiasis. *Antimicrob. Agents Chemother.* 42, 129–134, 1998.

41. Anaissie, E., Kontoyiannis, D.P., Huls, C., Vartivarian, S., Karl, C., Prince, R.A., Bosso, J., and Bodey, G.P. Safety, plasma concentrations, and efficacy of high-dose fluconazole in invasive mold infections. *J. Inf. Dis.* 1972:, 599, 1995.

42. Pittrow, A.P. Plasma and tissue concentrations of fluconazole and their correlation to breakpoints. *Mycoses* 40, 25–32, 1997.

15 Molecular Methods for Bacterial Strain Typing

Sophie Michaud and Donna Berg

CONTENTS

15.1 INTRODUCTION

Determining whether two or more isolates of the same species represent the same strain is often needed to understand and control the spread of disease in both hospitals and communities [1]. Typical problems include investigating a putative outbreak of a nosocomial pathogen, such as methicillin-resistant *Staphylococcus aureus* (MRSA), or establishing whether the isolation of a common pathogen such as *Campylobacter jejuni* from two successive episodes of enteritis in a single patient represents a relapse or a reinfection [2].

Biotyping (the pattern of biochemical reactions that can be produced by an isolate) and antimicrobial susceptibility testing are the two phenotypic typing methods performed by the clinical microbiology laboratory during routine assessment of essentially all isolates. These methods are typically characterized by both poor reproducibility and poor discriminatory power. First, most isolates of a species have similar metabolic reactions and therefore represent relatively few biotypes. Second, microorganisms are able to alter unpredictably the expression of many cellular products. Finally, antibiotic resistance is under strong selective pressure in hospitals, is often associated with mobile genetic elements such as transposons and plasmids, or may reflect spontaneous point mutations, for example, resistance to quinolones. Consequently, unrelated isolates may have indistinguishable resistance profiles, and conversely, isolates that are otherwise genetically indistinguishable may show different antimicrobial susceptibilities [1].

Biotyping and antimicrobial susceptibility testing are thus currently most useful as screening techniques. Culturing a set of isolates with a distinctive biotype or antimicrobial susceptibility pattern is often the first indication of an outbreak, which must then be confirmed by clinical and

TABLE 15.1

Definitions of the Main Terms Describing Genotypic and Epidemiological Relationships Among Isolates

Isolate	Pure culture of bacteria obtained by subculture of a single colony from a primary isolation plate and presumed to be derived from a single organism.
Strain	Isolate or set of isolates that can be differentiated from other isolates of the same genus and species by phenotypic and/or genotypic characteristics. A strain is a relative concept, a descriptive subdivision of a species based on one or more analyses, and therefore should not be used as a synonym for isolate.
Epidemiologically related isolates	Isolates cultured from specimens taken from patients or the environment during a specific time frame or from a particular area as part of an epidemiological investigation that suggests that the isolates may be derived from a common source.
Genetically related isolates (clones)	Isolates that are indistinguishable from each other by a variety of genetic tests or that are so similar that they are presumed to originate from a common precursor. Such isolates are often referred to as having a particular "genotype," representing a specific "genetic lineage" or to be "clonal."
Outbreak	Increased incidence of an infectious disease in a specific place during a given period that is above the baseline rate for that place and time frame.
Outbreak strains	Isolates of the same species that are both genetically and epidemiologically related (e.g., by time, place, and common source); by implication, the outbreak represents a set of isolates that are derived from a common parent.
Endemic strains	Isolates that are recovered frequently from infected or colonized patients in a particular place and that are indistinguishable or closely related to each other by typing methods, but for which no direct or epidemiological relationship can be identified.

Adapted from Tenover, F.C., Arbeit, R.D., Goering, R.V., Mickelsen, P.A., Murray, B.E., Persing, D.H., and Swaminathan, B. *J. Clin. Microbiol.,* 33(9), 2233–2239, 1995 [3] and Arbeit, R.D. *IDCP,* 5(4), 260–264, 1996 [4].

molecular epidemiological data. The main terms describing genotypic and epidemiological relationships among isolates are defined in Table 15.1.

The primary goal of strain typing studies is to provide laboratory evidence that epidemiologically related isolates are also genetically related and thus represent the same strain. Although molecular typing may contribute substantially to deciphering complex epidemiological processes, it complements, but does not replace basic clinical and epidemiological investigations. The integration of clinical, epidemiological, and typing data are essential for deriving valid and useful conclusions. Bacterial typing is most effective as an aid to outbreak investigations when it is applied to small sets of epidemiologically related isolates in the context of carefully defined questions developed by the clinician or epidemiologist. While typing may indicate that isolates recovered from multiple individuals or from both individuals and the environment represent a single strain, typing alone cannot establish the mode or the direction of transmission [5]. To avoid misinterpretations due to bias or preconceptions, typing should be performed independently and the data should be analyzed according to clear, predefined criteria. The results should then be considered by the infectious diseases or infection control practitioner in collaboration with the microbiology laboratory [1]. Genotypic methods are especially valuable when the epidemiological hypothesis is incorrect; in such instances, analysis of the isolates helps reorient the infection control decisions [5].

Molecular typing may also contribute to understanding the pathophysiology and managing infections in individual patients, based on the assumption that acute infections due to a single species are monoclonal. For example, when multiple isolates of the same species are cultured during distinct episodes of infection in a single patient, bacterial strain typing may help distinguish between a relapse with the same strain, indicating a residual focus or persistent colonization by a virulent organism, and a reinfection with a different strain. Studying the clonality of acute and chronic infections may also help to define the portal of entry of systemic infection when isolates of the same species are recovered from multiple samples in individual patients. For example, when multiple isolates of *Staphylococcus epidermidis* are recovered from independent cultures of patients with implanted foreign devices (e.g., prosthetic heart valves or joints), isolates representing a single strain are presumed to indicate the presence of an active infection, whereas the identification of multiple different strains is most compatible with contamination with the patient's own colonizing flora [5].

Molecular strain typing performed with standardized protocols and computer-assisted normalized databases has also been applied successfully to national and international surveys of the emergence, molecular evolution, and geographical spread of epidemic clones of MRSA [6,7], *Streptococcus pneumoniae* [8–10], *Salmonella typhimurium* [11], *Pseudomonas aeruginosa* [12], *Neisseria meningitidis* [13], and *Mycobacterium tuberculosis* [14]. PulseNet, coordinated by the Centers for Disease Control (CDC), enables standardized pulsed-field gel electrophoresis (PFGE) typing of foodborne pathogens (*Escherichia coli* O157:H7, typhoidal and nontyphoidal Salmonella serotypes, *Listeria monocytogenes, Campylobacter, Vibriocholera*, and *Shigella* spp.) to be used by a network of public health laboratories; data can be compared directly in the central database after transfer on the Internet (www.cdc.gov/ncidod/dbmd/pulsenet/pulsenet.htm) [15]. Similar procedures are now being piloted in Europe, for example, the Enter-Net (the human enteric pathogen surveillance network; www.phls.co.uk/International/Enter-Net/enter-net.htm) and the HARMONY networks (harmonization of antibiotic resistant measurement, methods of typing organisms and ways of using these and other tools to increase the effectiveness of nosocomial infection control; www.phls.co.uk/international/ harmony.htm).

Several DNA-based methods have been used for molecular strain typing of bacteria, including analysis of plasmid DNA, restriction endonuclease analysis of chromosomal DNA, Southern blot analysis of restriction fragment length polymorphisms (RFLP) of ribosomal RNA (ribotyping), macrorestriction fragment polymorphisms resolved by PFGE, polymerase chain reaction (PCR), and amplified fragment length polymorphism analysis (AFLP). A detailed description of the typeability, reproducibility, discriminatory power, ease of interpretation, ease of performance, and extent of use of these genotypic methods has been published elsewhere [16,17]. This chapter particularly focuses on PFGE, which is considered the reference typing method for most bacterial species [18].

15.1.1 PFGE

Developed by Schwartz and Cantor in 1984, PFGE is a variation of agarose gel electrophoresis in which the electric field across the gel periodically changes direction and/or intensity ("pulsed") rather than being kept constant as in conventional agarose gel electrophoresis. The pulsed field allows clear separation of very large molecular length DNA fragments ranging from 10 to 800 kbase [19], in contrast to unidirectional electrophoresis, which cannot separate DNA molecules larger than about 50 kbase in size because of molecular trapping in the gel [20].

Macrorestriction analysis of microbial genomes consists in PFGE separation of a limited number (<30) of large (>50 kbase) fragments of a bacterial chromosome digested with infrequently cutting restriction enzymes. This technique has emerged during the 1990s as the method of choice for studying the molecular epidemiology of bacterial pathogens [17,18,20–22]. It has been proven to be highly discriminatory (95%–100%) and reproducible for most bacterial species so far evaluated with large collections of unrelated isolates [20,23–25], and its performance has been found comparable or superior to that of other available techniques [18,23,25–39]. The high resolving power of PFGE is related to the fact that macrorestriction patterns scan >90% of the chromosome for large rearrangements (affecting >5% of fragment length) and approximately 0.05% of the genome for point mutations affecting restriction sites [20]. Of note, DNA prepared in agarose contains both chromosomal and plasmid DNA [40].

15.1.1.1 Performing PFGE

Conventional DNA extraction methods in solution are unsuitable for macrorestriction analysis because mechanical shearing degrades genomic DNA into fragments of several hundred kilobases that are inadequate for megabase-size restriction digestions [20]. Suitable chromosomal DNA is obtained by incorporating bacteria into agarose plugs. The cell preparation depends on the particular organism. Nonfastidious organisms are normally grown overnight in appropriate broth medium with orbital shaking, whereas fastidious organisms are preferably harvested from colonies grown on an appropriate solid medium [20].

Bacteria are suspended in an appropriate buffer, recovered by centrifugation, and then resuspended to a density of $1–5 \times 10^9$ CFU/mL, depending on the organism. The standardization of the DNA concentration in the agarose plugs is essential to obtaining comparable and informative fragment patterns [20]: Insufficient DNA will produce faint or incomplete patterns, whereas excess DNA will generate smears and result in retarded mobility of fragments during PFGE. The DNA concentration can be estimated from the bacterial cell density measured with a spectrophotometer or a densitometer, and adjusted to a standard value for a given species.

The embedded bacteria are then subjected to in situ detergent–enzyme lysis with a solution typically containing N-lauryl sarcosine, ethylenediaminetetraacetic acid (EDTA), proteinase K [2,41,42], RNAse, lysozyme, lysostaphin (for staphylococci [43]), and/or mutanolysin (for enterococci [44]). The detergent and proteolytic enzyme act together to remove cellular constituents, while the high EDTA concentration inhibits nuclease activity. To reduce the incubation time, researchers mix these cell-wall lytic enzymes with the cell suspension immediately prior to incorporation in the agarose [2,42,44–46].

After cellular and protein lysis, the agarose plugs are extensively washed with water and Tris-EDTA (TE) to remove proteolytic activity, detergent, and excess EDTA. The embedded high molecular size DNA is then digested with a restriction enzyme selected on the basis of the rarity of its recognition sequence in the target genome [20]. Hexamer endonucleases with G + C recognition sequences are rare cutters of A + T rich genomes, and vice versa [47]. Examples of restriction endonucleases commonly used for macrorestriction analysis of important human pathogens are shown in Table 15.2. In general, the enzyme *Sma*I is used for PFGE typing of *S. aureus* [46], *S. epidermidis*, *S. pneumoniae* [48], and *Enterococcus* spp. [44], and *Xba*I for *enterobacteriaceae*, *P. aeruginosa* (some authors rather recommend *Spe*I [40]), and *Stenotrophomonas maltophilia* [41]. The application of multiple enzymes can be used to dictate especially stringent criteria for strain identity.

Slices of agarose containing the chromosomal DNA fragments are inserted into the wells of an agarose gel, and the electrophoresis resolves chromosomal restriction profiles typically composed of 5 to 20 distinct fragments ranging from approximately 10 to 800 kbase. The relative simplicity of the restriction profiles greatly facilitates the analysis and comparison of multiple isolates [18].

The optimal running parameters used for separation of DNA digests depend on the organism, enzyme, and PFGE apparatus. The most popular PFGE system used for bacterial typing is the contour-clamped homogeneous electric field (CHEF) apparatus, in which an hexagonal array of electrodes periodically alternates uniform fields with an angle of reorientation of 120°. Large DNA fragments migrate through the agarose in a zig-zagging motion, in response to changes in the direction of the electric field; the larger the molecule, the longer the time required for the migration. Thus, the time interval between changes of field direction (or pulse time) will primarily determine the size window for separation of DNA molecules by PFGE [49]. A typical ramp time from 5 to 40 s enables optimal separation of DNA fragments from 50 to 600 kbase, while increasing the pulse time to 75 s extends the separation to 1 Mbase with standard CHEF conditions [20].

The mobility of the DNA fragments in an agarose gel further depends on DNA concentration, the type and concentration of the agarose, voltage, ionic strength of the electrophoresis buffer, electrophoresis time and temperature [50]. Changes in any of these factors can lead to alterations

TABLE 15.2
Suitable Restriction Enzymes for PFGE Typing of Selected Bacteria

Organism	Enzymes
Staphylococcus aureus	*Sma*I, *Sst*II, *Csp*I, *Bam*H1
Staphylococcus epidermidis	*Sma*I, *Sst*II, *Kpn*I
Enterococcus spp.	*Sma*I, *Apa*I
Streptococcus pneumoniae	*Sma*I, *Apa*I
Listeria monocytogenes	*Apa*I, *Sma*I, *Not*I
Escherichia coli	*Xba*I, *Not*I, *Sfi*I
Klebsiella pneumoniae	*Xba*I, *Asn*I
Enterobacter spp.	*Xba*I, *Spe*I
Serratia marcescens	*Xba*I
Citrobacter spp.	*Xba*I
Salmonella spp.	*Xba*I
Shigella spp.	*Xba*I, *Sfi*I
Proteus mirabilis	*Sfi*I, *Not*I
Haemophilus influenzae	*Sma*I, *Rsr*II
Bordetella pertussis	*Xba*I, *Asn*I, *Dra*I
Neisseria meningitidis	*Not*I, *Bgl*II, *Spe*I, *Sfi*I
Pseudomonas aeruginosa	*Spe*I, *Dra*I, *Ssp*I, *Xba*I
Stenotrophomonas maltophilia	*Xba*I
Acinetobacter baumanii	*Sma*I, *Apa*I
Burkholderia spp.	*Spe*I
Campylobacter spp.	*Kpn*I, *Sma*I
Bacteroides spp.	*Not*I
Mycobacterium spp.	*Ase*I, *Xba*I, *Dra*I, *Asn*I
Legionella pneumophila	*Sfi*I, *Not*I

Adapted from Struelens, M.J., de Ryck, R., and Deplano, A. in Dijkshoorn, L., Towner, K., Struelens, M., Eds., *New Approaches for the Generation and Analysis of Microbial Typing Data*, Elsevier, 2001, pp. 159, and Maslow, J.N., Slutsky, A.M., and Arbeit, R.D. in Persing, D.H., Smith, T.F., Tenover, F.C., White, T.J., Eds., *Diagnostic Molecular Microbiology, Principles and Applications*. American Society for Microbiology, Washington, DC, 1993, 563.

in the profiles, which then influence the comparability of patterns both within a single gel as well as between different gels.

PFGE gels are normally run at a temperature of 14°C, which is maintained with the use of a buffer cooling and recirculating system to prevent the generation of temperature gradients within the gel during the run [20]. Low ionic strength buffers (e.g., 0.25–0.5 × Tris-Acetic acid EDTA (TAE) or Tris-Boric acid EDTA (TBE)) are preferred to reduce heat generation and shorten the run times [49]. A voltage of 6 V/cm is used for the separation of molecules from 50 kbase to 1.5 Mbase in size. An agarose concentration of 1% is normally used for the separation of DNA fragments ranging from 50 kbase to 1 Mbase. Special PFGE-grade agarose with a high physical strength and low electro-endosmosis allows for a more rapid electrophoresis without loss of resolution [41].

Gels are stained with a fluorescent dye such as ethidium bromide [22], and the electrophoretic patterns are visualized by photography or digital image capture under UV light. The DNA restriction patterns of the isolates are then compared with one another to determine their relatedness. With the aid of the computerized gel scanning and analysis software, it is possible to create data banks of PFGE patterns for all organisms, enabling the creation of reference databases to which any new strain can be compared for identifying its phylogenetic relationship to other similar strains [22].

A detailed PFGE protocol suitable for both gram-positive and gram-negative organisms is described in the Appendix. Rapid PFGE protocols have been published for *E. coli* O157:H7 and other gram-negative organisms [41], *C. jejuni* [2, 42], *Enterococcus* spp. [44], *S. pneumoniae* [51], and MRSA [46].

15.1.1.2 Troubleshooting

The most common problems encountered in preparing DNA for PFGE are inadequate cell lysis, DNA degradation, incomplete protein digestion, partial restriction digests, and migration difficulties (Figure 15.1).

When the lysis step is insufficient, intact cells remain in the agarose after proteinase K digestion and very little DNA migrates out of the plug during the electrophoresis. This results in intense staining of the materiel remaining in the well, the migration of a single, very large DNA fragment, and very faint chromosome bands [40] (Figure 15.1, lanes 2–3). Agarose plugs containing incompletely lysed bacteria can be reprocessed by using the TE washout procedure to remove the proteinase K and then recycling the plugs through the entire procedure beginning with lysis solution [40].

Faint bands or a broad smear at the lower half of the gel may indicate DNA degradation by endogenous nucleases, which most commonly results from the failure to chill and wash the bacteria promptly when harvesting the broth culture [20,40] (Figure 15.1, lane 4). DNA degradation frequently occurs with isolates of *Clostridium* spp., and occasionally with *C. jejuni* or *P. aeruginosa*. Some *C. jejuni* PFGE protocols recommend treatment of the bacterial suspension in 10% formaldehyde for 15 min to inhibit DNAse activity [2,52].

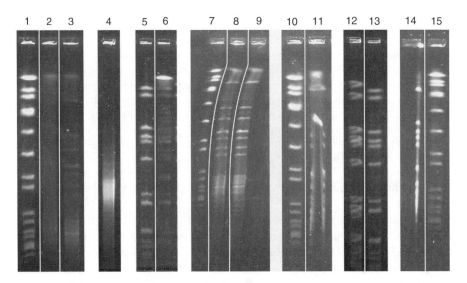

FIGURE 15.1 Composite of seven PFGE agarose gels demonstrating frequently encountered problems. Lanes 1, 7, 10, and 15 contain the molecular size standard *S. aureus* NCTC 8325 digested with *Sma*I. Lanes 2 and 3 contain two *C. jejuni* isolates with inadequate lysis, shown by the migration of a single, very large DNA fragment and faint chromosome bands. Lane 4 contains degraded DNA prepared from an isolate of *C. jejuni*; the broad smear observed reflects DNA that has been spontaneously and randomly fragmented by endogenous endonucleases. Lane 5 contains a complete *Sma*I digest of a clinical isolate of MRSA and lane 6, a partial *Sma*I digest of the same clinical isolate; typical characteristics of the partial digest demonstrated here include an unusually large fragment and intermediate-sized fragments of variable intensity. Lanes 7 to 9 illustrate distorted lanes due to an unleveled PFGE chamber. Lane 11 illustrates a partial *Kpn*I digest of a clinical isolate of *C. jejuni* that migrated inadequately due to an artifact in the gel. Lanes 12 and 13 contain the same clinical *Sma*I digest of MRSA, but the agarose plug was damaged during its insertion in the well of lane 12. In lane 14, only a small part of the agarose plug was inserted in the gel.

Incomplete protein digestion typically results in smearing proximal to the highest DNA band as well as between the DNA fragments. This can be rectified by increasing the amount of proteinase K or the length of digestion. Partial restriction digests are characterized by an unusually large fragment and intermediate-sized fragments of variable intensity between the DNA fragments (Figure 15.1, lane 6) [40]. All the reagents used to prepare the DNA (proteinase K, EDTA, detergent) will inhibit the activity of restriction enzymes if not completely removed; extensive washes in water and TE are thus required to remove all traces of these agents from the samples [53]. If the cell lysis is believed to be adequate but the restriction enzyme is suspect, the plugs can be redigested with fresh restriction enzyme after a TE washout [40].

The most common cause of curved lanes is heterogeneity in either the electric fields (e.g., because of the failure of several electrodes) or the temperature across the gel [49]. If the gel or the chamber are not level, the gel is covered by different depths of buffer and the current varies across the gel. Therefore, temperature gradients can form, leading to DNA moving faster in the warmer regions of the gel (Figure 15.1, lanes 7–9). Lanes can also become distorted if the gel is not fastened securely during electrophoresis or if air bubbles are trapped underneath and generate localized heating in the gel. Finally, bands can become distorted if the plugs are unevenly cut, only partially inserted into the gel, or damaged during insertion (Figure 15.1, lanes 11, 12, and 14).

15.1.1.3 Analyzing Typing Data

15.1.1.3.1 Visual Analysis of the Restriction Patterns

The use of molecular epidemiology data for infection control decisions is based on the assumption that isolates representing the outbreak strain have recently derived from a single (or common) precursor; this implies that outbreak isolates will have the same genotype, and that epidemiologically unrelated isolates will have different genotypes [3]. Demonstrating that isolates represent distinctly different strains indicates that they are not derived from a common source, but the final assignment of isolates with related genotypes requires careful consideration. Even for isolates with indistinguishable genotypes, the discriminatory power of the typing method and the genetic diversity within the species influence the likelihood that the result actually reflects epidemiological relatedness [5]. For example, some epidemiologically unrelated isolates may, by chance, have similar or indistinguishable genotypes, particularly if there is limited genetic diversity within a species. This is especially true for MRSA, a common nosocomial pathogen for which most strains originate from a small number of ancestral clones [54]. Thus, when MRSA is endemic in a hospital, it can be difficult to confirm the occurrence of an MRSA outbreak, particularly if the endemic strain is responsible.

The visual analysis of the restriction patterns for a discrete set of epidemiologically related isolates consists of three steps: (*a*) the examination of the patterns to identify the most common band profile among the isolates, which is presumed to represent the outbreak strain pattern; (*b*) the comparison of the size and number of the fragments in the outbreak pattern with the fragments that make up the patterns of the other isolates; and (*c*) the classification of each isolate's pattern for its relatedness to the outbreak pattern, on the basis of pairwise, fragment-for-fragment comparisons [4]. The absence of a common pattern indicates that the isolates are most likely unrelated and therefore refutes the idea that they represent an outbreak.

Tenover et al. [3] have developed stringent criteria for interpreting chromosomal DNA restriction patterns produced by PFGE. These interpretative criteria are intended for use in analyzing discrete sets of isolates (typically 40 or less) obtained during epidemiological studies of putative outbreaks in hospitals or communities spanning relatively short periods (1 to 3 months); they are not appropriate for studies of large populations of organisms collected over extended periods of 1 year or longer [18]. They can be used when PFGE resolves at least 10 fragments; when fewer bands are detected, the robustness and discriminatory power of the criteria are unknown.

Patterns are classified into four categories: indistinguishable, closely related, possibly related, and unrelated to the outbreak pattern. Isolates are designated genetically indistinguishable if their restriction patterns have the same numbers of bands and if the corresponding bands are the same apparent size. Such isolates are considered to represent the same strain and to be part of the outbreak. However, PFGE patterns are often altered by random genetic events (e.g., point mutations, insertions and deletions of DNA), during the course of an outbreak or even during the course of a single infection when strains are cultured repeatedly over time or isolated multiple times from the same patient [3]. Therefore, patterns that differ from the outbreak pattern by two to three bands (i.e., changes consistent with a single genetic event such as simple insertions or deletions of DNA or the gain or loss of restriction sites) are considered to be closely related to the outbreak pattern. Isolates that differ from the outbreak strain by four to six bands (i.e., changes consistent with two independent genetic events) are considered to be possibly related to the outbreak strain. Although such isolates may have derived from the same genetic precursor as the outbreak strain, they are not as closely related genetically and are likely to differ by other typing techniques; consequently, they are less likely to be related epidemiologically. Such variation has been observed among isolates collected over long periods (≥6 months) or taken from large numbers of patients involved in extended outbreaks. Finally, isolates are considered to be unrelated to the outbreak strain if their PFGE profile differs from the outbreak pattern by seven or more bands (i.e., changes consistent with three or more independent genetic events).

In reporting the typing results for a discrete set of isolates, the outbreak profile is typically reported as type A and all isolates whose restriction patterns are indistinguishable from this pattern are considered as representing the outbreak strain. Patterns that are closely or possibly related to the outbreak pattern are considered as subtypes of A (e.g., A1, A2, etc.), and are considered to be probably or possibly epidemiologically related, respectively. The final determination of whether to include indistinguishable, probably, and possibly related isolates in the epidemiological case definition of the outbreak requires the integration of both molecular and clinical analyses [4]. Finally, patterns that differ substantially from the outbreak pattern are designated as different types (e.g., B, C, etc.) and are considered to be unrelated epidemiologically.

15.1.1.3.2 *Analyzing Electrophoresis Gels by Software*

Numerization of PFGE profiles, together with computer-assisted normalization and introduction of data into a relational database, is necessary to analyze patterns from large series of isolates compared on multiple gels. Computer-assisted analysis allows systematic quality control of DNA fingerprints, rapid identification of identical or closely related patterns, and quantitative analysis of pattern similarity in large databases of several hundred profiles assembled following multicenter surveys or long term surveillance programs [20]. Several specialized software packages are commercially available, including GelCompar and BioNumerics (Applied Maths, Kortrijk, Belgium), BioImage (BioImage, Ann Arbor, MI, USA), and Taxotron (Taxolab, Institut Pasteur, Paris, France).

The process of analyzing electrophoresis gels by software consists of five sequential steps: (1) creation of a digitized image; (2) importation of this image into a computer analysis software; (3) recognition of the different lanes containing the images of the DNA fingerprints; (4) normalization of the different lanes to remove distortions; and (5) analysis and comparison of the electrophoretic profiles [50].

The gel image is digitized either by direct image capture with a digital camera or by scanning a gel photograph with a flatbed document scanner. Digitized images are saved in TIFF files (tagged image file format) with 8-bit optical density (OD) depth (256 gray values). Once imported into a fingerprint analysis software, the lanes of the gel are defined by determining the overall borderlines of the desired parts of the gel and of the different "raw" DNA fingerprints. At the end of this step, each selected DNA pattern has its own individual entry in the computer database and is thereby separated from the rest of the gel [50].

The normalization phase allows the alignment of patterns by associating bands to an external reference pattern and by subsequent interpolation of the intermediate values. Molecular size standards should be loaded on each side and in every fifth well of the gel so that when normalizing the patterns no isolate should be more than two lanes from a standard. The other (nonreference) tracks are aligned gradually according to the closest neighboring reference tracks on either side [50]. Since the normalized band positions are calculated through extrapolation, the external reference standard should cover at least the whole molecular size range of the fragments to be analyzed; if this condition is not respected, the results of the normalization phase will be unpredictable for those bands that reflect fragments with a higher or lower molecular size than the highest or lowest bands of the external reference standard. If a pattern has only one neighboring external reference standard, the normalization process will also lead to unpredictable results [50]. Finally, gels should have the same reference system to be compatible.

Restriction patterns are compared through a cluster analysis followed by the calculation of similarity coefficients. The result of this process is usually shown as a phylogenetic tree (dendrogram), in which the sequential union of clusters, together with the similarity value leading to this union, is depicted (Figure 15.2).

Cluster analysis involves a stepwise reduction in the number of isolates by placing them into groups with similar DNA patterns [50]. The most neutral and commonly used algorithm for clustering DNA patterns is the unweighted pair group method using arithmetic averages (UPGMA) [24]. Similarity coefficients (SCs) are then calculated for all patterns; each SC value is a number between 0 (no similarity at all) and 1 (100% identical patterns). The Dice coefficient is the most reliable coefficient for measuring genetic distances between fragment analysis patterns and is the preferred measure for comparing PFGE patterns [24]. The Dice coefficient is calculated as the number of matching size fragments multiplied by two and divided by the total number of fragments in a pair of patterns. It is also known as the coefficient of Nei and Li when it is applied to RFLP data [20].

$$\text{Dice} = \frac{2 \times N_{\text{common}}}{N_1 + N_2}$$

Isolates whose PFGE patterns are highly similar, as indicated by a Dice coefficient ≥ 0.90, are likely to be related genetically and epidemiologically. Typically, such putative matches must be confirmed by visual examination of the original patterns or direct side-by-side comparisons. In general, the correlation of PFGE pattern similarity with genomic relatedness decreases rapidly below 70% similarity values [20]. Still, the loss of one band or the addition of an extra band does not have a dramatic effect. For example, when applying the Dice coefficient in the case of a profile with 13 bands being compared to a pattern where one band is missing, the Dice SC is SC = $2 \times 12/(12 + 13) = 0.96$. Even in a large database containing many thousands of patterns, these two patterns will group in a similar branch of the dendrogram [50].

Even in the best laboratory situation, the different steps will almost always lead to disturbances or misalignments, thereby influencing the reproducibility of the DNA patterns. Optimization and position tolerance are two software parameters that allow correction of these misalignments to a certain degree. The position tolerance is the maximal shift (in percentage of the pattern length) between two bands allowed to consider the bands as matching. The optimization is the shift allowed between any two patterns and within which the program will look for the best possible matching; it allows track-to-track corrections to compensate for the remaining misalignments by shifting one or both tracks with respect to the other until they reach their maximum correlation [55]. Both settings can be adjusted by the user, but can also be defined automatically by the program [50].

15.1.1.4 Molecular Size Standards, Reproducibility Isolate, and Controls

To ensure accurate fragment size estimates (and adequate normalization of patterns when analyzing gels by software), researchers should include suitable molecular size markers in at least every fifth

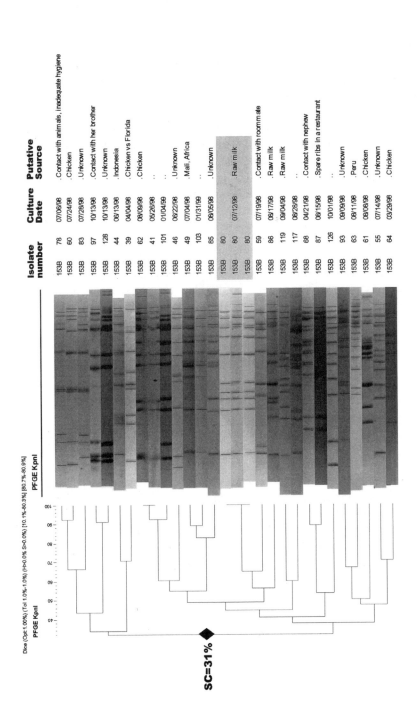

Isolate number	Culture Date	Putative Source
153B 78	07/06/98	Contact with animals, inadequate hygiene
153B 60	07/24/98	Chicken
153B 83	07/28/98	Unknown
153B 97	10/13/98	Contact with her brother
153B 128	10/13/98	Unknown
153B 44	06/13/98	Indonesia
153B 39	04/04/98	Chicken vs Florida
153B 62	09/09/98	Chicken
153B 41	05/26/98	
153B 101	01/04/99	
153B 46	06/22/98	Unknown
153B 49	07/04/96	Mali, Africa
153B 103	01/31/99	
153B 85	09/05/98	Unknown
153B 80	07/12/98	Raw milk
153B 80		
153B 80		
153B 59	07/19/98	Contact with roommate
153B 86	06/17/96	Raw milk
153B 119	09/04/96	Raw milk
153B 117	08/28/98	
153B 68	04/21/96	Contact with nephew
153B 87	06/15/98	Spare ribs in a restaurant
153B 126	10/01/98	
153B 93	09/09/98	Unknown
153B 63	08/11/98	Peru
153B 61	08/08/98	Chicken
153B 55	07/14/98	Unknown
153B 64	03/29/98	Chicken

SC=31%

FIGURE 15.2 Example of a dendrogram generated by BioNumerics version 2.0 (Applied Maths, Kortrijk, Belgium) representing relatedness among PFGE profiles of *Kpn*I digests of 27 isolates of *C. jejuni*. Optimization and a position tolerance of 1.0% were applied. The overall Dice similarity coefficient (SC) among the isolates was 31%. The SC among the reproducibility isolate (153B-80) was 100%. The software allows analysis of both genotypic and clinical epidemiological data together by displaying both the band profile and the pertinent epidemiological information of each isolate.

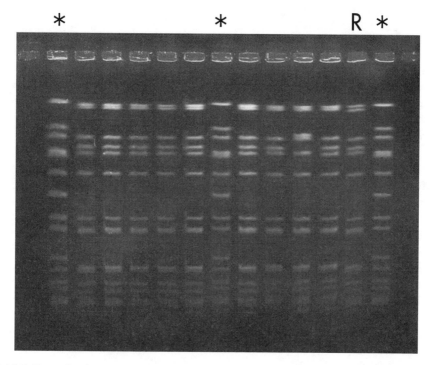

FIGURE 15.3 Example of a 15-lane PFGE gel of *Sma*I digests of MRSA. Lanes 2, 8, and 14 include *Sma*I digests of *S. aureus* NCTC 8325 as a reference standard (shown as * in the gel). Lane 13 contains the *Sma*I digest of an MRSA strain used as a reproducibility control (R). Lanes 1 and 15 were left blank; the remaining lanes were used for study isolates. These isolates were typed without suspecting a nosocomial outbreak of MRSA; the similarity of the patterns illustrates the low discriminatory power of PFGE for MRSA due to the limited genetic diversity within this species, and the importance of interpreting the typing results in the light of clinical epidemiological data and of a specific question defined by the epidemiologist.

lane, that is, in the outside lanes and in the middle of the gel (Figure 15.3) [3,20]. Examples of molecular size standards are phage lambda concatemers, referred to as "lambda ladder," preparations containing restriction endonuclease-digested *Saccharomyces cerevisiae* DNA, and DNA restriction fragment patterns of several well-characterized organisms in which the size of each chromosomal fragment has been determined, such as *S. aureus* NCTC 8325, *Enterococcus faecium* ATCC 51558, *E. coli* ATCC 47076, and *Enterococcus faecalis* ATCC 47077[3].

When multiple gels are analyzed by software, a well-characterized reproducibility isolate should also be processed along with the unknown isolates being tested [56]. Obtaining expected results with the reproducibility organism affirms that the procedure, including the cell lysis, washing, and endonuclease digestion steps, the gel, and the electrophoretic conditions have been appropriate [3]. In addition, since both optimization and position tolerance settings can influence the results of the clustering analysis, they should be validated by comparing the DNA profiles for a given set of gels: optimal settings should result in a Dice SC of 100% among the reproducibility isolates, being a measure for the analysis of the clinical isolates fingerprints [50]. The reproducibility isolate also allows quality control of the reproducibility of the gel: Any gel with reproducibility values lower than 100%, using the Dice coefficient, should not be included in the database [20].

Finally, when typing a set of isolates suspected of being part of an outbreak, it is helpful to include a sample of epidemiologically unrelated isolates as well to ensure that endemic strains can be differentiated from outbreak strains. This is particularly important for analyzing outbreaks of MRSA in which the overall number of PFGE patterns is limited [3].

15.1.1.5 Limitations of PFGE

PFGE requires relatively expensive, specialized equipment, costing from $15,000 to $20,000 [16,18]. Although technical protocols have been simplified over recent years and the duration of some of the incubation periods has been shortened, the technique remains technically demanding and still requires 24–72 h turnaround time [2,20,41,42,46,48]. This effort is partially offset because DNA in agarose is stable for years at 4°C and can be easily released into solution for use in other protocols [18].

In practice, a technique is statistically useful when the most commonly detected types represent less than 5% of random unrelated isolates [5]. This may be difficult to achieve for some pathogens such as MRSA, *Haemophilus influenzae* type b, and *E. coli* O157:H7, which represent genetically restricted subsets of strains within a species [54,57,58]; consequently, epidemiologically unrelated isolates may have very similar genotypes and may be indistinguishable by PFGE, as well as by other typing methods [18,23,59]. Some isolates of a given species may be untypeable by PFGE and must be resolved by using other genotypic techniques such as PCR. In addition, certain organisms such as *Clostridium difficile* and *Aspergillus* spp. may not be typeable by PFGE because their DNA cannot be extracted intact [16].

The level of reproducibility achievable between PFGE patterns obtained within and between gels is a limitation that can be only partially offset by normalization of the gels. PFGE is not suited for population genetics studies of bacterial species because the distance between two isolates in the dendrogram does not represent the genetic distance between them; for these purposes, techniques such as multilocus enzyme electrophoresis (MLEE), or most recently, multilocus sequence typing (MLST), are preferable.

15.2 RIBOTYPING

In the early 1980s researchers began examining ribosomal RNA sequences as a means of understanding relationships between organisms. Practical requirements, time, and technical skill limited the method's use. In 1995 the DuPont Company (Wilmington, DE) introduced an automated ribotyping instrument, the RiboPrinter Microbial Characterization System [60].

The RiboPrinter consists of a characterization unit (Figure 15.4) and a computer workstation. The technician picks bacterial cells from an agar plate, suspends them in buffer, and transfers them to a sample carrier. A heat treatment station inactivates the samples. The technician adds two lysing agents and places the sample carrier in the RiboPrinter. For most isolates, the system uses *EcoRI* to digest the DNA, but the user can substitute other restriction enzymes. Electrophoresis separates the DNA fragments by size on a precast agarose gel. The result is transferred to a nylon membrane. The RiboPrinter exposes the membrane to a series of chemical and enzymatic treatments, causing the DNA fragments to chemiluminesce. The RiboPrinter captures the resulting band pattern image using a digitizing camera and stores the pattern in the computer's memory. This digital representation of the ribosomal RNA pattern is the RiboPrint pattern.

The RiboPrinter system includes built-in analysis software and a database of RiboPrint patterns. Each sample can be identified (given a genus, species, or serovar name) by comparing the generated RiboPrint pattern with the identification patterns in the database. Each sample is also compared with previously processed samples and grouped into dynamic RiboGroups, groups of patterns within a specific similarity range, that reflect the genetic relatedness of the samples. At the end of each run, the RiboPrinter generates a Microbial Characterization System Report (Figure 15.5). Sophisticated data analysis tools enable the operator to further process this information and share it with a network of users [61].

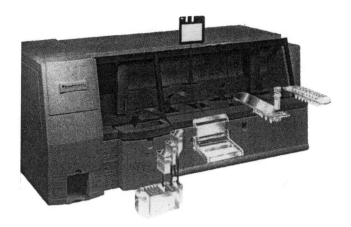

FIGURE 15.4 RiboPrinter Characterization Unit. Illustrates the loading of disposables for the processing of a batch of isolates.

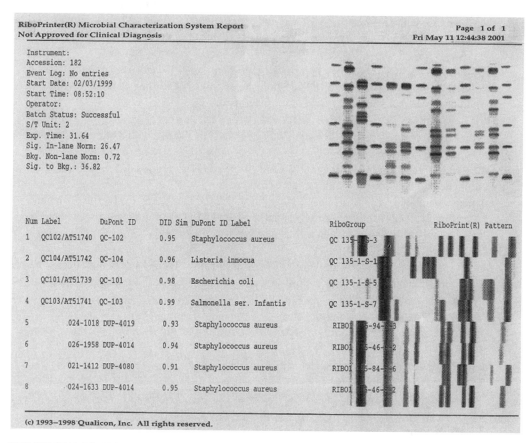

RiboPrinter(R) Microbial Characterization System Report
Not Approved for Clinical Diagnosis

Page 1 of 1
Fri May 11 12:44:38 2001

Instrument:
Accession: 182
Event Log: No entries
Start Date: 02/03/1999
Start Time: 08:52:10
Operator:
Batch Status: Successful
S/T Unit: 2
Exp. Time: 31.64
Sig. In-lane Norm: 26.47
Bkg. Non-lane Norm: 0.72
Sig. to Bkg.: 36.82

Num	Label	DuPont ID	DID Sim	DuPont ID Label	RiboGroup	RiboPrint(R) Pattern
1	QC102/AT51740	QC-102	0.95	Staphylococcus aureus	QC 135-1-S-3	
2	QC104/AT51742	QC-104	0.96	Listeria innocua	QC 135-1-S-1	
3	QC101/AT51739	QC-101	0.98	Escherichia coli	QC 135-1-S-5	
4	QC103/AT51741	QC-103	0.99	Salmonella ser. Infantis	QC 135-1-S-7	
5	.024-1018	DUP-4019	0.93	Staphylococcus aureus	RIBO 5-94-3	
6	026-1958	DUP-4014	0.94	Staphylococcus aureus	RIBO 5-46-2	
7	021-1412	DUP-4080	0.91	Staphylococcus aureus	RIBO 5-84-6	
8	.024-1633	DUP-4014	0.95	Staphylococcus aureus	RIBO 5-46-2	

FIGURE 15.5 RiboPrinter Microbial Characterization System Report. The system report prints automatically at the end of each run. Details of run conditions and image data for the batch are printed on the top half of the report. Identification, the digital representation of the ribosomal RNA pattern (the RiboPrint pattern), and the assigned Ribogroup are shown on the bottom half of the report.

Potential uses for automated ribotyping are growing. It can provide quality assurance in the food, agricultural, and pharmaceutical industries. Hospital infection control practitioners will benefit from timely epidemiological information [60,62].

The main limitation to expanding usage is the system's cost. The unit, its disposables, and maintenance may be prohibitively expensive. It is also not approved by the U.S. Food and Drug Administration at this time. However, the system's many benefits may outweigh its costs. Results are available in 8 h, and new batches of eight organisms can be loaded every 2 h. Automation minimizes errors due to technique, and computerized data analysis eliminates subjective interpretation of results [61].

APPENDIX 15.1 — PREPARATION PROTOCOL FOR PFGE BUFFERS AND REAGENTS

Adapted from Maslow et al. [40].

0.5 M EDTA (pH 7.6 and 8.0):
> Dissolve 10–15 g of NaOH pellets into approximately 700 mL of distilled water and then add 186.1 g of solid sodium EDTA. When completely dissolved, bring pH to exactly 7.6 or 8.0 with concentrated HCl and make up to a final volume of 1,000 mL with distilled water. Autoclave and store at room temperature.

1 M Tris (pH 7.6):
> Dissolve 60.5 g of Tris base into approximately 300 mL distilled water and carefully bring to pH 7.6 with concentrated HCl. Then make up to a final volume of 500 mL with distilled water. Autoclave and store at room temperature.

PIV (Phage buffer IV) (10 mM Tris, pH 7.6; 1 M NaCl):
> Dilute 5 mL of 1 M Tris (pH 7.6) and 29.25 g of NaCl to 500 mL with distilled water. Autoclave and store at 4°C.

Lysis buffer (6 mM Tris, pH 7.6; 1 M NaCl; 100 mM EDTA, pH 7.6; 0.5% Brij-35; 0.2% sodium deoxycholate; 0.5% sodium lauroyl sarcosine):
> Dilute 6.0 mL of 1 M Tris (pH 7.6), 58.0 g of NaCl, 200 mL of 0.5 M EDTA (pH 7.6), 5 mL of Brij-35, 2.0 g of sodium deoxycholate acid, and 5.0 g of sodium lauroyl sarcosine to 1,000 mL with distilled water. Filter sterilize and store at 4°C.

RNAse (10 mg/ml; stock solution):
> A 50-mg stock vial of RNAse has 5,400 U/ml enzyme. To get a concentration of 10 mg/ml, dilute the stock vial in 5 mL of sterile water. Aliquot 0.3 mL into ~16 Eppendorf tubes. Store at –20°C.

Lysozyme (50 mg/ml; stock solution):
> Dilute 0.5 g lysozyme in 10 mL of sterile water. Aliquot 0.5 mL into 20 Eppendorf tubes. Store at –20°C.

Lysostaphin buffer (50 mM Tris, pH 7.6; 0.15 M NaCl):
> Dilute 1.5 mL of 1 M Tris (pH 7.6) and 0.26 g of NaCl to 30 mL with distilled water. Filter sterilize and store at 4°C.

Lysostaphin stock solution (for *Staphylococcus* spp.):
> Five milligrams of stock lysostaphin has 5,150 U enzyme. To get a concentration of 500 U/mL, dilute the stock vial to 10.30 mL with lysostaphin buffer. Aliquot 0.5 mL into 20 Eppendorf tubes. Store at –20°C.

Lysis solution (20 µg RNAse/mL, 1 mg lysozyme/mL, and for *Staphylococcus* spp., 5 U lysostaphin/mL):
> When ready to use, add *to each milliliter of lysis buffer stock solution* 2 µl of RNAse

(10 µg/mL), 20 µL* of lysozyme (50 mg/mL), and for *Staphylococcus* spp., 10 µL of lysostaphin (500 U/mL).

*For *Enterococcus* spp., use 60 µL of lysozyme (for a final concentration of 3 mg/mL).

ES buffer (0.5 M EDTA, pH 8.0; 0.1% sodium lauroyl sarcosine):

Dilute 10 g of *N*-lauroyl sarcosine in 1,000 mL of 0.5 M EDTA (pH 8.0). Filter sterilize and store at 4°C.

ESP stock solution (2 mg/mL):

Dilute 100 mg of proteinase K (1 vial) in 50 mL of ES buffer. Shake well and then separate solution in half into two 50-mL centrifuge tubes (so that all 50 mL is submerged in the water bath). Place in a floatie and incubate in a 50°C water bath for approximately 1 h to dissolve the powder. After incubation, mix back together into one 50-mL centrifuge tube and store at 4°C.

ESP working solution (100 µg/mL):

Add 5 mL of ESP stock solution to 95 mL of ES buffer. Store at 4°C.

TE buffer (10 mM Tris, 0.1 mM EDTA; pH 7.6):

Dilute 5.0 mL of 1 M Tris (pH 7.6) and 0.1 mL of 0.5 M EDTA (pH 7.6) to a total volume of 500 mL with distilled water. Autoclave and store at room temperature.

5X TBE (stock solution) (0.45 M Tris, 0.45 M boric acid, 0.01 M EDTA; pH 8.0):

Dissolve 163.5 g Tris base, 83.4 g boric acid, and 60.0 mL of 0.5 M EDTA (pH 8.0) to a total volume of 3,000 mL with distilled water. Store at room temperature in a 3-L amber bottle.

0.5X TBE (working solution):

Dilute 300 mL of 5X TBE solution to a total volume of 3,000 mL with distilled water. Store at room temperature in a 3-L amber bottle.

APPENDIX 15.2 — GENERAL PROTOCOL FOR PFGE

Adapted from Maslow et al. [40] and Gautom [41].

Sample preparation

Day –2

1. For each isolate, inoculate a single colony from the clinical plate or glycerol into 0.5 mL trypticase soy (TS) or brain heart infusion (BHI) broth.
2. Grow for 2 h or until turbid.
3. Streak out onto 5% sheep blood TS agar and incubate overnight (ON).

Day –1

Pick a single colony, inoculate 5 mL of TS broth, and incubate ON on a roller at 37°C. To prevent overgrowth of culture and release of nucleases, inoculate broth just before leaving at night and put on ice in the morning, provided there is sufficient growth.

Plug Preparation

Day 1

Material Preparation

1. For each isolate, label one 15-mL snap-top tube, one 5-mL snap-top tube, one 7-mL scintillation vial, one 40-mL flat-bottom tube, and two 2-mL freezer tubes that have been filled with 0.4 mL of glycerol and sterilized.

2. Label one plug mold per isolate. Tape the bottom of the plug molds, place them in a metal tray, put this tray in a glass tray filled with ice, and place it in the refrigerator for at least 30 min. Cold molds are essential to the rapid gelling of the plugs.
3. Turn on a heat block to 50°C. Place one 5-mL snap-top tube per isolate in the heat block to warm up.
4. Take the cultures out of the warm room and place them on ice.

Preparation of Bacterial Suspension and Agarose

1. Put 5 mL of cold PIV into each 15-mL snap-top tube and place on ice.
2. Dispense 1.5 mL of each ON culture into the appropriately labeled 15-mL snap-top tube containing cold PIV.
3. Centrifuge the 15-mL snap-top tubes at $500 \times g$ for 15 min at 4°C.
4. While the cells are centrifuging, dispense 1.4 mL of the ON culture into each of the two freezer tubes. Cap the tubes securely and vortex them vigorously. Store them at –70°C. Preparing frozen stocks from the ON broth ensures that the exact colony being analyzed by PFGE has been saved.
5. Decant the PIV buffer from the cell pellet, resuspend the cells in 1.5 mL of fresh cold PIV, and place on ice.
6. Mix InCert agarose (1.3% [wt/vol]) in PIV buffer in a 15-mL tube. Prepare 1 mL per isolate (plus 1 mL extra), vortex, and place into boiling water to dissolve. Revortex prior to aliquoting.
7. Carefully dispense 1 mL of dissolved agarose into each 5-mL snap-top tube, and keep the tubes in the 50°C heat block.
8. Take the chilled plug molds placed in the ice-filled glass tray out of the refrigerator. Do not let chilled trays sit on the bench for a long time.
9. Add 1 mL of cells in PIV to the 5-mL snap-top tube with 1 mL of molten InCert agarose, pipet up and down a few times, and promptly aliquot the mixture down the side of each well of the plug molds, being careful not to trap any bubbles in the plugs. Mix cells with agarose one sample at a time. Do not prepare all isolates at once before aliquoting, or the organisms will start to produce nucleases while waiting in hot agarose. Keeping the bacteria and agarose plugs cold during the above procedures is critical to preparing high-quality plugs with intact DNA. The cold decreases premature cell lysis, decreases the activity of endonucleases, and facilitates homogeneous gelling of the agarose. The final concentration of organisms is $\sim 1 \times 10^9$ CFU/ml. Since 1 CFU $\approx 1 \times 10^{-14}$ g of DNA, each plug has $\sim$ 1 μg of DNA.
10. Place the molds (in their trays) at 4°C for 30 min to solidify.

Lysis

1. While the plugs are solidifying, thaw the RNAse and lysozyme (and lysostaphin if needed) on ice for approximately 20 min.
2. Make fresh lysis solution and keep on ice. Use 4 mL of lysis solution per isolate. For each milliliter of lysis solution, add 2 μL of RNAse (10 mg/mL), 20 μL of lysozyme* (50 mg/ml), and, if needed, 10 μl of lysostaphin (500 U/ml).
   * For *Enterococcus* spp., use 60 μL of lysozyme.
3. Dispense 4 mL of lysis solution into each labeled scintillation vial.
4. Wearing gloves, remove the tape gently from the plug molds and place it in contaminated waste (the tape has live organisms on it). Using a spatula, push out all plugs into the appropriate scintillation vial with lysis solution. Disinfect the trays and rinse with water, and place the contaminated plug molds in 15% bleach solution ON.

5. Incubate the scintillation vials at 37°C ON on a roller.
6. Turn on the 50°C water bath to have it ready early on day 2.

Day 2. Protease Digestion

1. Carefully aspirate the lysis solution using a bulb syringe and Pasteur pipette.
2. Dispense 4 mL of ESP solution into each tube and incubate ON at 50°C, shaking gently.

Day 3

Restriction Enzyme Digestion

1. Turn on a water bath at the temperature appropriate for the restriction enzyme.
2. Chill the scintillation vials with plugs on ice for about 10 min. The plugs can now be used for restriction enzyme digestion as outlined below or can be placed in fresh ESP solution and stored at 4°C. DNA in the plugs is stable at 4°C in ESP for at least 2 years.
3. Using a spatula, carefully take out one plug and put it in its respective 40-mL flat-bottom tube.
4. Wash the plugs six times, 10 min each wash, in a 50°C water bath with constant agitation (150 rpm), twice with 15 mL of preheated (50°C) sterile water, and four times with 10 mL of preheated (50°C) TE.
5. Label one 1.5-mL Eppendorf tube for each isolate.
6. Thaw on ice bovine sterile albumin (BSA) and the enzyme buffer.
7. Aliquot into each Eppendorf tube, *in order*, 267 µL of sterile water, 3.0 µL of BSA, 30 µL of enzyme buffer, and the washed plug.
8. Add restriction enzyme, mix gently, and incubate for 2–4 h at the appropriate temperature.
9. Chill the tubes before handling the inserts.
10. Carefully remove the digestion mixture from each Eppendorf tube.
11. Add 1 mL of ESP into each Eppendorf tube. Plugs can be stored in ESP buffer at 4°C indefinitely (>1 year).

Gel Preparation and Loading

1. Make the gel with SeaKem high-melting-temperature agarose (1% [wt/vol]) dissolved in 0.5X TBE (for a 15-lane gel, dissolve 0.8 mg Seakem agarose in 80 mL of TBE). Boil on hot plate, then cool to 50°C in a water bath.
2. Pour agarose slowly into the gel mold; avoid air bubbles. Let the gel solidify at room temperature for 15–30 min.
3. Using a surgical blade, cut a slice ~1–1.5 mm thick off the end of the plug and load it into a well of the gel using the narrow end of a Teflon-coated spatula. Make sure the slice is at bottom–front of the well and is not twisted.
4. Place the plugs in the gel in the following order (when using a 15-lane gel): lanes 1 and 15: no plug; lanes 2, 8, and 14: *S.aureus* NCTC 8325 or molecular weight standard; lanes 3–7 and 9–12: isolates to be tested; and lane 13: reproducibility isolate.
5. Return the remainder of the plug to the Eppendorf tube and store at 4°C.
6. Fill all the wells with agarose and place the gel in a PFGE gel box with recirculating 0.5X TBE cooled to 14°C. Run at 200 V (6 V/cm), with linear ramping (from 1 to 40 s), for 22 h.

Day 4. Gel Visualization

Stain the gel for 20 min in 1 L of sterile water containing 1 µg/mL ethidium bromide. Destain the gel by 2 washes of 30 min each in 1 L of sterile water, and photograph it under UV light. Since it is a powerful mutagen, always wear gloves when handling solutions containing ethidium bromide and dispose these solutions into an appropriate dangerous waste container.

REFERENCES

1. Maslow, J.N. and Arbeit, R.D. Molecular epidemiology for the clinician: I. Selected techniques, *IDCP,* 4(2), 128, 1995.
2. Michaud, S., Arbeit, R.D., and Gaudreau, C. Molecular strain typing of *Campylobacter jejuni* by pulsed-field gel electrophoresis in a single day, *Can. J. Microbiol,.* 47(7), 667, 2001.
3. Tenover, F.C., Arbeit, R.D., Goering, R.V., Mickelsen, P.A., Murray, B.E., Persing, D.H., and Swaminathan, B. Interpreting chromosomal DNA restriction patterns produced by pulsed-field gel electrophoresis, criteria for bacterial strain typing, *J. Clin. Microbiol.,* 33(9), 2233–2239, 1995.
4. Arbeit, R.D. Molecular epidemiology for the clinician, II. Interpretation and application of molecular typing,. *IDCP,* 5(4), 260–264, 1996.
5. Arbeit, R.D. Laboratory procedures for epidemiological analysis, in Crossley, K.B. and Archer, G.L., Eds. *The Staphylococci in Human Disease.* Churchill Livingstone, New York, 1997, 253–286.
6. Deplano, A., Witte, W., van Leeuwen, W.J., Brun, Y., and Struelens, M.J. Clonal dissemination of epidemic methicillin-resistant *Staphylococcus aureus* in Belgium and neighboring countries, *Clin. Microbiol. Infect.,* 6(5), 239–245, 2000.
7. Simor, A.E., Ofner-Agostini, M., Bryce, E., Green, K., McGeer, A., Mulvey, M., and Paton, S. The evolution of methicillin-resistant *Staphylococcus aureus* in Canadian hospitals, 5 years of national surveillance, *CMAJ,* 165(1), 21–26, 2001.
8. Ip, M., Lyon, D.J., Yung, R.W., Chan, C., and Cheng, A.F. Evidence of clonal dissemination of multidrug-resistant *Streptococcus pneumoniae* in Hong Kong, *J. Clin. Microbiol.,* 37(9), 2834–2839, 1999.
9. Greenberg, D., Speert, D.P., Mahenthiralingam, E., Henry, D.A., Campbell, M.E., and Scheifele, D.W. Emergence of penicillin-nonsusceptible *Streptococcus pneumoniae* invasive clones in Canada, *J. Clin. Microbiol.,* 40(1), 68–74, 2002.
10. Richter, S.S., Heilmann, K.P., Coffman, S.L., Huynh, H.K., Brueggemann, A.B., Pfaller, M.A., and Doern, G.V. The molecular epidemiology of penicillin-resistant *Streptococcus pneumoniae* in the United States, 1994-2000. *Clin. Infect. Dis.,* 34(3), 330–339, 2002.
11. Tassios, P.T., Gazouli, M., Tzelepi, E., Milch, H., Kozlova, N., Sidorenko, S., Legakis, N.J., and Tzouvelekis, L.S. Spread of a *Salmonella typhimurium* clone resistant to expanded-spectrum cephalosporins in three European countries, *J. Clin. Microbiol.,* 37(11), 3774–3777, 1999.
12. Tassios, P.T., Gennimata, V., Maniatis, A.N., Fock, C., and Legakis, N.J. Emergence of multidrug resistance in ubiquitous and dominant *Pseudomonas aeruginosa* serogroup O, 11. The Greek *Pseudomonas Aeruginosa* Study Group, *J. Clin. Microbiol.,* 36(4), 897–901, 1998.
13. Van Looveren, M., Vandamme, P, Hauchecorn, M., Wijdooghe, M., Carion, F., Caugant, D.A., and Goossens, H. Molecular epidemiology of recent Belgian isolates of *Neisseria meningitidis* serogroup B, *J. Clin. Microbiol.,* 36(10), 2828–2834, 1998.
14. Crawford, J.T., Braden, C., Schable, B.A., and Onorato, I.M. National tuberculosis genotyping and surveillance network, design and methods, *Emerg. Infect. Dis.,* 8(11), 1192–1196, 2002.
15. Swaminathan, B., Barrett, T.J., Hunter, S.B., and Tauxe, R.V. PulseNet, the molecular subtyping network for foodborne bacterial disease surveillance, United States, *Emerg. Infect. Dis.,* 7(3), 382–389, 2001.
16. Weber, S., Pfaller, M.A., and Herwaldt. L.A., Role of molecular epidemiology in infection control, in Rutala, W.A. and Weber, D.J., Eds., *Nosocomial Infections,* W.B. Saunders, Philadelphia, 1997, 257–278.
17. Tenover, F.C. Arbeit, R.D., and Goering, R.V. How to select and interpret molecular strain typing methods for epidemiological studies of bacterial infections, a review for healthcare epidemiologists. Molecular Typing Working Group of the Society for Healthcare Epidemiology of America, *Infect. Control Hosp. Epidemiol,* 18(6), 426–439, 1997.
18. Arbeit, R.D. Laboratory procedures for the epidemiological analysis of microorganisms, in Murray, P.R., Baron, E.J., Pfaller, M.A., Tenover, F.C., and Yolken, R.H., Eds., *Manual of Clinical Microbiology.* American Society for Microbiology, Washington, DC, 1999, 116.

19. Schwartz, D.C. and Cantor, C.R. Separation of yeast chromosome-sized DNAs by pulsed field gradient gel electrophoresis, *Cell,* 37(1), 67–75, 1984.

20. Struelens, M.J., de Ryck, R., and Deplano, A. Analysis of microbial genomic macrorestriction patterns by pulsed-field gel electrophoresis typing, in Dijkshoorn, L., Towner, K., and Struelens, M., Eds., *New Approaches for the Generation and Analysis of Microbial Typing Data,* Elsevier, Amsterdam, 2001, 159–176.

21. Struelens, M.J., De Gheldre, Y., and Deplano, A. Comparative and library epidemiological typing systems, outbreak investigations versus surveillance systems, *Infect. Control Hosp. Epidemiol.,* 19(8), 565–569, 1998.

22. Olive, D.M. and Bean, P. Principles and applications of methods for DNA-based typing of microbial organisms, *J. Clin. Microbiol.,* 37(6), 1661–1669, 1999.

23. Tenover, F.C., Arbeit, R., Archer, G., Biddle, J., Byrne, S., Goering, R., Hancock, G., Hebert, G.A, Hill, B., Hollis, R. et al. Comparison of traditional and molecular methods of typing isolates of *Staphylococcus aureus, J. Clin. Microbiol.,* 32(2), 407–415, 1994.

24. Struelens, M.J. Consensus guidelines for appropriate use and evaluation of microbial epidemiological typing systems, *Clin. Microbiol. Infect.,* 2(1), 2–11, 1996.

25. Grundmann, H., Schneider, C., Hartung, D., Daschner, F.D., and Pitt, T.L. Discriminatory power of three DNA-based typing techniques for *Pseudomonas aeruginosa, J. Clin. Microbiol.,* 33(3), 528–534, 1995.

26. Arbeit, R.D., Arthur, M., Dunn, R., Kim, C., Selander, R.K., and Goldstein, R. Resolution of recent evolutionary divergence among *Escherichia coli* from related lineages, the application of pulsed field electrophoresis to molecular epidemiology, *J. Infect. Dis.,* 161(2), 230–235, 1990.

27. Arbeit, R.D., Slutsky, A., Barber, T.W., Maslow, J.N., Niemczyk, S., Falkinham, J.O. 3rd, O'Connor, G.T., and von Reyn, C.F. Genetic diversity among strains of *Mycobacterium avium* causing monoclonal and polyclonal bacteremia in patients with AIDS, *J. Infect. Dis.,* 167(6), 1384–1390, 1993.

28. Murray, B.E., Singh, K.V., Heath, J.D., Sharma, B.R., and Weinstock GM. Comparison of genomic DNAs of different enterococcal isolates using restriction endonucleases with infrequent recognition sites, *J. Clin. Microbiol.,* 28(9), 2059–2063, 1990.

29. Poh, C.L., Yeo, C.C., and Tay, L. Genome fingerprinting by pulsed-field gel electrophoresis and ribotyping to differentiate *Pseudomonas aeruginosa* serotype O11 strains, *Eur. J. Clin. Microbiol. Infect. Dis.,* 11(9), 817–822, 1992.

30. Prevost, G., Jaulhac, B., and Piemont, Y. DNA fingerprinting by pulsed-field gel electrophoresis is more effective than ribotyping in distinguishing among methicillin-resistant *Staphylococcus aureus* isolates, *J. Clin. Microbiol.,* 30(4), 967–973, 1992.

31. Struelens, M.J., Bax, R., Deplano, A., Quint, W.G., and Van Belkum, A. Concordant clonal delineation of methicillin-resistant *Staphylococcus aureus* by macrorestriction analysis and polymerase chain reaction genome fingerprinting, *J. Clin. Microbiol.,* 31(8), 1064–1070, 1993.

32. Kristjansson, M., Samore, M.H., Gerding, D.N., DeGirolami, P.C., Bettin, K.M., Karchmer, A.W., and Arbeit, R.D. Comparison of restriction endonuclease analysis, ribotyping, and pulsed-field gel electrophoresis for molecular differentiation of *Clostridium difficile* strains, *J. Clin. Microbiol.,* 32(8), 1963–1969, 1994.

33. Bannerman, T.L., Hancock, G.A., Tenover, F.C., and Miller J.M. Pulsed-field gel electrophoresis as a replacement for bacteriophage typing of *Staphylococcus aureus, J. Clin. Microbiol.,* 33(3), 551–555, 1995.

34. Kersulyte, D., Struelens, M.J., Deplano, A., and Berg, D.E. Comparison of arbitrarily primed PCR and macrorestriction (pulsed-field gel electrophoresis) typing of *Pseudomonas aeruginosa* strains from cystic fibrosis patients, *J. Clin. Microbiol.,* 33(8), 2216–2219, 1995.

35. Seifert, H. and Gerner-Smidt, P. Comparison of ribotyping and pulsed-field gel electrophoresis for molecular typing of Acinetobacter isolates, *J. Clin. Microbiol.,* 33(5), 1402–1407, 1995.

36. Hermans, P.W, Sluijter, M., Hoogenboezem, T., Heersma, H., van Belkum, A., and de Groot, R. Comparative study of five different DNA fingerprint techniques for molecular typing of *Streptococcus pneumoniae* strains, *J. Clin. Microbiol.,* 33(6), 1606–1612, 1995.

37. Gori, A., Espinasse, F., Deplano, A., Nonhoff, C., Nicolas, M.H., and Struelens, M.J. Comparison of pulsed-field gel electrophoresis and randomly amplified DNA polymorphism analysis for typing extended-spectrum-beta-lactamase-producing *Klebsiella pneumoniae, J. Clin. Microbiol.,* 34(10), 2448–2453, 1996.

38. Kerouanton, A., Brisabois, A., Denoyer, E., Dilasser, F., Grout, J., Salvat, G., and Picard, B. Comparison of five typing methods for the epidemiological study of *Listeria monocytogenes*, *Int. J. Food Microbiol.*, 43(1–2), 61–71, 1998.

39. Wassenaar, T.M. and Newell, D.G. Genotyping of *Campylobacter* spp., *Appl. Environ. Microbiol.*, 66(1), 1–9, 2000.

40. Maslow, J.N., Slutsky, A.M., and Arbeit, R.D. Application of pulsed-field gel electrophoresis to molecular epidemiology, in Persing, D.H., Smith, T.F., Tenover, F.C., and White, T.J., Eds., *Diagnostic Molecular Microbiology, Principles and Applications*. American Society for Microbiology, Washington, DC, 1993, 563–572.

41. Gautom, R.K. Rapid pulsed-field gel electrophoresis protocol for typing of *Escherichia coli* O157, H7 and other gram-negative organisms in 1 day, *J. Clin. Microbiol.*, 35(11), 2977–2980, 1997.

42. Ribot, E.M., Fitzgerald, C., Kubota, K., Swaminathan, B., and Barrett, T.J. Rapid pulsed-field gel electrophoresis protocol for subtyping of *Campylobacter jejuni*, *J. Clin. Microbiol.*, 39(5), 1889–1894, 2001.

43. Maslow, J.N., Slutsky, A.M., and Arbeit, R.D. Application of pulsed-field gel electrophoresis to molecular epidemiology, in Persing, D.H., Smith, T.F., Tenover, F.C., and White, T.J., Eds., *Diagnostic Microbiology, Principles and Applications*. American Society for Microbiology, Washington, DC, 1993, 563–572.

44. Turabelidze, D., Kotetishvili, M., Kreger, A., Morris, J.G. Jr., and Sulakvelidze, A. Improved pulsed-field gel electrophoresis for typing vancomycin-resistant enterococci, *J. Clin. Microbiol.*, 38(11), 4242–4245, 2000.

45. Goering, R.V. and Winters, M.A. Rapid method for epidemiological evaluation of gram-positive cocci by field inversion gel electrophoresis, *J. Clin. Microbiol.*, 30(3), 577–850, 1992.

46. Mulvey, M.R., Chui, L., Ismail, J., Louie, L., Murphy, C., Chang, N., Alfa, M., and The Canadian Committee for the Standardization of Molecular Methods. Development of a Canadian standardized protocol for subtyping methicillin-resistant *Staphylococcus aureus* using pulsed-field gel electrophoresis, *J. Clin. Microbiol.*, 39(10), 3481–3485, 2001.

47. McClelland, M., Jones, R., Patel, Y., and Nelson, M. Restriction endonucleases for pulsed field mapping of bacterial genomes, *Nucleic Acids Res.*, 15(15), 5985–6005, 1987.

48. McEllistrem, M.C., Stout, J.E., and Harrison, L.H. Simplified protocol for pulsed-field gel electrophoresis analysis of *Streptococcus pneumoniae*, *J. Clin. Microbiol.*, 38(1), 351–353, 2000.

49. Birren, B.W., Lai, E., Clark, S.M., Hood, L., and Simon, M.I. Optimized conditions for pulsed field gel electrophoretic separations of DNA, *Nucleic Acids Res.*, 16(15), 7563–7582, 1988.

50. Heersma, H.F., Kremer, K., van Soolingen, D., and Hauman, J. Setting-up intra- and inter-laboratory databases of electrophoretic profiles, in Dijkshoorn, L., Towner, K., and Struelens, M., Eds., *New Approaches for the Generation and Analysis of Microbial Typing Data*, Elsevier, Amsterdam, 2001, 47–75.

51. McEllistrem, M.C., Stout, J.E., and Harrison, L.H. Simplified protocol for pulsed-field gel electrophoresis analysis of *Streptococcus pneumoniae*, *J. Clin. Microbiol.*, 38(1), 351–353, 2000.

52. Gibson, J.R., Sutherland, K., and Owen, R.J. Inhibition of DNAse activity in PFGE analysis of DNA from *Campylobacter jejuni*, *Lett. Appl. Microbiol.*, 19(5), 357–358, 1994.

53. Birren, B. and Lai, E. Trouble shooting, in *Pulsed Field Gel Electrophoresis, a Practical Guide*. Academic Press, San Diego, 1993, 167–175.

54. Kreiswirth, B., Kornblum, J., Arbeit, R.D., Eisner, W., Maslow, J.N., McGeer, A., Low, D.E., and Novick, R.P. Evidence for a clonal origin of methicillin resistance in *Staphylococcus aureus*, *Science*, 259(5092), 227–230, 1993.

55. *BioNumerics — The Integral Study of Biological Relationships*, Applied Maths, Kortrijk, Belgium 2000, 230.

56. Michaud, S., Ménard, S,, Gaudreau, C., and Arbeit, R.D. Comparison of *Sma*I-defined genotypes of *Campylobacter jejuni* examined by *Kpn*I, A population-based study, *J. Med. Microbiol.*, 50, 1075–1081, 2001.

57. Musser, J.M., Kroll, J.S., Moxon, E.R., and Selander, R.K. Evolutionary genetics of the encapsulated strains of *Haemophilus influenzae*, *Proc. Natl. Acad. Sci. USA*, 85(20), 7758–7762, 1988.

58. Whittam, T.S., Wachsmuth, I.K., and Wilson, R.A. Genetic evidence of clonal descent of *Escherichia coli* O157, H7 associated with hemorrhagic colitis and hemolytic uremic syndrome, *J. Infect. Dis.*, 157(6), 1124–1133, 1988.

59. Bohm, H. and Karch, H. DNA fingerprinting of *Escherichia coli* O157, H7 strains by pulsed-field gel electrophoresis, *J. Clin. Microbiol.,* 30(8), 2169–2172, 1992.
60. *Fragments*, Volume 3, Number 1, DuPont Qualicon, March 1999, pp. 1–3.
61. RiboPrinter Microbial Characterization System Operations User's Guide, DuPont Qualicon,1998.
62. *Fragments*, Volume 2, Number 3, DuPont Qualicon, August 1998, 5–6.

16 Pharmacy and Microbiology: Interactive Synergy

Beulah Perdue Sabundayo and Cassandra B. Calderón

CONTENTS

16.1 INTRODUCTION

Traditionally, pharmacists and microbiologists have been allocated to the basement of most hospitals, having little or no contact with each other except when passing in the hallways. Today, managed care has forced these two departments to work together as part of a team. Many of the decisions concerning patient care including safety, efficacy, and cost containment are a cooperative effort among physicians, pharmacists, and microbiologists, especially in the field of infectious diseases. The work these individuals perform and their specialized view on matters make each member invaluable, and together, a winning team. This chapter discusses the pharmacy and therapeutics committee, the antimicrobial subcommittee, and the role pharmacists and microbiologists play on such committees. It emphasizes the cooperative and sometimes dependent relationship between the two departments. This chapter also discusses the tools used in managed care, such as the drug formulary, antimicrobial streamlining, medication usage evaluations, and critical pathways as they pertain to the interaction between pharmacists and microbiologists.

16.2 PHARMACY AND THERAPEUTICS COMMITTEE

The continued success of many large companies and institutions depends upon work performed in committees, subcommittees, and task forces. Hospitals are no different. Even though the committee structure of institutions may differ slightly, most hospitals have established a pharmacy and therapeutics (P&T) committee. First established in the 1930s, this committee was responsible for developing a formal list of medications available in the hospital, now known as the formulary [1]. Then in 1959, the American Society of Hospital Pharmacists and the American Hospital Association officially described the role of the P&T committee in maintaining the formulary [2]. Today, most hospitals have created a P&T committee, as stipulated in their medical staff's bylaws, as an advisory committee to the medical executive committee [1]. They act as the primary governing body to ensure the appropriate use of medications within the hospital and as the formal communication link between the medical staff and the department of pharmacy.

The P&T committee is responsible for all matters related to medication use in the hospital. Their basic objectives are to specify drugs of choice and alternatives, to minimize therapeutic redundancies, and to maximize cost-effectiveness [3]. These objectives are accomplished through a variety of programs overseen by the committee, including maintaining the hospital's formulary, overseeing medication usage evaluations, and approving clinical pathways. In addition, the P&T committee reviews adverse drug reactions and drug-use policies and procedures, and discusses continuous quality improvement projects. They also serve in an educational capacity by establishing policies and procedures to help ensure safe, effective, and cost-effective drug therapy. In addition, they arrange educational programs for the staff on matters related to drug use and disseminate information regarding the actions approved by the committee [4]. Other committees, subcommittees, and task forces usually facilitate the work done by this committee. For example, the antimicrobial subcommittee and the infection control committee usually present information and recommendations to the P&T committee.

The infrastructure, membership, and chairperson of the P&T committee can vary among hospitals and the roles played by these members are specific to the needs of the individual hospital. Most P&T committees are multidisciplinary groups of members, primarily elected from the medical staff, pharmacy department, and nursing. Among the physicians, these members are usually practicing physicians and represent different medical and surgical subspecialties. Members from the department of pharmacy usually include the director of pharmacy, a clinical pharmacist, and possibly other representatives from the department. Some hospitals have a hospital administrator sit on the committee. The chairperson of the committee is usually a physician, but may be a pharmacist or hospital administrator. Microbiologists may or may not be members of the P&T committee, but play a vital role on the antimicrobial surveillance and infection control committees, which usually report to this committee. Representatives from ancillary departments or committees are invited, as needed. A survey of 267 teaching hospitals showed that these committees are very large, averaging almost 20 members, with the majority being physicians. It also revealed that each P&T committee had at least one pharmacist, with an average of 3.2 pharmacist members. Two to three members were nurses, and a hospital administrator may have been elected to the committee. In 98.9% of the hospitals, the chair of the committee was a physician [5].

16.3 ANTIMICROBIAL SUBCOMMITTEE OF THE P&T COMMITTEE

The antimicrobial or antibiotic subcommittee of the P&T committee is a multidisciplinary group responsible for reviewing each classification of antimicrobials. Members of this subcommittee may also be members of the P&T committee, but often times include additional health professionals from a variety of departments. The chair is typically a well-respected physician from the infectious disease department. Other members of the subcommittee include a clinical pharmacist, a clinical microbiologist, physicians representing medical, surgical, obstetrics and gynecology, oncology, and pediatric subspecialties. These physicians generally have an interest in infectious diseases or may be trained specifically in infectious diseases [6].

Having an antimicrobial subcommittee allows for more involvement by the medical, pharmacy, and microbiology staff in drug policy decisions specific to their hospital. The subcommittee extensively reviews each antimicrobial class and makes formal recommendations to the P&T committee on the preferred drugs for that class. Usually, the pharmacist reviews the literature, compares the drugs to each other, and presents the data to the group. The microbiologist presents data on resistance patterns seen throughout the hospital and in specific units. Decisions are based on *in vitro* activity, safety, efficacy, and cost resulting in minimal duplication of therapeutically equivalent drugs. A subcommittee allows for more extensive education of the medical staff through one-on-one consultations with its members or through formal educational programs developed by the subcommittee and endorsed by the P&T committee. The subcommittee provides continuous data about the use and misuse of antimicrobials within the institution through the review and publication of the antibiogram and medication use evaluations [6,7].

16.4 THE DRUG FORMULARY SYSTEM

As previously described, one of the major responsibilities of the P&T committee is to develop and maintain the hospital's drug formulary. The antimicrobial subcommittee is usually responsible for the antimicrobial section of the formulary. The formulary is a continually revised list of drugs with information pertaining to the appropriate and safe use of each medication [8]. The first formulary was introduced in a private hospital in 1816 [9]. Since then, its utility has grown more important and complex. The formulary should represent the clinical judgment of the P&T committee members in the diagnosis, management, and prevention of disease. There are three types of drug formularies: open, closed (restrictive), and managed. An open formulary allows for the use of all drugs and drug products currently available on the market. Drugs are used without a formal, objective review and approval process. In a closed or restrictive formulary, there is a limited list of drugs that are available for use. The drugs on this list have undergone a rigorous review process by members of the P&T committee before being included on the formulary. A managed formulary is an open formulary with preferred products that have guidelines for use. Most institutions use a closed formulary, which allows the department of pharmacy to maintain a manageable inventory by only having the medications that are on formulary readily available for use. When extenuating circumstances arise, these institutions usually have a method for obtaining drugs that are not on the formulary upon the request of the physician. Future use of that drug will depend on the review and approval by the P&T committee so that it may then be included on the formulary, if deemed necessary [8,10].

The drug formulary system is the process by which the P&T committee maintains policies for drug use [11]. The goal of the formulary system is to optimize pharmaceutical care for patients in terms of efficacy, safety, and cost. Information in the medical and pharmacy literature and economic concerns are coupled to form a comprehensive, unbiased profile of the drug. Initially a drug is evaluated in terms of efficacy and safety. The side effects of drugs are always considered as well as patient adherence to the specific drug regimen. After a drug is deemed acceptable in terms of safety and efficacy, then economic factors are evaluated. The drug must be evaluated for how it will affect total health care costs for the institution. Through this comprehensive process, drugs may either be added, deleted, or have restricted use within the formulary system [8,10–14].

The formulary system is responsible for the maintenance of the drug formulary. This entails medication usage reviews to assure appropriate use, evaluation, and analysis of treatment protocols; procedures such as critical pathways, as well as monitoring, analyzing, and reporting adverse events. The formulary system should provide educational programs to the medical staff about institution specific policies and procedures about the appropriate use of the drugs. This is accomplished by providing in-services, newsletters, and publications within the institution. The formulary system should also proactively inform the medical staff of changes to the formulary and be able to provide rationales for specific formulary decisions when asked. A well-defined process should be in place so that physicians can request drugs be added or removed from the formulary. The formulary system should also provide a process to educate patients about their medications by interacting with medical, nursing, and/or pharmacy staff based on the guidelines within the institution. Depending on the type of formulary system used, a well defined process enables the department of pharmacy to maintain a manageable inventory and therefore control costs by only having drugs that are on the formulary readily available within the institution [8,10,11,13].

16.5   ANTIMICROBIAL STREAMLINING

Antimicrobial medications often make up the majority of a hospital's formulary, accounting for 20%–40% of total drug expenditures [15,16]. For this reason, along with the propensity for the development of drug resistance with overuse and inappropriate use, antimicrobials are often the target of drug monitoring and control programs. In general, the initial choice of an antibiotic is empiric, based on the physician's knowledge of the type of infection and the microorganism believed to inhabit the institution (obtained from the antibiogram). Often times with empiric therapy the belief is that therapy must be broad and intravenous in the hospital setting. Review of empiric therapy has demonstrated that without intervention from other sources (i.e., integrated monitoring programs), many physicians will continue the agents that were originally chosen for empiric therapy even if less expensive, easier to administer (i.e., oral) agents are available. Many clinical pharmacy programs have been developed to affect empiric antibiotic usage (the first 2–3 days of therapy). Data on the individual patient's infecting organism is often available from the microbiology lab within 2–3 days of initiation of therapy, allowing the physician to modify therapy if needed. Cultures may show susceptibility to a less expensive agent than what was originally chosen. It is at this point that streamlining of therapy comes into play [17,18].

Streamlining of drugs involves changing to a less expensive agent or discontinuing therapy when appropriate [17,19]. Intervention programs are generally targeted at one or more of the following: dosage adjustment, parenteral regimen change, change from intravenous to oral, early discontinuation of therapy, or change to management by a clinical pharmacokinetic service (i.e., aminoglycoside dosage adjustments based on serum concentrations) [17,19,20]. The key to the success of such a program is making sure that selected patients have an organism with susceptibilities identified and the patient is showing signs of improvement prior to intervention. Antimicrobial streamlining may be the most crucial place where physicians, clinical pharmacists, and microbiologists interact to improve quality of care for the patient and control the costs of antimicrobial agents. While a major goal of streamlining therapy is to contain costs, it is imperative that patient outcomes be well-documented [17,20].

Many programs have been developed to implement streamlining. The most successful programs have resulted from strong leadership from the infectious disease division, a clinical pharmacy service responsible for the daily running of the program, and computer software that easily interacts with the microbiology laboratory. Support from the antimicrobial subcommittee and hence the P&T committee is essential in the form of review and approval of all policies and procedures [17,20].

16.6   MEDICATION USAGE EVALUATIONS

A medication usage evaluation (MUE), previously referred to as a drug usage evaluation (DUE), is a method to evaluate and improve the appropriate, safe, and cost-effective use of medications within the hospital or clinic setting. They can be performed on an individual medication (i.e., ciprofloxacin or imipenem/cilastatin), a therapeutic class (i.e., fluoroquinolones or β-lactam antibiotics) or a specific disease state or condition (i.e., treatment of urinary tract infections or drug causes for *Clostridium difficile* diarrhea). The goal of an MUE is to improve an individual patient's quality of life through achievement of predefined, medication-related outcomes [21]. MUEs are usually developed for high-volume, high-cost, and/or high-risk medication, diagnoses or procedures.

Hospital specific guidelines or criteria are written based on current medical and pharmacy literature and are then approved by the P&T committee. These guidelines incorporate the Joint Commission on Accreditation of Healthcare Organizations (JCAHO) medication-use indicators emphasizing all aspects of the medication experience. Items reviewed include prescribing, dispensing, and administering the medication, as well as monitoring the patient's response. Within each category there are processes listed that help the institution identify areas for specific improvement. For example, the dispensing indicator requires the reviewer to determine if the order was reviewed and processed correctly, and the medication prepared correctly and dispensed in a timely manner [22]. The proper use of medications is a cooperative goal among the prescribing physician, the dispensing pharmacist, the administering nurse, and all those who monitor the patient for appropriate outcomes. Through this process, we can improve the medication experience of the patient by identifying and resolving actual or potential medication-related problems [23].

Many institutions have an ongoing medication usage evaluation program solely dedicated to antibiotics primarily because unlike all other medications, the overuse or misuse of antibiotics carries the risk of selecting resistance to certain microorganisms. The goal of this program is similar to the MUE described previously, which is to promote the rational, safe, and cost-conscious use of antimicrobials within the hospital. For example, with the aid of a medication usage evaluation, the Veterans Affairs Medical Center affiliated with the University of Arizona determined that clindamycin usage was associated with an epidemic of *C. difficile* infections in their institution [24]. This is where input from microbiology lab personnel alerting physicians to increasing resistance to certain antimicrobials is important in identifying which agents require more careful monitoring.

16.7 CRITICAL PATHWAYS

With the rapid growth of managed care, many health care organizations are looking to critical pathways as a means of maintaining high quality health care while at the same time reducing costs. Critical pathways, also known as clinical pathways, were first implemented in the health care arena in the 1980s, when hospital reimbursement became competitive and capitated [25]. Today they are comprehensive medical management plans for patient care. Pathways cover the entire patient experience from admission, diagnosis, throughout the hospital stay, and after discharge. Unlike MUEs, which focus only on pharmacologic interventions, a critical pathway encompasses all aspects of patient care, including pharmacologic and nonpharmacological therapies, interventions, activities, and outcomes. They optimize the sequence and timing of different interventions performed by physicians, nurses, and other health professionals, to minimize delays and resources while maximizing quality of care. Similar to MUEs, critical pathways are usually developed based on the JCAHO indicator criteria for high-volume, high-cost, and/or high-risk diagnoses or procedures within a given institution [26]. Some goals of critical pathways are to improve patient care, reduce the variation in medical practice, increase continuity of care, and improve the utilization of resources. They are also used as a guide for other members of the health care team as well as patients and family members on what to expect from the hospital experience.

Although potentially beneficial, no controlled study has proven that critical pathways decrease resource use or improve patient satisfaction or outcomes [27]. Nonetheless, many health care organizations are actively developing critical pathways. A directory listing over 2,000 critical pathways developed in various institutions was published in 1995 [28]. The experiences of some hospitals have been published in the literature on various disease states including lumbar laminectomy, stroke, and cesarean section [29,30].

16.8 CONCLUSION

This chapter illustrates a few ways in which pharmacy and microbiology may interact. Primarily through a cooperative effort on the antimicrobial subcommittee, the antibiotic formulary is maintained and infectious disease-related critical pathways are reviewed and approved. The department of microbiology also provides information that assists in the antibiotic streamlining and MUEs being performed efficiently. However, many of the more interesting interactions are on a daily basis, involving the diagnosis and management of patients. The treatment of patients with infectious diseases is dependent on the department of microbiology. Physicians rely on the microbiology department to provide accurate and timely information on the microorganisms that are isolated from clinical specimens. It is the role of the clinical pharmacist to help the physicians interpret those data and decide on the best and most cost-effective treatment for that specific patient. The complete acceptance of policies, procedures, and monitoring programs is based on the multidisciplinary work of both the pharmacy and microbiology departments in conjunction with the medical staff. This work is displayed through the P&T committee, in particular the antibiotic subcommittee, and through the publication of policies and procedures for the appropriate use of antimicrobials. Ongoing information is gathered through the process of MUEs, antibiotic streamlining, and critical pathways. Through this interdisciplinary work, patients benefit from the knowledge and expertise of all those involved in their care.

REFERENCES

1. Hoffman, R.P. Perspectives on the hospital formulary system, *Hosp. Pharm.,* 19, 359–364, 1984.
2. Lipman, A.C. A new formulary statement and formulary service, editorial, *Hosp. Formul.,* 18, 771, 1983.
3. Summer, K.H. and Szeinbach, S.L. Formularies, the role of pharmacy and therapeutics (P&T) committees, *Clin. Ther.,* 15(2), 433–441, 1993.
4. ASHP statement on pharmacy and therapeutics committee, *Am. J. Hosp. Pharm.,* 49(8), 2008–2009, Aug. 1992.
5. Mannebach, M.A., Ascione, F.J., Gaither, C.A., Bagozzi, R.P., Cohen, I.A., and Ryan, M.L. Activities, functions, and structure of pharmacy and therapeutics committees in large teaching hospitals, *Am. J. Health Syst. Pharm..* 56, 622–628, 1999.
6. Cook, A.A. and Sanchez, M.L. A multidisciplinary process to determine, communicate, and manage an antibiotic form, *Hosp. Pharm.,* 27(10), 867–882, 1992.
7. Klopp, D.L. and Ramphal R. Antibiotics review and role of a representative subcommittee, *Qual. Rev. Bull.,* 8, 15–19, 1982. American Society of Hospital Pharmacists. ASHP statement on the formulary system, *Am. J. Hosp. Pharm.,* 40, 1384–1385, 1983.
8. Pearce, M.J. A review of limited lists and formularies, *Pharmacoeco,* 1(3), 191–202, 1992.
9. Consensus panel. Principles of a sound drug formulary system. *U.S. Pharm.* American Society of Hospital Pharmacists. ASHP guidelines on formulary system management, *Am. J. Hosp. Pharm.,* 49, 648–652, 1992. http://www.uspharmacist.com.
10. Benjamin, D.M. Selecting new drugs for the hospital formulary, *Med. Sci. Bull.,* 237, 239, 1997.
11. Rush, D.R. Antimicrobial formulary management, meeting the challenge in the community hospital, *Pharmacotherapy,* 11, 19S-26S, 1991.
12. MacKinnon, G.E. and Sever, C.M. Development of a criteria-based anti-infective formulary, *Pharm. Ther.,* 18(3), 248–254, 1993.
13. Powers, D.A. Antimicrobial surveillance in a VAMC hospital-resulting cost avoidance, *Drug. Intell. Clin. Pharm.,* 20, 803–805, 1986.
14. Himmelberg, C.J., Pleasants, R.A., Wever, D.J. et al. Use of antimicrobial drugs in adults before and after removal of a restriction policy, *Am. J. Hosp. Pharm.,* 48, 1220–1227, 1991.
15. Schentag, J.J., Ballow, C.H., Fritz, A.L. et al. Changes in antimicrobial agent usage resulting from interactions among clinical pharmacy, the infectious disease division, and the microbiology laboratory, *Diagn. Microbiol. Infect. Dis.,* 16, 255–264, 1993.
16. Quintiliani, R. and Nightingale, C.H. Antimicrobials and therapeutic decision making, a historical perspective, *Pharmacotherapy,* 11, 6S–13S, 1991.
17. Briceland, L.L., Nightingale, C.H., Quintiliani R. et al. Antibiotic streamlining from combination therapy to monotherapy utilizing an interdisciplinary approach, *Arch. Intern. Med.,* 148, 2019–2022, 1988.
18. Lesar, T.S. and Briceland, L.L. Survey of antibiotic control policies in university-affiliated teaching institutions, *Ann. Pharmacother.,* 30, 31–34, 1996.
19. ASHP guidelines on the pharmacist's role in drug-use evaluation, *Am. J. Hosp. Pharm.,* 45, 385–386, 1988.

20. Nadzam, D.M. Development of medication-use indicators by the Joint Commission on Accreditation of Healthcare Organizations, *Am. J. Hosp. Pharm.,* 48, 1925–1930, 1991.

21. ASHP guidelines on medication-use evaluation, *Am. J. Health-Syst. Pharm.,* 3, 1953–1955, 1996.

22. Pear, S.M., Williamson, T.H., Bettin, K.M., Gerding, D.N., and Galgiana, J.N. Decrease in nosocomial *Clostridium difficile*-associated diarrhea by restricting clindamycin use, *Ann. Intern. Med.,* 120, 272–277, 1994.

23. Coffey, R.J., Richards, J.S., Remmert, C.S,. LeRoy, S.S,. Schoville, R.R., and Baldwin, P.J. An introduction to critical paths, *Qual. Manage. Health Care,* 1(1), 45–54, 1992.

24. (Kirk-20) Joint Commission on Accreditation of Healthcare Organizations. 1995 comprehensive accreditation manual for hospitals. Joint Commission on Accreditation of Healthcare Organizations, Oakbrook Terrace, IL, 1995.

25. (Pearson-13) Falconer, J.A., Roth, E.J., Sutin, J.A., Strasser, D.C., and Chang, R.W. The critical path method in strike rehabilitation, lessons from an experiment in cost containment and outcome improvement, *Qual. Rev. Bull.,* 19, 8–16, 1993.

26. Anonymous. National directory of healthcare critical pathways. Cor Healthcare Resources, Santa Barbara, CA, 1995.

27. Ivey, M.F., Armitistead, J.A., and Sangha, K.S. Critical pathways at University of Cincinnati Hospital, *Am. J. Health Syst. Pharm.,* 52, 1053–1058, 1995.

28. Nelson, S.P. Critical pathways at University of Iowa Hospitals and Clinics, *Am. J. Health Syst. Pharm.,* 52, 1058–1060, 1995.

17 Interactions between Clinicians and the Microbiology Laboratory

John H. Powers

CONTENTS

17.1 INTRODUCTION

The treatment and prevention of infectious diseases is unique. Symptomatic illness in infectious diseases is the result of the host response to invading microorganisms. In the treatment of most human diseases, clinicians administer drugs that bind to some receptor site that is part of the human host. However, in most infectious diseases, other than vaccines and immunological therapies, therapy is directed at the invading organism rather than the human host. Inhibition or killing of the microorganisms will aid the human immune system in eradicating the invading pathogens with a subsequent resolution in the signs and symptoms of the disease. We have learned that some antimicrobials also may have a direct effect in modulating the host immune system as well [1,2]. The ultimate goal, of course, is the cure of the patient's signs and symptoms, and not merely the elimination of the pathogens. The microbiology laboratory provides information to clinicians that allows them to treat patients most appropriately. The microbiology laboratory interacts with clinicians in other important ways as well, including providing information related to infection control, educating clinicians and house staff, and participating in clinical research. The efficient functioning of the microbiology laboratory is dependent upon good communication between clinicians and their colleagues in the microbiology laboratory [3].

17.2 DIRECT PATIENT CARE

The most important interactions between clinicians and the microbiology laboratory are in the day-to-day context of direct patient care [4]. The information that clinicians obtain from the microbiology laboratory serves several important purposes. First, the results from appropriately obtained specimens sent to the microbiology laboratory allow clinicians to confirm that the patient's illness indeed is due to an infection and not some other noninfectious cause [5]. An erroneous diagnosis of infection may result in unnecessary exposure of patients to antimicrobial drugs. This may result in unnecessary adverse events related to antimicrobials, or eliminating the patient's protective normal flora with resulting colonization with antimicrobial-resistant organisms [6]. Most importantly, however, is that clinicians may wait two to three days to observe a potential response to antimicrobial therapy, thereby delaying finding the correct diagnosis. This delay in diagnosis may result in a delay in the appropriate therapy for the patient's illness, which may in turn result in increased morbidity or even mortality for some infections [7].

The information from the microbiology laboratory is one factor which helps clinicians to choose the most appropriate antimicrobial therapy for a given patient. In some cases clinicians may wait for the results of microbiological testing before initiating treatment. For instance, in a child who presents with less severe disease such as pharyngitis, the clinician may await the results of a throat culture before starting treatment. In a severe or serious illness such as acute bacterial meningitis, clinicians empirically initiate antimicrobial therapy based on the most likely pathogens implicated in that type of infection. In both cases the results from the microbiology laboratory obtained in a timely fashion aid the clinician in choosing the most appropriate therapy. Data indicate that in some infections, especially more serious diseases, a delay in the initiation of appropriate therapy may result in worse outcomes for patients [7]. Inappropriately broad therapy may also result in increased adverse events for patients or the selection of resistant organisms [6].

The results of microbiologic testing can also help clinicians determine which antimicrobials may be potentially effective against the pathogenic microorganisms by evaluating the ability of the antimicrobial to inhibit or kill the microorganisms *in vitro* [8]. While the most relevant information on drug efficacy comes from clinical outcomes in clinical trials establishing the safety and efficacy of that drug for a given infection in a specific patient population, the microbiological results also are helpful. The causative pathogen may be resistant *in vitro* to drugs commonly used to treat that infection, in some cases making clinical cure less likely. Also, clinicians may encounter patients infected with organisms that are sufficiently rare that there is little information from clinical trials on treatment. In the absence of clinical trial data, *in vitro* testing may provide clinicians with useful information about the potential for antimicrobial efficacy.

The microbiology laboratory provides a useful service for clinicians by interpreting the results of *in vitro* testing [9]. Many clinicians, other than infectious disease specialists, may not be familiar with how *in vitro* testing translates into susceptibility or resistance of an organism for a given antimicrobial. The microbiology laboratory compares the amount of drug necessary to inhibit growth of the organisms *in vitro* (the minimum inhibitory concentration or MIC) for an antimicrobial to standard breakpoints put forth for that antimicrobial–organism combination. The U.S. Food and Drug Administration includes susceptibility breakpoints in drug labeling. This allows the laboratory to determine whether the organism is considered susceptible or resistant *in vitro* to the antimicrobial. Laboratories, in turn, relay the information about susceptibility or resistance to clinicians, greatly simplifying the clinician's task in interpreting such data. In some situations, however, it is still useful to know the actual MIC value. It is important to keep in mind that susceptibility testing is one factor among many used in making treatment decisions for patients. In some cases, the definition of "resistance" may not accurately reflect clinical outcomes in patients [11].

The usefulness of microbiological testing in patient care depends upon adequate communication between clinicians and the microbiology laboratory [3]. Clinicians and microbiologists must also ensure adequate quality control in their respective parts of the testing process. First, clinicians must know when it is useful to obtain microbiological data and when it is not. For instance, in most young, healthy women with an uncomplicated urinary tract infection, the results of microbiological testing of urine cultures are sufficiently predictable that obtaining culture data adds little to clinical management [12]. Obtaining culture data in such cases results in unnecessary work for the micro-biologists and increases the cost of treating such infections. Similarly, clinicians should evaluate carefully the utility of repeating microbiological testing in selected patients. For instance, daily sputum cultures on patients receiving mechanical ventilation add little useful information for clinical decision making. On the other hand, clinicians often repeat blood cultures in bacteremic patients, especially those with endocarditis, to document clearing of the organisms [13].

When clinicians decide that microbiological information will be helpful in clinical decision making, they should ensure that they obtain specimens properly [4,14]. This entails obtaining an adequate amount of specimen. For instance, the yield of blood cultures is directly related to the amount of specimen obtained. The source of the specimen is also important. For instance, in patients with pneumonia sputum specimens obtained by deep cough are more helpful than saliva. Adequate labeling of specimens may also help in determining their clinical importance. For instance, cultures from existing drains may not be helpful and may be potentially misleading in that such drains may be colonized with commensal flora.

Clinicians and microbiologists should communicate when deciding whether susceptibility testing is warranted in specific situations. The decision to perform susceptibility testing is based on the source of the specimen, the types of organisms isolated, whether the organisms are present in pure or mixed culture, and the predictability of the susceptibility of the isolated organisms and host factors in the infected person. For instance, isolation of viridans streptococci from a throat culture could be considered "normal oral flora" and require no further testing, but isolation of the same organisms from a blood culture in a patient with a presumptive diagnosis of endocarditis may be an indication for more extensive testing. Isolation of coagulase-negative staphylococci may be a contaminent in otherwise healthy persons, but may be clinically significant in immuno compromised persons or patients with medical devices in place. These examples also illustrates that it is helpful to provide the microbiology laboratory with a differential diagnosis for the patient. This may cause the lab to continue to incubate the cultures for a longer time looking for fastidious organisms, or in other cases to use selective media. A differential diagnosis of "fever" is sufficiently nonspecific as to add little useful information to clinical decision making. When the differential diagnosis contains diseases that may be potentially transmitted to laboratory staff, such as tularemia, the clinicians should make sure to communicate this information to the laboratory staff.

When there are questions about how to properly obtain a specimen, it is helpful to communicate with the microbiology laboratory in advance. This is especially important when specimens are difficult to obtain, such as those obtained intra-operatively. Some institutions have manuals distributed throughout patient care areas or computer access to such manuals to aid clinicians in properly obtaining and labeling specimens.

The microbiology laboratory should provide most routine microbiological testing, including susceptibility testing for most bacteria. Occasionally, clinicians may require more specialized testing, such as susceptibility testing for anaerobic organisms. Laboratory personnel can aid clinicians in determining when such testing is appropriate. Other specialized testing may be sent out to reference laboratories. When testing is not performed on site, laboratory personnel should ensure that specimens are transported to the outside laboratory as soon as possible.

Microbiology laboratory personnel should ensure that results are provided to clinicians in a timely manner regardless of whether testing is performed on site or sent out to a reference laboratory. When laboratory personnel obtain critically important information, such as positive results from blood cultures, it is often helpful for the microbiologist to communicate this information directly to clinicians or other patient caregivers. This ensures that clinicians can act on this information as soon as possible. These results may require immediate changes in the patient's antimicrobial therapy and may have an important impact on the outcome of the patient's illness.

In conjunction with clinicians, laboratory personnel should decide which antimicrobials are appropriate to include in routine susceptibility testing and which results to report to clinicians [15]. This decision entails considerations of the site of infection, local antimicrobial resistance patterns, and the cost of the antimicrobials. In some cases, laboratory staff and clinicians may decide to test the susceptibility of organisms to certain antimicrobials but not routinely report the results. This is usually done in an effort to encourage use of narrower spectrum or less expensive but similarly efficacious alternatives for therapy [16]. Lab staff should provide unreported results to clinicians upon request because special circumstances such as patient allergies may necessitate the use of these antimicrobials.

Laboratory personnel and clinicians should also collaborate on how to report results. In some institutions, clinicians prefer to only receive the interpretation of results, that is, designating an organism as susceptible or resistant to an antimicrobial based on standardized breakpoints. In other cases, clinicians wish to receive the actual MIC values in addition to the interpretation of the results. Results may be reported as soon as they are received in the microbiology laboratory in institutions where results are provided through a computerized database. When a computer database is not available, the laboratory may need to designate staff to reply to phone inquiries from clinicians.

17.3 INFECTION CONTROL

The microbiology laboratory can provide important information related to infection control concerns in both the hospital and outpatient setting [17,18]. The susceptibility patterns of organisms vary greatly by geographic location and from institution to institution. Microbiology laboratories can provide an antibiogram of the susceptibility patterns of common organisms that can aid clinicians in empiric therapy in their practice location. The laboratory should ensure that the antibiogram does not contain duplicate organisms cultured multiple times from the same patient. This may give a spurious indication of the susceptibility pattern for an organism in that institution. Often, laboratories only tabulate the results of susceptibility testing on inpatient isolates or combine results of isolates on inpatients and outpatients. If possible, it is helpful to provide clinicians with separate results on inpatient and outpatient isolates. The widespread use of antimicrobials in the inpatient setting may result in resistance patterns that do not reflect those in the outpatient setting. On the other hand, increasing reports of antimicrobial resistance in outpatient infections, such as the description of methicillin-resistant *Staphylococcus aureus*–related skin infections, should prompt surveillance for such organisms. Clinicians need to know if such organisms are prevalent enough in their practice area to warrant a change in the empiric therapy of these common infections when data from clinical trials supports such a change.

Microbiology laboratory personnel should have a close working relationship with hospital infection control staff. As the hub of microbiological information in an institution, the microbiology laboratory may detect increases in infections with specific organisms in a given unit in the hospital, or may note changes in resistance patterns in certain organisms that may not be apparent to individual clinicians [19]. Laboratory personnel also can alert infection control practitioners to the presence of patients in the hospital who are colonized or infected with organisms that may require various forms of isolation, such as tuberculosis, or specific types of antimicrobial-resistant organisms.

17.4 EDUCATION

The microbiology laboratory can serve as a source of education about microbiological issues for clinicians and house staff. Seminars, grand rounds, and regularly scheduled tutorials can help keep clinicians informed about such topics as resistance patterns in the hospital, new antimicrobials on susceptibility panels, and new microbiological diagnostic tests. While aiding clinicians in the use of these tests for patient care, educational efforts can also help to decrease unnecessary microbiologic testing and ease the workload on laboratory staff [4]. For instance, microbiology staff can help clinicians in deciding when susceptibility testing is sufficiently predictable that it is not necessary, as with penicillin susceptibility testing for group A streptococci. Educational efforts can also give clinicians and house staff appropriate expectations about the timing of results. For instance, if house staff are not aware that a test is run only on specific days of the week, they may unnecessarily call the laboratory daily in anticipation of pending results.

17.5 RESEARCH

The microbiology laboratory is also an important participant in clinical research. The laboratory may participate in the evaluation of new diagnostic microbiological methods to ascertain their accuracy and to determine if those tests are cost-efficient for their particular institution [20]. The microbiology laboratory may also participate in evaluating new methods for susceptibility testing. Also, the microbiology laboratory is an important partner in clinical research, testing the safety and efficacy of new antimicrobials. The microbiology laboratory is often responsible for the initial testing of isolates from subjects participating in a clinical trial. The laboratory is often responsible for storing and shipping such isolates to a central laboratory as well. Finally, the laboratory is an important partner in epidemiological research on infection control related issues in the hospital and outpatient setting [19].

17.6 CONCLUSIONS

Infectious disease physicians have the ability to make a specific diagnosis of infection and gauge the most appropriate treatments for patients based on the results of microbiological testing performed in the laboratory. Perhaps in no other subspecialty in medicine is there such a symbiotic relationship between caregiver and laboratory personnel. The efficient functioning of the microbiology laboratory and a good relationship of the laboratory with patient caregivers are dependent upon good communication between the various groups. Good communication between the laboratory and clinicians results in the most appropriate use of microbiological testing, well-informed clinicians with realistic expectations of the laboratory, and the most cost-efficient use of resources. In the final analysis, smooth interactions between the microbiology laboratory and patient caregivers result in better care for patients, the common goal of all those involved in the treatment of infectious diseases.

REFERENCES

1. Labro, M.T. Interference of antibacterial agents with phagocyte functions: immunomodulation or "immuno-fairy tales"? *Clin. Microbiol. Rev.,* 134, 615–650, 2000.
2. Nau, R. and Eiffert, H. Modulation of release of proinflammatory bacterial compounds by antibacterials: potential impact on course of inflammation and outcome in sepsis and meningitis, *Clin. Microbiol. Rev.,* 151, 95–110, 2002.
3. Christenson, J.C. and Overall, J.C., Jr. Proper use of the clinical microbiology laboratory, *Pediatr. Rev.,* 162, 62–68, 1995.
4. Rosenblatt, J.E. Maximizing the productive interface between the clinical microbiologist and the infectious disease clinician, *Am. J. Clin. Pathol.,* 903, 355–357, 1988.
5. Thomson, R.B., Jr. and Peterson, L.R. Role of the clinical microbiology laboratory in the diagnosis of infections, *Cancer Treat. Res.,* 96, 143–165, 1998.
6. Colgan, R. and Powers, J.H. Appropriate antimicrobial prescribing: approaches that limit antibiotic resistance, *Am. Fam. Physician,* 646, 999–1004, 2001.
7. Ibrahim, E.H., Ward, S., Sherman, G., and Kollef, M.H. A comparative analysis of patients with early-onset vs late-onset nosocomial pneumonia in the ICU setting, *Chest,* 1175, 1434–1442, 2000.
8. Steinbach, W.J. and Shetty, A.K. Use of the diagnostic bacteriology laboratory: a practical review for the clinician. *Postgrad. Med. J.* 77905, 148, 2001.
9. Baron, E.J. Quality management and the clinical microbiology laboratory, *Diagn. Microbiol. Infect. Dis.,* 231–2, 23–34, 1995.
10. O'Brien, T.F., Eskildsen, M.A., Stelling, ,J.M. Using internet discussion of antimicrobial susceptibility databases for continuous quality improvement of the testing and management of antimicrobial resistance, *Clin. Infect. Dis.,* 33(Suppl 3), S118–S123, 2001.
11. Bishai, W. The *in vivo–in vitro* paradox in pneumococcal respiratory tract infections. *J. Antimicrob. Chemother.,* 49, 433–436, 2002.
12. Warren, J.W., Abrutyn, E., Hebel, J.R., Johnson, J.R., Schaeffer, A.J., and Stamm, W.E. Guidelines for antimicrobial treatment of uncomplicated acute bacterial cystitis and acute pyelonephritis in women. Infectious Diseases Society of America (IDSA), *Clin. Infect. Dis.,* 294, 745–758, 1999.
13. Chang, F.Y., Peacock, J.E. Jr., Musher, D.M., Triplett, P., MacDonald, B.B., Mylotte, J.M. et al. *Staphylococcus aureus* bacteremia: recurrence and the impact of antibiotic treatment in a prospective multicenter study, *Med. Baltimore,* 25, 333–339, 2003.

14. Gyssens, I.C., Smits-Caris, C., Stolk-Engelaar, M.V., Slooff, T.J., and Hoogkamp-Korstanje, J.A. An audit of microbiology laboratory utilization: the diagnosis of infection in orthopedic surgery, *Clin. Microbiol. Infect.,* 35, 518–522, 1997.

15. Cunney, R.J. and Smyth, E.G. The impact of laboratory reporting practice on antibiotic utilisation, *Int. J. Antimicrob. Agents,* 141, 13–19, 2000.

16. Stratton, C.W. The role of the microbiology laboratory in guiding formulary decisions, *Hosp. Formul.,* 238, 654–657, 1988.

17. Kolmos, H.J. Role of the clinical microbiology laboratory in infection control — a Danish perspective, *J. Hosp. Infect.,* 48 (Suppl A), S50–S54, 2001.

18. Peterson, L.R., Hamilton, J.D., Baron, E.J., Tompkins, L.S., Miller, J.M., Wilfert, C.M. et al. Role of clinical microbiology laboratories in the management and control of infectious diseases and the delivery of health care, *Clin. Infect. Dis.,* 324, 605–611, 2001.

19. Pfaller, M.A. and Herwaldt, L.A. The clinical microbiology laboratory and infection control: emerging pathogens, antimicrobial resistance, and new technology, *Clin. Infect. Dis.,* 254, 858–870, 1997.

20. Jenkins, S.G. Evaluation of new technology in the clinical microbiology laboratory, *Diagn. Microbiol. Infect. Dis.,* 231–2, 53–60, 1995.

18 Clinical Microbiology in the Development of New Antimicrobial Agents

C. Douglas Webb and Barbara G. Painter

CONTENTS

18.1 INTRODUCTION

The insidious, unrelenting ability of microorganisms to develop resistance poses a constant challenge for the pharmaceutical industry to devise new antimicrobial agents with improved spectrum and potency. This challenge is underscored by the vast array of currently available antibacterial agents ranging from penicillin and the extended-spectrum penicillins to the various generations of tetracyclines, macrolides, aminoglycosides, cephalosporins, carbapenems, and quinolones.

The microbiological procedures necessary for approval of a new antibiotic by regulatory agencies in the United States are rigorous and extensive, involving a wide variety of preclinical and clinical studies by numerous investigators and laboratories. In this chapter, we discuss the various types of information required for the microbiological section of new drug applications (NDAs). The requirements are essentially similar for all antibiotic classes. However, for purposes of illustration, most of our discussion centers on the second- and third-generation quinolones.

18.2 MECHANISMS OF ACTION

An in-depth description of the mechanism of action of the antibiotic is one of the first requirements. Details also are provided regarding chemical structure and any structural or other similarities with marketed antimicrobial drugs. Such details can provide information that is important in the drug's potential for resistance or scope of antimicrobial spectrum. For example, the major mechanism of bacterial killing by the quinolones involves inhibition of the activities of DNA gyrase, a Type II topoisomerase enzyme found in bacterial cells. By binding to a complex created by gyrase and DNA, quinolones prevent bacterial DNA synthesis and transcription. This unique interaction of quinolones with the gyrase–DNA complex explains their relative lack of cross-resistance with other classes of antimicrobial agents.

In addition to inhibiting DNA gyrase, newer quinolones like gatifloxacin, moxifloxacin, and trovafloxacin also inhibit the *in vitro* activity of topoisomerase IV. This bacterial cell enzyme plays a key role in chromosome partitioning during cell division and appears to be the primary target of quinolone activity in gram-positive bacteria (most notably *Staphylococcus aureus* and *Streptococcus pneumoniae*). In contrast, DNA gyrase is the main quinolone target in gram-negative bacteria like *Escherichia coli, Klebsiella pneumoniae,* and *Pseudomonas aeruginosa.*

18.3 STRUCTURE-ACTIVITY RELATIONSHIPS

Structural changes within members of an antibiotic class can significantly alter activity, spectrum, and propensity for development of resistance.

Figure 18.1 illustrates the chemical structures of representative first-, second-, and third-generation quinolones. All of these molecules are synthetic analogs of nalidixic acid, the first member of the quinolone class. Chemical modification of nalidixic acid, which has a limited spectrum and rapid development of resistance, began with carbon-for-nitrogen substitution at position 8 and other side-chain modifications. The resultant second-generation quinolones like ciprofloxacin and ofloxacin displayed greater potency, increased spectrum, and less tendency toward resistance. The striking superiority of ciprofloxacin over older quinolones paved the way for use of these agents in a variety of infections caused by a wide range of organisms. Substitutions based on the 6-fluoro, 7 piperazinyl molecule led to development of the other second-generation quinolones, sparfloxacin and clinafloxacin.

The third-generation quinolone, trovafloxacin, was created by a 7-azabicyclo modification of the ciprofloxacin molecule while the newer third-generation drugs, gatifloxacin and moxifloxacin, are characterized by an 8-methoxy side-chain modification at the C-8 position. These features maintain or exceed the potent antibacterial activity of ciprofloxacin against most enterobacteriaceae,

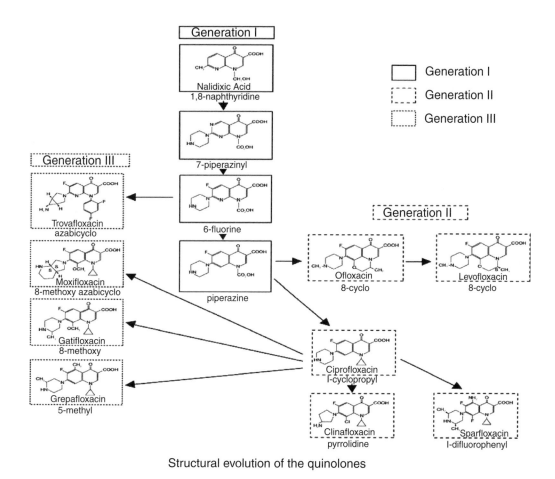

Structural evolution of the quinolones

FIGURE 18.1 Structural evolution of the quinolones. Reprinted from Blondeau, J.M. *Clin. Ther.,* 21, 3, 1999. With permission [15].

while improving activity against gram-positive organisms, anaerobes, and atypical pathogens like *Mycoplasma pneumoniae*, *Chlamydia pneumonia,* and *Legionella* spp.

18.4 SPECTRUM OF *IN VITRO* ACTIVITY

Studies determining the activity spectrum and relative potency of the new antibiotic form a lengthy part of NDAs. The initial step in the investigative process is to determine the minimal inhibitory concentration (MIC) of the drug against pathogenic bacteria that are within the spectrum of marketed members of the antibiotic class. Here, the MIC is defined as the lowest concentration of drug that inhibits the visible growth of an organism in microbroth dilution tests run under standard conditions recommended by the Clinical and Laboratory Standards Institute (CLSI). Some laboratories may perform macrobroth or agar dilution tests rather than the microbroth dilution. In the case of quinolones, pathogenic organisms tested would include gram-positive and gram-negative species, both aerobic and anaerobic, atypical organisms, and acid-fast mycobacteria (Table 18.1).

In addition to type strains obtained from the American Type Culture Collection (ATCC), the bacterial panel includes isolates with known mechanisms of resistance to ciprofloxacin and other second-generation quinolones, for example, methicillin-resistant *S. aureus*. The panel would also

TABLE 18.1
Major Organisms Tested for *In Vitro* Activity of Third-Generation Quinolones

Gram-positive organisms
Streptococcus pneumoniae
Streptococcus pyogenes
Staphylococcus aureus, S. epidermidis
MRSA/CRSA[a]
Enterococci
Gram-negative organisms
Haemophilus influenzae
Moraxella catarrhalis
Enterobacteriaceae
Pseudomonas aeruginosa, other nonfermentative gram-negative bacilli
Neisseria gonorrhoeae
Anaerobes
Bacteroides spp.
Fusobacterium
Peptostreptococcus
Clostridium spp.
Prevotella
Atypical bacteria
Chlamydia spp.
Mycoplasma pneumoniae
Legionella spp.
Acid-fast bacteria
Mycobacterium tuberculosis
Mycobacterium avium
Mycobacterium kansasii

[a] Methicillin- and ciprofloxacin-resistant *S. aureus*.

include organisms against which older quinolones are only minimally or moderately effective, for example, *S. pneumoniae* and anaerobes including *Bacteroides fragilis*.

18.4.1 CLINICAL ISOLATES

If the early type–strain studies are promising, the activity of the new antibiotic is evaluated against recent isolates from a variety of clinical environments such as outpatient and inpatient settings and community, teaching, and federal hospitals. In these studies, the new antibiotic is directly compared with currently approved drugs, especially those within the same class. In the case of quinolones, typical comparative agents would include ciprofloxacin, gatifloxacin, levofloxacin, and moxifloxacin. Against certain organisms, for example, *S. pneumoniae* or *M. pneumoniae*, the comparison might also include nonquinolone drugs approved for treatment of these infections, such as certain cephalosporins, amoxicillin and clavulanate, and macrolides. Comparative nonquinolone drugs in the evaluation of anaerobic activity would include metronidazole or the combination of piperacillin and tazobactam.

18.4.2 MICROBIOLOGICAL CRITERIA

Comparative *in vitro* activity data submitted to regulatory agencies are presented as a compilation of all available data from carefully conducted trials by the pharmaceutical company and independent

TABLE 18.2
Potential Indications for New Quinolones

Respiratory tract infections	Nosocomial pneumonia
	Community-acquired pneumonia
	Sinusitis
	Acute exacerbations of chronic bronchitis
Surgical infections	Intra-abdominal infections
	Gynecologic and pelvic infections
	Surgical prophylaxis
Urinary tract infections (UTIs)	Uncomplicated and complicated UTIs
	Prostatitis
Sexually transmitted infections	Pelvic inflammatory disease
	Nongonococcal urethritis and cervicitis
	Gonorrhea
Skin infections	Complicated and uncomplicated skin and skin structure infections

investigators. Examples of microbiological criteria for study inclusion are use of quality control strains recommended by the CLSI, susceptibility testing by the latest methods approved by CLSI, and standardization of all assay techniques. To be deemed effective *in vitro*, a minimum of 100 clinical isolates tested by both diffusion and dilution techniques is required for the common causative organisms. Fewer isolates are acceptable only for fastidious bacteria, infrequently isolated pathogens, *Chlamydia* spp., or other organisms with difficult growth or testing methodology issues.

The results of *in vitro* activity tests are compiled for all proposed clinical indications. Data for each species are reported as the concentration of drug necessary to inhibit 50% and 90% of strains (MIC_{50} and MIC_{90}, respectively), the range of MIC, and median MIC_{90} of common organisms associated with these conditions. Because of the broad spectrum of activity of third-generation quinolones, data on *in vitro* activity may include pathogens found in about 14 infections, ranging from acute sinusitis, community and nosocomial pneumonias, and skin and soft tissue infections, to complicated intra-abdominal or pelvic infections (Table 18.2).

Since antibiotic susceptibility varies among geographical areas, the majority of studies are conducted on isolates from patients at a variety of locations across the United States. Any data derived from other countries must be demonstrated as microbiologically relevant, that is, similar antimicrobial activity, to the treatment of patients in the United States.

18.4.3 PROTOTYPE *IN VITRO* STUDIES

The following are examples of the types of *in vitro* studies that would be incorporated into the database of an application for a new third-generation quinolone.

Gram-positive activity. A multicenter study [1] comparing the activity of trovafloxacin, gatifloxacin, and sparfloxacin against over 1,600 ciprofloxacin-resistant gram-positive cocci isolated from patients with significant bloodstream, respiratory tract, wound, and urinary tract infections. The majority of the organisms were *S. aureus*, enterococci, and coagulase-negative staphylococci.

Anaerobic activity. A study [2] comparing the MICs of gatifloxacin, trovafloxacin, ciprofloxacin, sparfloxacin, ampicillin, ampicillin and sulbactam, clindamycin, and metronidazole against 351 recent clinical isolates of *B. fragilis, Fusobacterium,* and other anaerobes.

Gram-negative activity. A study [3] comparing the activity of gatifloxacin, ciprofloxacin, and ofloxacin against *Enterobacteriaceae* and nonfermenting gram-negative bacteria. MICs were determined for 450 clinical isolates representing 25 species.

Activity against atypical organisms. A study [4] comparing the activity of gatifloxacin, ofloxacin, and ciprofloxacin against 172 strains of *Mycoplasma*, *Ureaplasma*, *Chlamydia*, and anaerobes.

18.5 PHARMACOKINETIC EVALUATION

Like *in vitro* activity, pharmacokinetic (PK) evaluation is started early in the development of a new antibiotic. After all, *in vitro* activity alone is useless when an antibiotic is not sufficiently concentrated in serum or at the infection site.

The first PK studies are performed in animal models from which appropriate dosage for humans is calculated following administration of multiple dosing regimens. Afterward, single and multiple oral and intravenous dosage regimens are administered to small groups of healthy human volunteers to obtain more precise information on the absorption, bioavailability, distribution, extent of protein binding, metabolism, and excretion of the drug. PK parameters include peak serum concentrations (C_{max}), terminal elimination half-life ($T_{1/2}$), and area under the serum concentration-time curve (AUC). C_{max} and AUC data collected from these preclinical phase I studies are especially useful in helping to establish proposed breakpoints for MIC and disk-diffusion testing. Tentative breakpoints are, of course, essential before the start of clinical trials in patients with various infections.

Other studies include investigation of the effects of food on drug absorption and any drug interactions that might alter the PK behavior of the new antibiotic. For example, ciprofloxacin and other second-generation quinolones undergo metabolism via the hepatic cytochrome P450 system, and drugs that compete for this pathway, such as theophylline, are known to accumulate when administered with these quinolones. In contrast, trovafloxacin and gatifloxacin undergo less oxidative metabolism and do not interact with P450.

Data on the volume of distribution, which reflects tissue penetration, are supplemented with those obtained using representative models of tissue penetration such as inflammatory blister fluid and cells obtained by bronchial lavage. The NDA may also include tissue distribution studies showing that the antibiotic diffuses into infection sites and maintains concentrations equal to or greater than the MIC_{90} of a pathogen for an adequate period.

On oral administration, ciprofloxacin is highly bioavailable with a high volume of distribution and low protein binding. Thus, its concentrations in body tissues and fluids are higher or similar to blood concentration. Compared with ciprofloxacin, the newer quinolones have equal or greater bioavailability, higher peak plasma concentrations, and greater volume of distribution, leading to even better tissue penetration. Longer serum half-lives permit once-daily dosage with most of these drugs.

18.5.1 PHARMACODYNAMICS

Pharmacodynamic (PD) factors are critical considerations because they help establish the relationship between antibiotic dosage regimens and antimicrobial activity. Such evaluations can be performed using *in vitro* or animal models of infection or, less often, during clinical trials. A combined PK/PD evaluation includes relating drug concentrations in plasma to the *in vitro* susceptibility of the target organism. Such studies have shown that for some antibiotics, for example, β-lactams, the most significant PK parameter in estimating clinical and microbiological efficacy is the time that antibiotic serum levels exceed the MIC for the pathogen. In contrast, the activity of quinolones is concentration rather than time dependent, so that the ratio of peak serum concentrations or area under the curve (AUC) to MIC become the most predictive parameters of potential clinical and microbiological efficacy.

This concept is illustrated in Figure 18.2, which shows the relationship of the AUC/MIC ratio (AUIC) to bacteriologic eradication in 94 hospitalized patients treated with intravenous ciprofloxacin

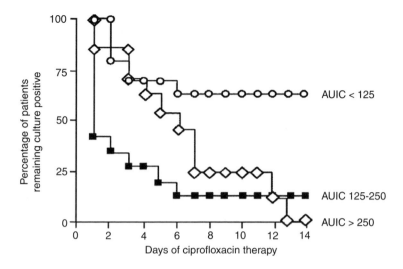

FIGURE 18.2 Time (number of days of therapy) to bacterial eradication vs. area under the concentration–time curve/MIC (AUIC) ratio, illustrated by a time-to-event (survival) plot. The day of therapy vs. the percentage of patients remaining culture positive on that day is shown. The three AUIC groups differed significantly (*P* < 0.005). Reprinted from Lode, H., Borner, K., and Koeppe, P. *Clin. Infect. Dis.*, 27, 33, 1998, with permission.

for serious acute infections. At an AUIC < 125, the probability of microbiological cure was only 26% while at an AUIC > 125, it was 80% [5].

18.6 QUALITATIVE ASPECTS OF ANTIBACTERIAL ACTIVITY

Qualitative microbiological aspects such as determination of minimal bactericidal concentration (MBC), the rate of bacterial killing, intracellular activity, and culture conditions that might alter *in vitro* activity are all evaluated. Similar to *in vitro* spectrum studies, these evaluations are conducted using comparative quinolones or other classes of antibiotics and all assays are standardized as required by regulatory agencies.

18.6.1 BACTERICIDAL ACTIVITY

Bactericidal activity is usually assessed by assays measuring the MBC in single time point susceptibility studies performed in broth. In these studies, the MBC is defined as the lowest concentration of drug that kills 99.9% (>3 $\log_{10}$) of the initial inoculum in 24 h. This may be supplemented by another method that samples for viability at timed intervals over 24 h. The ideal MBC is identical to or only 1 to 3 log above the MIC concentrations for the representative pathogen. With the third-generation quinolones, MBCs are usually within one dilution of the MIC for representative strains of *S. aureus, S. pneumoniae, E. coli, Enterobacter cloacae,* and *P. aeruginosa* as well as anaerobes like *B. fragilis* and *Peptostreptococcus.* MBCs for penicillin-resistant *S. pneumoniae* range from one to two dilutions above the MIC.

18.6.2 KILLING KINETICS

The rate of bacterial killing is yet another important NDA requirement. With some organisms and infections, for example, bacterial endocarditis, this may be a more important determinant of clinical outcome than are MBCs. *In vitro* time–kill studies of clinical isolates most frequently use a macrodilution technique to evaluate the speed of bacterial killing. The evaluation includes representative

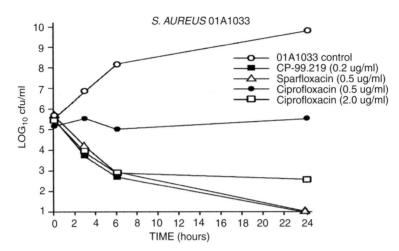

FIGURE 18.3 Kill curve performed in brain–heart infusion broth against a quinolone–methicillin-susceptible *Staphylococcus aureus* strain (01A1033). Reprinted from Gootz, T.D., Brighty, K.E., Anderson, M.R. et al. *Diagn. Microbiol. Infect. Dis.,* 19, 235, 1994, with permission.

organisms with high and reduced susceptibility to available quinolones. The increments of time are spaced to allow quantification of both speed and duration of bactericidal effect of the antibiotics, usually at their MIC and at concentrations 4 and 8 times their MICs. The time–kill curve shown in Figure 18.3 plots the killing rate of trovafloxacin, ciprofloxacin, and sparfloxacin against a strain of quinolone–methicillin-susceptible *S. aureus* (MSSA).

At its MIC of 0.5 µg/mL, ciprofloxacin exhibited only a bacteriostatic effect and was not highly bactericidal even at 4 times its MIC. In contrast, trovafloxacin and sparfloxacin at their respective MICs of 0.25 µg/mL and 0.5 µg/mL produced a bactericidal effect at 24 h [6]. Clinically, cipro-floxacin is effective against MSSA.

More recently, techniques called *in vitro* pharmacokinetic models have also been used. These methods simulate human pharmacokinetics so that the projected peak drug dose achieved in human serum can be evaluated for its time to killing. In a study [7] using this method, the third-generation quinolone, moxifloxacin, was found to kill *S. pneumoniae* at a significantly faster rate than spar-floxacin or levofloxacin. A similar study [8] of gatifloxacin found that the projected human dose was effective in killing strains of penicillin and erythromycin susceptible and resistant *S. pneumoniae* within 6 to 10 h.

18.6.3 ANTIBIOTIC SYNERGY

Standard time-kill methods and *in vitro* dynamic models are also used to evaluate antibiotic synergy [9]. In standard time-kill studies, synergy is defined as a decrease of 2 log units in colony-forming units (CFU) for the combination of antibiotics versus the bactericidal activity of the most active single agent. Synergy studies are most often performed on organisms that are known to rapidly develop resistance to a class of antibiotics. With ciprofloxacin, for example, it has been demonstrated that *P. aeruginosa* is less likely to develop resistance when the quinolone is administered with azlocillin.

18.6.4 INTRACELLULAR UPTAKE

Quinolones are known to accumulate in phagocytic cells at levels from 10- to 28-fold higher than extracellular concentrations. Thus, the degree of intracellular antibiotic uptake must be evaluated to verify activity of the new antibiotic against intracellular pathogens such as *Legionella* and *Mycobac-terium.* Since these organisms replicate exclusively within phagocyte cells, their eradication depends on intracellular levels of antibiotic above the MICs rather than serum or tissue antibiotic levels. Studies measuring the speed and extent of antibiotic accumulation in guinea pig macrophages, human neutrophils, and tissue cultured epithelial cells may be presented in the NDA. In such studies, the intracellular activity of the new quinolone at various concentrations is compared with that of erythromycin or other marketed drugs effective against infections caused by intracellular pathogens.

18.6.5 Drug Metabolites

The *in vitro* activity of any drug's metabolites detected during the early pharmacokinetic studies in humans may also be included in NDAs. Such activity, if greater than the parent compound, may be important in the treatment of urinary tract infections and pyelonephritis when limited levels of the parent compound are recovered in urine.

18.6.6 Postantibiotic Effect (PAE)

Quantification of the PAE (defined as the continued suppression of bacterial growth after short exposure to an antibiotic) is recommended by regulatory agencies. Either *in vitro* methods or *in vivo* animal models may be used to evaluate this effect.

Although the clinical significance of PAE is uncertain, the phenomenon may be important in devising dosage regimens and reducing development of resistance due to subinhibitory concentrations of antibiotic between doses. Most antibiotics display some PAE against gram-positive bacteria but quinolones also display a PAE against gram-negative organisms. The PAEs of third-generation quinolones vary with the pathogen; overall, the effect appears to range from 1 to 6 h.

18.6.7 Culture Conditions

The *in vitro* activity of ciprofloxacin and other marketed quinolones is affected by a variety of culture conditions. Acidic pH diminishes their activity for gram-negative organisms, especially at a pH of 6 or less. Likewise, significant MIC increases in certain organisms are observed with inocula of 10^7 CFU or more.

Since susceptibility testing methods must be standardized, a new quinolone is evaluated to determine if its MICs for various selected bacterial species are affected by these and other culture conditions. Determination of the inoculum size effect is accomplished by exposing the antibiotic to inocula of a clinical isolate from 10- to 100-fold less to 10- to100-fold greater than the standard inoculum for broth and agar dilution. Differences in MIC values signify that inoculum size can interfere with test accuracy. MIC values are also compared using microbroth and agar dilution test methods, at varying pH levels and with the addition of cations. All of these variables can interfere with test accuracy and must be clarified before the appropriate growth medium for susceptibility testing can be determined.

18.7 ASSESSMENT OF BACTERIAL RESISTANCE

Unlike β-lactam antibiotics, plasmid-encoded resistance and enzyme inactivation have not been observed with quinolones. Acquired resistance to quinolones is tied to their mechanism of action and involves spontaneous mutations in the bacterial chromosomal genes. Most often, resistance arises from mutations in bacterial DNA gyrase that impair the ability of these drugs to bind with the gyrase–DNA complex. The other mechanism involves mutations of chromosomally encoded drug influx and efflux systems resulting in prevention of quinolone entry into the bacterial cell or expulsion of drug from the cell. Single mutations of genes result in a stepwise selection of resistance. Over time, mutations in both DNA gyrase and topoisomerase IV or double DNA gyrase mutations may occur. Such multiple site mutations seem to have an additive effect in raising the level of resistance.

18.7.1 Selection Potential

The stability of a new quinolone against strains of various species is usually assessed by means of *in vitro* cell population analyses. These include measurements of MIC on daily passage of strains in media containing increasing concentrations of drug or plating of large inocula into media containing high antibiotic concentrations. Such studies have shown that, even with second-generation quinolones, resistance is rarely encountered in organisms like *E. coli* and other *Enterobacteriaceae* that are innately highly susceptible to quinolones. Resistant mutants are more often found among *P. aeruginosa* and *S. aureus*, organisms against which these antibiotics are less active.

The frequency of resistant mutants among gram-negative bacteria exposed to newer quinolones reportedly ranges from 10^6 at twice the MIC to 10^{10} at 16 to 32 times the MIC. Mutants with *P. aeruginosa* and *E. coli* appear to occur at rates similar to those of ciprofloxacin. However, resistant mutants of gram-positive bacteria appear to occur less often with newer quinolones than with ciprofloxacin and other second-generation agents.

For example, one study [10] found that selection for less susceptible mutants of MRSA and *S. pneumoniae* was 10- to 100-fold higher with ciprofloxacin and ofloxacin than with the third-generation quinolone, gatifloxacin. A lower selection tendency for these organisms has also been observed with trovafloxacin and moxifloxacin in comparison with ciprofloxacin. The reduced potential for resistance appears to be related to the fact that substantially more mutational steps are required before gram-positive organisms become resistant to third-generation quinolones. In most cases, the early step mutants remain susceptible to these newer agents.

18.7.2 Cross Resistance

Yet another aspect of study is to determine whether the new quinolone antibiotic displays cross resistance with strains resistant to marketed quinolones or other classes of antibiotics. This involves determination and comparison of the MICs of the various test antibiotics.

The third-generation quinolones have not demonstrated any consistent advantage over ciprofloxacin for gram-negative strains with high-level ciprofloxacin resistance or multidrug-resistant enterococci. They are, however, active against ciprofloxacin-resistant pneumococci and *S. aureus*, and potent against some strains of MRSA with high-level resistance to ciprofloxacin. In addition, the new quinolones are more active than ceftriaxone or erythromycin against penicillin-resistant pneumococci, and they are highly active against multiresistant *Enterobacteriaceae* susceptible to quinolones but resistant to β-lactams and aminoglycosides.

18.8 CLINICAL LABORATORY TEST METHODS

Several more laboratory procedures are required before a new antibiotic is evaluated for efficacy in clinical trials. Most of these tests revolve around defining standards and quality control parameters for disk diffusion tests. Regulatory agencies recommend that both MIC dilution and disk diffusion techniques be used for testing during clinical trials.

18.8.1 Disk Potency

The first step is to determine the appropriate antibiotic potency for the disks used in diffusion tests. This is done by comparing various concentrations of the new antibiotic with the disks of marketed quinolones with similar spectra and MICs. Generally, about 100 strains of bacteria with known and different MICs are tested with disks containing at least three different concentrations of the new antibiotic, for example, 5 μg, 10 μg, and 20 μg.

Once an antibiotic disk concentration is selected, it must be correlated with the MIC values already obtained by macrobroth dilution. Usually, this involves constructing regression lines of a zone of inhibition versus MIC for about 50 isolates covering the spectrum of the new antibiotic.